QUANTITATIVE APTITUDE

For Competitive Examinations

(Fully Solved)

QUANTITATIVE APTITUDE

FOR COMPETITIVE EXAMINATIONS
(Fully Solved)

An ideal book for :

Bank P.O., S.B.I. P.O; I.B.P.S., R.B.I. Exam.

A.A.O. Exam–L.I.C., G.I.C.

Railway Recruitment Board Exams.

S.S.C. Combined Preliminary Exam.

IGNOU, M.B.A., Hotel Management, N.I.F.T.

Sub-Inspectors of Police, C.B.I., C.P.O. Exam.

Dr. R.S. AGGARWAL

S. CHAND & COMPANY PVT. LTD.

(AN ISO 9001 : 2008 COMPANY)

RAM NAGAR, NEW DELHI - 110 055

S. CHAND & COMPANY PVT. LTD.
(An ISO 9001 : 2008 Company)
Head Office: 7361, RAM NAGAR, NEW DELHI - 110 055
Phone: 23672080-81-82, 9899107446, 9911310888 Fax: 91-11-23677446
www.schandpublishing.com; e-mail: helpdesk@schandpublishing.com

Branches

Ahmedabad : Ph: 27541965, 27542369, ahmedabad@schandpublishing.com
Bengaluru : Ph: 22268048, 22354008, bangalore@schandpublishing.com
Bhopal : Ph: 4274723, 4209587, bhopal@schandpublishing.com
Chandigarh : Ph: 2625356, 2625546, chandigarh@schandpublishing.com
Chennai : Ph. 28410027, 28410058, chennai@schandpublishing.com
Coimbatore : Ph: 2323620, 4217136, coimbatore@schandpublishing.com (Marketing Office)
Cuttack : Ph: 2332580; 2332581, cuttack@schandpublishing.com
Dehradun : Ph: 2711101, 2710861, dehradun@schandpublishing.com
Guwahati : Ph: 2738811, 2735640, guwahati@schandpublishing.com
Hyderabad : Ph: 27550194, 27550195, hyderabad@schandpublishing.com
Jaipur : Ph: 2219175, 2219176, jaipur@schandpublishing.com
Jalandhar : Ph: 2401630, 5000630, jalandhar@schandpublishing.com
Kochi : Ph: 2378740, 2378207-08, cochin@schandpublishing.com
Kolkata : Ph: 22367459, 22373914, kolkata@schandpublishing.com
Lucknow : Ph: 4026791, 4065646 lucknow@schandpublishing.com
Mumbai : Ph: 22690881, 22610885, mumbai@schandpublishing.com
Nagpur : Ph: 6451311, 2720523, 2777666, nagpur@schandpublishing.com
Patna : Ph: 2300489, 2302100, patna@schandpublishing.com
Pune : Ph: 64017298, pune@schandpublishing.com
Raipur : Ph: 2443142, raipur@schandpublishing.com (Marketing Office)
Ranchi : Ph: 2361178, ranchi@schandpublishing.com
Siliguri : Ph: 2520750, siliguri@schandpublishing.com (Marketing Office)
Visakhapatnam : Ph: 2782609 visakhapatnam@schandpublishing.com (Marketing Office)

First Edition 1989; Subsequent Editions and Reprints 1995, 96 (Twice), 97, 98, 99, 2000, 2001, 2002, 2003, 2004, 2005 (Twice), 2006 (Twice), 2007 (Twice), 2008 (Twice), 2009 (Thrice, 2010 (Twice), 2011 (Thrice), 2012, 2013 (Twice); 2014 (Twice); 2015 (Twice) Reprint 2016

(Revised by Deepak Aggarwal & Vikas Aggarwal)

ISBN : 978-81-219-2498-6 **Code :** 1006B 139

This book is for sale in India & other SAARC countries only.

PRINTED IN INDIA

By Nirja Publishers & Printers Pvt. Ltd., 54/3/2, Jindal Paddy Compound, Kashipur Road, Rudrapur-263153, Uttarakhand and published by S. Chand & Company Pvt. Ltd., 7361, Ram Nagar, New Delhi -110 055.

Preface to the Seventh Revised Edition

The tremendous response to the previous edition necessitated a thorough revision of this book. Hence, this revised edition is in your hands.

This book on *Quantitative Aptitude* in its revised from is expected to be an asset to those who plan to appear in competitive examinations for an executive post.

Most of the books which are in circulation in the market carry a very small number of objective type questions with their answers. But, how to get these answers, is not given there. Moreover, how to solve a mathematical question is not significant in such examinations. The most important aspect is to solve a question in a fraction of a minute, using short-cut methods. This has been taken care of in this revised edition. It also contains a huge collection of objective-type questions with their solutions by short-cut methods.

Every possible effort has been made to accommodate previous years' questions of various competitive examinations, on memory basis.

It is hoped that the subject matter of this revised edition will instil confidence among the candidates and the book will help them like an ideal teacher.

I convey my gratitude to the entire Management of S. Chand & Company Pvt. Ltd. for taking all pains in the publication of the book.

Constructive suggestions for improvement of this book will be highly appreciated.

R.S. AGGARWAL

Veenalaya
330, Deepali,
Pitampura, Delhi

Salient Features of the Book

- ✶ A Whole lot of objective-type questions, with their solutions by short-cut methods.
- ✶ A full coverage of every topic via fully solved examples given at the beginning of each chapter.
- ✶ A separate exercise on Data-Sufficiency-Type Questions given in each topic, along with explanatory solutions.
- ✶ A new, enriched section on Data Interpretation.
- ✶ Questions from latest years' examination papers (on memory basis) have been incorporated.

CONTENTS

1. SECTION–I

ARITHMETICAL ABILITY 1–568

2. SECTION–II

SECTION-I : ARITHMETICAL ABILITY

1. OPERATIONS ON NUMBERS

1. NUMBERS: In Hindu- Arabic system, we have ten **digits**, namely 0, 1, 2, 3, 4, 5, 6, 7, 8, 9 called zero, one two, three, four, five, six, seven, eight and nine respectively.

A number is denoted by a group of digits, called **numeral.**

For denoting a numeral, we use the place-value chart, given below.

Ex. 1. *Write each of the following numerals in words.*

	Ten-Crores	*Crores*	*Ten-Lakhs*	*Lakhs*	*Ten-Thousands*	*Thousands*	*Hundreds*	*Tens*	*Units*
(*i*)				6	3	8	5	4	9
(*ii*)			2	3	8	0	9	1	7
(*iii*)		8	5	4	1	6	0	0	8
(*iv*)	5	6	1	3	0	7	0	9	0

Sol. The given numerals in words are:

(*i*) Six lakh thirty-eight thousand five hundred forty-nine.

(*ii*) Twenty-three lakh eighty thousand nine hundred seventeen.

(*iii*) Eight crore fifty-four lakh sixteen thousand eight.

(*iv*) Fifty-six crore thirteen lakh seven thousand ninety.

Ex. 2. *Write each of the following numbers in figures:*

(*i*) Nine crore four lakh six thousand two

(*ii*) Twelve crore seven lakh nine thousand two hundred seven.

(*iii*) Four lakh four thousand forty.

(*iv*) Twenty-one crore sixty lakh five thousand fourteen.

Sol. Using the place value chart, we may write

	Ten-Crores	Crores	Ten-Lakhs	Lakhs	Ten-Thousands	Thousands	Hundreds	Tens	Ones
(*i*)		9	0	4	0	6	0	0	2
(*ii*)	1	2	0	7	0	9	2	0	7
(*iii*)				4	0	4	0	4	0
(*iv*)	2	1	6	0	0	5	0	1	4

2. Face value and Place value (or Local Value) of a Digit In a Numeral

(*i*) The face value of a digit in a numeral is its own value, at whatever place it may be

Ex. In the numeral 6872, the face value of 2 is 2, the face value of 7 is 7, the face value of 8 is 8 and the face value of 6 is 6.

(*ii*) In a given numeral:

Place value of unit digit = (unit digit) × 1,

Place value of tens digit = (tens digit) × 10,

Place value of hundreds digit = (hundreds digit) × 100 and so on.

Ex. In the numeral 70984, we have

Place value of 4 = (4 × 1) = 4

Place value of 8 = (8 × 10) = 80,

Place value of 9 = (9 × 100) = 900,

Place value of 7 = (7 × 10000) = 70000.

Note: Place value of 0 in a given numeral is 0, at whatever place it may be.

Ex. 3. *In the numeral 8734925, write down:*

(*i*) *Face value of 7* (*ii*) *Face value of 9* (*iii*) *Place value of 4*

(*iv*) *Place value of 3* (*iv*) *Place value of 8* (*v*) *Place value of 5*

Sol. Writing the given numeral in place-value chart, we get

Ten-Lakhs	Lakhs	Ten-thousands	Thousands	Hundreds	Tens	Ones
8	7	3	4	9	2	5

(*i*) Face value of 7 is 7.

(*ii*) Face value of 9 is 9.

(*iii*) Place value of 4 = (4 × 1000) = 4000.

(*iv*) Place value of 3 = (3 × 10000) = 30000.

(*v*) Place value of 8 = (8 × 1000000) = 8000000.

(*vi*) Place value of 5 = (5 × 1) = 5.

3. Various Types of Numbers:

(*i*) **Natural Numbers:** *Counting numbers are called natural numbers.*

Thus 1, 2, 3, 4, 5, 6, ... are all natural numbers.

(*ii*) **Whole Numbers:** *All counting numbers and 0 form the set of whole numbers.*

Thus 0, 1, 2, 3, 4, 5, ... etc. are whole numbers.

Clearly, every natural number is a whole number and 0 is a whole number which is not a natural number.

(*iii*) **Integers:** All counting numbers, zero and negatives of counting numbers form the set of integers.

Thus, ..., –3, –2, –1, 0, 1 , 2, 3, ... are all integers.

Set of positive integers = {1, 2, 3, 4, 5, 6, ...}

Set of negative integers = {–1, –2, –3, –4, ...}

Set of all non-negative integers = {0, 1, 2, 3, 4, 5, ...}.

4. Even And Odd Numbers:

(*i*) **Even Numbers:** *A counting number divisible by 2 is called an even number.*

Thus 0, 2, 4, 6, 8, 10, 12, ... etc. are all even numbers.

(*ii*) **Odd Numbers:** *A counting number not divisible by 2 is called an odd number.*

Thus 1, 3, 5, 7, 9, 11, 13, 15, ... etc. are all odd numbers.

5. Prime Numbers: *A counting number is called a prime number if it has exactly two factors, namely itself and 1.*

Ex. All prime numbers less than 100 are:

2, 3, 5, 7, 11, 13, 17, 19, 23, 29, 31, 37, 41, 43, 47, 53, 59, 61, 67, 71, 73, 79, 83, 89, 97

Test For a Number To be Prime:

Let p be a given number and let n be the smallest counting number such that $n^2 \geq p$.

Now, test whether p is divisible by any of the prime numbers less than or equal to n. If yes, then p is not prime otherwise, p is prime.

Ex. 4. *Test, which of the following are prime numbers ?*

(*i*) 137 (*ii*) 173 (*iii*) 319 (*iv*) 437 (*v*) 811

Sol. (*i*) We know that $(12)^2 > 137$.

Prime numbers less than 12 are 2, 3, 5, 7, 11.

Clearly, none of them divides 137.

$\therefore$ 137 is a prime number.

(*ii*) We known that $(14)^2 > 173$.

Prime numbers less than 14 are 2, 3, 5, 7, 11, 13.

Clearly, none of them divides 173.

$\therefore$ 173 is a prime number.

(*iii*) We know that $(18)^2 > 319$.

Prime numbers less than 18 are 2, 3, 5, 7, 11, 13, 17.

Out of these prime numbers, 11 divides 319 completely.

$\therefore$ 319 is not a prime number.

(*iv*) We know that $(21)^2 > 437$.

Prime numbers less than 21 are 2, 3, 5, 7, 11, 13, 17, 19.

Clearly, 437 is divisible by 19.

$\therefore$ 437 is not a prime number.

(*v*) We know that $(29)^2 > 811$.

Prime numbers less than 29 are 2, 3, 5, 7, 11, 13, 17, 19, 23.

Clearly, none of these numbers divides 811.

$\therefore$ 811 is a prime number.

Composite Numbers: *The natural numbers which are not prime, are called composite numbers.*

6. Co Primes: Two natural numbers a and b are said to be co-prime if their HCF is 1.

Ex. (2, 3), (4, 5), (7, 9), (8, 11) etc. are pairs of co-primes.

TESTS OF DIVISIBILITY

I. Divisibility By 2:

A number is divisible by 2 if its unit digit is any of 0, 2, 4, 6, 8.

Ex. 58694 is divisible by 2, while 86945 is not divisible by 2.

II. Divisibility By 3:

A number is divisible by 3 only when the sum of its digits is divisible by 3.

Ex. (*i*) In the number 695421, the sum of digits = 27, which is divisible by 3.

$\therefore$ 695421 is divisible by 3.

(*ii*) In the number 948653, the sum of digits = 35, which is not divisible by 3.

$\therefore$ 948653 is not divisible by 3.

III. Divisibility By 9:

A number is divisible by 9 only when the sum of its digits is divisible by 9.

Ex. (*i*) In the number 246591, the sum of digits = 27, which is divisible by 9.

$\therefore$ 246591 is divisible by 9.

(*ii*) In the number 734519, the sum of digits = 29, which is not divisible by 9.

$\therefore$ 734519 is not divisible by 9.

IV. Divisibility By 4:

A number is divisible by 4 if the number formed by its last two digits is divisible by 4.

Ex. (*i*) 6879376 is divisible by 4, since 76 is divisible by 4.

(*ii*) 496138 is not divisible by 4, since 38 is not divisible by 4.

V. Divisibility By 8:

A number is divisible by 8 if the number formed by hundred's, ten's and unit's digit of the given number is divisible by 8.

Ex. (*i*) In the number 16789352, the number formed by last 3 digits, namely 352 is divisible by 8.

∴ 16789352 is divisible by 8.

(*ii*) In the number 576484, the number formed by last 3 digits, namely 484 is not divisible by 8.

∴ 576484 is not divisible by 8.

VI. Divisibility By 10:

A number is divisible by 10 only when its unit digit is 0.

Ex. (*i*) 7849320 is divisible by 10, since its unit digit is 0.

(*ii*) 678405 is not divisible by 10, since its unit digit is not 0.

VII. Divisibility By 5:

A number is divisible by 5 only when its unit digit is 0 or 5.

Ex. Each of the numbers 76895 and 68790 is divisible by 5.

VIII. Divisibility By 11:

A number is divisible by 11 if the difference between the sum of its digits at odd places and the sum of its digits at even places is either 0 or a number divisible by 11.

Ex. (*i*) Consider the number 29435417.

(Sum of its digits at odd places) – (Sum of its digits at even places)

= (7 + 4 + 3 + 9) – (1 + 5 + 4 + 2) = (23 – 12) = 11, which is divisible by 11.

∴ 29435417 is divisible by 11.

(*ii*) Consider the number 57463822.

(Sum of its digits at odd places) – (Sum of its digits at even places)

= (2 + 8 + 6 + 7) – (2 + 3 + 4 + 5) = (23 – 14) = 9, which is not divisible by 11.

∴ 57463822 is not divisible by 11.

SOLVED EXAMPLES

Ex. 1. *9587 – ? = 7429 – 4358.*

Sol. Let 9587 – x = 7429 – 4358. Then,

9587 – x = 3071 ⇒ x = 9587 – 3071 = 6516.

$$\begin{array}{r} 7429 \\ -\ 4358 \\ \hline 3071 \end{array}$$

Ex. 2. *5793405 × 9999 = ?*

Sol. 5793405 × 9999 = 5793405 × (10000 – 1)

= 57934050000 – 5793405

= 57928256595.

$$\begin{array}{r} 57934050000 \\ -5793405 \\ \hline 57928256595 \end{array}$$

Ex. 3. *839478 × 625 = ?*

Sol. 839478 × 625 = 839478 × 5^4

$$= 839478 \times \left(\frac{10}{2}\right)^4 = \frac{839478 \times 10^4}{2^4}$$

$$= \frac{8394780000}{16} = 524673750.$$

Ex. 4. *976 × 237 + 976 × 763 = ?*

Sol. Using distributive law, we get:

$976 \times 237 + 976 + 763 = 976 \times (237 + 763)$

$= 976 \times 1000 = 976000.$

Ex. 5. *986 × 307 – 986 × 207 = ?*

Sol. By distributive law, we get

$986 \times 307 - 986 \times 207 = 986 \times (307 - 207)$

$= 986 \times 100 = 98600.$

Ex. 6. *1607 × 1607 = ?*

Sol. $1607 \times 1607 = (1607)^2$

$= (1600 + 7)^2 = (1600)^2 + 7^2 + 2 \times 1600 \times 7$

$= 2560000 + 49 + 22400 = 2582449.$

$$\begin{array}{r} 2560000 \\ +\ 49 \\ +\ 22400 \\ \hline 2582449 \\ \hline \end{array}$$

Ex. 7. *1396 × 1396 = ?*

Sol. $1396 \times 1396 = (1396)^2$

$= (1400 - 4)^2 = (1400)^2 + 4^2 - 2 \times 1400 \times 4$

$= 1960000 + 16 - 11200 = 1948816.$

$$\begin{array}{r} 1960016 \\ -11200 \\ \hline 1948816 \\ \hline \end{array}$$

Ex. 8. *(475 × 475 + 125 × 125) = ?*

Sol. We have $(a^2 + b^2) = \frac{1}{2}\left[(a+b)^2 + (a-b)^2\right]$

$\therefore\ (475)^2 + (125)^2 = \frac{1}{2} \cdot \left[(475+125)^2 + (475-125)^2\right]$

$= \frac{1}{2} \cdot \left[(600)^2 + (350)^2\right] = \frac{1}{2} \cdot [360000 + 122500]$

$= \frac{1}{2} \times 482500 = 241250.$

Ex. 9. *(796 × 796 – 204 × 204) = ?*

Sol. $796 + 796 - 204 \times 204 = (796)^2 - (204)^2$

$= (796 + 204)\ (796 - 204)$

$= (1000 \times 592) = 592000.$

$[\because (a^2 - b^2) = (a + b)\ (a - b)]$

Ex. 10. *(387 × 387 + 113 × 113 + 2 × 387 × 113) = ?*

Sol. Given Exp. $= (387)^2 + (113)^2 + 2 \times 387 \times 113$

$= (a^2 + b^2 + 2ab)$, where $a = 387$ and $b = 113$

$= (a + b)^2 = (387 + 113)^2 = (500)^2 = 250000.$

Ex. 11. *(87 × 87 + 61 × 61 – 2 × 87 × 61) = ?*

Sol. Given Exp. $= (87)^2 + (61)^2 - 2 \times 87 \times 61$

$= (a^2 + b^2 - 2ab)$, where $a = 87$ and $b = 61$

$= (a - b)^2 = (87 - 61)^2 = (26)^2 = (20 + 6)^2$

$= (20)^2 + 6^2 + 2 \times 20 \times 6 = (400 + 36 + 240)$

$= (436 + 240) = 676.$

Ex. 12. *Find the least value of * for which 5967 * 13 is divisible by 3.*

Sol. Let the required value be x. Then,

$(5 + 9 + 6 + 7 + x + 1 + 3) = (31 + x)$ is divisible by 3.

$\therefore$ Least value of x is 2.

Ex. 13. *Find the least value of * for which 7 * 5462 is divisible by 9.*

Sol. Let the required value be x. Then.

$(7 + x + 5 + 4 + 6 + 2) = (24 + x)$ is divisible by 9.

$\therefore$ Least value of * is 3.

Ex. 14. *Find the least value of * for which 4832 * 18 is divisible by 11.*

Sol. (Sum of digits at odd places) – (Sum of digits at even places)

$= (8 + x + 3 + 4) - (1 + 2 + 8) = (4 + x)$, which should be divisible by 11.

$\therefore \quad x = 7.$

Ex. 15. *Show that 52563744 is divisible by 24.*

Sol. $24 = 3 \times 8$, where 3 and 8 are co-prime.

Sum of digits = 36, which is divisible by 3.

So, the given number is divisible by 3.

The number formed by last 3 digits = 744, which is divisible by 8.

So, the given number is divisible by 8.

Hence, it is divisible by (3×8), *i.e.*, 24.

Ex. 16. *What least number must be subtracted from 1672 to obtain a number which is completely divisible by 17 ?*

Sol.
```
17 ) 1672 ( 98
     153
     ---
      142
      136
      ---
        6
```
Number to be subtracted = 6.

Ex. 17. *What least number must be added to 2010 to obtain a number which is completely divisible by 19?*

Sol.
```
19 ) 2010 ( 105
     19
     ---
      110
       95
      ---
       15
```
Number to be added = (19 – 15) = 4.

Ex. 18. *On dividing 12401 by a certain number, we get 76 as quotient and 13 as remainder. What is the divisor ?*

Sol. [(Divisor) × (Quotient)] + Remainder = Dividend

$$\therefore \quad \text{Divisor} = \frac{(\text{Dividend}) - (\text{Remainder})}{\text{Quotient}}$$

$$= \frac{(12401 - 13)}{76} = \frac{\cancel{12388}\ \cancel{3097}\ 163}{\cancel{76}\ \cancel{19}\ 1} = 163.$$

Ex. 19. *On dividing a certain number by 342, we get 47 as remainder. If the same number is divided by 18, what will be the remainder ?*

Sol. Suppose that on dividing the given number by 342, we get quotient = k and remainder = 47. Then,

Number = $342k + 47$

$= (18 \times 19k) + (18 \times 2) + 11$

$= 18 \times (19k + 2) + 11.$

So, the number when divided by 18 gives remainder = 11.

Ex. 20. *Simplify:*

$$\frac{789\times789\times789+211\times211\times211}{789\times789-789\times211+211\times211}=?$$

Sol. Given Ex.p. $=\frac{(789)^3+(211)^3}{(789)^2-(789\times211)+(211)^2}$

$=\frac{(a^3+b^3)}{(a^2-ab+b^2)}$, where a = 789 and b = 211

$= (a + b) = (789 + 211) = 1000.$

Ex. 21. *Simplify:*

$$\frac{658\times658\times658-328\times328\times328}{658\times658+658\times328+328\times328}=?$$

Sol. Given Exp. $=\frac{(658)^3-(328)^3}{(658)^2+658\times328+(328)^2}$

$=\frac{(a^3-b^3)}{(a^2+ab+b^2)}$, where a = 658 and b = 328

$= (a - b) = (658 - 328) = 330.$

Ex. 22. *Simplify:*

$$\frac{(893+786)^2-(893-786)^2}{(893\times786)}=?$$

Sol. Given Exp. $=\frac{(a+b)^2-(a-b)^2}{ab}$, where a = 893 and b = 786

$=\frac{4ab}{ab}=4$

Ex. 23. *What is the unit digit in the product (684 × 759 × 413 × 676) ?*

Sol. Unit digit in the given product

= Unit digit in the product (4 × 9 × 3 × 6) = 8.

Ex. 24. *What is the unit digit in the product* $(3547)^{153} \times (251)^{72}$?

Sol. Required digit = unit digit in $(7^{153} \times 1^{72})$

Now, 7^4 gives unit digit 1 and $1^{72} = 1$.

$(7^{153} \times 1^{72}) = [(7^4)^{38} \times 7 \times 1]$

∴ Required unit digit = (1 × 7 × 1) = 7.

Ex. 25. *What is the unit digit in* $\{(264)^{102} + (264)^{103}\}$?

Sol. $(264)^{102} + (264)^{103} = (264)^{102}\{1 + 264\} = (264)^{102} \times 265$.

Required unit digit = unit digit in $[(4)^{102} \times 5]$

= unit digit in $[(4^4)^{25} \times 4^2 \times 5]$

= unit digit in (6 × 6 × 5) = 0.

Ex. 26. *Find the total number of prime factors in the product* $\{(4)^{11} \times 7^5 \times (11)^2\}$.

Sol. $\{(4)^{11} \times 7^5 \times (11)^2\} = (2 \times 2)^{11} \times 7^5 \times (11)^2 = (2^2)^{11} \times 7^5 \times (11)^2$

$= (2^{22} \times 7^5 \times 11^2)$

Required number of factors = (22 + 5 + 2) = 29.

Ex. 27. *Find the remainder when 2^{31} is divided by 5.*

Sol. $2^{31} = (2^{10} \times 2^{10} \times 2^{10}) \times 2 = (2^{10})^3 \times 2 = (1024)^3 \times 2$

Unit digit in 2^{31} = Unit digit in $\{(1024)^3 \times 2\} = (4 \times 2) = 8$.

Now, 8 when divided by 5 gives 3 as remainder

$\therefore$ 2^{31} when divided by 5 gives remainder = 3.

Ex. 28. *A number when successively divided by 1, 5 and 8 leaves remainders 1, 4 and 7 respectively. Find the respective remainders if the order of divisors be reversed.*

Sol.

3	x
5	$y - 1$
8	$z - 4$
	$1 - 7$

$\therefore z = (8 \times 1 + 7) = 15,\ y = (5 \times z + 4) = (5 \times 15 + 4) = 79,$
$x = (3y + 1) = (3 \times 79 + 1) = (237 + 1) = 238.$

8	238
5	$29 - 6$
3	$5 - 4$
	$1 - 2$

Hence, the respective remainders are 6, 4, 2.

Results On Some Series (Formulae)

(*i*) $(1+2+3+...+n) = \frac{1}{2}n(n+1)$

(*ii*) $(1^2+2^2+3^2+...+n^2) = \frac{1}{6}n(n+1)(2n+1)$

(*iii*) $(1^3+2^3+3^3+...+n^3) = \frac{1}{4}n^2(n+1)^2$

(*iv*) **Arithmetic Progression (A.P.)**

$a,\ a+d,\ a+2d,\ a+3d,$ .... are said to be in A.P. in which first term = a and common difference = d.

Let the nth term be t_n and let last term = l. Then

I. nth term = $a + (n-1)d$

II. Sum of n terms $= \frac{n}{2}[2a + (n-1)d]$

III. Sum of n terms $= \frac{n}{2}(a + l)$, where l is the last term.

(*v*) **Geometric Progression (G.P)**

$a, ar, ar^2, ar^3, ...$ are said to be in G.P. in which first term = a and common ratio = r

I. nth term = ar^{n-1}

II. Sum of n terms $= \begin{cases} \frac{a(1-r^n)}{(1-r)}, & \text{when } r < 1 \\ \frac{a(r^n-1)}{(r-1)}, & \text{when } r > 1 \end{cases}$

Ex. 29. *How many natural numbers between 17 and 80 are divisible by 6 ?*

Sol. These numbers are 18, 24, 30, 36, ..., 78.

This is an A.P. in which $a = 18$, $d = (24 - 18) = 6$ and $l = 78$.

Let the number of these terms be n. Then,

$t_n = 78 \Rightarrow a + (n-1)d = 78$

$\Rightarrow 18 + (n-1) \times 6 = 78 \Rightarrow (n-1) \times 6 = 60 \Rightarrow (n-1) = 10 \Rightarrow n = 11.$

Required number of numbers = 11.

Ex. 30. *Find the sum of all even natural numbers less than 75.*

Sol. Required sum = 2 + 4 + 6 + ...+ 74

This is an A.P. in which $a = 2$, $d = (4 - 2) = 2$, $l = 74$.

Clearly, $n = 37$.

$$\therefore \quad \text{Required sum} = \frac{n}{2}(a+l) = \frac{37}{2} \times (2+74) = (37 \times 38)$$
$$= 37 \times (40 - 2) = (37 \times 40) - (37 \times 2)$$
$$= (1480 - 74) = 1406.$$

Ex. 31. *(6 + 15 + 24 + 33 + ... + 105) = ?*

Sol. Given series in an A.P. in which $a = 6$, $d = (15 - 6) = 9$ and $l = 105$

Let the number of terms in it be n. Then,

$a + (n - 1) d = 105 \Rightarrow 6 + (n - 1) \times 9 = 105$
$\Rightarrow (n - 1) \times 9 = 99 \Rightarrow (n - 1) = 11 \Rightarrow n = 12.$

$$\text{Required sum} = \frac{n}{2}(a+l) = \frac{12}{2} \times (6+105) = (6 \times 111) = 666.$$

Ex. 32. *Find the sum $(2 + 2^2 + 2^3 + 2^4 + ... + 2^{10})$*

Sol. This is a G.P. in which $a = 2$, $r = \frac{2^2}{2} = \frac{4}{2} = 2$.

$$\text{Required sum} = \frac{a(r^n - 1)}{(r-1)} = \frac{2 \times (2^{10} - 1)}{(2-1)} = (2 \times 1023) = 2046.$$

EXERCISE 1

Mark (✔) against the correct answer in each of the following:

1. The difference between the place value and the face value of 6 in the numeral 856973 is
(a) 973 (b) 6973 (c) 5994 (d) none of these
2. The difference between the local value and the face value of 7 in the numeral 32675149 is
(a) 75142 (b) 64851 (c) 5149 (d) 69993
(e) none of these
3. The difference between the place values of two sevens in the numeral 69758472 is
(a) 0 (b) 6993 (c) 699930 (d) none of these
4. The unit digit in the product (784 × 618 × 917 × 463) is:
(a) 2 (b) 3 (c) 4 (d) 5
(S.S.C. 2005)
5. What is the unit digit in 7^{105} ?
(a) 1 (b) 5 (c) 7 (d) 9
(L.I.C. 2003)
6. What is the unit digit in the product $(3^{65} \times 6^{59} \times 7^{71})$?
(a) 1 (b) 2 (c) 4 (d) 6
7. What is the unit digit in $(7^{95} - 3^{58})$?
(a) 0 (b) 4 (c) 6 (d) 7
8. What is the unit digit in $(4137)^{754}$?
(a) 1 (b) 3 (c) 7 (d) 9
9. What is the unit digit in $\{(6374)^{1793} \times (625)^{317} \times (341)^{491}\}$?
(a) 0 (b) 2 (c) 3 (d) 5
(Bank P.O. 2003)
10. 7589 – ? = 3434
(a) 4242 (b) 4155 (c) 1123 (d) 11023
(e) none of these
11. 8597 – ? = 7429 – 4358
(a) 5426 (b) 5706 (c) 5526 (d) 5476
(e) none of these
(Bank P.O. 2007)
12. 3251 + 587 + 369 – ? = 3007
(a) 1250 (b) 1300 (c) 1375 (d) 1200
(e) none of these

13. (4300731) – ? = 2535618 *(Bank P.O. 2007)*
(*a*) 1865113 (*b*) 1775123 (*c*) 1765113 (*d*) 1675123
(*e*) none of these

14. (?) – 19657 – 33994 = 9999
(*a*) 63650 (*b*) 53760 (*c*) 59640 (*d*) 61560
(*e*) none of these

15. 3 + 33 + 333 + 3.33 = ?
(*a*) 362.3 (*b*) 372.33 (*c*) 702.33 (*d*) 702
(*e*) none of these

16. $9\frac{3}{4}+7\frac{2}{17}-9\frac{1}{15}=?$ *(Bank P.O. 2006)*
(*a*) $7\frac{719}{1020}$ (*b*) $9\frac{817}{1020}$ (*c*) $9\frac{719}{1020}$ (*d*) $7\frac{817}{1020}$
(*e*) none of these

17. –84 × 29 + 365 = ? *(Bank P.O. 2007)*
(*a*) 2436 (*b*) 2801 (*c*) –2801 (*d*) –2071
(*e*) none of these

18. (35423 + 7164 + 41720) – (317 × 89) = ?
(*a*) 28213 (*b*) 84307 (*c*) 56094 (*d*) 54094
(*e*) none of these

19. 9548 + 7314 = 8362 + ?
(*a*) 8230 (*b*) 8410 (*c*) 8500 (*d*) 8600
(*e*) none of these

20. (?) + 3699 + 1985 – 2047 = 31111
(*a*) 34748 (*b*) 27474 (*c*) 30154 (*d*) 27574
(*e*) none of these

21. 4500 × ? = 3375 *(Bank P.O. 2007)*
(*a*) $\frac{2}{5}$ (*b*) $\frac{3}{4}$ (*c*) $\frac{1}{4}$ (*d*) $\frac{3}{5}$
(*e*) none of these

22. If 1400 × x = 1050. Then, x = ?
(*a*) $\frac{1}{4}$ (*b*) $\frac{3}{5}$ (*c*) $\frac{2}{3}$ (*d*) $\frac{3}{4}$
(*e*) none of these

23. $(1000)^9 \div 10^{24} = ?$ *(Bank P.O. 2006)*
(*a*) 10000 (*b*) 1000 (*c*) 100 (*d*) 10
(*e*) none of these

24. 8988 ÷ 8 ÷ 4 = ? *(Bank P.O. 2007)*
(*a*) 4494 (*b*) 561.75 (*c*) 2247 (*d*) 280.875
(*e*) none of these

25. 666 ÷ 6 ÷ 3 = ? *(Bank P.O. 2006)*
(*a*) 37 (*b*) 333 (*c*) 111 (*d*) 84
(*e*) none of these

26. (800 ÷ 64) × (1296 ÷ 36) = ? *(Bank P.O. 2007)*
(*a*) 420 (*b*) 460 (*c*) 500 (*d*) 540
(*e*) none of these

27. $(12)^3 \times 6^4 \div 432 = ?$ *(Bank P.O. 2007)*
(*a*) 5184 (*b*) 5060 (*c*) 5148 (*d*) 5084
(*e*) none of these

28. 35 + 15 × 1.5 = ? *(Bank P.O. 2006)*
(*a*) 75 (*b*) 51.5 (*c*) 57.5 (*d*) 5.25
(*e*) none of these

(R.B.I. 2003)

29. $5358 \times 51 = ?$
(a) 273258 (b) 273268 (c) 273348 (d) 273358

30. $587 \times 999 = ?$
(a) 586413 (b) 587523 (c) 614823 (d) 615173

31. $3897 \times 999 = ?$
(a) 3883203 (b) 3893103 (c) 3639403 (d) 3791203
(e) none of these

32. $72519 \times 9999 = ?$
(a) 725117481 (b) 674217481 (c) 685126481 (d) 696217481
(e) none of these

33. $2056 \times 987 = ?$
(a) 1936372 (b) 2029272 (c) 1896172 (d) 1923472
(e) none of these

34. $1904 \times 1904 = ?$
(a) 3654316 (b) 3632646 (c) 3625216 (d) 3623436
(e) none of these

35. $1397 \times 1397 = ?$
(a) 1951609 (b) 1981709 (c) 18362619 (d) 2031719
(e) none of these

36. $107 \times 107 + 93 \times 93 = ?$
(a) 19578 (b) 19418 (c) 20098 (d) 21908
(e) none of these

(Hotel Management 2002)

37. $217 \times 217 + 183 \times 183 = ?$
(a) 79698 (b) 80578 (c) 80698 (d) 81268

(R.R.B. 2006)

38. $106 \times 106 - 94 \times 94 = ?$
(a) 2400 (b) 2000 (c) 1904 (d) 1906
(e) none of these

39. $8796 \times 223 + 8796 \times 77 = ?$
(a) 2736900 (b) 2638800 (c) 2658560 (d) 2716740
(e) none of these

40. $287 \times 287 + 269 \times 269 - 2 \times 287 \times 269 = ?$
(a) 534 (b) 446 (c) 354 (d) 324
(e) none of these

41. $\{(476 + 424)^2 - 4 \times 476 \times 424\} = ?$
(a) 2906 (b) 3116 (c) 2704 (d) 2904
(e) none of these

(M.B.A. 2002)

42. $(112 \times 5^4) = ?$
(a) 67000 (b) 70000 (c) 76500 (d) 77200

43. $(935421 \times 625) = ?$
(a) 575648125 (b) 584638125 (c) 584649125 (d) 585628125

44. $(12345679 \times 72) = ?$
(a) 88888888 (b) 888888888 (c) 898989898 (d) 9999999998

45. $397 \times 397 + 104 \times 104 + 2 \times 397 \times 104 = ?$
(a) 250001 (b) 251001 (c) 260101 (d) 261001

46. If $(64)^2 - (36)^2 = 20 \times x$, then $x = ?$
(a) 70 (b) 120 (c) 180 (d) 140
(e) none of these

47. $\dfrac{(489+375)^2 - (489-375)^2}{(489 \times 375)} = ?$
(a) 144 (b) 864 (c) 2 (d) 4
(e) none of these

48. $\dfrac{(963+476)^2 + (963-476)^2}{(963 \times 963 + 476 \times 476)} = ?$

(*a*) 1449 (*b*) 497 (*c*) 2 (*d*) 4
(*e*) none of these

49. $\dfrac{768 \times 768 \times 768 + 232 \times 232 \times 232}{768 \times 768 - 768 \times 232 + 232 \times 232} = ?$

(*a*) 1000 (*b*) 536 (*c*) 500 (*d*) 268
(*e*) none of these

50. $\dfrac{854 \times 854 \times 854 - 276 \times 276 \times 276}{854 \times 854 + 854 \times 276 + 276 \times 276} = ?$

(*a*) 1130 (*b*) 578 (*c*) 565 (*d*) 1156
(*e*) none of these

51. $\dfrac{753 \times 753 + 247 \times 247 - 753 \times 247}{753 \times 753 \times 753 + 247 \times 247 \times 247} = ?$

(*a*) $\dfrac{1}{1000}$ (*b*) $\dfrac{1}{506}$ (*c*) $\dfrac{253}{500}$ (*d*) none of these

52. If the number 517 * 324 is completely divisible by 3, then the smallest whole number in place of * will be:
(*a*) 0 (*b*) 1 (*c*) 2 (*d*) none of these

53. If the number 481 * 673 is completely divisible by 9, then the smallest whole number in place of * will be:
(*a*) 2 (*b*) 5 (*c*) 6 (*d*) 7
(*e*) none of these

54. If the number 97215 * 6 is completely divisible by 11, then the smallest whole number in place of * will be:
(*a*) 3 (*b*) 2 (*c*) 1 (*d*) 5
(*e*) none of these

55. If the number 91876 * 2 is completely divisible by 8, then the smallest whole number in place of * will be:
(*a*) 1 (*b*) 2 (*c*) 3 (*d*) 4
(*e*) none of these

56. Which one of the following numbers is completely divisible by 45 ?
(*a*) 181560 (*b*) 331145 (*c*) 202860 (*d*) 203550
(*e*) none of these

57. Which one of the following numbers is completely divisible by 99 ?
(*a*) 3572404 (*b*) 135792 (*c*) 913464 (*d*) 114345
(*e*) none of these

58. If the number 42573 * is exactly divisible by 72, then the minimum value of * is:
(*a*) 4 (*b*) 5 (*c*) 6 (*d*) 7 (*e*) 8

59. If x and y are the two digits of the number 653 xy such that this number is divisible by 80, then $x + y = ?$
(*a*) 2 (*b*) 3 (*c*) 4 (*d*) 6
(*e*) none of these

60. If the product 4864 × 9 P 2 is divisible by 12, the value of P is:
(*a*) 2 (*b*) 5 (*c*) 6 (*d*) 8
(*e*) none of these

61. If the number 5 * 2 is divisible by 6, then * = ?
(*a*) 2 (*b*) 3 (*c*) 6 (*d*) 7

62. Which of the following numbers is divisible by 24 ?
(*a*) 35718 (*b*) 63810 (*c*) 537804 (*d*) 3125736

63. How many of the following numbers are divisible by 132 ?
264, 396, 462, 792, 968, 2178, 5184, 6336 (*Hotel Management, 2002*)
(*a*) 4 (*b*) 5 (*c*) 6 (*d*) 7

64. 476 ** 0 is divisible by both 3 and 11. The non-zero digits in the hundred's and ten's places are respectively:
(*a*) 7 and 4 (*b*) 7 and 5 (*c*) 8 and 5 (*d*) none of these

65. Which one of the following numbers is exactly divisible by 11 ? *(C.D.S. 2003)*
(*a*) 235641 (*b*) 245642 (*c*) 315624 (*d*) 415624

66. How many 3 digit numbers are divisible by 6 in all ?
(*a*) 149 (*b*) 150 (*c*) 151 (*d*) 166

67. The sum of first 45 natural numbers is :
(*a*) 1035 (*b*) 1280 (*c*) 2070 (*d*) 2140

68. The sum of even numbers between 1 and 31 is :
(*a*) 6 (*b*) 128 (*c*) 240 (*d*) 512

69. (51 + 52 + 53 + ... + 100) = ?
(*a*) 2525 (*b*) 2975 (*c*) 3225 (*d*) 3775

70. The smallest prime number is:
(*a*) 0 (*b*) 1 (*c*) 2 (*d*) 3

71. The sum of first five prime numbers is :
(*a*) 11 (*b*) 18 (*c*) 26 (*d*) 28

72. How many prime numbers are less than 50 ?
(*a*) 16 (*b*) 15 (*c*) 14 (*d*) 18

73. Which of the following is a prime number ?
(*a*) 33 (*b*) 81 (*c*) 93 (*d*) 97

74. Which one of the following is not a prime number ?
(*a*) 31 (*b*) 61 (*c*) 71 (*d*) 91

75. Which one of the following is a prime number ?
(*a*) 161 (*b*) 221 (*c*) 373 (*d*) 437
(*e*) none of these

76. Which one of the following is a prime number ?
(*a*) 119 (*b*) 187 (*c*) 247 (*d*) 551
(*e*) none of these

77. The smallest 3-digit prime number is:
(*a*) 103 (*b*) 107 (*c*) 109 (*d*) 113
(*e*) none of these

78. If a and b are odd numbers, then which of the following is even ?
(*a*) $a + b$ (*b*) $a + b + 1$ (*c*) ab (*d*) $ab + 2$
(*e*) none of these

79. Which one of the following cannot be the square of a natural number ?
(*a*) 30976 (*b*) 75625 (*c*) 28561 (*d*) 143642
(*e*) none of these

80. Which one of the following cannot be the square of a natural number ?
(*a*) 32761 (*b*) 81225 (*c*) 42437 (*d*) 20164
(*e*) none of these

81. What smallest number should be added to 4456 so that the sum is completely divisible by 6 ?
(*a*) 4 (*b*) 3 (*c*) 2 (*d*) 1
(*e*) none of these

82. Which natural number is nearest to 9217, which is completely divisible by 88 ?
(*a*) 9152 (*b*) 9240 (*c*) 9064 (*d*) 9184
(*e*) none of these

83. Which natural number is nearest to 8485, which is completely divisible by 75 ?
(*a*) 8475 (*b*) 8500 (*c*) 8550 (*d*) 8525
(*e*) none of these

84. The largest 4-digit number exactly divisible by 88 is
(*a*) 9944 (*b*) 9768 (*c*) 9988 (*d*) 8888
(*e*) none of these

85. The largest 5-digit number exactly divisible by 91 is
(*a*) 99921 (*b*) 99918 (*c*) 99981 (*d*) 99971
(*e*) none of these

86. What least number must be subtracted from 13601, so that the remainder is divisible by 87 ?
(*a*) 23 (*b*) 31 (*c*) 29 (*d*) 37
(*e*) 49

87. What least number must be added to 1056, so that the sum is completely divisible by 23?
(*a*) 2 (*b*) 3 (*c*) 18 (*d*) 21
(*e*) none of these

88. The smallest 5-digit number exactly divisible by 41 is :
(*a*) 10041 (*b*) 10004 (*c*) 10045 (*d*) 10025
(*e*) none of these

89. The smallest 6-digit number exactly divisible by 111 is :
(*a*) 111111 (*b*) 110011 (*c*) 100011 (*d*) 110101
(*e*) none of these

90. In a division sum, the divisor is 10 times the quotient and 5 times the remainder. If the remainder is 46, what is the dividend ?
(*a*) 4236 (*b*) 4306 (*c*) 4336 (*d*) 5336
(*e*) none of these

91. On dividing a number by 68, we get 269 as quotient and 0 as remainder. On dividing the same number by 67, what will be the remainder ? (*S.S.C. 2005*)
(*a*) 0 (*b*) 1 (*c*) 2 (*d*) 3

92. On dividing a number by 56, we get 29 as remainder. On dividing the same number by 8, what will be the remainder ? (*S.S.C 2007*)
(*a*) 4 (*b*) 5 (*c*) 6 (*d*) 7

93. On dividing a number by 357, we get 39 as remainder. On dividing the same number by 17, what will be the remainder ? (*S.S.C. 2005*)
(*a*) 0 (*b*) 3 (*c*) 5 (*d*) 11

94. On dividing a number by 5, we get 3 as remainder. What will be the remainder when the square of this number is divided by 5 ? (*S.S.C. 2005*)
(*a*) 0 (*b*) 1 (*c*) 2 (*d*) 4

95. The difference of two numbers is 1365. On dividing the larger number by the smaller, we get 6 as quotient and 15 as remainder. What is the smaller number ? (*L.I.C. 2003*)
(*a*) 240 (*b*) 270 (*c*) 295 (*d*) 360

96. In a division sum, the remainder is 0. A student mistook the divisor by 12 instead of 21 and obtained 35 as quotient. What is the correct quotient ? (*S.S.C. 2003*)
(*a*) 0 (*b*) 12 (*c*) 13 (*d*) 20

97. The sum of the two numbers is 12 and their product is 35. What is the sum of the reciprocals of these numbers ? (*S.S.C. 2007*)
(*a*) $\frac{12}{35}$ (*b*) $\frac{1}{35}$ (*c*) $\frac{35}{8}$ (*d*) $\frac{7}{32}$

98. If 60% of $\frac{3}{5}$ of a number is 36, then the number is :
(*a*) 80 (*b*) 100 (*c*) 75 (*d*) 90

99. The difference between a positive proper fraction and its reciprocal is $\frac{9}{20}$. The fraction is : (*S.S.C. 2006*)
(*a*) $\frac{3}{5}$ (*b*) $\frac{3}{10}$ (*c*) $\frac{4}{5}$ (*d*) $\frac{5}{4}$

100. On dividing 2272 as well as 875 by 3-digit number N, we get the same remainder. The sum of the digits of N is : (*S.S.C. 2007*)
(*a*) 10 (*b*) 11 (*c*) 12 (*d*) 13

101. On multiplying a number by 7, the product is a number each of whose digits is 3. The smallest such number is : (*S.S.C. 2006*)
(*a*) 47619 (*b*) 47719 (*c*) 48619 (*d*) 47649

102. The difference of the squares of two consecutive even integers is divisible by which of the following integers ? (*M.B.A. 2003*)
(*a*) 3 (*b*) 4 (*c*) 6 (*d*) 7

103. The difference of the squares of two consecutive odd integers is divisible by which of the following integers ? (*M.B.A. 2003*)
(*a*) 3 (*b*) 6 (*c*) 7 (*d*) 8

104. If n is a natural number, then $(6n^2 + 6n)$ is always divisible by : *(M.B.A. 2005)*
(*a*) 6 only (*b*) 6 and 12 both (*c*) 12 only (*d*) by 18 only

105. n is a whole number which when divided by 4 gives 3 as remainder. What will be the remainder when $2n$ is divided by 4 ?
(*a*) 3 (*b*) 2 (*c*) 1 (*d*) 0

106. What will be the remainder when $(67^{67} + 67)$ is divided by 68 ?
(*a*) 1 (*b*) 63 (*c*) 66 (*d*) 67

107. Which of the following numbers will completely divide $(49^{15} - 1)$?
(*a*) 8 (*b*) 14 (*c*) 48 (*d*) 50

108. $(x^n - a^n)$ is completely divisible by $(x - a)$, when
(*a*) n is any natural number (*b*) n is an even natural number
(*c*) n is an odd natural number (*d*) n is prime

109. What will be the remainder when 17^{200} is divided by 18 ? *(S.S.C. 2006)*
(*a*) 17 (*b*) 16 (*c*) 1 (*d*) 2

110. Which one of the following is the common factor of $(47^{43} + 43^{43})$ and $(47^{47} + 43^{47})$?
(*a*) $(47 - 43)$ (*b*) $(47 + 43)$ (*c*) $(47^{43} + 43^{43})$ (*d*) none of these

111. It is being given that $(2^{32} + 1)$ is completely divisible by a whole number. Which of the following numbers is completely divisible by this number ? *(S.S.C. 2007)*
(*a*) $(2^{16} + 1)$ (*b*) $(2^{16} - 1)$ (*c*) 7×2^{33} (*d*) $(2^{96} + 1)$

112. Which one of the following numbers will completely divide $(4^{61} + 4^{62} + 4^{63} + 4^{64})$?
(*a*) 3 (*b*) 10 (*c*) 11 (*d*) 13

113. Which one of the following numbers will completely divide $(3^{25} + 3^{26} + 3^{27} + 3^{28})$?
(*a*) 11 (*b*) 16 (*c*) 25 (*d*) 30

114. A 3-digit number $4a3$ is added to another 3-digit number 984 to give a 4-digit number $13b7$, which is divisible by 11. Then, $(a + b) = ?$
(*a*) 10 (*b*) 11 (*c*) 12 (*d*) 15

115. If x and y are positive integers such that $(3x + 7y)$ is a multiple of 11, then which of the following will be divisible by 11 ?
(*a*) $4x + 6y$ (*b*) $x + y + 4$ (*c*) $9x + 4y$ (*d*) $4x - 9y$

116. If the number 653 xy is divisible by 90, then $(x + y) = ?$
(*a*) 2 (*b*) 3 (*c*) 4 (*d*) 6

117. How many of the following numbers are divisible by 3 but not by 9 ?
2133, 2343, 3474, 4131, 5286, 5340, 6336, 7347, 8115, 9276
(*a*) 5 (*b*) 6 (*c*) 7 (*d*) none of these

118. Which of the following numbers is divisible by each one of 3, 7, 9 and 11 ?
(*a*) 639 (*b*) 2079 (*c*) 3791 (*d*) 37911
(*e*) none of these

119. How many of the following numbers are divisible by 132 ? *(Hotel Management, 2002)*
264, 396, 462, 792, 968, 2178, 5184, 6336
(*a*) 4 (*b*) 5 (*c*) 6 (*d*) 7

120. A number when divided by 6 leaves a remainder 3. When the square of the number is divided by 6, the remainder is :
(*a*) 0 (*b*) 1 (*c*) 2 (*d*) 3

121. A number when divided successively by 4 and 5 leaves remainders 1 and 4 respectively. When it is successively divided by 5 and 4, then the respective remainders will be *(S.S.C. 2003)*
(*a*) 1, 2 (*b*) 2, 3 (*c*) 3, 2 (*d*) 4, 1

122. A number was divided successively in order by 4, 5 and 6. The remainders were respectively 2, 3 and 4. The number is
(*a*) 214 (*b*) 476 (*c*) 954 (*d*) 1908

123. In dividing a number by 585, a student employed the method of short division. He divided the number successively by 5, 9 and 13 (factors of 585) and got the remainders 4, 8, 12 respectively. If he had divided the number by 585, the remainder would have been
(*a*) 24 (*b*) 144 (*c*) 292 (*d*) 584

124. When a number is divided by 13, the remainder is 11. When the same number is divided by 17, the remainder is 9. What is the number ?
(*a*) 339 (*b*) 349 (*c*) 369
(*d*) data inadequate

125. A number when divided by 296 leaves 75 as remainder. When the same number is divided by 37, the remainder will be : (*C.B.I. 2003*)
(*a*) 1 (*b*) 2 (*c*) 8 (*d*) 11

126. A boy multiplied 987 by a certain number and obtained 559981 as his answer. If in the answer both 9s are wrong and the other digits are correct, then the correct answer would be :
(*a*) 553681 (*b*) 555181 (*c*) 555681 (*d*) 556581

127. How many 3-digit numbers are completely divisible by 6 ?
(*a*) 149 (*b*) 150 (*c*) 151 (*d*) 166

128. The sum of first 45 natural numbers is :
(*a*) 1035 (*b*) 1280 (*c*) 2070 (*d*) 2140

129. The sum of all even natural numbers between 1 and 31 is
(*a*) 16 (*b*) 128 (*c*) 240 (*d*) 512

130. (51 + 52 + 53 + ... + 100) = ?
(*a*) 2525 (*b*) 2975 (*c*) 3225 (*d*) 3775

131. $\left(1-\frac{1}{n}\right)+\left(1-\frac{2}{n}\right)+\left(1-\frac{3}{n}\right)+\ldots$ upto n terms = ?
(*a*) $\frac{1}{2}n$ (*b*) $\frac{1}{2}(n-1)$ (*c*) $\frac{1}{2}n(n-1)$ (*d*) none of these

132. How many natural numbers are there between 23 and 100 which are exactly divisible by 6 ?
(*a*) 8 (*b*) 11 (*c*) 12 (*d*) 13
(*e*) none of these

133. The sum of all two digit numbers divisible by 5 is
(*a*) 1035 (*b*) 1245 (*c*) 1230 (*d*) 945
(*e*) none of these

134. The sum of how many terms of the series 6 + 12 + 18 + 24 + ... is 1800 ?
(*a*) 16 (*b*) 24 (*c*) 20 (*d*) 18
(*e*) 22

135. How many terms are there in the G.P. 3, 6, 12, 24, ..., 384 ?
(*a*) 8 (*b*) 9 (*c*) 10 (*d*) 11
(*e*) 7

136. $2 + 2^2 + 2^3 + \ldots + 2^9$ = ?
(*a*) 2044 (*b*) 1022 (*c*) 1056 (*d*) none of these

137. $(1^2 + 2^2 + 3^2 + \ldots + 10^2)$ = ?
(*a*) 330 (*b*) 345 (*c*) 365 (*d*) 385

138. $(2^2 + 4^2 + 6^2 + \ldots + 20^2)$ = ?
(*a*) 770 (*b*) 1155 (*c*) 1540 (*d*) 385 × 385

139. $(11^2 + 12^2 + 13^2 + \ldots + 20^2)$ = ?
(*a*) 385 (*b*) 2485 (*c*) 2870 (*d*) 3255

ANSWERS

1. (*c*)	**2.** (*d*)	**3.** (*c*)	**4.** (*a*)	**5.** (*c*)	**6.** (*c*)	**7.** (*b*)	**8.** (*d*)
9. (*a*)	**10.** (*b*)	**11.** (*c*)	**12.** (*d*)	**13.** (*c*)	**14.** (*a*)	**15.** (*b*)	**16.** (*d*)
17. (*d*)	**18.** (*c*)	**19.** (*c*)	**20.** (*b*)	**21.** (*b*)	**22.** (*d*)	**23.** (*b*)	**24.** (*d*)
25. (*a*)	**26.** (*e*)	**27.** (*a*)	**28.** (*c*)	**29.** (*a*)	**30.** (*a*)	**31.** (*b*)	**32.** (*a*)
33. (*b*)	**34.** (*c*)	**35.** (*a*)	**36.** (*c*)	**37.** (*b*)	**38.** (*a*)	**39.** (*b*)	**40.** (*d*)
41. (*c*)	**42.** (*b*)	**43.** (*b*)	**44.** (*b*)	**45.** (*b*)	**46.** (*d*)	**47.** (*d*)	**48.** (*c*)
49. (*a*)	**50.** (*b*)	**51.** (*a*)	**52.** (*c*)	**53.** (*d*)	**54.** (*a*)	**55.** (*c*)	**56.** (*c*)
57. (*d*)	**58.** (*c*)	**59.** (*a*)	**60.** (*e*)	**61.** (*a*)	**62.** (*d*)	**63.** (*a*)	**64.** (*c*)
65. (*d*)	**66.** (*b*)	**67.** (*a*)	**68.** (*c*)	**69.** (*d*)	**70.** (*c*)	**71.** (*d*)	**72.** (*b*)
73. (*d*)	**74.** (*d*)	**75.** (*c*)	**76.** (*e*)	**77.** (*e*)	**78.** (*a*)	**79.** (*d*)	**80.** (*c*)
81. (*c*)	**82.** (*b*)	**83.** (*a*)	**84.** (*a*)	**85.** (*b*)	**86.** (*c*)	**87.** (*a*)	**88.** (*b*)
89. (*c*)	**90.** (*d*)	**91.** (*b*)	**92.** (*b*)	**93.** (*c*)	**94.** (*d*)	**95.** (*b*)	**96.** (*d*)
97. (*a*)	**98.** (*b*)	**99.** (*c*)	**100.** (*a*)	**101.** (*a*)	**102.** (*b*)	**103.** (*d*)	**104.** (*b*)
105. (*b*)	**106.** (*c*)	**107.** (*a*)	**108.** (*a*)	**109.** (*c*)	**110.** (*b*)	**111.** (*d*)	**112.** (*b*)
113. (*d*)	**114.** (*a*)	**115.** (*d*)	**116.** (*c*)	**117.** (*b*)	**118.** (*b*)	**119.** (*a*)	**120.** (*d*)
121. (*b*)	**122.** (*a*)	**123.** (*d*)	**124.** (*b*)	**125.** (*a*)	**126.** (*c*)	**127.** (*b*)	**128.** (*a*)
129. (*c*)	**130.** (*d*)	**131.** (*b*)	**132.** (*d*)	**133.** (*d*)	**134.** (*b*)	**135.** (*a*)	**136.** (*b*)
137. (*d*)	**138.** (*c*)	**139.** (*b*)					

SOLUTIONS

1. (Place value of 6) – (Face Value of 6)

$= (6000 - 6) = 5994.$

2. (Local value of 7) – (Face value of 7)

$= (70000 - 7) = 69993.$

3. Required difference $= (700000 - 70) = 699930.$

4. Unit digit in the given product = Unit digit in $(4 \times 8 \times 7 \times 3) = 2.$

5. Unit digit in 7^{105} = Unit digit in $[(7^4)^{26} \times 7]$.

But, unit digit in $(7^4)^{26} = 1.$

$\therefore$ Unit digit in $7^{105} = (1 \times 7) = 7.$

6. Unit digit in $3^4 = 1 \Rightarrow$ Unit digit in $(3^4)^{16} = 1.$

$\therefore$ Unit digit in 3^{65} = Unit digit in $[(3^4)^{16} \times 3] = (1 \times 3) = 3.$

Unit digit in $6^{59} = 6.$

Unit digit in $7^4 = 1 \Rightarrow$ Unit digit in $(7^4)^{17}$ is 1.

Unit digit in 7^{71} = Unit digit in $[(7^4)^{17} \times 7^3] = (1 \times 3) = 3.$

$\therefore$ Required digit = Unit digit in $(3 \times 6 \times 3) = 4.$

7. Unit digit in 7^{95} = Unit digit in $[(7^4)^{23} \times 7^3] = (1 \times 3) = 3.$

Unit digit in 3^{58} = Unit digit in $[(3^4)^{14} \times 3^2] = (1 \times 9) = 9.$

Unit digit in $(7^{95} - 3^{58}) = (13 - 9) = 4.$

8. Unit digit in $(4137)^{754}$ = Unit digit in $\left\{\left\{(4137)^4\right\}^{188} \times (4137)^2\right\} = (1 \times 9) = 9.$

9. Unit digit in $(6374)^{1793}$ = Unit digit in $(4)^{1793}$

= Unit digit in $[(4^2)^{896} \times 4]$

= Unit digit in $(6 \times 4) = 4.$

Unit digit in $(625)^{317}$ = Unit digit in $(5)^{317} = 5.$

Unit digit in $(341)^{491}$ = Unit digit in $(1)^{491} = 1.$

Required digit = Unit digit in $(4 \times 5 \times 1) = 0.$

10. Let $7589 - x = 3434$.
Then, $x = 7589 - 3434 = 4155$

$$\begin{array}{r} 7589 \\ -\ 3434 \\ \hline 4155 \end{array}$$

11.
$$\begin{array}{r} 7429 \\ -4358 \\ \hline 3071 \end{array}$$

Let $8597 - x = 3071$
Then, $x = 8597 - 3071$

$$\begin{array}{r} 8597 \\ -\ 3071 \\ \hline 5526 \end{array}$$

12.
$$\begin{array}{r} 3251 \\ +\ 587 \\ +\ 369 \\ \hline 4207 \end{array}$$

Let $4207 - x = 3007$
Then, $x = 4207 - 3007 = 1200$.

13. Let $4300731 - x = 2535618$
Then, $x = 4300731 - 2535618$

$$\begin{array}{r} 4300731 \\ -2535618 \\ \hline 1765113 \end{array}$$

14.
$$\begin{array}{r} 19657 \\ 33994 \\ \hline 53651 \end{array}$$

Let $x - 53651 = 9999$
Then, $x = 9999 + 53651 = 9999 + 1 + 53650$
$= 10000 + 53650 = 63650$.

15.
$$\begin{array}{r} 3 \\ +\ 33 \\ +\ 333 \\ +\ 3.33 \\ \hline 372.33 \end{array}$$

16. Given sum $= 9+\frac{3}{4}+7+\frac{2}{17}-\left(9+\frac{1}{15}\right)$

$$=(9+7-9)+\left(\frac{3}{4}+\frac{2}{17}-\frac{1}{15}\right)$$

$$=7+\frac{765+120-68}{1020}=7\frac{817}{1020}$$

17. Given Exp. $= -84 \times (30 - 1) + 365$
$= -(84 \times 30) + 84 + 365$
$= -2520 + 449 = -2071$

$$\begin{array}{r} -\ 2520 \\ +\ 449 \\ \hline -\ 2071 \end{array}$$

18.
$$\begin{array}{r} 35423 \\ +\ 7164 \\ +\ 41720 \\ \hline 84307 \\ -\ 28213 \\ \hline 56094 \end{array}$$

$317 \times 89 = 317 \times (90 - 1)$
$= (317 \times 90 - 317)$
$= (28530 - 317) = 28213$

19.
$$\begin{array}{r} 9548 \\ +\ 7314 \\ \hline 16862 \end{array}$$

$16862 = 8362 + x \Rightarrow x = 16862 - 8362 = 8500$.

20. $x + 3699 + 1985 - 2047 = 31111$

$\Rightarrow \quad x + 3699 + 1985 = 31111 + 2047$

$\Rightarrow \quad x + 5684 = 33158$

$\Rightarrow \quad x = 33158 - 5684 = 27474.$

$$\begin{array}{r} 33158 \\ -5684 \\ \hline 27474 \end{array}$$

21. $4500 \times x = 3375 \quad \Rightarrow \quad x = \frac{\cancel{3375}^{75}}{\cancel{4500}_{100}} = \frac{3}{4}$

$$\begin{array}{r} 45\,)3375(\,75 \\ 315 \\ \hline 225 \\ 225 \\ \hline \times \end{array}$$

22. $1400 \times x = 1050 \Rightarrow x = \frac{1050}{1400} = \frac{3}{4}.$

23. Given Exp. $= \frac{(1000)^9}{10^{24}} = \frac{(10^3)^9}{10^{24}} = \frac{10^{27}}{10^{24}} = 10^{(27-24)} = 10^3 = 1000.$

24. Given Exp. $= 8988 \times \frac{1}{8} \times \frac{1}{4} = \frac{2247}{8} = 280.875.$

25. Given Exp. $= 666 \times \frac{1}{6} \times \frac{1}{3} = 37.$

26. Given Exp. $= \frac{\cancel{800}^{50}}{\cancel{64}_{4}} \times \frac{\cancel{1296}^{\cancel{216}^{\cancel{36}^{9}}}}{\cancel{36}_{6}} = 450.$

27. Given Exp. $= \frac{(12)^3 \times 6^4}{432} = \frac{(12)^3 \times 6^4}{12 \times 6^2} = (12)^2 \times 6^2 = (72)^2 = 5184.$

28. Given Exp. $= 35 + 15 \times \frac{3}{2} = 35 + \frac{45}{2} = 35 + 22.5 = 57.5.$

29. $5358 \times 51 = 5358 \times (50 + 1)$

$= 5358 \times 50 + 5358 \times 1$

$= 267900 + 5358 = 273258.$

$$\begin{array}{r} 267900 \\ +\,5358 \\ \hline 273258 \end{array}$$

30. $587 \times 999 = 587 \times (1000 - 1)$

$= 587 \times 1000 \times 587 \times 1 = 587000 - 587 = 586413.$

31. $3897 \times 999 = 3897 \times (1000 - 1)$

$= 3897 \times 1000 - 3897 \times 1$

$= 3897000 - 3897 = 3893103.$

$$\begin{array}{r} 3897000 \\ -\,3897 \\ \hline 3893103 \end{array}$$

32. $72519 \times 9999 = 72519 \times (10000 - 1)$

$= 72519 \times 10000 - 72519 \times 1$

$= 725190000 - 72519 = 725117481.$

$$\begin{array}{r} 725190000 \\ -72519 \\ \hline 725117481 \end{array}$$

33. $2056 \times 987 = 2056 \times (1000 - 13)$

$= 2056 \times 1000 - 2056 \times 13$

$= 2056000 - 26728 = 2029272$

$$\begin{array}{r} 2056000 \\ -26728 \\ \hline 2029272 \end{array}$$

34. $1904 \times 1904 = (1904)^2 = (1900 + 4)^2$

$= (1900)^2 + 4^2 + 2 \times 1900 \times 4 = 3610000 + 16 + 15200$

$= 3610016 + 15200 = 3625216.$

35. $1397 \times 1397 = (1397)^2 = (1400 - 3)^2$

$= (1400)^2 + 3^2 - 2 \times 1400 \times 3 = 1960000 + 9 - 8400$

$= 1960009 - 8400 = 1951609.$

$$\begin{array}{r} 1960009 \\ -8400 \\ \hline 1951609 \\ \hline \end{array}$$

36. $107 \times 107 + 93 \times 93 = (107)^2 + (93)^2 = (100 + 7)^2 + (100 - 7)^2$

$= 2 \times [(100)^2 + 7^2] = 2\ (10000 + 49) = 2 \times 10049 = 20098$

$[\because (a + b)^2 + (a - b)^2 = 2(a^2 + b^2)]$

37. $(217)^2 + (183)^2 = (200 + 17)^2 + (200 - 17)^2$

$= 2[(200)^2 + (17)^2]$ $\quad [(a + b)^2 + (a - b)^2 = 2(a^2 + b^2)]$

$= 2[40000 + 289] = (2 \times 40289) = 80578.$

38. $106 \times 106 - 94 \times 94 = (106)^2 - (94)^2 = (106 + 94)\ (106 - 94)$ $\quad [(a^2 - b^2) = (a + b)\ (a - b)]$

$= (200 \times 12) = 2400.$

39. $8796 \times 223 + 8796 \times 77 = 8796 \times (223 + 77)$ [*by distributive law*]

$= (8796 \times 300) = 2638800.$

40. Given Exp. $= a^2 + b^2 - 2ab$, where $a = 287$ and $b = 269$

$= (a - b)^2 = (287 - 269)^2 = (18)^2 = 324.$

41. Given Exp. $= [(a + b)^2 - 4ab]$, where $a = 476$ and $b = 424$

$= (a - b)^2$

$= (476 - 424)^2$

$= (52)^2 = 2704.$

42. $(112 \times 5^4) = 112 \times \left(\frac{10}{2}\right)^4 = \frac{112 \times 10^4}{2^4} = \frac{1120000}{16} = 70000.$

43. $935421 \times 625 = 935421 \times 5^4 = 935421 \times \left(\frac{10}{2}\right)^4$

$= \frac{935421 \times 10^4}{2^4} = \frac{9354210000}{16}$

$= 584638125.$

44. $12345679 \times 72 = 12345679 \times (70 + 2)$

$= 12345679 \times 70 + 12345679 \times 2$

$= 864197530 + 24691358$

$= 888888888$

$$\begin{array}{r} 864197530 \\ 24691358 \\ \hline 888888888 \\ \hline \end{array}$$

45. Given Exp. $= (397)^2 + (104)^2 + 2 \times 397 \times 104$

$= (397 + 104)^2 = (501)^2 = (500 + 1)^2$

$= (500)^2 + 1^2 + 2 \times 500 \times 1 = 250000 + 1 + 1000$

$= 251001.$

46. $20 \times x = (64 + 36)\ (64 - 36) = 100 \times 28$

$\Rightarrow \quad x = \frac{100 \times 28}{20} = 140.$

47. Given Exp. $= \frac{(a+b)^2 - (a-b)^2}{ab} = \frac{4ab}{ab} = 4.$

48. Given Exp. $= \frac{(a+b)^2 + (a-b)^2}{(a^2 + b^2)} = \frac{2(a^2 + b^2)}{(a^2 + b^2)} = 2.$

49. Given Exp. $= \frac{(a^3 + b^3)}{(a^2 - ab + b^2)} = (a + b) = (768 + 232) = 1000.$

50. Given Exp. $\frac{(a^3-b^3)}{(a^2+ab+b^2)} = (a-b) = (854-276) = 578.$

51. Given Exp. $= \frac{(a^2+b^2-ab)}{(a^3+b^3)} = \frac{1}{(a+b)} = \frac{1}{(753+247)} = \frac{1}{1000}.$

52. Sum of digits = (5 + 1 + 7 + x + 3 + 2 + 4) = (22 + x), which must be divisible by 3.
∴ $x = 2$.

53. Sum of digits = (4 + 8 + 1 + x + 6 + 7 + 3) = (29 + x), which must be divisible by 9.
∴ $x = 7$.

54. Given number = 97215x6
(6 + 5 + 2 + 9) – (x + 1 + 7) = (14 – x), which must be divisible by 11.
∴ $x = 3$.

55. The number 6x2 must be divisible by 8.
∴ x = 3, as 632 is divisible by 8.

56. 45 = 5 × 9, where 5 and 9 are co-primes.
Unit digit must be 0 or 5 and sum of digits must be divisible by 9.
Among given numbers, such number is 202860.

57. 99 = 11 × 9, where 11 and 9 are co-primes.
Clearly, 114345 is divisible by 11 as well as 9. So, it is divisible by 99.

58. 72 = 9 × 8, where 9 and 8 are co-prime.
The minimum value of x for which 73x is divisible by 8 is, x = 6.
Sum of digits in 425736 = (4 + 2 + 5 + 7 + 3 + 6) = 27, which is divisible by 9.
∴ Required value of * is 6.

59. 80 = 2 × 5 × 8.
Since 653 xy is divisible by 2 and 5 both, so y = 0.
Now, 653 x0 is divisible by 8, so 3x0 should be divisible by 8. This happens when x = 2.
∴ $x + y$ = (2 + 0) = 2.

60. Clearly, 4864 is divisible by 4.
So, 9P2 must be divisible by 3. So, (9 + P + 2) must be divisible by 3.
∴ P = 1.

61. 6 = 3 × 2. Clearly, 5 * 2 is divisible by 2. Replace * by x.
Then, (5 + x + 2) must be divisible by 3. So, x = 2.

62. 24 = 3 × 8, where 3 and 8 are co-primes.
Clearly, 35718 is not divisible by 8, as 718 is not divisible by 8
Similarly, 63810 is not divisible by 8 and 537804 is not divisible by 8.
Consider part (d).
Sum of digits = (3 + 1 + 2 + 5 + 7 + 3 + 6) = 27, which is divisible by 3.
Also, 736 is divisible by 8.
∴ 3125736 is divisible by (3 × 8), *i.e.*, 24.

63. 132 = 11 × 3 × 4.
Clearly, 968 is not divisible by 3
None of 462 and 2178 is divisible by 4.
And, 5184 is not divisible by 11.
Each one of the remaining four numbers is divisible by each one of 4, 3 and 11. So, there are 4 such numbers.

64. Let the given number be 476 xy 0.

Then $(4 + 7 + 6 + x + y + 0) = (17 + x + y)$ must be divisible by 3.

And, $(0 + x + 7) - (y + 6 + 4) = (x - y - 3)$ must be either 0 or 11.

$x - y - 3 = 0 \Rightarrow y = x - 3$

$(17 + x + y) = (17 + x + x - 3) = (2x + 14) \Rightarrow x = 2$ or $x = 8$.

$\therefore x = 8$ and $y = 5$.

65. $(4 + 5 + 2) - (1 + 6 + 3) = 1$, not divisible by 11.

$(2 + 6 + 4) - (4 + 5 + 2) = 1$, not divisible by 11.

$(4 + 6 + 1) - (2 + 5 + 3) = 1$, not divisible by 11.

$(4 + 6 + 1) - (2 + 5 + 4) = 0$, So, 415624 is divisible by 11.

66. Required numbers are 102, 108, 114, ..., 996

This is an A.P. in which $a = 102$, $d = 6$ and $l = 996$.

Let the number of terms be n. Then,

$a + (n - 1)d = 996 \Rightarrow 102 + (n - 1) \times 6 = 996.$

$\Rightarrow 6 \times (n - 1) = 894 \Rightarrow (n - 1) = 149 \Rightarrow n = 150.$

Required number of terms = 150.

67. Let $S_n = (1 + 2 + 3 + ... + 45)$. This is an A.P. in which $a = 1, d = 1, n = 45$.

$$S_n = \frac{n}{2}[2a + (n-1)d] = \frac{45}{2} \times [2 \times 1 + (45-1) \times 1] = \left(\frac{45}{2} \times 46\right) = (45 \times 23)$$

$= 45 \times (20 + 3) = (45 \times 20 + 45 \times 3) = (900 + 135) = 1035.$

68. Let $S_n = (2 + 4 + 6 + ... + 30)$. This is an A.P. in which $a = 2$, $d = 2$ and $l = 30$.

Let the number of terms be n. Then.

$a + (n - 1)d = 30 \Rightarrow 2 + (n - 1) \times 2 = 30 \Rightarrow n = 15.$

$$\therefore S_n = \frac{n}{2}(a + l) = \frac{15}{2} \times (2 + 30) = (15 \times 16) = 240.$$

69. $S_n = (1 + 2 + 3 + ... + 50 + 51 + 52 + ... + 100) - (1 + 2 + 3 + ... + 50)$

$$= \frac{100}{2} \times (1 + 100) - \frac{50}{2} \times (1 + 50) = (50 \times 101) - (25 \times 51) = (5050 - 1275) = 3775.$$

70. The smallest prime number is 2.

71. Required sum = $(2 + 3 + 5 + 7 + 11) = 28$.

72. Prime numbers less than 50 are :

2, 3, 5, 7, 11, 13, 17, 19, 23, 29, 31, 37, 41, 43, 47

Their number is 15.

73. Clearly, 97 is a prime number.

74. 91 is divisible by 7. So, it is not a prime number.

75. $\sqrt{437} > 20$

All prime numbers less than 20 are 2, 3, 5, 7, 11, 13, 17, 19.

161 is divisible by 7, 221 is divisible by 13 and 437 is divisible by 19.

373 is not divisible by any of the above prime numbers.

$\therefore$ 373 is prime.

76. $\sqrt{551} > 23$

All prime numbers less than 23 are 2, 3, 5, 7, 11, 13, 17, 19.

119 is divisible by 7; 187 is divisible by 11; 247 is divisible by 13 and 551 is divisible by 19.

So, none of the given numbers is prime.

77. The smallest 3-digit number is 100, which is divisible by 2.

$\therefore$ 100 is not a prime number.

$\sqrt{101} < 11$ and 101 is not divisible by any of the prime numbers 2, 3, 5, 7, 11.

$\therefore$ 101 is a prime number

Hence 101 is the smallest 3-digit prime number.

78. The sum of two odd numbers is even. So, $a + b$ is even.

79. The square of a natural number never ends in 2, 3, 7 or 8.

$\therefore$ 143642 is not the square of a natural number.

80. The square of a natural number never ends in 2, 3, 7 or 8.

$\therefore$ 42437 is not the square of a natural number.

81. 6) 4456 (742

42
25
24
16
12
4

Required number = (6 – 4) = 2.

82. On dividing, we get

88) 9217 (104
88
417
352
65

$\therefore$ Required number = 9217 + (88 – 65) = 9217 + 23 = 9240.

83. On dividing, we get: 75) 8485 (113

75
98
75
235
225
10

$\therefore$ Required number = (8485 – 10) = 8475.

84. Largest 4-digit number = 9999.

88) 9999 (113
88
119
88
319
264
55

Required number = (9999 – 55) = 9944.

85. Largest 5-digit number = 99999.

```
91 ) 99999 ( 1098
     91
     ---
      899
      819
      ---
       809
       728
       ---
        81
```

Required number = (99999 – 81) = 99918.

86.

```
87 ) 13601( 156
     87
     ---
     490
     435
     ---
      551
      522
      ---
       29
```

∴ Required number = 29

87.

```
23 ) 1056 ( 45
     92
     ---
     136
     115
     ---
      21
```

Required number = (23 – 21) = 2.

88. The smallest 5-digit number = 10000.

```
41 ) 10000 ( 243
     82
     ---
     180
     164
     ---
      160
      123
      ---
       37
```

Required number = 10000 + (41 – 37) = 10004.

89. The smallest 6-digit number = 100000.

```
111 ) 100000 ( 900
      999
      ---
       100
```

Required number = 100000 + (111 – 100) = 100011.

90. Divisor = (5 × 46) = 230.

∴ 10 × quotient = 230 ⇒ Quotient $= \frac{230}{10} = 23$.

Dividend = (Divisor × Quotient) + Remainder
= (230 × 23) + 46 = (5290 + 46) = 5336.

91. Number = 269 × 68 + 0 = 18292.

```
   269
 × 68
 -----
  2152
 1614
 -----
 18292
```

```
67 ) 18292 ( 273
     134
     ---
      489
      469
      ---
       202
       201
       ---
         1
```

∴ Required remainder = 1

92. Let x be the number & y be the quotient. Then,

$$x = 56 \times y + 29 = (8 \times 7y) + (8 \times 3) + 5 = 8 \times (7y + 3) + 5.$$

$\therefore$ Required remainder = 5.

93. Let x be the number and y be the quotient. Then,

$$x = 357 \times y + 39$$
$$= (17 \times 21 \times y) + (17 \times 2) + 5$$
$$= 17 \times (21y + 2) + 5.$$

$\therefore$ Required remainder = 5.

94. Let the number be x and on dividing x by 5, we get k as quotient and 3 as remainder.

$\therefore \quad x = 5k + 3 \Rightarrow x^2 = (5k + 3)^2 = (25k^2 + 30k + 9) = 5\,(5k^2 + 6k + 1) + 4$

$\therefore$ On dividing x^2 by 5, we get 4 as remainder.

95. Let the smaller number be x. Then larger number = $(x + 1365)$.

$\therefore\ x + 1365 = 6x + 15 \Rightarrow 5x = 1350 \Rightarrow x = 270.$

$\therefore$ Smaller number = 270.

96. Number = $(12 \times 35) = 420$.

Correct Quotient = $420 \div 21 = 20$.

97. Let the numbers be a and b. Then, $a + b = 12$ and $ab = 35$.

$$\therefore \quad \frac{a+b}{ab} = \frac{12}{35} \quad \Rightarrow \left(\frac{1}{b} + \frac{1}{a}\right) = \frac{12}{35}$$

$\therefore$ Sum of reciprocals of given numbers $= \frac{12}{35}$.

98. Let the number be x. Then

$$60\% \text{ of } \frac{3}{5} \text{ of } x = 36 \Rightarrow \frac{60}{100} \times \frac{3}{5} \times x = 36 \Rightarrow x = \left(36 \times \frac{25}{9}\right) = 100.$$

$\therefore \quad$ Required number = 100.

99. Let the required fraction be x. Then, $\frac{1}{x} - x = \frac{9}{20}$

$$\therefore \quad \frac{1 - x^2}{x} = \frac{9}{20} \Rightarrow 20 - 20x^2 = 9x \Rightarrow 20x^2 + 9x - 20 = 0$$

$$\Rightarrow \quad 20x^2 + 25x - 16x - 20 = 0 \quad \Rightarrow 5x\,(4x + 5) - 4(4x + 5) = 0$$

$$\Rightarrow \quad (4x + 5)\,(5x - 4) = 0 \Rightarrow x = \frac{4}{5}.$$

100. Clearly, $(2272 - 875) = 1397$, is exactly divisible by N.

Now , $1397 = 11 \times 127$

$\therefore$ The required 3-digit number is 127, the sum of whose digits is 10.

101. We go on dividing a string of 3's by 7 till we get remainder 0.

```
7 ) 333333 ( 47619
    28
    --
     53
     49
     --
      43
      42
      --
       13
        7
       --
        63
        63
        --
         ×
        --
```

102. Let the two consecutive even integers be $2n$ and $(2n + 2)$. Then,

$(2n + 2)^2 - (2n)^2 = (2n + 2 + 2n)(2n + 2 - 2n)$

$= 2(4n + 2) = 4(2n + 1)$, which is divisible by 4.

103. Let the two consecutive odd integers be $(2n + 1)$ and $(2n + 3)$. Then,

$(2n + 3)^2 - (2n + 1)^2 = (2n + 3 + 2n + 1)(2n + 3 - 2n - 1)$

$= (4n + 4) \times 2 = 8(n + 1)$, which is divisible by 8.

104. $(6n^2 + 6n) = 6n(n + 1)$, which is always divisible by 6 and 12 both, since $n(n + 1)$ is always even.

105. Let $n = 4q + 3$. Then, $2n = 8q + 6 = 4(2q + 1) + 2$.

Thus, when $2n$ is divided by 4, the remainder is 2.

106. $(x^n + 1)$ will be divisible by $(x + 1)$ only when n is odd.

$\therefore$ $(67^{67} + 1)$ will be divisible by $(67 + 1)$

$\therefore$ $(67^{67} + 1) + 66$, when divided by 68 will give 66 as remainder.

107. $(x^n - 1)$ will be divisible by $(x + 1)$ only when n is even.

$(49^{15} - 1) = \{(7^2)^{15} - 1\} = (7^{30} - 1)$, which is divisible by $(7 + 1)$, *i.e.*, 8.

108. For every natural number n, $(x^n - a^n)$ is always divisible by $(x - a)$.

109. When n is even, $(x^n - a^n)$ is completely divisible by $(x + a)$

$(17^{200} - 1^{200})$ is completely divisible by $(17 + 1)$, *i.e.*, 18.

$\Rightarrow$ $(17^{200} - 1)$ is completely divisible by 18.

$\Rightarrow$ On dividing 17^{200} by 18, we get 1 as remainder.

110. When n is odd, $(x^n + a^n)$ is always divisible by $(x + a)$.

$\therefore$ Each one of $(47^{43} + 43^{43})$ and $(47^{47} + 43^{43})$ is divisible by $(47 + 43)$.

111. Let $2^{32} = x$. Then, $(2^{32} + 1) = (x + 1)$.

Let $(x + 1)$ be completely divisible by the natural number N. Then,

$(2^{96} + 1) = [(2^{32})^3 + 1] = (x^3 + 1) = (x + 1)(x^2 - x + 1)$, which is completely divisible by N, since $(x + 1)$ is divisible by N.

112. $(4^{61} + 4^{62} + 4^{63} + 4^{64}) = 4^{61} \times (1 + 4 + 4^2 + 4^3) = 4^{61} \times 85$

$= 4^{60} \times (4 \times 85) = (4^{60} \times 340)$, which is divisible by 10.

113. $(3^{25} + 3^{26} + 3^{27} + 3^{28}) = 3^{25} \times (1 + 3 + 3^2 + 3^3) = 3^{25} \times 40$

$= 3^{24} \times 3 \times 4 \times 10 = (3^{24} \times 4 \times 30)$, which is divisible by 30.

114. $\left.\begin{array}{r} 4\ a\ 3 \\ 9\ 8\ 4 \\ \hline 13\ b\ 7 \end{array}\right\} \Rightarrow a + 8 = b \Rightarrow b - a = 8$

Also, $13\,b7$ is divisible by 11 $\Rightarrow (7 + 3) - (b + 1) = (9 - b) \Rightarrow (9 - b) = 0 \Rightarrow b = 9$.

$\therefore$ $(b = 9$ and $a = 1) \Rightarrow (a + b) = 10$.

115. By hit and trial, we put $x = 5$ and $y = 1$ so that $(3x + 7y) = (3 \times 5 + 7 \times 1) = 22$, which is divisible by 11.

$\therefore$ $(4x + 6y) = (4 \times 5 + 6 \times 1) = 26$, which is not divisible by 11;

$(x + y + 4) = (5 + 1 + 4) = 10$, which is not divisible by 11;

$(9x + 4y) = (9 \times 5 + 4 \times 1) = 49$, which is not divisible by 11;

$(4x - 9y) = (4 \times 5 - 9 \times 1) = 11$, which is divisible by 11.

116. $90 = 10 \times 9$

Clearly, $653xy$ is divisible by 10, so $y = 0$.

Now, $653x0$ is divisible by 9. So, $(6 + 5 + 3 + x + 0) = (14 + x)$ is divisible by 9. So, $x = 4$.

Hence, $(x + y) = (4 + 0) = 4$.

117. Marking (✓) those which are divisible by 3 but not by 9 and the others by (x), by taking the sum of digits, we get:

$2133 \to 9$ (✗), $2343 \to 12$ (✓), $3474 \to 18$ (✗), $4131 \to 9$ (✗), $5286 \to 21$ (✓),

$5340 \to 12$ (✓), $6336 \to 18$ (✗), $7347 \to 21$ (✓), $8115 \to 15$ (✓), $9276 \to 24$ (✓)

Required number of numbers = 6

118. 639 is not divisible by 7.

2079 is divisible by each one of 3, 7, 9, 11.

119. $132 = 4 \times 3 \times 11$

$264 \to 11, 3, 4$ (✓); $396 \to 11, 3, 4$ (✓); $462 \to 11, 3$ (✓); $792 \to 11, 3, 4$ (✓)

$968 \to 11, 4$ (✗); $2178 \to 11, 3$ (✗); $5184 \to 3, 4$ (✗); $6336 \to 11, 3, 4$ (✓)

Required number of numbers = 4.

120. Let $x = 6q + 3$. Then, $x^2 = (6q + 3)^2 = 36q^2 + 36q + 9 = 6(6q^2 + 6q + 1) + 3$

Thus, when x^2 is divided by 6, then remainder = 3.

121.

4	x
5	$y - 1$
	$1 - 4$

$\therefore y = (5 \times 1 + 4) = 9.$

$x = (4 \times y + 1) = (4 \times 9 + 1) = 37.$

Now, 37 when divided successively by 5 and 4, we get

5	37
4	7 – 2
	1 – 3

Respective remainders are 2 and 3.

122.

4	x
5	$y - 2$
6	$z - 3$
	$1 - 4$

$\therefore z = 6 \times 1 + 4 = 10.$

$y = 5 \times z + 3 = 5 \times 10 + 3 = 53.$

$x = 4 \times y + 2 = 4 \times 53 + 2 = 212 + 2 = 214.$

Hence, required number = 214.

123.

5	x
9	$y - 4$
13	$z - 8$
	$1 - 12$

$\therefore z = 13 \times 1 + 12 = 25,$

$y = 9 \times z + 8 = 9 \times 25 + 8 = 233,$

$x = 5 \times y + 4 = 5 \times 233 + 4 = 1169.$

585) 1169 (1
585
584

$\therefore$ On dividing the number by 585, remainder = 584.

124. $x = 13p + 11$ and $x = 17q + 9.$

$\therefore \quad 13p + 11 = 17q + 9 \Rightarrow 17q - 13p = 2 \Rightarrow q = \frac{2 + 13p}{17}.$

The least value of p for which $q = \frac{2 + 13p}{17}$ is a whole number is $p = 26$.

$\therefore x = (13 \times 26 + 11) = (338 \times 11) = 349.$

125. Let $x = 296\,q + 75 = (37 \times 8q + 37 \times 2) + 1$

$= 37 \times (8q + 2) + 1$

Thus, when the number is divided by 37, the remainder is 1.

126. $987 = 3 \times 7 \times 47.$

So, the required number must be divisible by each one of 3, 7, 47

553681 $\to$ (Sum of digits = 28, not divisible by 3)

555181 → (Sum of digits = 25, not divisible by 3)

555681 is divisible by each one of 3, 7, 47.

127. 3-digit numbers divisible by 6 are:
102, 108, 114, ..., 996

This is an A.P. in which $a = 102$, $d = 6$ and $l = 996$.

Let the number of terms be n. Then $t_n = 996$.

$\therefore a + (n-1)d = 996 \Rightarrow 102 + (n-1) \times 6 = 996.$

$\Rightarrow 6 \times (n-1) = 894 \Rightarrow (n-1) = 149 \Rightarrow n = 150.$

$\therefore$ Number of terms = 150.

128. Let $S_n = (1 + 2 + 3 + ... + 45)$.

This is an A.P. in which $a = 1$, $d = 1$, $n = 45$ and $l = 45$.

$$\therefore S_n = \frac{n}{2}(a+l) = \frac{45}{2} \times (1+45) = (45 \times 23) = 45 \times (20+3)$$

$$= (45 \times 20) + (45 \times 3) = 900 + 135 = 1035.$$

Required sum = 1035.

129. Required sum = (2 + 4 + 6 + ... + 30)

This is an A.P. in which $a = 2$, $d = (4 - 2) = 2$ and $l = 30$.

Let the number of terms be n. Then

$t_n = 30 \Rightarrow a + (n-1)d = 30$

$\Rightarrow 2 + (n-1) \times 2 = 30 \Rightarrow n - 1 = 14 \Rightarrow n = 15.$

$$\therefore S_n = \frac{n}{2}(a+l) = \frac{15}{2} \cdot (2+30) = 240.$$

130. This is an A.P. in which $a = 51$, $l = 100$ and $n = 50$.

$$\therefore Sum = \frac{n}{2}(a+l) = \frac{50}{2} \times (51+100) = (25 \times 151) = 3775.$$

131. Given sum $= (1 + 1 + 1 + ... \text{ to } n \text{ terms}) - \left(\frac{1}{n} + \frac{2}{n} + \frac{3}{n} + ... \text{ to } n \text{ terms}\right)$

$$= n - \frac{n}{2}\left(\frac{1}{n} + 1\right) \qquad [\because l = n\text{th term} = \frac{n}{n} = 1]$$

$$= n - \frac{n+1}{2} = \frac{1}{2}(n-1).$$

132. Required numbers are 24, 30, 36, 42 ..., 96.

This is an A.P. in which $a = 24$, $d = 6$ and $l = 96$.

Let the number of terms in it be n.

Then, $t_n = 96 \Rightarrow a + (n-1)d = 96.$

$\Rightarrow 24 + (n-1) \times 6 = 96 \Rightarrow (n-1) \times 6 = 72 \Rightarrow (n-1) = 12 \Rightarrow n = 13.$

Required number of numbers = 13.

133. Required numbers are 10, 15, 20, 25, ..., 95.

This is an A.P. in which $a = 10$, $d = 5$ and $l = 95$.

Let the number of terms in it be n. Then

$t_n = 95 \Rightarrow a + (n-1)d = 95$

$\Rightarrow 10 + (n-1) \times 5 = 95 \Rightarrow (n-1) \times 5 = 85 \Rightarrow (n-1) = 17 \Rightarrow n = 18.$

Required sum $= \frac{n}{2}(a+l) = \frac{18}{2}\cdot(10+95) = (9\times105) = 945.$

134. This is an A.P. in which $a = 6$, $d = 6$ and $S_n = 1800$.

Then, $\frac{n}{2}[2a+(n-1)d] = 1800 \Rightarrow \frac{n}{2}\cdot[2\times6+(n-1)\times6] = 1800$

$\Rightarrow 3n\,(n + 1) = 1800 \Rightarrow n(n + 1) = 600$

$\Rightarrow n^2 + n - 600 = 0 \Rightarrow n^2 + 25\,n - 24n - 600 = 0$

$\Rightarrow n(n + 25) - 24(n + 25) = 0 \Rightarrow (n + 25)\,(n - 24) = 0 \Rightarrow n = 24.$

Number of terms = 24.

135. Here $a = 3$ and $r = \frac{6}{3} = 2$. Let the number of terms be n.

Then, $t_n = 384 \Rightarrow ar^{n-1} = 384$

$\Rightarrow 3 \times 2^{n-1} = 384 \Rightarrow 2^{n-1} = 128 = 2^7$

$\Rightarrow n - 1 = 7 \Rightarrow n = 8.$

$\therefore$ Number of terms = 8.

136. This is a G.P. in which $a = 2$, $r = \frac{2^2}{2} = 2$ and $n = 9$.

$$S_n = \frac{a(r^n-1)}{(r-1)} = \frac{2\times(2^9-1)}{(2-1)} = 2\times(512-1) = 2\times511 = 1022.$$

137. We know that $(1^2+2^2+3^2+...+n^2) = \frac{1}{6}n(n+1)(2n+1).$

Putting $n = 10$, required sum $= \left(\frac{1}{6}\times10\times11\times21\right) = 385.$

138. $(2^2 + 4^2 + 6^2 + ... + 20^2) = (1 \times 2)^2 + (2 \times 2)^2 + (2 \times 3)^2 + ... + (2 \times 10)^2$

$= (2^2 \times 1^2) + (2^2 \times 2^2) + (2^2 \times 3^2) + ... + (2 \times 10)^2$

$= 2^2 \times [1^2 + 2^2 + 3^2 + ... + 10^2]$

$= \left(4\times\frac{1}{6}\times10\times11\times21\right) \quad \left[\because (1^2+2^2+3^2+...+n^2) = \frac{1}{6}n(n+1)\,(2n+1)\right]$

$= (4 \times 5 \times 77) = 1540.$

139. $(11^2 + 12^2 + 13^2 + ... + 20^2) = (1^2 + 2^2 + ... + 20^2) - (1^2 + 2^2 + ... + 10^2)$

$= \left\{\frac{20\times21\times41}{6} - \frac{10\times11\times21}{6}\right\} \quad \left[\because (1^2+2^2+...+n^2) = \frac{1}{6}n(n+1)\,(2n+1)\right]$

$= (2870 - 385) = 2485.$

2. H.C.F. AND L.C.M. OF NUMBERS

IMPORTANT FACTS AND FORMULAE

I. Factors and Multiples : If a number a divides another number b exactly, we say that a is a ***factor*** of b. In this case, b is called a ***multiple*** of a.

II. Highest Common Factor (H.C.F.) or Greatest Common Measure (G.C.M.) or Greatest Common Divisor (G.C.D.) : The H.C.F. of two or more than two numbers is the greatest number that divides each of them exactly.

There are two methods of finding the H.C.F. of a given set of numbers :

1. ***Factorization Method*** : *Express each one of the given numbers as the product of prime factors. The product of least powers of common prime factors gives H.C.F.*
2. ***Division Method*** : *Suppose we have to find the H.C.F. of two given numbers. Divide the larger number by the smaller one. Now, divide the divisor by the remainder. Repeat the process of dividing the preceding number by the remainder last obtained till zero is obtained as remainder. The last divisor is the required H.C.F.*

Finding the H.C.F. of more than two numbers : Suppose we have to find the H.C.F. of three numbers. Then, H.C.F. of [(H.C.F. of any two) and (the third number)] gives the H.C.F. of three given numbers.

Similarly, the H.C.F. of more than three numbers may be obtained.

III. Least Common Multiple (L.C.M.) : The least number which is exactly divisible by each one of the given numbers is called their L.C.M.

1. ***Factorization Method of Finding L.C.M.*** : *Resolve each one of the given numbers into a product of prime factors. Then, L.C.M. is the product of highest powers of all the factors.*
2. ***Common Division Method (Short-cut Method) of Finding L.C.M.*** : *Arrange the given numbers in a row in any order. Divide by a number which divides exactly at least two of the given numbers and carry forward the numbers which are not divisible. Repeat the above process till no two of the numbers are divisible by the same number except 1. The product of the divisors and the undivided numbers is the required L.C.M. of the given numbers.*

IV. Product of two numbers = Product of their H.C.F. and L.C.M.

V. Co-primes : Two numbers are said to be co-primes if their H.C.F. is 1.

VI. H.C.F. and L.C.M. of Fractions :

1. $\text{H.C.F.} = \dfrac{\text{H.C.F. of Numerators}}{\text{L.C.M. of Denominators}}$ 2. $\text{L.C.M.} = \dfrac{\text{L.C.M. of Numerators}}{\text{H.C.F. of Denominators}}$.

VII. H.C.F. and L.C.M. of Decimal Fractions : *In given numbers, make the same number of decimal places by annexing zeros in some numbers, if necessary. Considering these numbers without decimal point, find H.C.F. or L.C.M. as the case may be. Now, in the result, mark off as many decimal places as are there in each of the given numbers.*

VIII. Comparison of Fractions : *Find the L.C.M. of the denominators of the given fractions. Convert each of the fractions into an equivalent fraction with L.C.M. as the denominator, by multiplying both the numerator and denominator by the same number. The resultant fraction with the greatest numerator is the greatest.*

SOLVED EXAMPLES

Ex. 1. ***Find the H.C.F. of $2^3 \times 3^2 \times 5 \times 7^4$, $2^2 \times 3^5 \times 5^2 \times 7^3$, $2^3 \times 5^3 \times 7^2$.***

Sol. The prime numbers common to given numbers are 2, 5 and 7.

$\therefore$ H.C.F. $= 2^2 \times 5 \times 7^2 = 980$.

Ex. 2. ***Find the H.C.F. of 108, 288 and 360.***

Sol. $108 = 2^2 \times 3^3$, $288 = 2^5 \times 3^2$ and $360 = 2^3 \times 5 \times 3^2$.

$\therefore$ H.C.F. $= 2^2 \times 3^2 = 36$.

Ex. 3. ***Find the H.C.F. of 513, 1134 and 1215.***

Sol.

```
1134 ) 1215 ( 1
       1134
       ----
         81 ) 1134 ( 14
                81
              ----
               324
               324
              ----
                 ×
```

$\therefore$ H.C.F. of 1134 and 1215 is 81.

So, Required H.C.F. = H.C.F. of 513 and 81.

```
81 ) 513 ( 6
     486
     ---
      27 ) 81 ( 3
           81
           --
            ×
```

$\therefore$ H.C.F. of given numbers = 27.

Ex. 4. ***Reduce $\frac{391}{667}$ to lowest terms.***

Sol. H.C.F. of 391 and 667 is 23.

On dividing the numerator and denominator by 23, we get :

$$\frac{391}{667} = \frac{391 \div 23}{667 \div 23} = \frac{17}{29}.$$

Ex. 5. ***Find the L.C.M. of $2^2 \times 3^3 \times 5 \times 7^2$, $2^3 \times 3^2 \times 5^2 \times 7^4$, $2 \times 3 \times 5^3 \times 7 \times 11$.***

Sol. L.C.M. = Product of highest powers of 2, 3, 5, 7 and 11 $= 2^3 \times 3^3 \times 5^3 \times 7^4 \times 11$.

Ex. 6. ***Find the L.C.M. of 72, 108 and 2100.***

Sol. $72 = 2^3 \times 3^2$, $108 = 3^3 \times 2^2$, $2100 = 2^2 \times 5^2 \times 3 \times 7$.

$\therefore$ L.C.M. $= 2^3 \times 3^3 \times 5^2 \times 7 = 37800$.

Ex. 7. ***Find the L.C.M. of 16, 24, 36 and 54.***

Sol.

2	16 – 24 – 36 – 54
2	8 – 12 – 18 – 27
2	4 – 6 – 9 – 27
3	2 – 3 – 9 – 27
3	2 – 1 – 3 – 9
	2 – 1 – 1 – 3

$\therefore$ L.C.M. $= 2 \times 2 \times 2 \times 3 \times 3 \times 2 \times 3 = 432$.

Ex. 8. ***Find the H.C.F. and L.C.M. of*** $\frac{2}{3}, \frac{8}{9}, \frac{16}{81}$ ***and*** $\frac{10}{27}$.

Sol. H.C.F. of given fractions $= \frac{\text{H.C.F. of } 2, 8, 16, 10}{\text{L.C.M. of } 3, 9, 81, 27} = \frac{2}{81}$.

L.C.M. of given fractions $= \frac{\text{L.C.M. of } 2, 8, 16, 10}{\text{H.C.F. of } 3, 9, 81, 27} = \frac{80}{3}$.

Ex. 9. ***Find the H.C.F. and L.C.M. of 0.63, 1.05 and 2.1.***

Sol. Making the same number of decimal places, the given numbers are 0.63, 1.05 and 2.10.

Without decimal places, these numbers are 63, 105 and 210.

Now, H.C.F. of 63, 105 and 210 is 21.

$\therefore$ H.C.F. of 0.63, 1.05 and 2.1 is 0.21.

L.C.M. of 63, 105 and 210 is 630.

$\therefore$ L.C.M. of 0.63, 1.05 and 2.1 is 6.30.

Ex. 10. ***Two numbers are in the ratio of 15 : 11. If their H.C.F. is 13, find the numbers.***

Sol. Let the required numbers be $15x$ and $11x$.

Then, their H.C.F. is x. So, $x = 13$.

$\therefore$ The numbers are $(15 \times 13$ and $11 \times 13)$ *i.e.*, 195 and 143.

Ex. 11. ***The H.C.F. of two numbers is 11 and their L.C.M. is 693. If one of the numbers is 77, find the other.***

Sol. Other number $= \left(\frac{11 \times 693}{77}\right) = 99$.

Ex. 12. ***Find the greatest possible length which can be used to measure exactly the lengths 4 m 95 cm, 9 m and 16 m 65 cm.***

Sol. Required length = H.C.F. of 495 cm, 900 cm and 1665 cm.

$495 = 3^2 \times 5 \times 11,\ 900 = 2^2 \times 3^2 \times 5^2,\ 1665 = 3^2 \times 5 \times 37.$

$\therefore$ H.C.F. $= 3^2 \times 5 = 45$.

Hence, required length = 45 cm.

Ex. 13. ***Find the greatest number which on dividing 1657 and 2037 leaves remainders 6 and 5 respectively.***

Sol. Required number = H.C.F. of (1657 – 6) and (2037 – 5) = H.C.F. of 1651 and 2032

```
1651 ) 2032 ( 1
       1651
       ----
        381 ) 1651 ( 4
              1524
              ----
               127 ) 381 ( 3
                     381
                     ---
                      ×
                     ---
```

$\therefore$ Required number = 127.

Ex. 14. ***Find the largest number which divides 62, 132 and 237 to leave the same remainder in each case.***

Sol. Required number = H.C.F. of (132 – 62), (237 – 132) and (237 – 62)

= H.C.F. of 70, 105 and 175 = 35.

Ex. 15. ***Find the least number exactly divisible by 12, 15, 20 and 27.***

Sol. Required number = L.C.M. of 12, 15, 20, 27.

3	12	15	20	27
4	4	5	20	9
5	1	5	5	9
	1	1	1	9

∴ L.C.M. = 3 × 4 × 5 × 9 = 540.

Hence, required number = 540.

Ex. 16. ***Find the least number which when divided by 6, 7, 8, 9 and 12 leaves the same remainder 1 in each case.***

Sol. Required number = (L.C.M. of 6, 7, 8, 9, 12) + 1

3	6	7	8	9	12
2	2	7	8	3	4
2	1	7	4	3	2
	1	7	2	3	1

∴ L.C.M. = 3 × 2 × 2 × 7 × 2 × 3 = 504.

Hence, required number = (504 + 1) = 505.

Ex. 17. ***Find the largest number of four digits exactly divisible by 12, 15, 18 and 27.***

Sol. The largest number of four digits is 9999.

Required number must be divisible by L.C.M. of 12, 15, 18, 27 *i.e.*, 540.

On dividing 9999 by 540, we get 279 as remainder.

∴ Required number = (9999 − 279) = 9720.

Ex. 18. ***Find the smallest number of five digits exactly divisible by 16, 24, 36 and 54.***

Sol. Smallest number of five digits is 10000.

Required number must be divisible by L.C.M. of 16, 24, 36, 54 *i.e.*, 432.

On dividing 10000 by 432, we get 64 as remainder.

∴ Required number = 10000 + (432 − 64) = 10368.

Ex. 19. ***Find the least number which when divided by 20, 25, 35 and 40 leaves remainders 14, 19, 29 and 34 respectively.***

Sol. Here, (20 − 14) = 6, (25 − 19) = 6, (35 − 29) = 6 and (40 − 34) = 6.

∴ Required number = (L.C.M. of 20, 25, 35, 40) − 6 = 1394.

Ex. 20. ***Find the least number which when divided by 5, 6, 7 and 8 leaves a remainder 3, but when divided by 9 leaves no remainder.***

Sol. L.C.M. of 5, 6, 7, 8 = 840.

∴ Required number is of the form $840k + 3$.

Least value of k for which $(840k + 3)$ is divisible by 9 is $k = 2$.

∴ Required number = (840 × 2 + 3) = 1683.

Ex. 21. ***The traffic lights at three different road crossings change after every 48 sec., 72 sec. and 108 sec. respectively. If they all change simultaneously at 8 : 20 : 00 hours, then at what time will they again change simultaneously ?***

Sol. Interval of change = (L.C.M. of 48, 72, 108) sec. = 432 sec.

So, the lights will again change simultaneously after every 432 seconds *i.e.*, 7 min. 12 sec.

Hence, next simultaneous change will take place at 8 : 27 : 12 hrs.

Ex. 22. ***Arrange the fractions*** $\frac{17}{18}, \frac{31}{36}, \frac{43}{45}, \frac{59}{60}$ ***in the ascending order.***

Sol. L.C.M. of 18, 36, 45 and 60 = 180.

Now, $\frac{17}{18} = \frac{17 \times 10}{18 \times 10} = \frac{170}{180}$; $\frac{31}{36} = \frac{31 \times 5}{36 \times 5} = \frac{155}{180}$;

$\frac{43}{45} = \frac{43 \times 4}{45 \times 4} = \frac{172}{180}$; $\frac{59}{60} = \frac{59 \times 3}{60 \times 3} = \frac{177}{180}$.

Since, 155 < 170 < 172 < 177, so, $\frac{155}{180} < \frac{170}{180} < \frac{172}{180} < \frac{177}{180}$.

Hence, $\frac{31}{36} < \frac{17}{18} < \frac{43}{45} < \frac{59}{60}$.

EXERCISE 2

(OBJECTIVE TYPE QUESTIONS)

Directions : *Mark (✓) against the correct answer* :

1. 252 can be expressed as a product of primes as : **(IGNOU, 2002)**
(a) $2 \times 2 \times 3 \times 3 \times 7$ (b) $2 \times 2 \times 2 \times 3 \times 7$
(c) $3 \times 3 \times 3 \times 3 \times 7$ (d) $2 \times 3 \times 3 \times 3 \times 7$

2. Which of the following has most number of divisors ? **(M.B.A. 2002)**
(a) 99 (b) 101 (c) 176 (d) 182

3. A number *n* is said to be perfect if the sum of all its divisors (excluding *n* itself) is equal to *n*. An example of perfect number is :
(a) 6 (b) 9 (c) 15 (d) 21

4. $\frac{1095}{1168}$ when expressed in simplest form is : **(M.B.A. 1998)**
(a) $\frac{13}{16}$ (b) $\frac{15}{16}$ (c) $\frac{17}{26}$ (d) $\frac{25}{26}$

5. Reduce $\frac{128352}{238368}$ to its lowest terms. **(IGNOU, 2003)**
(a) $\frac{3}{4}$ (b) $\frac{5}{13}$ (c) $\frac{7}{13}$ (d) $\frac{9}{13}$

6. The H.C.F. of $2^2 \times 3^3 \times 5^5$, $2^3 \times 3^2 \times 5^2 \times 7$ and $2^4 \times 3^4 \times 5 \times 7^2 \times 11$ is :
(a) $2^2 \times 3^2 \times 5$ (b) $2^2 \times 3^2 \times 5 \times 7 \times 11$
(c) $2^4 \times 3^4 \times 5^5$ (d) $2^4 \times 3^4 \times 5^5 \times 7 \times 11$

7. The H.C.F. of $2^4 \times 3^2 \times 5^3 \times 7$, $2^3 \times 3^3 \times 5^2 \times 7^2$ and $3 \times 5 \times 7 \times 11$ is :
(a) 105 (b) 1155 (c) 2310 (d) 27720

8. H.C.F. of $4 \times 27 \times 3125$, $8 \times 9 \times 25 \times 7$ & $16 \times 81 \times 5 \times 11 \times 49$ is : **(C.B.I. 1997)**
(a) 180 (b) 360 (c) 540 (d) 1260

9. Find the highest common factor of 36 and 84. **(R.R.B. 2003)**
(a) 4 (b) 6 (c) 12 (d) 18

10. The H.C.F. of 204, 1190 and 1445 is :
(a) 17 (b) 18 (c) 19 (d) 21

11. Which of the following is a pair of co-primes ?
(a) (16, 62) (b) (18, 25) (c) (21, 35) (d) (23, 92)

12. The H.C.F. of 2923 and 3239 is :
(*a*) 37 (*b*) 47 (*c*) 73 (*d*) 79

13. The H.C.F. of 3556 and 3444 is :
(*a*) 23 (*b*) 25 (*c*) 26 (*d*) 28

14. The L.C.M. of $2^3 \times 3^2 \times 5 \times 11$, $2^4 \times 3^4 \times 5^2 \times 7$ and $2^5 \times 3^3 \times 5^3 \times 7^2 \times 11$ is :
(*a*) $2^3 \times 3^2 \times 5$ (*b*) $2^5 \times 3^4 \times 5^3$
(*c*) $2^3 \times 3^2 \times 5 \times 7 \times 11$ (*d*) $2^5 \times 3^4 \times 5^3 \times 7^2 \times 11$

(R.R.B. 2003)

15. Find the lowest common multiple of 24, 36 and 40.
(*a*) 120 (*b*) 240 (*c*) 360 (*d*) 480

(M.B.A. 1998)

16. The L.C.M. of 22, 54, 108, 135 and 198 is :
(*a*) 330 (*b*) 1980 (*c*) 5940 (*d*) 11880

17. The L.C.M. of 148 and 185 is :
(*a*) 680 (*b*) 740 (*c*) 2960 (*d*) 3700

18. The H.C.F. of $\frac{2}{3}, \frac{8}{9}, \frac{64}{81}$ and $\frac{10}{27}$ is :
(*a*) $\frac{2}{3}$ (*b*) $\frac{2}{81}$ (*c*) $\frac{160}{3}$ (*d*) $\frac{160}{81}$

19. The H.C.F. of $\frac{9}{10}, \frac{12}{25}, \frac{18}{35}$ and $\frac{21}{40}$ is .
(*a*) $\frac{3}{5}$ (*b*) $\frac{252}{5}$ (*c*) $\frac{3}{2800}$ (*d*) $\frac{63}{700}$

20. The L.C.M. of $\frac{1}{3}, \frac{5}{6}, \frac{2}{9}, \frac{4}{27}$ is :
(*a*) $\frac{1}{54}$ (*b*) $\frac{10}{27}$ (*c*) $\frac{20}{3}$ (*d*) None of these

21. The L.C.M. of $\frac{2}{3}, \frac{3}{5}, \frac{4}{7}, \frac{9}{13}$ is :
(*a*) 36 (*b*) $\frac{1}{36}$ (*c*) $\frac{1}{1365}$ (*d*) $\frac{12}{455}$

22. The H.C.F. of 1.75, 5.6 and 7 is :
(*a*) 0.07 (*b*) 0.7 (*c*) 3.5 (*d*) 0.35

(Hotel Management, 2002)

23. The G.C.D. of 1.08, 0.36 and 0.9 is :
(*a*) 0.03 (*b*) 0.9 (*c*) 0.18 (*d*) 0.108

24. The H.C.F. of 0.54, 1.8 and 7.2 is :
(*a*) 1.8 (*b*) 0.18 (*c*) 0.018 (*d*) 18

25. The L.C.M. of 3, 2.7 and 0.09 is :
(*a*) 2.7 (*b*) 0.27 (*c*) 0.027 (*d*) 27

26. H.C.F. of 3240, 3600 and a third number is 36 and their L.C.M. is $2^4 \times 3^5 \times 5^2 \times 7^2$. The third number is :

(S.S.C. 1999)

(*a*) $2^2 \times 3^5 \times 7^2$ (*b*) $2^2 \times 5^3 \times 7^2$ (*c*) $2^5 \times 5^2 \times 7^2$ (*d*) $2^3 \times 3^5 \times 7^2$

27. Three numbers are in the ratio 1 : 2 : 3 and their H.C.F. is 12. The numbers are :
(*a*) 4, 8, 12 (*b*) 5, 10, 15 (*c*) 10, 20, 30 (*d*) 12, 24, 36

(Section Officers', 2001)

28. The ratio of two numbers is 3 : 4 and their H.C.F. is 4. Their L.C.M. is :
(*a*) 12 (*b*) 16 (*c*) 24 (*d*) 48

(S.S.C. 2002)

29. The sum of two numbers is 216 and their H.C.F. is 27. The numbers are :
(*a*) 27, 189 (*b*) 81, 189 (*c*) 108, 108 (*d*) 154, 162

30. The sum of two numbers is 528 and their H.C.F. is 33. The number of pairs of numbers satisfying the above conditions is : **(C.B.I. 1997)**
(*a*) 4 (*b*) 6 (*c*) 8 (*d*) 12

31. The number of number-pairs lying between 40 and 100 with their H.C.F. as 15 is :
(*a*) 3 (*b*) 4 (*c*) 5 (*d*) 6

32. The H.C.F. of two numbers is 12 and their difference is 12. The numbers are :
(*a*) 66, 78 (*b*) 70, 82 (*c*) 94, 106 (*d*) 84, 96

33. The product of two numbers is 4107. If the H.C.F. of these numbers is 37, then the greater number is : **(S.S.C. 2003)**
(*a*) 101 (*b*) 107 (*c*) 111 (*d*) 185

34. The product of two numbers is 2028 and their H.C.F. is 13. The number of such pairs is : **(C.B.I. 2003)**
(*a*) 1 (*b*) 2 (*c*) 3 (*d*) 4

35. Three numbers which are co-prime to each other are such that the product of the first two is 551 and that of the last two is 1073. The sum of the three numbers is :
(*a*) 75 (*b*) 81 (*c*) 85 (*d*) 89
(S.S.C. 2003)

36. The L.C.M. of two numbers is 48. The numbers are in the ratio 2 : 3. The sum of the numbers is : **(S.S.C. 2003)**
(*a*) 28 (*b*) 32 (*c*) 40 (*d*) 64

37. Three numbers are in the ratio of 3 : 4 : 5 and their L.C.M. is 2400. Their H.C.F. is :
(*a*) 40 (*b*) 80 (*c*) 120 (*d*) 200
(M.B.A. 2003)

38. The H.C.F. of two numbers is 11 and their L.C.M. is 7700. If one of the numbers is 275, then the other is : **(Section Officers', 2001)**
(*a*) 279 (*b*) 283 (*c*) 308 (*d*) 318

39. The sum of two numbers is 2000 and their L.C.M. is 21879. The two numbers are :
(*a*) 1993, 7 (*b*) 1991, 9 (*c*) 1989, 11 (*d*) 1987, 13

40. The H.C.F. and L.C.M. of two numbers are 84 and 21 respectively. If the ratio of the two numbers is 1 : 4, then the larger of the two numbers is : **(M.A.T. 1997)**
(*a*) 12 (*b*) 48 (*c*) 84 (*d*) 108

41. The L.C.M. of two numbers is 495 and their H.C.F. is 5. If the sum of the numbers is 10, then their difference is : **(S.S.C. 1999)**
(*a*) 10 (*b*) 46 (*c*) 70 (*d*) 90

42. The product of the L.C.M. and H.C.F. of two numbers is 24. The difference of two numbers is 2. Find the numbers.
(*a*) 2 and 4 (*b*) 6 and 4 (*c*) 8 and 6 (*d*) 8 and 10

43. If the sum of two numbers is 55 and the H.C.F. and L.C.M. of these numbers are 5 and 120 respectively, then the sum of the reciprocals of the numbers is equal to :
(*a*) $\frac{55}{601}$ (*b*) $\frac{601}{55}$ (*c*) $\frac{11}{120}$ (*d*) $\frac{120}{11}$
(C.D.S. 2003)

44. The L.C.M. of two numbers is 45 times their H.C.F. If one of the numbers is 125 and the sum of H.C.F. and L.C.M. is 1150, the other number is :
(*a*) 215 (*b*) 220 (*c*) 225 (*d*) 235

45. The H.C.F. and L.C.M. of two numbers are 50 and 250 respectively. If the first number is divided by 2, the quotient is 50. The second number is :
(*a*) 50 (*b*) 100 (*c*) 125 (*d*) 250

46. The product of two numbers is 1320 and their H.C.F. is 6. The L.C.M. of the numbers is :
(*a*) 220 (*b*) 1314 (*c*) 1326 (*d*) 7920

47. Product of two co-prime numbers is 117. Their L.C.M. should be : **(C.B.I. 1997)**
(*a*) 1 (*b*) 117 (*c*) equal to their H.C.F. (*d*) cannot be calculated

48. The L.C.M. of three different numbers is 120. Which of the following cannot be their H.C.F. ?
(*a*) 8 (*b*) 12 (*c*) 24 (*d*) 35

49. The H.C.F. of two numbers is 8. Which one of the following can never be their L.C.M. ?
(*a*) 24 (*b*) 48 (*c*) 56 (*d*) 60
(S.S.C. 2000)

50. The H.C.F. of two numbers is 23 and the other two factors of their L.C.M. are 13 and 14. The larger of the two numbers is : **(S.S.C. 2004)**
(*a*) 276 (*b*) 299 (*c*) 322 (*d*) 345

51. About the number of pairs which have 16 as their H.C.F. and 136 as their L.C.M., we can definitely say that :
(*a*) no such pair exists (*b*) only one such pair exists
(*c*) only two such pairs exist (*d*) many such pairs exist

52. The H.C.F. and L.C.M. of two numbers are 11 and 385 respectively. If one number lies between 75 and 125, then that number is : **(C.B.I. 1998)**
(*a*) 77 (*b*) 88 (*c*) 99 (*d*) 110

53. Two numbers, both greater than 29, have H.C.F. 29 and L.C.M. 4147. The sum of the numbers is : **(S.S.C. 2002)**
(*a*) 666 (*b*) 669 (*c*) 696 (*d*) 966

54. L.C.M. of two prime numbers x and y $(x > y)$ is 161. The value of $3y - x$ is :
(*a*) -2 (*b*) -1 (*c*) 1 (*d*) 2
(S.S.C. 1999)

55. The greatest number that exactly divides 105, 1001 and 2436 is :
(*a*) 3 (*b*) 7 (*c*) 11 (*d*) 21

56. The greatest possible length which can be used to measure exactly the lengths 7 m, 3 m 85 cm, 12 m 95 cm is : **(R.R.B. 2003)**
(*a*) 15 cm (*b*) 25 cm (*c*) 35 cm (*d*) 42 cm

57. Three different containers contain 496 litres, 403 litres and 713 litres of mixtures of milk and water respectively. What biggest measure can measure all the different quantities exactly ?
(*a*) 1 litre (*b*) 7 litres (*c*) 31 litres (*d*) 41 litres

58. The maximum number of students among them 1001 pens and 910 pencils can be distributed in such a way that each student gets the same number of pens and same number of pencils is : **(S.S.C. 1999)**
(*a*) 91 (*b*) 910 (*c*) 1001 (*d*) 1911

59. A rectangular courtyard 3.78 metres long and 5.25 metres wide is to be paved exactly with square tiles, all of the same size. What is the largest size of the tile which could be used for the purpose ? **(N.I.F.T. 2000)**
(*a*) 14 cms (*b*) 21 cms (*c*) 42 cms (*d*) None of these

60. Find the greatest number that will divide 43, 91 and 183 so as to leave the same remainder in each case. **(L.I.C. 2003)**
(*a*) 4 (*b*) 7 (*c*) 9 (*d*) 13

61. Let N be the greatest number that will divide 1305, 4665 and 6905, leaving the same remainder in each case. Then sum of the digits in N is : **(S.S.C. 2004)**
(*a*) 4 (*b*) 5 (*c*) 6 (*d*) 8

62. The greatest number which can divide 1356, 1868 and 2764 leaving the same remainder 12 in each case, is :
(*a*) 64 (*b*) 124 (*c*) 156 (*d*) 260

63. The greatest number which on dividing 1657 and 2037 leaves remainders 6 and 5 respectively, is : **(R.R.B. 2004)**

(*a*) 123 (*b*) 127 (*c*) 235 (*d*) 305

64. Which of the following fractions is the largest ? **(IGNOU, 2003)**

(*a*) $\frac{7}{8}$ (*b*) $\frac{13}{16}$ (*c*) $\frac{31}{40}$ (*d*) $\frac{63}{80}$

65. What will be the least number which when doubled will be exactly divisible by 12, 18, 21 and 30 ? **(S.S.C. 2003)**

(*a*) 196 (*b*) 630 (*c*) 1260 (*d*) 2520

66. The smallest fraction, which each of $\frac{6}{7}, \frac{5}{14}, \frac{10}{21}$ will divide exactly, is : **(S.S.C. 1998)**

(*a*) $\frac{30}{7}$ (*b*) $\frac{30}{98}$ (*c*) $\frac{60}{147}$ (*d*) $\frac{50}{294}$

67. The least number of five digits which is exactly divisible by 12, 15 and 18, is :

(*a*) 10010 (*b*) 10015 (*c*) 10020 (*d*) 10080

68. The greatest number of four digits which is divisible by 15, 25, 40 and 75 is :

(*a*) 9000 (*b*) 9400 (*c*) 9600 (*d*) 9800 **(S.S.C. 2002)**

69. The least number which should be added to 2497 so that the sum is exactly divisible by 5, 6, 4 and 3 is : **(Hotel Management, 2003)**

(*a*) 3 (*b*) 13 (*c*) 23 (*d*) 33

70. The least number which is a perfect square and is divisible by each of the numbers 16, 20 and 24, is :

(*a*) 1600 (*b*) 3600 (*c*) 6400 (*d*) 14400

71. The smallest number which when diminished by 7, is divisible by 12, 16, 18, 21 and 28 is : **(L.I.C. 2003)**

(*a*) 1008 (*b*) 1015 (*c*) 1022 (*d*) 1032

72. The least number which when increased by 5 is divisible by each one of 24, 32, 36 and 54, is :

(*a*) 427 (*b*) 859 (*c*) 869 (*d*) 4320

73. The least number, which when divided by 12, 15, 20 and 54 leaves in each case a remainder of 8, is : **(R.R.B. 2003)**

(*a*) 504 (*b*) 536 (*c*) 544 (*d*) 548

74. The largest four-digit number which when divided by 4, 7 or 13 leaves a remainder of 3 in each case, is :

(*a*) 8739 (*b*) 9831 (*c*) 9834 (*d*) 9893

75. Let the least number of six digits, which when divided by 4, 6, 10 and 15, leaves in each case the same remainder of 2, be N. The sum of the digits in N is : **(S.S.C. 2003)**

(*a*) 3 (*b*) 4 (*c*) 5 (*d*) 6

76. The least multiple of 7, which leaves a remainder of 4, when divided by 6, 9, 15 and 18 is : **(A.A.O. Exam, 2003)**

(*a*) 74 (*b*) 94 (*c*) 184 (*d*) 364

77. The least number, which when divided by 48, 60, 72, 108 and 140 leaves 38, 50, 62, 98 and 130 as remainders respectively, is : **(C.B.I. 1997)**

(*a*) 11115 (*b*) 15110 (*c*) 15120 (*d*) 15210

78. Find the least multiple of 23, which when divided by 18, 21 and 24 leaves remainders 7, 10 and 13 respeetively.

(*a*) 3002 (*b*) 3013 (*c*) 3024 (*d*) 3036

79. The least number which when divided by 5, 6, 7 and 8 leaves a remainder 3, but when divided by 9 leaves no remainder, is : **(L.I.C.A.A.O. 2003)**

(*a*) 1677 (*b*) 1683 (*c*) 2523 (*d*) 3363

80. Find the least number which when divided by 16, 18, 20 and 25 leaves 4 as remainder in each case, but when divided by 7 leaves no remainder.
(a) 17004 (b) 18000 (c) 18002 (d) 18004

81. Six bells commence tolling together and toll at intervals of 2, 4, 6, 8, 10 and 12 seconds respectively. In 30 minutes, how many times do they toll together ?
(a) 4 (b) 10 (c) 15 (d) 16

82. Four different electronic devices make a beep after every 30 minutes, 1 hour, $1\frac{1}{2}$ hour and 1 hour 45 minutes respectively. All the devices beeped together at 12 noon. They will again beep together at :
(a) 12 midnight (b) 3 a.m. (c) 6 a.m. (d) 9 a.m.

83. A, B and C start at the same time in the same direction to run around a circular stadium. A completes a round in 252 seconds, B in 308 seconds and C in 198 seconds, all starting at the same point. After what time will they meet again at the starting point ? **(S.S.C. 2003)**
(a) 26 minutes 18 seconds (b) 42 minutes 36 seconds
(c) 45 minutes (d) 46 minutes 12 seconds

ANSWERS

1. (a)	**2.** (c)	**3.** (a)	**4.** (b)	**5.** (c)	**6.** (a)	**7.** (a)	**8.** (a)	**9.** (c)
10. (a)	**11.** (b)	**12.** (d)	**13.** (d)	**14.** (d)	**15.** (c)	**16.** (c)	**17.** (b)	**18.** (b)
19. (c)	**20.** (c)	**21.** (a)	**22.** (d)	**23.** (c)	**24.** (b)	**25.** (d)	**26.** (a)	**27.** (d)
28. (d)	**29.** (a)	**30.** (a)	**31.** (b)	**32.** (d)	**33.** (c)	**34.** (b)	**35.** (c)	**36.** (c)
37. (a)	**38.** (c)	**39.** (c)	**40.** (c)	**41.** (a)	**42.** (b)	**43.** (c)	**44.** (c)	**45.** (c)
46. (a)	**47.** (b)	**48.** (d)	**49.** (d)	**50.** (c)	**51.** (a)	**52.** (a)	**53.** (c)	**54.** (a)
55. (b)	**56.** (c)	**57.** (c)	**58.** (a)	**59.** (b)	**60.** (a)	**61.** (a)	**62.** (a)	**63.** (b)
64. (a)	**65.** (b)	**66.** (a)	**67.** (d)	**68.** (c)	**69.** (c)	**70.** (b)	**71.** (b)	**72.** (b)
73. (d)	**74.** (b)	**75.** (c)	**76.** (d)	**77.** (b)	**78.** (b)	**79.** (b)	**80.** (d)	**81.** (d)
82. (d)	**83.** (d)							

SOLUTIONS

1. Clearly, $252 = 2 \times 2 \times 3 \times 3 \times 7$.

2. $99 = 1 \times 3 \times 3 \times 11$; $101 = 1 \times 101$;
$176 = 1 \times 2 \times 2 \times 2 \times 2 \times 11$; $182 = 1 \times 2 \times 7 \times 13$.
So, divisors of 99 are 1, 3, 9, 11, 33 and 99;
divisors of 101 are 1 and 101;
divisors of 176 are 1, 2, 4, 8, 16, 22, 44, 88 and 176;
divisors of 182 are 1, 2, 7, 13, 14, 26, 91 and 182.
Hence, 176 has the most number of divisors.

3.

n	*Divisors excluding n*	*Sum of divisors*
6	1, 2, 3	6
9	1, 3	4
15	1, 3, 5	9
21	1, 3, 7	11

Clearly, 6 is a perfect number.

4. 1095) 1168 (1
1095
73) 1095 (15
73
365
365
×

So, H.C.F. of 1095 and 1168 = 73.

$\therefore \quad \frac{1095}{1168} = \frac{1095 \div 73}{1168 \div 73} = \frac{15}{16}.$

5. 128352) 238368 (1
128352
110016) 128352 (1
110016
18336) 110016 (6
110016
×

So, H.C.F. of 128352 and 238368 = 18336.

$\therefore \quad \frac{128352}{238368} = \frac{128352 \div 18336}{238368 \div 18336} = \frac{7}{13}.$

6. H.C.F. = Product of lowest powers of common factors = $2^2 \times 3^2 \times 5$.

7. H.C.F. = Product of lowest powers of common factors = $3 \times 5 \times 7 = 105$.

8. $4 \times 27 \times 3125 = 2^2 \times 3^3 \times 5^5$; $8 \times 9 \times 25 \times 7 = 2^3 \times 3^2 \times 5^2 \times 7$;
$16 \times 81 \times 5 \times 11 \times 49 = 2^4 \times 3^4 \times 5 \times 7^2 \times 11$.
$\therefore$ H.C.F. = $2^2 \times 3^2 \times 5 = 180$.

9. $36 = 2^2 \times 3^2$; $84 = 2^2 \times 3 \times 7$.
$\therefore$ H.C.F. = $2^2 \times 3 = 12$.

10. $204 = 2^2 \times 3 \times 17$; $1190 = 2 \times 5 \times 7 \times 17$; $1445 = 5 \times 17^2$.
$\therefore$ H.C.F. = 17.

11. H.C.F. of 18 and 25 is 1. So, they are co-primes.

12. 2923) 3239 (1
2923
316) 2923 (9
2844
79) 316 (4
316
×

$\therefore$ H.C.F. = 79.

13. 3444) 3556 (1
3444
112) 3444 (30
3360
84) 112 (1
84
28) 84 (3
84
×

$\therefore$ H.C.F. = 28.

14. L.C.M. = Product of highest powers of prime factors = $2^5 \times 3^4 \times 5^3 \times 7^2 \times 11$.

15.

2	24	36	40
2	12	18	20
2	6	9	10
3	3	9	5
	1	3	5

L.C.M. = $2 \times 2 \times 2 \times 3 \times 3 \times 5 = 360$.

16.

2	22	54	108	135	198
3	11	27	54	135	99
3	11	9	18	45	33
3	11	3	6	15	11
11	11	1	2	5	11
	1	1	2	5	1

L.C.M. = $2 \times 3 \times 3 \times 3 \times 11 \times 2 \times 5 = 5940$.

17. H.C.F. of 148 and 185 is 37.

$\therefore \quad \text{L.C.M.} = \left(\frac{148 \times 185}{37}\right) = 740.$

18. Required H.C.F. = $\frac{\text{H.C.F. of } 2, 8, 64, 10}{\text{L.C.M. of } 3, 9, 81, 27} = \frac{2}{81}.$

19. Required H.C.F. $= \frac{\text{H.C.F. of } 9, 12, 18, 21}{\text{L.C.M. of } 10, 25, 35, 40} = \frac{3}{2800}$.

20. Required L.C.M. $= \frac{\text{L.C.M. of } 1, 5, 2, 4}{\text{H.C.F. of } 3, 6, 9, 27} = \frac{20}{3}$.

21. Required L.C.M. $= \frac{\text{L.C.M. of } 2, 3, 4, 9}{\text{H.C.F. of } 3, 5, 7, 13} = \frac{36}{1} = 36$.

22. Given numbers with two decimal places are : 1.75, 5.60 and 7.00. Without decimal places, these numbers are : 175, 560 and 700, whose H.C.F. is 35.

∴ H.C.F. of given numbers = 0.35.

23. Given numbers are 1.08, 0.36 and 0.90. H.C.F. of 108, 36 and 90 is 18.

∴ H.C.F. of given numbers = 0.18.

24. Given numbers are 0.54, 1.80 and 7.20. H.C.F. of 54, 180 and 720 is 18.

∴ H.C.F. of given numbers = 0.18.

25. Given numbers are 3.00, 2.70 and 0.09. L.C.M. of 300, 270 and 9 is 2700.

∴ L.C.M. of given numbers = 27.00 = 27.

26. $3240 = 2^3 \times 3^4 \times 5$; $3600 = 2^4 \times 3^2 \times 5^2$; H.C.F. $= 36 = 2^2 \times 3^2$.

Since H.C.F. is the product of lowest powers of common factors, so the third number must have $(2^2 \times 3^2)$ as its factor.

Since L.C.M. is the product of highest powers of common prime factors, so the third number must have 3^5 and 7^2 as its factors.

∴ Third number $= 2^2 \times 3^5 \times 7^2$.

27. Let the required numbers be x, $2x$ and $3x$. Then, their H.C.F. = x. So, $x = 12$.

∴ The numbers are 12, 24 and 36.

28. Let the numbers be $3x$ and $4x$. Then, their H.C.F. = x. So, $x = 4$.

So, the numbers are 12 and 16.

L.C.M. of 12 and 16 = 48.

29. Let the required numbers be $27a$ and $27b$. Then, $27a + 27b = 216 \Rightarrow a + b = 8$.

Now, co-primes with sum 8 are (1, 7) and (3, 5).

∴ Required numbers are $(27 \times 1, 27 \times 7)$ and $(27 \times 3, 27 \times 5)$ *i.e.*, (27, 189) and (81, 135).

Out of these, the given one in the answer is the pair (27, 189).

30. Let the required numbers be $33a$ and $33b$. Then, $33a + 33b = 528 \Rightarrow a + b = 16$.

Now, co-primes with sum 16 are (1, 15), (3, 13), (5, 11) and (7, 9).

∴ Required numbers are $(33 \times 1, 33 \times 15)$, $(33 \times 3, 33 \times 13)$, $(33 \times 5, 33 \times 11)$, $(33 \times 7, 33 \times 9)$.

The number of such pairs is 4.

31. Numbers with H.C.F. 15 must contain 15 as a factor.

Now, multiples of 15 between 40 and 100 are 45, 60, 75 and 90.

∴ Number-pairs with H.C.F. 15 are (45, 60), (45, 75), (60, 75) and (75, 90).

[∵ H.C.F. of (60, 90) is 30 and that of (45, 90) is 45]

Clearly, there are 4 such pairs.

32. Out of the given numbers, the two with H.C.F. 12 and difference 12 are 84 and 96.

33. Let the numbers be $37a$ and $37b$. Then, $37a \times 37b = 4107 \Rightarrow ab = 3$.

Now, co-primes with product 3 are (1, 3).

So, the required numbers are $(37 \times 1, 37 \times 3)$ *i.e.*, (1, 111).

∴ Greater number = 111.

34. Let the numbers be $13a$ and $13b$. Then, $13a \times 13b = 2028 \Rightarrow ab = 12$.
Now, co-primes with product 12 are (1, 12) and (3, 4).
So, the required numbers are $(13 \times 1, 13 \times 12)$ and $(13 \times 3, 13 \times 4)$.
Clearly, there are 2 such pairs.

35. Since the numbers are co-prime, they contain only 1 as the common factor.
Also, the given two products have the middle number in common.
So, middle number = H.C.F. of 551 and 1073 = 29;
First number $= \left(\frac{551}{29}\right) = 19$; Third number $= \left(\frac{1073}{29}\right) = 37$.
$\therefore$ Required sum $= (19 + 29 + 37) = 85$.

36. Let the numbers be $2x$ and $3x$. Then, their L.C.M. $= 6x$. So, $6x = 48$ or $x = 8$.
$\therefore$ The numbers are 16 and 24.
Hence, required sum $= (16 + 24) = 40$.

37. Let the numbers be $3x$, $4x$ and $5x$. Then, their L.C.M. $= 60x$. So, $60x = 2400$ or $x = 40$.
$\therefore$ The numbers are (3×40), (4×40) and (5×40).
Hence, required H.C.F. = 40.

38. Other number $= \left(\frac{11 \times 7700}{275}\right) = 308$.

39. Let the numbers be x and $(2000 - x)$. Then, their L.C.M. $= x(2000 - x)$.
So, $x(2000 - x) = 21879 \Leftrightarrow x^2 - 2000x + 21879 = 0$
$\Leftrightarrow (x - 1989)(x - 11) = 0 \Leftrightarrow x = 1989$ or $x = 11$.
Hence, the numbers are 1989 and 11.

40. Let the numbers be x and $4x$. Then, $x \times 4x = 84 \times 21 \Leftrightarrow x^2 = \left(\frac{84 \times 21}{4}\right) \Leftrightarrow x = 21$.
Hence, larger number $= 4x = 84$.

41. Let the numbers be x and $(100 - x)$.
Then, $x(100 - x) = 5 \times 495 \Leftrightarrow x^2 - 100x + 2475 = 0$
$\Leftrightarrow (x - 55)(x - 45) = 0 \Leftrightarrow x = 55$ or $x = 45$.
$\therefore$ The numbers are 45 and 55.
Required difference $= (55 - 45) = 10$.

42. Let the numbers be x and $(x + 2)$.
Then, $x(x + 2) = 24 \Leftrightarrow x^2 + 2x - 24 = 0 \Leftrightarrow (x - 4)(x + 6) = 0 \Leftrightarrow x = 4$.
So, the numbers are 4 and 6.

43. Let the numbers be a and b. Then, $a + b = 55$ and $ab = 5 \times 120 = 600$.
$\therefore$ Required sum $= \frac{1}{a} + \frac{1}{b} = \frac{a + b}{ab} = \frac{55}{600} = \frac{11}{120}$.

44. Let H.C.F. be h and L.C.M. be l. Then, $l = 45h$ and $l + h = 1150$.
$\therefore$ $45h + h = 1150$ or $h = 25$. So, $l = (1150 - 25) = 1125$.
Hence, other number $= \left(\frac{25 \times 1125}{125}\right) = 225$.

45. First number $= (50 \times 2) = 100$. Second number $= \left(\frac{50 \times 250}{100}\right) = 125$.

46. L.C.M. $= \frac{\text{Product of numbers}}{\text{H.C.F.}} = \frac{1320}{6} = 220$.

47. H.C.F of co-prime numbers is 1. So, L.C.M. $= \frac{117}{1} = 117$.

48. Since H.C.F. is always a factor of L.C.M., we cannot have three numbers with H.C.F. 35 and L.C.M. 120.

49. H.C.F. of two numbers divides their L.C.M. exactly. Clearly, 8 is not a factor of 60.

50. Clearly, the numbers are (23×13) and (23×14).

$\therefore$ Larger number $= (23 \times 14) = 322$.

51. Since 16 is not a factor of 136, it follows that there does not exist any pair of numbers with H.C.F. 16 and L.C.M. 136.

52. Product of numbers $= 11 \times 385 = 4235$.

Let the numbers be $11a$ and $11b$. Then, $11a \times 11b = 4235 \Rightarrow ab = 35$.

Now, co-primes with product 35 are (1, 35) and (5, 7).

So, the numbers are $(11 \times 1, 11 \times 35)$ and $(11 \times 5, 11 \times 7)$.

Since one number lies between 75 and 125, the suitable pair is (55, 77).

Hence, required number = 77.

53. Product of numbers $= 29 \times 4147$.

Let the numbers be $29a$ and $29b$. Then, $29a \times 29b = (24 \times 4147) \Rightarrow ab = 143$.

Now, co-primes with product 143 are (1, 143) and (11, 13).

So, the numbers are $(29 \times 1, 29 \times 143)$ and $(29 \times 11, 29 \times 13)$.

Since both numbers are greater than 29, the suitable pair is $(29 \times 11, 29 \times 13)$ *i.e.*, (319, 377).

$\therefore$ Required sum $= (319 + 377) = 696$.

54. H.C.F. of two prime numbers is 1. Product of numbers $= (1 \times 161) = 161$.

Let the numbers be a and b. Then, $ab = 161$.

Now, co-primes with product 161 are (1, 161) and (7, 23).

Since x and y are prime numbers and $x > y$, we have $x = 23$ and $y = 7$.

$\therefore$ $3y - x = (3 \times 7) - 23 = -2$.

55. H.C.F. of 2436 and 1001 is 7. Also, H.C.F. of 105 and 7 is 7.

$\therefore$ H.C.F. of 105, 1001 and 2436 is 7.

56. Required length = H.C.F. of 700 cm, 385 cm and 1295 cm = 35 cm.

57. Required measurement = (H.C.F. of 496, 403, 713) litres = 31 litres.

58. Required number of students = H.C.F. of 1001 and 910 = 91.

59. Largest size of the tile = H.C.F. of 378 cm and 525 cm = 21 cm.

60. Required number = H.C.F. of $(91 - 43)$, $(183 - 91)$ and $(183 - 43)$

= H.C.F. of 48, 92 and 140 = 4.

61. N = H.C.F. of $(4665 - 1305)$, $(6905 - 4665)$ and $(6905 - 1305)$

= H.C.F. of 3360, 2240 and 5600 = 1120.

Sum of digits in N $= (1 + 1 + 2 + 0) = 4$.

62. Required number = H.C.F. of $(1356 - 12)$, $(1868 - 12)$ and $(2764 - 12)$

= H.C.F. of 1344, 1856 and 2752 = 64.

63. Required number = H.C.F. of $(1657 - 6)$ and $(2037 - 5)$

= H.C.F. of 1651 and 2032 = 127.

64. L.C.M. of 8, 16, 40 and 80 = 80.

$$\frac{7}{8} = \frac{70}{80}; \frac{13}{16} = \frac{65}{80}; \frac{31}{40} = \frac{62}{80}.$$

Since, $\frac{70}{80} > \frac{63}{80} > \frac{65}{80} > \frac{62}{80}$, so $\frac{7}{8} > \frac{63}{80} > \frac{13}{16} > \frac{31}{40}$.

So, $\frac{7}{8}$ is the largest.

65. L.C.M. of 12, 18, 21, 30

$= 2 \times 3 \times 2 \times 3 \times 7 \times 5 = 1260.$

2	12 – 18 – 21 – 30
3	6 – 9 – 21 – 15
	2 – 3 – 7 – 5

$\therefore$ Required number $= (1260 \div 2) = 630.$

66. Required fraction = L.C.M. of $\frac{6}{7}, \frac{5}{14}, \frac{10}{21} = \frac{\text{L.C.M. of 6, 5, 10}}{\text{H.C.F. of 7, 14, 21}} = \frac{30}{7}.$

67. Least number of 5 digits is 10000. L.C.M. of 12, 15 and 18 is 180.
On dividing 10000 by 180, the remainder is 100.
$\therefore$ Required number $= 10000 + (180 - 100) = 10080.$

68. Greatest number of 4 digits is 9999. L.C.M. of 15, 25, 40 and 75 is 600.
On dividing 9999 by 600, the remainder is 399.
$\therefore$ Required number $= (9999 - 399) = 9600.$

69. L.C.M. of 5, 6, 4 and 3 = 60. On dividing 2497 by 60, the remainder is 37.
$\therefore$ Number to be added $= (60 - 37) = 23.$

70. The least number divisible by 16, 20, 24
$= \text{L.C.M. of } 16, 20, 24 = 240 = 2 \times 2 \times 2 \times 2 \times 3 \times 5.$
To make it a perfect square, it must be multiplied by 3×5.
$\therefore$ Required number $= 240 \times 3 \times 5 = 3600.$

71. Required number = (L.C.M. of 12, 16, 18, 21, 28) + 7 = 1008 + 7 = 1015.

72. Required number = (L.C.M. of 24, 32, 36, 54) – 5 = 864 – 5 = 859.

73. Required number = (L.C.M. of 12, 15, 20, 54) + 8 = 540 + 8 = 548.

74. Greatest number of 4 digits is 9999. L.C.M. of 4, 7 and 13 = 364.
On dividing 9999 by 364, remainder obtained is 171.
$\therefore$ Greatest number of 4 digits divisible by 4, 7 and 13 = (9999 – 171) = 9828.
Hence, required number = (9828 + 3) = 9831.

75. Least number of 6 digits is 100000. L.C.M. of 4, 6, 10 and 15 = 60.
On dividing 100000 by 60, the remainder obtained is 40.
$\therefore$ Least number of 6 digits divisible by 4, 6, 10 and 15 = 100000 + (60 – 40) = 100020.
$\therefore$ N = (100020 + 2) = 100022. Sum of digits in N = (1 + 2 + 2) = 5.

76. L.C.M. of 6, 9, 15 and 18 is 90.
Let required number be $90k + 4$, which is a multiple of 7.
Least value of k for which $(90k + 4)$ is divisible by 7 is $k = 4$.
$\therefore$ Required number $= 90 \times 4 + 4 = 364.$

77. Here (48 – 38) = 10, (60 – 50) = 10, (72 – 62) = 10, (108 – 98) = 10 & (140 – 130) = 10.
$\therefore$ Required number = (L.C.M. of 48, 60, 72, 108, 140) – 10 = 15120 – 10 = 15110.

78. Here (18 – 7) = 11, (21 – 10) = 11 and (24 – 13) = 11. L.C.M. of 18, 21 and 24 is 504.
Let required number be $504k - 11$.
Least value of k for which $(504k - 11)$ is divisible by 23 is $k = 6$.
$\therefore$ Required number $= 504 \times 6 - 11 = 3024 - 11 = 3013.$

79. L.C.M. of 5, 6, 7, 8 = 840.
$\therefore$ Required number is of the form $840k + 3$.
Least value of k for which $(840k + 3)$ is divisible by 9 is $k = 2$.
$\therefore$ Required number $= (840 \times 2 + 3) = 1683.$

80. L.C.M. of 16, 18, 20, 25 = 3600. Required number is of the form $3600k + 4$.
Least value of k for which $(3600k + 4)$ is divisible by 7 is $k = 5$.
$\therefore$ Required number $= (3600 \times 5 + 4) = 18004.$

81 L.C.M. of 2, 4, 6, 8, 10, 12 is 120.

So, the bells will toll together after every 120 seconds, *i.e.*, 2 minutes.

In 30 minutes, they will toll together $\left[\left(\frac{30}{2}\right)+1\right]$ = 16 times.

82. Interval after which the devices will beep together

= (L.C.M. of 30, 60, 90, 105) min. = 1260 min. = 21 hrs.

So, the devices will again beep together 21 hrs. after 12 noon *i.e.*, at 9 a.m.

83. L.C.M. of 252, 308 and 198 = 2772.

So, A, B and C will again meet at the starting point in 2772 sec. *i.e.*, 46 min. 12 sec.

---

3. DECIMAL FRACTIONS

IMPORTANT FACTS AND FORMULAE

I. Decimal Fractions : Fractions in which denominators are powers of 10 are known as ***decimal fractions.***

Thus, $\frac{1}{10}$ = 1 tenth = .1; $\frac{1}{100}$ = 1 hundredth = .01;

$\frac{99}{100}$ = 99 hundredths = .99; $\frac{7}{1000}$ = 7 thousandths = .007, etc.

II. Conversion of a Decimal Into Vulgar Fraction : Put 1 in the denominator under the decimal point and annex with it as many zeros as is the number of digits after the decimal point. Now, remove the decimal point and reduce the fraction to its lowest terms.

Thus, $0.25 = \frac{25}{100} = \frac{1}{4}$; $2.008 = \frac{2008}{1000} = \frac{251}{125}$.

III. 1. Annexing zeros to the extreme right of a decimal fraction does not change its value.

Thus, 0.8 = 0.80 = 0.800, etc.

2. If numerator and denominator of a fraction contain the same number of decimal places, then we remove the decimal sign.

Thus, $\frac{1.84}{2.99} = \frac{184}{299} = \frac{8}{13}$; $\frac{.365}{.584} = \frac{365}{584} = \frac{5}{8}$

IV. Operations on Decimal Fractions :

1. **Addition and Subtraction of Decimal Fractions :** The given numbers are so placed under each other that the decimal points lie in one column. The numbers so arranged can now be added or subtracted in the usual way.

2. **Multiplication of a Decimal Fraction By a Power of 10 :** Shift the decimal point to the right by as many places as is the power of 10.

Thus, 5.9632 × 100 = 596.32; 0.073 × 10000 = 0.0730 × 10000 = 730.

3. **Multiplication of Decimal Fractions :** Multiply the given numbers considering them without the decimal point. Now, in the product, the decimal point is marked off to obtain as many places of decimal as is the sum of the number of decimal places in the given numbers.

Suppose we have to find the product (.2 × .02 × .002).

Now, 2 × 2 × 2 = 8. Sum of decimal places = (1 + 2 + 3) = 6.

∴ .2 × .02 × .002 = .000008.

4. **Dividing a Decimal Fraction By a Counting Number :** Divide the given number without considering the decimal point, by the given counting number. Now, in the quotient, put the decimal point to give as many places of decimal as there are in the dividend.

Suppose we have to find the quotient (0.0204 ÷ 17). Now, 204 ÷ 17 = 12.

Dividend contains 4 places of decimal. So, 0.0204 ÷ 17 = 0.0012.

5. **Dividing a Decimal Fraction By a Decimal Fraction :** Multiply both the dividend and the divisor by a suitable power of 10 to make divisor a whole number. Now, proceed as above.

Thus, $\frac{0.00066}{0.11} = \frac{0.00066 \times 100}{0.11 \times 100} = \frac{0.066}{11} = .006.$

V. Comparison of Fractions : Suppose some fractions are to be arranged in ascending or descending order of magnitude. Then, convert each one of the given fractions in the decimal form, and arrange them accordingly.

Suppose, we have to arrange the fractions $\frac{3}{5}, \frac{6}{7}$ and $\frac{7}{9}$ in descending order.

Now, $\frac{3}{5} = 0.6, \frac{6}{7} = 0.857, \frac{7}{9} = 0.777.....$

Since $0.857 > 0.777 ..... > 0.6$, so $\frac{6}{7} > \frac{7}{9} > \frac{3}{5}$.

VI. Recurring Decimal : If in a decimal fraction, a figure or a set of figures is repeated continuously, then such a number is called a ***recurring decimal.***

In a recurring decimal, if a single figure is repeated, then it is expressed by putting a dot on it. If a set of figures is repeated, it is expressed by putting a bar on the set.

Thus, $\frac{1}{3} = 0.333 ..... = 0.\dot{3}; \frac{22}{7} = 3.142857142857 ..... = 3.\overline{142857}.$

Pure Recurring Decimal : A decimal fraction in which all the figures after the decimal point are repeated, is called a pure recurring decimal.

Converting a Pure Recurring Decimal Into Vulgar Fraction : Write the repeated figures only once in the numerator and take as many nines in the denominator as is the number of repeating figures.

Thus, $0.\bar{5} = \frac{5}{9}; 0.\overline{53} = \frac{53}{99}; 0.\overline{067} = \frac{67}{999}$; etc.

Mixed Recurring Decimal : A decimal fraction in which some figures do not repeat and some of them are repeated, is called a mixed recurring decimal.

e.g., $0.17333 ..... = 0.17\bar{3}$.

Converting a Mixed Recurring Decimal Into Vulgar Fraction : In the numerator, take the difference between the number formed by all the digits after decimal point (taking repeated digits only once) and that formed by the digits which are not repeated. In the denominator, take the number formed by as many nines as there are repeating digits followed by as many zeros as is the number of non-repeating digits.

Thus, $0.1\bar{6} = \frac{16-1}{90} = \frac{15}{90} = \frac{1}{6}; 0.22\overline{73} = \frac{2273-22}{9900} = \frac{2251}{9900}$.

VII. Some Basic Formulae :

1. $(a + b)(a - b) = (a^2 - b^2)$.
2. $(a + b)^2 = (a^2 + b^2 + 2ab)$.
3. $(a - b)^2 = (a^2 + b^2 - 2ab)$.
4. $(a + b + c)^2 = a^2 + b^2 + c^2 + 2(ab + bc + ca)$.
5. $(a^3 + b^3) = (a + b)(a^2 - ab + b^2)$
6. $(a^3 - b^3) = (a - b)(a^2 + ab + b^2)$.
7. $(a^3 + b^3 + c^3 - 3abc) = (a + b + c)(a^2 + b^2 + c^2 - ab - bc - ac)$.
8. When $a + b + c = 0$, then $a^3 + b^3 + c^3 = 3abc$.

SOLVED EXAMPLES

Ex. 1. ***Convert the following into vulgar fractions :***

(i) 0.75 (ii) 3.004 (iii) .0056.

Sol. (i) $0.75 = \frac{75}{100} = \frac{3}{4}$. (ii) $3.004 = \frac{3004}{1000} = \frac{751}{250}$. (iii) $.0056 = \frac{56}{10000} = \frac{7}{1250}$.

Ex. 2. ***Arrange the fractions*** $\frac{5}{8}, \frac{7}{12}, \frac{13}{16}, \frac{16}{29}$ ***and*** $\frac{3}{4}$ ***in ascending order of magnitude.***

Sol. Converting each of the given fractions into decimal form, we get :

$\frac{5}{8} = 0.625, \frac{7}{12} = 0.5833, \frac{13}{16} = 0.8125, \frac{16}{29} = 0.5517$ and $\frac{3}{4} = 0.75$.

Now, $0.5517 < 0.5833 < 0.625 < 0.75 < 0.8125$.

$\therefore \quad \frac{16}{29} < \frac{7}{12} < \frac{5}{8} < \frac{3}{4} < \frac{13}{16}$.

Ex. 3. ***Arrange the fractions*** $\frac{3}{5}, \frac{4}{7}, \frac{8}{9}$ ***and*** $\frac{9}{11}$ ***in their descending order.*** **(R.B.I. 2003)**

Sol. Clearly, $\frac{3}{5} = 0.6, \frac{4}{7} = 0.571, \frac{8}{9} = 0.88, \frac{9}{11} = 0.818$.

Now, $0.88 > 0.818 > 0.6 > 0.571$.

$\therefore \quad \frac{8}{9} > \frac{9}{11} > \frac{3}{5} > \frac{4}{7}$.

Ex. 4. ***Evaluate :*** ***(i) 6202.5 + 620.25 + 62.025 + 6.2025 + 0.62025*** **(L.I.C. 2003)**

(ii) 5.064 + 3.98 + .7036 + 7.6 + .3 + 2

Sol. (i)

```
   6202.5
    620.25
     62.025
      6.2025
+     0.62025
-------------
   6891.59775
```

(ii)

```
    5.064
    3.98
    0.7036
    7.6
    0.3
+   2.0
---------
   19.6476
```

Ex. 5. ***Evaluate : (i) 31.004 − 17.2386 (ii) 13 − 5.1967***

Sol. (i)

```
  31.0040
− 17.2386
---------
  13.7654
```

(ii)

```
  13.0000
−  5.1967
---------
   7.8033
```

Ex. 6. ***What value will replace the question mark in the following equations ?***

(i) 5172.49 + 378.352 + ? = 9318.678 **(B.S.R.B. 1998)**

(ii) ? − 7328.96 = 5169.38 **(B.S.R.B. 2003)**

Sol. (i) Let $5172.49 + 378.352 + x = 9318.678$.

Then, $x = 9318.678 - (5172.49 + 378.352) = 9318.678 - 5550.842 = 3767.836$.

(ii) Let $x - 7328.96 = 5169.38$. Then, $x = 5169.38 + 7328.96 = 12498.34$.

Ex. 7. ***Find the products : (i) 6.3204 × 100 (ii) .069 × 10000***

Sol. (i) $6.3204 \times 100 = 632.04$. (ii) $.069 \times 10000 = .0690 \times 10000 = 690$.

Ex. 8. ***Find the products :***

(i) 2.61 × 1.3 ***(ii) 2.1693 × 1.4*** ***(iii) .4 × .04 × .004 × 40.***

Sol. (*i*) 261 × 13 = 3393. Sum of decimal places of given numbers = (2 + 1) = 3.

∴ 2.61 × 1.3 = 3.393.

(*ii*) 21693 × 14 = 303702. Sum of decimal places = (4 + 1) = 5.

∴ 2.1693 × 1.4 = 3.03702.

(*iii*) 4 × 4 × 4 × 40 = 2560. Sum of decimal places = (1 + 2 + 3) = 6.

∴ .4 × .04 × .004 × 40 = .002560.

Ex. 9. ***Given that 268 × 74 = 19832, find the value of 2.68 × .74.***

Sol. Sum of decimal places = (2 + 2) = 4.

∴ 2.68 × .74 = 1.9832.

Ex. 10. ***Find the quotient :***

(i) 0.63 ÷ 9 ***(ii) 0.0204 ÷ 17*** ***(iii) 3.1603 ÷ 13.***

Sol. (*i*) 63 ÷ 9 = 7. Dividend contains 2 places of decimal.

∴ 0.63 ÷ 9 = .07.

(*ii*) 204 ÷ 17 = 12. Dividend contains 4 places of decimal.

∴ 0.0204 ÷ 17 = .0012.

(*iii*) 31603 ÷ 13 = 2431. Dividend contains 4 places of decimal.

∴ 3.1603 ÷ 13 = .2431.

Ex. 11. ***Evaluate :***

(i) 35 ÷ .07 ***(ii) 2.5 ÷ 0.0005*** **(M.B.A. 1998)**

(iii) 136.09 ÷ 43.9 **(Hotel Management, 2000)**

Sol. (*i*) $\frac{35}{.07} = \frac{35 \times 100}{.07 \times 100} = \frac{3500}{7} = 500.$

(*ii*) $\frac{2.5}{0.0005} = \frac{2.5 \times 10000}{0.0005 \times 10000} = \frac{25000}{5} = 5000.$

(*iii*) $\frac{136.09}{43.9} = \frac{136.09 \times 10}{43.9 \times 10} = \frac{1360.9}{439} = 3.1.$

Ex. 12. ***What value will come in place of question mark in the following equations?***

(i) 0.006 ÷ ? = 0.6 ***(ii) ? ÷ .025 = 80***

Sol. (*i*) Let $\frac{0.006}{x} = 0.6$. Then, $x = \frac{0.006}{0.6} = \frac{0.006 \times 10}{0.6 \times 10} = \frac{0.06}{6} = 0.01.$

(*ii*) Let $\frac{x}{.025} = 80$. Then, $x = 80 \times .025 = 2.$

Ex. 13. ***If*** $\frac{1}{3.718} = .2689$, ***then find the value of*** $\frac{1}{.0003718}$.

Sol. $\frac{1}{.0003718} = \frac{10000}{3.718} = \left(10000 \times \frac{1}{3.718}\right) = 10000 \times .2689 = 2689.$

Ex. 14. ***Express as vulgar fractions : (i)*** $0.\overline{37}$ ***(ii)*** $0.\overline{053}$ ***(iii)*** $3.\overline{142857}$.

Sol. (*i*) $0.\overline{37} = \frac{37}{99}$. (*ii*) $0.\overline{053} = \frac{53}{999}$.

(*iii*) $3.\overline{142857} = 3 + 0.\overline{142857} = 3 + \frac{142857}{999999} = 3\frac{142857}{999999}$.

Ex. 15. ***Express as vulgar fractions : (i)*** $0.1\overline{7}$ ***(ii)*** $0.12\overline{54}$ ***(iii)*** $2.53\overline{6}$

Sol. (*i*) $0.1\overline{7} = \frac{17-1}{90} = \frac{16}{90} = \frac{8}{45}$. (*ii*) $0.12\overline{54} = \frac{1254-12}{9900} = \frac{1242}{9900} = \frac{69}{550}$.

(*iii*) $2.53\bar{6} = 2 + 0.53\bar{6} = 2 + \frac{536 - 53}{900} = 2 + \frac{483}{900} = 2 + \frac{161}{300} = 2\frac{161}{300}$.

Ex. 16. ***Simplify*** : $\frac{0.05 \times 0.05 \times 0.05 + 0.04 \times 0.04 \times 0.04}{0.05 \times 0.05 - 0.05 \times 0.04 + 0.04 \times 0.04}$. **(IGNOU, 2003)**

Sol. Given expression $= \left(\frac{a^3 + b^3}{a^2 - ab + b^2}\right)$, where $a = 0.05$, $b = 0.04$

$= (a + b) = (0.05 + 0.04) = 0.09.$

EXERCISE 3

(OBJECTIVE TYPE QUESTIONS)

Directions : *Mark (✓) against the correct answer* :

1. The fraction $101\frac{27}{100000}$ in decimal form is :
   (*a*) .01027 (*b*) .10127 (*c*) 101.00027 (*d*) 101.000027
2. When .36 is written in simplest fractional form, the sum of the numerator and the denominator is :
   (*a*) 15 (*b*) 45 (*c*) 114 (*d*) 135
3. What decimal of an hour is a second ?
   (*a*) .0025 (*b*) .0256 (*c*) .00027 (*d*) .000126
4. If $47.2506 = 4A + \frac{7}{B} + 2C + \frac{5}{D} + 6E$, then the value of $5A + 3B + 6C + D + 3E$ is : **(S.S.C. 2003)**
   (*a*) 53.6003 (*b*) 53.603 (*c*) 153.6003 (*d*) 213.0003
5. Which of the following has fractions in ascending order ? **(Bank P.O. 2003)**
   (*a*) $\frac{1}{3}, \frac{2}{5}, \frac{4}{7}, \frac{3}{5}, \frac{5}{6}, \frac{6}{7}$ (*b*) $\frac{1}{3}, \frac{2}{5}, \frac{3}{5}, \frac{4}{7}, \frac{5}{6}, \frac{6}{7}$
   (*c*) $\frac{1}{3}, \frac{2}{5}, \frac{3}{5}, \frac{5}{6}, \frac{4}{7}, \frac{6}{7}$ (*d*) $\frac{2}{5}, \frac{3}{5}, \frac{1}{3}, \frac{4}{7}, \frac{5}{6}, \frac{6}{7}$
6. Which of the following has fractions in ascending order ? **(NABARD, 2002)**
   (*a*) $\frac{2}{3}, \frac{3}{5}, \frac{7}{9}, \frac{9}{11}, \frac{8}{9}$ (*b*) $\frac{3}{5}, \frac{2}{3}, \frac{9}{11}, \frac{7}{9}, \frac{8}{9}$ (*c*) $\frac{3}{5}, \frac{2}{3}, \frac{7}{9}, \frac{9}{11}, \frac{8}{9}$
   (*d*) $\frac{8}{9}, \frac{9}{11}, \frac{7}{9}, \frac{2}{3}, \frac{3}{5}$ (*e*) $\frac{8}{9}, \frac{9}{11}, \frac{7}{9}, \frac{3}{5}, \frac{2}{3}$
7. Which of the following are in descending order of their value ? **(R.R.B. 2002)**
   (*a*) $\frac{5}{9}, \frac{7}{11}, \frac{8}{15}, \frac{11}{17}$ (*b*) $\frac{5}{9}, \frac{8}{15}, \frac{11}{17}, \frac{7}{11}$
   (*c*) $\frac{11}{17}, \frac{7}{11}, \frac{8}{15}, \frac{5}{9}$ (*d*) $\frac{11}{17}, \frac{7}{11}, \frac{5}{9}, \frac{8}{15}$
8. What is the difference between the biggest and the smallest fraction among $\frac{2}{3}, \frac{3}{4}, \frac{4}{5}$ and $\frac{5}{6}$? **(C.B.I. 1998)**
   (*a*) $\frac{1}{6}$ (*b*) $\frac{1}{12}$ (*c*) $\frac{1}{20}$ (*d*) $\frac{1}{30}$

9. Which part contains the fractions in ascending order ?

(a) $\frac{11}{14}, \frac{16}{19}, \frac{19}{21}$ (b) $\frac{16}{19}, \frac{11}{14}, \frac{19}{21}$ (c) $\frac{16}{19}, \frac{19}{21}, \frac{11}{14}$ (d) $\frac{19}{21}, \frac{11}{14}, \frac{16}{19}$

(S.S.C. 2002)

10. Which of the following fractions is the smallest ?

(a) $\frac{13}{16}$ (b) $\frac{15}{19}$ (c) $\frac{17}{21}$ (d) $\frac{7}{8}$

11. Which of the following fractions is greater than $\frac{3}{4}$ and less than $\frac{5}{6}$?

(S.S.C. 1999)

(a) $\frac{1}{2}$ (b) $\frac{2}{3}$ (c) $\frac{4}{5}$ (d) $\frac{9}{10}$

12. Which of the following fractions is less than $\frac{7}{8}$ and greater than $\frac{1}{3}$?

(a) $\frac{1}{4}$ (b) $\frac{23}{24}$ (c) $\frac{11}{12}$ (d) $\frac{17}{24}$

13. Which of the following numbers does not lie between $\frac{4}{5}$ and $\frac{7}{13}$?

(a) $\frac{1}{2}$ (b) $\frac{2}{3}$ (c) $\frac{3}{4}$ (d) $\frac{5}{7}$

14. The arrangement of rational numbers $\frac{-7}{10}, \frac{5}{-8}, \frac{2}{-3}$ in ascending order is :

(a) $\frac{2}{-3}, \frac{5}{-8}, \frac{-7}{10}$ (b) $\frac{5}{-8}, \frac{-7}{10}, \frac{2}{-3}$ (c) $\frac{-7}{10}, \frac{5}{-8}, \frac{2}{-3}$ (d) $\frac{-7}{10}, \frac{2}{-3}, \frac{5}{-8}$

(S.S.C. 1998)

15. 337.62 + 8.591 + 34.4 = ?

(a) 370.611 (b) 380.511 (c) 380.611 (d) 426.97

16. The value of (1 + .1 + .01 + .001) is :

(a) 1.001 (b) 1.011 (c) 1.003 (d) 1.111

(Bank P.O. 2002)

17. 34.95 + 240.016 + 23.98 = ?

(a) 298.0946 (b) 298.111 (c) 298.946 (d) 299.09

(M.B.A. 1998)

18. 617 + 6.017 + 0.617 + 6.0017 = ?

(a) 6.2963 (b) 62.965 (c) 629.6357 (d) None of these

(I.B.P.S. 2002)

19. 48.95 − 32.006 = ?

(a) 16.089 (b) 16.35 (c) 16.89 (d) 16.944

(NABARD, 2002)

20. 792.02 + 101.32 − 306.76 = ?

(a) 586.58 (b) 893.34 (c) 997.11 (d) 1200.10

(B.S.R.B. 2003)

21. 12.1212 + 17.0005 − 9.1102 = ?

(a) 20.0015 (b) 20.0105 (c) 20.0115 (d) 20.1015

22. 892.7 − 573.07 − 95.007 = ?

(a) 224.623 (b) 224.777 (c) 233.523 (d) 414.637

(Bank P.O. 2002)

23. 3889 + 12.952 − ? = 3854.002

(a) 47.095 (b) 47.752 (c) 47.932 (d) 47.95

(Bank P.O. 1999)

24. 138.009 + 341.981 − 146.305 = 123.6 + ?

(a) 120.085 (b) 120.85 (c) 220.085 (d) None of these

(B.S.R.B. 1998)

25. 832.58 − 242.31 = 779.84 − ?

(a) 179.57 (b) 199.57 (c) 295.05 (d) None of these

26. What will come in place of question mark in the following equation ?

54. (?) 3 + 543 + 5.43 = 603.26 **(Hotel Management, 2001)**

(a) 5 (b) 6 (c) 8 (d) None of these

27. Which of the following is equal to 3.14×10^6 ? **(Hotel Management, 2003)**

(a) 314 (b) 3140 (c) 3140000 (d) None of these

28. The number 518,000,000 when expressed in scientific notation, equals :

(a) 51.8×10^6 (b) 51.8×10^7 (c) 5.18×10^8 (d) 5.18×10^9

29. 0.000006723 when expressed in scientific notation, is :

(a) 6723×10^{-5} (b) 67.23×10^{-7} (c) 6.723×10^{-6} (d) None of these

30. If $1.125 \times 10^k = 0.001125$, then the value of k is :

(a) – 4 (b) – 3 (c) – 2 (d) – 1

31. 0.002 × 0.5 = ? **(Bank P.O. 2003)**

(a) 0.0001 (b) 0.001 (c) 0.01 (d) 0.1

32. 16.02 × 0.001 = ? **(Bank P.O. 2002)**

(a) 0.001602 (b) 0.01602 (c) 0.1602 (d) 1.6021

33. 0.014 × 0.014 = ? **(Hotel Management, 2001)**

(a) 0.000196 (b) 0.00196 (c) 19.6 (d) 196

34. 40.83 × 1.02 × 1.2 = ? **(S.B.I.P.O. 2003)**

(a) 41.64660 (b) 42.479532 (c) 49.97592 (d) 58.7952

35. 0.04 × 0.0162 is equal to : **(M.B.A. 1998)**

(a) 6.48×10^{-3} (b) 6.48×10^{-4} (c) 6.48×10^{-5} (d) 6.48×10^{-6}

36. 3 × 0.3 × 0.03 × 0.003 × 30 = ? **(Hotel Management, 2002)**

(a) 0.0000243 (b) 0.000243 (c) 0.00243 (d) 0.0243

37. How many digits will be there to the right of the decimal point in the product of 95.75 and .02554 ? **(I.A.M. 2002)**

(a) 5 (b) 6 (c) 7 (d) None of these

38. $\left(.00625 \text{ of } \frac{23}{5}\right)$, when expressed as a vulgar fraction, equals :

(a) $\frac{23}{80}$ (b) $\frac{23}{800}$ (c) $\frac{23}{8000}$ (d) $\frac{125}{23}$

39. Which is the closest approximation to the product 0.3333 × 0.25 × 0.499 × 0.125 × 24 ?

(a) $\frac{1}{8}$ (b) $\frac{3}{4}$ (c) $\frac{3}{8}$ (d) $\frac{2}{5}$

40. Consider the following quotients :

1. 368.39 divided by 17 2. 170.50 divided by 62 3. 875.65 divided by 83

Their correct sequence in decreasing order is : **(C.D.S. 2003)**

(a) 1, 3, 2 (b) 2, 1, 3 (c) 2, 3, 1 (d) 3, 1, 2

41. 0.213 ÷ 0.00213 = ?

(a) 1 (b) 10 (c) 100 (d) None of these

42. 4.036 divided by 0.04 gives : **(Hotel Management, 2003)**

(a) 1.009 (b) 10.09 (c) 100.9 (d) None of these

43. $\frac{1}{0.04}$ is equal to : **(S.S.C. 2000)**

(a) $\frac{1}{40}$ (b) $\frac{2}{5}$ (c) 2.5 (d) 25

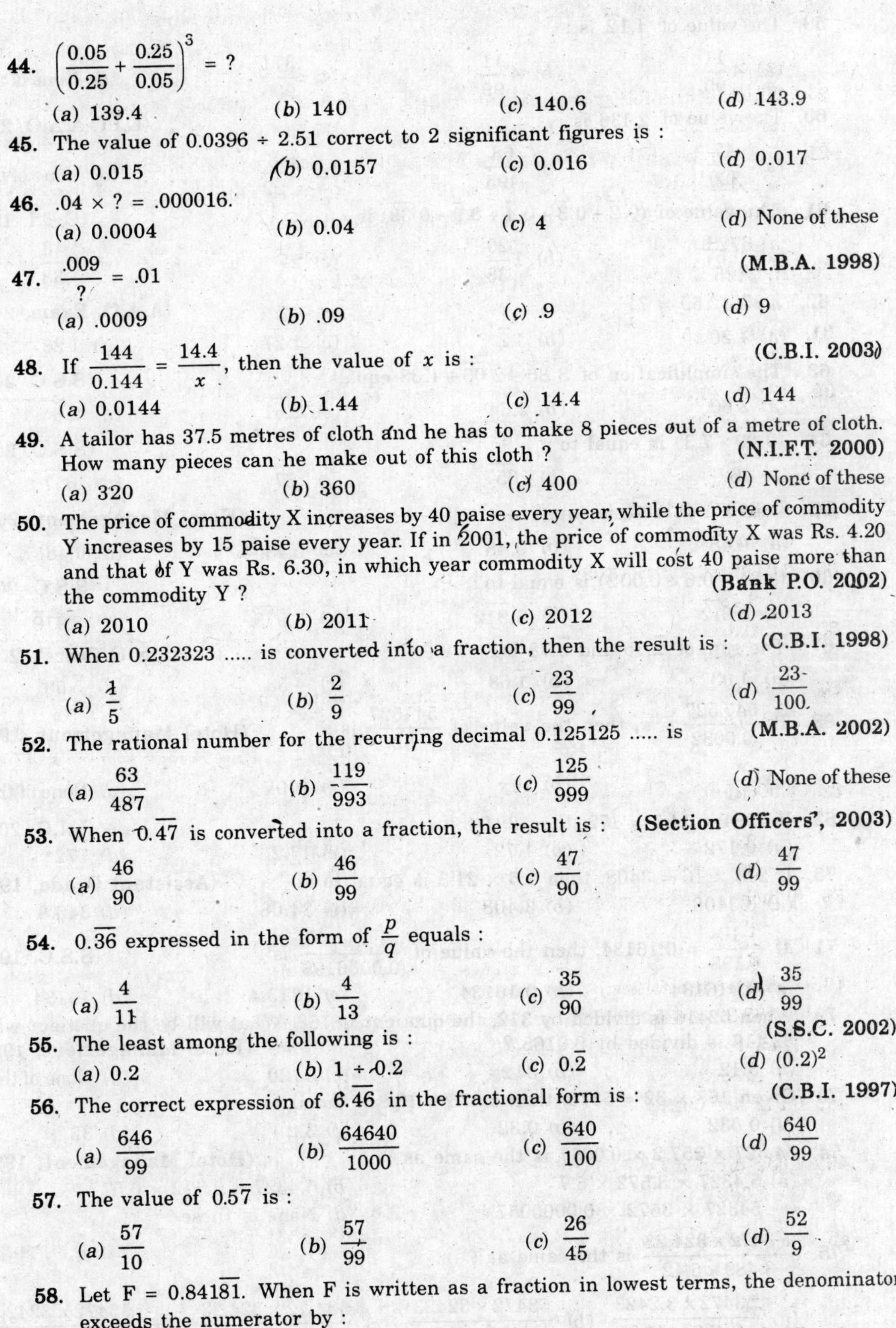

44. $\left(\dfrac{0.05}{0.25}+\dfrac{0.25}{0.05}\right)^3 = ?$

(a) 139.4 (b) 140 (c) 140.6 (d) 143.9

45. The value of 0.0396 ÷ 2.51 correct to 2 significant figures is :

(a) 0.015 (b) 0.0157 (c) 0.016 (d) 0.017

46. .04 × ? = .000016.

(a) 0.0004 (b) 0.04 (c) 4 (d) None of these

47. $\dfrac{.009}{?} = .01$ **(M.B.A. 1998)**

(a) .0009 (b) .09 (c) .9 (d) 9

48. If $\dfrac{144}{0.144} = \dfrac{14.4}{x}$, then the value of x is : **(C.B.I. 2003)**

(a) 0.0144 (b) 1.44 (c) 14.4 (d) 144

49. A tailor has 37.5 metres of cloth and he has to make 8 pieces out of a metre of cloth. How many pieces can he make out of this cloth ? **(N.I.F.T. 2000)**

(a) 320 (b) 360 (c) 400 (d) None of these

50. The price of commodity X increases by 40 paise every year, while the price of commodity Y increases by 15 paise every year. If in 2001, the price of commodity X was Rs. 4.20 and that of Y was Rs. 6.30, in which year commodity X will cost 40 paise more than the commodity Y ? **(Bank P.O. 2002)**

(a) 2010 (b) 2011 (c) 2012 (d) 2013

51. When 0.232323 ..... is converted into a fraction, then the result is : **(C.B.I. 1998)**

(a) $\dfrac{1}{5}$ (b) $\dfrac{2}{9}$ (c) $\dfrac{23}{99}$ (d) $\dfrac{23}{100}$

52. The rational number for the recurring decimal 0.125125 ..... is **(M.B.A. 2002)**

(a) $\dfrac{63}{487}$ (b) $\dfrac{119}{993}$ (c) $\dfrac{125}{999}$ (d) None of these

53. When $0.\overline{47}$ is converted into a fraction, the result is : **(Section Officers', 2003)**

(a) $\dfrac{46}{90}$ (b) $\dfrac{46}{99}$ (c) $\dfrac{47}{90}$ (d) $\dfrac{47}{99}$

54. $0.\overline{36}$ expressed in the form of $\dfrac{p}{q}$ equals :

(a) $\dfrac{4}{11}$ (b) $\dfrac{4}{13}$ (c) $\dfrac{35}{90}$ (d) $\dfrac{35}{99}$

55. The least among the following is : **(S.S.C. 2002)**

(a) 0.2 (b) 1 ÷ 0.2 (c) $0.\overline{2}$ (d) $(0.2)^2$

56. The correct expression of $6.\overline{46}$ in the fractional form is : **(C.B.I. 1997)**

(a) $\dfrac{646}{99}$ (b) $\dfrac{64640}{1000}$ (c) $\dfrac{640}{100}$ (d) $\dfrac{640}{99}$

57. The value of $0.5\overline{7}$ is :

(a) $\dfrac{57}{10}$ (b) $\dfrac{57}{99}$ (c) $\dfrac{26}{45}$ (d) $\dfrac{52}{9}$

58. Let F = $0.84\overline{181}$. When F is written as a fraction in lowest terms, the denominator exceeds the numerator by :

(a) 13 (b) 14 (c) 29 (d) 87

59. The value of $4.1\overline{2}$ is :

(a) $4\frac{11}{90}$ (b) $4\frac{11}{99}$ (c) $\frac{371}{900}$ (d) None of these

60. The value of $2.1\overline{36}$ is : **(L.I.C.A.A.O. 2003)**

(a) $\frac{47}{220}$ (b) $\frac{68}{495}$ (c) $2\frac{3}{22}$ (d) None of these

61. The value of $(0.\overline{2} + 0.\overline{3} + 0.\overline{4} + 0.\overline{9} + 0.\overline{39})$ is : **(C.B.I. 1997)**

(a) $0.\overline{57}$ (b) $1\frac{20}{33}$ (c) $2\frac{1}{3}$ (d) $2\frac{13}{33}$

62. $3.\overline{87} - 2.59 = ?$ **(A.A.O. Exam, 2003)**

(a) 1.20 (b) $1.\overline{2}$ (c) $1.\overline{27}$ (d) $1.\overline{28}$

63. The simplification of $3.\overline{36} - 2.\overline{05} + 1.\overline{33}$ equals : **(S.S.C. 2003)**

(a) 2.60 (b) 2.64 (c) $2.\overline{61}$ (d) $2.\overline{64}$

64. $(0.\overline{09} \times 7.\overline{3})$ is equal to : **(S.S.C. 2003)**

(a) $.\overline{6}$ (b) $.\overline{657}$ (c) $.\overline{67}$ (d) $.6\overline{57}$

65. $(0.34\overline{67} + 0.13\overline{33})$ is equal to : **(Hotel Management, 2002)**

(a) $0.4\overline{8}$ (b) $0.\overline{48}$ (c) $0.48\overline{01}$ (d) 0.48

66. $(8.3\overline{1} + 0.\overline{6} + 0.00\overline{2})$ is equal to : **(S.S.C. 2002)**

(a) $8.9\overline{12}$ (b) $8.\overline{912}$ (c) $8.9\overline{79}$ (d) $8.97\overline{9}$

67. The sum of $\overline{2}.75$ and $\overline{3}.78$ is : **(Section Officers', 2001)**

(a) 1.03 (b) $\overline{1}.53$ (c) $\overline{4}.53$ (d) $\overline{5}.53$

68. If $\frac{547.527}{0.0082} = x$, then the value of $\frac{547527}{82}$ is : **(Hotel Management, 1999)**

(a) $\frac{x}{10}$ (b) $10x$ (c) $100x$ (d) None of these

69. If $2994 \div 14.5 = 172$, then $29.94 \div 1.45 = ?$ **(L.I.C. 2003)**

(a) 0.172 (b) 1.72 (c) 17.2 (d) 172

70. If $213 \times 16 = 3408$, then 1.6×21.3 is equal to : **(Assistant Grade, 1998)**

(a) 0.3408 (b) 3.408 (c) 34.08 (d) 340.8

71. If $\frac{1}{6.198} = 0.16134$, then the value of $\frac{1}{0.0006198}$ is : **(S.S.C. 1997)**

(a) 0.016134 (b) 0.16134 (c) 1613.4 (d) 16134

72. When 52416 is divided by 312, the quotient is 168. What will be the quotient when 52.416 is divided by 0.0168 ? **(Hotel Management, 1998)**

(a) 3.12 (b) 312 (c) 3120 (d) None of these

73. Given $168 \times 32 = 5376$, then $5.376 \div 16.8$ is equal to :

(a) 0.032 (b) 0.32 (c) 3.2 (d) 32

74. $54.327 \times 357.2 \times 0.0057$ is the same as : **(Hotel Management, 1997)**

(a) $5.4327 \times 3.572 \times 5.7$ (b) $5.4327 \times 3.572 \times 0.57$

(c) $54327 \times 3572 \times 0.0000057$ (d) None of these

75. $\frac{5.3472 \times 324.23}{3.489 \times 5.42}$ is the same as :

(a) $\frac{53472 \times 3.2423}{3.489 \times 54.2}$ (b) $\frac{53472 \times 32423}{3489 \times 542}$ (c) $\frac{534.72 \times 324.23}{34.89 \times 5.42}$ (d) $\frac{53472 \times 3242.3}{3489 \times 542}$

76. $\frac{96.54 - 89.63}{96.54 + 89.63} \div \frac{965.4 - 896.3}{9.654 + 8.963} = ?$

(a) 10^{-2} (b) 10^{-1} (c) 10 (d) None of these

77. If $1^3 + 2^3 + ... + 9^3 = 2025$, then the value of $(0.11)^3 + (0.22)^3 + ... + (0.99)^3$ is close to : **(S.S.C. 2003)**

(a) 0.2695 (b) 0.3695 (c) 2.695 (d) 3.695

78. $8.7 - [7.6 - \{6.5 - (5.4 - \overline{4.3 - 2})\}]$ is simplified to : **(S.S.C. 2004)**

(a) 2.5 (b) 3.5 (c) 4.5 (d) 5.5

79. The value of $\frac{1}{4} + \frac{1}{4 \times 5} + \frac{1}{4 \times 5 \times 6}$ correct to 4 decimal places is :

(a) 0.3075 (b) 0.3082 (c) 0.3083 (d) 0.3085

80. Find the value of the following expression upto four places of decimals.

$\left[1 + \frac{1}{1 \times 2} + \frac{1}{1 \times 2 \times 4} + \frac{1}{1 \times 2 \times 4 \times 8} + \frac{1}{1 \times 2 \times 4 \times 8 \times 16}\right]$ **(Hotel Management, 2002)**

(a) 1.6414 (b) 1.6415 (c) 1.6416 (d) 1.6428

81. The sum of the first 20 terms of the series $\frac{1}{5 \times 6} + \frac{1}{6 \times 7} + \frac{1}{7 \times 8} + ...$ is :

(a) 0.16 (b) 1.6 (c) 16 (d) None of these

(Hotel Management, 1998)

82. If $1.5x = 0.04y$, then the value of $\left(\frac{y - x}{y + x}\right)$ is :

(a) $\frac{730}{77}$ (b) $\frac{73}{77}$ (c) $\frac{7.3}{77}$ (d) None of these

83. The value of $\left[35.7 - \left(3 + \frac{1}{3 + \frac{1}{3}}\right) - \left(2 + \frac{1}{2 + \frac{1}{2}}\right)\right]$ is :

(a) 30 (b) 34.8 (c) 36.6 (d) 41.4

84. $\frac{(0.1667)\,(0.8333)\,(0.3333)}{(0.2222)\,(0.6667)\,(0.1250)}$ is approximately equal to : **(M.B.A. 1998)**

(a) 2 (b) 2.40 (c) 2.43 (d) 2.50

85. The value of $\frac{3.6 \times 0.48 \times 2.50}{0.12 \times 0.09 \times 0.5}$ is : **(S.S.C. 1998)**

(a) 80 (b) 800 (c) 8000 (d) 80000

86. $\frac{0.0203 \times 2.92}{0.0073 \times 14.5 \times 0.7} = ?$ **(R.R.B. 1998)**

(a) 0.8 (b) 1.45 (c) 2.40 (d) 3.25

87. The value of $\frac{3.157 \times 4126 \times 3.198}{63.972 \times 2835.121}$ is closest to : **(C.B.I. 2003)**

(a) 0.002 (b) 0.02 (c) 0.2 (d) 2

88. The value of $\frac{489.1375 \times 0.0483 \times 1.956}{0.0873 \times 92.581 \times 99.749}$ is closest to : **(C.B.I. 1997)**

(a) 0.006 (b) 0.06 (c) 0.6 (d) 6

89. The value of $\frac{241.6 \times 0.3814 \times 6.842}{0.4618 \times 38.25 \times 73.65}$ is close to :

(a) 0.2 (b) 0.4 (c) 0.6 (d) 1

90. $(0.2 \times 0.2 + 0.01)(0.1 \times 0.1 + 0.02)^{-1}$ is equal to : **(Section Officers', 2003)**

(*a*) $\frac{5}{3}$ (*b*) $\frac{9}{5}$ (*c*) $\frac{41}{4}$ (*d*) $\frac{41}{12}$

91. $\frac{5 \times 1.6 - 2 \times 1.4}{1.3} = ?$ **(Bank P.O. 2003)**

(*a*) 0.4 (*b*) 1.2 (*c*) 1.4 (*d*) 4

92. The value of $(4.7 \times 13.26 + 4.7 \times 9.43 + 4.7 \times 77.31)$ is : **(IGNOU, 2003)**

(*a*) 0.47 (*b*) 47 (*c*) 470 (*d*) 4700

93. Simplify : $\frac{0.2 \times 0.2 + 0.2 \times 0.02}{0.044}$. **(S.S.C. 1999)**

(*a*) 0.004 (*b*) 0.4 (*c*) 1 (*d*) 2

94. The value of $\left(\frac{8.6 \times 5.3 + 8.6 \times 4.7}{4.3 \times 9.7 - 4.3 \times 8.7}\right)$ is :

(*a*) 3.3 (*b*) 6.847 (*c*) 13.9 (*d*) 20

95. The value of $\left(\frac{.896 \times .763 + .896 \times .237}{.7 \times .064 + .7 \times .936}\right)$ is :

(*a*) .976 (*b*) 9.76 (*c*) 1.28 (*d*) 12.8

96. The value of $(68.237)^2 - (31.763)^2$ i :

(*a*) 3.6474 (*b*) 36.474 (*c*) 364.74 (*d*) 3647.4

97. Evaluate : $\frac{(2.39)^2 - (1.61)^2}{2.39 - 1.61}$. **(R.R.B. 2003)**

(*a*) 2 (*b*) 4 (*c*) 6 (*d*) 8

98. On simplification of $\frac{(2.644)^2 - (2.356)^2}{0.288}$, we get : **(S.S.C. 1999)**

(*a*) 1 (*b*) 4 (*c*) 5 (*d*) 6

99. $\frac{(36.54)^2 - (3.46)^2}{?} = 40.$

(*a*) 3.308 (*b*) 4 (*c*) 33.08 (*d*) 330.8

100. The value of $\frac{(67.542)^2 - (32.458)^2}{75.458 - 40.374}$ is : **(Hotel Management, 1997)**

(*a*) 1 (*b*) 10 (*c*) 100 (*d*) None of these

101. $\left(\frac{1.49 \times 14.9 - 0.51 \times 5.1}{14.9 - 5.1}\right)$ is equal to : **(S.S.C. 2004)**

(*a*) 0.20 (*b*) 2.00 (*c*) 20 (*d*) 22

102. $\frac{4.2 \times 4.2 - 1.9 \times 1.9}{2.3 \times 6.1} = ?$ **(R.R.B. 1998)**

(*a*) 0.5 (*b*) 1 (*c*) 1.9 (*d*) 4.2

103. Simplify : $\frac{5.32 \times 56 + 5.32 \times 44}{(7.66)^2 - (2.34)^2}$.

(*a*) 7.2 (*b*) 8.5 (*c*) 10 (*d*) 12

104. $\frac{(0.6)^4 - (0.5)^4}{(0.6)^2 + (0.5)^2}$ is equal to :

(*a*) 0.1 (*b*) 0.11 (*c*) 1.1 (*d*) 11

105. $(7.5 \times 7.5 + 37.5 + 2.5 \times 2.5)$ is equal to : **(S.S.C. 2000)**

(*a*) 30 (*b*) 60 (*c*) 80 (*d*) 100

106. The simplification of $\frac{0.2 \times 0.2 + 0.02 \times 0.02 - 0.4 \times 0.02}{0.36}$ gives :

(*a*) 0.009 (*b*) 0.09 (*c*) 0.9 (*d*) 9

107. The expression $(11.98 \times 11.98 + 11.98 \times x + 0.02 \times 0.02)$ will be a perfect square for x equal to .

(*a*) 0.02 (*b*) 0.2 (*c*) 0.04 (*d*) 0.4

108. The value of $\frac{(2.697 - 0.498)^2 + (2.697 + 0.498)^2}{2.697 \times 2.697 + 0.498 \times 0.498}$ is :

(*a*) 0.5 (*b*) 2 (*c*) 2.199 (*d*) 3.195

109. The value of $\frac{(0.137 + 0.098)^2 - (0.137 - 0.098)^2}{0.137 \times 0.098}$ is :

(*a*) 0.039 (*b*) 0.235 (*c*) 0.25 (*d*) 4

110. The value of $\left(\frac{0.051 \times 0.051 \times 0.051 + 0.041 \times 0.041 \times 0.041}{0.051 \times 0.051 - 0.051 \times 0.041 + 0.041 \times 0.041}\right)$ is : **(S.S.C. 2003)**

(*a*) 0.00092 (*b*) 0.0092 (*c*) 0.092 (*d*) 0.92

111. The value of $\left(\frac{.953 \times .953 - .953 \times .047 + .047 \times .047}{.953 \times .953 \times .953 + .047 \times .047 \times .047}\right)$ is :

(*a*) .32 (*b*) .886 (*c*) 1.1286 (*d*) None of these

112. The value of $\left(\frac{0.125 + 0.027}{0.5 \times 0.5 + 0.09 - 0.15}\right)$ is : **(S.S.C. 2002)**

(*a*) 0.08 (*b*) 0.2 (*c*) 0.8 (*d*) 1

113. $\left(\frac{10.3 \times 10.3 \times 10.3 + 1}{10.3 \times 10.3 - 10.3 + 1}\right)$ is equal to : **(S.S.C. 2004)**

(*a*) 9.3 (*b*) 10.3 (*c*) 11.3 (*d*) 12.3

114. $\left[\frac{8\,(3.75)^3 + 1}{(7.5)^2 - 6.5}\right]$ is equal to : **(S.S.C. 2003)**

(*a*) $\frac{9}{5}$ (*b*) 2.75 (*c*) 4.75 (*d*) 8.5

115. The value of $\left(\frac{0.1 \times 0.1 \times 0.1 + 0.02 \times 0.02 \times 0.02}{0.2 \times 0.2 \times 0.2 + 0.04 \times 0.04 \times 0.04}\right)$ is : **(Hotel Management, 2003)**

(*a*) 0.0125 (*b*) 0.125 (*c*) 0.25 (*d*) 0.5

116. The value of $\left(\frac{8.94 \times 8.94 \times 8.94 - 3.56 \times 3.56 \times 3.56}{8.94 \times 8.94 + 8.94 \times 3.56 + 3.56 \times 3.56}\right)$ is :

(*a*) 0.538 (*b*) 5.38 (*c*) 0.0538 (*d*) 53.8

117. The value of $\frac{(0.96)^3 - (0.1)^3}{(0.96)^2 + 0.096 + (0.1)^2}$ is : **(S.S.C. 2004)**

(*a*) 0.86 (*b*) 0.95 (*c*) 0.97 (*d*) 1.06

118. The value of $\frac{(2.3)^3 - .027}{(2.3)^2 + .69 + .09}$ is : **(S.S.C. 1997)**

(*a*) 0 (*b*) 1.6 (*c*) 2 (*d*) 3.4

119. The value of $\frac{(0.06)^2 + (0.47)^2 + (0.079)^2}{(0.006)^2 + (0.047)^2 + (0.0079)^2}$ is :

(*a*) 0.1 (*b*) 10 (*c*) 100 (*d*) 1000

ANSWERS

1. (c)	2. (a)	3. (c)	4. (c)	5. (a)	6. (c)	7. (d)	8. (a)	9. (a)
10. (b)	11. (c)	12. (d)	13. (a)	14. (d)	15. (c)	16. (d)	17. (c)	18. (c)
19. (d)	20. (a)	21. (c)	22. (a)	23. (d)	24. (d)	25. (d)	26. (c)	27. (c)
28. (c)	29. (c)	30. (b)	31. (b)	32. (b)	33. (a)	34. (c)	35. (b)	36. (c)
37. (b)	38. (b)	39. (a)	40. (a)	41. (c)	42. (c)	43. (d)	44. (c)	45. (c)
46. (a)	47. (c)	48. (a)	49. (d)	50. (b)	51. (c)	52. (c)	53. (d)	54. (a)
55. (d)	56. (d)	57. (c)	58. (d)	59. (a)	60. (c)	61. (d)	62. (d)	63. (d)
64. (a)	65. (c)	66. (d)	67. (c)	68. (a)	69. (c)	70. (c)	71. (c)	72. (c)
73. (b)	74. (a)	75. (d)	76. (a)	77. (c)	78. (c)	79. (c)	80. (c)	81. (a)
82. (b)	83. (a)	84. (d)	85. (b)	86. (a)	87. (c)	88. (b)	89. (b)	90. (a)
91. (d)	92. (c)	93. (c)	94. (d)	95. (c)	96. (d)	97. (b)	98. (c)	99. (c)
100. (c)	101. (b)	102. (b)	103. (c)	104. (b)	105. (d)	106. (b)	107. (c)	108. (b)
109. (d)	110. (c)	111. (d)	112. (c)	113. (c)	114. (d)	115. (b)	116. (b)	117. (a)
118. (c)	119. (c)							

SOLUTIONS

1. $101\frac{27}{100000} = 101 + \frac{27}{100000} = 101 + .00027 = 101.00027.$

2. $0.36 = \frac{36}{100} = \frac{9}{25}$. Sum of Numerator and Denominator = 9 + 25 = 34.

3. Required decimal $= \frac{1}{60 \times 60} = \frac{1}{3600} = .00027.$

4. $4A + \frac{7}{B} + 2C + \frac{5}{D} + 6E = 47.2506$

$\Rightarrow \quad 4A + \frac{7}{B} + 2C + \frac{5}{D} + 6E = 40 + 7 + 0.2 + 0.05 + 0.0006$

Comparing the terms on both sides, we get :

$4A = 40, \frac{7}{B} = 7, 2C = 0.2, \frac{5}{D} = 0.05, 6E = 0.0006$

or $A = 10, B = 1, C = 0.1, D = 100, E = 0.0001.$

$\therefore \quad 5A + 3B + 6C + D + 3E = (5 \times 10) + (3 \times 1) + (6 \times 0.1) + 100 + (3 \times 0.0001)$

$= 50 + 3 + 0.6 + 100 + 0.0003 = 153.6003.$

5. Converting each of the given fractions into decimal form, we get :

$\frac{1}{3} = 0.33, \frac{2}{5} = 0.4, \frac{4}{7} = 0.57, \frac{3}{5} = 0.6, \frac{5}{6} = 0.82, \frac{6}{7} = 0.857.$

Clearly, 0.33 < 0.4 < 0.57 < 0.6 < 0.82 < 0.857. So, $\frac{1}{3} < \frac{2}{5} < \frac{4}{7} < \frac{3}{5} < \frac{5}{6} < \frac{6}{7}$.

6. Converting each of the given fractions into decimal form, we get :

$\frac{2}{3} = 0.66, \frac{3}{5} = 0.6, \frac{7}{9} = 0.77, \frac{9}{11} = 0.81, \frac{8}{9} = 0.88.$

Clearly, 0.6 < 0.66 < 0.77 < 0.81 < 0.88. So, $\frac{3}{5} < \frac{2}{3} < \frac{7}{9} < \frac{9}{11} < \frac{8}{9}$.

7. Converting each of the given fractions into decimal form, we get :

$\frac{5}{9} = 0.55$, $\frac{7}{11} = 0.63$, $\frac{8}{15} = 0.533$, $\frac{11}{17} = 0.647$.

Clearly, $0.647 > 0.63 > 0.55 > 0.533$. So, $\frac{11}{17} > \frac{7}{11} > \frac{5}{9} > \frac{8}{15}$.

8. Converting each of the given fractions into decimal form, we get :

$\frac{2}{3} = 0.66$, $\frac{3}{4} = 0.75$, $\frac{4}{5} = 0.8$, $\frac{5}{6} = 0.833$.

Since $0.833 > 0.8 > 0.75 > 0.66$, so $\frac{5}{6} > \frac{4}{5} > \frac{3}{4} > \frac{2}{3}$.

$\therefore$ Required difference $= \left(\frac{5}{6} - \frac{2}{3}\right) = \frac{1}{6}$.

9. Clearly, $\frac{11}{14} = 0.785$, $\frac{16}{19} = 0.842$, $\frac{19}{21} = 0.904$.

Now, $0.785 < 0.842 < 0.904$. So, $\frac{11}{14} < \frac{16}{19} < \frac{19}{21}$.

10. We have : $\frac{13}{16} = 0.8125$, $\frac{15}{19} = 0.7894$, $\frac{17}{21} = 0.8095$ and $\frac{7}{8} = 0.875$.

Since 0.7894 is the smallest, so $\frac{15}{19}$ is the smallest.

11. $\frac{3}{4} = 0.75$, $\frac{5}{6} = 0.833$, $\frac{1}{2} = 0.5$, $\frac{2}{3} = 0.66$, $\frac{4}{5} = 0.8$, $\frac{9}{10} = 0.9$.

Clearly, 0.8 lies between 0.75 and 0.833.

$\therefore$ $\frac{4}{5}$ lies between $\frac{3}{4}$ and $\frac{5}{6}$.

12. $\frac{7}{8} = 0.875$, $\frac{1}{3} = 0.333$, $\frac{1}{4} = 0.25$, $\frac{23}{24} = 0.958$, $\frac{11}{12} = 0.916$, $\frac{17}{24} = 0.708$.

Clearly, 0.708 lies between 0.333 and 0.875.

$\therefore$ $\frac{17}{24}$ lies between $\frac{1}{3}$ and $\frac{7}{8}$.

13. $\frac{4}{5} = 0.8$, $\frac{7}{13} = 0.53$, $\frac{1}{2} = 0.5$, $\frac{2}{3} = 0.66$, $\frac{3}{4} = 0.75$, $\frac{5}{7} = 0.714$.

Clearly, 0.5 does not lie between 0.53 and 0.8.

$\therefore$ $\frac{1}{2}$ does not lie between $\frac{4}{5}$ and $\frac{7}{13}$.

14. $\frac{-7}{10} = -0.7$, $\frac{5}{-8} = -\frac{5}{8} = -0.625$, $\frac{2}{-3} = -\frac{2}{3} = -0.66$.

Since $-0.7 < -0.66 < -0.625$, so $\frac{-7}{10} < \frac{2}{-3} < \frac{5}{-8}$.

15.
$$\begin{array}{r} 337.62 \\ 8.591 \\ +\ 34.4 \\ \hline 380.611 \\ \hline \end{array}$$

16.
$$\begin{array}{r} 1.0 \\ 0.1 \\ 0.01 \\ +\ 0.001 \\ \hline 1.111 \\ \hline \end{array}$$

17.
$$\begin{array}{r} 34.95 \\ 240.016 \\ +\ 23.98 \\ \hline 298.946 \\ \hline \end{array}$$

18.
$$\begin{array}{r} 617.00 \\ 6.017 \\ 0.617 \\ +\ 6.0017 \\ \hline 629.6357 \\ \hline \end{array}$$

19.
$$\begin{array}{r} 48.950 \\ -\ 32.006 \\ \hline 16.944 \\ \hline \end{array}$$

20.
$$\begin{array}{r} 792.02 \\ +\ 101.32 \\ \hline 893.34 \\ \hline \end{array} \qquad \begin{array}{r} 893.34 \\ -\ 306.76 \\ \hline 586.58 \\ \hline \end{array}$$

21. Given expression = (12.1212 + 17.0005) − 9.1102 = (29.1217 − 9.1102) = 20.0115.

22. Given expression = 892.7 − (573.07 + 95.007) = 892.7 − 668.077 = 224.623.

23. Let 3889 + 12.952 − x = 3854.002.

Then, x = (3889 + 12.952) − 3854.002 = 3901.952 − 3854.002 = 47.95.

24. Let 138.009 + 341.981 − 146.305 = 123.6 + x.

Then, x = (138.009 + 341.981) − (146.305 + 123.6) = 479.99 − 269.905 = 210.085.

25. Let 832.58 − 242.31 = 779.84 − x.

Then, x = (779.84 + 242.31) − 832.58 = 1022.15 − 832.58 = 189.57.

26. Let x + 543 + 5.43 = 603.26. Then, x = 603.26 − (543 + 5.43) = 603.26 − 548.43 = 54.83.

∴ Missing digit = 8.

27. $3.14 \times 10^6 = 3.140000 \times 1000000 = 3140000$.

28. $518{,}000{,}000 = 5.18 \times 100000000 = 5.18 \times 10^8$.

29. $0.000006723 = \dfrac{0.000006723 \times 10^6}{10^6} = \dfrac{6.723}{10^6} = 6.723 \times 10^{-6}$.

30. $10^k = \dfrac{0.001125}{1.125} = \dfrac{1.125}{1125} = \dfrac{1.125 \times 10^3}{1125 \times 10^3} = \dfrac{1}{10^3} = 10^{-3}$.

∴ $k = -3$.

31. 2 × 5 = 10. Sum of decimal places = 4.

∴ 0.002 × 0.5 = 0.0010 = 0.001.

32. 1602 × 1 = 1602. Sum of decimal places = 5.

∴ 16.02 × 0.001 = 0.01602.

33. 14 × 14 = 196. Sum of decimal places = 6.

∴ 0.014 × 0.014 = 0.000196.

34. 4083 × 102 × 12 = 4997592. Sum of decimal places = 5.

∴ 40.83 × 1.02 × 1.2 = 49.97592.

35. 4 × 162 = 648. Sum of decimal places = 6.

∴ $0.04 \times 0.0162 = 0.000648 = 6.48 \times 10^{-4}$.

36. 3 × 3 × 3 × 3 × 30 = 2430. Sum of decimal places = 6.

∴ 3 × 0.3 × 0.03 × 0.003 × 30 = 0.002430 = 0.00243.

37. Sum of decimal places = 7.

Since the last digit to the extreme right will be zero (∵ 5 × 4 = 20), so there will be 6 significant digits to the right of the decimal point.

38 $\left(.00625 \text{ of } \dfrac{23}{5}\right) = \left(\dfrac{625}{100000} \times \dfrac{23}{5}\right) = \dfrac{23}{800}$.

39. Given product $= 0.3 \times 0.25 \times 0.5 \times 0.125 \times 24$

$$= \left(\frac{3}{10} \times \frac{25}{100} \times \frac{5}{10} \times \frac{125}{1000} \times 24\right) = \frac{9}{80} = \frac{1}{8} \text{ (App.)}$$

40. 1. 36839 ÷ 17 = 2167. Dividend contains 2 places of decimal.

∴ 368.39 ÷ 17 = 21.67.

2. 17050 ÷ 62 = 275. Dividend contains 2 places of decimal.

∴ 170.50 ÷ 62 = 2.75.

3. 87565 ÷ 83 = 1055. Dividend contains 2 places of decimal.

∴ 875.65 ÷ 83 = 10.55.

Since 21.67 > 10.55 > 2.75, the desired order is 1, 3, 2.

41. $\frac{0.213}{0.00213} = \frac{0.213 \times 100000}{0.00213 \times 100000} = \frac{213 \times 100}{213} = 100.$

42. $\frac{4.036}{0.04} = \frac{403.6}{4} = 100.9.$

43. $\frac{1}{0.04} = \frac{100}{4} = 25.$

44. $\left(\frac{0.05}{0.25} + \frac{0.25}{0.05}\right)^3 = \left(\frac{5}{25} + \frac{25}{5}\right)^3 = \left(\frac{1}{5} + 5\right)^3 = \left(\frac{26}{5}\right)^3 = (5.2)^3 = 140.608.$

45. $\frac{0.0396}{2.51} = \frac{3.96}{251} = \left(\frac{396}{251 \times 100}\right) = \frac{1.577}{100} = 0.01577 \approx 0.016.$

46. Let $.04 \times x = .000016$. Then, $x = \frac{.000016}{.04} = \frac{.0016}{4} = .0004.$

47. Let $\frac{.009}{x} = .01$. Then, $x = \frac{.009}{.01} = \frac{.9}{1} = .9.$

48. $\frac{144}{0.144} = \frac{14.4}{x} \Leftrightarrow \frac{144 \times 1000}{144} = \frac{14.4}{x} \Leftrightarrow x = \frac{14.4}{1000} = 0.0144.$

49. Length of each piece $= \left(\frac{1}{8}\right)$ m = 0.125 m.

∴ Required number of pieces $= \left(\frac{37.5}{0.125}\right) = \left(\frac{375 \times 100}{125}\right) = 300.$

50. Suppose commodity X will cost 40 paise more than Y after z years. Then,

$(4.20 + 0.40z) - (6.30 + 0.15z) = 0.40$

$\Leftrightarrow 0.25z = 0.40 + 2.10 \Leftrightarrow z = \frac{2.50}{0.25} = \frac{250}{25} = 10.$

∴ X will cost 40 paise more than Y 10 years after 2001 *i.e.*, in 2011.

51. $0.232323 \ldots\ldots = 0.\overline{23} = \frac{23}{99}.$

52. $0.125125 \ldots\ldots = 0.\overline{125} = \frac{125}{999}.$

53. $0.\overline{47} = \frac{47}{99}.$

54. $0.\overline{36} = \frac{36}{99} = \frac{4}{11}.$

55. $1 \div 0.2 = \frac{1}{0.2} = \frac{10}{2} = 5;\ 0.\overline{2} = 0.222 \ldots\ldots;\ (0.2)^2 = 0.04.$

$0.04 < 0.2 < 0.22 \ldots\ldots < 5.$

Since 0.04 is the least, so $(0.2)^2$ is the least.

56. $6.\overline{46} = 6 + 0.\overline{46} = 6 + \frac{46}{99} = \frac{594 + 46}{99} = \frac{640}{99}.$

57. $0.5\overline{7} = \frac{57 - 5}{90} = \frac{52}{90} = \frac{26}{45}.$

58. $0.841\overline{81} = \frac{84181 - 841}{99000} = \frac{83340}{99000} = \frac{463}{550}.$

∴ Required difference = (550 − 463) = 87.

59. $4.1\bar{2} = 4 + 0.1\bar{2} = 4 + \frac{12-1}{90} = 4\frac{11}{90}$.

60. $2.1\overline{36} = 2 + 0.1\overline{36} = 2 + \frac{136-1}{990} = 2 + \frac{3}{22} = 2\frac{3}{22}$.

61. $0.\bar{2} + 0.\bar{3} + 0.\bar{4} + 0.\bar{9} + 0.\overline{39} = \left(\frac{2}{9} + \frac{3}{9} + \frac{4}{9} + \frac{9}{9} + \frac{39}{99}\right) = \left(\frac{9}{9} + \frac{9}{9} + \frac{39}{99}\right) = 2 + \frac{13}{33} = 2\frac{13}{33}$.

62. $3.\overline{87} - 2.\overline{59} = (3 + 0.\overline{87}) - (2 + 0.\overline{59}) = \left(3 + \frac{87}{99}\right) - \left(2 + \frac{59}{99}\right) = 1 + \left(\frac{87}{99} - \frac{59}{99}\right)$

$= 1 + \frac{28}{99} = 1.\overline{28}$.

63. $3.\overline{36} - 2.\overline{05} + 1.\overline{33} = [(3 + 0.\overline{36}) + (1 + 0.\overline{33})] - (2 + 0.\overline{05})$

$= \left[4 + \left(\frac{36}{99} + \frac{33}{99}\right)\right] - \left[2 + \frac{5}{99}\right] = 2 + \left(\frac{36}{99} + \frac{33}{99} - \frac{5}{99}\right) = 2 + \frac{64}{99} = 2.\overline{64}$.

64. $0.\overline{09} \times 7.\bar{3} = \frac{9}{99} \times 7\frac{3}{9} = \frac{1}{11} \times \frac{66}{9} = \frac{2}{3} = 0.\bar{6}$.

65. $0.34\overline{67} + 0.13\overline{33} = \frac{3467-34}{9900} + \frac{1333-13}{9900} = \frac{3433+1320}{9900} = \frac{4753}{9900} = \frac{4801-48}{9900} = 0.48\overline{01}$.

66. $(8.3\bar{1} + 0.\bar{6} + 0.00\bar{2}) = 8 + \frac{31-3}{90} + \frac{6}{9} + \frac{2}{900} = \frac{7200+280+600+2}{900}$

$= \frac{8082}{900} = 8\frac{882}{900} = 8 + \frac{979-97}{900} = 8.97\bar{9}$.

67. $\bar{2}.75 + \bar{3}.78 = (-2 + 0.75) + (-3 + 0.78) = -5 + (0.75 + 0.78) = -5 + 1.53$

$= -5 + 1 + 0.53 = -4 + 0.53 = \bar{4}.53$.

68. $\frac{547527}{82} = \frac{54.7527}{0.0082} = \left(\frac{547.527}{0.0082} \times \frac{1}{10}\right) = \frac{x}{10}$.

69. $\frac{29.94}{1.45} = \frac{299.4}{14.5} = \left(\frac{2994}{14.5} \times \frac{1}{10}\right) = \frac{172}{10} = 17.2$.

70. $1.6 \times 21.3 = \left(\frac{16}{10} \times \frac{213}{10}\right) = \left(\frac{16 \times 213}{100}\right) = \frac{3408}{100} = 34.08$.

71. $\frac{1}{0.0006198} = \frac{10000}{6.198} = \left(10000 \times \frac{1}{6.198}\right) = (10000 \times 0.16134) = 1613.4$.

72. Given, $\frac{52416}{312} = 168 \Leftrightarrow \frac{52416}{168} = 312$.

Now, $\frac{52.416}{0.0168} = \frac{524160}{168} = \left(\frac{52416}{168} \times 10\right) = (312 \times 10) = 3120$.

73. Given, $168 \times 32 = 5376$ or $5376 \div 168 = 32$.

Now, $\frac{5.376}{16.8} = \frac{53.76}{168} = \left(\frac{5376}{168} \times \frac{1}{100}\right) = \frac{32}{100} = 0.32$.

74. Number of decimal places in the given expression = 8.
Number of decimal places in (*a*) = 8.
Number of decimal places in (*b*) = 9.
Number of decimal places in (*c*) = 7.
Clearly, the expression in (*a*) is the same as the given expression

75. For the expressions to be equivalent, the difference between the sum of the decimal places in the numerator and that in the denominator must be equal.
This difference is 1 in the given expression and 1 in (*d*). So, (*d*) is the answer.

76. Given expression $= \frac{(96.54 - 89.63)}{(96.54 + 89.63)} \times \frac{(9.654 + 8.963)}{(965.4 - 896.3)} = \frac{(96.54 - 89.63)}{(965.4 - 896.3)} \times \frac{(9.654 + 8.963)}{(96.54 + 89.63)}$

$= \frac{(96.54 - 89.63)}{10\,(96.54 - 89.63)} \times \frac{(96.54 + 89.63)}{10\,(96.54 + 89.63)}$

$= \frac{1}{10} \times \frac{1}{10} = \frac{1}{100} = \frac{1}{10^2} = 10^{-2}.$

77. $(0.11)^3 + (0.22)^3 + \ldots\ldots + (0.99)^3 = (0.11)^3\,(1^3 + 2^3 + \ldots\ldots + 9^3)$

$= 0.001331 \times 2025 = 2.695275 \approx 2.695.$

78. Given expression $= 8.7 - [7.6 - \{6.5 - (5.4 - 2.3)\}] = 8.7 - [7.6 - (6.5 - 3.1)]$

$= 8.7 - (7.6 - 3.4) = 8.7 - 4.2 = 4.5.$

79. $\frac{1}{4} + \frac{1}{4 \times 5} + \frac{1}{4 \times 5 \times 6} = \frac{1}{4}\left(1 + \frac{1}{5} + \frac{1}{30}\right) = \frac{1}{4}\left(\frac{30 + 6 + 1}{30}\right) = \frac{1}{4} \times \frac{37}{30} = \frac{37}{120} = 0.3083.$

80. Given expression $= \frac{2 \times 4 \times 8 \times 16 + 4 \times 8 \times 16 + 8 \times 16 + 16 + 1}{2 \times 4 \times 8 \times 16}$

$= \frac{1024 + 512 + 128 + 16 + 1}{1024} = \frac{1681}{1024} = 1.6416.$

81. Given expression $= \frac{1}{5 \times 6} + \frac{1}{6 \times 7} + \frac{1}{7 \times 8} + \ldots\ldots + \frac{1}{24 \times 25}$

$= \left(\frac{1}{5} - \frac{1}{6}\right) + \left(\frac{1}{6} - \frac{1}{7}\right) + \left(\frac{1}{7} - \frac{1}{8}\right) + \ldots\ldots + \left(\frac{1}{24} - \frac{1}{25}\right)$

$= \left(\frac{1}{5} - \frac{1}{25}\right) = \frac{4}{25} = 0.16.$

82. $\frac{x}{y} = \frac{0.04}{1.5} = \frac{4}{150} = \frac{2}{75} \Rightarrow \frac{y - x}{y + x} = \frac{1 - \frac{x}{y}}{1 + \frac{x}{y}} = \frac{1 - \frac{2}{75}}{1 + \frac{2}{75}} = \frac{73}{77}.$

83. Given expression $= 35.7 - \left(\frac{3 + \frac{1}{10}}{3}\right) - \left(\frac{2 + \frac{1}{5}}{2}\right) = 35.7 - \left(3 + \frac{3}{10}\right) - \left(2 + \frac{2}{5}\right)$

$= 35.7 - \frac{33}{10} - \frac{12}{5} = 35.7 - \left(\frac{33}{10} + \frac{12}{5}\right) = 35.7 - \frac{57}{10} = 35.7 - 5.7 = 30.$

84. Given expression $= \frac{(0.3333)}{(0.2222)} \times \frac{(0.1667)\,(0.8333)}{(0.6667)\,(0.1250)} = \frac{3333}{2222} \times \frac{\frac{1}{6} \times \frac{5}{6}}{\frac{2}{3} \times \frac{125}{1000}}$

$= \left(\frac{3}{2} \times \frac{1}{6} \times \frac{5}{6} \times \frac{3}{2} \times 8\right) = \frac{5}{2} = 2.50.$

85. $\frac{3.6 \times 0.48 \times 2.50}{0.12 \times 0.09 \times 0.5} = \frac{36 \times 48 \times 250}{12 \times 9 \times 5} = 800.$

86. $\frac{0.0203 \times 2.92}{0.0073 \times 14.5 \times 0.7} = \frac{203 \times 292}{73 \times 145 \times 7} = \frac{4}{5} = 0.8.$

87. $\dfrac{3.157 \times 4126 \times 3.198}{63.972 \times 2835.121} \approx \dfrac{3.2 \times 4126 \times 3.2}{64 \times 2835} = \dfrac{32 \times 4126 \times 32}{64 \times 2835} \times \dfrac{1}{100}$

$= \dfrac{66016}{2835} \times \dfrac{1}{100} = \dfrac{23.28}{100} = 0.23 \approx 0.2.$

88. $\dfrac{489.1375 \times 0.0483 \times 1.956}{0.0873 \times 92.581 \times 99.749} \approx \dfrac{489 \times 0.05 \times 2}{0.09 \times 93 \times 100} = \dfrac{489}{9 \times 93 \times 10}$

$= \dfrac{163}{279} \times \dfrac{1}{10} = \dfrac{0.58}{10} = 0.058 \approx 0.06.$

89. $\dfrac{241.6 \times 0.3814 \times 6.842}{0.4618 \times 38.25 \times 73.65} \approx \dfrac{240 \times 0.38 \times 6.9}{0.46 \times 38 \times 75} = \dfrac{240 \times 38 \times 69}{46 \times 38 \times 75} \times \dfrac{1}{10}$

$= \left(\dfrac{24}{5} \times \dfrac{1}{10}\right) = \dfrac{4.8}{10} = 0.48.$

So, the value is close to 0.4.

90. Given expression $= \dfrac{(0.2 \times 0.2 + 0.01)}{(0.1 \times 0.1 + 0.02)} = \dfrac{0.04 + 0.01}{0.01 + 0.02} = \dfrac{0.05}{0.03} = \dfrac{5}{3}.$

91. Given expression $= \dfrac{8 - 2.8}{1.3} = \dfrac{5.2}{1.3} = \dfrac{52}{13} = 4.$

92. Given expression $= 4.7 \times (13.26 + 9.43 + 77.31) = 4.7 \times 100 = 470.$

93. Given expression $= \dfrac{0.2\,(0.2 + 0.02)}{0.044} = \dfrac{0.2 \times 0.22}{0.044} = \dfrac{0.044}{0.044} = 1.$

94. Given expression $= \dfrac{8.6 \times (5.3 + 4.7)}{4.3 \times (9.7 - 8.7)} = \dfrac{8.6 \times 10}{4.3 \times 1} = 20.$

95. Given expression $= \dfrac{.896 \times (.763 + .237)}{.7 \times (.064 + .936)} = \dfrac{.896 \times 1}{.7 \times 1} = \dfrac{8.96}{7} = 1.28.$

96. Given expression $= (a^2 - b^2) = (a + b)\,(a - b) = (68.237 + 31.763)\,(68.237 - 31.763)$

$(100 \times 36.474) = 3647.4.$

97. Given expression $= \dfrac{a^2 - b^2}{a \quad b} = \dfrac{(a + b)\,(a - b)}{(a - b)} = (a + b) = (2.39 + 1.61) = 4.$

98. Given expression $= \dfrac{(2.644)^2 - (2.356)^2}{2.644 - 2.356} = \dfrac{a^2 - b^2}{a - b} = (a + b) = (2.644 + 2.356) = 5.$

99. Let $\dfrac{(36.54)^2 - (3.46)^2}{x} = 40$. Then, $x = \dfrac{(36.54)^2 - (3.46)^2}{40} = \dfrac{(36.54)^2 - (3.46)^2}{36.54 + 3.46}$

$= \dfrac{a^2 - b^2}{a + b} = (a - b) = (36.54 - 3.46) = 33.08.$

100. Given expression $= \dfrac{(67.542)^2 - (32.458)^2}{(67.542 + 7.196) - (32.458 + 7.916)}$

$= \dfrac{(67.542)^2 - (32.458)^2}{67.542 - 32.458} = (67.542 + 32.458) = 100.$

101. Given expression $= \left(\dfrac{1.49 \times 1.49 \times 10 - 0.51 \times 0.51 \times 10}{1.49 \times 10 - 0.51 \times 10}\right)$

$= \dfrac{10\,[(1.49)^2 - (0.51)^2]}{10\,(1.49 - 0.51)} = (1.49 + 0.51) = 2.$

102. Given expression $= \dfrac{(a^2 - b^2)}{(a+b)(a-b)} = \dfrac{(a^2 - b^2)}{(a^2 - b^2)} = 1.$

103. Given expression $= \dfrac{5.32 \times (56 + 44)}{(7.66 + 2.34)(7.66 - 2.34)} = \dfrac{5.32 \times 100}{10 \times 5.32} = 10.$

104. Given expression $= \dfrac{[(0.6)^2]^2 - [(0.5)^2]^2}{(0.6)^2 + (0.5)^2} = \dfrac{[(0.6)^2 + (0.5)^2][(0.6)^2 - (0.5)^2]}{(0.6)^2 + (0.5)^2}$

$= (0.6)^2 - (0.5)^2 = (0.6 + 0.5)(0.6 - 0.5) = (1.1 \times 0.1) = 0.11.$

105. Given expression $= (7.5 \times 7.5 + 2 \times 7.5 \times 2.5 + 2.5 \times 2.5)$

$= (a^2 + 2ab + b^2) = (a + b)^2 = (7.5 + 2.5)^2 = 10^2 = 100.$

106. $0.2 \times 0.2 + 0.02 \times 0.02 - 0.4 \times 0.02 = 0.2 \times 0.2 + 0.02 \times 0.02 - 2 \times 0.2 \times 0.02$

$\Rightarrow (a^2 + b^2 - 2ab) = (a - b)^2 = (0.2 - 0.02)^2$

$= (0.18)^2.$

$\therefore$ Given expression $= \dfrac{(0.18 \times 0.18)}{0.36} = 0.09.$

107. Given expression $= (11.98)^2 + (0.02)^2 + 11.98 \times x.$

For the given expression to be a perfect square, we must have

$11.98 \times x = 2 \times 11.98 \times 0.02$ or $x = 0.04.$

108. Given expression $= \dfrac{(a-b)^2 + (a+b)^2}{a^2 + b^2} = \dfrac{2(a^2 + b^2)}{(a^2 + b^2)} = 2.$

109. Given expression $= \dfrac{(a+b)^2 - (a-b)^2}{ab} = \dfrac{4ab}{ab} = 4.$

110. Given expression $= \dfrac{(0.051)^3 + (0.041)^3}{(0.051)^2 - (0.051 \times 0.041) + (0.041)^2} = \left(\dfrac{a^3 + b^3}{a^2 - ab + b^2}\right)$

$= (a + b) = (0.051 + 0.041) = 0.092.$

111. Given expression $= \dfrac{(.953)^2 - (.953 \times .047) + (.047)^2}{(.953)^3 + (.047)^3}$

$= \left(\dfrac{a^2 - ab + b^2}{a^3 + b^3}\right) = \dfrac{1}{a+b} = \dfrac{1}{.953 + .047} = 1.$

112. Given expression $= \dfrac{(0.5)^3 + (0.3)^3}{(0.5)^2 + (0.3)^2 - (0.5 \times 0.3)} = \left(\dfrac{a^3 + b^3}{a^2 + b^2 - ab}\right)$

$= (a + b) = (0.5 + 0.3) = 0.8.$

113. Given expression $= \dfrac{(10.3)^3 + (1)^3}{(10.3)^2 - (10.3 \times 1) + (1)^2} = \left(\dfrac{a^3 + b^3}{a^2 - ab + b^2}\right)$

$= (a + b) = (10.3 + 1) = 11.3.$

114. Given expression $= \dfrac{(2 \times 3.75)^3 + (1)^3}{(7.5)^2 - (7.5 \times 1) + (1)^2} = \dfrac{(7.5)^3 + (1)^3}{(7.5)^2 - (7.5 \times 1) + (1)^2}$

$= \left(\dfrac{a^3 + b^3}{a^2 - ab + b^2}\right) = (a + b) = (7.5 + 1) = 8.5.$

115. Given expression $= \dfrac{(0.1)^3 + (0.02)^3}{2^3\,[(0.1)^3 + (0.02)^3]} = \dfrac{1}{8} = 0.125.$

116. Given expression $= \dfrac{(8.94)^3 - (3.56)^3}{(8.94)^2 + 8.94 \times 3.56 + (3.56)^2} = \left(\dfrac{a^3 - b^3}{a^2 + ab + b^2}\right)$

$= (a - b) = (8.94 - 3.56) = 5.38.$

117. Given expression $= \dfrac{(0.96)^3 - (0.1)^3}{(0.96)^2 + (0.96 \times 0.1) + (0.1)^2} = \left(\dfrac{a^3 - b^3}{a^2 + ab + b^2}\right)$

$= (a - b) = (0.96 - 0.1) = 0.86.$

118. Given expression $= \dfrac{(2.3)^3 - (0.3)^3}{(2.3)^2 + (2.3 \times 0.3) + (0.3)^2} = \left(\dfrac{a^3 - b^3}{a^2 + ab + b^2}\right)$

$= (a - b) = (2.3 - 0.3) = 2.$

119. Given expression $= \dfrac{a^2 + b^2 + c^2}{\left(\dfrac{a}{10}\right)^2 + \left(\dfrac{b}{10}\right)^2 + \left(\dfrac{c}{10}\right)^2}$, where $a = 0.6$, $b = 0.47$ and $c = 0.079$.

$= \dfrac{100\,(a^2 + b^2 + c^2)}{(a^2 + b^2 + c^2)} = 100.$

---

4. SIMPLIFICATION

IMPORTANT CONCEPTS

I. 'BODMAS' Rule : This rule depicts the correct sequence in which the operations are to be executed, so as to find out the value of a given expression.

Here, 'B' stands for '***Bracket***', 'O' for '***of***', 'D' for '***Division***', 'M' for '***Multiplication***', 'A' for '***Addition***' and 'S' for '***Subtraction***'.

Thus, in simplifying an expression, first of all the brackets must be removed, strictly in the order (), {} and [].

After removing the brackets, we must use the following operations strictly in the order :

(*i*) of (*ii*) Division (*iii*) Multiplication (*iv*) Addition (*v*) Subtraction.

II. Modulus of a Real Number : Modulus of a real number a is defined as

$$|a| = \begin{cases} a, & \text{if } a > 0 \\ -a, & \text{if } a < 0. \end{cases}$$

Thus, $|5| = 5$ and $|-5| = -(-5) = 5$.

III. Virnaculum (or Bar) : When an expression contains Virnaculum, before applying the 'BODMAS' rule, we simplify the expression under the Virnaculum.

SOLVED EXAMPLES

Ex. 1. ***Simplify* : (*i*) 5005 – 5000 ÷ 10 (*ii*) 18800 ÷ 470 ÷ 20.**

Sol. (*i*) $5005 - 5000 \div 10 = 5005 - \frac{5000}{10} = 5005 - 500 = 4505.$

(*ii*) $18800 \div 470 \div 20 = \frac{18800}{470} \div 20 = 40 \div 20 = 2.$

Ex. 2. ***Simplify* : $b - [b - (a + b) - \{b - (b - \overline{a - b})\} + 2a]$.** **(Hotel Management, 2002)**

Sol. Given expression $= b - [b - (a + b) - \{b - (b - a + b)\} + 2a]$

$= b - [b - a - b - \{b - 2b + a\} + 2a]$

$= b - [-a - \{b - 2b + a + 2a\}]$

$= b - [-a - \{-b + 3a\}] = b - [-a + b - 3a]$

$= b - [-4a + b] = b + 4a - b = 4a.$

Ex. 3. *What value will replace the question mark in the following equation ?*

$$4\frac{1}{2} + 3\frac{1}{6} + ? + 2\frac{1}{3} = 13\frac{2}{5}.$$

Sol. Let $\frac{9}{2} + \frac{19}{6} + x + \frac{7}{3} = \frac{67}{5}$

Then, $x = \frac{67}{5} - \left(\frac{9}{2} + \frac{19}{6} + \frac{7}{3}\right) \Leftrightarrow x = \frac{67}{5} - \left(\frac{27 + 19 + 14}{6}\right) = \left(\frac{67}{5} - \frac{60}{6}\right)$

$\Leftrightarrow x = \left(\frac{67}{5} - 10\right) = \frac{17}{5} = 3\frac{2}{5}.$

Hence, missing fraction $= 3\frac{2}{5}$.

Ex. 4. $\frac{4}{15}$ ***of*** $\frac{5}{7}$ ***of a number is greater than*** $\frac{4}{9}$ ***of*** $\frac{2}{5}$ ***of the same number by 8. What is half of that number ?*** **(S.B.I.P.O. 2000)**

Sol. Let the number be x. Then, $\frac{4}{15}$ of $\frac{5}{7}$ of $x - \frac{4}{9}$ of $\frac{2}{5}$ of $x = 8 \Leftrightarrow \frac{4}{21}x - \frac{8}{45}x = 8$

$$\Leftrightarrow \left(\frac{4}{21} - \frac{8}{45}\right)x = 8 \Leftrightarrow \left(\frac{60-56}{315}\right)x = 8 \Leftrightarrow \frac{4}{315}x = 8$$

$$\Leftrightarrow x = \left(\frac{8 \times 315}{4}\right) = 630 \Leftrightarrow \frac{1}{2}x = 315.$$

Hence, required number = 315.

Ex. 5. ***Simplify :*** $\left[3\frac{1}{4} \div \left\{1\frac{1}{4} - \frac{1}{2}\left(2\frac{1}{2} - \overline{\frac{1}{4} - \frac{1}{6}}\right)\right\}\right]$.

Sol. Given exp. $= \left[\frac{13}{4} \div \left\{\frac{5}{4} - \frac{1}{2}\left(\frac{5}{2} - \frac{3-2}{12}\right)\right\}\right] = \left[\frac{13}{4} \div \left\{\frac{5}{4} - \frac{1}{2}\left(\frac{5}{2} - \frac{1}{12}\right)\right\}\right]$

$$= \left[\frac{13}{4} \div \left\{\frac{5}{4} - \frac{1}{2}\left(\frac{30-1}{12}\right)\right\}\right] = \left[\frac{13}{4} \div \left\{\frac{5}{4} - \frac{29}{24}\right\}\right]$$

$$= \left[\frac{13}{4} \div \left\{\frac{30-29}{24}\right\}\right] = \left[\frac{13}{4} \div \frac{1}{24}\right] = \left[\frac{13}{4} \times 24\right] = 78.$$

Ex. 6. ***Simplify :*** $108 \div 36$ ***of*** $\frac{1}{4} + \frac{2}{5} \times 3\frac{1}{4}$.

Sol. Given exp. $= 108 \div 9 + \frac{2}{5} \times \frac{13}{4} = \frac{108}{9} + \frac{13}{10} = \left(12 + \frac{13}{10}\right) = \frac{133}{10} = 13\frac{3}{10}$.

Ex. 7. ***Simplify :*** $\dfrac{\frac{7}{2} \div \frac{5}{2} \times \frac{3}{2}}{\frac{7}{2} \div \frac{5}{2} \text{ of } \frac{3}{2}} \div 5.25$. **(S.S.C. 1999)**

Sol. Given exp. $= \dfrac{\frac{7}{2} \times \frac{2}{5} \times \frac{3}{2}}{\frac{7}{2} \div \frac{15}{4}} \div 5.25 = \dfrac{\frac{21}{10}}{\frac{7}{2} \times \frac{4}{15}} \div \frac{525}{100} = \frac{21}{10} \times \frac{15}{14} \times \frac{100}{525} = \frac{6}{14} = \frac{3}{7}$.

Ex. 8. ***Simplify :*** **(*i*)** ***12.05 × 5.4 ÷ 0.6*** **(*ii*)** ***.6 × .6 + .6 ÷ 6.*** **(Bank P.O. 2003)**

Sol. (*i*) Given exp. $= 12.05 \times \frac{5.4}{0.6} = 12.05 \times 9 = 108.45$.

(*ii*) Given exp. $= .6 \times .6 + \frac{.6}{6} = .36 + .1 = .46$.

Ex. 9. ***Find the value of x in each of the following equations :***

(*i*) $\dfrac{17.28 \div x}{3.6 \times 0.2} = 2$ (*ii*) $3648.24 + 364.824 + x - 36.4824 = 3794.1696$

(*iii*) $8.5 - \left\{5\frac{1}{2} - \left(7\frac{1}{2} + 2.8 \div x\right)\right\} \times 4.25 \div (0.2)^2 = 306.$ **(Hotel Management, 1997)**

Sol. (*i*) $\frac{17.28}{x} = 2 \times 3.6 \times 0.2 \Leftrightarrow x = \frac{17.28}{1.44} = \frac{1728}{144} = 12.$

(ii) $\dfrac{364.824}{x} = (3794.1696 + 36.4824) - 3648.24 = 3830.652 - 3648.24 = 182.412$

$\Leftrightarrow \quad x = \dfrac{364.824}{182.412} = 2.$

(iii) $8.5 - \left\{5.5 - \left(7.5 + \dfrac{2.8}{x}\right)\right\} \times \dfrac{4.25}{0.04} = 306 \Leftrightarrow 8.5 - \left\{5.5 - \left(\dfrac{7.5x + 2.8}{x}\right)\right\} \times \dfrac{425}{4} = 306$

$\Leftrightarrow \quad 8.5 - \left\{\dfrac{5.5x - 7.5x - 2.8}{x}\right\} \times \dfrac{425}{4} = 306 \Leftrightarrow 8.5 - \left\{\dfrac{-2x - 2.8}{x}\right\} \times 106.25 = 306$

$\Leftrightarrow \quad 8.5 - \left\{\dfrac{-212.5x - 297.5}{x}\right\} = 306 \Leftrightarrow \dfrac{8.5x + 212.5x + 297.5}{x} = 306$

$\Leftrightarrow \quad (306 - 221)\,x = 297.5 \Leftrightarrow x = \dfrac{297.5}{85} = 3.5.$

Ex. 10. ***If*** $\dfrac{x}{y} = \dfrac{6}{5}$, ***find the value of*** $\dfrac{x^2 + y^2}{x^2 - y^2}$.

Sol. $\dfrac{x^2 + y^2}{x^2 - y^2} = \dfrac{\dfrac{x^2}{y^2} + 1}{\dfrac{x^2}{y^2} - 1} = \dfrac{\left(\dfrac{x}{y}\right)^2 + 1}{\left(\dfrac{x}{y}\right)^2 - 1} = \dfrac{\left(\dfrac{6}{5}\right)^2 + 1}{\left(\dfrac{6}{5}\right)^2 - 1} = \dfrac{\dfrac{36}{25} + 1}{\dfrac{36}{25} - 1} = \dfrac{61}{25} \times \dfrac{25}{11} = \dfrac{61}{11}.$

Ex. 11. ***Find the value of*** $4 - \dfrac{5}{1 + \dfrac{1}{3 + \dfrac{1}{2 + \dfrac{1}{4}}}}$.

Sol. Given exp. $= 4 - \dfrac{5}{1 + \dfrac{1}{3 + \dfrac{1}{(9/4)}}} = 4 - \dfrac{5}{1 + \dfrac{1}{3 + \dfrac{4}{9}}} = 4 - \dfrac{5}{1 + \dfrac{1}{(31/9)}}$

$= 4 - \dfrac{5}{1 + \dfrac{9}{31}} = 4 - \dfrac{5}{(40/31)} = 4 - \dfrac{5 \times 31}{40} = 4 - \dfrac{31}{8} = \dfrac{1}{8}.$

Ex. 12. ***If*** $\dfrac{2x}{1 + \dfrac{1}{1 + \dfrac{x}{1 - x}}} = 1$, ***then find the value of*** x. **(M.A.T. 1998)**

Sol. We nave : $\dfrac{2x}{1 + \dfrac{1}{\dfrac{(1-x) + x}{1 - x}}} = 1 \Leftrightarrow \dfrac{2x}{1 + \dfrac{1}{[1/(1-x)]}} = 1 \Leftrightarrow \dfrac{2x}{1 + (1 - x)} = 1$

$\Leftrightarrow 2x = 2 - x \Leftrightarrow 3x = 2 \Leftrightarrow x = \dfrac{2}{3}.$

Ex. 13. (*i*) ***If*** $\dfrac{a}{b} = \dfrac{3}{4}$ ***and*** $8a + 5b = 22$, ***then find the value of*** a. **(R.R.B. 2002)**

(*ii*) ***If*** $\dfrac{x}{4} - \dfrac{x - 3}{6} = 1$, ***then find the value of*** x. **(R.R.B. 2000)**

Sol. (*i*) $\frac{a}{b} = \frac{3}{4} \Rightarrow b = \frac{4}{3}a.$

$\therefore \quad 8a + 5b = 22 \Rightarrow 8a + 5 \times \frac{4}{3}a = 22 \Rightarrow 8a + \frac{20}{3}a = 22$

$\Rightarrow 44a = 66 \Rightarrow a = \frac{66}{44} = \frac{3}{2}.$

(*ii*) $\frac{x}{4} - \frac{x-3}{6} = 1 \Leftrightarrow \frac{3x - 2(x-3)}{12} = 1 \Leftrightarrow 3x - 2x + 6 = 12 \Leftrightarrow x = 6.$

Ex. 14. ***If $2x + 3y = 34$ and $\frac{x+y}{y} = \frac{13}{8}$, then find the value of $5y + 7x$.*** **(S.B.I.P.O. 2001)**

Sol. The given equations are :

$2x + 3y = 34$ ...(*i*) and, $\frac{x+y}{y} = \frac{13}{8} \Rightarrow 8x + 8y = 13y \Rightarrow 8x - 5y = 0$ ...(*ii*)

Multiplying (*i*) by 5, (*ii*) by 3 and adding, we get : $34x = 170$ or $x = 5$.

Putting $x = 5$ in (*i*), we get : $y = 8$.

$\therefore \quad 5y + 7x = (5 \times 8 + 7 \times 5) = 40 + 35 = 75.$

Ex. 15. ***If $2x + 3y + z = 55$, $x + z - y = 4$ and $y - x + z = 12$, then what are the values of x, y and z ?*** **(Bank P.O. 2003)**

Sol. The given equations are :

$2x + 3y + z = 55$ ...(*i*) ; $x + z - y = 4$ ...(*ii*) ; $y - x + z = 12$ ...(*iii*)

Subtracting (*ii*) from (*i*), we get : $x + 4y = 51$ ...(*iv*)

Subtracting (*iii*) from (*i*), we get : $3x + 2y = 43$ ...(*v*)

Multiplying (*v*) by 2 and subtracting (*iv*) from it, we get : $5x = 35$ or $x = 7$.

Putting $x = 7$ in (*iv*), we get : $4y = 44$ or $y = 11$.

Putting $x = 7$, $y = 11$ in (*i*), we get : $z = 8$.

Ex. 16. ***Find the value of $\left(1 - \frac{1}{3}\right)\left(1 - \frac{1}{4}\right)\left(1 - \frac{1}{5}\right) \ldots \left(1 - \frac{1}{100}\right)$.*** **(S.S.C. 2003)**

Sol. Given expression $= \frac{2}{3} \times \frac{3}{4} \times \frac{4}{5} \times \ldots \times \frac{99}{100} = \frac{2}{100} = \frac{1}{50}.$

Ex. 17. ***Find the value of $\frac{1}{2 \times 3} + \frac{1}{3 \times 4} + \frac{1}{4 \times 5} + \frac{1}{5 \times 6} + \ldots + \frac{1}{9 \times 10}$.***

Sol. Given expression $= \left(\frac{1}{2} - \frac{1}{3}\right) + \left(\frac{1}{3} - \frac{1}{4}\right) + \left(\frac{1}{4} - \frac{1}{5}\right) + \left(\frac{1}{5} - \frac{1}{6}\right) + \ldots + \left(\frac{1}{9} - \frac{1}{10}\right)$

$= \left(\frac{1}{2} - \frac{1}{10}\right) = \frac{4}{10} = \frac{2}{5}.$

Ex. 18. ***Simplify : $99\frac{48}{49} \times 245$.*** **(R.R.B. 2000)**

Sol. Given expression $= \left(100 - \frac{1}{49}\right) \times 245 = \frac{4899}{49} \times 245 = 4899 \times 5 = 24495.$

Ex. 19. ***A board 7 ft. 9 inches long is divided into 3 equal parts. What is the length of each part ?*** **(Hotel Management, 2003)**

Sol. Length of board = 7 ft. 9 inches = $(7 \times 12 + 9)$ inches = 93 inches.

$\therefore$ Length of each part $= \left(\frac{93}{3}\right)$ inches = 31 inches = 2 ft. 7 inches.

Ex. 20. ***A man divides Rs. 8600 among 5 sons, 4 daughters and 2 nephews. If each daughter receives four times as much as each nephew, and each son receives five times as much as each nephew, how much does each daughter receive ?*** **(S.S.C. 2000)**

Sol. Let the share of each nephew be Rs. x.

Then, share of each daughter = Rs. $(4x)$; share of each son = Rs. $(5x)$.

So, $5 \times 5x + 4 \times 4x + 2 \times x = 8600 \Leftrightarrow 25x + 16x + 2x = 8600$

$\Leftrightarrow 43x = 8600 \Leftrightarrow x = 200.$

$\therefore$ Share of each daughter = Rs. (4×200) = Rs. 800.

Ex. 21. ***A man spends $\frac{2}{5}$ of his salary on house rent, $\frac{3}{10}$ of his salary on food and $\frac{1}{8}$ of his salary on conveyance. If he has Rs. 1400 left with him, find his expenditure on food and conveyance.***

Sol. Part of the salary left $= 1 - \left(\frac{2}{5} + \frac{3}{10} + \frac{1}{8}\right) = 1 - \frac{33}{40} = \frac{7}{40}$

Let the monthly salary be Rs. x.

Then, $\frac{7}{40}$ of $x = 1400 \Leftrightarrow x = \left(\frac{1400 \times 40}{7}\right) = 8000.$

$\therefore$ Expenditure on food = Rs. $\left(\frac{3}{10} \times 8000\right)$ = Rs. 2400.

Expenditure on conveyance = Rs. $\left(\frac{1}{8} \times 8000\right)$ = Rs. 1000.

Ex. 22. ***A third of Arun's marks in Mathematics exceeds a half of his marks in English by 30. If he got 240 marks in the two subjects together, how many marks did he get in English ?***

Sol. Let Arun's marks in Mathematics and English be x and y respectively.

Then, $\frac{1}{3}x - \frac{1}{2}y = 30 \Leftrightarrow 2x - 3y = 180$ ...(*i*) and $x + y = 240$ ...(*ii*)

Solving (*i*) and (*ii*), we get : $x = 180$ and $y = 60$.

Ex. 23. ***A tin of oil was $\frac{4}{5}$ full. When 6 bottles of oil were taken out and four bottles of oil were poured into it, it was $\frac{3}{4}$ full. How many bottles of oil can the tin contain?*** **(Section Officers', 2001)**

Sol. Suppose x bottles can fill the tin completely.

Then, $\frac{4}{5}x - \frac{3}{4}x = (6 - 4) \Leftrightarrow \frac{x}{20} = 2 \Leftrightarrow x = 40.$

$\therefore$ Required number of bottles = 40.

Ex. 24. ***If $\frac{1}{8}$ of a pencil is black, $\frac{1}{2}$ of the remaining is white and the remaining $3\frac{1}{2}$ cm is blue, find the total length of the pencil.***

Sol. Let the total length of the pencil be x cm. Then.

Black part = $\left(\frac{x}{8}\right)$ cm. Remaining part = $\left(x - \frac{x}{8}\right)$ cm = $\left(\frac{7x}{8}\right)$ cm.

White part $= \left(\frac{1}{2} \times \frac{7x}{8}\right)$ cm $= \left(\frac{7x}{16}\right)$ cm. Remaining part $= \left(\frac{7x}{8} - \frac{7x}{16}\right)$ cm $= \frac{7x}{16}$ cm.

$\therefore \quad \frac{7x}{16} = \frac{7}{2}$ or $x = \frac{16}{2} = 8$ cm.

Hence, total length of the pencil = 8 cm.

Ex. 25. ***In a certain office, $\frac{1}{3}$ of the workers are women, $\frac{1}{2}$ of the women are married and $\frac{1}{3}$ of the married women have children. If $\frac{3}{4}$ of the men are married and $\frac{2}{3}$ of the married men have children, what part of workers are without children ?***

Sol. Let the total number of workers be x. Then,

Number of women $= \frac{x}{3}$ and number of men $= \left(x - \frac{x}{3}\right) = \frac{2x}{3}$.

Number of women having children $= \frac{1}{3}$ of $\frac{1}{2}$ of $\frac{x}{3} = \frac{x}{18}$.

Number of men having children $= \frac{2}{3}$ of $\frac{3}{4}$ of $\frac{2x}{3} = \frac{x}{3}$.

Number of workers having children $= \left(\frac{x}{18} + \frac{x}{3}\right) = \frac{7x}{18}$.

$\therefore$ Workers having no children $= \left(x - \frac{7x}{18}\right) = \frac{11x}{18} = \frac{11}{18}$ of all workers.

Ex. 26. ***A crate of mangoes contains one bruised mango for every 30 mangoes in the crate. If 3 out of every 4 bruised mangoes are considered unsalable, and there are 12 unsalable mangoes in the crate, then how many mangoes are there in the crate ?***

Sol. Let the total number of mangoes in the crate be x. Then,

Number of bruised mangoes $= \frac{1}{30}x$.

Number of unsalable mangoes $= \left(\frac{3}{4} \times \frac{1}{30}x\right) = \frac{1}{40}x$.

$\therefore \quad \frac{1}{40}x = 12$ or $x = (12 \times 40) = 480$.

Hence, total number of mangoes in the crate = 480.

Ex. 27. ***A train starts full of passengers. At the first station, it drops one-third of the passengers and takes 280 more. At the second station, it drops one-half of the new total and takes 12 more. On arriving at the third station, it is found to have 248 passengers. Find the number of passengers in the beginning.***

Sol. Let the number of passengers in the beginning be x.

After 1st station, number of passengers $= \left(x - \frac{x}{3}\right) + 280 = \left(\frac{2x}{3} + 280\right)$.

After 2nd station, number of passengers $= \frac{1}{2}\left(\frac{2x}{3} + 280\right) + 12$.

$\therefore \quad \frac{1}{2}\left(\frac{2x}{3} + 280\right) + 12 = 248 \Leftrightarrow \frac{2x}{3} + 280 = 2 \times 236 \Leftrightarrow \frac{2x}{3} = 192$

$\Leftrightarrow x = \left(192 \times \frac{3}{2}\right) = 288.$

Ex. 28. ***If $a^2 + b^2 = 117$ and $ab = 54$, then find the value of $\frac{a+b}{a-b}$.***

Sol. $(a + b)^2 = a^2 + b^2 + 2ab = 117 + 2 \times 54 = 225 \Rightarrow a + b = 15.$

$(a - b)^2 = a^2 + b^2 - 2ab = 117 - 2 \times 54 = 9 \Rightarrow a - b = 3.$

$\therefore \quad \frac{a+b}{a-b} = \frac{15}{3} = 5.$

Ex. 29. ***Find the value of*** $\left(\frac{75983 \times 75983 - 45983 \times 45983}{30000}\right)$.

Sol. Given expression $= \frac{(75983)^2 - (45983)^2}{(75983 - 45983)} = \frac{(a^2 - b^2)}{(a - b)}$, where $a = 75983$, $b = 45983$

$= \frac{(a+b)(a-b)}{(a-b)} = (a + b) = (75983 + 45983) = 121966.$

Ex. 30. ***Find the value of*** $\left(\frac{343 \times 343 \times 343 - 113 \times 113 \times 113}{343 \times 343 + 343 \times 113 + 113 \times 113}\right)$.

Sol. Given expression $= \frac{(a^3 - b^3)}{(a^2 + ab + b^2)}$, where $a = 343$, $b = 113$

$= (a - b) = (343 - 113) = 230.$

Ex. 31. ***Village X has a population of 68000, which is decreasing at the rate of 1200 per year. Village Y has a population of 42000, which is increasing at the rate of 800 per year. In how many years will the population of the two villages be equal ?***

Sol. Let the population of villages X and Y be equal after p years.

Then, $68000 - 1200p = 42000 + 800p \Rightarrow 2000p = 26000 \Rightarrow p = 13.$

So, their population will be equal after 13 years.

Ex. 32. ***From a group of boys and girls, 15 girls leave. There are then left 2 boys for each girl. After this, 45 boys leave. There are then 5 girls for each boy. Find the number of girls in the beginning.***

Sol. Let at present there be x boys. Then, number of girls at present = $5x$.

Before the boys had left : Number of boys = $x + 45$ and number of girls = $5x$.

$\therefore \quad x + 45 = 2 \times 5x \Leftrightarrow 9x = 45 \Leftrightarrow x = 5.$

Hence, number of girls in the beginning = $5x + 15 = 25 + 15 = 40$.

Ex. 33. ***An employer pays Rs. 20 for each day a worker works, and forfeits Rs. 3 for each day he is idle. At the end of 60 days, a worker gets Rs. 280. For how many days did the worker remain idle ?***

Sol. Suppose the worker remained idle for x days. Then, he worked for $(60 - x)$ days.

$\therefore \quad 20(60 - x) - 3x = 280 \Leftrightarrow 1200 - 23x = 280 \Leftrightarrow 23x = 920 \Leftrightarrow x = 40.$

So, the worker remained idle for 40 days.

Ex. 34. ***Kiran had 85 currency notes in all, some of which were of Rs. 100 denomination and the remaining of Rs. 50 denomination. The total amount of all these currency notes was Rs. 5000. How much amount did she have in the denomination of Rs. 50 ?*** **(R.B.I. 2000)**

Sol. Let the number of 50-rupee notes be x.

Then, the number of 100-rupee notes = $(85 - x)$.

$\therefore \quad 50x + 100(85 - x) = 5000 \Leftrightarrow x + 2(85 - x) = 100 \Leftrightarrow x = 70.$

So, required amount = Rs. (50×70) = Rs. 3500.

Ex. 35. ***When an amount was distributed among 14 boys, each of them got Rs. 80 more than the amount received by each boy when the same amount is distributed equally among 18 boys. What was the amount ?*** **(S.B.I.P.O. 1998)**

Sol. Let the total amount be Rs. x. Then,

$$\frac{x}{14} - \frac{x}{18} = 80 \Leftrightarrow \frac{2x}{126} = 80 \Leftrightarrow \frac{x}{63} = 80 \Leftrightarrow x = 63 \times 80 = 5040.$$

Hence, total amount = Rs. 5040.

Ex. 36. ***Mr. Bhaskar is on tour and he has Rs. 360 for his expenses. If he exceeds his tour by 4 days, he must cut down his daily expenses by Rs. 3. For how many days is Mr. Bhaskar on tour ?***

Sol. Suppose Mr. Bhaskar is on tour for x days. Then,

$$\frac{360}{x} - \frac{360}{x+4} = 3 \Leftrightarrow \frac{1}{x} - \frac{1}{x+4} = \frac{1}{120} \Leftrightarrow x(x+4) = 4 \times 120 = 480$$

$$\Leftrightarrow x^2 + 4x - 480 = 0 \Leftrightarrow (x + 24)(x - 20) = 0 \Leftrightarrow x = 20.$$

Hence, Mr. Bhaskar is on tour for 20 days.

Ex. 37. ***Two pens and three pencils cost Rs. 86. Four pens and a pencil cost Rs. 112. Find the cost of a pen and that of a pencil.*** **(Bank P.O. 2002)**

Sol. Let the cost of a pen and a pencil be Rs. x and Rs. y respectively.

Then, $2x + 3y = 86$ ...(*i*) and $4x + y = 112$ ...(*ii*)

Solving (*i*) and (*ii*), we get : $x = 25$ and $y = 12$.

$\therefore$ Cost of a pen = Rs. 25 and cost of a pencil = Rs. 12.

Ex. 38. ***Arun and Sajal are friends. Each has some money. If Arun gives Rs. 30 to Sajal, then Sajal will have twice the money left with Arun. But, if Sajal gives Rs. 10 to Arun, then Arun will have thrice as much as is left with Sajal. How much money does each have ?***

Sol. Suppose Arun has Rs. x and Sajal has Rs. y. Then,

$2(x - 30) = y + 30 \Rightarrow 2x - y = 90$ ...(*i*)

and $x + 10 = 3(y - 10) \Rightarrow x - 3y = -40$ ...(*ii*)

Solving (*i*) and (*ii*), we get : $x = 62$ and $y = 34$.

$\therefore$ Arun has Rs. 62 and Sajal has Rs. 34.

Ex. 39. ***In a caravan, in addition to 50 hens there are 45 goats and 8 camels with some keepers. If the total number of feet be 224 more than the number of heads, find the number of keepers.***

Sol. Let the number of keepers be x. Then,

Total number of heads = $(50 + 45 + 8 + x) = (103 + x)$.

Total number of feet = $(45 + 8) \times 4 + (50 + x) \times 2 = (312 + 2x)$.

$\therefore$ $(312 + 2x) - (103 + x) = 224 \Leftrightarrow x = 15$.

Hence, number of keepers = 15.

EXERCISE 4

(OBJECTIVE TYPE QUESTIONS)

Directions : *Mark (✓) against the correct answer :*

1. $100 + 50 \times 2 = ?$ **(Bank P.O. 2003)**

(*a*) 75 (*b*) 150 (*c*) 200 (*d*) 300 (*e*) None of these

2. $(3080 + 6160) \div 28 = ?$ **(B.S.R.B. 1998)**

(*a*) 320 (*b*) 440 (*c*) 3320 (*d*) 3350 (*e*) None of these

3. $5004 \div 139 - 6 = ?$ **(R.B.I. 2003)**

(*a*) 24 (*b*) 30 (*c*) 36 (*d*) 42 (*e*) None of these

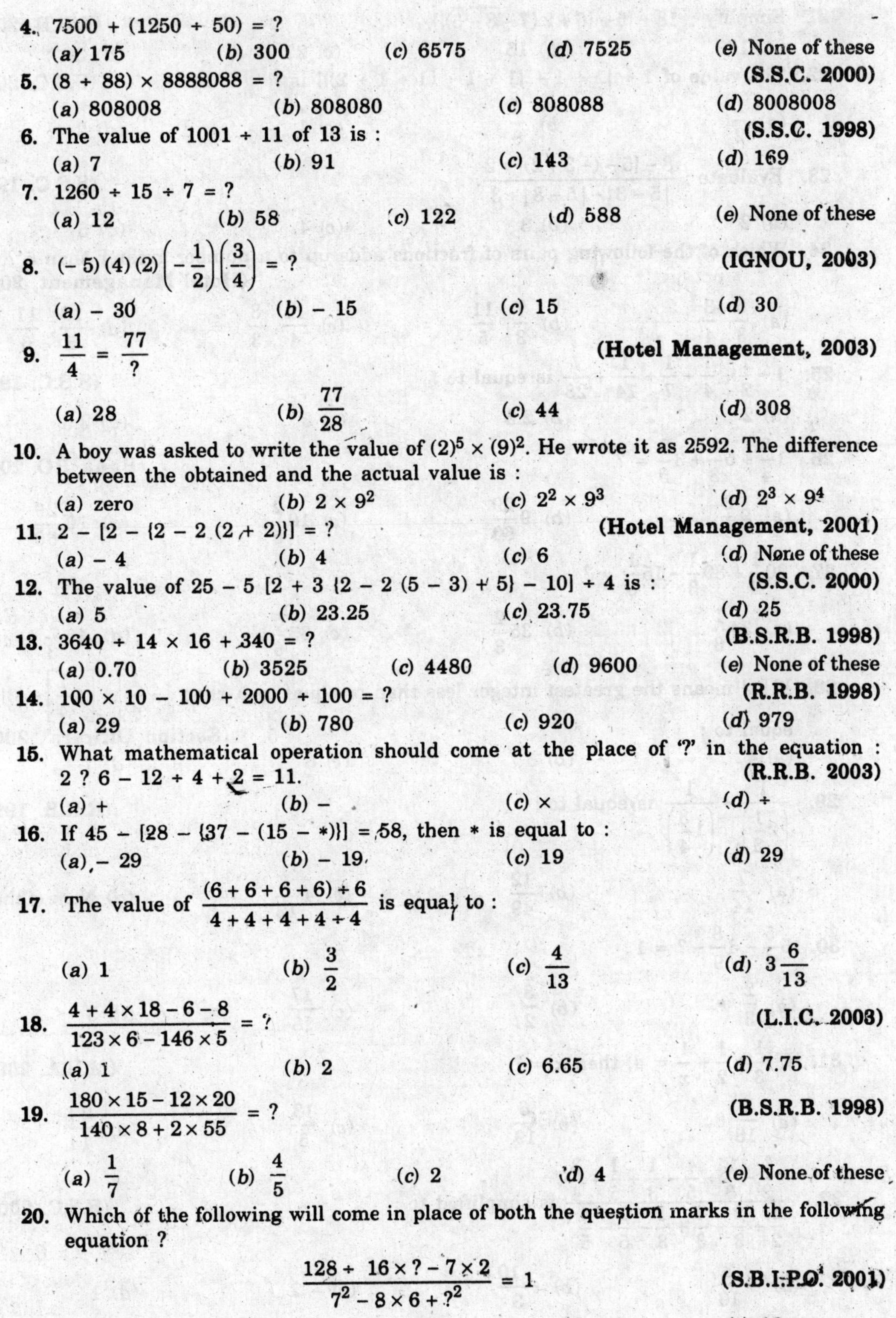

4. $7500 \div (1250 \div 50) = ?$
(a) 175 (b) 300 (c) 6575 (d) 7525 (e) None of these

5. $(8 \div 88) \times 8888088 = ?$ **(S.S.C. 2000)**
(a) 808008 (b) 808080 (c) 808088 (d) 8008008

6. The value of $1001 \div 11$ of 13 is : **(S.S.C. 1998)**
(a) 7 (b) 91 (c) 143 (d) 169

7. $1260 \div 15 \div 7 = ?$
(a) 12 (b) 58 (c) 122 (d) 588 (e) None of these

8. $(-5)(4)(2)\left(-\frac{1}{2}\right)\left(\frac{3}{4}\right) = ?$ **(IGNOU, 2003)**
(a) − 30 (b) − 15 (c) 15 (d) 30

9. $\frac{11}{4} = \frac{77}{?}$ **(Hotel Management, 2003)**
(a) 28 (b) $\frac{77}{28}$ (c) 44 (d) 308

10. A boy was asked to write the value of $(2)^5 \times (9)^2$. He wrote it as 2592. The difference between the obtained and the actual value is :
(a) zero (b) 2×9^2 (c) $2^2 \times 9^3$ (d) $2^3 \times 9^4$

11. $2 - [2 - \{2 - 2(2 + 2)\}] = ?$ **(Hotel Management, 2001)**
(a) − 4 (b) 4 (c) 6 (d) None of these

12. The value of $25 - 5[2 + 3\{2 - 2(5 - 3) + 5\} - 10] \div 4$ is : **(S.S.C. 2000)**
(a) 5 (b) 23.25 (c) 23.75 (d) 25

13. $3640 \div 14 \times 16 + 340 = ?$ **(B.S.R.B. 1998)**
(a) 0.70 (b) 3525 (c) 4480 (d) 9600 (e) None of these

14. $100 \times 10 - 100 + 2000 \div 100 = ?$ **(R.R.B. 1998)**
(a) 29 (b) 780 (c) 920 (d) 979

15. What mathematical operation should come at the place of '?' in the equation : $2 ? 6 - 12 \div 4 + 2 = 11$. **(R.R.B. 2003)**
(a) + (b) − (c) × (d) ÷

16. If $45 - [28 - \{37 - (15 - *)\}] = 58$, then * is equal to :
(a) − 29 (b) − 19 (c) 19 (d) 29

17. The value of $\frac{(6 + 6 + 6 + 6) \div 6}{4 + 4 + 4 + 4 \div 4}$ is equal to :
(a) 1 (b) $\frac{3}{2}$ (c) $\frac{4}{13}$ (d) $3\frac{6}{13}$

18. $\frac{4 + 4 \times 18 - 6 - 8}{123 \times 6 - 146 \times 5} = ?$ **(L.I.C. 2003)**
(a) 1 (b) 2 (c) 6.65 (d) 7.75

19. $\frac{180 \times 15 - 12 \times 20}{140 \times 8 + 2 \times 55} = ?$ **(B.S.R.B. 1998)**
(a) $\frac{1}{7}$ (b) $\frac{4}{5}$ (c) 2 (d) 4 (e) None of these

20. Which of the following will come in place of both the question marks in the following equation ?

$$\frac{128 \div 16 \times ? - 7 \times 2}{7^2 - 8 \times 6 + ?^2} = 1$$ **(S.B.I.P.O. 2001)**

(a) 3 (b) 14 (c) 16 (d) 17 (e) 18

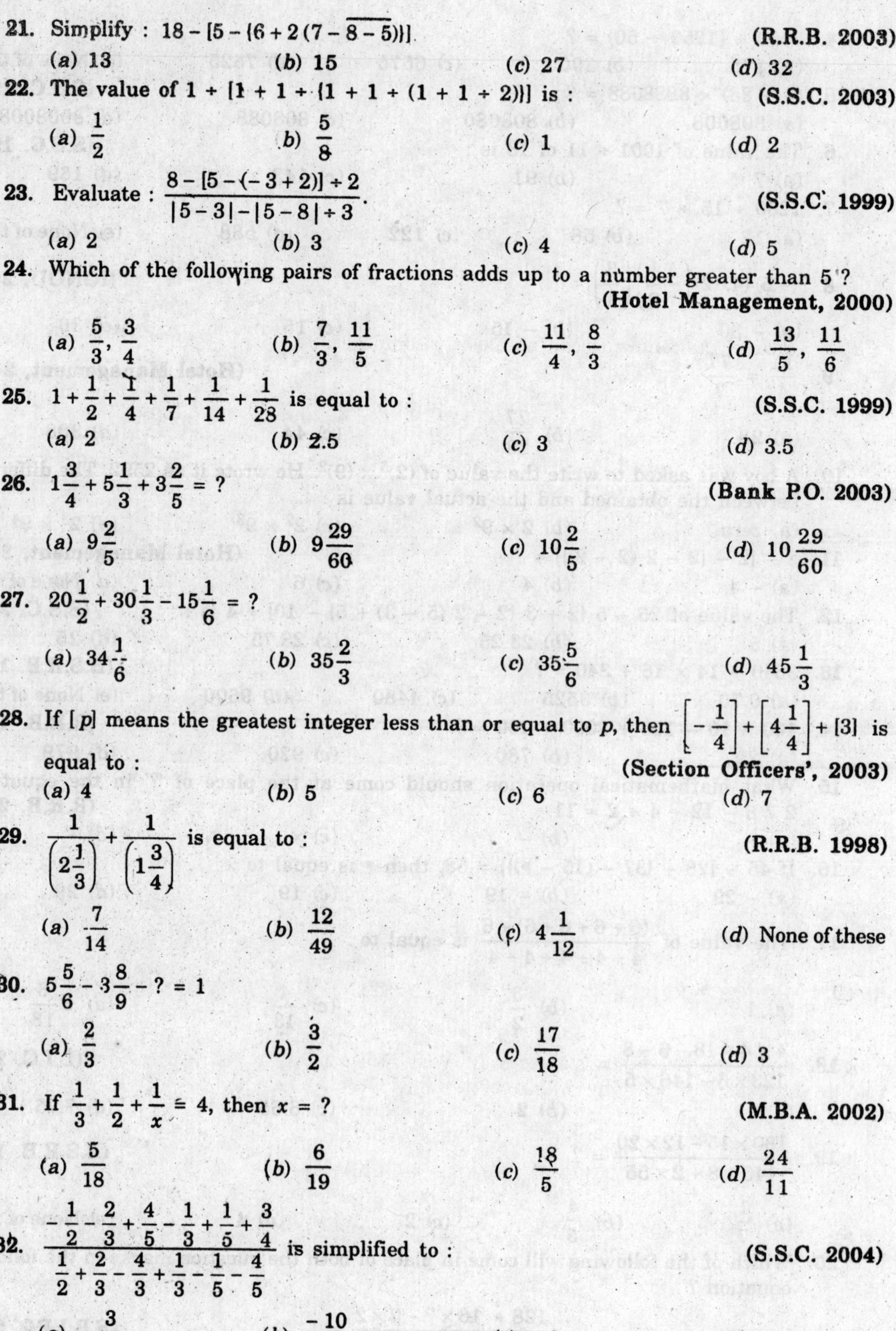

21. Simplify : $18 - [5 - \{6 + 2(7 - \overline{8 - 5})\}]$. **(R.R.B. 2003)**

(*a*) 13 (*b*) 15 (*c*) 27 (*d*) 32

22. The value of $1 + [1 + 1 \div \{1 + 1 \div (1 + 1 \div 2)\}]$ is : **(S.S.C. 2003)**

(*a*) $\frac{1}{2}$ (*b*) $\frac{5}{8}$ (*c*) 1 (*d*) 2

23. Evaluate : $\dfrac{8 - [5 - (-3 + 2)] \div 2}{|5 - 3| - |5 - 8| \div 3}$. **(S.S.C. 1999)**

(*a*) 2 (*b*) 3 (*c*) 4 (*d*) 5

24. Which of the following pairs of fractions adds up to a number greater than 5 ? **(Hotel Management, 2000)**

(*a*) $\frac{5}{3}, \frac{3}{4}$ (*b*) $\frac{7}{3}, \frac{11}{5}$ (*c*) $\frac{11}{4}, \frac{8}{3}$ (*d*) $\frac{13}{5}, \frac{11}{6}$

25. $1 + \frac{1}{2} + \frac{1}{4} + \frac{1}{7} + \frac{1}{14} + \frac{1}{28}$ is equal to : **(S.S.C. 1999)**

(*a*) 2 (*b*) 2.5 (*c*) 3 (*d*) 3.5

26. $1\frac{3}{4} + 5\frac{1}{3} + 3\frac{2}{5} = ?$ **(Bank P.O. 2003)**

(*a*) $9\frac{2}{5}$ (*b*) $9\frac{29}{60}$ (*c*) $10\frac{2}{5}$ (*d*) $10\frac{29}{60}$

27. $20\frac{1}{2} + 30\frac{1}{3} - 15\frac{1}{6} = ?$

(*a*) $34\frac{1}{6}$ (*b*) $35\frac{2}{3}$ (*c*) $35\frac{5}{6}$ (*d*) $45\frac{1}{3}$

28. If $[p]$ means the greatest integer less than or equal to p, then $\left[-\frac{1}{4}\right] + \left[4\frac{1}{4}\right] + [3]$ is equal to : **(Section Officers', 2003)**

(*a*) 4 (*b*) 5 (*c*) 6 (*d*) 7

29. $\dfrac{1}{\left(2\frac{1}{3}\right)} + \dfrac{1}{\left(1\frac{3}{4}\right)}$ is equal to : **(R.R.B. 1998)**

(*a*) $\frac{7}{14}$ (*b*) $\frac{12}{49}$ (*c*) $4\frac{1}{12}$ (*d*) None of these

30. $5\frac{5}{6} - 3\frac{8}{9} - ? = 1$

(*a*) $\frac{2}{3}$ (*b*) $\frac{3}{2}$ (*c*) $\frac{17}{18}$ (*d*) 3

31. If $\frac{1}{3} + \frac{1}{2} + \frac{1}{x} = 4$, then $x = ?$ **(M.B.A. 2002)**

(*a*) $\frac{5}{18}$ (*b*) $\frac{6}{19}$ (*c*) $\frac{18}{5}$ (*d*) $\frac{24}{11}$

32. $\dfrac{-\frac{1}{2} - \frac{2}{3} + \frac{4}{5} - \frac{1}{3} + \frac{1}{5} + \frac{3}{4}}{\frac{1}{2} + \frac{2}{3} - \frac{4}{3} + \frac{1}{3} - \frac{1}{5} - \frac{4}{5}}$ is simplified to : **(S.S.C. 2004)**

(*a*) $-\frac{3}{10}$ (*b*) $\frac{-10}{3}$ (*c*) -2 (*d*) 1

33. $5 - \left[\frac{3}{4} + \left\{2\frac{1}{2} - \left(0.5 + \overline{\frac{1}{6} - \frac{1}{7}}\right)\right\}\right]$ is equal to :

(*a*) $1\frac{19}{84}$ (*b*) $2\frac{61}{84}$ (*c*) $2\frac{23}{84}$ (*d*) $2\frac{47}{84}$

34. When $\left(\frac{1}{2} - \frac{1}{4} + \frac{1}{5} - \frac{1}{6}\right)$ is divided by $\left(\frac{2}{5} - \frac{5}{9} + \frac{3}{5} - \frac{7}{18}\right)$, the result is : **(S.S.C. 2000)**

(*a*) $2\frac{1}{18}$ (*b*) $3\frac{1}{6}$ (*c*) $3\frac{3}{10}$ (*d*) $5\frac{1}{10}$

35. Which of the following can be used to compute $\left(34 \times 4\frac{1}{2}\right)$?

(*a*) $(30 \times 4) + \left(4 \times 4\frac{1}{2}\right)$ (*b*) $(34 \times 40) + \left(34 \times \frac{1}{2}\right)$

(*c*) $\left(30 \times 4\frac{1}{2}\right) + (4 \times 4)$ (*d*) $\left(34 \times \frac{1}{2}\right) + (30 \times 4) + (4 \times 4)$

36. $\frac{3}{5}$ of $\frac{4}{7}$ of $\frac{5}{9}$ of $\frac{21}{24}$ of 504 = ? **(Bank P.O. 2003)**

(*a*) 63 (*b*) 69 (*c*) 96 (*d*) 109 (*e*) None of these

37. $6\frac{5}{6} \times 5\frac{1}{3} + 17\frac{2}{3} \times 4\frac{1}{2} = ?$ **(Bank P.O. 2003)**

(*a*) $112\frac{1}{3}$ (*b*) $116\frac{2}{3}$ (*c*) 240 (*d*) 663 (*e*) None of these

38. $\frac{3}{8}$ of $168 \times 15 \div 5 + ? = 549 \div 9 + 235$ **(S.B.I.P.O. 2000)**

(*a*) 107 (*b*) 174 (*c*) 1 (*d*) 296 (*e*) None of these

39. Find the value of * in the following :

$$1\frac{2}{3} \div \frac{2}{7} \times \frac{*}{7} = 1\frac{1}{4} \times \frac{2}{3} \div \frac{1}{6}$$ **(S.S.C. 2002)**

(*a*) 0.006 (*b*) $\frac{1}{6}$ (*c*) 0.6 (*d*) 6

40. $5\frac{2}{3} \div ?\frac{5}{6} = 2$ **(Hotel Management, 1998)**

(*a*) 2 (*b*) 3 (*c*) 4 (*d*) None of these

41. Supply the two missing figures in order indicated by *x* and *y* in the given equation, the fractions being in their lowest terms, **(IGNOU, 2003)**

$$5\frac{1}{x} \times y\frac{3}{4} = 20$$

(*a*) 3, 1 (*b*) 3, 3 (*c*) 4, 1 (*d*) 5, 3

42. The difference of $1\frac{3}{16}$ and its reciprocal is equal to : **(M.A.T. 2002)**

(*a*) $1\frac{1}{8}$ (*b*) $\frac{4}{3}$ (*c*) $\frac{15}{16}$ (*d*) None of these

43. How many $\frac{1}{8}$s are there in $37\frac{1}{2}$?

(*a*) 300 (*b*) 400 (*c*) 500 (*d*) Cannot be determined

44. $\frac{3}{8}$ is what part of $\frac{1}{12}$?

(*a*) $\frac{3}{7}$ (*b*) $\frac{1}{12}$ (*c*) $\frac{4}{3}$ (*d*) None of these

45. The smallest fraction which should be subtracted from the sum of $1\frac{3}{4}$, $2\frac{1}{2}$, $5\frac{7}{12}$, $3\frac{1}{3}$ and $2\frac{1}{4}$ to make the result a whole number is :

(*a*) $\frac{5}{12}$ (*b*) $\frac{7}{12}$ (*c*) $\frac{1}{2}$ (*d*) 7

46. If x is a positive number, then which of the following fractions has the greatest value ?

(*a*) $\frac{x}{x}$ (*b*) $\frac{x}{x+1}$ (*c*) $\frac{x+1}{x}$ (*d*) $\frac{x+2}{x+3}$

47. By how much is three-fifth of 350 greater than four-seventh of 210 ?

(*a*) 95 (*b*) 110 (*c*) 120 (*d*) 210 (*e*) None of these

(S.B.I.P.O. 2003)

48. By how much does $\frac{6}{7/8}$ exceed $\frac{6/7}{8}$? **(Section Officers', 2003)**

(*a*) $6\frac{1}{8}$ (*b*) $6\frac{3}{4}$ (*c*) $7\frac{3}{4}$ (*d*) $7\frac{5}{6}$

49. If $\frac{4}{5}$ of an estate be worth Rs. 16,800, then the value of $\frac{3}{7}$ of the estate is :

(*a*) Rs. 9000 (*b*) Rs. 21,000 (*c*) Rs. 72,000 (*d*) Rs. 90,000

(S.S.C. 2002)

50. Two-fifth of one-fourth of three-seventh of a number is 15. What is half of that number ?

(*a*) 94 (*b*) 96 (*c*) 188 (*d*) 196 (*e*) None of these

(Bank P.O. 1999)

51. One-fifth of a number exceeds one-seventh of the same by 10. The number is :

(*a*) 125 (*b*) 150 (*c*) 175 (*d*) 200

52. If $x * y = x^2 + y^2 - xy$, then the value of $9 * 11$ is : **(S.S.C. 2003)**

(*a*) 93 (*b*) 103 (*c*) 113 (*d*) 121

53. If $a * b = \frac{ab}{a+b}$, find the value of $3 * (3 * -1)$. **(M.B.A. 2002)**

(*a*) -3 (*b*) -1.5 (*c*) -1 (*d*) $\frac{2}{3}$

54. If $a * b = 2a - 3b + ab$, then $3 * 5 + 5 * 3$ is equal to : **(S.S.C. 1999)**

(*a*) 22 (*b*) 24 (*c*) 26 (*d*) 28

55. If $x \oplus y = x^2 + 2y$, what is the value of p if $4 \oplus (3 \oplus p) = 50$? **(N.I.F.T. 1997)**

(*a*) 4 (*b*) 7 (*c*) 8 (*d*) 12.5

56. If $a * b * c$ means $\frac{a+b}{c}$ for all numbers except 0, then $(a * b * c) * a * b$ is equal to :

(*a*) 0 (*b*) 1 (*c*) $\frac{a+b+c}{ab}$ (*d*) $\frac{a+b+ac}{bc}$ (*e*) $\frac{ab+bc+ca}{a+b+c}$

57. 7 is added to a certain number; the sum is multiplied by 5; the product is divided by 9 and 3 is subtracted from the quotient. The remainder left is 12. The number is :

(*a*) 20 (*b*) 30 (*c*) 40 (*d*) 60

(S.S.C. 2000)

58. The value of $\left(\frac{5}{7} \text{ of } 1\frac{6}{13}\right) \div \left(2\frac{5}{7} \div 3\frac{1}{4}\right)$ is : **(R.R.B. 2001)**

(a) $\frac{20}{169}$ (b) 1 (c) $\frac{5}{4}$ (d) $1\frac{119}{180}$

59. $2\frac{3}{4} \div 2\frac{2}{3} \div 1\frac{1}{12} = ?$ **(Hotel Management, 2001)**

(a) $\frac{39}{48}$ (b) $1\frac{1}{4}$ (c) $\frac{169}{144}$ (d) None of these

60. $4\frac{1}{2} \times 4\frac{1}{3} - 8\frac{1}{3} \div 5\frac{2}{3} = ?$ **(Bank P.O. 1999)**

(a) $\frac{7}{17}$ (b) $1\frac{33}{34}$ (c) 8 (d) $18\frac{1}{34}$

61. $\frac{4335}{4(?)24} \div 1\frac{7}{8} = \frac{289}{528}$ **(Hotel Management, 2000)**

(a) 1 (b) 2 (c) 8 (d) None of these

62. $5\frac{1}{3} - 3\frac{2}{3} \div 1\frac{1}{3} \div ? + 3\frac{1}{5} \div 1\frac{1}{5} = 7$

(a) $1\frac{1}{2}$ (b) $2\frac{1}{3}$ (c) $3\frac{1}{4}$ (d) None of these

63. $9 - 1\frac{2}{9} \text{ of } 3\frac{3}{11} \div 5\frac{1}{7} \text{ of } \frac{7}{9} = ?$ **(S.S.C. 2002)**

(a) $\frac{5}{4}$ (b) 8 (c) $8\frac{32}{81}$ (d) 9

64. $\frac{5}{6} \div \frac{6}{7} \times ? - \frac{8}{9} \div 1\frac{3}{5} + \frac{3}{4} \times 3\frac{1}{3} = 2\frac{7}{9}$

(a) $\frac{7}{6}$ (b) $\frac{6}{7}$ (c) 1 (d) None of these

65. $\frac{3}{4} \div 2\frac{1}{4} \text{ of } \frac{2}{3} - \frac{\frac{1}{2} - \frac{1}{3}}{\frac{1}{2} + \frac{1}{3}} \times 3\frac{1}{3} + \frac{5}{6} = ?$

(a) $\frac{7}{18}$ (b) $\frac{49}{54}$ (c) $\frac{2}{3}$ (d) $\frac{1}{6}$

66. A student was asked to solve the fraction $\frac{\frac{7}{3} + 1\frac{1}{2} \text{ of } \frac{5}{3}}{2 + 1\frac{2}{3}}$ and his answer was $\frac{1}{4}$. By how much was his answer wrong ? **(N.I.F.T. 1997)**

(a) 1 (b) $\frac{1}{55}$ (c) $\frac{1}{220}$ (d) None of these

67. Simplify : $\frac{\frac{1}{3} + \frac{3}{4}\left(\frac{2}{5} - \frac{1}{3}\right)}{1\frac{2}{3} \text{ of } \frac{3}{4} - \frac{1}{4} \text{ of } \frac{4}{5}}$ **(C.B.I. 1998)**

(a) $\frac{1}{63}$ (b) $\frac{23}{40}$ (c) $\frac{23}{55}$ (d) $\frac{23}{63}$

68. The simplified value of $\dfrac{\frac{1}{3} \div \frac{1}{3} \times \frac{1}{3}}{\frac{1}{3} \div \frac{1}{3} \text{ of } \frac{1}{3}} - \dfrac{1}{9}$ is : **(S.S.C. 2003)**

(*a*) 0 (*b*) $\frac{1}{9}$ (*c*) $\frac{1}{3}$ (*d*) 1

69. The value of $\dfrac{\frac{1}{2} \div \frac{1}{2} \text{ of } \frac{1}{2}}{\frac{1}{2} + \frac{1}{2} \text{ of } \frac{1}{2}}$ is :

(*a*) 1 (*b*) $1\frac{1}{3}$ (*c*) $2\frac{2}{3}$ (*d*) 3

70. $\dfrac{3\frac{1}{4} - \frac{4}{5} \text{ of } \frac{5}{6}}{4\frac{1}{3} \div \frac{1}{5} - \left(\frac{3}{10} + 21\frac{1}{5}\right)}$ is equal to :

(*a*) $\frac{1}{6}$ (*b*) $2\frac{7}{12}$ (*c*) $15\frac{1}{2}$ (*d*) $21\frac{1}{2}$

71. $\dfrac{7\frac{1}{2} - 5\frac{3}{4}}{3\frac{1}{2} + ?} \div \dfrac{\frac{1}{2} + 1\frac{1}{4}}{1\frac{1}{5} + 3\frac{1}{2}} = 0.6$

(*a*) $4\frac{1}{3}$ (*b*) $4\frac{1}{2}$ (*c*) $4\frac{2}{3}$ (*d*) None of these

72 On simplification, 3034 – (1002 ÷ 20.04) is equal to : **(S.S.C. 2000)**

(*a*) 2543 (*b*) 2984 (*c*) 2993 (*d*) 3029

73. 52.416 ÷ 18.72 + 6.28 = ?

(*a*) 2.09664 (*b*) 8.36 (*c*) 9.08 (*d*) 9.80

74. $8\frac{2}{7}$ of 1568 + 265.75 = ? + 2455.60 : **(S.B.I.P.O. 1998)**

(*a*) 10354.15 (*b*) 10578.15 (*c*) 10802.15 (*d*) 11250.15

75. 5.8 × 2.5 + 0.6 × 6.75 + 139.25 = ? **(Bank P.O. 1998)**

(*a*) 157.30 (*b*) 157.80 (*c*) 158.40 (*d*) 160.30

76. $8\frac{1}{4} - 4\frac{1}{5} + 2.8 + \frac{4}{?} - 2.32 = 5.33$

(*a*) .05 (*b*) .5 (*c*) 5 (*d*) None of these

77. The value of 0.008 × 0.01 × 0.0072 ÷ (0.12 × 0.0004) is : **(S.S.C. 2002)**

(*a*) 0.012 (*b*) 0.12 (*c*) 1.02 (*d*) 1.2

78. 2.375 × 5.22 + 0.87 – 1.425 × 0.02 = ?

(*a*) 0.142215 (*b*) 1.42215 (*c*) 14.2215 (*d*) None of these

79. 0.2 + 0.2 – 0.2 ÷ 0.2 × (0.2 × 0.2), on simplification, gives :

(*a*) 0.04 (*b*) 0.2 (*c*) 0.36 (*d*) 1

80. 11.6 + 9.28 ÷ 0.464 – 0.2828 ÷ 0.07 = ? **(R.R.B. 1998)**

(*a*) 9.2 (*b*) 9.56 (*c*) 27.2 (*d*) 27.56

81. $4.59 \times 1.8 \div 3.6 + 5.4 \text{ of } \frac{1}{9} - \frac{1}{5} = ?$

(*a*) 2.695 (*b*) 2.705 (*c*) 3.105 (*d*) None of these

82. $\dfrac{64\frac{2}{5} - 34.7125}{6.25 \text{ of } ?} = 1 :$

(*a*) $2\frac{2}{3}$ (*b*) 2.75 (*c*) $4\frac{3}{4}$ (*d*) None of these

83. 2.002 + 7.9 {2.8 − 6.3 (3.6 − 1.5) + 15.6} = ? **(S.S.C. 1997)**

(*a*) 2.002 (*b*) 4.2845 (*c*) 40.843 (*d*) 42.845

84. 24 − [2.4 −{.24 × 2 − (.024 − ?)}] = 22.0584

(*a*) 0.0024 (*b*) 0.024 (*c*) 0.24 (*d*) None of these

85. 3 − [1.6 − {3.2 − (3.2 + 2.25 ÷ *x*)}] = 0.65. The value of *x* is : **(R.R.B. 2002)**

(*a*) 0.3 (*b*) 0.7 (*c*) 3 (*d*) 7

86. $587.4 + 58.74 \times 2 - 5.874 \div 2\frac{?}{4} = 702.744$

(*a*) 1 (*b*) 2 (*c*) 3 (*d*) None of these

87. 54.27 − [12.84 − {(?).87 − (3.41 × 2 − 1.85)}] = 38.33

(*a*) 2 (*b*) 3 (*c*) 4 (*d*) None of these

88. $6\frac{2}{3}$ of 7.26 ÷ 0.45 of ? = $8\frac{32}{117}$

(*a*) $\frac{1}{13}$ (*b*) 13 (*c*) $13\frac{1}{9}$ (*d*) None of these

89. What is the value of $\dfrac{(P+Q)}{(P-Q)}$ if $\dfrac{P}{Q} = 7$? **(Hotel Management, 2000)**

(*a*) $\frac{1}{3}$ (*b*) $\frac{2}{3}$ (*c*) $\frac{4}{3}$ (*d*) $\frac{7}{8}$

90. If $\dfrac{x}{y} = \dfrac{4}{5}$ then the value of $\left(\dfrac{4}{7} + \dfrac{2y - x}{2y + x}\right)$ is : **(R.R.B. 2003)**

(*a*) $\frac{3}{7}$ (*b*) 1 (*c*) $1\frac{1}{7}$ (*d*) 2

91. If $\dfrac{a}{b} = \dfrac{4}{3}$, then the value of $\dfrac{6a + 4b}{6a - 5b}$ is :

(*a*) − 1 (*b*) 3 (*c*) 4 (*d*) 5

92. If $\dfrac{x}{2y} = \dfrac{6}{7}$, the value of $\dfrac{x - y}{x + y} + \dfrac{14}{19}$ is :

(*a*) $\frac{13}{19}$ (*b*) $\frac{15}{19}$ (*c*) 1 (*d*) $1\frac{1}{19}$

93. If $\dfrac{a}{b} = \dfrac{4}{5}$ and $\dfrac{b}{c} = \dfrac{15}{16}$, then $\dfrac{c^2 - a^2}{c^2 + a^2}$ is :

(*a*) $\frac{1}{7}$ (*b*) $\frac{7}{25}$ (*c*) $\frac{3}{4}$ (*d*) None of these

94. If (*a* − *b*) is 6 more than (*c* + *d*) and (*a* + *b*) is 3 less than (*c* − *d*), then (*a* − *c*) is :

(*a*) 0.5 (*b*) 1 (*c*) 1.5 (*d*) None of these

95. If $x = \dfrac{a}{a-1}$ and $y = \dfrac{1}{a-1}$, then : **(Bank P.O. 2003)**

(*a*) x is equal to y (*b*) x is equal to y only if $a < 1$
(*c*) x is greater than y (*d*) x is greater than y only if $a < 1$
(*e*) y is greater than x only if $a < 1$

96. If $0 < a < 1$, then the value of $a + \frac{1}{a}$ is : **(S.S.C. 1997)**

(*a*) less than 2 (*b*) greater than 2 (*c*) less than 4 (*d*) greater than 4

97. If $\frac{a}{x} + \frac{y}{b} = 1$ and $\frac{b}{y} + \frac{z}{c} = 1$, then $\frac{x}{a} + \frac{c}{z}$ will be equal to : **(C.D.S. 2003)**

(*a*) 0 (*b*) $\frac{b}{y}$ (*c*) 1 (*d*) $\frac{y}{b}$

98. If a, b, c are integers; $a^2 + b^2 = 45$ and $b^2 + c^2 = 40$, then the values of a, b and c respectively are :

(*a*) 2, 6, 3 (*b*) 3, 2, 6 (*c*) 5, 4, 3 (*d*) None of these.

99. If $\frac{a}{3} = \frac{b}{4} = \frac{c}{7}$, then the value of $\frac{a+b+c}{c}$ is : **(C.B.I. 2003)**

(*a*) $\frac{1}{\sqrt{7}}$ (*b*) $\sqrt{2}$ (*c*) 2 (*d*) 7

100. If $3x + 7 = x^2 + P = 7x + 5$, what is the value of P ? **(S.B.I.P.O. 2000)**

(*a*) $\frac{1}{2}$ (*b*) $8\frac{1}{4}$ (*c*) $8\frac{1}{2}$ (*d*) Cannot be determined

101. If $\frac{2a+b}{a+4b} = 3$, then find the value of $\frac{a+b}{a+2b}$. **(S.S.C. 2002)**

(*a*) $\frac{2}{7}$ (*b*) $\frac{5}{9}$ (*c*) $\frac{10}{7}$ (*d*) $\frac{10}{9}$

102. If $(2a + 3b)(2c - 3d) = (2a - 3b)(2c + 3d)$, then :

(*a*) $\frac{a}{b} = \frac{c}{d}$ (*b*) $\frac{a}{d} = \frac{c}{b}$ (*c*) $\frac{a}{b} = \frac{d}{c}$ (*d*) $\frac{b}{a} = \frac{c}{d}$

103. If $(a + b + 2c + 3d)(a - b - 2c + 3d) = (a - b + 2c - 3d)(a + b - 2c - 3d)$, then $2bc$ is equal to : **(M.A.T. 2003)**

(*a*) $\frac{3}{2}$ (*b*) $\frac{3a}{2d}$ (*c*) $3ad$ (*d*) a^2d^2

104. The value of $\cfrac{1}{2+\cfrac{1}{2+\cfrac{1}{2-\cfrac{1}{2}}}}$ is : **(S.S.C. 1999)**

(*a*) $\frac{3}{8}$ (*b*) $\frac{19}{8}$ (*c*) $\frac{8}{3}$ (*d*) $\frac{8}{19}$

105. If $2 = x + \cfrac{1}{1+\cfrac{1}{3+\cfrac{1}{4}}}$, then the value of x is : **(S.S.C. 2003)**

(*a*) $\frac{12}{17}$ (*b*) $\frac{13}{17}$ (*c*) $\frac{18}{17}$ (*d*) $\frac{21}{17}$

106. If $\dfrac{2+\dfrac{1}{3\frac{4}{5}}}{2+\dfrac{1}{3+\dfrac{1}{1+\dfrac{1}{4}}}} = x$, then the value of x is : **(C.B.I. 1998)**

(*a*) $\frac{1}{7}$ (*b*) $\frac{3}{7}$ (*c*) 1 (*d*) $\frac{8}{7}$

107. $8 - 8 \times \dfrac{2\frac{1}{5} - 1\frac{2}{7}}{2 - \dfrac{1}{6 - \dfrac{1}{6}}}$ is equal to : **(S.S.C. 2002)**

(*a*) 2 (*b*) 4 (*c*) 6 (*d*) 8

108. $\dfrac{2}{2 + \dfrac{2}{3 + \dfrac{2}{3 + \dfrac{2}{3}}} \times 0.39}$ is simplified to : **(S.S.C. 2004)**

(*a*) $\frac{1}{3}$ (*b*) 2 (*c*) 6 (*d*) None of these

109. Simplify : $\dfrac{1}{1 + \dfrac{\frac{2}{3}}{1 + \frac{2}{3} + \dfrac{\frac{8}{9}}{1 - \frac{2}{3}}}}$. **(S.S.C. 2003)**

(*a*) $\frac{11}{13}$ (*b*) $\frac{13}{15}$ (*c*) $\frac{15}{11}$ (*d*) $\frac{15}{13}$

110. If $\dfrac{37}{13} = 2 + \dfrac{1}{x + \dfrac{1}{y + \dfrac{1}{z}}}$, where x, y, z are natural numbers, then x, y, z are :

(*a*) 1, 2, 5 (*b*) 1, 5, 2 (*c*) 5, 2, 11 (*d*) 11, 2, 5

(Assistant Grade, 1998)

111. If $x = 1 - q$ and $y = 2q + 1$, then for what value of q, x is equal to y ?

(*a*) -1 (*b*) 0 (*c*) $\frac{1}{2}$ (*d*) 2

112. Find x if $\frac{x}{5} - \frac{x}{6} = 4$. **(B.S.F. 2001)**

(*a*) -120 (*b*) -100 (*c*) 100 (*d*) 120

113. If $4x + 5y = 83$ and $\frac{3x}{2y} = \frac{21}{22}$, then $y - x = ?$ **(Bank P.O. 2002)**

(*a*) 3 (*b*) 4 (*c*) 7 (*d*) 11

114. Which of the following values of x and y satisfy the following equations I and II ?

I. $3x + y = 19$ II. $x - y = 9$ **(B.S.R.B. 2003)**

(*a*) $-7, -2$ (*b*) $-7, 2$ (*c*) $7, -2$ (*d*) 7, 2

115. If $a + b = 5$ and $3a + 2b = 20$, then $(3a + b)$ will be : **(M.B.A. 1998)**

(a) 10 (b) 15 (c) 20 (d) 25

116. If $2p + 3q = 18$ and $2p - q = 2$, then $2p + q = ?$

(a) 6 (b) 7 (c) 10 (d) 20

117. If $2x + y = 5$ and $3x - 4y = 2$, then the value of $2xy$ is :

(a) 4 (b) 6 (c) 8 (d) 10

118. If $3x - 5y = 5$ and $\frac{x}{x+y} = \frac{5}{7}$, then what is the value of $x - y$? **(Bank P.O. 2002)**

(a) 3 (b) 4 (c) 6 (d) 9 (e) None of these

119. If $4x + 3y = 18xy$ and $2x - 5y + 4xy = 0$, then the values of x and y will be respectively :

(a) $-\frac{1}{2}$ and $-\frac{1}{3}$ (b) -1 and -3 (c) $\frac{1}{2}$ and $\frac{1}{3}$ (d) $\frac{1}{4}$ and $\frac{1}{3}$

120. If $2x + y = 17$; $y + 2z = 15$ and $x + y = 9$, then what is the value of $4x + 3y + z$?

(a) 41 (b) 43 (c) 45 (d) 55 (e) None of these

(S.B.I.P.O. 1999)

121. If $3x - 4y + z = 7$; $2x - z + 3y = 19$; $x + 2y + 2z = 24$, then what is the value of z ?

(a) 4 (b) 5 (c) 6 (d) 8

122. If $2x + y = 15$, $2y + z = 25$ and $2z + x = 26$, what is the value of z ?

(a) 4 (b) 7 (c) 9 (d) 11

123. If $2x + 3y = 31$, $y - z = 4$ and $x + 2z = 11$, then what is the value of $x + y + z$?

(a) 12 (b) 13 (c) 15 (d) 16

(Bank P.O. 2003)

124. $\frac{3}{4}\left(1+\frac{1}{3}\right)\left(1+\frac{2}{3}\right)\left(1-\frac{2}{5}\right)\left(1+\frac{6}{7}\right)\left(1-\frac{12}{13}\right) = ?$ **(Hotel Management, 2001)**

(a) $\frac{1}{5}$ (b) $\frac{1}{6}$ (c) $\frac{1}{7}$ (d) None of these

125. When simplified, the product $\left(1-\frac{1}{2}\right)\left(1-\frac{1}{3}\right)\left(1-\frac{1}{4}\right) \ldots\ldots \left(1-\frac{1}{n}\right)$ gives **(S.S.C. 2004)**

(a) $\frac{1}{n}$ (b) $\frac{2}{n}$ (c) $\frac{2(n-1)}{n}$ (d) $\frac{2}{n(n+1)}$

126. The value of $\left(1+\frac{1}{2}\right)\left(1+\frac{1}{3}\right)\left(1+\frac{1}{4}\right) \ldots\ldots \left(1+\frac{1}{120}\right)$ is : **(S.S.C. 2003)**

(a) 30 (b) 40.5 (c) 60.5 (d) 121

127. When simplified, the product $\left(2-\frac{1}{3}\right)\left(2-\frac{3}{5}\right)\left(2-\frac{5}{7}\right) \ldots\ldots \left(2-\frac{999}{1001}\right)$ is equal to :

(a) $\frac{991}{1001}$ (b) $\frac{1001}{13}$ (c) $\frac{1003}{13}$ (d) None of these

128. Find the sum : $\frac{1}{2}+\frac{1}{6}+\frac{1}{12}+\frac{1}{20}+\frac{1}{30}+\frac{1}{42}+\frac{1}{56}+\frac{1}{72}+\frac{1}{90}+\frac{1}{110}+\frac{1}{132}$.

(a) $\frac{7}{8}$ (b) $\frac{11}{12}$ (c) $\frac{15}{16}$ (d) $\frac{17}{18}$

129. The sum of the first 35 terms of the series $\frac{1}{2}+\frac{1}{3}-\frac{1}{4}-\frac{1}{2}-\frac{1}{3}+\frac{1}{4}+\frac{1}{2}+\frac{1}{3}-\frac{1}{4} \ldots\ldots$ is :

(a) $-\frac{1}{2}$ (b) $-\frac{1}{4}$ (c) $\frac{1}{4}$ (d) None of these

130. The value of $999\frac{995}{999} \times 999$ is : **(S.S.C. 2003)**

(a) 990809 (b) 998996 (c) 998999 (d) 999824

131. $\left(999\frac{1}{7} + 999\frac{2}{7} + 999\frac{3}{7} + 999\frac{4}{7} + 999\frac{5}{7} + 999\frac{6}{7}\right)$ is simplified to : **(S.S.C. 2004)**

(a) 2997 (b) 5979 (c) 5994 (d) 5997

132. The value of $1 + \frac{1}{4 \times 3} + \frac{1}{4 \times 3^2} + \frac{1}{4 \times 3^3}$ is :

(a) $\frac{121}{108}$ (b) $\frac{3}{2}$ (c) $\frac{31}{2}$ (d) None of these

133. $\frac{1}{1 \cdot 2 \cdot 3} + \frac{1}{2 \cdot 3 \cdot 4} + \frac{1}{3 \cdot 4 \cdot 5} + \frac{1}{4 \cdot 5 \cdot 6}$ is equal to :

(a) $\frac{7}{30}$ (b) $\frac{11}{30}$ (c) $\frac{13}{30}$ (d) $\frac{17}{30}$

134. The value of $\frac{3}{1^2 \cdot 2^2} + \frac{5}{2^2 \cdot 3^2} + \frac{7}{3^2 \cdot 4^2} + \frac{9}{4^2 \cdot 5^2} + \frac{11}{5^2 \cdot 6^2} + \frac{13}{6^2 \cdot 7^2} + \frac{15}{7^2 \cdot 8^2} + \frac{17}{8^2 \cdot 9^2} + \frac{19}{9^2 \cdot 10^2}$ is:

(a) $\frac{1}{100}$ (b) $\frac{99}{100}$ (c) 1 (d) $\frac{101}{100}$

(S.S.C. 2004)

135. How may pieces of 85 cm length can be cut from a rod 42.5 metres long ?

(a) 30 (b) 40 (c) 60 (d) None of these

136. Income of a company doubles after every one year. If the initial income was Rs. 4 lakhs, what would be the income after 5 years ? **(Bank P.O. 2003)**

(a) Rs. 1.24 crores (b) Rs. 1.28 crores (c) Rs. 2.52 crores
(d) Rs. 2.56 crores (e) None of these

137. On sports day, if 30 children were made to stand in a column, then 16 columns could be formed. If 24 children were made to stand in a column, then how many columns could be formed ? **(Hotel Management, 2002)**

(a) 20 (b) 22 (c) 29 (d) 45

138. The number of students in each section of a school is 24. After admitting new students, three new sections were started. Now, the total number of sections is 16 and there are 21 students in each section. The number of new students admitted is :

(a) 14 (b) 24 (c) 48 (d) 114

139. A class starts at 10 a.m. and lasts till 1.27 p.m. Four periods are held during this interval. After every period, 5 minutes are given free to the students. The exact duration of each period is :

(a) 42 minutes (b) 48 minutes (c) 51 minutes (d) 53 minutes

140. A light was seen at intervals of 13 seconds. It was seen for the first time at 1 hr. 54 min 50 secs. a.m. and the last time at 3 hrs. 17 min. 49 secs. a.m. How many times was the light seen ? **(A.A.O. Exam, 2003)**

(a) 360 (b) 375 (c) 378 (d) 384

141. A man earns Rs. 20 on the first day and spends Rs. 15 on the next day. He again earns Rs. 20 on the third day and spends Rs. 15 on the fourth day. If he continues to save like this, how soon will he have Rs. 60 in hand ? **(IGNOU, 2003)**

(a) On 17th day (b) On 27th day (c) On 30th day (d) On 40th day

142. It costs Rs. x each to make the first thousand copies of a compact disc and Rs. y to make each subsequent copy. If z is greater than 1000, how much will it cost to make z copies of the compact disc ? **(R.R.B. 2001)**

(*a*) $zx - zy$ (*b*) $1000x + yz$
(*c*) $1000(x - y) + yz$ (*d*) $1000(z - y) + xz$

143. Along a yard 225 metres long, 26 trees are planted at equal distances, one tree being at each end of the yard. What is the distance between two consecutive trees ?

(*a*) 8 metres (*b*) 9 metres (*c*) 10 metres (*d*) 15 metres

(R.R.B. 2002)

144. A boy was asked to multiply a number by 25. He instead multiplied the number by 52 and got the answer 324 more than the correct answer. The number to be multiplied was :

(*a*) 12 (*b*) 15 (*c*) 25 (*d*) 32

145. A boy multiplied 423 by a number and obtained 65589 as his answer. If both the fives in the answer are wrong and all other figures are correct, the correct answer is :

(*a*) 60489 (*b*) 61189 (*c*) 62189 (*d*) 62389

146. The total monthly salary of 4 men and 2 women is Rs. 46,000. If a woman earns Rs. 500 more than a man, what is the monthly salary of a woman ?

(*a*) Rs. 6500 (*b*) Rs. 7500 (*c*) Rs. 8000 (*d*) Rs. 9000

(Bank P.O. 1999)

147. David got two and a half times as many marks in English as in History. If his total marks in the two subjects are 140, the marks obtained by him in English are :

(*a*) 40 (*b*) 75 (*c*) 90 (*d*) 100

(Assistant Grade, 1998)

148. A pineapple costs Rs. 7 each. A watermelon costs Rs. 5 each. X spends Rs. 38 on these fruits. The number of pineapples purchased is : **(M.B.A. 1998)**

(*a*) 2 (*b*) 3 (*c*) 4 (*d*) Data inadequate

149. The number of girls in a class is 5 times the number of boys. Which of the following cannot be the total number of children in the class ? **(R.R.B. 2002)**

(*a*) 24 (*b*) 30 (*c*) 35 (*d*) 42 (*e*) 54

150. Water boils at 212°F or 100°C and melts at 32°F or 0°C. If the temperature of a particular day is 35°C, it is equivalent to : **(R.R.B. 2000)**

(*a*) 85°F (*b*) 90°F (*c*) 95°F (*d*) 99°F

151. A sum of Rs. 750 is distributed among A, B, C and D in such a manner that A gets as much as B and C together, B gets Rs. 125 more than C and D gets as much as C. What is A's share ?

(*a*) Rs. 100 (*b*) Rs. 225 (*c*) Rs. 275 (*d*) Rs. 325

152. A bonus of Rs. 1000 is to be divided among three people so that Rohit receives twice as much as Sachin, who receives one-fifth as much as Gagan. How much money should Gagan receive ?

(*a*) Rs. 100 (*b*) Rs. 250 (*c*) Rs. 375 (*d*) Rs. 625

153. The total number of digits used in numbering the pages of a book having 366 pages, is : **(S.C.R.A. 1998)**

(*a*) 732 (*b*) 990 (*c*) 1098 (*d*) 1305

154. A printer numbers the pages of a book starting with 1 and uses 3189 digits in all. How many pages does the book have ? **(M.A.T. 2002)**

(*a*) 1000 (*b*) 1074 (*c*) 1075 (*d*) 1080

155. In a garden, there are 10 rows and 12 columns of mango trees. The distance between the two trees is 2 metres and a distance of one metre is left from all sides of the boundary of the garden. The length of the garden is :

(*a*) 20 m (*b*) 22 m (*c*) 24 m (*d*) 26 m

156. What fraction of an hour is a second ?

(a) $\frac{1}{24}$ (b) $\frac{1}{60}$ (c) $\frac{1}{120}$ (d) $\frac{1}{3600}$

157. When a ball bounces, it rises to $\frac{3}{4}$ of the height from which it fell. If the ball is dropped from a height of 32 m, how high will it rise at the third bounce ? **(S.S.C. 2000)**

(a) 13 m (b) $13\frac{1}{2}$ m (c) $14\frac{1}{2}$ m (d) None of these

158. Sankēt earns twice as much in the month of March as in each of the other months of the year. What part of his entire annual earnings was earned in March ?

(a) $\frac{1}{7}$ (b) $\frac{1}{6}$ (c) $\frac{2}{11}$ (d) $\frac{2}{13}$

159. If one-third of a tank holds 80 litres of water, then the quantity of water that half of the tank holds is : **(S.S.C. 1999)**

(a) $\frac{80}{3}$ litres (b) 100 litres (c) 120 litres (d) 240 litres

160. A person travels 3.5 km from place A to place B. Out of this distance, he travels $1\frac{2}{3}$ km on bicycle, $1\frac{1}{6}$ km on scooter and the rest on foot. What portion of the whole distance does he cover on foot ? **(S.S.C. 2003)**

(a) $\frac{3}{19}$ (b) $\frac{4}{11}$ (c) $\frac{4}{21}$ (d) $\frac{5}{6}$

161. What fraction of $\frac{4}{7}$ must be added to itself to make the sum $1\frac{1}{14}$? **(S.S.C. 2002)**

(a) $\frac{1}{2}$ (b) $\frac{4}{7}$ (c) $\frac{7}{8}$ (d) $\frac{15}{14}$

162. Express $\frac{2}{3}$ of $\frac{1}{4}$ of Rs. 25.20 as a fraction of $1\frac{1}{2}$ of Rs. 36.

(a) $\frac{5}{8}$ (b) $\frac{5}{42}$ (c) $\frac{7}{90}$ (d) $\frac{11}{90}$

163. A 70 cm long wire is to be cut into two pieces such that one piece will be $\frac{2}{5}$ as long as the other. How many centimetres will the shorter piece be ?

(a) 10 (b) 14 (c) 20 (d) 28

164. A certain amount is distributed among A, B and C. A gets $\frac{3}{16}$ and B gets $\frac{1}{4}$ of the whole amount. If C gets Rs. 81, then B gets :

(a) Rs. 30 (b) Rs. 32 (c) Rs. 36 (d) Rs. 40

165. $\frac{1}{10}$ of a pole is coloured red, $\frac{1}{20}$ white, $\frac{1}{30}$ blue, $\frac{1}{40}$ black, $\frac{1}{50}$ violet, $\frac{1}{60}$ yellow and the rest is green. If the length of the green portion of the pole is 12.08 metres, then the length of the pole is : **(S.S.C. 2004)**

(a) 16 m (b) 18 m (c) 20 m (d) 30 m

166. In an examination, a student was asked to find $\frac{3}{14}$ of a certain number. By mistake, he found $\frac{3}{4}$ of that number. His answer was 150 more than the correct answer. The number is : **(R.R.B. 2003)**

(a) 180 (b) 240 (c) 280 (d) 290

167. A student was asked to find the value of $\frac{3}{8}$ of a sum of money. The student made a mistake by dividing the sum by $\frac{3}{8}$ and thus got an answer which exceeded the correct answer by Rs. 55. The correct answer was :

(*a*) Rs. 9 (*b*) Rs. 18 (*c*) Rs. 24 (*d*) Rs. 64

168. If we multiply a fraction by itself and divide the product by its reciprocal, the fraction thus obtained is $18\frac{26}{27}$. The original fraction is :

(*a*) $\frac{8}{27}$ (*b*) $1\frac{1}{3}$ (*c*) $2\frac{2}{3}$ (*d*) None of these

169. The marks scored in an examination are converted from 50 to 10 for the purpose of internal assessment. The highest marks were 47 and the lowest were 14. The difference between the maximum and the minimum internal assessment scores is :

(*a*) 3.3 (*b*) 4.8 (*c*) 6.6 (*d*) 7.4

(S.S.C. 2000)

170. One-third of Rahul's savings in National Savings Certificate is equal to one-half of his savings in Public Provident Fund. If he has Rs. 1,50,000 as total savings, how much has he saved in Public Provident Fund ? **(Bank P.O. 2002)**

(*a*) Rs. 30,000 (*b*) Rs. 50,000 (*c*) Rs. 60,000 (*d*) Rs. 90,000

171. In a family, the father took $\frac{1}{4}$ of the cake and he had 3 times as much as each of the other members had. The total number of family members is :

(*a*) 3 (*b*) 7 (*c*) 10 (*d*) 12

172. A waiter's salary consists of his salary and tips. During one week his tips were $\frac{5}{4}$ of his salary. What fraction of his income came from tips ?

(*a*) $\frac{4}{9}$ (*b*) $\frac{5}{4}$ (*c*) $\frac{5}{8}$ (*d*) $\frac{5}{9}$

173. A sum of Rs. 1360 has been divided among A, B and C such that A gets $\frac{2}{3}$ of what B gets and B gets $\frac{1}{4}$ of what C gets. B's share is : **(M.A.T. 2002)**

(*a*) Rs. 120 (*b*) Rs. 160 (*c*) Rs. 240 (*d*) Rs. 300

174. Three friends had dinner at a restaurant. When the bill was received, Amita paid $\frac{2}{3}$ as much as Veena paid and Veena paid $\frac{1}{2}$ as much as Tanya paid. What fraction of the bill did Veena pay ?

(*a*) $\frac{1}{3}$ (*b*) $\frac{3}{11}$ (*c*) $\frac{12}{31}$ (*d*) $\frac{5}{8}$

175. $\frac{1}{4}$ of a tank holds 135 litres of water. What part of the tank is full if it contains 180 litres of water ? **(S.S.C. 1999)**

(*a*) $\frac{1}{6}$ (*b*) $\frac{1}{3}$ (*c*) $\frac{2}{3}$ (*d*) $\frac{2}{5}$

176. A tank is $\frac{2}{5}$ full. If 16 litres of water is added to the tank, it becomes $\frac{6}{7}$ full. The capacity of the tank is :

(*a*) 28 litres (*b*) 32 litres (*c*) 35 litres (*d*) 42 litres

177. The fluid contained in a bucket can fill four large bottles or seven small bottles. A full large bottle is used to fill an empty small bottle. What fraction of the fluid is left over in the large bottle when the small one is full ? **(D.M.R.C. 2003)**

(*a*) $\frac{2}{7}$ (*b*) $\frac{3}{7}$ (*c*) $\frac{4}{7}$ (*d*) $\frac{5}{7}$

178. To fill a tank, 25 buckets of water is required. How many buckets of water will be required to fill the same tank if the capacity of the bucket is reduced to two-fifth of its present ? **(R.B.I. 2003)**

(*a*) 10 (*b*) 35 (*c*) $62\frac{1}{2}$

(*d*) Cannot be determined (*e*) None of these

179. Peter gave one-fourth of the amount he had to Michael. Michael in turn gave half of what he received from Peter to Sam. If the difference between the remaining amount with Peter and the amount received by Sam is Rs. 500, how much money did Michael receive from Peter ? **(S.B.I.P.O. 1999)**

(*a*) Rs. 100 (*b*) Rs. 200 (*c*) Rs. 400

(*d*) Data inadequate (*e*) None of these

180. Four children A, B, C and D divide a bag of sweets. A takes $\frac{1}{3}$ of them, B $\frac{2}{5}$th of the remainder and the rest is equally shared between C and D. What fraction of the sweets did C or D get ?

(*a*) $\frac{1}{4}$ (*b*) $\frac{1}{5}$ (*c*) $\frac{1}{6}$ (*d*) $\frac{1}{17}$

181. A boy read $\frac{3}{8}$th of a book on one day and $\frac{4}{5}$th of the remainder on another day. If there were 30 pages unread, how many pages did the book contain ? **(I.M.T. 2002)**

(*a*) 240 (*b*) 300 (*c*) 600 (*d*) None of these

182. A man has divided his total money in his will in such a way that half of it goes to his wife, $\frac{2}{3}$rd of the remaining among his three sons equally and the rest among his four daughters equally. If each daughter gets Rs. 20,000, how much money will each son get ? **(S.B.I.P.O. 2000)**

(*a*) Rs. 48,233.33 (*b*) Rs. 50,333.33 (*c*) Rs. 53,333.33

(*d*) Data inadequate (*e*) None of these

183. An institute organised a fete and $\frac{1}{5}$ of the girls and $\frac{1}{8}$ of the boys participated in the same. What fraction of the total number of students took part in the fete ?

(*a*) $\frac{2}{13}$ (*b*) $\frac{13}{40}$ (*c*) Data inadequate (*d*) None of these

(N.I.F.T. 2000)

184. At an International Dinner, $\frac{1}{5}$ of the people attending were French men. If the number of French women at the dinner was $\frac{2}{3}$ greater than the number of French men, and there were no other French people at the dinner, then what fraction of the people at the dinner were not French ? **(M.B.A. 2003)**

(*a*) $\frac{1}{5}$ (*b*) $\frac{2}{5}$ (*c*) $\frac{2}{3}$ (*d*) $\frac{7}{15}$

185. In a class, $\frac{3}{5}$ of the students are girls and rest are boys. If $\frac{2}{9}$ of the girls and $\frac{1}{4}$ of the boys are absent, what part of the total number of students is present ?

(a) $\frac{17}{25}$ (b) $\frac{18}{49}$ (c) $\frac{23}{30}$ (d) $\frac{23}{36}$

186. One-third of the boys and one-half of the girls of a college participated in a social work project. If the number of participating students is 300 out of which 100 are boys, what is the total number of students in the college ? **(Bank P.O. 2000)**

(a) 500 (b) 600 (c) 700 (d) 800

187. To win an election, a candidate needs $\frac{3}{4}$ of the votes cast. If after $\frac{2}{3}$ of the votes have been counted, a candidate has $\frac{5}{6}$ of what he needs, then what part of the remaining votes does he still need ?

(a) $\frac{1}{8}$ (b) $\frac{3}{8}$ (c) $\frac{1}{10}$ (d) $\frac{1}{4}$

188. In an office, $\frac{3}{4}$ of the staff can neither type nor take shorthand. However, $\frac{1}{5}$th can type and $\frac{1}{3}$rd can take shorthand. What part of the whole staff can do both ?

(a) $\frac{1}{5}$ (b) $\frac{3}{40}$ (c) $\frac{13}{40}$ (d) $\frac{17}{60}$

189. The charges of hired car are Rs. 4 per km for the first 60 km, Rs. 5 per km for the next 60 km and Rs. 8 for every 5 km for further journey. If the balance amount left over with Rohit is one-fourth of what he paid towards the charges of the hired car for travelling 320 km, how much money did he have initially with him ?

(a) Rs. 1075 (b) Rs. 1255 (c) Rs. 1540 (d) None of these

190. A fires 5 shots to B's 3 but A kills only once in 3 shots while B kills once in 2 shots. When B has missed 27 times, A has killed : **(C.B.I. 1997)**

(a) 30 birds (b) 60 birds (c) 72 birds (d) 90 birds

191. If every 2 out of 3 readymade shirts need alterations in the collar, every 3 out of 4 need alterations in the sleeves, and every 4 out of 5 need it in the body, how many alterations will be required for 60 shirts ?

(a) 24 (b) 123 (c) 133 (d) 143

192. The sum of three fractions is $2\frac{11}{24}$. When the largest fraction is divided by the smallest, the fraction thus obtained is $\frac{7}{6}$ which is $\frac{1}{3}$ more than the middle one. The fractions are :

(a) $\frac{3}{5}, \frac{4}{7}, \frac{2}{3}$ (b) $\frac{7}{8}, \frac{5}{6}, \frac{3}{4}$ (c) $\frac{7}{9}, \frac{2}{3}, \frac{3}{5}$ (d) None of these

193. One test tube contains some acid and another test tube contains an equal quantity of water. To prepare a solution, 20 grams of the acid is poured into the second test tube. Then, two-thirds of the so-formed solution is poured from the second tube into the first. If the fluid in first test tube is four times that in the second, what quantity of water was taken initially ?

(a) 40 grams (b) 60 grams (c) 80 grams (d) 100 grams

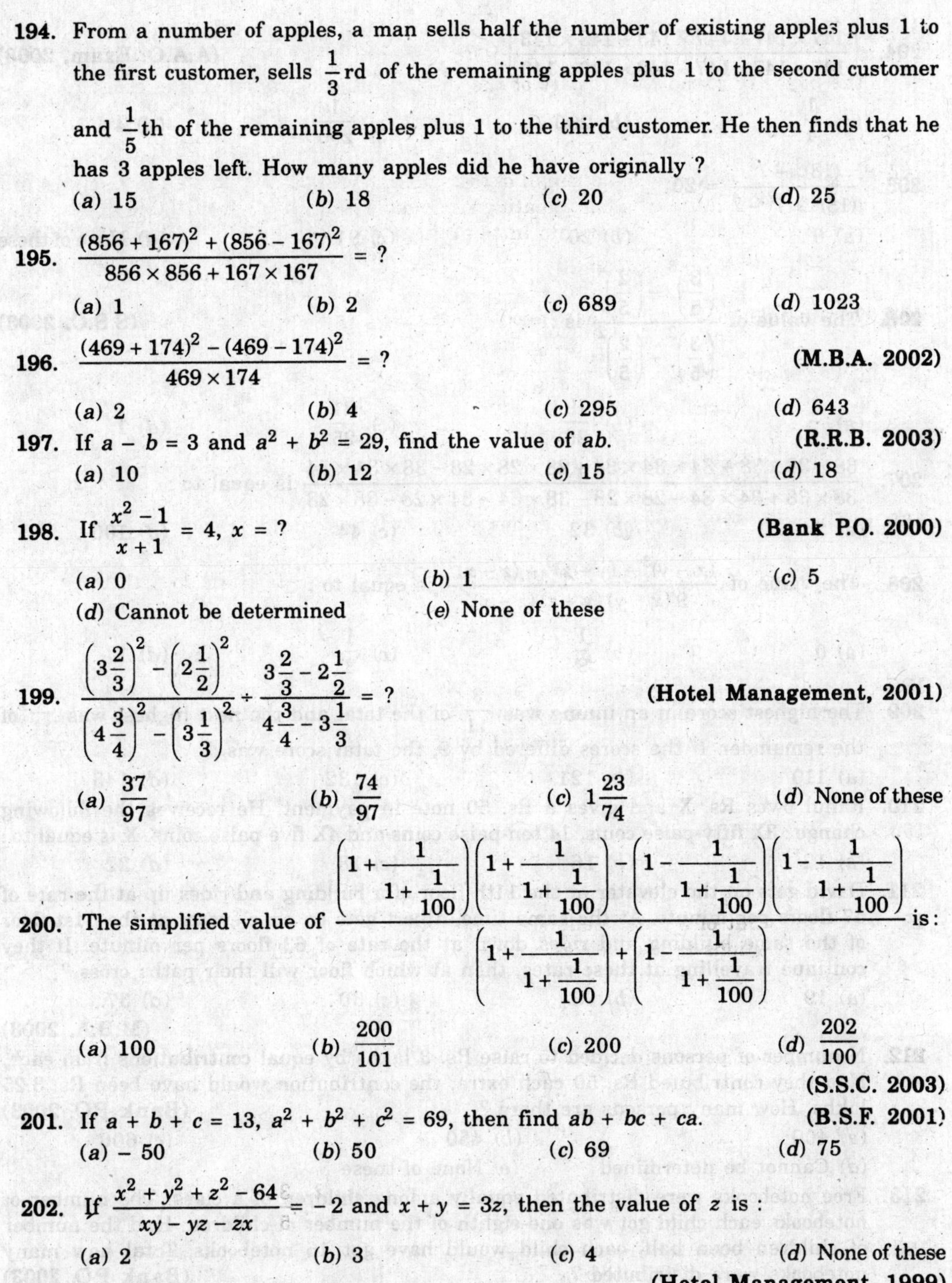

194. From a number of apples, a man sells half the number of existing apples plus 1 to the first customer, sells $\frac{1}{3}$rd of the remaining apples plus 1 to the second customer and $\frac{1}{5}$th of the remaining apples plus 1 to the third customer. He then finds that he has 3 apples left. How many apples did he have originally ?

(*a*) 15 (*b*) 18 (*c*) 20 (*d*) 25

195. $\dfrac{(856+167)^2+(856-167)^2}{856\times 856+167\times 167}=?$

(*a*) 1 (*b*) 2 (*c*) 689 (*d*) 1023

196. $\dfrac{(469+174)^2-(469-174)^2}{469\times 174}=?$ **(M.B.A. 2002)**

(*a*) 2 (*b*) 4 (*c*) 295 (*d*) 643

197. If $a-b=3$ and $a^2+b^2=29$, find the value of ab. **(R.R.B. 2003)**

(*a*) 10 (*b*) 12 (*c*) 15 (*d*) 18

198. If $\dfrac{x^2-1}{x+1}=4$, $x=?$ **(Bank P.O. 2000)**

(*a*) 0 (*b*) 1 (*c*) 5

(*d*) Cannot be determined (*e*) None of these

199. $\dfrac{\left(3\frac{2}{3}\right)^2-\left(2\frac{1}{2}\right)^2}{\left(4\frac{3}{4}\right)^2-\left(3\frac{1}{3}\right)^2}\div\dfrac{3\frac{2}{3}-2\frac{1}{2}}{4\frac{3}{4}-3\frac{1}{3}}=?$ **(Hotel Management, 2001)**

(*a*) $\frac{37}{97}$ (*b*) $\frac{74}{97}$ (*c*) $1\frac{23}{74}$ (*d*) None of these

200. The simplified value of $\dfrac{\left(1+\frac{1}{1+\frac{1}{100}}\right)\left(1+\frac{1}{1+\frac{1}{100}}\right)-\left(1-\frac{1}{1+\frac{1}{100}}\right)\left(1-\frac{1}{1+\frac{1}{100}}\right)}{\left(1+\frac{1}{1+\frac{1}{100}}\right)+\left(1-\frac{1}{1+\frac{1}{100}}\right)}$ is:

(*a*) 100 (*b*) $\frac{200}{101}$ (*c*) 200 (*d*) $\frac{202}{100}$

(S.S.C. 2003)

201. If $a+b+c=13$, $a^2+b^2+c^2=69$, then find $ab+bc+ca$. **(B.S.F. 2001)**

(*a*) -50 (*b*) 50 (*c*) 69 (*d*) 75

202. If $\dfrac{x^2+y^2+z^2-64}{xy-yz-zx}=-2$ and $x+y=3z$, then the value of z is :

(*a*) 2 (*b*) 3 (*c*) 4 (*d*) None of these

(Hotel Management, 1999)

203. $\left(\dfrac{785\times 785\times 785+435\times 435\times 435}{785\times 785+435\times 435-785\times 435}\right)$ simplifies to : **(S.S.C. 2000)**

(*a*) 350 (*b*) 785 (*c*) 1220 (*d*) 1320

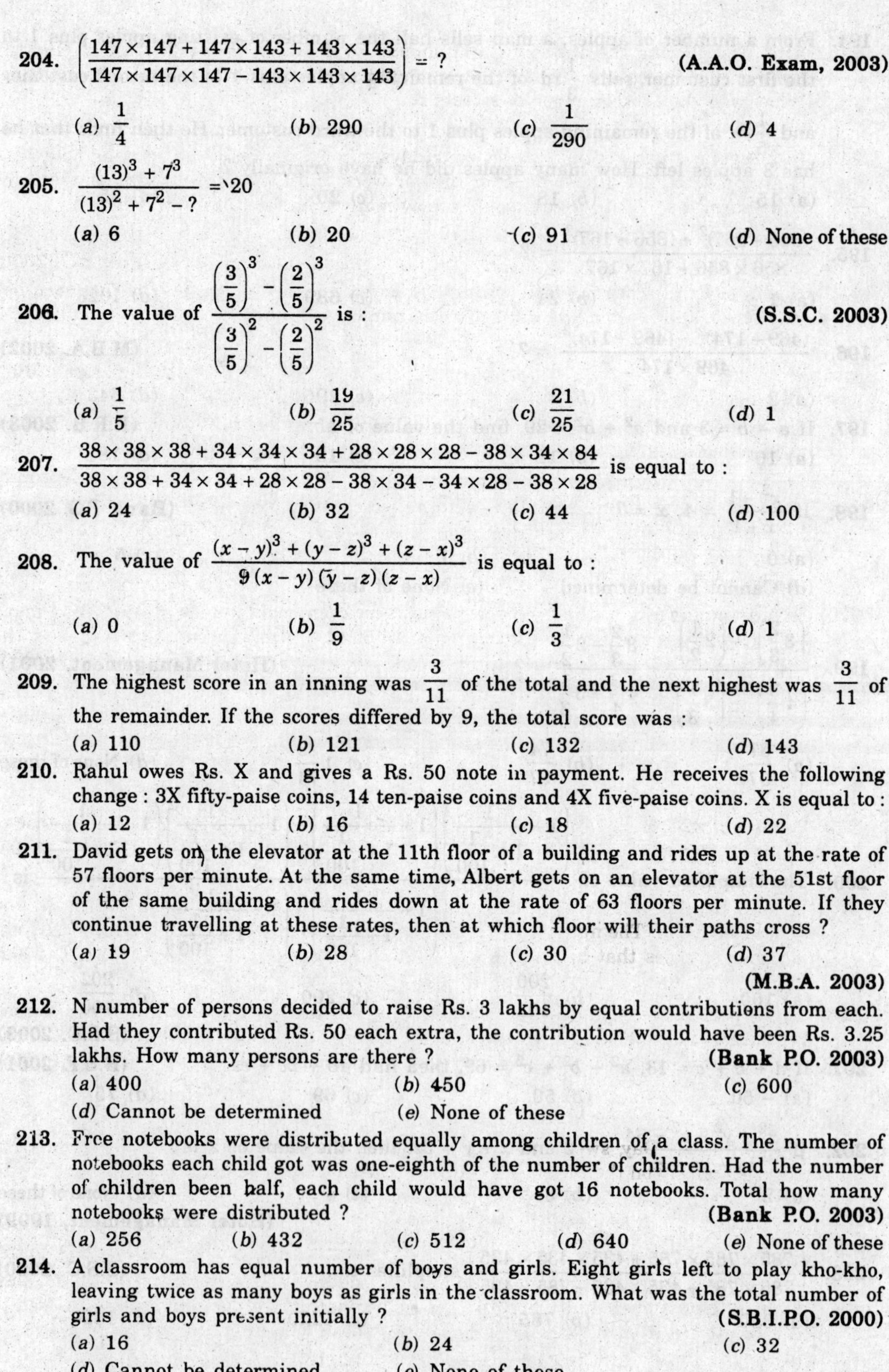

204. $\left(\dfrac{147 \times 147 + 147 \times 143 + 143 \times 143}{147 \times 147 \times 147 - 143 \times 143 \times 143}\right) = ?$ **(A.A.O. Exam, 2003)**

(*a*) $\frac{1}{4}$ (*b*) 290 (*c*) $\frac{1}{290}$ (*d*) 4

205. $\dfrac{(13)^3 + 7^3}{(13)^2 + 7^2 - ?} = 20$

(*a*) 6 (*b*) 20 (*c*) 91 (*d*) None of these

206. The value of $\dfrac{\left(\frac{3}{5}\right)^3 - \left(\frac{2}{5}\right)^3}{\left(\frac{3}{5}\right)^2 - \left(\frac{2}{5}\right)^2}$ is : **(S.S.C. 2003)**

(*a*) $\frac{1}{5}$ (*b*) $\frac{19}{25}$ (*c*) $\frac{21}{25}$ (*d*) 1

207. $\dfrac{38 \times 38 \times 38 + 34 \times 34 \times 34 + 28 \times 28 \times 28 - 38 \times 34 \times 84}{38 \times 38 + 34 \times 34 + 28 \times 28 - 38 \times 34 - 34 \times 28 - 38 \times 28}$ is equal to :

(*a*) 24 (*b*) 32 (*c*) 44 (*d*) 100

208. The value of $\dfrac{(x - y)^3 + (y - z)^3 + (z - x)^3}{9(x - y)(y - z)(z - x)}$ is equal to :

(*a*) 0 (*b*) $\frac{1}{9}$ (*c*) $\frac{1}{3}$ (*d*) 1

209. The highest score in an inning was $\frac{3}{11}$ of the total and the next highest was $\frac{3}{11}$ of the remainder. If the scores differed by 9, the total score was :

(*a*) 110 (*b*) 121 (*c*) 132 (*d*) 143

210. Rahul owes Rs. X and gives a Rs. 50 note in payment. He receives the following change : 3X fifty-paise coins, 14 ten-paise coins and 4X five-paise coins. X is equal to :

(*a*) 12 (*b*) 16 (*c*) 18 (*d*) 22

211. David gets on the elevator at the 11th floor of a building and rides up at the rate of 57 floors per minute. At the same time, Albert gets on an elevator at the 51st floor of the same building and rides down at the rate of 63 floors per minute. If they continue travelling at these rates, then at which floor will their paths cross ?

(*a*) 19 (*b*) 28 (*c*) 30 (*d*) 37

(M.B.A. 2003)

212. N number of persons decided to raise Rs. 3 lakhs by equal contributions from each. Had they contributed Rs. 50 each extra, the contribution would have been Rs. 3.25 lakhs. How many persons are there ? **(Bank P.O. 2003)**

(*a*) 400 (*b*) 450 (*c*) 600
(*d*) Cannot be determined (*e*) None of these

213. Free notebooks were distributed equally among children of a class. The number of notebooks each child got was one-eighth of the number of children. Had the number of children been half, each child would have got 16 notebooks. Total how many notebooks were distributed ? **(Bank P.O. 2003)**

(*a*) 256 (*b*) 432 (*c*) 512 (*d*) 640 (*e*) None of these

214. A classroom has equal number of boys and girls. Eight girls left to play kho-kho, leaving twice as many boys as girls in the classroom. What was the total number of girls and boys present initially ? **(S.B.I.P.O. 2000)**

(*a*) 16 (*b*) 24 (*c*) 32
(*d*) Cannot be determined (*e*) None of these

215. After distributing the sweets equally among 25 children, 8 sweets remain. Had the number of children been 28, 22 sweets would have been left after equally distributing. What was the total number of sweets ?

(*a*) 328 (*b*) 348 (*c*) 358 (*d*) Data inadequate

216. In a regular week, there are 5 working days and for each day, the working hours are 8. A man gets Rs. 2.40 per hour for regular work and Rs. 3.20 per hours for overtime. If he earns Rs. 432 in 4 weeks, then how many hours does he work for ?

(*a*) 160 (*b*) 175 (*c*) 180 (*d*) 195

(Bank P.O. 2003)

217. A sum of Rs. 312 was divided among 100 boys and girls in such a way that each boy gets Rs. 3.60 and each girl Rs. 2.40. The number of girls is :

(*a*) 35 (*b*) 40 (*c*) 60 (*d*) 65

(A.A.O. Exam, 2003)

218. Each boy contributed rupees equal to the number of girls and each girl contributed rupees equal to the number of boys in a class of 60 students. If the total contribution thus collected is Rs. 1600, how many boys are there in the class ?

(*a*) 25 (*b*) 30 (*c*) 50 (*d*) Data inadequate

219. A worker may claim Rs. 1.50 for each km which he travels by taxi and 50 p for each km he drives his own car. If in one week he claimed Rs. 50 for travelling 80 km, how many kms did he travel by taxi ?

(*a*) 10 (*b*) 20 (*c*) 30 (*d*) 40

220. In an examination, a student scores 4 marks for every correct answer and loses 1 mark for every wrong answer. If he attempts in all 60 questions and secures 130 marks, the number of questions he attempts correctly, is : **(L.I.C. A.A.O. 2003)**

(*a*) 35 (*b*) 38 (*c*) 40 (*d*) 42

221. A cricket team won 3 matches more than they lost. If a win gives them 2 points and loss (– 1) point, how many matches, in all, have they played if their score is 23 ?

(S.S.C. 2000)

(*a*) 17 (*b*) 20 (*c*) 37 (*d*) 40.

222. A total of 324 coins of 20 paise and 25 paise make a sum of Rs. 71. The number of 25-paise coins is : **(N.I.F.T. 2003)**

(*a*) 120 (*b*) 124 (*c*) 144 (*d*) 200

223. A man has Rs. 480 in the denominations of one-rupee notes, five-rupee notes and ten-rupee notes. The number of notes of each denomination is equal. What is the total number of notes that he has ? **(M.A.T. 2002)**

(*a*) 45 (*b*) 60 (*c*) 75 (*d*) 90

224. Eight people are planning to share equally the cost of a rental car. If one person withdraws from the arrangement and the others share equally the entire cost of the car, then the share of each of the remaining persons increased by : **(M.B.A. 2002)**

(*a*) $\frac{1}{7}$ (*b*) $\frac{1}{8}$ (*c*) $\frac{1}{9}$ (*d*) $\frac{7}{8}$

225. On Children's Day, sweets were to be equally distributed among 175 children in a school. Actually on the Children's Day, 35 children were absent and therefore each child got 4 sweets extra. Total how many sweets were available for distribution ?

(*a*) 2400 (*b*) 2480 (*c*) 2680 (*d*) 2750 (*e*) None of these

(Bank P.O. 2003)

226. A number of friends decided to go on a picnic and planned to spend Rs. 96 on eatables. Four of them, however, did not turn up. As a consequence, the remaining ones had to contribute Rs. 4 each extra. The number of those who attended the picnic was :

(*a*) 8 (*b*) 12 (*c*) 16 (*d*) 24

227. A certain number of tennis balls were purchased for Rs. 450. Five more balls could have been purchased in the same amount if each ball was cheaper by Rs. 15. The number of balls purchased was : **(Bank P.O. 1999)**

(*a*) 10 (*b*) 15 (*c*) 20 (*d*) 25

228. A piece of cloth costs Rs. 35. If the length of the piece would have been 4 m longer and each metre costs Re. 1 less, the cost would have remained unchanged. How long is the piece ?

(*a*) 9 m (*b*) 10 m (*c*) 12 m (*d*) 14 m

229. The price of 10 chairs is equal to that of 4 tables. The price of 15 chairs and 2 tables together is Rs. 4000. The total price of 12 chairs and 3 tables is : **(S.S.C. 2002)**

(*a*) Rs. 3500 (*b*) Rs. 3750 (*c*) Rs. 3840 (*d*) Rs. 3900

230. In a certain shop, 9 oranges cost as much as 5 apples, 5 apples cost as much as 3 mangoes and 4 mangoes cost as much as 9 lemons. If 3 lemons cost Rs. 4.80, the price of an orange is :

(*a*) Rs. 1.20 (*b*) Rs. 1.30 (*c*) Rs. 1.40 (*d*) Rs. 1.50

231. The price of 2 sarees and 4 shirts is Rs. 1600. With the same money one can buy 1 saree and 6 shirts. If one wants to buy 12 shirts, how much shall he have to pay ?

(*a*) Rs. 1200 (*b*) Rs. 2400 (*c*) Rs. 4800
(*d*) Cannot be determined (*e*) None of these **(Bank P.O. 2002)**

232. If 2 tables and 3 chairs cost Rs. 3500 and 3 tables and 2 chairs cost Rs. 4000, then how much does a table cost ? **(Hotel Management, 2003)**

(*a*) Rs. 500 (*b*) Rs. 750 (*c*) Rs. 1000 (*d*) Rs. 1500

233. The taxi charges in a city comprise of a fixed charge, together with the charge of the distance covered. For a journey of 16 km, the charges paid are Rs. 156 and for a journey of 24 km, the charges paid are Rs. 204. What will a person have to pay for travelling a distance of 30 km ?

(*a*) Rs. 236 (*b*) Rs. 240 (*c*) Rs. 248 (*d*) Rs. 252

234. In a classroom, if 6 students per bench are assigned to accommodate all students, one more bench will be required. However, if 7 students are accommodated per bench, there would be a space left for 5 students. What is the number of students in the class ?

(*a*) 30 (*b*) 42 (*c*) 72 (*d*) None of these

(S.S.C. 2000)

235. There are two examination rooms A and B. If 10 students are sent from A to B, then the number of students in each room is the same. If 20 candidates are sent from B to A, then the number of students in A is double the number of students in B. The number of students in room A is : **(M.A.T. 2002)**

(*a*) 20 (*b*) 80 (*c*) 100 (*d*) 200

236. In a group of buffaloes and ducks, the number of legs are 24 more than twice the number of heads. What is the number of buffaloes in the group ? **(R.R.B. 2002)**

(*a*) 6 (*b*) 8 (*c*) 10 (*d*) 12

237. A man has some hens and cows. If the number of heads be 48 and the number of feet equals 140, then the number of hens will be : **(R.R.B. 2003)**

(*a*) 22 (*b*) 23 (*c*) 24 (*d*) 26

238. Vidushi and Sanya distribute Rs. 100 each in charity. Vidushi distributes money to 5 more people than Sanya and Sanya gives each Re. 1 more than Vidushi. How many people are recipients of the charity ?

(*a*) 45 (*b*) 60 (*c*) 90 (*d*) None of these

ANSWERS

1. (c)	2. (e)	3. (b)	4. (d)	5. (a)	6. (a)	7. (a)	8. (c)
9. (a)	10. (a)	11. (d)	12. (c)	13. (e)	14. (c)	15. (c)	16. (c)
17. (c)	18. (d)	19. (c)	20. (a)	21. (c)	22. (b)	23. (d)	24. (c)
25. (a)	26. (d)	27. (b)	28. (c)	29. (d)	30. (c)	31. (b)	32. (a)
33. (c)	34. (d)	35. (d)	36. (e)	37. (e)	38. (a)	39. (d)	40. (a)
41. (b)	42. (d)	43. (a)	44. (d)	45. (a)	46. (c)	47. (e)	48. (b)
49. (a)	50. (e)	51. (c)	52. (b)	53. (a)	54. (a)	55. (a)	56. (d)
57. (a)	58. (c)	59. (d)	60. (d)	61. (b)	62. (d)	63. (b)	64. (b)
65. (c)	66. (d)	67. (d)	68. (a)	69. (c)	70. (c)	71. (a)	72. (b)
73. (c)	74. (c)	75. (b)	76. (c)	77. (a)	78. (c)	79. (c)	80. (d)
81. (a)	82. (c)	83. (d)	84. (a)	85. (c)	86. (c)	87. (d)	88. (b)
89. (c)	90. (b)	91. (c)	92. (c)	93. (b)	94. (c)	95. (c)	96. (b)
97. (c)	98. (b)	99. (c)	100. (b)	101. (d)	102. (a)	103. (c)	104. (d)
105. (d)	106. (c)	107. (b)	108. (d)	109. (b)	110. (b)	111. (b)	112. (d)
113. (b)	114. (c)	115. (d)	116. (c)	117. (a)	118. (a)	119. (c)	120. (e)
121. (b)	122. (d)	123. (c)	124. (c)	125. (a)	126. (c)	127. (d)	128. (b)
129. (b)	130. (b)	131. (d)	132. (a)	133. (a)	134. (b)	135. (d)	136. (b)
137. (a)	138. (b)	139. (b)	140. (d)	141. (a)	142. (c)	143. (b)	144. (a)
145. (a)	146. (c)	147. (d)	148. (c)	149. (c)	150. (c)	151. (d)	152. (d)
153. (b)	154. (b)	155. (b)	156. (d)	157. (b)	158. (d)	159. (c)	160. (c)
161. (c)	162. (c)	163. (c)	164. (c)	165. (a)	166. (c)	167. (a)	168. (c)
169. (c)	170. (c)	171. (c)	172. (d)	173. (c)	174. (b)	175. (b)	176. (c)
177. (b)	178. (c)	179. (b)	180. (b)	181. (a)	182. (c)	183. (a)	184. (d)
185. (c)	186. (c)	187. (b)	188. (d)	189. (a)	190. (a)	191. (c)	192. (b)
193. (a)	194. (c)	195. (b)	196. (b)	197. (a)	198. (c)	199. (b)	200. (b)
201. (b)	202. (c)	203. (c)	204. (a)	205. (c)	206. (b)	207. (d)	208. (c)
209. (b)	210. (c)	211. (c)	212. (e)	213. (c)	214. (c)	215. (c)	216. (b)
217. (b)	218. (d)	219. (a)	220. (b)	221. (c)	222. (b)	223. (d)	224. (a)
225. (e)	226. (b)	227. (a)	228. (b)	229. (d)	230. (a)	231. (b)	232. (c)
233. (b)	234. (c)	235. (c)	236. (d)	237. (d)	238. (a)		

SOLUTIONS

1. Given expression = 100 + 100 = 200.
2. Given expression = 9240 ÷ 28 = 330.
3. Given expression = $\frac{5004}{139} - 6 = 36 - 6 = 30$.
4. Given expression = 7500 + 25 = 7525.
5. Given expression = $\frac{8}{88} \times 8888088 = \frac{1}{11} \times 8888088 = 808008$.
6. Given expression = 1001 ÷ 143 = 7.
7. Given expression = $\frac{1260}{15} \div 7 = 84 \div 7 = 12$.
8. Given expression = $\left(5 \times 4 \times 2 \times \frac{1}{2} \times \frac{3}{4}\right) = 15$.

9. Let $\frac{11}{4} = \frac{77}{x}$. Then, $11x = 77 \times 4$ or $x = \left(\frac{77 \times 4}{11}\right) = 28$.

10. $2^5 \times 9^2 = 32 \times 81 = 2592$.

11. Given exp. $= 2 - [2 - \{2 - 2 \times 4\}] = 2 - [2 - \{2 - 8\}] = 2 - [2 - (-6)]$
$= 2 - [2 + 6] = 2 - 8 = -6$.

12. Given exp. $= 25 - 5\ [2 + 3\ \{2 - 2 \times 2 + 5\} - 10] \div 4$
$= 25 - 5\ [2 + 3\ \{2 - 4 + 5\} - 10] \div 4 = 25 - 5\ [2 + 3 \times 3 - 10] \div 4$
$= 25 - 5\ [2 + 9 - 10] \div 4 = 25 - 5 \div 4 = 25 - 1.25 = 23.75$.

13. Given exp. $= 260 \times 16 + 340 = 4160 + 340 = 4500$.

14. Given exp. $= 100 \times 10 - 100 + 20 = 1000 - 100 + 20 = 1020 - 100 = 920$.

15. Let $2\ x\ 6 - 12 \div 4 + 2 = 11$. Then, $2\ x\ 6 - 3 + 2 = 11 \Leftrightarrow 2\ x\ 6 = 11 + 3 - 2 = 12$.
So, x must be replaced by '$\times$'.

16. Let $45 - [28 - \{37 - (15 - x)\}] = 58$.
Then, $45 - [28 - \{37 - 15 + x\}] = 58 \Leftrightarrow 45 - [28 - \{22 + x\}] = 58$
$\Leftrightarrow 45 - [28 - 22 - x] = 58 \Leftrightarrow 45 - [6 - x] = 58 \Leftrightarrow 45 - 6 + x = 58$
$\Leftrightarrow 39 + x = 58 \Leftrightarrow x = 58 - 39 = 19$.

17. Given exp. $= \frac{24 \div 6}{4 + 4 + 4 + 1} = \frac{4}{13}$.

18. Given exp. $= \frac{4 + 72 - 6 - 8}{738 - 730} = \frac{76 - 14}{8} = \frac{62}{8} = 7.75$.

19. Given exp. $= \frac{2700 - 240}{1120 + 110} = \frac{2460}{1230} = 2$.

20. Let $\frac{128 \div 16 \times x - 7 \times 2}{7^2 - 8 \times 6 + x^2} = 1$.
Then, $8x - 7 \times 2 = 49 - 48 + x^2 \Leftrightarrow 8x - 14 = 1 + x^2 \Leftrightarrow x^2 - 8x + 15 = 0$
$\Leftrightarrow (x - 3)(x - 5) = 0 \Leftrightarrow x = 3$ or $x = 5$.

21. Given exp. $= 18 - [5 - \{6 + 2\ (7 - 3)\}] = 18 - [5 - \{6 + 2 \times 4\}]$
$= 18 - [5 - \{6 + 8\}] = 18 - [5 - 14] = 18 - [-9] = 18 + 9 = 27$.

22. Given exp. $= 1 \div \left[1 + 1 \div \left\{1 + 1 \div \left(1 + \frac{1}{2}\right)\right\}\right] = 1 \div \left[1 + 1 \div \left\{1 + 1 \div \frac{3}{2}\right\}\right]$
$= 1 \div \left[1 + 1 \div \left\{1 + 1 \times \frac{2}{3}\right\}\right] = 1 \div \left[1 + 1 \div \left\{1 + \frac{2}{3}\right\}\right]$
$= 1 \div \left[1 + 1 \div \frac{5}{3}\right] = 1 \div \left[1 + 1 \times \frac{3}{5}\right] = 1 \div \left[1 + \frac{3}{5}\right] = 1 \div \frac{8}{5} = 1 \times \frac{5}{8} = \frac{5}{8}$.

23. Given exp. $= \frac{8 - [5 - (-1)] \div 2}{|2| - |-3| + 3} = \frac{8 - [5 + 1] \div 2}{2 - 3 + 3} = \frac{8 - 6 \div 2}{2 - 1} = 8 - 3 = 5$.

24. $\frac{5}{3} + \frac{3}{4} = \frac{20 + 9}{12} = \frac{29}{12} = 2\frac{5}{12} < 5$; $\frac{7}{3} + \frac{11}{5} = \frac{35 + 33}{15} = \frac{68}{15} = 4\frac{8}{15} < 5$;
$\frac{11}{4} + \frac{8}{3} = \frac{33 + 32}{12} = \frac{65}{12} = 5\frac{5}{12} > 5$; $\frac{13}{5} + \frac{11}{6} = \frac{78 + 55}{30} = \frac{133}{30} = 4\frac{13}{30} < 5$.

25. Given exp. $= \frac{28 + 14 + 7 + 4 + 2 + 1}{28} = \frac{56}{28} = 2$.

26. Given exp. $= \frac{7}{4} + \frac{16}{3} + \frac{17}{5} = \frac{105 + 320 + 204}{60} = \frac{629}{60} = 10\frac{29}{60}$.

27. Given exp. $= \frac{41}{2} + \frac{91}{3} - \frac{91}{6} = \left(\frac{123 + 182}{6}\right) - \frac{91}{6} = \frac{305}{6} - \frac{91}{6} = \frac{214}{6} = \frac{107}{3} = 35\frac{2}{3}$.

28. Given exp. = – 1 + 4 + 3 = 6.

29. Given exp. = $\frac{1}{(7/3)}+\frac{1}{(7/4)}=\frac{3}{7}+\frac{4}{7}=\frac{7}{7}=1.$

30. Let $\frac{35}{6}-\frac{35}{9}-x=1.$

Then, $x=\frac{35}{6}-\frac{35}{9}-1=\frac{35}{6}-\left(\frac{35}{9}+1\right)=\frac{35}{6}-\frac{44}{9}=\frac{105-88}{18}=\frac{17}{18}.$

31. $\frac{1}{x}=4-\left(\frac{1}{3}+\frac{1}{2}\right)=4-\left(\frac{2+3}{6}\right)=4-\frac{5}{6}=\frac{24-5}{6}=\frac{19}{6}\Rightarrow x=\frac{6}{19}.$

32. Given exp. = $\frac{\left(-\frac{2}{3}-\frac{1}{3}\right)+\left(\frac{4}{5}+\frac{1}{5}\right)+\left(\frac{3}{4}-\frac{1}{2}\right)}{\left(\frac{2}{3}-\frac{4}{3}+\frac{1}{3}\right)-\left(\frac{1}{5}+\frac{4}{5}\right)+\frac{1}{2}}$

$=\frac{-1+1+\frac{1}{4}}{-\frac{1}{3}-1+\frac{1}{2}}=\frac{\frac{1}{4}}{\frac{-2-6+3}{6}}=\frac{\frac{1}{4}}{-\frac{5}{6}}=\frac{1}{4}\times\left(-\frac{6}{5}\right)=\frac{-3}{10}.$

33. Given exp. = $5-\left[\frac{3}{4}+\left\{\frac{5}{2}-\left(\frac{1}{2}+\frac{7-6}{42}\right)\right\}\right]=5-\left[\frac{3}{4}+\left\{\frac{5}{2}-\left(\frac{1}{2}+\frac{1}{42}\right)\right\}\right]$

$=5-\left[\frac{3}{4}+\left\{\frac{5}{2}-\frac{22}{42}\right\}\right]=5-\left[\frac{3}{4}+\frac{83}{42}\right]=5-\frac{229}{84}$

$=\left(\frac{420-229}{84}\right)=\frac{191}{84}=2\frac{23}{84}.$

34. $\frac{\left(\frac{1}{2}-\frac{1}{4}+\frac{1}{5}-\frac{1}{6}\right)}{\left(\frac{2}{5}-\frac{5}{9}+\frac{3}{5}-\frac{7}{18}\right)}=\frac{\left(\frac{30-15+12-10}{60}\right)}{\left(\frac{2}{5}+\frac{3}{5}\right)-\left(\frac{5}{9}+\frac{7}{18}\right)}=\frac{\left(\frac{17}{60}\right)}{1-\frac{17}{18}}=\left(\frac{17}{60}\times 18\right)=\frac{51}{10}=5\frac{1}{10}.$

35. $\left(34\times 4\frac{1}{2}\right)=34\times\left(4+\frac{1}{2}\right)=(34\times 4)+\left(34\times\frac{1}{2}\right)$

$=(30+4)\times 4+\left(34\times\frac{1}{2}\right)=(30\times 4)+(4\times 4)+\left(34\times\frac{1}{2}\right).$

36. Given exp. = $\left(\frac{3}{5}\times\frac{4}{7}\times\frac{5}{9}\times\frac{21}{24}\times 504\right)=84.$

37. Given exp. = $\left(\frac{41}{6}\times\frac{16}{3}+\frac{53}{3}\times\frac{9}{2}\right)=\left(\frac{328}{9}+\frac{159}{2}\right)=\frac{656+1431}{18}=\frac{2087}{18}=115\frac{17}{18}.$

38. Let $\frac{3}{8}$ of $168\times 15\div 5+x=549\div 9+235.$

Then, $63\times 15\div 5+x=61+235\Leftrightarrow 63\times 3+x=296$

$\Leftrightarrow 189+x=296\Leftrightarrow x=107.$

39. Let $\frac{5}{3}\div\frac{2}{7}\times\frac{x}{7}=\frac{5}{4}\times\frac{2}{3}\div\frac{1}{6}$. Then,

$\frac{5}{3}\times\frac{7}{2}\times\frac{x}{7}=\frac{5}{4}\times\frac{2}{3}\times 6\Leftrightarrow\frac{5}{6}x=5\Leftrightarrow x=\left(\frac{5\times 6}{5}\right)=6.$

40. Let $5\frac{2}{3} \div x\frac{5}{6} = 2$. Then, $\frac{17}{3} \div x\frac{5}{6} = 2 \Leftrightarrow x\frac{5}{6} = \frac{17}{3} \times \frac{1}{2} = \frac{17}{6} \Leftrightarrow x\frac{5}{6} = 2\frac{5}{6}$.

$\therefore \quad x = 2$.

41. Given equation is : $\frac{(5x+1)}{x} \times \frac{(4y+3)}{4} = 20 \Leftrightarrow (5x+1)(4y+3) = 80x \quad ...(i)$

Clearly, $x = 3$ and $y = 3$ satisfy (*i*).

42. Required difference $= \frac{19}{16} - \frac{16}{19} = \frac{19^2 - 16^2}{304} = \frac{(19+16)(19-16)}{304} = \frac{35 \times 3}{304} = \frac{105}{304}$.

43. Required number $= \frac{37\frac{1}{2}}{1/8} = \frac{75/2}{1/8} = \frac{75}{2} \times 8 = 300$.

44. Let x of $\frac{1}{12} = \frac{3}{8}$. Then, $\frac{x}{12} = \frac{3}{8} \Leftrightarrow x = \left(\frac{3}{8} \times 12\right) = \frac{9}{2}$.

45. Sum of given fractions $= \frac{7}{4} + \frac{5}{2} + \frac{67}{12} + \frac{10}{3} + \frac{9}{4} = \left(\frac{21+30+67+40+27}{12}\right) = \frac{185}{12}$.

The whole number just less than $\frac{185}{12}$ is 15.

Let $\frac{185}{12} - x = 15$. Then, $x = \left(\frac{185}{12} - 15\right) = \frac{5}{12}$.

46. Clearly, $\frac{x+1}{x}$ is the only fraction in which the numerator is greater than the denominator. So, it is the greatest fraction.

47. $\frac{3}{5}$ of $350 - \frac{4}{7}$ of $210 = 210 - 120 = 90$.

48. $\frac{6}{7/8} - \frac{6/7}{8} = 6 \times \frac{8}{7} - \frac{6}{7} \times \frac{1}{8} = \frac{48}{7} - \frac{6}{56} = \frac{384-6}{56} = \frac{378}{56} = \frac{27}{4} = 6\frac{3}{4}$.

49. Let the value of the estate be Rs. x.

Then, $\frac{4}{5}$ of $x = 16800 \Leftrightarrow x = \left(\frac{16800 \times 5}{4}\right) = 21000 \Leftrightarrow \frac{3}{7}x = \left(\frac{3}{7} \times 21000\right) = 9000$.

50. Let the number be x. Then,

$\frac{2}{5}$ of $\frac{1}{4}$ of $\frac{3}{7}$ of $x = 15 \Leftrightarrow x = \left(15 \times \frac{7}{3} \times 4 \times \frac{5}{2}\right) = 350 \Leftrightarrow \frac{1}{2}x = 175$.

51. Let the number be x. Then,

$\frac{1}{5}x - \frac{1}{7}x = 10 \Leftrightarrow \frac{7x - 5x}{35} = 10 \Leftrightarrow \frac{2x}{35} = 10 \Leftrightarrow x = \left(\frac{10 \times 35}{2}\right) = 175$.

52. $9 * 11 = 9^2 + (11)^2 - 9 \times 11 = 81 + 121 - 99 = 103$.

53. $(3 * -1) = \frac{3 \times (-1)}{3 + (-1)} = \frac{-3}{2}$. So, $3 * (3 * -1) = 3 * \left(\frac{-3}{2}\right) = \frac{3 \times \left(\frac{-3}{2}\right)}{3 + \left(\frac{-3}{2}\right)} = \frac{-9}{2} \times \frac{2}{3} = -3$.

54. $3 * 5 + 5 * 3 = (2 \times 3 - 3 \times 5 + 3 \times 5) + (2 \times 5 - 3 \times 3 + 5 \times 3)$

$= (6 + 10 - 9 + 15) = 22$.

55. $4 \oplus (3 \oplus p) = 4 \oplus (3^2 + 2p) = 4 \oplus (9 + 2p) = 4^2 + 2(9 + 2p) = 34 + 4p$.

$\therefore \quad 34 + 4p = 50 \Rightarrow 4p = 50 - 34 = 16 \Rightarrow p = 4$.

56. $(a * b * c) * a * b = \left(\frac{a+b}{c}\right) * a * b = \frac{\left(\frac{a+b}{c}\right)+a}{b} = \frac{a+b+ac}{bc}$.

57. Let the number be x. Then,

$\frac{5(x+7)}{9} - 3 = 12 \Leftrightarrow 5(x+7) - 27 = 108 \Leftrightarrow 5x + 35 = 135 \Leftrightarrow 5x = 100 \Leftrightarrow x = 20.$

58. Given exp. $= \left(\frac{5}{7} \times \frac{19}{13}\right) \div \left(\frac{19}{7} \times \frac{4}{13}\right) = \frac{5 \times 19}{7 \times 13} \times \frac{7 \times 13}{19 \times 4} = \frac{5}{4}$.

59. Given exp. $= \frac{11}{4} \div \frac{8}{3} \div \frac{13}{12} = \frac{11}{4} \times \frac{3}{8} \times \frac{12}{13} = \frac{99}{104}$.

60. Given exp. $= \frac{9}{2} \times \frac{13}{3} - \frac{25}{3} \div \frac{17}{3} = \frac{9}{2} \times \frac{13}{3} - \frac{25}{3} \times \frac{3}{17}$

$= \frac{39}{2} - \frac{25}{17} = \frac{663-50}{34} = \frac{613}{34} = 18\frac{1}{34}$.

61. Let $\frac{4335}{x} \div \frac{15}{8} = \frac{289}{528}$. Then,

$\frac{4335}{x} = \frac{289}{528} \times \frac{15}{8} \Leftrightarrow \frac{4335}{x} = \frac{289 \times 5}{176 \times 8} \Leftrightarrow x = \left(\frac{4335 \times 176 \times 8}{289 \times 5}\right) = 4224.$

$\therefore$ Missing digit = 2.

62. Let $\frac{16}{3} - \frac{11}{3} \div \frac{4}{3} \div x + \frac{16}{5} \div \frac{6}{5} = 7$. Then,

$\frac{16}{3} - \frac{11}{3} \times \frac{3}{4} \times \frac{1}{x} + \frac{16}{5} \times \frac{5}{6} = 7 \Leftrightarrow \frac{16}{3} - \frac{11}{4x} + \frac{8}{3} = 7 \Leftrightarrow \frac{24}{3} - \frac{11}{4x} = 7$

$\Leftrightarrow \frac{11}{4x} = 8 - 7 = 1 \Leftrightarrow 4x = 11 \Leftrightarrow x = \frac{11}{4} = 2\frac{3}{4}$.

63. Given exp. $= 9 - \frac{11}{9}$ of $\frac{36}{11} \div \frac{36}{7}$ of $\frac{7}{9} = 9 - 4 \div 4 = 9 - 1 = 8$.

64. Let $\frac{5}{6} \div \frac{6}{7} \times x - \frac{8}{9} \div \frac{8}{5} + \frac{3}{4} \times \frac{10}{3} = \frac{25}{9}$. Then

$\frac{5}{6} \times \frac{7}{6} \times x - \frac{8}{9} \times \frac{5}{8} + \frac{3}{4} \times \frac{10}{3} = \frac{25}{9} \Leftrightarrow \frac{35}{36}x - \frac{5}{9} + \frac{5}{2} = \frac{25}{9}$

$\Leftrightarrow \frac{35}{36}x = \frac{25}{9} + \frac{5}{9} - \frac{5}{2} = \frac{10}{3} - \frac{5}{2} \Leftrightarrow \frac{35}{36}x = \frac{5}{6} \Leftrightarrow x = \left(\frac{5}{6} \times \frac{36}{35}\right) = \frac{6}{7}$.

65. Given exp. $= \frac{3}{4} \div \frac{9}{4}$ of $\frac{2}{3} - \frac{\left(\frac{3-2}{6}\right)}{\left(\frac{3+2}{6}\right)} \times \frac{10}{3} + \frac{5}{6} = \frac{3}{4} \div \frac{3}{2} - \frac{1}{6} \times \frac{6}{5} \times \frac{10}{3} + \frac{5}{6}$

$= \frac{3}{4} \times \frac{2}{3} - \frac{2}{3} + \frac{5}{6} = \left(\frac{1}{2} - \frac{2}{3} + \frac{5}{6}\right) = \left(\frac{3-4+5}{6}\right) = \frac{4}{6} = \frac{2}{3}$.

66. $\frac{\frac{7}{3} + 1\frac{1}{2} \text{ of } \frac{5}{3}}{2 + 1\frac{2}{3}} = \frac{\frac{7}{3} + \frac{3}{2} \text{ of } \frac{5}{3}}{2 + \frac{5}{3}} = \frac{\frac{7}{3} + \frac{5}{2}}{\frac{11}{3}} = \frac{29}{6} \times \frac{3}{11} = \frac{29}{22}$.

$\therefore$ Required answer $= \frac{29}{22} - \frac{1}{4} = \frac{58-11}{44} = \frac{47}{44} = 1\frac{3}{44}$.

67. Given exp. $= \dfrac{\dfrac{1}{3}+\dfrac{3}{4}\left(\dfrac{6-5}{15}\right)}{\dfrac{5}{3} \text{ of } \dfrac{3}{4}-\dfrac{1}{5}} = \dfrac{\dfrac{1}{3}+\dfrac{3}{4}\times\dfrac{1}{15}}{\dfrac{5}{4}-\dfrac{1}{5}} = \dfrac{\dfrac{1}{3}+\dfrac{1}{20}}{\dfrac{25-4}{20}} = \dfrac{23}{60}\times\dfrac{20}{21} = \dfrac{23}{63}.$

68. Given exp. $= \dfrac{\dfrac{1}{3}\times 3\times\dfrac{1}{3}}{\dfrac{1}{3}\div\dfrac{1}{9}} - \dfrac{1}{9} = \dfrac{\dfrac{1}{3}}{\dfrac{1}{3}\times 9} - \dfrac{1}{9} = \dfrac{1}{3}\times\dfrac{1}{3}-\dfrac{1}{9} = \dfrac{1}{9}-\dfrac{1}{9} = 0.$

69. Given exp. $= \dfrac{\dfrac{1}{2}\div\dfrac{1}{4}}{\dfrac{1}{2}+\dfrac{1}{4}} = \dfrac{\dfrac{1}{2}\times 4}{\dfrac{2+1}{4}} = 2\times\dfrac{4}{3} = \dfrac{8}{3} = 2\dfrac{2}{3}.$

70. Given exp. $= \dfrac{\dfrac{13}{4}-\dfrac{4}{5} \text{ of } \dfrac{5}{6}}{\dfrac{13}{3}\div\dfrac{1}{5}-\left(\dfrac{3}{10}+\dfrac{106}{5}\right)} = \dfrac{\dfrac{13}{4}-\dfrac{2}{3}}{\dfrac{13}{3}\times 5-\dfrac{215}{10}} = \dfrac{\dfrac{31}{12}}{\dfrac{65}{3}-\dfrac{43}{2}} = \left(\dfrac{31}{12}\times 6\right) = \dfrac{31}{2} = 15\dfrac{1}{2}.$

71. Let $\dfrac{\dfrac{15}{2}-\dfrac{23}{4}}{\dfrac{7}{2}+x} \div \dfrac{\dfrac{1}{2}-\dfrac{5}{4}}{\dfrac{6}{5}+\dfrac{7}{2}} = \dfrac{6}{10}$. Then, $\left[\dfrac{7}{4}\times\dfrac{2}{(7+2x)}\right]\div\left[\dfrac{7}{4}\times\dfrac{10}{47}\right] = \dfrac{3}{5}$

$\Leftrightarrow \quad \dfrac{7}{2(7+2x)} = \dfrac{3}{5}\times\dfrac{7}{4}\times\dfrac{10}{47} = \dfrac{21}{94} \quad \Leftrightarrow \quad 7+2x = \left(\dfrac{7}{2}\times\dfrac{94}{21}\right) = \dfrac{47}{3}$

$\Leftrightarrow \quad 2x = \dfrac{47}{3}-7 = \dfrac{26}{3} \quad \Leftrightarrow \quad x = \left(\dfrac{26}{3}\times\dfrac{1}{2}\right) = \dfrac{13}{3} = 4\dfrac{1}{3}.$

72. Given exp. $= 3034-\left(\dfrac{1002}{2004}\times 100\right) = 3034-50 = 2984.$

73. Given exp. $= \dfrac{5241.6}{1872}+6.28 = 2.8+6.28 = 9.08.$

74. Let $\dfrac{58}{7}$ of $1568+265.75 = x+2455.60.$

Then, $12992+265.75 = x+2455.60$

$\Leftrightarrow \quad x = 12992+265.75-2455.60 = 13257.75-2455.60 = 10802.15.$

75. Given exp. $= 14.5+4.05+139.25 = 157.80.$

76. Let $8.25-4.20+2.8+\dfrac{4}{x}-2.32 = 5.33.$

Then, $\dfrac{4}{x} = (5.33+4.20+2.32)-(8.25+2.8) = 11.85-11.05 = 0.80 \Leftrightarrow x = \dfrac{4}{0.80} = \dfrac{40}{8} = 5.$

77. Given exp. $= 0.008\times 0.01\times 0.0072\div 0.000048$

$= 0.00008\times\dfrac{0.0072}{0.000048} = \dfrac{8}{48}\times\dfrac{72}{1000} = 0.012.$

78. Given exp. $= 2.375\times\dfrac{522}{87}-0.0285 = 2.375\times 6-0.0285 = 14.25-0.0285 = 14.2215.$

79. Given exp. $= 0.2+0.2-1\times 0.04 = 0.4-0.04 = 0.36.$

80. Given exp. $= 11.6+\dfrac{9280}{464}-\dfrac{28.28}{7} = 11.6+20-4.04 = 27.56.$

81. Given exp. $= 4.59\times\dfrac{18}{36}+0.6-0.2 = \dfrac{4.59}{2}+0.6-0.2 = 2.295+0.6-0.2 = 2.695.$

82. Let $\dfrac{64.4 - 34.7125}{6.25 \text{ of } x} = 1$. Then, 6.25 of $x = 29.6875$.

$\therefore \quad x = \dfrac{29.6875}{6.25} = \dfrac{2968.75}{625} = 4.75 = 4\dfrac{3}{4}$.

83. Given exp. $= 2.002 + 7.9 \{2.8 - 6.3 \times 2.1 + 15.6\}$
$= 2.002 + 7.9 \{2.8 - 13.23 + 15.6\} = 2.002 + 7.9 \times 5.17$
$= 2.002 + 40.843 = 42.845$.

84. Let $24 - [2.4 - \{.24 \times 2 - (.024 - x)\}] = 22.0584$.
Then, $24 - [2.4 - \{.48 - .024 + x\}] = 22.0584 \Leftrightarrow 24 - [2.4 - 0.456 - x] = 22.0584$
$\Leftrightarrow \quad 24 - 1.944 + x = 22.0584 \Leftrightarrow x = 22.0584 - 22.056 = 0.0024$.

85. Let $3 - \left[1.6 - \left\{3.2 - \left(3.2 + \dfrac{2.25}{x}\right)\right\}\right] = 0.65$.

Then, $3 - \left[1.6 - \left\{3.2 - 3.2 - \dfrac{2.25}{x}\right\}\right] = 0.65 \Leftrightarrow 3 - \left[1.6 + \dfrac{2.25}{x}\right] = 0.65$

$\Leftrightarrow \quad 3 - 1.6 - \dfrac{2.25}{x} = 0.65 \Leftrightarrow \dfrac{2.25}{x} = 1.4 - 0.65 \Leftrightarrow x = \dfrac{2.25}{0.75} = 3$.

86. Let $587.4 + 58.74 \times 2 - \dfrac{5.874}{x} = 702.744$.

Then, $\dfrac{5.874}{x} = 587.4 + 117.48 - 702.744 = 2.136 \Leftrightarrow x = \dfrac{5.874}{2.136} = \dfrac{5874}{2136} = \dfrac{11}{4} = 2\dfrac{3}{4}$.

$\therefore$ Missing digit = 3.

87. Let $54.27 - [12.84 - \{x - (6.82 - 1.85)\}] = 38.33$.
Then, $54.27 - [12.84 - \{x - 4.97\}] = 38.33$
$\Leftrightarrow \quad 54.27 - [12.84 - x + 4.97] = 38.33 \Leftrightarrow 54.27 - [17.81 - x] = 38.33$
$\Leftrightarrow \quad 54.27 - 17.81 + x = 38.33 \Leftrightarrow x = 38.33 - 36.46 = 1.87$.

88. Let $\dfrac{20}{3}$ of $\dfrac{726}{100} \div \dfrac{45}{100}$ of $x = \dfrac{968}{117}$.

Then, $\dfrac{242}{5} \div \dfrac{45x}{100} = \dfrac{968}{117} \Leftrightarrow \dfrac{242}{5} \times \dfrac{100}{45x} = \dfrac{968}{117} \Leftrightarrow x = \dfrac{242}{5} \times \dfrac{100}{45} \times \dfrac{117}{968} = 13$.

89. $\dfrac{P+Q}{P-Q} = \dfrac{\dfrac{P}{Q}+1}{\dfrac{P}{Q}-1} = \dfrac{7+1}{7-1} = \dfrac{8}{6} = \dfrac{4}{3}$.

90. $\left(\dfrac{4}{7} + \dfrac{2y-x}{2y+x}\right) = \left(\dfrac{4}{7} + \dfrac{2-\dfrac{x}{y}}{2+\dfrac{x}{y}}\right) = \dfrac{4}{7} + \dfrac{2-\dfrac{4}{5}}{2+\dfrac{4}{5}} = \dfrac{4}{7} + \dfrac{(6/5)}{(14/5)} = \dfrac{4}{7} + \left(\dfrac{6}{5} \times \dfrac{5}{14}\right) = \dfrac{4}{7} + \dfrac{3}{7} = \dfrac{7}{7} = 1$.

91. $\dfrac{6a+4b}{6a-5b} = \dfrac{6\left(\dfrac{a}{b}\right)+4}{6\left(\dfrac{a}{b}\right)-5} = \dfrac{6 \times \dfrac{4}{3} + 4}{6 \times \dfrac{4}{3} - 5} = \dfrac{8+4}{8-5} = \dfrac{12}{3} = 4$.

92. $\dfrac{x}{2y} = \dfrac{6}{7} \Rightarrow \dfrac{x}{y} = \left(2 \times \dfrac{6}{7}\right) = \dfrac{12}{7}$.

$$\therefore \quad \frac{x-y}{x+y}+\frac{14}{19}=\frac{\frac{x}{y}-1}{\frac{x}{y}+1}+\frac{14}{19}=\frac{\frac{12}{7}-1}{\frac{12}{7}+1}+\frac{14}{19}=\frac{(5/7)}{(19/7)}+\frac{14}{19}$$

$$=\left(\frac{5}{7}\times\frac{7}{19}\right)+\frac{14}{19}=\frac{5}{19}+\frac{14}{19}=\frac{19}{19}=1.$$

93. $\frac{a}{b}=\frac{4}{5}$ and $\frac{b}{c}=\frac{15}{16} \Rightarrow \left(\frac{a}{b}\times\frac{b}{c}\right)=\left(\frac{4}{5}\times\frac{15}{16}\right) \Rightarrow \frac{a}{c}=\frac{3}{4}.$

$$\therefore \quad \frac{c^2-a^2}{c^2+a^2}=\frac{1-\left(\frac{a^2}{c^2}\right)}{1+\left(\frac{a^2}{c^2}\right)}=\frac{1-\left(\frac{a}{c}\right)^2}{1+\left(\frac{a}{c}\right)^2}=\frac{1-\frac{9}{16}}{1+\frac{9}{16}}=\frac{(7/16)}{(25/16)}=\frac{7}{25}.$$

94. $(a-b)-(c+d)=6$ and $(c-d)-(a+b)=3$

$\Rightarrow \ (a-c)-(b+d)=6$ and $(c-a)-(b+d)=3$

$\Rightarrow \ (b+d)=(a-c)-6$ and $(b+d)=(c-a)-3$

$\Rightarrow \ (a-c)-6=(c-a)-3 \Rightarrow 2(a-c)=3 \Rightarrow (a-c)=\frac{3}{2}=1.5.$

95. $x=\frac{a}{a-1}=1+\frac{1}{a-1}=1+y. \quad \therefore \ x>y.$

96. a is positive and $a<1 \Rightarrow \frac{1}{a}>1. \quad \therefore \ \left(a+\frac{1}{a}\right)>2.$

97. $\frac{a}{x}+\frac{y}{b}=1 \Rightarrow \frac{a}{x}=1-\frac{y}{b}=\frac{b-y}{b} \Rightarrow \frac{x}{a}=\frac{b}{b-y}.$

$\frac{b}{y}+\frac{z}{c}=1 \Rightarrow \frac{z}{c}=1-\frac{b}{y}=\frac{y-b}{y} \Rightarrow \frac{c}{z}=\frac{y}{y-b}=\frac{-y}{(b-y)}.$

$$\therefore \quad \frac{x}{a}+\frac{c}{z}=\frac{b}{(b-y)}-\frac{y}{(b-y)}=\frac{(b-y)}{(b-y)}=1.$$

98. $a^2+b^2=45$ ...(*i*) and $b^2+c^2=40$ ...(*ii*)

Subtracting, we get : $a^2-c^2=5 \Rightarrow (a+c)(a-c)=5.$

$\therefore \ (a+c)=5$ and $(a-c)=1.$

Solving, we get : $a=3, c=2$. Putting $c=2$ in (*ii*), we get $b=6$.

99. $\frac{a}{3}=\frac{b}{4}=\frac{c}{7}=k$ (say). Then, $a=3k, b=4k, c=7k.$

$$\therefore \quad \frac{a+b+c}{c}=\frac{3k+4k+7k}{7k}=\frac{14k}{7k}=2.$$

100. $3x+7=7x+5 \Rightarrow 7x-3x=2 \Rightarrow 4x=2 \Rightarrow x=\frac{1}{2}.$

Now, $3x+7=x^2+\text{P} \Rightarrow \frac{3}{2}+7=\frac{1}{4}+\text{P} \Rightarrow \text{P}=\frac{17}{2}-\frac{1}{4}=\frac{33}{4}=8\frac{1}{4}.$

101. $\frac{2a+b}{a+4b}=3 \Rightarrow 2a+b=3(a+4b) \Rightarrow a=-11b.$

$$\therefore \quad \frac{a+b}{a+2b}=\frac{-11b+b}{-11b+2b}=\frac{-10b}{-9b}=\frac{10}{9}.$$

102. $(2a + 3b)(2c - 3d) = (2a - 3b)(2c + 3d)$

$$\Rightarrow \frac{(2a+3b)}{(2a-3b)} = \frac{(2c+3d)}{(2c-3d)} \Rightarrow \frac{2\left(\frac{a}{b}\right)+1}{2\left(\frac{a}{b}\right)-1} = \frac{2\left(\frac{c}{d}\right)+1}{2\left(\frac{c}{d}\right)-1} \Rightarrow \frac{a}{b} = \frac{c}{d}.$$

103. $(a + b + 2c + 3d)(a - b - 2c + 3d) = (a - b + 2c - 3d)(a + b - 2c - 3d)$

$\Rightarrow [(a + b) + (2c + 3d)]\,[(a - b) - (2c - 3d)]$

$= [(a - b) + (2c - 3d)]\,[(a + b) - (2c + 3d)]$

$\Rightarrow (a + b)(a - b) - (a + b)(2c - 3d) + (a - b)(2c + 3d) - (2c + 3d)(2c - 3d)$

$= (a - b)(a + b) - (a - b)(2c + 3d) + (a + b)(2c - 3d) - (2c + 3d)(2c - 3d)$

$\Rightarrow (a + b)(2c - 3d) = (a - b)(2c + 3d)$

$\Rightarrow 2ac - 3ad + 2bc - 3bd = 2ac + 3ad - 2bc - 3bd$

$\Rightarrow 4bc = 6ad \Rightarrow 2bc = 3ad.$

104. Given exp. $= \dfrac{1}{2+\dfrac{1}{2+\dfrac{1}{(3/2)}}} = \dfrac{1}{2+\dfrac{1}{2+\dfrac{2}{3}}} = \dfrac{1}{2+\dfrac{1}{(8/3)}} = \dfrac{1}{2+\dfrac{3}{8}} = \dfrac{1}{(19/8)} = \dfrac{8}{19}.$

105. $x = 2-\dfrac{1}{1+\dfrac{1}{(13/4)}} = 2-\dfrac{1}{1+\dfrac{4}{13}} = 2-\dfrac{1}{(17/13)} = 2-\dfrac{13}{17} = \dfrac{21}{17}.$

106. $x = \dfrac{2+\dfrac{1}{(19/5)}}{2+\dfrac{1}{3+\dfrac{1}{(5/4)}}} = \dfrac{2+\dfrac{5}{19}}{2+\dfrac{1}{3+\dfrac{4}{5}}} = \dfrac{2+\dfrac{5}{19}}{2+\dfrac{1}{(19/5)}} = \dfrac{2+\dfrac{5}{19}}{2+\dfrac{5}{19}} = 1.$

107. Given exp. $= 8-8\times\dfrac{\dfrac{11}{5}-\dfrac{9}{7}}{2-\dfrac{1}{(35/6)}} = 8-8\times\dfrac{\dfrac{32}{35}}{2-\dfrac{6}{35}} = 8-8\times\dfrac{32}{35}\times\dfrac{35}{64} = 8-4 = 4.$

108. Given exp. $= \dfrac{2}{2+\dfrac{2}{3+\dfrac{2}{(11/3)}}\times 0.39} = \dfrac{2}{2+\dfrac{2}{3+\dfrac{6}{11}}\times 0.39} = \dfrac{2}{2+\dfrac{2}{(39/11)}\times 0.39}$

$= \dfrac{2}{2+\dfrac{22}{39}\times\dfrac{39}{100}} = \dfrac{2}{2+\dfrac{22}{100}} = \dfrac{2}{2+\dfrac{11}{50}} = \dfrac{2}{(111/50)} = \dfrac{100}{111}.$

109. Given exp. $= \dfrac{1}{1+\dfrac{\dfrac{2}{3}}{\dfrac{5}{3}+\dfrac{\dfrac{8}{9}}{(1/3)}}} = \dfrac{1}{1+\dfrac{2/3}{\dfrac{5}{3}+\dfrac{8}{9}\times 3}} = \dfrac{1}{1+\dfrac{2/3}{(13/3)}} = \dfrac{1}{1+\dfrac{2}{13}} = \dfrac{13}{15}.$

110. $2+\dfrac{1}{x+\dfrac{1}{y+\dfrac{1}{z}}} = \dfrac{37}{13} = 2\dfrac{11}{13} = 2+\dfrac{11}{13} \Rightarrow \dfrac{1}{x+\dfrac{1}{y+\dfrac{1}{z}}} = \dfrac{11}{13} \Rightarrow x+\dfrac{1}{y+\dfrac{1}{z}} = \dfrac{13}{11}$

$\Rightarrow x+\dfrac{1}{y+\dfrac{1}{z}} = 1+\dfrac{2}{11} \Rightarrow x = 1,\ y+\dfrac{1}{z} = \dfrac{11}{2} = 5\dfrac{1}{2} = 5+\dfrac{1}{2} \Rightarrow x = 1,\ y = 5,\ z = 2.$

111. $x = y \Leftrightarrow 1 - q = 2q + 1 \Leftrightarrow 3q = 0 \Leftrightarrow q = 0.$

112. $\frac{x}{5} - \frac{x}{6} = 4 \Leftrightarrow \frac{6x - 5x}{30} = 4 \Leftrightarrow x = 120.$

113. $\frac{3x}{2y} = \frac{21}{22} \Rightarrow \frac{x}{y} = \left(\frac{21}{22} \times \frac{2}{3}\right) = \frac{7}{11} \Rightarrow x = \frac{7}{11}y.$

$4x + 5y = 83 \Rightarrow 4 \times \frac{7}{11}y + 5y = 83 \Rightarrow \frac{28}{11}y + 5y = 83 \Rightarrow 83y = 83 \times 11 \Rightarrow y = 11.$

$\therefore \quad x = \frac{7}{11}y = \left(\frac{7}{11} \times 11\right) = 7.$

So, $y - x = 11 - 7 = 4.$

114. $3x + y = 19$ ...(*i*) and $x - y = 9$ ...(*ii*)

Adding (*i*) and (*ii*), we get : $4x = 28$ or $x = 7$. Putting $x = 7$ in (*i*), we get : $y = -2$.

115. $a + b = 5$ ...(*i*) and $3a + 2b = 20$ ...(*ii*)

Multiplying (*i*) by 2 and subtracting from (*ii*), we get : $a = 10$.

Putting $a = 10$ in (*i*), we get : $b = -5$.

$\therefore \quad (3a + b) = 3 \times 10 + (-5) = 30 - 5 = 25.$

116. $(2p + 3q) + (2p - q) = 18 + 2 \Rightarrow 4p + 2q = 20 \Rightarrow 2(2p + q) = 20$

$\Rightarrow 2p + q = 10.$

117. $2x + y = 5$ ...(*i*) and $3x - 4y = 2$ ...(*ii*)

Multiplying (*i*) by 4 and adding (*ii*) to it, we get : $11x = 22$ or $x = 2$.

Putting $x = 2$ in (*i*), we get : $y = 1$. So, $2xy = 2 \times 2 \times 1 = 4$.

118. $3x - 5y = 5$ ...(*i*) and $\frac{x}{x + y} = \frac{5}{7} \Rightarrow 7x = 5x + 5y \Rightarrow 2x - 5y = 0$ ...(*ii*)

Subtracting (*ii*) from (*i*), we get : $x = 5$.

Putting $x = 5$ in (*i*), we get : $y = 2$. So, $x - y = 5 - 2 = 3$.

119. $4x + 3y = 18xy$ ...(*i*) and $2x - 5y = -4xy$ ...(*ii*)

Dividing (*i*) and (*ii*) by xy, we get : $\frac{3}{x} + \frac{4}{y} = 18$ ...(*iii*) and $\frac{5}{x} - \frac{2}{y} = 4$ ...(*iv*)

Multiplying (*iv*) by 2 and adding (*iii*) to it, we get : $\frac{13}{x} = 26$ or $x = \frac{1}{2}$.

Putting $x = \frac{1}{2}$ in (*iii*), we get : $y = \frac{1}{3}$.

120. $2x + y = 17$ ...(*i*) ; $y + 2z = 15$ ...(*ii*) and $x + y = 9$ ...(*iii*)

Subtracting (*iii*) from (*i*), we get : $x = 8$.

Putting $x = 8$ in (*i*), we get : $y = 1$. Putting $y = 1$ in (*ii*), we get : $2z = 14$ or $z = 7$.

$\therefore \quad 4x + 3y + z = 4 \times 8 + 3 \times 1 + 7 = 42.$

121. $3x - 4y + z = 7$ ...(*i*) ; $2x + 3y - z = 19$ ...(*ii*) and $x + 2y + 2z = 24$ ...(*iii*)

Adding (*i*) and (*ii*), we get ; $5x - y = 26$ ...(*iv*)

Subtracting (*i*) from (*ii*) and adding to (*iii*), we get : $9y = 36$ or $y = 4$.

Putting $y = 4$ in (*iv*), we get : $5x = 30$ or $x = 6$.

Putting $x = 6$, $y = 4$ in (*iii*), we get : $2z = 10$ or $z = 5$.

122. $2x + y = 15$ ...(*i*) ; $2y + z = 25$ ...(*ii*) and $2z + x = 26$ ...(*iii*)

Adding (*i*), (*ii*) and (*iii*), we get : $3(x + y + z) = 66$ or $x + y + z = 22$ ...(*iv*)

From (*ii*), we have : $y = \frac{25 - z}{2}$. From (*iii*), we have : $x = 26 - 2z$.

$\therefore \quad (26 - 2z) + \left(\frac{25 - z}{2}\right) + z = 22 \Leftrightarrow 77 - 3z = 44 \Leftrightarrow 3z = 33 \Leftrightarrow z = 11.$

123. $2x + 3y = 31$ ...(*i*) ; $y - z = 4$ ...(*ii*) and $x + 2z = 11$ ...(*iii*)
Multiplying (*iii*) by 2 and subtracting from (*i*), we get : $3y - 4z = 9$ ...(*iv*)
Solving (*ii*) and (*iv*), we get : $y = 7$, $z = 3$. Putting $y = 7$ in (*i*), we get : $x = 5$.
$\therefore$ $x + y + z = (5 + 7 + 3) = 15$.

124. Given exp. $= \left(\frac{3}{4} \times \frac{4}{3} \times \frac{5}{3} \times \frac{3}{5} \times \frac{13}{7} \times \frac{1}{13}\right) = \frac{1}{7}$.

125. Given exp. $= \frac{1}{2} \times \frac{2}{3} \times \frac{3}{4} \times \ldots\ldots \times \frac{(n-1)}{n} = \frac{1}{n}$.

126. Given exp. $= \frac{3}{2} \times \frac{4}{3} \times \frac{5}{4} \times \ldots\ldots \times \frac{121}{120} = \frac{121}{2} = 60.5$.

127. Given exp. $= \frac{5}{3} \times \frac{7}{5} \times \frac{9}{7} \times \ldots\ldots \times \frac{1003}{1001} = \frac{1003}{3}$.

128. Given exp. $= \left(1 - \frac{1}{2}\right) + \left(\frac{1}{2} - \frac{1}{3}\right) + \left(\frac{1}{3} - \frac{1}{4}\right) + \left(\frac{1}{4} - \frac{1}{5}\right) + \ldots\ldots + \left(\frac{1}{11} - \frac{1}{12}\right) = \left(1 - \frac{1}{12}\right) = \frac{11}{12}$.

129. Clearly, sum of first 6 terms is zero. So, sum of first 30 terms = 0.
$\therefore$ Required sum $= \left(\frac{1}{2} + \frac{1}{3} - \frac{1}{4} - \frac{1}{2} - \frac{1}{3}\right) = -\frac{1}{4}$.

130. Given exp. $= \left(1000 - \frac{4}{999}\right) \times 999 = 999000 - 4 = 998996$.

131. Given exp.

$$= \left(1000 - \frac{6}{7}\right) + \left(1000 - \frac{5}{7}\right) + \left(1000 - \frac{4}{7}\right) + \left(1000 - \frac{3}{7}\right) + \left(1000 - \frac{2}{7}\right) + \left(1000 - \frac{1}{7}\right)$$

$$= 6000 - \left(\frac{6}{7} + \frac{5}{7} + \frac{4}{7} + \frac{3}{7} + \frac{2}{7} + \frac{1}{7}\right) = 6000 - \frac{21}{7} = 6000 - 3 = 5997.$$

132. Given exp. $= \frac{4 \times 3^3 + 3^2 + 3 + 1}{4 \times 3^3} = \frac{108 + 9 + 3 + 1}{108} = \frac{121}{108}$.

133. Given exp. $= \frac{4 \cdot 5 \cdot 6 + 5 \cdot 6 + 2 \cdot 6 + 2 \cdot 3}{1 \cdot 2 \cdot 3 \cdot 4 \cdot 5 \cdot 6} = \frac{120 + 30 + 12 + 6}{720} = \frac{168}{720} = \frac{7}{30}$.

134. Given exp. $= \left(\frac{1}{1^2} - \frac{1}{2^2}\right) + \left(\frac{1}{2^2} - \frac{1}{3^2}\right) + \left(\frac{1}{3^2} - \frac{1}{4^2}\right) + \left(\frac{1}{4^2} - \frac{1}{5^2}\right) + \ldots\ldots + \left(\frac{1}{9^2} - \frac{1}{10^2}\right)$

$$= \left(\frac{1}{1^2} - \frac{1}{10^2}\right) = \left(1 - \frac{1}{100}\right) = \frac{99}{100}.$$

135. Number of pieces $= \left(\frac{42.5 \times 100}{85}\right) = \frac{4250}{85} = 50$.

136. Income after 1 year = Rs. (4×2^1) lakhs.
Income after 2 years = Rs. $(4 \times 2 \times 2)$ lakhs = Rs. (4×2^2) lakhs
$\therefore$ Income after 5 years = Rs. (4×2^5) lakhs = Rs. 128 lakhs = Rs. 1.28 crores.

137. Total number of children $= (30 \times 16) = 480$.
$\therefore$ Number of columns of 24 children each $= \left(\frac{480}{24}\right) = 20$.

138. Original number of sections $= (16 - 3) = 13$.
Original number of students $= (24 \times 13) = 312$.
Present number of students $= (21 \times 16) = 336$.
Number of new students admitted $= (336 - 312) = 24$.

139. Time between 10 a.m. and 13.27 hours = 3 hrs. 27 min. = 207 min.
For three periods in between free time = 15 min.
Remaining time = (207 − 15) min. = 192 min.

$\therefore$ Duration of each of the 4 periods = $\left(\frac{192}{4}\right)$ min. = 48 min.

140.

	Hrs.	Min.	Sec.
	3	17	49
(−)	1	54	50
	1	22	59

Total time = (1 × 60 + 22) min. + 59 sec. = (82 × 60 + 59) sec. = 4979 sec.

$\therefore$ Number of times the light is seen = $\left(\frac{4979}{13}+1\right)$ = 384.

141. Money earned in 2 days = Rs. (20 − 15) = Rs. 5.

Money earned in 16 days = Rs. $\left(\frac{5}{2}\times 16\right)$ = Rs. 40.

On 17th day, money in hand = Rs. (40 + 20) = Rs. 60.

142. Required cost = Rs. $[1000 \times x + (z - 1000) \times y]$ = Rs. $(1000x + zy - 1000y)$
= Rs. $[1000\,(x - y) + yz]$.

143. 26 trees have 25 gaps between them. Hence, required distance = $\left(\frac{225}{25}\right)$ m = 9 m.

144. Let the number be x. Then, $52x - 25x = 324 \Leftrightarrow 27x = 324 \Leftrightarrow x = 12$.

145. Among the given numbers, only 60489 is a multiple of 423.

146. Let the monthly salary of a man be Rs. x.
Then, monthly salary of a woman = Rs. $(x + 500)$.

$\therefore\ 4x + 2\,(x + 500) = 46000 \Leftrightarrow 6x = 45000 \Leftrightarrow x = 7500.$

Monthly salary of a woman = $x + 500$ = Rs. 8000.

147. Let marks in History = x. Then, marks in English = $\frac{5}{2}x$.

$\therefore\ x + \frac{5}{2}x = 140 \Leftrightarrow \frac{7}{2}x = 140 \Leftrightarrow x = \left(\frac{140\times 2}{7}\right) = 40.$

Hence, marks in English = $\frac{5}{2}x = \left(\frac{5}{2}\times 40\right) = 100$.

148. Let the number of pineapples and watermelons be x and y respectively.

Then, $7x + 5y = 38$ or $5y = (38 - 7x)$ or $y = \frac{38 - 7x}{5}$.

Clearly, y is a whole number, only when $(38 - 7x)$ is divisible by 5. This happens when $x = 4$.

149. Let number of boys = x. Then, number of girls = $5x$.
Total number of children = $(x + 5x) = 6x$.
Thus, the total number of children must be a multiple of 6.

150. Let F and C denote the temperatures in Fahrenheit and Celsius respectively.

Then, $\frac{F - 32}{212 - 32} = \frac{C - 0}{100 - 0} \Leftrightarrow \frac{F - 32}{180} = \frac{C}{100}$.

If C = 35, then F = $\left(\frac{35}{100}\times 180\right) + 32 = 63 + 32 = 95$.

151. Let D's share = Rs. x. Then, C's share = Rs. x.
B's share = Rs. $(x + 125)$. A's share = Rs. $(x + x + 125)$ = Rs. $(2x + 125)$
$\therefore \quad (2x + 125) + (x + 125) + x + x = 750 \Leftrightarrow 5x = 500 \Leftrightarrow x = 100.$
Hence, A's share = $2x + 125$ = Rs. $(2 \times 100 + 125)$ = Rs. 325.

152. Let Gagan's share = Rs. x.
Then, Sachin's share = Rs. $\left(\frac{x}{5}\right)$ and Rohit's share = Rs. $\left(\frac{2x}{5}\right)$.
$\therefore \quad \frac{2x}{5} + \frac{x}{5} + x = 1000 \Leftrightarrow 8x = 5000 \Leftrightarrow x = 625.$

153. Total number of digits = (No. of digits in 1-digit page nos. + No. of digits in 2-digit page nos. + No. of digits in 3-digit page nos.)
$= (1 \times 9 + 2 \times 90 + 3 \times 267) = (9 + 180 + 801) = 990.$

154. No. of digits in 1-digit page nos. = $1 \times 9 = 9$.
No. of digits in 2-digit page nos. = $2 \times 90 = 180$.
No. of digits in 3-digit page nos. = $3 \times 900 = 2700$.
No. of digits in 4-digit page nos. = $3189 - (9 + 180 + 2700) = 3189 - 2889 = 300.$
$\therefore$ No. of pages with 4-digit page nos. = $\left(\frac{300}{4}\right) = 75.$
Hence, total number of pages = $(999 + 75) = 1074$

155. Each row contains 12 plants.
Leaving 2 corner plants, 10 plants in between have (10×2) metres and 1 metre on each side is left.
$\therefore$ Length = $(20 + 2)$ m = 22 m.

156. Required fraction $= \frac{1 \text{ sec.}}{1 \text{ hr.}} = \frac{1 \text{ sec.}}{(1 \times 60 \times 60) \text{ sec.}} = \frac{1}{3600}.$

157. Height at the third bounce $= \left[32 \times \left(\frac{3}{4}\right)^3\right] \text{m} = \left(32 \times \frac{27}{64}\right) \text{m} = \frac{27}{2} \text{ m} = 13\frac{1}{2} \text{ m}.$

158. Suppose Sanket earns Rs. x in each of the other eleven months.
Then, Sanket's earning in March = Rs. $(2x)$.
Sanket's annual earning = Rs. $(11x + 2x)$ = Rs. $(13x)$.
$\therefore$ Required fraction $= \frac{2x}{13x} = \frac{2}{13}.$

159. Let the capacity of the tank be x litres. Then, $\frac{1}{3}x = 80 \Leftrightarrow x = 240 \Leftrightarrow \frac{1}{2}x = 120.$

160. Distance travelled on foot $= \left[\frac{7}{2} - \left(\frac{5}{3} + \frac{7}{6}\right)\right] \text{km} = \left(\frac{7}{2} - \frac{17}{6}\right) \text{km} = \frac{2}{3} \text{ km}$
$\therefore$ Required fraction $= \frac{(2/3)}{(7/2)} = \left(\frac{2}{3} \times \frac{2}{7}\right) = \frac{4}{21}.$

161. Let the required fraction be x. Then,
$\frac{4}{7}x + \frac{4}{7} = \frac{15}{14} \Leftrightarrow \frac{4}{7}x = \left(\frac{15}{14} - \frac{4}{7}\right) = \frac{7}{14} = \frac{1}{2} \Leftrightarrow x = \left(\frac{1}{2} \times \frac{7}{4}\right) = \frac{7}{8}$

162. Required fraction $= \dfrac{\frac{2}{3} \text{ of } \frac{1}{4} \text{ of Rs. } 25.20}{\frac{3}{2} \text{ of Rs. } 36} = \frac{\text{Rs. } 4.20}{\text{Rs. } 54} = \frac{42}{540} = \frac{7}{90}.$

163. Let the length of longer piece be x cm. Then, length of shorter piece $= \left(\frac{2}{5}x\right)$ cm.

$\therefore \; x + \frac{2}{5}x = 70 \Leftrightarrow \frac{7x}{5} = 70 \Leftrightarrow x = \left(\frac{70 \times 5}{7}\right) = 50.$

Hence, length of shorter piece $= \frac{2}{5}x = \left(\frac{2}{5} \times 50\right)$ cm $= 20$ cm.

164. Let the whole amount be Rs. x. Then, A's share = Rs. $\left(\frac{3}{16}x\right)$; B's share = Rs. $\left(\frac{x}{4}\right)$;

and C's share = Rs. $\left[x - \left(\frac{3x}{16} + \frac{x}{4}\right)\right]$ = Rs. $\left(\frac{9x}{16}\right)$.

$\therefore \; \frac{9x}{16} = 81 \Leftrightarrow x = \left(\frac{81 \times 16}{9}\right) = 144.$

Hence, B's share = Rs. $\left(\frac{144}{4}\right)$ = Rs. 36.

165. Green portion $= \left[1 - \left(\frac{1}{10} + \frac{1}{20} + \frac{1}{30} + \frac{1}{40} + \frac{1}{50} + \frac{1}{60}\right)\right]$

$= \left[1 - \frac{1}{10}\left(1 + \frac{1}{2} + \frac{1}{3} + \frac{1}{4} + \frac{1}{5} + \frac{1}{6}\right)\right] = 1 - \frac{1}{10} \times \frac{147}{60} = 1 - \frac{147}{600} = \frac{453}{600}.$

Let the length of the pole be x metres.

Then, $\frac{453}{600}x = 12.08 \Leftrightarrow x = \left(\frac{12.08 \times 600}{453}\right) = 16.$

166. Let the number be x. Then,

$\frac{3}{4}x - \frac{3}{14}x = 150 \Leftrightarrow 21x - 6x = 150 \times 28 \Leftrightarrow 15x = 150 \times 28 \Leftrightarrow x = 280.$

167. Let the sum be Rs. x. Then,

$\frac{8}{3}x - \frac{3}{8}x = 55 \Leftrightarrow 64x - 9x = 55 \times 24 \Leftrightarrow x = \left(\frac{55 \times 24}{55}\right) = 24.$

$\therefore$ Correct answer = Rs. $\left(\frac{3}{8} \times 24\right)$ = Rs. 9.

168. Let the fraction be $\frac{a}{b}$. Then,

$\left(\frac{a}{b} \times \frac{a}{b}\right) \div \frac{b}{a} = \frac{512}{27} \Leftrightarrow \frac{a}{b} \times \frac{a}{b} \times \frac{a}{b} = \frac{512}{27} \Leftrightarrow \left(\frac{a}{b}\right)^3 = \left(\frac{8}{3}\right)^3 \Leftrightarrow \frac{a}{b} = \frac{8}{3} = 2\frac{2}{3}.$

169. Maximum internal assessment score $= \left(\frac{47}{50} \times 10\right) = 9.4.$

Minimum internal assessment score $= \left(\frac{14}{50} \times 10\right) = 2.8.$

$\therefore$ Required difference $= (9.4 - 2.8) = 6.6.$

170. Let savings in N.S.C. and P.P.F. be Rs. x and Rs. $(150000 - x)$ respectively. Then

$\frac{1}{3}x = \frac{1}{2}(150000 - x) \Leftrightarrow \frac{x}{3} + \frac{x}{2} = 75000 \Leftrightarrow \frac{5x}{6} = 75000 \Leftrightarrow x = \left(\frac{75000 \times 6}{5}\right) = 90000.$

$\therefore$ Savings in Public Provident Fund = Rs. $(150000 - 90000)$ = Rs. 60000

171. Let there be $(x + 1)$ members. Then,

Father's share $= \frac{1}{4}$, share of each other member $= \frac{3}{4x}$.

$\therefore\ 3\left(\frac{3}{4x}\right) = \frac{1}{4} \Leftrightarrow 4x = 36 \Leftrightarrow x = 9.$

Hence, total number of family members = 10.

172. Let salary = Rs. x. Then, tips = Rs. $\left(\frac{5}{4}x\right)$.

Total income = Rs. $\left(x + \frac{5}{4}x\right)$ = Rs. $\left(\frac{9x}{4}\right)$.

$\therefore$ Required fraction $= \left(\frac{5x}{4} \times \frac{4}{9x}\right) = \frac{5}{9}$.

173. Let C's share = Rs. x. Then, B's share = Rs. $\left(\frac{x}{4}\right)$, A's share = Rs. $\left(\frac{2}{3} \times \frac{x}{4}\right)$ = Rs. $\frac{x}{6}$

$\therefore\ \frac{x}{6} + \frac{x}{4} + x = 1360 \Leftrightarrow \frac{17x}{12} = 1360 \Leftrightarrow x = \left(\frac{1360 \times 12}{17}\right)$ = Rs. 960.

Hence, B's share = Rs. $\left(\frac{960}{4}\right)$ = Rs. 240.

174. Let Tanya's share = Rs. x. Then, Veena's share = Rs. $\left(\frac{x}{2}\right)$,

Amita's share = Rs. $\left(\frac{2}{3} \times \frac{x}{2}\right)$ = Rs. $\left(\frac{x}{3}\right)$. Total bill = Rs. $\left(x + \frac{x}{2} + \frac{x}{3}\right)$ = Rs. $\left(\frac{11x}{6}\right)$.

$\therefore$ Required fraction $= \left(\frac{x}{2} \times \frac{6}{11x}\right) = \frac{3}{11}$.

175. Let the capacity of the tank be x litres. Then, $\frac{1}{4}x = 135 \Leftrightarrow x = 135 \times 4 = 540.$

$\therefore$ Required fraction $= \left(\frac{180}{540}\right) = \frac{1}{3}$.

176. Let the capacity of the tank be x litres.

Then, $\frac{6}{7}x - \frac{2}{5}x = 16 \Leftrightarrow 30x - 14x = 16 \times 35 \Leftrightarrow 16x = 560 \Leftrightarrow x = 35.$

177. Let the capacity of the bucket be x litres. Then,

Capacity of 1 large bottle $= \frac{x}{4}$; Capacity of 1 small bottle $= \frac{x}{7}$.

Fluid left in large bottle $= \left(\frac{x}{4} - \frac{x}{7}\right) = \frac{3x}{28}$.

$\therefore$ Required fraction $= \left(\frac{3x/28}{x/4}\right) = \left(\frac{3x}{28} \times \frac{4}{x}\right) = \frac{3}{7}$.

178. Let the capacity of 1 bucket = x. Then, capacity of tank = $25x$.

New capacity of bucket $= \frac{2}{5}x$.

$\therefore$ Required number of buckets $= \frac{25x}{(2x/5)} = \left(25x \times \frac{5}{2x}\right) = \frac{125}{2} = 62\frac{1}{2}$.

179. Suppose initially Peter had Rs. x. Then,

Amount received by Michael = Rs. $\left(\frac{x}{4}\right)$.

Amount remaining with Peter = Rs. $\left(x - \frac{x}{4}\right)$ = Rs. $\left(\frac{3x}{4}\right)$.

Amount received by Sam = Rs. $\left(\frac{1}{2} \times \frac{x}{4}\right)$ = Rs. $\left(\frac{x}{8}\right)$.

$\therefore \quad \frac{3x}{4} - \frac{x}{8} = 500 \Leftrightarrow 5x = 4000 \Leftrightarrow x = 800.$

Hence, amount received by Michael = $(x/4)$ = Rs. 200.

180. A's share = $\frac{1}{3}$. Remainder = $\left(1 - \frac{1}{3}\right) = \frac{2}{3}$.

B's share = $\frac{2}{5}$ of $\frac{2}{3} = \frac{4}{15}$. Rest = $\left(\frac{2}{3} - \frac{4}{15}\right) = \frac{6}{15} = \frac{2}{5}$.

C's share = D's share = $\frac{1}{2}$ of $\frac{2}{5} = \frac{1}{5}$

181. Part read on first day = $\frac{3}{8}$. Remaining part = $\left(1 - \frac{3}{8}\right) = \frac{5}{8}$.

Part read on second day = $\frac{4}{5}$ of $\frac{5}{8} = \frac{1}{2}$. Unread part = $\left[1 - \left(\frac{3}{8} + \frac{1}{2}\right)\right] = \frac{1}{8}$.

Let the number of pages be x. Then, $\frac{1}{8}x = 30$ or $x = 30 \times 8 = 240$.

182. Wife's share = $\frac{1}{2}$. Remaining part = $\left(1 - \frac{1}{2}\right) = \frac{1}{2}$.

Share of 3 sons = $\left(\frac{2}{3} \text{ of } \frac{1}{2}\right) = \frac{1}{3}$. Remaining part = $\left(\frac{1}{2} - \frac{1}{3}\right) = \frac{1}{6}$.

Each daughter's share = $\frac{1}{4} \times \frac{1}{6} = \frac{1}{24}$.

Let the total money be Rs. x. Then, $\frac{1}{24}x = 20000 \Leftrightarrow x = 20000 \times 24 = 480000$.

$\therefore$ Each son's share = Rs. $\left[\frac{1}{3} \times \left(\frac{1}{3} \times 480000\right)\right]$ = Rs. 53,333.33.

183. Out of 5 girls, 1 took part in fete. Out of 8 boys, 1 took part in fete.

$\therefore$ Out of 13 students, 2 took part in fete.

Hence, $\frac{2}{13}$ of the total number took part in fete.

184. French men = $\frac{1}{5}$; French women = $\left(\frac{1}{5} + \frac{2}{3} \times \frac{1}{5}\right) = \frac{5}{15} = \frac{1}{3}$.

French people = $\left(\frac{1}{5} + \frac{1}{3}\right) = \frac{8}{15}$. $\quad\therefore$ Not-French = $\left(1 - \frac{8}{15}\right) = \frac{7}{15}$.

185. Girls $= \frac{3}{5}$; Boys $= \left(1 - \frac{3}{5}\right) = \frac{2}{5}$.

Fraction of students absent $= \frac{2}{9}$ of $\frac{3}{5} + \frac{1}{4}$ of $\frac{2}{5} = \frac{6}{45} + \frac{1}{10} = \frac{21}{90} = \frac{7}{30}$

$\therefore$ Fraction of students present $= \left(1 - \frac{7}{30}\right) = \frac{23}{30}$.

186. Number of boys who participate = 100.

$\therefore$ $\frac{1}{3}$ of boys = 100 or total number of boys = 300.

Number of girls who participate = 200.

$\therefore$ $\frac{1}{2}$ of girls = 200 or total number of girls = 400.

Hence, total number of students = (300 + 400) = 700.

187. Let the number of votes cast be x. Then, number of votes required $= \frac{3x}{4}$.

Counted votes $= \frac{2x}{3}$. Uncounted votes $= \left(x - \frac{2x}{3}\right) = \frac{x}{3}$.

Votes won by the candidate $= \frac{5}{6}$ of $\frac{3x}{4} = \frac{5x}{8}$.

Remaining votes required $= \left(\frac{3x}{4} - \frac{5x}{8}\right) = \frac{x}{8}$.

$\therefore$ Required fraction $= \frac{(x/8)}{(x/3)} = \left(\frac{x}{8} \times \frac{3}{x}\right) = \frac{3}{8}$.

188. Let the total number of staff members be x.

Then, the number who can type or take shorthand $= \left(x - \frac{3x}{4}\right) = \frac{x}{4}$.

Let A and B represent the sets of persons who can type and take shorthand respectively.

Then, $n(A \cup B) = \frac{x}{4}$, $n(A) = \frac{x}{5}$ and $n(B) = \frac{x}{3}$.

$n(A \cap B) = n(A) + n(B) - n(A \cup B) = \left(\frac{x}{5} + \frac{x}{3} - \frac{x}{4}\right) = \left(\frac{12x + 20x - 15x}{60}\right) = \frac{17x}{60}$.

189. Hire charges = Rs. $\left(60 \times 4 + 60 \times 5 + \frac{8}{5} \times 200\right)$ = Rs. 860.

Suppose Rohit had Rs. x with him initially. Then, $x - 860 = \frac{1}{4} \times 860 \Leftrightarrow x = 1075$.

190. Let the total number of shots be x. Then,

Shots fired by A $= \frac{5}{8}x$; Shots fired by B $= \frac{3}{8}x$.

Killing shots by A $= \frac{1}{3}$ of $\frac{5}{8}x = \frac{5x}{24}$; Shots missed by B $= \frac{1}{2}$ of $\frac{3}{8}x = \frac{3}{16}x$.

$\therefore$ $\frac{3x}{16} = 27$ or $x = \left(\frac{27 \times 16}{3}\right) = 144$. Birds killed by A $= \frac{5x}{24} = \left(\frac{5}{24} \times 144\right) = 30$.

191. Number of alterations required in 1 shirt $= \left(\frac{2}{3} + \frac{3}{4} + \frac{4}{5}\right) = \frac{133}{60}$.

$\therefore$ Number of alterations required in 60 shirts $= \left(\frac{133}{60} \times 60\right) = 133$.

192. Let the largest fraction be x and the smallest be y. Then, $\frac{x}{y} = \frac{7}{6}$ or $y = \frac{6}{7}x$.

Let the middle one be z. Then, $x + \frac{6}{7}x + z = \frac{59}{24}$ or $z = \left(\frac{59}{24} - \frac{13x}{7}\right)$.

$\therefore \quad \frac{59}{24} - \frac{13x}{7} + \frac{1}{3} = \frac{7}{6} \Leftrightarrow \frac{13x}{7} = \frac{59}{24} + \frac{1}{3} - \frac{7}{6} = \frac{39}{24} \Leftrightarrow x = \left(\frac{39}{24} \times \frac{7}{13}\right) = \frac{7}{8}.$

So, $x = \frac{7}{8}$, $y = \frac{6}{7} \times \frac{7}{8} = \frac{3}{4}$ and $z = \frac{59}{24} - \frac{13}{7} \times \frac{7}{8} = \frac{20}{24} = \frac{5}{6}$.

Hence, the fractions are $\frac{7}{8}, \frac{5}{6}$ and $\frac{3}{4}$.

193. Suppose each tube contains x grams initially. Then,

$4\left[\frac{1}{3}(x+20)\right] = x + \frac{2}{3}(x+20) \Leftrightarrow \frac{2}{3}(x+20) = x \Leftrightarrow \frac{x}{3} = \frac{40}{3} \Leftrightarrow x = 40.$

194. Let the total number of apples be x. Then,

Apples sold to 1st customer $= \left(\frac{x}{2} + 1\right)$. Remaining apples $= x - \left(\frac{x}{2} + 1\right) = \left(\frac{x}{2} - 1\right)$.

Apples sold to 2nd customer $= \frac{1}{3}\left(\frac{x}{2} - 1\right) + 1 = \frac{x}{6} - \frac{1}{3} + 1 = \left(\frac{x}{6} + \frac{2}{3}\right)$.

Remaining apples $= \left(\frac{x}{2} - 1\right) - \left(\frac{x}{6} + \frac{2}{3}\right) = \left(\frac{x}{2} - \frac{x}{6}\right) - \left(1 + \frac{2}{3}\right) = \left(\frac{x}{3} - \frac{5}{3}\right)$.

Apples sold to 3rd customer $= \frac{1}{5}\left(\frac{x}{3} - \frac{5}{3}\right) + 1 = \left(\frac{x}{15} + \frac{2}{3}\right)$.

Remaining apples $= \left(\frac{x}{3} - \frac{5}{3}\right) - \left(\frac{x}{15} + \frac{2}{3}\right) = \left(\frac{x}{3} - \frac{x}{15}\right) - \left(\frac{5}{3} + \frac{2}{3}\right) = \left(\frac{4x}{15} - \frac{7}{3}\right)$.

$\therefore \quad \frac{4x}{15} - \frac{7}{3} = 3 \Leftrightarrow \frac{4x}{15} = \frac{16}{3} \Leftrightarrow x = \left(\frac{16}{3} \times \frac{15}{4}\right) = 20.$

195. Given exp. $= \frac{(a+b)^2 + (a-b)^2}{a^2 + b^2}$, where $a = 856$, $b = 167$

$= \frac{2(a^2 + b^2)}{(a^2 + b^2)} = 2.$

196. Given exp. $= \frac{(a+b)^2 - (a-b)^2}{ab} = \frac{4ab}{ab} = 4$ (where $a = 469$, $b = 174$).

197. $2ab = (a^2 + b^2) - (a - b)^2 = 29 - 9 = 20 \Rightarrow ab = 10.$

198. $\frac{x^2 - 1}{x + 1} = 4 \Leftrightarrow \frac{(x+1)(x-1)}{x+1} = 4 \Leftrightarrow x - 1 = 4 \Leftrightarrow x = 5.$

199. If $a = 3\frac{2}{3}$, $b = 2\frac{1}{2}$, $c = 4\frac{3}{4}$, $d = 3\frac{1}{3}$, then

Given exp. $= \frac{(a^2 - b^2)}{(c^2 - d^2)} \div \frac{(a-b)}{(c-d)} = \frac{(a^2 - b^2)}{(c^2 - d^2)} \times \frac{(c-d)}{(a-b)} = \frac{(a+b)}{(c+d)}$

$= \frac{3\frac{2}{3} + 2\frac{1}{2}}{4\frac{3}{4} + 3\frac{1}{3}} = \frac{\frac{11}{3} + \frac{5}{2}}{\frac{19}{4} + \frac{10}{3}} = \frac{37}{6} \times \frac{12}{97} = \frac{74}{97}.$

200. Given exp. $= \dfrac{a^2-b^2}{a+b} = a-b = \left(1+\dfrac{1}{1+\dfrac{1}{100}}\right) - \left(1-\dfrac{1}{1+\dfrac{1}{100}}\right)$

$= 2 \times \dfrac{1}{(101/100)} = 2 \times \dfrac{100}{101} = \dfrac{200}{101}$.

201. $(a+b+c)^2 = a^2+b^2+c^2+2(ab+bc+ca)$

$\Rightarrow\ 2(ab+bc+ca) = (a+b+c)^2 - (a^2+b^2+c^2) = 169 - 69 = 100$

$\Rightarrow\ ab+bc+ca = 50.$

202. Given : $x^2+y^2+z^2-64 = -2(xy-yz-zx)$ ...(*i*)

Now, $[x+y+(-z)]^2 = x^2+y^2+z^2+2(xy-yz-zx)$

$\Rightarrow\ (3z-z)^2 = x^2+y^2+z^2+2(xy-yz-zx)$

$\Rightarrow\ -2(xy-yz-zx) = (x^2+y^2+z^2)-(2z)^2$ ...(*ii*)

From (*i*) and (*ii*), we get : $(2z)^2 = 64 \Leftrightarrow 4z^2 = 64 \Leftrightarrow z^2 = 16 \Leftrightarrow z = 4.$

203. Given exp. $= \left(\dfrac{a^3+b^3}{a^2+b^2-ab}\right) = (a+b)$, where $a = 785$, $b = 435$

$= (785 + 435) = 1220.$

204. Given exp. $= \left(\dfrac{a^2+ab+b^2}{a^3-b^3}\right) = \left(\dfrac{1}{a-b}\right)$, where $a = 147$, $b = 143$

$= \left(\dfrac{1}{147-143}\right) = \dfrac{1}{4}.$

205. Let $\dfrac{13^3+7^3}{13^2+7^2-x} = 20$. Then,

$\dfrac{13^3+7^3}{13+7} = 13^2+7^2-x \Leftrightarrow 13^2+7^2-13\times 7 = 13^2+7^2-x \Leftrightarrow x = 13\times 7 = 91.$

206. Given exp. $= \dfrac{a^3-b^3}{a^2-b^2} = \dfrac{(a-b)(a^2+ab+b^2)}{(a-b)(a+b)} = \dfrac{(a^2+ab+b^2)}{(a+b)}$

$= \dfrac{\left(\dfrac{3}{5}\right)^2 + \left(\dfrac{3}{5}\times\dfrac{2}{5}\right) + \left(\dfrac{2}{5}\right)^2}{\left(\dfrac{3}{5}+\dfrac{2}{5}\right)} = \dfrac{9}{25}+\dfrac{6}{25}+\dfrac{4}{25} = \dfrac{19}{25}.$

207. Given exp. $= \dfrac{a^3+b^3+c^3-3abc}{a^2+b^2+c^2-ab-bc-ca} = a+b+c = (38+34+28) = 100.$

208. Since $(x-y)+(y-z)+(z-x) = 0$, so $(x-y)^3+(y-z)^3+(z-x)^3$

$= 3(x-y)(y-z)(z-x).$

$\therefore$ Given exp. $= \dfrac{3(x-y)(y-z)(z-x)}{9(x-y)(y-z)(z-x)} = \dfrac{1}{3}.$

209. Let total score be x. Then, highest score $= \dfrac{3x}{11}$.

Remainder $= \left(x-\dfrac{3x}{11}\right) = \dfrac{8x}{11}$. Next highest score $= \dfrac{3}{11}$ of $\dfrac{8x}{11} = \dfrac{24x}{121}$.

$\therefore\ \dfrac{3x}{11}-\dfrac{24x}{121} = 9 \Leftrightarrow 33x-24x = 9\times 121 \Leftrightarrow 9x = 9\times 121 \Leftrightarrow x = 121.$

210. $X + 3X \times 0.50 + 14 \times 0.10 + 4X \times 0.05 = 50$
$\Leftrightarrow X + 1.5X + 1.40 + 0.2X = 50 \Leftrightarrow 2.7X = 48.60 \Leftrightarrow X = 18.$

211. Suppose their paths cross after x minutes.

Then, $11 + 57x = 51 - 63x \Leftrightarrow 120x = 40 \Leftrightarrow x = \frac{1}{3}.$

Number of floors covered by David in (1/3) min. $= \left(\frac{1}{3} \times 57\right) = 19.$

So, their paths cross at (11 + 19) *i.e.* 30th floor.

212. $N \times 50 = (325000 - 300000) = 25000 \Leftrightarrow N = 500.$

213. Let total number of children be x. Then, $x \times \frac{1}{8} x = \frac{x}{2} \times 16 \Leftrightarrow x = 64.$

$\therefore$ Number of notebooks $= \frac{1}{8} x^2 = \left(\frac{1}{8} \times 64 \times 64\right) = 512.$

214. Let number of boys = x. Then, number of girls = x.
Now, $2(x - 8) = x$ or $x = 16$.
$\therefore$ Total number of students $= 2x = (2 \times 16) = 32.$

215. Let the total number of sweets be $(25x + 8)$.
Then, $(25x + 8) - 22$ is divisible by 28
$\Leftrightarrow (25x - 14)$ is divisible by 28 $\Leftrightarrow 28x - (3x + 14)$ is divisible by 28
$\Leftrightarrow (3x + 14)$ is divisible by 28 $\Leftrightarrow x = 14.$
$\therefore$ Total number of sweets $= (25 \times 14 + 8) = 358.$

216. Suppose the man works overtime for x hours.
Now, working hours in 4 weeks $= (5 \times 8 \times 4) = 160.$
$\therefore 160 \times 2.40 + x \times 3.20 = 432 \Leftrightarrow 3.20x = 432 - 384 = 48 \Leftrightarrow x = 15.$
Hence, total hours of work $= (160 + 15) = 175.$

217. Let number of boys = x. Then, number of girls $= (100 - x)$.
$\therefore 3.60x + 2.40(100 - x) = 312 \Leftrightarrow 1.20x = 312 - 240 = 72 \Leftrightarrow x = 60.$
Hence, number of girls $= (100 - x) = 40.$

218. Let number of boys = x. Then, number of girls $= (60 - x)$.
$\therefore x(60 - x) + (60 - x)x = 1600 \Leftrightarrow 60x - x^2 + 60x - x^2 = 1600$
$\Leftrightarrow 2x^2 - 120x + 1600 = 0 \Leftrightarrow x^2 - 60x + 800 = 0$
$\Leftrightarrow (x - 40)(x - 20) = 0 \Leftrightarrow x = 40$ or $x = 20$.
So, we are not definite. Hence, data is inadequate.

219. Let the distance covered by taxi be x km. Then, distance covered by car $= (80 - x)$ km.
$\therefore 1.5x + 0.5(80 - x) = 50 \Leftrightarrow x = 50 - 40 = 10$ km.

220. Let the number of correct answers be x. Number of incorrect answers $= (60 - x)$.
$\therefore 4x - (60 - x) = 130 \Leftrightarrow 5x = 190 \Leftrightarrow x = 38.$

221. Let number of matches lost = x. Then, number of matches won = $x + 3$.
$\therefore 2(x + 3) - x = 23 \Leftrightarrow x = 17.$
Hence, total number of matches played $= x + (x + 3) = 2x + 3 = 37.$

222. Let the number of 20-paise coins be x. Then, number of 25-paise coins $= (324 - x)$.
$\therefore 0.20 \times x + 0.25(324 - x) = 71 \Leftrightarrow 20x + 25(324 - x) = 7100$
$\Leftrightarrow 5x = 1000 \Leftrightarrow x = 200.$
Hence, number of 25-paise coins $= (324 - x) = 124.$

223. Let number of notes of each denomination be x.
Then, $x + 5x + 10x = 480 \Leftrightarrow 16x = 480 \Leftrightarrow x = 30.$
Hence, total number of notes $= 3x = 90.$

224. Original share of 1 person $= \frac{1}{8}$. New share of 1 person $= \frac{1}{7}$

Increase $= \left(\frac{1}{7} - \frac{1}{8}\right) = \frac{1}{56}$.

$\therefore$ Required fraction $= \frac{(1/56)}{(1/8)} = \left(\frac{1}{56} \times 8\right) = \frac{1}{7}$.

225. Let total number of sweets be x. Then,

$\frac{x}{140} - \frac{x}{175} = 4 \Leftrightarrow 5x - 4x = 4 \times 700 \Leftrightarrow x = 2800$.

226. Let the number of persons be x. Then,

$\frac{96}{x-4} - \frac{96}{x} = 4 \Leftrightarrow \frac{1}{x-4} - \frac{1}{x} = \frac{4}{96} \Leftrightarrow \frac{x-(x-4)}{x(x-4)} = \frac{1}{24}$

$\Leftrightarrow x^2 - 4x - 96 = 0 \Leftrightarrow (x - 12)(x + 8) = 0 \Leftrightarrow x = 12$.

227. Let the number of balls purchased be x.

Then, $\frac{450}{x} - \frac{450}{x+5} = 15 \Leftrightarrow \frac{1}{x} - \frac{1}{x+5} = \frac{15}{450} \Leftrightarrow \frac{x+5-x}{x(x+5)} = \frac{1}{30}$

$\Leftrightarrow x^2 + 5x - 150 = 0 \Leftrightarrow (x + 15)(x - 10) = 0 \Leftrightarrow x = 10$.

228. Let the length of the piece be x metres. Then, cost of 1 m of piece = Rs. $\left(\frac{35}{x}\right)$

$\therefore \quad (x+4)\left(\frac{35}{x} - 1\right) = 35 \Leftrightarrow 35 - x + \frac{140}{x} - 4 = 35 \Leftrightarrow \frac{140}{x} - x = 4$

$\Leftrightarrow x^2 + 4x - 140 = 0 \Leftrightarrow (x + 14)(x - 10) = 0 \Leftrightarrow x = 10$.

229. Let the cost of a chair and that of a table be Rs. x and Rs. y respectively.

Then, $10x = 4y$ or $y = \frac{5}{2}x$.

$\therefore \quad 15x + 2y = 4000 \Leftrightarrow 15x + 2 \times \frac{5}{2}x = 4000 \Leftrightarrow 20x = 4000 \Leftrightarrow x = 200$.

So, $y = \left(\frac{5}{2} \times 200\right) = 500$.

Hence, cost of 12 chairs and 3 tables $= 12x + 3y$ = Rs. (2400 + 1500) = Rs. 3900.

230. Cost of 4 mangoes = Cost of 9 lemons = Rs. $\left(\frac{4.80}{3} \times 9\right)$ = Rs. 14.40

Cost of 1 mango = Rs. $\left(\frac{14.40}{4}\right)$ = Rs. 3.60.

Cost of 5 apples = Cost of 3 mangoes = Rs. (3.60 × 3) = Rs. 10.80.

Cost of 9 oranges = Cost of 5 apples = Rs. 10.80.

$\therefore$ Cost of 1 orange = Rs. $\left(\frac{10.80}{9}\right)$ = Rs. 1.20.

231. Let the price of a saree and a shirt be Rs. x and Rs. y respectively.

Then, $2x + 4y = 1600$ ...(*i*) and $x + 6y = 1600$ ...(*ii*)

Solving (*i*) and (*ii*), we get : $x = 400$, $y = 200$.

$\therefore$ Cost of 12 shirts = Rs. (12 × 200) = Rs. 2400.

232. Let the cost of a table and that of a chair be Rs. x and Rs. y respectively.

Then, $2x + 3y = 3500$ ...(*i*) and $3x + 2y = 4000$ ...(*ii*)

Solving (*i*) and (*ii*), we get : $x = 1000$ and $y = 500$.

233. Let the fixed charge be Rs. x and variable charge be Rs. y per km.
Then, $x + 16y = 156$ ...(*i*) and $x + 24y = 204$ ...(*ii*)
Solving (*i*) and (*ii*), we get : $x = 60, y = 6$.
$\therefore$ Cost of travelling 30 km = Rs. $(60 + 30 \times 6)$ = Rs. 240.

234. Let the number of benches in the class be x. Then, $6(x + 1) = 7x - 5 \Leftrightarrow x = 11$.
Hence, number of students in the class $= 6(x + 1) = 6 \times 12 = 72$.

235. Let the number of students in rooms A and B be x and y respectively. Then,
$x - 10 = y + 10 \Rightarrow x - y = 20$ ...(*i*) and $x + 20 = 2(y - 20) \Rightarrow x - 2y = -60$ ...(*ii*)
Solving (*i*) and (*ii*), we get : $x = 100, y = 80$.

236. Let the number of buffaloes be x and the number of ducks be y.
Then, $4x + 2y = 2(x + y) + 24 \Leftrightarrow 2x = 24 \Leftrightarrow x = 12$.

237. Let the number of hens be x and the number of cows be y. Then,
$x + y = 48$ ...(*i*) and $2x + 4y = 140 \Rightarrow x + 2y = 70$ ...(*ii*)
Solving (*i*) and (*ii*), we get : $x = 26, y = 22$.

238. Suppose, Sanya and Vidushi donate money to x and $(x + 5)$ people respectively.

Then, $\frac{100}{x} - \frac{100}{x+5} = 1 \Leftrightarrow 100(x + 5) - 100x = x(x + 5) \Leftrightarrow x^2 + 5x - 500 = 0$

$\Leftrightarrow (x - 20)(x + 25) = 0 \Leftrightarrow x = 20$.

$\therefore$ Total number of recipients of charity $= x + (x + 5) = 2x + 5 = 45$.

5. SQUARE ROOTS AND CUBE ROOTS

IMPORTANT FACTS AND FORMULAE

Square Root : If $x^2 = y$, we say that the square root of y is x and we write, $\sqrt{y} = x$.

Thus, $\sqrt{4} = 2$, $\sqrt{9} = 3$, $\sqrt{196} = 14$.

Cube Root : The cube root of a given number x is the number whose cube is x. We denote the cube root of x by $\sqrt[3]{x}$.

Thus, $\sqrt[3]{8} = \sqrt[3]{2\times2\times2} = 2$, $\sqrt[3]{343} = \sqrt[3]{7\times7\times7} = 7$ etc.

Note :

1. $\sqrt{xy} = \sqrt{x}\times\sqrt{y}$
2. $\sqrt{\dfrac{x}{y}} = \dfrac{\sqrt{x}}{\sqrt{y}} = \dfrac{\sqrt{x}}{\sqrt{y}}\times\dfrac{\sqrt{y}}{\sqrt{y}} = \dfrac{\sqrt{xy}}{y}$.

SOLVED EXAMPLES

Ex. 1. ***Evaluate $\sqrt{6084}$ by factorization method.***

Sol. **Method** : Express the given number as the product of prime factors. Now, take the product of these prime factors choosing one out of every pair of the same primes. This product gives the square root of the given number.

2	6084
2	3042
3	1521
3	507
13	169
	13

Thus, resolving 6084 into prime factors, we get :

$6084 = 2^2 \times 3^2 \times 13^2$

$\therefore \quad \sqrt{6084} = (2\times3\times13) = 78.$

Ex. 2. ***Find the square root of 1471369.***

Sol. **Explanation** : In the given number, mark off the digits in pairs starting from the unit's digit. Each pair and the remaining one digit is called a period.

Now, $1^2 = 1$. On subtracting, we get 0 as remainder.

Now, bring down the next period *i.e.*, 47.

Now, trial divisor is $1\times2 = 2$ and trial dividend is 47.

So, we take 22 as divisor and put 2 as quotient.

The remainder is 3.

Next, we bring down the next period which is 13.

Now, trial divisor is $12\times2 = 24$ and trial dividend is 313. So, we take 241 as dividend and 1 as quotient.

The remainder is 72.

Bring down the next period *i.e.*, 69.

Now, the trial divisor is $121\times2 = 242$ and the trial dividend is 7269. So, we take 3 as quotient and 2423 as divisor. The remainder is then zero.

Divisor	Working
1	1471369 (1213
	1
22	47
	44
241	313
	241
2423	7269
	7269
	×

Hence, $\sqrt{1471369} = 1213$.

Ex. 3. *Evaluate :* $\sqrt{248+\sqrt{51+\sqrt{169}}}$.

Sol. Given expression $= \sqrt{248+\sqrt{51+13}} = \sqrt{248+\sqrt{64}} = \sqrt{248+8} = \sqrt{256} = 16.$

Ex. 4. *If* $a*b*c = \dfrac{\sqrt{(a+2)(b+3)}}{c+1}$, ***then find the value of*** $6*15*3$.

Sol. $6*15*3 = \dfrac{\sqrt{(6+2)(15+3)}}{3+1} = \dfrac{\sqrt{8\times 18}}{4} = \dfrac{\sqrt{144}}{4} = \dfrac{12}{4} = 3.$

Ex. 5. *Find the value of* $\sqrt{1\dfrac{9}{16}}$.

Sol. $\sqrt{1\dfrac{9}{16}} = \sqrt{\dfrac{25}{16}} = \dfrac{\sqrt{25}}{\sqrt{16}} = \dfrac{5}{4} = 1\dfrac{1}{4}.$

Ex. 6. *What is the square root of 0.0009 ?*

Sol. $\sqrt{0.0009} = \sqrt{\dfrac{9}{10000}} = \dfrac{\sqrt{9}}{\sqrt{10000}} = \dfrac{3}{100} = 0.03.$

Ex. 7. *Evaluate* $\sqrt{175.2976}$.

Sol. Method : We make even number of decimal places by affixing a zero, if necessary. Now, we mark off periods and extract the square root as shown.

$\therefore \quad \sqrt{175.2976} = 13.24.$

1	$\overline{1}\,\overline{75}.\overline{29}\,\overline{76}$ (13.24
	1
23	75
	69
262	629
	524
2644	10576
	10576
	×

Ex. 8. *What will come in place of question mark in each of the following questions?*

(i) $\sqrt{\dfrac{32.4}{?}} = 2$ (ii) $\sqrt{86.49} + \sqrt{5+(?)^2} = 12.3.$ **(R.R.B. 2002)**

Sol. (i) Let $\sqrt{\dfrac{32.4}{x}} = 2$. Then, $\dfrac{32.4}{x} = 4 \Leftrightarrow 4x = 32.4 \Leftrightarrow x = 8.1.$

(ii) Let $\sqrt{86.49} + \sqrt{5+x^2} = 12.3.$

Then, $9.3 + \sqrt{5+x^2} = 12.3 \Leftrightarrow \sqrt{5+x^2} = 12.3 - 9.3 = 3$

$\Leftrightarrow 5 + x^2 = 9 \Leftrightarrow x^2 = 9 - 5 = 4 \Leftrightarrow x = \sqrt{4} = 2.$

Ex. 9. *Find the value of* $\sqrt{\dfrac{0.289}{0.00121}}$. **(IGNOU, 2003)**

Sol. $\sqrt{\dfrac{0.289}{0.00121}} = \sqrt{\dfrac{0.28900}{0.00121}} = \sqrt{\dfrac{28900}{121}} = \dfrac{170}{11}.$

Ex. 10. *If* $\sqrt{1+\dfrac{x}{144}} = \dfrac{13}{12}$, ***then find the value of x.***

Sol. $\sqrt{1+\dfrac{x}{144}} = \dfrac{13}{12} \Rightarrow \left(1+\dfrac{x}{144}\right) = \left(\dfrac{13}{12}\right)^2 = \dfrac{169}{144} \Rightarrow \dfrac{x}{144} = \dfrac{169}{144} - 1$

$\Rightarrow \dfrac{x}{144} = \dfrac{25}{144} \Rightarrow x = 25.$

Ex. 11. ***Find the value of $\sqrt{3}$ upto three places of decimal.***

Sol.

```
   1 | 3.00 00 00 ( 1.732
     | 1
  27 | 200
     | 189
 343 |  1100
     |  1029
3462 |    7100
     |    6924
```

$\therefore \sqrt{3} = 1.732.$

Ex. 12. ***If $\sqrt{3} = 1.732$, find the value of $\sqrt{192} - \dfrac{1}{2}\sqrt{48} - \sqrt{75}$ correct to 3 places of decimal.*** **(S.S.C. 2004)**

Sol. $\sqrt{192} - \dfrac{1}{2}\sqrt{48} - \sqrt{75} = \sqrt{64\times3} - \dfrac{1}{2}\sqrt{16\times3} - \sqrt{25\times3} = 8\sqrt{3} - \dfrac{1}{2}\times4\sqrt{3} - 5\sqrt{3}$

$= 3\sqrt{3} - 2\sqrt{3} = \sqrt{3} = 1.732.$

Ex. 13. ***Evaluate : $\sqrt{\dfrac{9.5\times.0085\times18.9}{.0017\times1.9\times0.021}}$.***

Sol. Given exp. $= \sqrt{\dfrac{9.5\times.0085\times18.900}{.0017\times1.9\times0.021}}$.

Now, since the sum of decimal places in the numerator and denominator under the radical sign is the same, we remove the decimal.

$\therefore$ Given exp. $= \sqrt{\dfrac{95\times85\times18900}{17\times19\times21}} = \sqrt{5\times5\times900} = 5\times30 = 150.$

Ex. 14. ***Simplify : $\sqrt{[(12.1)^2 - (8.1)^2] + [(0.25)^2 + (0.25)(19.95)]}$.*** **(C.B.I. 2003)**

Sol. Given exp. $= \sqrt{\dfrac{(12.1+8.1)(12.1-8.1)}{(0.25)(0.25+19.95)}} = \sqrt{\dfrac{20.2\times4}{0.25\times20.2}}$

$= \sqrt{\dfrac{4}{0.25}} = \sqrt{\dfrac{400}{25}} = \sqrt{16} = 4.$

Ex. 15. ***If $x = 1+\sqrt{2}$ and $y = 1-\sqrt{2}$, find the value of (x^2+y^2).***

Sol. $x^2 + y^2 = (1+\sqrt{2})^2 + (1-\sqrt{2})^2 = 2[(1)^2 + (\sqrt{2})^2] = 2\times3 = 6.$

Ex. 16. ***Evaluate $\sqrt{0.9}$ upto 3 places of decimal.*** **(R.R.B. 2003)**

Sol.

```
   9 | 0.90 00 00 ( .948
     |   81
 184 |   900
     |   736
1888 |   16400
     |   15104
```

$\therefore \sqrt{0.9} = 0.948.$

Ex. 17. ***If*** $\sqrt{15} = 3.88$, ***find the value of*** $\sqrt{\frac{5}{3}}$. **(S.S.C. 2003)**

Sol. $\sqrt{\frac{5}{3}} = \sqrt{\frac{5 \times 3}{3 \times 3}} = \frac{\sqrt{15}}{3} = \frac{3.88}{3} = 1.2933..... = 1.29\bar{3}$.

Ex. 18. ***Find the least square number which is exactly divisible by 10, 12, 15 and 18.***

Sol. L.C.M. of 10, 12, 15, 18 = 180. Now, $180 = 2 \times 2 \times 3 \times 3 \times 5 = 2^2 \times 3^2 \times 5$.

To make it a perfect square, it must be multiplied by 5.

$\therefore$ Required number $= (2^2 \times 3^2 \times 5^2) = 900$.

Ex. 19. ***Find the greatest number of five digits which is a perfect square.*** **(R.R.B. 1998)**

Sol. Greatest number of 5 digits is 99999.

```
   3 | 9 99 99 ( 316
     | 9
     |------
  61 |   99
     |   61
     |------
 626 |   3899
     |   3756
     |------
     |    143
```

$\therefore$ Required number = (99999 − 143) = 99856.

Ex. 20. ***Find the smallest number that must be added to 1780 to make it a perfect square.***

Sol.

```
  4 | 17 80 (42
    | 16
    |------
 82 |  180
    |  164
    |------
    |   16
```

$\therefore$ Number to be added $= (43)^2 - 1780 = 1849 - 1780 = 69$.

Ex. 21. ***If*** $\sqrt{2} = 1.4142$, ***find the value of*** $\frac{\sqrt{2}}{(2 + \sqrt{2})}$.

Sol. $\frac{\sqrt{2}}{(2+\sqrt{2})} = \frac{\sqrt{2}}{(2+\sqrt{2})} \times \frac{(2-\sqrt{2})}{(2-\sqrt{2})} = \frac{2\sqrt{2}-2}{(4-2)} = \frac{2(\sqrt{2}-1)}{2} = (\sqrt{2}-1) = (1.4142 - 1) = 0.4142$.

Ex. 22. ***If*** $x = \left(\frac{\sqrt{5}+\sqrt{3}}{\sqrt{5}-\sqrt{3}}\right)$ ***and*** $y = \left(\frac{\sqrt{5}-\sqrt{3}}{\sqrt{5}+\sqrt{3}}\right)$, ***find the value of*** $(x^2 + y^2)$.

Sol. $x = \frac{(\sqrt{5}+\sqrt{3})}{(\sqrt{5}-\sqrt{3})} \times \frac{(\sqrt{5}+\sqrt{3})}{(\sqrt{5}+\sqrt{3})} = \frac{(\sqrt{5}+\sqrt{3})^2}{(5-3)} = \frac{5+3+2\sqrt{15}}{2} = 4 + \sqrt{15}$.

$y = \frac{(\sqrt{5}-\sqrt{3})}{(\sqrt{5}+\sqrt{3})} \times \frac{(\sqrt{5}-\sqrt{3})}{(\sqrt{5}-\sqrt{3})} = \frac{(\sqrt{5}-\sqrt{3})^2}{(5-3)} = \frac{5+3-2\sqrt{15}}{2} = 4 - \sqrt{15}$.

$\therefore$ $x^2 + y^2 = (4+\sqrt{15})^2 + (4-\sqrt{15})^2 = 2[(4)^2 + (\sqrt{15})^2] = 2 \times 31 = 62$.

Ex. 23. *Find the cube root of 2744.*

Sol. **Method :** Resolve the given number as the product of prime factors and take the product of prime factors, choosing one out of three of the same prime factors. Resolving 2744 as the product of prime factors, we get :

2	2744
2	1372
2	686
7	343
7	49
	7

$2744 = 2^3 \times 7^3$.

$\therefore \quad \sqrt[3]{2744} = 2 \times 7 = 14.$

Ex. 24. *By what least number 4320 be multiplied to obtain a number which is a perfect cube ?*

Sol. Clearly, $4320 = 2^3 \times 3^3 \times 2^2 \times 5$.

To make it a perfect cube, it must be multiplied by 2×5^2 *i.e.,* 50.

EXERCISE 5

(OBJECTIVE TYPE QUESTIONS)

Directions : *Mark (✓) against the correct answer* :

1. $\sqrt{53824} = ?$ **(Bank P.O. 2003)**
(*a*) 202 (*b*) 232 (*c*) 242 (*d*) 332
2. The square root of 64009 is : **(R.R.B. 2003)**
(*a*) 253 (*b*) 347 (*c*) 363 (*d*) 803
3. The value of $\sqrt{10+\sqrt{25+\sqrt{108+\sqrt{154+\sqrt{225}}}}}$ is : **(S.S.C. 1998)**
(*a*) 4 (*b*) 6 (*c*) 8 (*d*) 10
4. Evaluate : $\sqrt{41-\sqrt{21+\sqrt{19-\sqrt{9}}}}$ **(C.B.I. 1997)**
(*a*) 3 (*b*) 5 (*c*) 6 (*d*) 6.4
5. $\sqrt{176+\sqrt{2401}}$ is equal to :
(*a*) 14 (*b*) 15 (*c*) 18 (*d*) 24
6. $\left(\frac{\sqrt{625}}{11} \times \frac{14}{\sqrt{25}} \times \frac{11}{\sqrt{196}}\right)$ is equal to : **(S.S.C. 2000)**
(*a*) 5 (*b*) 6 (*c*) 8 (*d*) 11
7. $\left(\sqrt{\frac{225}{729}} - \sqrt{\frac{25}{144}}\right) \div \sqrt{\frac{16}{81}} = ?$
(*a*) $\frac{1}{48}$ (*b*) $\frac{5}{48}$ (*c*) $\frac{5}{16}$ (*d*) None of these
8. The square root of $(272^2 - 128^2)$ is : **(S.S.C. 2000)**
(*a*) 144 (*b*) 200 (*c*) 240 (*d*) 256
9. If $x * y = x + y + \sqrt{xy}$, the value of $6 * 24$ is : **(C.B.I. 1998)**
(*a*) 41 (*b*) 42 (*c*) 43 (*d*) 44
10. If $y = 5$, then what is the value of $10y\sqrt{y^3 - y^2}$? **(R.R.B. 1998)**
(*a*) $50\sqrt{2}$ (*b*) 100 (*c*) $200\sqrt{5}$ (*d*) 500

11. $\sqrt{110\frac{1}{4}} = ?$

(a) 10.25 (b) 10.5 (c) 11.5 (d) 19.5

12. $\sqrt{\frac{25}{81} - \frac{1}{9}} = ?$ (Hotel Management, 2002)

(a) $\frac{2}{3}$ (b) $\frac{4}{9}$ (c) $\frac{16}{81}$ (d) $\frac{25}{81}$

13. The digit in the unit's place in the square root of 15876 is : (S.S.C. 2000)

(a) 2 (b) 4 (c) 6 (d) 8

14. How many two-digit numbers satisfy this property : The last digit (unit's digit) of the square of the two-digit number is 8 ? (R.R.B. 2001)

(a) 1 (b) 2 (c) 3 (d) None of these

15. What is the square root of 0.16 ? (P.C.S. 1998)

(a) 0.004 (b) 0.04 (c) 0.4 (d) 4

16. The value of $\sqrt{0.000441}$ is : (S.S.C. 2002)

(a) 0.00021 (b) 0.0021 (c) 0.021 (d) 0.21

17. $\sqrt{0.00004761}$ equals : (C.B.I. 2003)

(a) 0.00069 (b) 0.0069 (c) 0.0609 (d) 0.069

18. $1.5^2 \times \sqrt{0.0225} = ?$ (Bank P.O. 2002)

(a) 0.0375 (b) 0.3375 (c) 3.275 (d) 32.75

19. $\sqrt{0.01 + \sqrt{0.0064}} = ?$

(a) 0.03 (b) 0.3 (c) 0.42 (d) None of these

20. The value of $\sqrt{0.01} + \sqrt{0.81} + \sqrt{1.21} + \sqrt{0.0009}$ is : (S.S.C. 2002)

(a) 2.03 (b) 2.1 (c) 2.11 (d) 2.13

21. $\sqrt{.0025} \times \sqrt{2.25} \times \sqrt{.0001} = ?$ (Hotel Management, 1998)

(a) .000075 (b) .0075 (c) .075 (d) None of these

22. $\sqrt{1.5625} = ?$ (S.B.I.P.O. 2003)

(a) 1.05 (b) 1.25 (c) 1.45 (d) 1.55

23. If $\sqrt{.00000676} = .0026$, the square root of 67,60,000 is :

(a) $\frac{1}{26}$ (b) 26 (c) 260 (d) 2600

24. If $\sqrt{18225} = 135$, then the value of

$(\sqrt{182.25} + \sqrt{1.8225} + \sqrt{0.018225} + \sqrt{0.00018225})$ is :

(a) 1.49985 (b) 14.9985 (c) 149.985 (d) 1499.85

25. Given that $\sqrt{13} = 3.605$ and $\sqrt{130} = 11.40$, find the value of $\sqrt{1.3} + \sqrt{1300} + \sqrt{0.013}$.

(a) 36.164 (b) 36.304 (c) 37.164 (d) 37.304

(S.S.C. 1999)

26. If $\frac{52}{x} = \sqrt{\frac{169}{289}}$, the value of x is : (C.B.I. 1998)

(a) 52 (b) 58 (c) 62 (d) 68

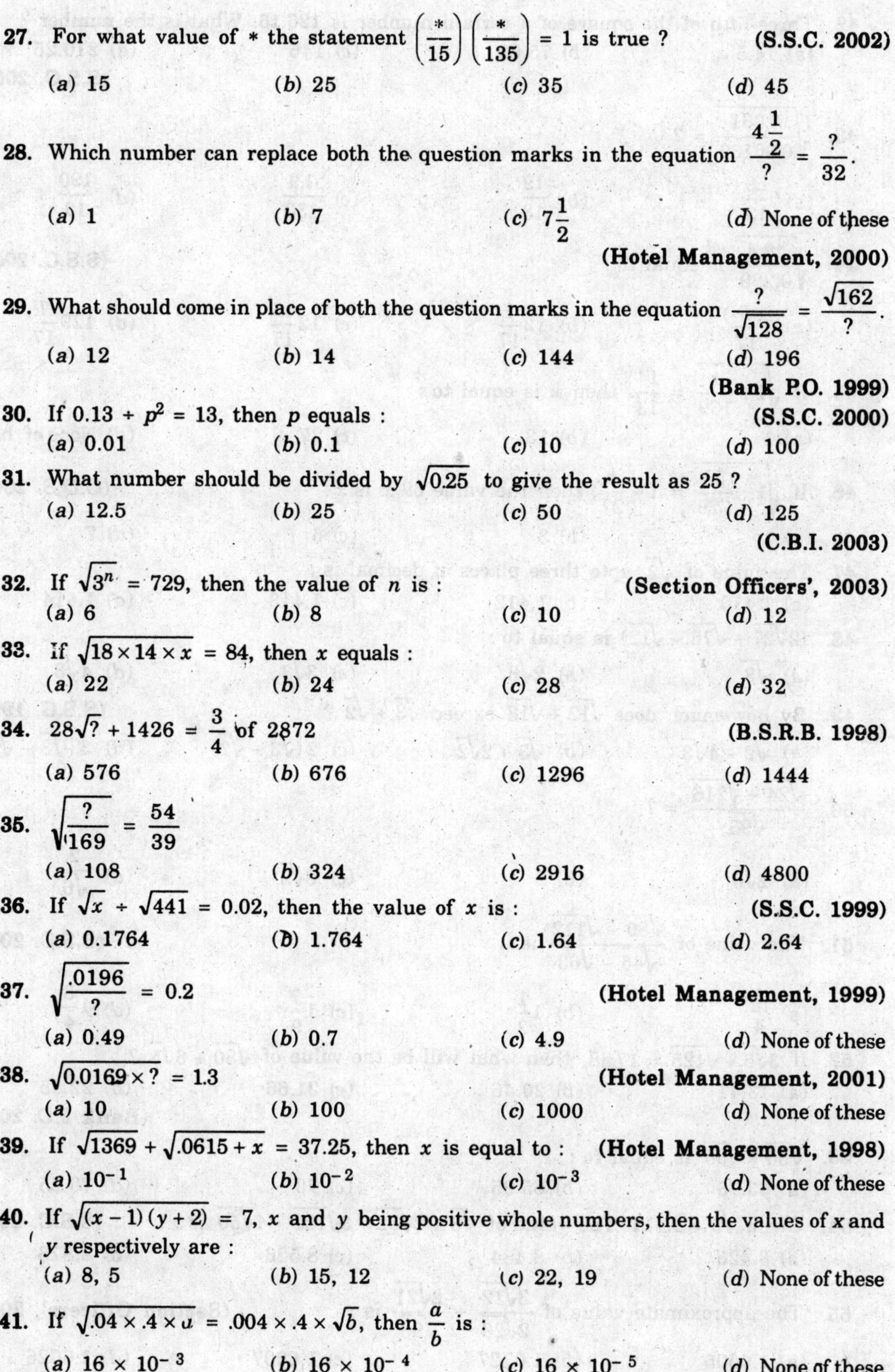

27. For what value of * the statement $\left(\frac{*}{15}\right)\left(\frac{*}{135}\right) = 1$ is true ? **(S.S.C. 2002)**

(*a*) 15 (*b*) 25 (*c*) 35 (*d*) 45

28. Which number can replace both the question marks in the equation $\frac{4\frac{1}{2}}{?} = \frac{?}{32}$.

(*a*) 1 (*b*) 7 (*c*) $7\frac{1}{2}$ (*d*) None of these

(Hotel Management, 2000)

29. What should come in place of both the question marks in the equation $\frac{?}{\sqrt{128}} = \frac{\sqrt{162}}{?}$.

(*a*) 12 (*b*) 14 (*c*) 144 (*d*) 196

(Bank P.O. 1999)

30. If $0.13 \div p^2 = 13$, then p equals : **(S.S.C. 2000)**

(*a*) 0.01 (*b*) 0.1 (*c*) 10 (*d*) 100

31. What number should be divided by $\sqrt{0.25}$ to give the result as 25 ?

(*a*) 12.5 (*b*) 25 (*c*) 50 (*d*) 125

(C.B.I. 2003)

32. If $\sqrt{3^n} = 729$, then the value of n is : **(Section Officers', 2003)**

(*a*) 6 (*b*) 8 (*c*) 10 (*d*) 12

33. If $\sqrt{18 \times 14 \times x} = 84$, then x equals :

(*a*) 22 (*b*) 24 (*c*) 28 (*d*) 32

34. $28\sqrt{?} + 1426 = \frac{3}{4}$ of 2872 **(B.S.R.B. 1998)**

(*a*) 576 (*b*) 676 (*c*) 1296 (*d*) 1444

35. $\sqrt{\frac{?}{169}} = \frac{54}{39}$

(*a*) 108 (*b*) 324 (*c*) 2916 (*d*) 4800

36. If $\sqrt{x} \div \sqrt{441} = 0.02$, then the value of x is : **(S.S.C. 1999)**

(*a*) 0.1764 (*b*) 1.764 (*c*) 1.64 (*d*) 2.64

37. $\sqrt{\frac{.0196}{?}} = 0.2$ **(Hotel Management, 1999)**

(*a*) 0.49 (*b*) 0.7 (*c*) 4.9 (*d*) None of these

38. $\sqrt{0.0169 \times ?} = 1.3$ **(Hotel Management, 2001)**

(*a*) 10 (*b*) 100 (*c*) 1000 (*d*) None of these

39. If $\sqrt{1369} + \sqrt{.0615 + x} = 37.25$, then x is equal to : **(Hotel Management, 1998)**

(*a*) 10^{-1} (*b*) 10^{-2} (*c*) 10^{-3} (*d*) None of these

40. If $\sqrt{(x-1)(y+2)} = 7$, x and y being positive whole numbers, then the values of x and y respectively are :

(*a*) 8, 5 (*b*) 15, 12 (*c*) 22, 19 (*d*) None of these

41. If $\sqrt{.04 \times .4 \times a} = .004 \times .4 \times \sqrt{b}$, then $\frac{a}{b}$ is :

(*a*) 16×10^{-3} (*b*) 16×10^{-4} (*c*) 16×10^{-5} (*d*) None of these

42. Three-fifth of the square of a certain number is 126.15. What is the number ?

(*a*) 14.5 (*b*) 75.69 (*c*) 145 (*d*) 210.25

(S.S.C. 2002)

43. $\sqrt{\frac{0.361}{0.00169}} = ?$

(*a*) $\frac{1.9}{13}$ (*b*) $\frac{19}{13}$ (*c*) $\frac{1.9}{130}$ (*d*) $\frac{190}{13}$

44 $\sqrt{\frac{48.4}{0.289}}$ is equal to : **(S.S.C. 2004)**

(*a*) $1\frac{5}{17}$ (*b*) $12\frac{1}{17}$ (*c*) $12\frac{16}{17}$ (*d*) $129\frac{7}{17}$

45. If $\sqrt{1+\frac{x}{169}} = \frac{14}{13}$, then x is equal to :

(*a*) 1 (*b*) 13 (*c*) 27 (*d*) None of these

46. If $\sqrt{1+\frac{55}{729}} = 1+\frac{x}{27}$, then the value of x is : **(C.D.S. 2003)**

(*a*) 1 (*b*) 3 (*c*) 5 (*d*) 7

47. The value of $\sqrt{2}$ upto three places of decimal is :

(*a*) 1.410 (*b*) 1.412 (*c*) 1.413 (*d*) 1.414

48. $(2\sqrt{27} - \sqrt{75} + \sqrt{12})$ is equal to :

(*a*) $\sqrt{3}$ (*b*) $2\sqrt{3}$ (*c*) $3\sqrt{3}$ (*d*) $4\sqrt{3}$

49. By how much does $\sqrt{12} + \sqrt{18}$ exceed $\sqrt{3} + \sqrt{2}$? **(S.S.C. 1999)**

(*a*) $\sqrt{2} - 4\sqrt{3}$ (*b*) $\sqrt{3} + 2\sqrt{2}$ (*c*) $2(\sqrt{3} - \sqrt{2})$ (*d*) $3(\sqrt{3} - \sqrt{2})$

50. $\frac{\sqrt{24} + \sqrt{216}}{\sqrt{96}} = ?$

(*a*) $2\sqrt{6}$ (*b*) 2 (*c*) $6\sqrt{2}$ (*d*) $\frac{2}{\sqrt{6}}$

51. The value of $\frac{\sqrt{80} - \sqrt{112}}{\sqrt{45} - \sqrt{63}}$ is : **(S.S.C. 2000)**

(*a*) $\frac{3}{4}$ (*b*) $1\frac{1}{3}$ (*c*) $1\frac{7}{9}$ (*d*) $1\frac{3}{4}$

52. If $3\sqrt{5} + \sqrt{125} = 17.88$, then what will be the value of $\sqrt{80} + 6\sqrt{5}$?

(*a*) 13.41 (*b*) 20.46 (*c*) 21.66 (*d*) 22.35

(Bank P.O. 2000)

53. $\sqrt{50} \times \sqrt{98}$ is equal to :

(*a*) 63.75 (*b*) 65.95 (*c*) 70 (*d*) 70.25

54. Given $\sqrt{2} = 1.414$. The value of $\sqrt{8} + 2\sqrt{32} - 3\sqrt{128} + 4\sqrt{50}$ is : **(S.S.C. 2003)**

(*a*) 8.426 (*b*) 8.484 (*c*) 8.526 (*d*) 8.876

55. The approximate value of $\frac{3\sqrt{12}}{2\sqrt{28}} \div \frac{2\sqrt{21}}{\sqrt{98}}$ is : **(Section Officers', 2003)**

(*a*) 1.0605 (*b*) 1.0727 (*c*) 1.6007 (*d*) 1.6026

56. $\sqrt{\frac{.081 \times .484}{.0064 \times 6.25}}$ is equal to : **(N.I.F.T. 1997)**

(a) 0.9 (b) 0.99 (c) 9 (d) 99

57. $\sqrt{\frac{0.204 \times 42}{0.07 \times 3.4}}$ is equal to :

(a) $\frac{1}{6}$ (b) 0.06 (c) 0.6 (d) 6

58. $\sqrt{\frac{0.081 \times 0.324 \times 4.624}{1.5625 \times 0.0289 \times 72.9 \times 64}}$ is equal to :

(a) 0.024 (b) 0.24 (c) 2.4 (d) 24

59. $\sqrt{\frac{9.5 \times .085}{.0017 \times .19}}$ equals :

(a) .05 (b) 5 (c) 50 (d) 500

60. The value of $\sqrt{\frac{(0.03)^2 + (0.21)^2 + (0.065)^2}{(0.003)^2 + (0.021)^2 + (0.0065)^2}}$ is : **(S.S.C. 2002)**

(a) 0.1 (b) 10 (c) 10^2 (d) 10^3

61. The square root of $(7 + 3\sqrt{5})(7 - 3\sqrt{5})$ is : **(S.S.C. 2004)**

(a) $\sqrt{5}$ (b) 2 (c) 4 (d) $3\sqrt{5}$

62. $\left(\sqrt{3} - \frac{1}{\sqrt{3}}\right)^2$ simplifies to : **(R.R.B. 2000)**

(a) $\frac{3}{4}$ (b) $\frac{4}{\sqrt{3}}$ (c) $\frac{4}{3}$ (d) None of these

63. $\left(\sqrt{2} + \frac{1}{\sqrt{2}}\right)^2$ is equal to :

(a) $2\frac{1}{2}$ (b) $3\frac{1}{2}$ (c) $4\frac{1}{2}$ (d) $5\frac{1}{2}$

64. If $a = 0.1039$, then the value of $\sqrt{4a^2 - 4a + 1} + 3a$ is : **(C.B.I. 2003)**

(a) 0.1039 (b) 0.2078 (c) 1.1039 (d) 2.1039

65. The square root of $\frac{(0.75)^3}{1 - 0.75} + [0.75 + (0.75)^2 + 1]$ is : **(S.S.C. 1999)**

(a) 1 (b) 2 (c) 3 (d) 4

66. If $3a = 4b = 6c$ and $a + b + c = 27\sqrt{29}$, then $\sqrt{a^2 + b^2 + c^2}$ is :

(a) $3\sqrt{29}$ (b) 81 (c) 87 (d) None of these

(Hotel Management, 1999)

67. The square root of $0.\overline{4}$ is : **(S.S.C. 2004)**

(a) $0.\overline{6}$ (b) $0.\overline{7}$ (c) $0.\overline{8}$ (d) $0.\overline{9}$

68. Which one of the following numbers has rational square root ?

(a) 0.4 (b) 0.09 (c) 0.9 (d) 0.025

69. The value of $\sqrt{0.4}$ is :

(a) 0.02 (b) 0.2 (c) 0.51 (d) 0.63

70. The value of $\sqrt{0.121}$ is :
(*a*) 0.011 (*b*) 0.11 (*c*) 0.347 (*d*) 1.1

71. The value of $\sqrt{0.064}$ is :
(*a*) 0.008 (*b*) 0.08 (*c*) 0.252 (*d*) 0.8

72. The value of $\sqrt{\dfrac{0.16}{0.4}}$ is : **(IGNOU, 2003)**
(*a*) 0.02 (*b*) 0.2 (*c*) 0.63 (*d*) None of these

73. The value of $\dfrac{1+\sqrt{0.01}}{1-\sqrt{0.1}}$ is close to : **(C.B.I. 1997)**
(*a*) 0.6 (*b*) 1.1 (*c*) 1.6 (*d*) 1.7

74. If $\sqrt{5} = 2.236$, then the value of $\dfrac{1}{\sqrt{5}}$ is :
(*a*) .367 (*b*) .447 (*c*) .745 (*d*) None of these

75. If $\sqrt{24} = 4.899$, the value of $\sqrt{\dfrac{8}{3}}$ is :
(*a*) 0.544 (*b*) 1.333 (*c*) 1.633 (*d*) 2.666

76. If $\sqrt{6} = 2.449$, then the value of $\dfrac{3\sqrt{2}}{2\sqrt{3}}$ is :
(*a*) 0.6122 (*b*) 0.8163 (*c*) 1.223 (*d*) 1.2245

77. If $\sqrt{5} = 2.236$, then the value of $\dfrac{\sqrt{5}}{2} - \dfrac{10}{\sqrt{5}} + \sqrt{125}$ is equal to : **(M.B.A. 1998)**
(*a*) 5.59 (*b*) 7.826 (*c*) 8.944 (*d*) 10.062

78. If $2*3 = \sqrt{13}$ and $3*4 = 5$, then the value of $5*12$ is :
(*a*) $\sqrt{17}$ (*b*) $\sqrt{29}$ (*c*) 12 (*d*) 13

79. The least perfect square number divisible by 3, 4, 5, 6 and 8 is :
(*a*) 900 (*b*) 1200 (*c*) 2500 (*d*) 3600

80. The least perfect square, which is divisible by each of 21, 36 and 66, is :
(*a*) 213444 (*b*) 214344 (*c*) 214434 (*d*) 231444
(C.B.I. 2003)

81. The least number by which 294 must be multiplied to make it a perfect square, is :
(*a*) 2 (*b*) 3 (*c*) 6 (*d*) 24

82. Find the smallest number by which 5808 should be multiplied so that the product becomes a perfect square. **(S.S.C. 1999)**
(*a*) 2 (*b*) 3 (*c*) 7 (*d*) 11

83. The least number by which 1470 must be divided to get a number which is a perfect square, is :
(*a*) 5 (*b*) 6 (*c*) 15 (*d*) 30

84. What is the smallest number to be subtracted from 549162 in order to make it a perfect square ?
(*a*) 28 (*b*) 36 (*c*) 62 (*d*) 81

85. What is the least number which should be subtracted from 0.000326 to make it a perfect square ? **(S.S.C. 2003)**
(*a*) 0.000002 (*b*) 0.000004 (*c*) 0.02 (*d*) 0.04

86. The smallest number added to 680621 to make the sum a perfect square is :
(*a*) 4 (*b*) 5 (*c*) 6 (*d*) 8
(S.S.C. 2002)

87. The greatest four-digit perfect square number is : **(Hotel Management, 2003)**
(*a*) 9000 (*b*) 9801 (*c*) 9900 (*d*) 9981

88. The least number of 4 digits which is a perfect square, is :
(*a*) 1000 (*b*) 1016 (*c*) 1024 (*d*) 1036

89. Given $\sqrt{5} = 2.2361$, $\sqrt{3} = 1.7321$, then $\frac{1}{\sqrt{5}-\sqrt{3}}$ is equal to : **(S.S.C. 2000)**
(*a*) 1.98 (*b*) 1.984 (*c*) 1.9841 (*d*) 2

90. $\frac{1}{(\sqrt{9}-\sqrt{8})} - \frac{1}{(\sqrt{8}-\sqrt{7})} + \frac{1}{(\sqrt{7}-\sqrt{6})} - \frac{1}{(\sqrt{6}-\sqrt{5})} + \frac{1}{(\sqrt{5}-\sqrt{4})}$ is equal to :
(*a*) 0 (*b*) $\frac{1}{3}$ (*c*) 1 (*d*) 5

91. $\left(2+\sqrt{2}+\frac{1}{2+\sqrt{2}}+\frac{1}{\sqrt{2}-2}\right)$ simplifies to : **(S.S.C. 2000)**
(*a*) $2-\sqrt{2}$ (*b*) 2 (*c*) $2+\sqrt{2}$ (*d*) $2\sqrt{2}$

92. If $\sqrt{2} = 1.4142$, the value of $\frac{7}{(3+\sqrt{2})}$ is :
(*a*) 1.5858 (*b*) 3.4852 (*c*) 3.5858 (*d*) 4.4142

93. $\left[\frac{3\sqrt{2}}{\sqrt{6}-\sqrt{3}} - \frac{4\sqrt{3}}{\sqrt{6}-\sqrt{2}} - \frac{6}{\sqrt{8}-\sqrt{12}}\right] = ?$ **(R.R.B. 2001)**
(*a*) $\sqrt{3}-\sqrt{2}$ (*b*) $\sqrt{3}+\sqrt{2}$ (*c*) $5\sqrt{3}$ (*d*) 1

94. $\frac{\sqrt{7}+\sqrt{5}}{\sqrt{7}-\sqrt{5}}$ is equal to : **(Section Officers', 2001)**
(*a*) 1 (*b*) 2 (*c*) $6-\sqrt{35}$ (*d*) $6+\sqrt{35}$

95. If $\frac{5+2\sqrt{3}}{7+4\sqrt{3}} = a + b\sqrt{3}$, then : **(R.R.B. 2001)**
(*a*) $a = -11, b = -6$ (*b*) $a = -11, b = 6$ (*c*) $a = 11, b = -6$ (*d*) $a = 6, b = 11$

96. If $\sqrt{2} = 1.414$, the square root of $\frac{\sqrt{2}-1}{\sqrt{2}+1}$ is nearest to : **(C.B.I. 2003)**
(*a*) 0.172 (*b*) 0.414 (*c*) 0.586 (*d*) 1.414

97. $\frac{3+\sqrt{6}}{5\sqrt{3}-2\sqrt{12}-\sqrt{32}+\sqrt{50}} = ?$ **(I.A.F. 2002)**
(*a*) 3 (*b*) $3\sqrt{2}$ (*c*) 6 (*d*) None of these

98. $\left(\frac{2+\sqrt{3}}{2-\sqrt{3}}+\frac{2-\sqrt{3}}{2+\sqrt{3}}+\frac{\sqrt{3}-1}{\sqrt{3}+1}\right)$ simplifies to : **(S.S.C, 2000)**
(*a*) $16-\sqrt{3}$ (*b*) $4-\sqrt{3}$ (*c*) $2-\sqrt{3}$ (*d*) $2+\sqrt{3}$

99. If $x = (7 - 4\sqrt{3})$, then the value of $\left(x + \frac{1}{x}\right)$ is : **(S.S.C. 2000)**

(*a*) $3\sqrt{3}$ (*b*) $8\sqrt{3}$ (*c*) 14 (*d*) $14 + 8\sqrt{3}$

100. If $x = \frac{\sqrt{3}+1}{\sqrt{3}-1}$ and $y = \frac{\sqrt{3}-1}{\sqrt{3}+1}$, then the value of $(x^2 + y^2)$ is : **(S.S.C. 2003)**

(*a*) 10 (*b*) 13 (*c*) 14 (*d*) 15

101. If $a = \frac{\sqrt{5}+1}{\sqrt{5}-1}$ and $b = \frac{\sqrt{5}-1}{\sqrt{5}+1}$, the value of $\left(\frac{a^2+ab+b^2}{a^2-ab+b^2}\right)$ is :

(*a*) $\frac{3}{4}$ (*b*) $\frac{4}{3}$ (*c*) $\frac{3}{5}$ (*d*) $\frac{5}{3}$

102. A man plants 15376 apple trees in his garden and arranges them so that there are as many rows as there are apples trees in each row. The number of rows is :

(*a*) 124 (*b*) 126 (*c*) 134 (*d*) 144

103. A General wishes to draw up his 36581 soldiers in the form of a solid square. After arranging them, he found that some of them are left over. How many are left ?

(*a*) 65 (*b*) 81 (*c*) 100 (*d*) None of these

104. A group of students decided to collect as many paise from each member of the group as is the number of members. If the total collection amounts to Rs. 59.29, the number of members in the group is :

(*a*) 57 (*b*) 67 (*c*) 77 (*d*) 87

105. The cube root of .000216 is :

(*a*) .6 (*b*) .06 (*c*) .006 (*d*) None of these

106. $\sqrt[3]{4\frac{12}{125}} = ?$

(*a*) $1\frac{2}{5}$ (*b*) $1\frac{3}{5}$ (*c*) $1\frac{4}{5}$ (*d*) $2\frac{2}{5}$

107. $\sqrt[3]{\sqrt{.000064}} = ?$

(*a*) .02 (*b*) .2 (*c*) 2 (*d*) None of these

108. The largest four-digit number which is a perfect cube, is :

(*a*) 8000 (*b*) 9261 (*c*) 9999 (*d*) None of these

109. By what least number 675 be multiplied to obtain a number which is a perfect cube ?

(*a*) 5 (*b*) 6 (*c*) 7 (*d*) 8

110. What is the smallest number by which 3600 be divided to make it a perfect cube ?

(*a*) 9 (*b*) 50 (*c*) 300 (*d*) 450.

ANSWERS

1. (*b*)	**2.** (*a*)	**3.** (*a*)	**4.** (*c*)	**5.** (*b*)	**6.** (*a*)	**7.** (*c*)	**8.** (*c*)	**9.** (*b*)
10. (*d*)	**11.** (*b*)	**12.** (*b*)	**13.** (*c*)	**14.** (*d*)	**15.** (*c*)	**16.** (*c*)	**17.** (*b*)	**18.** (*b*)
19. (*b*)	**20.** (*d*)	**21.** (*d*)	**22.** (*b*)	**23.** (*d*)	**24.** (*b*)	**25.** (*d*)	**26.** (*d*)	**27.** (*d*)
28. (*d*)	**29.** (*a*)	**30.** (*b*)	**31.** (*a*)	**32.** (*d*)	**33.** (*c*)	**34.** (*b*)	**35.** (*b*)	**36.** (*a*)

37. (*a*)	**38.** (*b*)	**39.** (*c*)	**40.** (*a*)	**41.** (*c*)	**42.** (*a*)	**43.** (*d*)	**44.** (*c*)	**45.** (*c*)
46. (*a*)	**47.** (*d*)	**48.** (*c*)	**49.** (*b*)	**50.** (*b*)	**51.** (*b*)	**52.** (*d*)	**53.** (*c*)	**54.** (*b*)
55. (*a*)	**56.** (*b*)	**57.** (*d*)	**58.** (*a*)	**59.** (*c*)	**60.** (*b*)	**61.** (*b*)	**62.** (*c*)	**63.** (*c*)
64. (*c*)	**65.** (*b*)	**66.** (*c*)	**67.** (*a*)	**68.** (*b*)	**69.** (*d*)	**70.** (*c*)	**71.** (*c*)	**72.** (*c*)
73. (*c*)	**74.** (*b*)	**75.** (*c*)	**76.** (*d*)	**77.** (*b*)	**78.** (*d*)	**79.** (*d*)	**80.** (*a*)	**81.** (*c*)
82. (*b*)	**83.** (*d*)	**84.** (*d*)	**85.** (*a*)	**86.** (*a*)	**87.** (*b*)	**88.** (*c*)	**89.** (*c*)	**90.** (*d*)
91. (*b*)	**92.** (*a*)	**93.** (*c*)	**94.** (*d*)	**95.** (*c*)	**96.** (*b*)	**97.** (*d*)	**98.** (*a*)	**99.** (*c*)
100. (*c*)	**101.** (*b*)	**102.** (*a*)	**103.** (*c*)	**104.** (*c*)	**105.** (*b*)	**106.** (*b*)	**107.** (*b*)	**108.** (*b*)
109. (*a*)	**110.** (*d*)							

SOLUTIONS

1.

```
     2 | 53824 ( 232
       | 4
       |------
    43 | 138
       | 129
       |------
   462 |   924
       |   924
       |------
       |    ×
```

$\therefore \quad \sqrt{53824} = 232.$

2.

```
     2 | 64009 ( 253
       | 4
       |------
    45 | 240
       | 225
       |------
   503 |  1509
       |  1509
       |------
       |    ×
```

$\therefore \quad \sqrt{64009} = 253.$

3. Given exp. $= \sqrt{10+\sqrt{25+\sqrt{108+\sqrt{154+15}}}} = \sqrt{10+\sqrt{25+\sqrt{108+\sqrt{169}}}}$

$= \sqrt{10+\sqrt{25+\sqrt{108+13}}} = \sqrt{10+\sqrt{25+\sqrt{121}}}$

$= \sqrt{10+\sqrt{25+11}} = \sqrt{10+\sqrt{36}} = \sqrt{10+6} = \sqrt{16} = 4.$

4. Given exp. $= \sqrt{41-\sqrt{21+\sqrt{19-3}}} = \sqrt{41-\sqrt{21+\sqrt{16}}} = \sqrt{41-\sqrt{21+4}}$

$= \sqrt{41-\sqrt{25}} = \sqrt{41-5} = \sqrt{36} = 6.$

5. Given exp. $= \sqrt{176+49} = \sqrt{225} = 15.$

```
     4 | 2401 ( 49
       | 16
       |------
    89 |  801
       |  801
       |------
       |   ×
```

6. Given exp. $= \dfrac{25}{11} \times \dfrac{14}{5} \times \dfrac{11}{14} = 5.$

7. Given exp. $= \left(\dfrac{\sqrt{225}}{\sqrt{729}} - \dfrac{\sqrt{25}}{\sqrt{144}}\right) \div \dfrac{\sqrt{16}}{\sqrt{81}} = \left(\dfrac{15}{27} - \dfrac{5}{12}\right) \div \dfrac{4}{9} = \left(\dfrac{15}{108} \times \dfrac{9}{4}\right) = \dfrac{5}{16}.$

8. $\sqrt{(272)^2 - (128)^2} = \sqrt{(272+128)(272-128)} = \sqrt{400 \times 144} = \sqrt{57600} = 240.$

9. $6 * 24 = 6 + 24 + \sqrt{6 \times 24} = 30 + \sqrt{144} = 30 + 12 = 42.$

10. $10y\sqrt{y^3 - y^2} = 10 \times 5\sqrt{5^3 - 5^2} = 50 \times \sqrt{125 - 25} = 50 \times \sqrt{100} = 50 \times 10 = 500.$

11. $\sqrt{110\frac{1}{4}} = \sqrt{\frac{441}{4}} = \frac{\sqrt{441}}{\sqrt{4}} = \frac{21}{2} = 10.5.$

12. $\sqrt{\frac{25}{81} - \frac{1}{9}} = \sqrt{\frac{25-9}{81}} = \sqrt{\frac{16}{81}} = \frac{\sqrt{16}}{\sqrt{81}} = \frac{4}{9}.$

13.
```
   1  | 1̄58̄76̄ ( 126
      | 1
      |-----
  22  | 58
      | 44
      |-----
 246  | 1476
      | 1476
      |-----
      |  ×
```

$\therefore \sqrt{15876} = 126.$

14. A number ending in 8 can never be a perfect square.

15. $\sqrt{0.16} = \sqrt{\frac{16}{100}} = \frac{\sqrt{16}}{\sqrt{100}} = \frac{4}{10} = 0.4.$

16. $\sqrt{0.000441} = \sqrt{\frac{441}{10^6}} = \frac{\sqrt{441}}{\sqrt{10^6}} = \frac{21}{10^3} = \frac{21}{1000} = 0.021.$

17. $\sqrt{0.00004761} = \sqrt{\frac{4761}{10^8}} = \frac{\sqrt{4761}}{\sqrt{10^8}} = \frac{69}{10^4} = \frac{69}{10000} = 0.0069.$

18. $1.5^2 \times \sqrt{0.0225} = 1.5^2 \times \sqrt{\frac{225}{10000}} = 2.25 \times \frac{15}{100} = 2.25 \times 0.15 = 0.3375.$

19. $\sqrt{0.01 + \sqrt{0.0064}} = \sqrt{0.01 + \sqrt{\frac{64}{10000}}} = \sqrt{0.01 + \frac{8}{100}} = \sqrt{0.01 + 0.08} = \sqrt{0.09} = 0.3.$

20. Given exp. $= \sqrt{\frac{1}{100}} + \sqrt{\frac{81}{100}} + \sqrt{\frac{121}{100}} + \sqrt{\frac{9}{10000}} = \frac{1}{10} + \frac{9}{10} + \frac{11}{10} + \frac{3}{100}$

$= 0.1 + 0.9 + 1.1 + 0.03 = 2.13.$

21. Given exp. $= \sqrt{\frac{25}{10000}} \times \sqrt{\frac{225}{100}} \times \sqrt{\frac{1}{10000}} = \frac{5}{100} \times \frac{15}{10} \times \frac{1}{100} = \frac{75}{100000} = 0.00075$

22.
```
   1  | 1̄.5̄62̄5̄ ( 1.25
      | 1
      |-----
  22  | 56
      | 44
      |-----
 245  | 1225
      | 1225
      |-----
      |  ×
```

$\therefore \sqrt{1.5625} = 1.25.$

23. $\sqrt{6760000} = \sqrt{0.00000676 \times 10^{12}} = \sqrt{0.00000676} \times \sqrt{10^{12}} = .0026 \times 10^6 = 2600.$

24. Given exp. $= \sqrt{\frac{18225}{10^2}} + \sqrt{\frac{18225}{10^4}} + \sqrt{\frac{18225}{10^6}} + \sqrt{\frac{18225}{10^8}}$

$= \frac{\sqrt{18225}}{10} + \frac{\sqrt{18225}}{10^2} + \frac{\sqrt{18225}}{10^3} + \frac{\sqrt{18225}}{10^4} = \frac{135}{10} + \frac{135}{100} + \frac{135}{1000} + \frac{135}{10000}$

$= 13.5 + 1.35 + 0.135 + 0.0135 = 14.9985.$

25. Given exp. $= \sqrt{1.30} + \sqrt{1300} + \sqrt{0.0130} = \sqrt{\frac{130}{100}} + \sqrt{13 \times 100} + \sqrt{\frac{130}{10000}}$

$= \frac{\sqrt{130}}{10} + \sqrt{13} \times 10 + \frac{\sqrt{130}}{100} = \frac{11.40}{10} + 3.605 \times 10 + \frac{11.40}{100}$

$= 1.14 + 36.05 + 0.114 = 37.304.$

26. $\frac{52}{x} = \sqrt{\frac{169}{289}} \Leftrightarrow \frac{52}{x} = \frac{13}{17} \Leftrightarrow x = \left(\frac{52 \times 17}{13}\right) = 68.$

27. Let the missing number be x.

Then, $x^2 = 15 \times 135 \Leftrightarrow x = \sqrt{15 \times 135} = \sqrt{15^2 \times 3^2} = 15 \times 3 = 45.$

28. Let $\frac{4\frac{1}{2}}{x} = \frac{x}{32}$. Then, $x^2 = 32 \times \frac{9}{2} = 144 \Leftrightarrow x = \sqrt{144} = 12.$

29. Let $\frac{x}{\sqrt{128}} = \frac{\sqrt{162}}{x}$.

Then, $x^2 = \sqrt{128 \times 162} = \sqrt{64 \times 2 \times 18 \times 9} = \sqrt{8^2 \times 6^2 \times 3^2} = 8 \times 6 \times 3 = 144.$

$\therefore \quad x = \sqrt{144} = 12.$

30. $\frac{0.13}{p^2} = 13 \Leftrightarrow p^2 = \frac{0.13}{13} = \frac{1}{100} \Leftrightarrow p = \sqrt{\frac{1}{100}} = \frac{1}{100} = \frac{1}{10} = 0.1.$

31. Let the required number be x. Then, $\frac{x}{\sqrt{0.25}} = 25 \Leftrightarrow \frac{x}{0.5} = 25 \Leftrightarrow x = 25 \times 0.5 = 12.5.$

32. $\sqrt{3^n} = 729 = 3^6 \Leftrightarrow (\sqrt{3^n})^2 = (3^6)^2 \Leftrightarrow 3^n = 3^{12} \Leftrightarrow n = 12.$

33. $\sqrt{18 \times 14 \times x} = 84 \Leftrightarrow 18 \times 14 \times x = 84 \times 84 \Leftrightarrow x = \frac{84 \times 84}{18 \times 14} = 28.$

34. Let $28\sqrt{x} + 1426 = 3 \times 718.$

Then, $28\sqrt{x} = 2154 - 1426 \Leftrightarrow 28\sqrt{x} = 728 \Leftrightarrow \sqrt{x} = 26 \Leftrightarrow x = (26)^2 = 676.$

35. Let $\sqrt{\frac{x}{169}} = \frac{54}{39}$. Then, $\frac{\sqrt{x}}{13} = \frac{54}{39} \Leftrightarrow \sqrt{x} = \left(\frac{54}{39} \times 13\right) = 18 \Leftrightarrow x = (18)^2 = 324.$

36. $\frac{\sqrt{x}}{\sqrt{441}} = 0.02 \Leftrightarrow \frac{\sqrt{x}}{21} = 0.02 \Leftrightarrow \sqrt{x} = 0.02 \times 21 = 0.42 \Leftrightarrow x = (0.42)^2 = 0.1764.$

37. Let $\sqrt{\frac{.0196}{x}} = 0.2$. Then, $\frac{.0196}{x} = 0.04 \Leftrightarrow x = \frac{.0196}{.04} = \frac{1.96}{4} = .49.$

38. Let $\sqrt{0.0169 \times x} = 1.3$. Then, $0.0169x = (1.3)^2 = 1.69 \Leftrightarrow x = \frac{1.69}{0.0169} = 100.$

39. $37 + \sqrt{.0615 + x} = 37.25 \Leftrightarrow \sqrt{.0615 + x} = 0.25$

$\Leftrightarrow .0615 + x = (0.25)^2 = 0.0625 \Leftrightarrow x = .001 = \frac{1}{10^3} = 10^{-3}$

40. $\sqrt{(x-1)(y+2)} = 7 \Rightarrow (x-1)(y+2) = (7)^2 \Rightarrow (x-1) = 7$ and $(y+2) = 7$

$\Rightarrow x = 8$ and $y = 5$.

41. $\dfrac{\sqrt{a}}{\sqrt{b}} = \dfrac{.004 \times .4}{\sqrt{.04 \times .4}} \Rightarrow \dfrac{a}{b} = \dfrac{.004 \times .4 \times .004 \times .4}{.04 \times .4} = \dfrac{.0000064}{.04}$

$\therefore \dfrac{a}{b} = \dfrac{.00064}{4} = .00016 = \dfrac{16}{10^5} = 16 \times 10^{-5}$.

42. Let the number be x. Then,

$\dfrac{3}{5}x^2 = 126.15 \Leftrightarrow x^2 = \left(126.15 \times \dfrac{5}{3}\right) = 210.25 \Leftrightarrow x = \sqrt{210.25} = 14.5$.

43. $\sqrt{\dfrac{0.361}{0.00169}} = \sqrt{\dfrac{0.36100}{0.00169}} = \sqrt{\dfrac{36100}{169}} = \dfrac{190}{13}$.

44. $\sqrt{\dfrac{48.4}{0.289}} = \sqrt{\dfrac{48.400}{0.289}} = \sqrt{\dfrac{48400}{289}} = \dfrac{220}{17} = 12\dfrac{16}{17}$.

45. $\sqrt{1 + \dfrac{x}{169}} = \dfrac{14}{13} \Rightarrow 1 + \dfrac{x}{169} = \dfrac{196}{169} \Rightarrow \dfrac{x}{169} = \left(\dfrac{196}{169} - 1\right) = \dfrac{27}{169} \Rightarrow x = 27$.

46. $\sqrt{1 + \dfrac{55}{729}} = 1 + \dfrac{x}{27} \Rightarrow \sqrt{\dfrac{784}{729}} = \dfrac{27 + x}{27} \Rightarrow \dfrac{28}{27} = \dfrac{27 + x}{27} \Rightarrow 27 + x = 28 \Rightarrow x = 1$.

47.

1	$\overline{2}.\overline{00}\,\overline{00}\,\overline{00}$ (1.414
	1
24	100
	96
281	400
	281
2824	11900
	11296

$\therefore \sqrt{2} = 1.414$.

48. $2\sqrt{27} - \sqrt{75} + \sqrt{12} = 2\sqrt{9 \times 3} - \sqrt{25 \times 3} + \sqrt{4 \times 3} = 6\sqrt{3} - 5\sqrt{3} + 2\sqrt{3} = 3\sqrt{3}$.

49. $(\sqrt{12} + \sqrt{18}) - (\sqrt{3} + \sqrt{2}) = (\sqrt{4 \times 3} + \sqrt{9 \times 2}) - (\sqrt{3} + \sqrt{2}) = (2\sqrt{3} + 3\sqrt{2}) - (\sqrt{3} + \sqrt{2})$

$= (2\sqrt{3} - \sqrt{3}) + (3\sqrt{2} - \sqrt{2}) = \sqrt{3} + 2\sqrt{2}$.

50. $\dfrac{\sqrt{24} + \sqrt{216}}{\sqrt{96}} = \dfrac{\sqrt{4 \times 6} + \sqrt{36 \times 6}}{\sqrt{16 \times 6}} = \dfrac{2\sqrt{6} + 6\sqrt{6}}{4\sqrt{6}} = \dfrac{8\sqrt{6}}{4\sqrt{6}} = 2$.

51. $\dfrac{\sqrt{80} - \sqrt{112}}{\sqrt{45} - \sqrt{63}} = \dfrac{\sqrt{16 \times 5} - \sqrt{16 \times 7}}{\sqrt{9 \times 5} - \sqrt{9 \times 7}} = \dfrac{4\sqrt{5} - 4\sqrt{7}}{3\sqrt{5} - 3\sqrt{7}} = \dfrac{4(\sqrt{5} - \sqrt{7})}{3(\sqrt{5} - \sqrt{7})} = \dfrac{4}{3} = 1\dfrac{1}{3}$.

52. $3\sqrt{5} + \sqrt{125} = 17.88 \Rightarrow 3\sqrt{5} + \sqrt{25 \times 5} = 17.88$

$\Rightarrow 3\sqrt{5} + 5\sqrt{5} = 17.88 \Rightarrow 8\sqrt{5} = 17.88 \Rightarrow \sqrt{5} = 2.235$.

$\therefore \sqrt{80} + 6\sqrt{5} = \sqrt{16 \times 5} + 6\sqrt{5} = 4\sqrt{5} + 6\sqrt{5} = 10\sqrt{5} = (10 \times 2.235) = 22.35$.

53. $\sqrt{50} \times \sqrt{98} = \sqrt{50 \times 98} = \sqrt{4900} = 70$.

54. Given exp. $= \sqrt{4\times 2} + 2\sqrt{16\times 2} - 3\sqrt{64\times 2} + 4\sqrt{25\times 2}$

$= 2\sqrt{2} + 8\sqrt{2} - 24\sqrt{2} + 20\sqrt{2} = 6\sqrt{2} = 6\times 1.414 = 8.484.$

55. Given exp. $= \dfrac{3\sqrt{12}}{2\sqrt{28}} \times \dfrac{\sqrt{98}}{2\sqrt{21}} = \dfrac{3\sqrt{4\times 3}}{2\sqrt{4\times 7}} \times \dfrac{\sqrt{49\times 2}}{2\sqrt{21}} = \dfrac{6\sqrt{3}}{4\sqrt{7}} \times \dfrac{7\sqrt{2}}{2\sqrt{21}} = \dfrac{21\sqrt{6}}{4\sqrt{7\times 21}} = \dfrac{21\sqrt{6}}{28\sqrt{3}}$

$= \dfrac{3}{4}\sqrt{2} = \dfrac{3}{4}\times 1.414 = 3\times 0.3535 = 1.0605.$

56. Sum of decimal places in the numerator and denominator under the radical sign being the same, we remove the decimal.

$\therefore$ Given exp. $= \sqrt{\dfrac{81\times 484}{64\times 625}} = \dfrac{9\times 22}{8\times 25} = 0.99.$

57. Given exp. $= \sqrt{\dfrac{204\times 42}{7\times 34}} = \sqrt{36} = 6.$

58. Given exp. $= \sqrt{\dfrac{81\times 324\times 4624}{15625\times 289\times 729\times 64}} = \dfrac{9\times 18\times 68}{125\times 17\times 27\times 8} = \dfrac{3}{125} = 0.024.$

59. Given exp. $= \sqrt{\dfrac{9.5\times .08500}{.19\times .0017}} = \sqrt{\dfrac{95\times 8500}{19\times 17}} = \sqrt{5\times 500} = \sqrt{2500} = 50.$

60. Given exp. $= \sqrt{\dfrac{(0.03)^2 + (0.21)^2 + (0.065)^2}{\left(\dfrac{0.03}{10}\right)^2 + \left(\dfrac{0.21}{10}\right)^2 + \left(\dfrac{0.065}{10}\right)^2}}$

$= \sqrt{\dfrac{100\,[(0.03)^2 + (0.21)^2 + (0.065)^2]}{(0.03)^2 + (0.21)^2 + (0.065)^2}} = \sqrt{100} = 10.$

61. $\sqrt{(7+3\sqrt{5})(7-3\sqrt{5})} = \sqrt{(7)^2 - (3\sqrt{5})^2} = \sqrt{49-45} = \sqrt{4} = 2.$

62. $\left(\sqrt{3} - \dfrac{1}{\sqrt{3}}\right)^2 = (\sqrt{3})^2 + \left(\dfrac{1}{\sqrt{3}}\right)^2 - 2\times\sqrt{3}\times\dfrac{1}{\sqrt{3}} = 3 + \dfrac{1}{3} - 2 = 1 + \dfrac{1}{3} = \dfrac{4}{3}.$

63. $\left(\sqrt{2} + \dfrac{1}{\sqrt{2}}\right)^2 = (\sqrt{2})^2 + \left(\dfrac{1}{\sqrt{2}}\right)^2 + 2\times\sqrt{2}\times\dfrac{1}{\sqrt{2}} = 2 + \dfrac{1}{2} + 2 = 4 + \dfrac{1}{2} = 4\dfrac{1}{2}.$

64. $\sqrt{4a^2 - 4a + 1} + 3a = \sqrt{(1)^2 + (2a)^2 - 2\times 1\times 2a} + 3a$

$= \sqrt{(1+2a)^2} + 3a = (1-2a) + 3a = (1+a) = (1+0.1039) = 1.1039.$

65. $\sqrt{\dfrac{(0.75)^3}{(1-0.75)} + [0.75 + (0.75)^2 + 1]} = \sqrt{\dfrac{(0.75)^3 + (1-0.75)\,[(1)^2 + (0.75)^2 + 1\times 0.75]}{1-0.75}}$

$= \sqrt{\dfrac{(0.75)^3 + [(1)^3 - (0.75)^3]}{1-0.75}} = \sqrt{\dfrac{1}{0.25}} = \sqrt{\dfrac{100}{25}} = \sqrt{4} = 2.$

66. $4b = 6c \Rightarrow b = \dfrac{3}{2}c$ and $3a = 4b \Rightarrow a = \dfrac{4}{3}b = \dfrac{4}{3}\left(\dfrac{3}{2}c\right) = 2c.$

$a + b + c = 27\sqrt{29} \Rightarrow 2c + \dfrac{3}{2}c + c = 27\sqrt{29} \Rightarrow \dfrac{9}{2}c = 27\sqrt{29} \Rightarrow c = 6\sqrt{29}.$

$$\therefore \quad \sqrt{a^2+b^2+c^2} = \sqrt{(a+b+c)^2 - 2(ab+bc+ca)}$$

$$= \sqrt{(27\sqrt{29})^2 - 2\left(2c \times \frac{3}{2}c + \frac{3}{2}c \times c + c \times 2c\right)}$$

$$= \sqrt{(729 \times 29) - 2\left(3c^2 + \frac{3}{2}c^2 + 2c^2\right)} = \sqrt{(729 \times 29) - 2 \times \frac{13}{2}c^2}$$

$$= \sqrt{(729 \times 29) - 13 \times (6\sqrt{29})^2} = \sqrt{29\,(729 - 468)}$$

$$= \sqrt{29 \times 261} = \sqrt{29 \times 29 \times 9} = 29 \times 3 = 87.$$

67. $\sqrt{0.\bar{4}} = \sqrt{\frac{4}{9}} = \frac{2}{3} = 0.666..... = 0.\bar{6}.$

68. $\sqrt{0.09} = \sqrt{\frac{9}{100}} = \frac{3}{10} = 0.3$, which is rational.

$\therefore$ 0.09 has rational square root.

69.

```
  6 | 0.40 00 00 ( .63
    |   36
123 |    400
    |    369
```

70.

```
  3 | 0.12 10 00 ( .347
    |    9
 64 |    310
    |    256
687 |     5400
    |     4809
```

71.

```
  2 | 0.06 40 00 ( .252
    |    4
 45 |    240
    |    225
502 |     1500
    |     1006
```

72. $\sqrt{\frac{0.16}{0.4}} = \sqrt{\frac{0.16}{0.40}} = \sqrt{\frac{16}{40}} = \sqrt{\frac{4}{10}} = \sqrt{0.4} = 0.63.$

73. $\frac{1+\sqrt{0.01}}{1-\sqrt{0.1}} = \frac{1+0.1}{1-0.316} = \frac{1.1}{0.684}$

$= \frac{1100}{684} = 1.6.$

```
 3 | 0.10 00 00 ( .316
   |    9
61 |    100
   |     61
62 |     3900
   |     3756
```

74. $\frac{1}{\sqrt{5}} = \frac{1}{\sqrt{5}} \times \frac{\sqrt{5}}{\sqrt{5}} = \frac{\sqrt{5}}{5} = \frac{2.236}{5} = 0.447.$

75. $\sqrt{\frac{8}{3}} = \sqrt{\frac{8 \times 3}{3 \times 3}} = \frac{\sqrt{24}}{3} = \frac{4.899}{3} = 1.633.$

76. $\frac{3\sqrt{2}}{2\sqrt{3}} = \frac{3\sqrt{2}}{2\sqrt{3}} \times \frac{\sqrt{3}}{\sqrt{3}} = \frac{3\sqrt{6}}{2 \times 3} = \frac{\sqrt{6}}{2} = \frac{2.449}{2} = 1.2245.$

77. $\frac{\sqrt{5}}{2} - \frac{10}{\sqrt{5}} + \sqrt{125} = \frac{(\sqrt{5})^2 - 20 + 2\sqrt{5} \times 5\sqrt{5}}{2\sqrt{5}} = \frac{5 - 20 + 50}{2\sqrt{5}}$

$= \frac{35}{2\sqrt{5}} \times \frac{\sqrt{5}}{\sqrt{5}} = \frac{35\sqrt{5}}{10} = \frac{7}{2} \times 2.236 = 7 \times 1.118 = 7.826.$

78. Clearly, $a * b = \sqrt{a^2 + b^2}$.

$\therefore \quad 5 * 12 = \sqrt{5^2 + 12^2} = \sqrt{25 + 144} = \sqrt{169} = 13.$

79. L.C.M. of 3, 4, 5, 6, 8 is 120. Now, $120 = 2 \times 2 \times 2 \times 3 \times 5$.
To make it a perfect square, it must be multiplied by $2 \times 3 \times 5$.
So, required number $= 2^2 \times 2^2 \times 3^2 \times 5^2 = 3600$.

80. L.C.M. of 21, 36, 66 = 2772. Now, $2772 = 2 \times 2 \times 3 \times 3 \times 7 \times 11$.
To make it a perfect square, it must be multiplied by 7×11.
So, required number $= 2^2 \times 3^2 \times 7^2 \times 11^2 = 213444$.

81. $294 = 7 \times 7 \times 2 \times 3$.
To make it a perfect square, it must be multiplied by 2×3 *i.e.*, 6.
$\therefore$ Required number = 6.

82. $5808 = 2 \times 2 \times 2 \times 2 \times 3 \times 11 \times 11 = 2^2 \times 2^2 \times 3 \times 11^2$
To make it a perfect square, it must be multiplied by 3.

83. $1470 = 7 \times 7 \times 5 \times 6$. To make it a perfect square, it must be divided by 5×6, *i.e.*, 30.

84.

```
   7  | 54 91 62 ( 741
      | 49
      |-----
 144  |  591
      |  576
      |-----
1481  |   1562
      |   1481
      |   -----
      |     81
```

$\therefore$ Required number to be subtracted = 81.

85. $0.000326 = \frac{326}{10^6}$.

```
  1 | 3 26 (18
    | 1
    |----
 28 | 226
    | 224
    |----
    |   2
```

$\therefore$ Required number to be subtracted $= \frac{2}{10^6} = 0.000002$.

86.

```
   8  | 68 06 21 ( 824
      | 64
      |-----
 162  |  406
      |  324
      |-----
1644  |   8221
      |   6576
      |   -----
      |   1645
```

$\therefore$ Number to be added $= (825)^2 - 680621 = 680625 - 680621 = 4$.

87. Greatest number of four digits is 9999.

```
  9  | 99 99 (99
     | 81
     |-----
189  | 1899
     | 1701
     |-----
     |  198
```

$\therefore$ Required number $= (9999 - 198) = 9801$.

88. Least number of 4 digits is 1000.

$$\begin{array}{r|l} 3 & \overline{10}\,\overline{00}\ (31 \\ & 9 \\ \hline 61 & 100 \\ & 61 \\ \hline & 39 \end{array}$$

$\therefore$ $(31)^2 < 1000 < (32)^2$. Hence, required number $= (32)^2 = 1024$.

89. $\dfrac{1}{(\sqrt{5}-\sqrt{3})} = \dfrac{1}{(\sqrt{5}-\sqrt{3})} \times \dfrac{(\sqrt{5}+\sqrt{3})}{(\sqrt{5}+\sqrt{3})} = \dfrac{(\sqrt{5}+\sqrt{3})}{(5-3)} = \dfrac{(2.2361+1.7321)}{2} = \dfrac{3.9682}{2} = 1.9841.$

90. Given exp. $= \dfrac{1}{(\sqrt{9}-\sqrt{8})} \times \dfrac{(\sqrt{9}+\sqrt{8})}{(\sqrt{9}+\sqrt{8})} - \dfrac{1}{(\sqrt{8}-\sqrt{7})} \times \dfrac{(\sqrt{8}+\sqrt{7})}{(\sqrt{8}+\sqrt{7})} + \dfrac{1}{(\sqrt{7}-\sqrt{6})} \times \dfrac{(\sqrt{7}+\sqrt{6})}{(\sqrt{7}+\sqrt{6})}$

$- \dfrac{1}{(\sqrt{6}-\sqrt{5})} \times \dfrac{(\sqrt{6}+\sqrt{5})}{(\sqrt{6}+\sqrt{5})} + \dfrac{1}{(\sqrt{5}-\sqrt{4})} \times \dfrac{(\sqrt{5}+\sqrt{4})}{(\sqrt{5}+\sqrt{4})}$

$= \dfrac{(\sqrt{9}+\sqrt{8})}{(9-8)} - \dfrac{(\sqrt{8}+\sqrt{7})}{(8-7)} + \dfrac{(\sqrt{7}+\sqrt{6})}{(7-6)} - \dfrac{(\sqrt{6}+\sqrt{5})}{(6-5)} + \dfrac{(\sqrt{5}+\sqrt{4})}{(5-4)}$

$= (\sqrt{9}+\sqrt{8}) - (\sqrt{8}+\sqrt{7}) + (\sqrt{7}+\sqrt{6}) - (\sqrt{6}+\sqrt{5}) + (\sqrt{5}+\sqrt{4}) = (\sqrt{9}+\sqrt{4}) = 3+2 = 5.$

91. Given exp. $= (2+\sqrt{2}) + \dfrac{1}{(2+\sqrt{2})} \times \dfrac{(2-\sqrt{2})}{(2-\sqrt{2})} - \dfrac{1}{(2-\sqrt{2})} \times \dfrac{(2+\sqrt{2})}{(2+\sqrt{2})}$

$= (2+\sqrt{2}) + \dfrac{(2-\sqrt{2})}{(4-2)} - \dfrac{(2+\sqrt{2})}{(4-2)} = (2+\sqrt{2}) + \dfrac{1}{2}(2-\sqrt{2}) - \dfrac{1}{2}(2+\sqrt{2}) = 2.$

92. $\dfrac{7}{(3+\sqrt{2})} = \dfrac{7}{(3+\sqrt{2})} \times \dfrac{(3-\sqrt{2})}{(3-\sqrt{2})} = \dfrac{7(3-\sqrt{2})}{(9-2)} = (3-\sqrt{2}) = (3-1.4142) = 1.5858.$

93. Given exp. $= \dfrac{3\sqrt{2}}{(\sqrt{6}-\sqrt{3})} \times \dfrac{(\sqrt{6}+\sqrt{3})}{(\sqrt{6}+\sqrt{3})} - \dfrac{4\sqrt{3}}{(\sqrt{6}-\sqrt{2})} \times \dfrac{(\sqrt{6}+\sqrt{2})}{(\sqrt{6}+\sqrt{2})} - \dfrac{6}{2(\sqrt{2}-\sqrt{3})}$

$= \dfrac{3\sqrt{2}(\sqrt{6}+\sqrt{3})}{(6-3)} - \dfrac{4\sqrt{3}(\sqrt{6}+\sqrt{2})}{(6-2)} + \dfrac{3}{(\sqrt{3}-\sqrt{2})} \times \dfrac{(\sqrt{3}+\sqrt{2})}{(\sqrt{3}+\sqrt{2})}$

$= \sqrt{2}(\sqrt{6}+\sqrt{3}) - \sqrt{3}(\sqrt{6}+\sqrt{2}) + 3(\sqrt{3}+\sqrt{2})$

$= \sqrt{12} + \sqrt{6} - \sqrt{18} - \sqrt{6} + 3\sqrt{3} + 3\sqrt{2}$

$= 2\sqrt{3} - 3\sqrt{2} + 3\sqrt{3} + 3\sqrt{2} = 5\sqrt{3}.$

94. $\dfrac{\sqrt{7}+\sqrt{5}}{\sqrt{7}-\sqrt{5}} = \dfrac{(\sqrt{7}+\sqrt{5})}{(\sqrt{7}-\sqrt{5})} \times \dfrac{(\sqrt{7}+\sqrt{5})}{(\sqrt{7}+\sqrt{5})} = \dfrac{(\sqrt{7}+\sqrt{5})^2}{(7-5)} = \dfrac{7+5+2\sqrt{35}}{2} = \dfrac{12+2\sqrt{35}}{2} = 6+\sqrt{35}.$

95. $a + b\sqrt{3} = \dfrac{(5+2\sqrt{3})}{(7+4\sqrt{3})} \times \dfrac{(7-4\sqrt{3})}{(7-4\sqrt{3})} = \dfrac{35-20\sqrt{3}+14\sqrt{3}-24}{(7)^2-(4\sqrt{3})^2} = \dfrac{11-6\sqrt{3}}{49-48} = 11-6\sqrt{3}.$

$\therefore$ $a = 11$, $b = -6$.

96. $\dfrac{\sqrt{2}-1}{\sqrt{2}+1} = \dfrac{(\sqrt{2}-1)}{(\sqrt{2}+1)} \times \dfrac{(\sqrt{2}-1)}{(\sqrt{2}-1)} = (\sqrt{2}-1)^2.$

$\therefore$ $\sqrt{\dfrac{\sqrt{2}-1}{\sqrt{2}+1}} = (\sqrt{2}-1) = (1.414-1) = 0.414.$

97. Given exp. $= \dfrac{3+\sqrt{6}}{5\sqrt{3}-4\sqrt{3}-4\sqrt{2}+5\sqrt{2}} = \dfrac{(3+\sqrt{6})}{(\sqrt{3}+\sqrt{2})}$

$= \dfrac{(3+\sqrt{6})}{(\sqrt{3}+\sqrt{2})} \times \dfrac{(\sqrt{3}-\sqrt{2})}{(\sqrt{3}-\sqrt{2})} = \dfrac{3\sqrt{3}-3\sqrt{2}+3\sqrt{2}-2\sqrt{3}}{(3-2)} = \sqrt{3}.$

98. Given exp. $= \dfrac{(2+\sqrt{3})}{(2-\sqrt{3})} \times \dfrac{(2+\sqrt{3})}{(2+\sqrt{3})} + \dfrac{(2-\sqrt{3})}{(2+\sqrt{3})} \times \dfrac{(2-\sqrt{3})}{(2-\sqrt{3})} + \dfrac{(\sqrt{3}-1)}{(\sqrt{3}+1)} \times \dfrac{(\sqrt{3}-1)}{(\sqrt{3}-1)}$

$= \dfrac{(2+\sqrt{3})^2}{(4-3)} + \dfrac{(2-\sqrt{3})^2}{(4-3)} + \dfrac{(\sqrt{3}-1)^2}{(3-1)} = [(2+\sqrt{3})^2 + (2-\sqrt{3})^2] + \dfrac{4-2\sqrt{3}}{2}$

$= 2(4+3) + 2 - \sqrt{3} = 16 - \sqrt{3}.$

99. $x + \dfrac{1}{x} = (7-4\sqrt{3}) + \dfrac{1}{(7-4\sqrt{3})} \times \dfrac{(7+4\sqrt{3})}{(7+4\sqrt{3})} = (7-4\sqrt{3}) + \dfrac{(7+4\sqrt{3})}{(49-48)}$

$= (7-4\sqrt{3}) + (7+4\sqrt{3}) = 14.$

100. $x = \dfrac{(\sqrt{3}+1)}{(\sqrt{3}-1)} \times \dfrac{(\sqrt{3}+1)}{(\sqrt{3}+1)} = \dfrac{(\sqrt{3}+1)^2}{(3-1)} = \dfrac{3+1+2\sqrt{3}}{2} = 2+\sqrt{3}.$

$y = \dfrac{(\sqrt{3}-1)}{(\sqrt{3}+1)} \times \dfrac{(\sqrt{3}-1)}{(\sqrt{3}-1)} = \dfrac{(\sqrt{3}-1)^2}{(3-1)} = \dfrac{3+1-2\sqrt{3}}{2} = 2-\sqrt{3}.$

$\therefore \quad x^2 + y^2 = (2+\sqrt{3})^2 + (2-\sqrt{3})^2 = 2(4+3) = 2 \times 7 = 14.$

101. $a = \dfrac{(\sqrt{5}+1)}{(\sqrt{5}-1)} \times \dfrac{(\sqrt{5}+1)}{(\sqrt{5}+1)} = \dfrac{(\sqrt{5}+1)^2}{(5-1)} = \dfrac{5+1+2\sqrt{5}}{4} = \left(\dfrac{3+\sqrt{5}}{2}\right)$

$b = \dfrac{(\sqrt{5}-1)}{(\sqrt{5}+1)} \times \dfrac{(\sqrt{5}-1)}{(\sqrt{5}-1)} = \dfrac{(\sqrt{5}-1)^2}{(5-1)} = \dfrac{5+1-2\sqrt{5}}{4} = \left(\dfrac{3-\sqrt{5}}{2}\right).$

$\therefore \quad a^2 + b^2 = \dfrac{(3+\sqrt{5})^2}{4} + \dfrac{(3-\sqrt{5})^2}{4} = \dfrac{(3+\sqrt{5})^2 + (3-\sqrt{5})^2}{4} = \dfrac{2(9+5)}{4} = 7.$

Also, $ab = \dfrac{(3+\sqrt{5})}{2} \cdot \dfrac{(3-\sqrt{5})}{2} = \dfrac{(9-5)}{4} = 1.$

$\therefore \quad \dfrac{a^2+ab+b^2}{a^2-ab+b^2} = \dfrac{(a^2+b^2)+ab}{(a^2+b^2)-ab} = \dfrac{7+1}{7-1} = \dfrac{8}{6} = \dfrac{4}{3}.$

102.

```
  1 | 15376 ( 124
    | 1
    |------
 22 | 53
    | 44
    |------
244 | 976
    | 976
    |------
    | ×
```

$\therefore$ Number of rows = 124.

103.

```
  1 | 36581 ( 191
    | 1
    |------
 29 | 265
    | 261
    |------
381 | 481
    | 381
    |------
    | 100
```

$\therefore$ Number of men left = 100

104. Money collected = (59.29 × 100) paise = 5929 paise.

$\therefore$ Number of members $= \sqrt{5929} = 77.$

105. $(.000216)^{1/3} = \left(\dfrac{216}{10^6}\right)^{1/3} = \left(\dfrac{6 \times 6 \times 6}{10^2 \times 10^2 \times 10^2}\right)^{1/3} = \dfrac{6}{10^2} = \dfrac{6}{100} = .06.$

106. $\sqrt[3]{4\frac{12}{125}} = \sqrt[3]{\frac{512}{125}} = \left(\frac{8\times8\times8}{5\times5\times5}\right)^{1/3} = \frac{8}{5} = 1\frac{3}{5}.$

107. $\sqrt{.000064} = \sqrt{\frac{64}{10^6}} = \frac{8}{10^3} = \frac{8}{1000} = .008.$

$\therefore \quad \sqrt[3]{\sqrt{.000064}} = \sqrt[3]{.008} = \sqrt[3]{\frac{8}{1000}} = \frac{2}{10} = 0.2.$

108. Clearly, 9261 is a perfect cube satisfying the given property.

109. $675 = 5 \times 5 \times 3 \times 3 \times 3.$

To make it a perfect cube, it must be multiplied by 5.

110. $3600 = 2^3 \times 5^2 \times 3^2 \times 2.$

To make it a perfect cube, it must be divided by $5^2 \times 3^2 \times 2$ *i.e.*, 450.

---

6. AVERAGE

IMPORTANT FACTS AND FORMULAE

1. Average $= \left(\dfrac{\text{Sum of observations}}{\text{Number of observations}}\right)$

2. Suppose a man covers a certain distance at x kmph and an equal distance at y kmph. Then, the average speed during the whole journey is $\left(\dfrac{2xy}{x+y}\right)$ kmph.

SOLVED EXAMPLES

Ex. 1. ***Find the average of all prime numbers between 30 and 50.***

Sol. There are five prime numbers between 30 and 50.

They are 31, 37, 41, 43 and 47.

$\therefore$ Required average $= \left(\dfrac{31+37+41+43+47}{5}\right) = \dfrac{199}{5} = 39.8.$

Ex. 2. ***Find the average of first 40 natural numbers.***

Sol. Sum of first n natural numbers $= \dfrac{n(n+1)}{2}$

So, sum of first 40 natural numbers $= \dfrac{40 \times 41}{2} = 820.$

$\therefore$ Required average $= \dfrac{820}{40} = 20.5.$

Ex. 3. ***Find the average of first 20 multiples of 7.***

Sol. Required average $= \dfrac{7(1+2+3+\ldots+20)}{20} = \left(\dfrac{7 \times 20 \times 21}{20 \times 2}\right) = \left(\dfrac{147}{2}\right) = 73.5.$

Ex. 4. ***The average of four consecutive even numbers is 27. Find the largest of these numbers.***

Sol. Let the numbers be x, $x + 2$, $x + 4$ and $x + 6$. Then,

$$\frac{x+(x+2)+(x+4)+(x+6)}{4} = 27 \Rightarrow \frac{4x+12}{4} = 27 \Rightarrow x+3 = 27 \Rightarrow x = 24.$$

$\therefore$ Largest number $= (x + 6) = 24 + 6 = 30.$

Ex. 5. ***There are two sections A and B of a class, consisting of 36 and 44 students respectively. If the average weight of section A is 40 kg and that of section B is 35 kg, find the average weight of the whole class.***

Sol. Total weight of (36 + 44) students $= (36 \times 40 + 44 \times 35)$ kg $= 2980$ kg.

$\therefore$ Average weight of the whole class $= \left(\dfrac{2980}{80}\right)$ kg $= 37.25$ kg.

Ex. 6. ***Nine persons went to a hotel for taking their meals. Eight of them spent Rs. 12 each on their meals and the ninth spent Rs. 8 more than the average expenditure of all the nine. What was the total money spent by them ?***

Sol. Let the average expenditure of all the nine be Rs. x.

Then, $12 \times 8 + (x + 8) = 9x$ or $8x = 104$ or $x = 13$.

$\therefore$ Total money spent $= 9x =$ Rs. $(9 \times 13) =$ Rs. 117.

Ex. 7. ***Of the three numbers, second is twice the first and is also thrice the third. If the average of the three numbers is 44, find the largest number.***

Sol. Let the third number be x. Then, second number $= 3x$. First number $= \frac{3x}{2}$.

$\therefore$ $x + 3x + \frac{3x}{2} = (44 \times 3)$ or $\frac{11x}{2} = 44 \times 3$ or $x = 24$.

So, largest number = 2nd number $= 3x = 72$.

Ex. 8. ***The average of 25 results is 18. The average of first twelve of them is 14 and that of last twelve is 17. Find the thirteenth result.***

Sol. Clearly, thirteenth result = (sum of 25 results) – (sum of 24 results)

$= (18 \times 25) - [(14 \times 12) + (17 \times 12)]$

$= 450 - (168 + 204) = 450 - 372 = 78.$

Ex. 9. ***The average of 11 results is 60. If the average of first six results is 58 and that of the last six is 63, find the sixth result.***

Sol. Sixth result $= (58 \times 6 + 63 \times 6 - 60 \times 11) = 66$.

Ex. 10. ***The average weight of A, B, C is 45 kg. If the average weight of A and B be 40 kg and that of B and C be 43 kg, find the weight of B.***

Sol. Let A, B and C represent their individual weights. Then,

$A + B + C = (45 \times 3)$ kg $= 135$ kg.

$A + B = (40 \times 2)$ kg $= 80$ kg and $B + C = (43 \times 2)$ kg $= 86$ kg.

$\therefore$ $B = (A + B) + (B + C) - (A + B + C) = (80 + 86 - 135)$ kg $= 31$ kg.

Ex. 11. ***The average age of a class of 39 students is 15 years. If the age of the teacher be included, then the average increases by 3 months. Find the age of the teacher.***

Sol. Total age of 39 persons $= (39 \times 15)$ years $= 585$ years.

Average age of 40 persons = 15 years 3 months $= \frac{61}{4}$ years.

Total age of 40 persons $= \left(\frac{61}{4} \times 40\right)$ years $= 610$ years.

$\therefore$ Age of the teacher $= (610 - 585)$ years $= 25$ years.

Ex. 12. ***The average weight of 10 oarsmen in a boat is increased by 1.8 kg when one of the crew, who weighs 53 kg is replaced by a new man. Find the weight of the new man.***

Sol. Total weight increased $= (1.8 \times 10)$ kg $= 18$ kg.

$\therefore$ Weight of the new man $= (53 + 18)$ kg $= 71$ kg.

Ex. 13. ***There were 35 students in a hostel. Due to the admission of 7 new students, the expenses of the mess were increased by Rs. 42 per day while the average expenditure per head diminished by Re 1. What was the original expenditure of the mess ?***

Sol. Let the original average expenditure be Rs. x. Then,

$42 (x - 1) - 35x = 42 \Leftrightarrow 7x = 84 \Rightarrow x = 12$.

$\therefore$ Original expenditure = Rs. (35×12) = Rs. 420.

Ex. 14. ***A batsman makes a score of 87 runs in the 17th inning and thus increases his average by 3. Find his average after 17th inning.***

Sol. Let the average after 17th inning = x.

Then, average after 16th inning = $(x - 3)$.

$\therefore$ $16(x-3) + 87 = 17x$ or $x = (87 - 48) = 39$.

Ex. 15. ***Distance between two stations A and B is 778 km. A train covers the journey from A to B at 84 km per hour and returns back to A with a uniform speed of 56 km per hour. Find the average speed of the train during the whole journey.***

Sol. Required average speed $= \left(\frac{2xy}{x+y}\right)$ km/hr $= \frac{2 \times 84 \times 56}{(84+56)}$ km/hr

$= \left(\frac{2 \times 84 \times 56}{140}\right)$ km/hr = 67.2 km/hr.

EXERCISE 6A

(OBJECTIVE TYPE QUESTIONS)

Directions : *Mark (✓) against the correct answer :*

1. David obtained 76, 65, 82, 67 and 85 marks (out of 100) in English, Mathematics, Physics, Chemistry and Biology. What are his average marks ? **(Bank P.O. 2003)**
   (a) 65 (b) 69 (c) 72
   (d) 76 (e) None of these
2. In Arun's opinion, his weight is greater than 65 kg but less than 72 kg. His brother does not agree with Arun and he thinks that Arun's weight is greater than 60 kg but less than 70 kg. His mother's view is that his weight cannot be greater than 68 kg. If all of them are correct in their estimation, what is the average of different probable weights of Arun ? **(S.B.I.P.O. 2000)**
   (a) 67 kg (b) 68 kg (c) 69 kg
   (d) Data inadequate (e) None of these
3. The average of 20 numbers is zero. Of them, at the most, how many may be greater than zero ? **(Hotel Management, 2002)**
   (a) 0 (b) 1 (c) 10 (d) 19
4. Find the average of all the numbers between 6 and 34 which are divisible by 5.
   (a) 18 (b) 20 (c) 24 (d) 30
   (C.B.I. 1997)
5. The average of first five multiples of 3 is : **(Assistant Grade, 1998)**
   (a) 3 (b) 9 (c) 12 (d) 15
6. The average of the first nine prime numbers is : **(C.B.I. 2003)**
   (a) 9 (b) 11 (c) $11\frac{1}{9}$ (d) $11\frac{2}{9}$
7. A student was asked to find the arithmetic mean of the numbers 3, 11, 7, 9, 15, 13, 8, 19, 17, 21, 14 and x. He found the mean to be 12. What should be the number in place of x ? **(Section Officers', 2003)**
   (a) 3 (b) 7 (c) 17 (d) 31
8. The average of 2, 7, 6 and x is 5 and the average of 18, 1, 6, x and y is 10. What is the value of y ?
   (a) 5 (b) 10 (c) 20 (d) 30

9. If the mean of 5 observations x, $x + 2$, $x + 4$, $x + 6$ and $x + 8$ is 11, then the mean of the last three observations is : **(C.D.S. 2003)**
(*a*) 11 (*b*) 13 (*c*) 15 (*d*) 17

10. If the mean of a, b, c is M and $ab + bc + ca = 0$, then the mean of a^2, b^2, c^2 is :
(*a*) M^2 (*b*) $3M^2$ (*c*) $6M^2$ (*d*) $9M^2$
(IITTM, 2003)

11. The average of the two-digit numbers, which remain the same when the digits interchange their positions, is : **(C.D.S. 2003)**
(*a*) 33 (*b*) 44 (*c*) 55 (*d*) 66

12. The average of first 50 natural numbers is :
(*a*) 12.25 (*b*) 21.25 (*c*) 25 (*d*) 25.5

13. The mean of 1^2, 2^2, 3^2, 4^2, 5^2, 6^2, 7^2 is :
(*a*) 10 (*b*) 20 (*c*) 30 (*d*) 40

14. The average of all odd numbers upto 100 is :
(*a*) 49 (*b*) 49.5 (*c*) 50 (*d*) 51

15. If a, b, c, d, e are five consecutive odd numbers, their average is :
(*a*) $5(a + 4)$ (*b*) $\frac{abcde}{5}$
(*c*) $5(a + b + c + d + e)$ (*d*) None of these

16. The average of a non-zero number and its square is 5 times the number. The number is : **(S.S.C. 2003)**
(*a*) 9 (*b*) 17 (*c*) 29 (*d*) 295

17. The average of 7 consecutive numbers is 20. The largest of these numbers is :
(*a*) 20 (*b*) 22 (*c*) 23 (*d*) 24
(S.S.C. 2000)

18. The average of five consecutive odd numbers is 61. What is the difference between the highest and lowest numbers ? **(Bank P.O. 2003)**
(*a*) 2 (*b*) 5 (*c*) 8
(*d*) Cannot be determined (*e*) None of these

19. The sum of three consecutive odd numbers is 38 more than the average of these numbers. What is the first of these numbers ? **(Bank P.O. 1998)**
(*a*) 13 (*b*) 17 (*c*) 19
(*d*) Data inadequate (*e*) None of these

20. The average age of the boys in a class is 16 years and that of the girls is 15 years. The average age for the whole class is : **(S.S.C. 2003)**
(*a*) 15 years (*b*) 15.5 years (*c*) 16 years
(*d*) Cannot be computed with the given information

21. The average annual income (in Rs.) of certain agricultural workers is S and that of other workers is T. The number of agricultural workers is 11 times that of other workers. Then the average monthly income (in Rs.) of all the workers is :
(*a*) $\frac{S + T}{2}$ (*b*) $\frac{S + 11T}{2}$ (*c*) $\frac{1}{11S} + T$ (*d*) $\frac{11S + T}{12}$
(S.S.C. 2004)

22. A family consists of grandparents, parents and three grandchildren. The average age of the grandparents is 67 years, that of the parents is 35 years and that of the grandchildren is 6 years. What is the average age of the family ? **(R.R.B. 2003)**
(*a*) $28\frac{4}{7}$ years (*b*) $31\frac{5}{7}$ years (*c*) $32\frac{1}{7}$ years (*d*) None of these

23. A library has an average of 510 visitors on Sundays and 240 on other days. The average number of visitors per day in a month of 30 days beginning with a Sunday is : **(M.A.T. 2003)**

(*a*) 250 (*b*) 276 (*c*) 280 (*d*) 285

24. If the average marks of three batches of 55, 60 and 45 students respectively is 50, 55 and 60, then the average marks of all the students is : **(C.B.I. 2003)**

(*a*) 53.33 (*b*) 54.68 (*c*) 55 (*d*) None of these

25. The average weight of 16 boys in a class is 50.25 kgs and that of the remaining 8 boys is 45.15 kgs. Find the average weight of all the boys in the class. **(I.M.T. 2002)**

(*a*) 47.55 kgs (*b*) 48 kgs (*c*) 48.55 kgs (*d*) 49.25 kgs

26. A car owner buys petrol at Rs 7.50, Rs. 8 and Rs. 8.50 per litre for three successive years. What approximately is the average cost per litre of petrol if he spends Rs. 4000 each year ? **(M.A.T. 2001)**

(*a*) Rs. 7.98 (*b*) Rs. 8 (*c*) Rs. 8.50 (*d*) Rs. 9

27. The average of six numbers is x and the average of three of these is y. If the average of the remaining three is z, then : **(Hotel Management, 2001)**

(*a*) $x = y + z$ (*b*) $2x = y + z$ (*c*) $x = 2y + 2z$ (*d*) None of these

28. Out of 9 persons, 8 persons spent Rs. 30 each for their meals. The ninth one spent Rs. 20 more than the average expenditure of all the nine. The total money spent by all of them was : **(C.B.I. 1998)**

(*a*) Rs. 260 (*b*) Rs. 290 (*c*) Rs. 292.50 (*d*) Rs. 400.50

29. The average of 50 numbers is 30. If two numbers, 35 and 40 are discarded, then the average of the remaining numbers is nearly : **(R.R.B. 2002)**

(*a*) 28.32 (*b*) 28.78 (*c*) 29.27 (*d*) 29.68

30. The average of five numbers is 27. If one number is excluded, the average becomes 25. The excluded number is : **(Section Officers', 2003)**

(*a*) 25 (*b*) 27 (*c*) 30 (*d*) 35

31. The average age of 35 students in a class is 16 years. The average age of 21 students is 14. What is the average age of remaining 14 students ? **(S.B.I.P.O. 1997)**

(*a*) 15 years (*b*) 17 years (*c*) 18 years (*d*) 19 years

32. 16 children are to be divided into two groups A and B of 10 and 6 children. The average percent marks obtained by the children of group A is 75 and the average percent marks of all the 16 children is 76. What is the average percent marks of children of group B ? **(B.S.R.B. 2003)**

(*a*) $77\frac{1}{3}$ (*b*) $77\frac{2}{3}$ (*c*) $78\frac{1}{3}$ (*d*) $78\frac{2}{3}$

33. The average score of a cricketer for ten matches is 38.9 runs. If the average for the first six matches is 42, then find the average for the last four matches.

(*a*) 33.25 (*b*) 33.5 (*c*) 34.25 (*d*) 35

(IGNOU, 2003)

34. The average of six numbers is 3.95. The average of two of them is 3.4, while the average of the other two is 3.85. What is the average of the remaining two numbers ?

(*a*) 4.5 (*b*) 4.6 (*c*) 4.7 (*d*) 4.8

(Bank P.O. 2003)

35. The batting average for 40 innings of a cricket player is 50 runs. His highest score exceeds his lowest score by 172 runs. If these two innings are excluded, the average of the remaining 38 innings is 48 runs. The highest score of the player is :

(*a*) 165 runs (*b*) 170 runs (*c*) 172 runs (*d*) 174 runs

36. The average price of 10 books is Rs. 12 while the average price of 8 of these books is Rs. 11.75. Of the remaining two books, if the price of one book is 60% more than the price of the other, what is the price of each of these two books ?
(*a*) Rs. 5, Rs. 7.50 (*b*) Rs. 8, Rs. 12 (*c*) Rs. 10, Rs. 16 (*d*) Rs. 12, Rs. 14
(Assistant Grade, 1997)

37. The average of runs of a cricket player of 10 innings was 32. How many runs must he make in his next innings so as to increase his average of runs by 4 ?
(*a*) 2 (*b*) 4 (*c*) 70 (*d*) 76
(S.S.C. 2004)

38. A grocer has a sale of Rs. 6435, Rs. 6927, Rs. 6855, Rs. 7230 and Rs. 6562 for 5 consecutive months. How much sale must he have in the sixth month so that he gets an average sale of Rs. 6500 ? **(S.S.C. 2003)**
(*a*) Rs. 4991 (*b*) Rs. 5991 (*c*) Rs. 6001 (*d*) Rs. 6991

39. A company produces on an average 4000 items per month for the first 3 months. How many items it must produce on an average per month over the next 9 months, to average 4375 items per month over the whole ? **(S.S.C. 1999)**
(*a*) 4500 (*b*) 4600 (*c*) 4680 (*d*) 4710

40. In the first 10 overs of a cricket game, the run rate was only 3.2. What should be the run rate in the remaining 40 overs to reach the target of 282 runs ? **(M.A.T. 2002)**
(*a*) 6.25 (*b*) 6.5 (*c*) 6.75 (*d*) 7

41. The average price of three items of furniture is Rs. 15000. If their prices are in the ratio 3 : 5 : 7, the price of the cheapest item is :
(*a*) Rs. 9000 (*b*) Rs. 15000 (*c*) Rs. 18000 (*d*) Rs. 21000

42. Of the four numbers, the first is twice the second, the second is one-third of the third and the third is 5 times the fourth. The average of the numbers is 24.75. The largest of these numbers is : **(Hotel Management, 1998)**
(*a*) 9 (*b*) 25 (*c*) 30 (*d*) None of these

43. Of the four numbers, whose average is 60, the first is one-fourth of the sum of the last three. The first number is : **(S.S.C. 2000)**
(*a*) 15 (*b*) 45 (*c*) 48 (*d*) 60.25

44. Of the three numbers, the first is twice the second and the second is twice the third. The average of the reciprocal of the numbers is $\frac{7}{72}$. The numbers are :
(*a*) 16, 8, 4 (*b*) 20, 10, 5 (*c*) 24, 12, 6 (*d*) 36, 18, 9
(C.B.I. 1997)

45. Of the three numbers, the average of the first and the second is greater than the average of the second and the third by 15. What is the difference between the first and the third of the three numbers ? **(S.B.I.P.O. 2000)**
(*a*) 15 (*b*) 45 (*c*) 60
(*d*) Data inadequate (*e*) None of these

46. The average of 8 numbers is 20. The average of first two numbers is $15\frac{1}{2}$ and that of the next three is $21\frac{1}{3}$. If the sixth number be less than the seventh and eighth numbers by 4 and 7 respectively, then the eighth number is : **(S.S.C. 2004)**
(*a*) 18 (*b*) 22 (*c*) 25 (*d*) 27

47. If the arithmetic mean of seventy-five numbers is calculated, it is 35. If each number is increased by 5, then mean of new numbers is : **(Assistant Grade, 1998)**
(*a*) 30 (*b*) 40 (*c*) 70 (*d*) 90

48. The average of ten numbers is 7. If each number is multiplied by 12, then the average of the new set of numbers is :

(a) 7 (b) 19 (c) 82 (d) 84

49. Average of ten positive numbers is $\overline{x}$. If each number is increased by 10%, then $\overline{x}$:

(a) remains unchanged (b) may decrease
(c) may increase (d) is increased by 10%

(I.M.T. 2002)

50. The mean of 50 observations was 36. It was found later that an observation 48 was wrongly taken as 23. The corrected new mean is : **(S.S.C. 2003)**

(a) 35.2 (b) 36.1 (c) 36.5 (d) 39.1

51. A pupil's marks were wrongly entered as 83 instead of 63. Due to that the average marks for the class got increased by half. The number of pupils in the class is :

(a) 10 (b) 20 (c) 40 (d) 73

(C.B.I. 1998)

52. The average age of 15 students of a class is 15 years. Out of these, the average age of 5 students is 14 years and that of the other 9 students is 16 years. The age of the 15th student is : **(S.S.C. 2003)**

(a) 11 years (b) 14 years (c) 15 years (d) $15\frac{2}{7}$ years

53. The average of 11 numbers is 10.9. If the average of the first six numbers is 10.5 and that of the last six numbers is 11.4, then the middle number is :

(a) 11 (b) 11.3 (c) 11.4 (d) 11.5

54. The average weight of three boys A, B and C is $54\frac{1}{3}$ kg, while the average weight of three boys B, D and E is 53 kg. What is the average weight of A, B, C, D and E ?

(a) 52.4 kg (b) 53.2 kg (c) 53.8 kg
(d) Data inadequate (e) None of these

(S.B.I.P.O. 2002)

55. The average temperature of the town in the first four days of a month was 58 degrees. The average for the second, third, fourth and fifth days was 60 degrees. If the temperatures of the first and fifth days were in the ratio 7 : 8, then what is the temperature on the fifth day ? **(NMIMS, 2003)**

(a) 64 degrees (b) 62 degrees (c) 56 degrees (d) None of these.

56. The average weight of A, B and C is 45 kg. If the average weight of A and B be 40 kg and that of B and C be 43 kg, then the weight of B is : **(S.S.C. 2004)**

(a) 17 kg (b) 20 kg (c) 26 kg (d) 31 kg

57. The average monthly income of P and Q is Rs. 5050. The average monthly income of Q and R is Rs. 6250 and the average monthly income of P and R is Rs. 5200. The monthly income of P is : **(R.R.B. 2004)**

(a) Rs. 3500 (b) Rs. 4000 (c) Rs. 4050 (d) Rs. 5000

58. The average age of 36 students in a group is 14 years. When teacher's age is included to it, the average increases by one. What is the teacher's age in years ?

(a) 31 (b) 36 (c) 51
(d) Cannot be determined (e) None of these **(R.B.I. 2003)**

59. The average monthly salary of 20 employees in an organisation is Rs. 1500. If the manager's salary is added, then the average salary increases by Rs. 100. What is the manager's monthly salary ? **(R.R.B. 2002)**

(a) Rs. 2000 (b) Rs. 2400 (c) Rs. 3600 (d) Rs. 4800

60. The average weight of a class of 24 students is 35 kg. If the weight of the teacher be included, the average rises by 400 g. The weight of the teacher is : **(S.S.C. 2003)**
(*a*) 45 kg (*b*) 50 kg (*c*) 53 kg (*d*) 55 kg

61. The average age of the mother and her six children is 12 years which is reduced by 5 years if the age of the mother is excluded. How old is the mother ?
(*a*) 40 years (*b*) 42 years (*c*) 48 years (*d*) 50 years

62. The captain of a cricket team of 11 members is 26 years old and the wicket keeper is 3 years older. If the ages of these two are excluded, the average age of the remaining players is one year less than the average age of the whole team. What is the average age of the team ? **(N.I.F.T. 2000)**
(*a*) 23 years (*b*) 24 years (*c*) 25 years (*d*) None of these

63. The average height of 25 boys is 1.4 m. When 5 boys leave the group, then the average height increases by 0.15 m. What is the average height of the 5 boys who leave ?
(*a*) 0.8 m (*b*) 0.9 m (*c*) 0.95 m (*d*) 1.05 m

64. The average weight of 8 persons increases by 2.5 kg when a new person comes in place of one of them weighing 65 kg. What might be the weight of the new person ?
(*a*) 76 kg (*b*) 76.5 kg (*c*) 85 kg
(*d*) Data inadequate (*e*) None of these **(Bank P.O. 2000)**

65. The average weight of 45 students in a class is 52 kg. Five of them whose average weight is 48 kg leave the class and other 5 students whose average weight is 54 kg join the class. What is the new average weight (in kg) of the class ? **(R.R.B. 2002)**
(*a*) $52\frac{1}{3}$ (*b*) $52\frac{1}{2}$ (*c*) $52\frac{2}{3}$ (*d*) None of these

66. The average age of 8 men is increased by 2 years when two of them whose ages are 21 years and 23 years are replaced by two new men. The average age of the two new men is : **(S.S.C. 2002)**
(*a*) 22 years (*b*) 24 years (*c*) 28 years (*d*) 30 years

67. The average of five consecutive numbers is *n*. If the next two numbers are also included, the average will :
(*a*) remain the same (*b*) increase by 1
(*c*) increase by 1.4 (*d*) increase by 2

68. A cricketer has a certain average for 10 innings. In the eleventh inning, he scored 108 runs, thereby increasing his average by 6 runs. His new average is :
(*a*) 48 runs (*b*) 52 runs (*c*) 55 runs (*d*) 60 runs
(A.A.O. Exam, 2003)

69. A cricketer whose bowling average is 12.4 runs per wicket takes 5 wickets for 26 runs and thereby decreases his average by 0.4. The number of wickets taken by him till the last match was : **(S.S.C. 2000)**
(*a*) 64 (*b*) 72 (*c*) 80 (*d*) 85

70. A team of 8 persons joins in a shooting competition. The best marksman scored 85 points. If he had scored 92 points, the average score for the team would have been 84. The number of points, the team scored was :
(*a*) 588 (*b*) 645 (*c*) 665 (*d*) 672

71. A motorist travels to a place 150 km away at an average speed of 50 km / hr and returns at 30 km / hr. His average speed for the whole journey in km / hr is :
(*a*) 35 (*b*) 37 (*c*) 37.5 (*d*) 40

72. The average weight of 3 men A, B and C is 84 kg. Another man D joins the group and the average now becomes 80 kg. If another man E, whose weight is 3 kg more than that of D, replaces A, then the average weight of B, C, D and E becomes 79 kg. The weight of A is : **(Bank P.O. 2003)**
(*a*) 70 kg (*b*) 72 kg (*c*) 75 kg (*d*) 80 kg

73. The average age of a husband and his wife was 23 years at the time of their marriage. After five years they have a one-year old child. The average age of the family now is :

(a) 19 years (b) 23 years (c) 28.5 years (d) 29.3 years

(Assistant Grade., 1998)

74. Three years ago, the average age of A and B was 18 years. With C joining them, the average age becomes 22 years. How old is C now ?

(a) 24 years (b) 27 years (c) 28 years (d) 30 years

75. The average age of husband, wife and their child 3 years ago was 27 years and that of wife and the child 5 years ago was 20 years. The present age of the husband is :

(a) 35 years (b) 40 years (c) 50 years (d) None of these

(Hotel Management, 2003)

76. 3 years ago, the average age of a family of 5 members was 17 years. A baby having been born, the average age of the family is the same today. The present age of the baby is **(S.S.C. 2004)**

(a) 1 year (b) $1\frac{1}{2}$ years (c) 2 years (d) 3 years

77. 10 years ago, the average age of a family of 4 members was 24 years. Two children having been born (with age difference of 2 years), the present average age of the family is the same. The present age of the youngest child is : **(S.S.C. 2003)**

(a) 1 year (b) 2 years (c) 3 years (d) 5 years

78. After replacing an old member by a new member, it was found that the average age of five members of a club is the same as it was 3 years ago. What is the difference between the ages of the replaced and the new member ?

(a) 2 years (b) 4 years (c) 8 years (d) 15 years

79. The average age of 3 children in a family is 20% of the average age of the father and the eldest child. The total age of the mother and the youngest child is 39 years. If the father's age is 26 years, what is the age of second child ?

(a) 15 years (b) 18 years (c) 20 years (d) Cannot be determined

80. The average age of a group of persons going for picnic is 16 years. Twenty new persons with an average age of 15 years join the group on the spot due to which their average age becomes 15.5 years. The number of persons initially going for picnic is :

(a) 5 (b) 10 (c) 20 (d) 30

81. A certain factory employed 600 men and 400 women and the average wage was Rs. 25.50 per day. If a woman got Rs. 5 less than a man, then what are their daily wages ?

(a) Man : Rs. 25; Woman : Rs. 20 (b) Man : Rs. 27.50, Woman : Rs. 22.50

(c) Man : Rs. 30, Woman : Rs. 25 (d) Man : Rs. 32.50, Woman : Rs. 27.50

82. The arithmetic mean of the scores of a group of students in a test was 52. The brightest 20% of them secured a mean score of 80 and the dullest 25% a mean score of 31. The mean score of remaining 55% is : **(S.S.C. 2000)**

(a) 45 (b) 50 (c) 51.4 approx. (d) 54.6 approx.

83. The average salary of all the workers in a workshop is Rs. 8000. The average salary of 7 technicians is Rs. 12000 and the average salary of the rest is Rs. 6000. The total number of workers in the workshop is : **(S.S.C. 2003)**

(a) 20 (b) 21 (c) 22 (d) 23

84. In a school with 600 students, the average age of the boys is 12 years and that of the girls is 11 years. If the average age of the school is 11 years 9 months, then the number of girls in the school is :

(a) 150 (b) 250 (c) 350 (d) 450

85. In an examination, a pupil's average marks were 63 per paper. If he had obtained 20 more marks for his Geography paper and 2 more marks for his History paper, his average per paper would have been 65. How many papers were there in the examination ?

(*a*) 8 (*b*) 9 (*c*) 10 (*d*) 11 (*e*) 12

(SCMHRD, 2001)

86. The average age of students of a class is 15.8 years. The average age of boys in the class is 16.4 years and that of the girls is 15.4 years. The ratio of the number of boys to the number of girls in the class is : **(S.B.I.P.O. 2002)**

(*a*) 1 : 2 (*b*) 2 : 3 (*c*) 3 : 4 (*d*) 3 : 5

ANSWERS

1. (*e*)	**2.** (*e*)	**3.** (*d*)	**4.** (*b*)	**5.** (*b*)	**6.** (*c*)	**7.** (*b*)	**8.** (*c*)	**9.** (*b*)
10. (*b*)	**11.** (*c*)	**12.** (*d*)	**13.** (*b*)	**14.** (*c*)	**15.** (*d*)	**16.** (*a*)	**17.** (*c*)	**18.** (*c*)
19. (*b*)	**20.** (*d*)	**21.** (*d*)	**22.** (*b*)	**23.** (*d*)	**24.** (*b*)	**25.** (*c*)	**26.** (*a*)	**27.** (*b*)
28. (*c*)	**29.** (*d*)	**30.** (*d*)	**31.** (*d*)	**32.** (*b*)	**33.** (*c*)	**34.** (*b*)	**35.** (*d*)	**36.** (*c*)
37. (*d*)	**38.** (*a*)	**39.** (*a*)	**40.** (*a*)	**41.** (*a*)	**42.** (*d*)	**43.** (*c*)	**44** (*c*)	**45.** (*e*)
46. (*c*)	**47.** (*b*)	**48.** (*d*)	**49.** (*d*)	**50.** (*c*)	**51.** (*c*)	**52.** (*a*)	**53.** (*d*)	**54.** (*d*)
55. (*a*)	**56.** (*d*)	**57.** (*b*)	**58.** (*c*)	**59.** (*c*)	**60.** (*a*)	**61.** (*b*)	**62.** (*d*)	**63.** (*a*)
64. (*c*)	**65.** (*c*)	**66.** (*d*)	**67.** (*b*)	**68.** (*a*)	**69.** (*d*)	**70.** (*c*)	**71.** (*c*)	**72.** (*c*)
73. (*a*)	**74.** (*a*)	**75.** (*b*)	**76.** (*c*)	**77.** (*c*)	**78.** (*d*)	**79.** (*d*)	**80.** (*c*)	**81.** (*b*)
82. (*c*)	**83.** (*b*)	**84.** (*a*)	**85.** (*d*)	**86.** (*b*)				

SOLUTIONS

1. Average $= \left(\frac{76+65+82+67+85}{5}\right) = \left(\frac{375}{5}\right) = 75.$

2. Let Arun's weight be X kg.

According to Arun, 65 < X < 72.

According to Arun's brother, 60 < X < 70.

According to Arun's mother, X < 68.

The values satisfying all the above conditions are 66 and 67.

$\therefore$ Required average $= \left(\frac{66+67}{2}\right) = \left(\frac{133}{2}\right) = 66.5$ kg.

3. Average of 20 numbers = 0.

$\therefore$ Sum of 20 numbers = $(0 \times 20) = 0$.

It is quite possible that 19 of these numbers may be positive and if their sum is *a*, then 20th number is $(-a)$.

4. Average $= \left(\frac{10+15+20+25+30}{5}\right) = \frac{100}{5} = 20.$

5. Average $= \frac{3(1+2+3+4+5)}{5} = \frac{45}{5} = 9.$

6. Average $= \left(\frac{2+3+5+7+11+13+17+19+23}{9}\right) = \frac{100}{9} = 11\frac{1}{9}.$

7. Clearly, we have $\left(\frac{3+11+7+9+15+13+8+19+17+21+14+x}{12}\right) = 12$

or $137 + x = 144$ or $x = 144 - 137 = 7$.

8. We have : $\left(\frac{2+7+6+x}{4}\right) = 5$ or $15 + x = 20$ or $x = 5$

Also, $\left(\frac{18+1+6+x+y}{5}\right) = 10$ or $25 + 5 + y = 50$ or $y = 20$.

9. We have : $\left[\frac{x+(x+2)+(x+4)+(x+6)+(x+8)}{5}\right] = 11$ or $5x + 20 = 55$ or $x = 7$.

So, the numbers are 7, 9, 11, 13, 15.

$\therefore$ Required mean $= \left(\frac{11+13+15}{3}\right) = \frac{39}{3} = 13$.

10. We have : $\left(\frac{a+b+c}{3}\right) = \text{M}$ or $(a + b + c) = 3\text{M}$.

Now, $(a + b + c)^2 = (3\text{M})^2 = 9\text{M}^2$.

$\Leftrightarrow \quad a^2 + b^2 + c^2 + 2\,(ab + bc + ca) = 9\text{M}^2$

$\Leftrightarrow \quad a^2 + b^2 + c^2 = 9\text{M}^2$. $\quad [\because (ab + bc + ca) = 0]$

$\therefore$ Required mean $= \left(\frac{a^2+b^2+c^2}{3}\right) = \frac{9\text{M}^2}{3} = 3\text{M}^2$.

11. Average $= \left(\frac{11+22+33+44+55+66+77+88+99}{9}\right)$

$= \left[\frac{(11+99)+(22+88)+(33+77)+(44+66)+55}{9}\right]$

$= \left(\frac{4\times 110+55}{9}\right) = \frac{495}{9} = 55$.

12. Sum of first n natural numbers $= \frac{n\,(n+1)}{2}$.

So, average of first n natural numbers $= \frac{n\,(n+1)}{2n} = \frac{n+1}{2}$.

$\therefore$ Required average $= \left(\frac{50+1}{2}\right) = \frac{51}{2} = 25.5$.

13. $1^2 + 2^2 + 3^2 + \ldots\ldots + n^2 = \frac{n\,(n+1)\,(2n+1)}{6}$

$\therefore \quad 1^2 + 2^2 + 3^2 + \ldots\ldots + 7^2 = \left(\frac{7\times 8\times 15}{6}\right) = 140$.

So, required average $= \left(\frac{140}{7}\right) = 20$.

14. Sum of odd numbers upto 100 $= 1 + 3 + 5 + 7 + \ldots\ldots + 95 + 97 + 99$.

$= (1 + 99) + (3 + 97) + (5 + 95) + \ldots\ldots +$ upto 25 pairs

$= 100 + 100 + 100 + \ldots\ldots$ (25 times) $= 2500$.

$\therefore$ Average $= \left(\frac{2500}{50}\right) = 50$.

15. Clearly, $b = a + 2$, $c = a + 4$, $d = a + 6$ and $e = a + 8$.

$\therefore$ Average $= \dfrac{a + (a+2) + (a+4) + (a+6) + (a+8)}{5} = \left(\dfrac{5a + 20}{5}\right) = (a + 4)$.

16. Let the number be x. Then,

$\dfrac{x + x^2}{2} = 5x \Leftrightarrow x^2 - 9x = 0 \Leftrightarrow x(x - 9) = 0 \Leftrightarrow x = 0$ or $x = 9$.

So, the number is 9.

17. Let the numbers be x, $x + 1$, $x + 2$, $x + 3$, $x + 4$, $x + 5$ and $x + 6$.

Then, $\dfrac{x + (x+1) + (x+2) + (x+3) + (x+4) + (x+5) + (x+6)}{7} = 20$

or $7x + 21 = 140$ or $7x = 119$ or $x = 17$.

$\therefore$ Largest number $= x + 6 = 23$.

18. Let the numbers be x, $x + 2$, $x + 4$, $x + 6$ and $x + 8$.

Then, $\dfrac{x + (x+2) + (x+4) + (x+6) + (x+8)}{5} = 61$ or $5x + 20 = 305$ or $x = 57$.

So, required difference $= (57 + 8) - 57 = 8$.

19. Let the numbers be x, $x + 2$ and $x + 4$.

Then, $(x + x + 2 + x + 4) - \dfrac{(x + x + 2 + x + 4)}{3} = 38$

or $(3x + 6) - \dfrac{(3x + 6)}{3} = 38$ or $2(3x + 6) = 114$ or $6x = 102$ or $x = 17$.

So, first number $= x = 17$.

20. Clearly, to find the average, we ought to know the number of boys, girls or students in the class, neither of which has been given.

So, the data provided is inadequate.

21. Let the number of other workers be x.

Then, number of agricultural workers $= 11x$.

Total number of workers $= 12x$.

$\therefore$ Average monthly income $= \dfrac{S \times 11x + T \times x}{12x} = \dfrac{11S + T}{12}$.

22. Required average $= \left(\dfrac{67 \times 2 + 35 \times 2 + 6 \times 3}{2 + 2 + 3}\right)$

$= \left(\dfrac{134 + 70 + 18}{7}\right) = \dfrac{222}{7} = 31\dfrac{5}{7}$ years.

23. Since the month begins with a Sunday, so there will be five Sundays in the month.

$\therefore$ Required average $= \left(\dfrac{510 \times 5 + 240 \times 25}{30}\right) = \dfrac{8550}{30} = 285$.

24. Required average $= \left(\dfrac{55 \times 50 + 60 \times 55 + 45 \times 60}{55 + 60 + 45}\right)$

$= \left(\dfrac{2750 + 3300 + 2700}{160}\right) = \dfrac{8750}{160} = 54.68$.

25. Required average $= \left(\dfrac{50.25 \times 16 + 45.15 \times 8}{16 + 8}\right)$

$= \left(\dfrac{804 + 361.20}{24}\right) = \dfrac{1165.20}{24} = 48.55$.

26. Total quantity of petrol consumed in 3 years $= \left(\frac{4000}{7.50} + \frac{4000}{8} + \frac{4000}{8.50}\right)$ litres

$= 4000\left(\frac{2}{15} + \frac{1}{8} + \frac{2}{17}\right) = \left(\frac{76700}{51}\right)$ litres.

Total amount spent = Rs. (3 × 4000) = Rs. 12000.

$\therefore$ Average cost = Rs. $\left(\frac{12000 \times 51}{76700}\right)$ = Rs. $\frac{6120}{767}$ = Rs. 7.98.

27. Clearly, we have : $x = \left(\frac{3y + 3z}{6}\right)$ or $2x = y + z$.

28. Let the average expenditure be Rs. x. Then,

$9x = 8 \times 30 + (x + 20)$ or $9x = x + 260$ or $8x = 260$ or $x = 32.50$.

$\therefore$ Total money spent = $9x$ = Rs. (9 × 32.50) = Rs 292. 50.

29. Sum of 50 numbers = 30 × 50 = 1500.

Sum of remaining 48 numbers = 1500 – (35 + 40) = 1425.

$\therefore$ Required average $= \left(\frac{1425}{48}\right) = \frac{475}{16} = 29.68$.

30. Excluded number = (27 × 5) – (25 × 4) = 135 – 100 = 35.

31. Sum of the ages of 14 students = (16 × 35) – (14 × 21) = 560 – 294 = 266.

$\therefore$ Required average $= \left(\frac{266}{14}\right)$ = 19 years.

32. Required average $= \frac{(76 \times 16) - (75 \times 10)}{6} = \left(\frac{1216 - 750}{6}\right) = \frac{466}{6} = \frac{233}{3} = 77\frac{2}{3}$.

33. Required average $= \frac{(38.9 \times 10) - (42 \times 6)}{4} = \frac{137}{4} = 34.25$.

34. Sum of the remaining two numbers $= (3.95 \times 6) - [(3.4 \times 2) + (3.85 \times 2)]$

$= 23.70 - (6.8 + 7.7) = 23.70 - 14.5 = 9.20$.

$\therefore$ Required average $= \left(\frac{9.2}{2}\right) = 4.6$.

35. Let the highest score be x. Then, lowest score = $(x - 172)$.

Then, $(50 \times 40) - [x + (x - 172)] = 38 \times 48$

$\Leftrightarrow$ $2x = 2000 + 172 - 1824 \Leftrightarrow 2x = 348 \Leftrightarrow x = 174$.

36. Total price of the two books = Rs. [(12 × 10) – (11.75 × 8)]

= Rs. (120 – 94) = Rs. 26.

Let the price of one book be Rs. x.

Then, the price of other book = Rs. (x + 60% of x) = Rs. $\left(x + \frac{3}{5}x\right)$ = Rs. $\left(\frac{8x}{5}\right)$

So, $x + \frac{8x}{5} = 26 \Leftrightarrow 13x = 130 \Leftrightarrow x = 10$.

$\therefore$ The prices of the two books are Rs. 10 and Rs. 16.

37. Average after 11 innings = 36.

$\therefore$ Required number of runs $= (36 \times 11) - (32 \times 10)$

$= 396 - 320 = 76$.

38. Total sale for 5 months = Rs. (6435 + 6927 + 6855 + 7230 + 6562) = Rs. 34009.

$\therefore$ Requred sale = Rs. $[(6500 \times 6) - 34009]$ = Rs. $(39000 - 34009)$ = Rs. 4991.

39. Required average $= \frac{(4375 \times 12) - (4000 \times 3)}{9} = \frac{52500 - 12000}{9} = \frac{40500}{9} = 4500.$

40. Required run rate $= \frac{282 - (3.2 \times 10)}{40} = \frac{250}{40} = 6.25.$

41. Let their prices be $3x$, $5x$ and $7x$.

Then, $3x + 5x + 7x = (15000 \times 3)$ or $x = 3000$.

$\therefore$ Cost of cheapest item $= 3x =$ Rs. 9000.

42. Let the fourth number be x.

Then, third number $= 5x$, second number $= \frac{5x}{3}$ and first number $= \frac{10x}{3}$.

$x + 5x + \frac{5x}{3} + \frac{10x}{3} = (24.75 \times 4)$ or $11x = 99$ or $x = 9$.

So, the numbers are 9, 45, 15 and 30.

$\therefore$ Largest number = 45.

43. Let the first number be x.

Then, sum of the four numbers $= x + 4x = 5x$.

So, $\frac{5x}{4} = 60$ or $x = \left(\frac{60 \times 4}{5}\right) = 48$.

44. Let the third number be x. Then, second number $= 2x$. First number $= 4x$.

$\therefore \quad \frac{1}{x} + \frac{1}{2x} + \frac{1}{4x} = \left(\frac{7}{72} \times 3\right)$ or $\frac{7}{4x} = \frac{7}{24}$ or $4x = 24$ or $x = 6$.

So, the numbers are 24, 12 and 6.

45. Let the numbers be x, y and z.

Then, $\left(\frac{x+y}{2}\right) - \left(\frac{y+z}{2}\right) = 15$ or $(x + y) - (y + z) = 30$ or $x - z = 30$.

46. Let the eighth number be x. Then, sixth number $= (x - 7)$.

Seventh number $= (x - 7) + 4 = (x - 3)$.

So, $\left(2 \times 15\frac{1}{2}\right) + \left(3 \times 21\frac{1}{3}\right) + (x - 7) + (x - 3) + x = 8 \times 20$

$\Leftrightarrow \quad 31 + 64 + (3x - 10) = 160 \Leftrightarrow 3x = 75 \Leftrightarrow x = 25.$

47. A.M. of 75 numbers = 35.

Sum of 75 numbers $= (75 \times 35) = 2625$.

Total increase $= (75 \times 5) = 375$.

Increased sum $= (2625 + 375) = 3000$.

Increased average $= \frac{3000}{75} = 40$.

48. Average of 10 numbers = 7.

Sum of these 10 numbers $= (10 \times 7) = 70$.

$\therefore \quad x_1 + x_2 + \ldots.. + x_{10} = 70.$

$\Rightarrow \quad 12x_1 + 12x_2 + \ldots.. + 12x_{10} = 840$

$\Rightarrow \quad \frac{12x_1 + 12x_2 + \ldots.. + 12x_{10}}{10} = 84$

$\Rightarrow$ Average of new numbers is 84.

49. $\frac{x_1 + x_2 + ... + x_{10}}{10} = \bar{x} \Rightarrow x_1 + x_2 + ... + x_{10} = 10\bar{x}$

$$\Rightarrow \frac{110}{100}x_1 + \frac{110}{100}x_2 + ... + \frac{110}{100}x_{10} = \frac{110}{100} \times 10\bar{x}$$

$$\Rightarrow \frac{\frac{110}{100}x_1 + \frac{110}{100}x_2 + ... + \frac{110}{100}x_{10}}{10} = \frac{11}{10}\bar{x}$$

$\Rightarrow$ **Average is increased by 10%.**

50. **Correct sum = (36 × 50 + 48 − 23) = 1825.**

$\therefore$ **Correct mean =** $\frac{1825}{50}$ **= 36.5.**

51. **Let there be** x **pupils in the class.**

Total increase in marks = $\left(x \times \frac{1}{2}\right) = \frac{x}{2}$.

$\therefore \frac{x}{2} = (83 - 63) \Rightarrow \frac{x}{2} = 20 \Rightarrow x = 40.$

52. **Age of the 15th student =** $[15 \times 15 - (14 \times 5 + 16 \times 9)] = (225 - 214) = 11$ **years.**

53. **Middle number =** $[(10.5 \times 6 + 11.4 \times 6) - 10.9 \times 11] = (131.4 - 119.9) = 11.5.$

54. **Total weight of (A + B + C) =** $\left(54\frac{1}{3} \times 3\right)$ **kg = 163 kg.**

Total weight of (B + D + E) = (53 × 3) kg = 159 kg.

Adding both, we get : A + 2B + C + D + E = (163 + 159) kg = 322 kg.

So, to find the average weight of A, B, C, D and E, we ought to know B's weight, which is not given. So, the data is inadequate.

55. **Sum of temperatures on 1st, 2nd, 3rd and 4th days = (58 × 4) = 232 degrees** ...(*i*)

Sum of temperatures on 2nd, 3rd, 4th and 5th days = (60 × 4) = 240 degrees ...(*ii*)

Subtracting (*i*) from (*ii*), we get :

Temp. on 5th day - Temp. on 1st day = 8 degrees.

Let the temperatures on 1st and 5th days be 7*x* and 8*x* degrees respectively.

Then, $8x - 7x = 8$ **or** $x = 8$.

$\therefore$ **Temperature on the 5th day =** $8x$ **= 64 degrees.**

56. **Let A, B, C represent their respective weights. Then, we have :**

A + B + C = (45 × 3) = 135 ...(*i*)

A + B = (40 × 2) = 80 ...(*ii*)

B + C = (43 × 2) = 86 ...(*iii*)

Adding (*ii*) and (*iii*), we get : A + 2B + C = 166 ...(*iv*)

Subtracting (*i*) from (*iv*), we get : B = 31.

$\therefore$ **B's weight = 31 kg.**

57. **Let P, Q and R represent their respective monthly incomes. Then, we have :**

P + Q = (5050 × 2) = 10100 ...(*i*)

Q + R = (6250 × 2) = 12500 ...(*ii*)

P + R = (5200 × 2) = 10400 ...(*iii*)

Adding (*i*), (*ii*) and (*iii*), we get : 2 (P + Q + R) = 33000 or P + Q + R = 16500 ...(*iv*)

Subtracting (*ii*) from (*iv*), we get P = 4000.

$\therefore$ **P's monthly income = Rs. 4000.**

58. Age of the teacher = $(37 \times 15 - 36 \times 14)$ years = 51 years.

59. Manager's monthly salary = Rs. $(1600 \times 21 - 1500 \times 20)$ = Rs. 3600.

60. Weight of the teacher = $(35.4 \times 25 - 35 \times 24)$ kg = 45 kg.

61. Age of the mother = $(12 \times 7 - 7 \times 6)$ years = 42 years.

62. Let the average age of the whole team be x years.

$\therefore \quad 11x - (26 + 29) = 9(x - 1) \Leftrightarrow 11x - 9x = 46 \Leftrightarrow 2x = 46 \Leftrightarrow x = 23.$

So, average age of the team is 23 years.

63. Sum of heights of the 5 boys = $(25 \times 1.4 - 20 \times 1.55)$ m = 4 m.

$\therefore \quad$ Required average = $\left(\frac{4}{5}\right)$ = 0.8 m.

64. Total weight increased = (8×2.5) kg = 20 kg.

Weight of new person = $(65 + 20)$ kg = 85 kg.

65. Sum of the weights of the students after replacement

$= [(52 \times 45) - (48 \times 5) + (54 \times 5)]$ kg = 2370 kg.

$\therefore \quad$ New average = $\left(\frac{2370}{45}\right)$ kg = $53\frac{2}{3}$ kg.

66. Total age increased = (8×2) years = 16 years.

Sum of ages of two new men = $(21 + 23 + 16)$ years = 60 years.

$\therefore \quad$ Average age of two new men = $\left(\frac{60}{2}\right)$ years = 30 years.

67. Let five consecutive numbers be $x, x + 1, x + 2, x + 3$ and $x + 4$.

Their average = $\frac{5x + 10}{5} = (x + 2)$.

Average of 7 numbers = $\frac{(5x + 10) + (x + 5) + (x + 6)}{7} = \frac{7x + 21}{7} = (x + 3)$.

So, the average increased by 1.

68. Let average for 10 innings be x. Then,

$\frac{10x + 108}{11} = x + 6 \Rightarrow 11x + 66 = 10x + 108 \Rightarrow x = 42.$

$\therefore \quad$ New average = $(x + 6)$ = 48 runs.

69. Let the number of wickets taken till the last match be x. Then,

$\frac{12.4x + 26}{x + 5} = 12 \Rightarrow 12.4x + 26 = 12x + 60 \Rightarrow 0.4x = 34 \Rightarrow x = \frac{34}{0.4} = \frac{340}{4} = 85.$

70. Let the total score be x.

$\therefore \quad \frac{x + 92 - 85}{8} = 84 \Rightarrow x + 7 = 672 \Rightarrow x = 665.$

71. Average speed = $\frac{2xy}{x + y}$ km/hr = $\left(\frac{2 \times 50 \times 30}{50 + 30}\right)$ km/hr = 37.5 km/hr.

72. Let A, B, C, D and E represent their respective weights. Then,

$A + B + C = (84 \times 3) = 252$ kg, $A + B + C + D = (80 \times 4) = 320$ kg.

$\therefore \quad D = (320 - 252)$ kg = 68 kg, $E = (68 + 3)$ kg = 71 kg.

$B + C + D + E = (79 \times 4) = 316$ kg.

Now, $(A + B + C + D) - (B + C + D + E) = (320 - 316)$ kg = 4 kg.

$\therefore \quad A - E = 4 \Rightarrow A = (4 + E) = 75$ kg.

73. Sum of the present ages of husband, wife and child = $(23 \times 2 + 5 \times 2) + 1 = 57$ years.

$\therefore$ Required average $= \left(\frac{57}{3}\right) = 19$ years.

74. Present age of (A + B) = $(18 \times 2 + 3 \times 2)$ years = 42 years.

Present age of (A + B + C) = (22×3) years = 66 years.

$\therefore$ C's age = $(66 - 42)$ years = 24 years.

75. Sum of the present ages of husband, wife and child = $(27 \times 3 + 3 \times 3)$ years = 90 years.

Sum of the present ages of wife and child = $(20 \times 2 + 5 \times 2)$ years = 50 years.

$\therefore$ Husband's present age = $(90 - 50)$ years = 40 years.

76. Total age of 5 members, 3 years ago = (17×5) years = 85 years.

Total age of 5 members now = $(85 + 3 \times 5)$ years = 100 years.

Total age of 6 members now = (17×6) years = 102 years.

$\therefore$ Age of the baby = $(102 - 100)$ years = 2 years.

77. Total age of 4 members, 10 years ago = (24×4) years = 96 years.

Total age of 4 members now = $(96 + 10 \times 4)$ years = 136 years.

Total age of 6 members now = (24×6) years = 144 years.

Sum of the ages of 2 children = $(144 - 136)$ years = 8 years.

Let the age of the younger child be x years.

Then, age of the elder child = $(x + 2)$ years.

So, $x + x + 2 = 8 \Leftrightarrow 2x = 6 \Leftrightarrow x = 3$.

$\therefore$ Age of younger child = 3 years.

78. Age decreased = (5×3) years = 15 years.

So, the required difference = 15 years.

79. Since the total or average age of all the family members is not given, the given data is inadequate. So, the age of second child cannot be determined.

80. Let the initial number of persons be x. Then,

$16x + 20 \times 15 = 15.5\,(x + 20) \Leftrightarrow 0.5x = 10 \Leftrightarrow x = 20$.

81. Let the daily wage of a man be Rs. x.

Then, daily wage of a woman = Rs. $(x - 5)$.

Now, $600x + 400\,(x - 5) = 25.50 \times (600 + 400) \Leftrightarrow 1000x = 27500 \Leftrightarrow x = 27.50$.

$\therefore$ Man's daily wages = Rs. 27.50; Woman's daily wages = $(x - 5)$ = Rs. 22.50.

82. Let the required mean score be x. Then,

$20 \times 80 + 25 \times 31 + 55 \times x = 52 \times 100$

$\Leftrightarrow 1600 + 775 + 55x = 5200 \Leftrightarrow 55x = 2825 \Leftrightarrow x = \frac{565}{11} \approx 51.4$.

83. Let the total number of workers be x. Then,

$8000x = (12000 \times 7) + 6000\,(x - 7) \Leftrightarrow 2000x = 42000 \Leftrightarrow x = 21$.

84. Let the number of girls be x. Then, number of boys = $(600 - x)$.

Then, $\left(11\frac{3}{4} \times 600\right) = 11x + 12\,(600 - x) \Leftrightarrow x = 7200 - 7050 \Leftrightarrow x = 150$.

85. Let the number of papers be x. Then, $63x + 20 + 2 = 65x$ or $2x = 22$ or $x = 11$.

86. Let the ratio be $k : 1$. Then,

$k \times 16.4 + 1 \times 15.4 = (k + 1) \times 15.8$

$\Leftrightarrow (16.4 - 15.8)\,k = (15.8 - 15.4) \Leftrightarrow k = \frac{0.4}{0.6} = \frac{2}{3}$.

$\therefore$ Required ratio $= \frac{2}{3} : 1 = 2 : 3$.

EXERCISE 6B

(DATA SUFFICIENCY TYPE QUESTIONS)

Directions *(Questions 1 to 10)* : ***Each of the questions given below consists of a statement and/or a question and two statements numbered I and II given below it. You have to decide whether the data provided in the statement(s) is/are sufficient to answer the given question. Read both the statements and***

Give answer (a) if the data in Statement I alone are sufficient to answer the question, while the data in Statement II alone are not sufficient to answer the question;

Give answer (b) if the data in Statement II alone are sufficient to answer the question, while the data in Statement I alone are not sufficient to answer the question;

Give answer (c) if the data either in Statement I or in Statement II alone are sufficient to answer the question;

Give answer (d) if the data even in both Statements I and II together are not sufficient to answer the question;

Give answer (e) if the data in both Statements I and II together are necessary to answer the question.

1. The total of the present ages of A, B, C and D is 96 years. What is B's present age ?

I. The average age of A, B and D is 20 years.

II. The average age of C and D is 25 years.

2. What is the average age of children in the class ? **(Bank P.O. 2003)**

I. Age of the teacher is as many years as the number of children.

II. Average age increased by 1 year if the teacher's age is also included.

3. What is the average weight of the three new team members who are recently included in the team ?

I. The average weight of the team increases by 20 kg.

II. The three new men substitute earlier members whose weights are 64 kg, 75 kg and 66 kg.

4. The average age of P, Q, R and S is 30 years. How old is R ? **(R.B.I. 2003)**

I. The sum of ages of P and R is 60 years.

II. S is 10 years younger than R.

5. How old will C be after 10 years ?

I. Five years ago, the average age of A and B was 15 years.

II. Average age of A, B and C today is 20 years.

6. How many children are there in the group ? **(Bank P.O. 2000)**

I. Average age of the children in this group is 15 years. The total age of all the children in this group is 240 years.

II. The total age of all the children in the group and the teacher is 264 years. The age of the teacher is 9 years more than the average age of the children.

7. Deepak's marks in Hindi are 15 more than the average marks obtained by him in Hindi, Economics, Sociology and Philosophy. What are his marks in Philosophy ?

I. The total marks obtained by him in Hindi and Philosophy together is 120.

II. The difference between the marks obtained by him in Sociology and Economics is 120.

8. How many candidates were interviewed everyday by the panel A out of the three panels A, B and C ? **(Bank P.O. 1999)**

I. The three panels on an average interview 15 candidates everyday.

II. Out of a total of 45 candidates interviewed everyday by the three panels, the number of candidates interviewed by panel A is more by 2 than the candidates interviewed by panel C and is more by 1 than the candidates interviewed by panel B.

9. The average age of teacher and students in a class is 3 years more than the average age of students. What is the age of the class teacher ? **(Bank P.O. 2000)**

I. There are 11 students in the class.

II. The average age of teacher and students is 14 years.

10. What will be the average weight of the remaining class ? **(Bank P.O. 1999)**

I. Average weight of 30 children out of total 46 in the class is 22.5 kg and that of the remaining children is 29.125 kg. A child having weight more than 40 kg is excluded.

II. Average weight of a class of 46 children is 23.5 kg. A child weighing 46 kg is dropped out.

Directions (*Questions 11 to 13*) : *Each of the questions given below consists of a question followed by three statements. You have to study the question and the statements and decide which of the statement(s) is/are necessary to answer the question.*

11. How many marks did Tarun secure in English ? **(S.B.I.P.O. 2000)**

I. The average marks obtained by Tarun in four subjects including English is 60.

II. The total marks obtained by him in English and Mathematics together is 170.

III. The total marks obtained by him in Mathematics and Science together is 180.

(*a*) I and II only (*b*) II and III only (*c*) I and III only

(*d*) All I, II and III (*e*) None of these

12. The mean temperature of Monday to Wednesday was 37°C and of Tuesday to Thursday was 34°C. What was the temperature on Thursday ?

I. The temperature on Thursday was $\frac{4}{5}$th that of Monday.

II. The mean temperature of Monday and Thursday was 40.5°C.

III. The difference between the temperature on Monday and that on Thursday was 9°C.

(*a*) I and II only (*b*) II and III only (*c*) Either I or II

(*d*) Either I, II or III (*e*) Any two of the three

13. In a cricket eleven, the average age of eleven players is 28 years. What is the age of the captain ?

I. The captain is eleven years older than the youngest player.

II. The average age of 10 players, other than the captain is 27.3 years.

III. Leaving aside the captain and the youngest player, the average ages of three groups of three players each are 25 years, 28 years and 30 years respectively.

(*a*) Any two of the three (*b*) All I, II and III

(*c*) II only or I and III only (*d*) II and III only

(*e*) None of these

Directions (*Question 14*) : *The given question is followed by three statements labelled I, II and III. You have to study the question and all the three statements given to decide whether any information provided in the statement(s) is/are redundant and can be dispensed with while answering the given question.*

14. What is the average salary of 15 employees ? **(S.B.I.P.O. 2001)**

I. Average salary of 7 clerical cadre (out of the 15 employees) is Rs. 8500.

II. Average salary of 5 officer cadre (out of the 15 employees) is Rs. 10000.

III. Average salary of the 3 sub-staff employees (out of the 15 employees) is Rs. 2500.

(*a*) None (*b*) Only I

(*c*) Only II (*d*) Only III

(*e*) Question cannot be answered even with information in all the three statements

ANSWERS

1. (d) 2. (d) 3. (d) 4. (d) 5. (e) 6. (a) 7. (d) 8. (b) 9. (e)
10. (b) 11. (e) 12. (c) 13. (c) 14. (a)

SOLUTIONS

1. A + B + C + D = 96 ...(i)
I gives, A + B + D = (3 × 20) ⇒ A + B + D = 60 ...(ii)
II gives, C + D = (2 × 50) ⇒ C + D = 100 ...(iii)
From (i), (ii) and (iii) also, we cannot find B.
∴ Correct answer is (d).

2. Let there be x children.
I gives, age of teacher = x years.
II gives, average age of $(x + 1)$ persons = $(x + 1)$ years.
∴ Teacher's age = $(x + 1)(x + 1) - x^2 = (x^2 + 1 + 2x) - x^2 = (1 + 2x)$.
Thus, teacher's age cannot be obtained.
∴ Correct answer is (d).

3. Let the number of team members be n.
I. Total increase in weight on replacement = $(20n)$ kg.
II. Total weight of new members = $[(64 + 75 + 66) + 20n]$ kg
= $(205 + 20n)$ kg.
∴ Required average = $\frac{(205 + 20n)}{3}$ kg and we need n to get the answer.
∴ Correct answer is (d).

4. P + Q + R + S = (30 × 4) ⇒ P + Q + R + S = 120 ...(i)
I. P + R = 60 ...(ii)
II. S = (R − 10) ...(iii)
From (i), (ii) and (iii), we cannot find R.
∴ Correct answer is (d).

5. I. A + B = (15 × 2) + (5 × 2) ⇒ A + B = 40 ...(i)
II. A + B + C = (20 × 3) ⇒ A + B + C = 60 ...(ii)
From (i) and (ii), we get C = 20.
C's age after 10 years = (20 + 10) years = 30 years.
∴ Correct answer is (e).

6. Let there be x children in the group.
I. Average age = 15 years.
∴ Total age = $15x$ years.
∴ $15x = 240 \Leftrightarrow x = \frac{240}{15} \Leftrightarrow x = 16$.
So, there are 16 children in the group.
II. Total age of x children and 1 teacher is 264 years.
Age of teacher = (15 + 9) years = 24 years.
Total age of x children = (264 − 24) years = 240 years.
This does not give the answer.
∴ Correct answer is (a).

7. $H = \dfrac{(H+E+S+P)}{4} + 15$

$\Rightarrow 4(H - 15) = H + E + S + P \Rightarrow 3H - 60 = E + S + P$ ...(*i*)

I. H + P = 120 ...(*ii*)

II. S − E = 120 ...(*iii*)

From (*i*), (*ii*) and (*iii*), we cannot find P.

∴ Correct answer is (*d*).

8. I. Total candidates interviewed by 3 panels = (15 × 3) = 45.

II. Let x candidates be interviewed by C.

Number of candidates interviewed by A = $(x + 2)$.

Number of candidates interviewed by B = $(x + 1)$.

∴ $x + (x + 2) + (x + 1) = 45 \Leftrightarrow 3x = 42 \Leftrightarrow x = 14$.

So, the number of candidates interviewed by A is 14.

Hence, the correct answer is (*b*).

9. Average age of 11 students and 1 teacher = 14 years

⇒ Total age of (11 students and 1 teacher) = (14 × 12) years = 168 years.

Average age of (11 students and 1 teacher) = (Average age of 11 students) + 3

⇒ Average age of 11 students = (14 − 3) years = 11 years

⇒ Total age of 11 students = (11 × 11) years = 121 years.

∴ Age of the teacher = (168 − 121) years = 47 years.

Thus, both I and II are needed to get the answer.

∴ Correct answer is (*e*).

10. I. Total weight of 46 children = [(22.5 × 30) + (29.125 × 16)] kg = 1141 kg.

Weight excluded is not exact. So, average of remaining class cannot be obtained.

II. Total weight of 45 children = [(23.5 × 46) − 46] kg = 1035 kg.

Average weight of 45 children = $\dfrac{1035}{45}$ kg = 23 kg.

∴ Data in II is sufficient to answer the question, while the data in I is not sufficient.

∴ Correct answer is (*b*).

11. I gives, total marks in 4 subjects = (60 × 4) = 240.

II gives, E + M = 170

III gives, M + S = 180.

Thus, none of (*a*), (*b*), (*c*), (*d*) is true.

∴ Correct answer is (*e*).

12. M + T + W = (37 × 3) ⇒ M + T + W = 111 ...(*i*)

T + W + Th = (34 × 3) ⇒ T + W + Th = 102 ...(*ii*)

I gives, $Th = \dfrac{4}{5}M \Rightarrow M = \dfrac{5}{4}Th$

Using it in (*i*), we get :

$$\frac{5}{4}Th + T + W = 111 \quad \text{...(iii)}$$

On subtracting (*ii*) from (*iii*), we get : $\dfrac{1}{4}Th = 9 \Rightarrow Th = 36$.

Thus, I alone gives the answer.

II gives, M + Th = (40.5 × 2) ⇒ M + Th = 81 ...(*iv*)

On subtracting (*ii*) from (*i*), we get M − Th = 9 ...(*v*)

From (*iv*) and (*v*), we get Th = 36.

Thus, II alone gives the answer.

III gives, M − Th = 9.

Clearly, III with given results, does not give the answer.

∴ Correct answer is (*c*).

13. Total age of 11 players = (28 × 11) years = 308 years.

I. C = Y + 11 ⇒ C − Y = 11 ...(*i*)

II. Total age of 10 players (excluding captain) = (27.3 × 10) years = 273 years.

∴ Age of captain = (308 − 273) years = 35 years.

Thus, C = 35. ...(*ii*)

From (*i*) and (*ii*), we get Y = 24.

III. Total age of 9 players = [(25 × 3) + (28 × 3) + (30 × 3)] years = 249 years.

∴ C + Y = (308 − 249) = 59 ...(*iii*)

From (*i*) and (*iii*), we get C = 35.

Thus, II alone gives the answer.

Also, I and III together give the answer.

∴ Correct answer is (*c*).

14. I. gives, total salary of 7 clerks = Rs. (8500 × 7) = Rs. 59500.

II. gives, total salary of 5 officers = Rs. (10000 × 5) = Rs. 50000.

III. gives, total salary of 3 sub-staff members = Rs. (2500 × 3) = Rs. 7500.

Total salary of 15 employees = Rs. (59500 + 50000 + 7500) = Rs. 117000.

∴ Average salary = Rs. $\left(\frac{117000}{15}\right)$ = Rs. 7800.

∴ All given statements are needed. Hence, none is redundant.

∴ Correct answer is (*a*).

---

7. PROBLEMS ON NUMBERS

In this section, questions involving a set of numbers are put in the form of a puzzle. You have to analyse the given conditions, assume the unknown numbers and form equations accordingly, which on solving yield the unknown numbers.

SOLVED EXAMPLES

Ex. 1. ***A number is as much greater than 36 as is less than 86. Find the number.***

Sol. Let the number be x. Then, $x - 36 = 86 - x \Leftrightarrow 2x = 86 + 36 = 122 \Leftrightarrow x = 61$.

Hence, the required number is 61.

Ex. 2. ***Find a number such that when 15 is subtracted from 7 times the number, the result is 10 more than twice the number.*** **(Hotel Management, 2002)**

Sol. Let the number be x. Then, $7x - 15 = 2x + 10 \Leftrightarrow 5x = 25 \Leftrightarrow x = 5$.

Hence, the required number is 5.

Ex. 3. ***The sum of a rational number and its reciprocal is*** $\frac{13}{6}$. ***Find the number.*** **(S.S.C. 2000)**

Sol. Let the number be x.

$$\text{Then, } x + \frac{1}{x} = \frac{13}{6} \Leftrightarrow \frac{x^2+1}{x} = \frac{13}{6} \Leftrightarrow 6x^2 - 13x + 6 = 0$$

$$\Leftrightarrow 6x^2 - 9x - 4x + 6 = 0 \Leftrightarrow (3x - 2)(2x - 3) = 0$$

$$\Leftrightarrow x = \frac{2}{3} \text{ or } x = \frac{3}{2}.$$

Hence, the required number is $\frac{2}{3}$ or $\frac{3}{2}$.

Ex. 4. ***The sum of two numbers is 184. If one-third of the one exceeds one-seventh of the other by 8, find the smaller number.***

Sol. Let the numbers be x and $(184 - x)$. Then,

$$\frac{x}{3} - \frac{(184 - x)}{7} = 8 \Leftrightarrow 7x - 3(184 - x) = 168 \Leftrightarrow 10x = 720 \Leftrightarrow x = 72.$$

So, the numbers are 72 and 112. Hence, smaller number = 72.

Ex. 5. ***The difference of two numbers is 11 and one-fifth of their sum is 9. Find the numbers.***

Sol. Let the numbers be x and y. Then,

$x - y = 11$ ...(i) and $\frac{1}{5}(x + y) = 9 \Rightarrow x + y = 45$ ...(ii)

Adding (i) and (ii), we get : $2x = 56$ or $x = 28$. Putting $x = 28$ in (i), we get : $y = 17$.

Hence, the numbers are 28 and 17.

Ex. 6. ***If the sum of two numbers is 42 and their product is 437, then find the absolute difference between the numbers.*** **(S.S.C. 2003)**

Sol. Let the numbers be x and y. Then, $x + y = 42$ and $xy = 437$.

$$x - y = \sqrt{(x+y)^2 - 4xy} = \sqrt{(42)^2 - 4 \times 437} = \sqrt{1764 - 1748} = \sqrt{16} = 4.$$

$\therefore$ Required difference = 4.

Ex. 7. ***The sum of two numbers is 15 and the sum of their squares is 113. Find the numbers.***

Sol. Let the numbers be x and $(15 - x)$.

Then, $x^2 + (15 - x)^2 = 113 \quad \Leftrightarrow \quad x^2 + 225 + x^2 - 30x = 113$

$\Leftrightarrow \quad 2x^2 - 30x + 112 = 0 \quad \Leftrightarrow \quad x^2 - 15x + 56 = 0$

$\Leftrightarrow \quad (x - 7)(x - 8) = 0 \quad \Leftrightarrow \quad x = 7$ or $x = 8$.

So, the numbers are 7 and 8.

Ex. 8. ***The average of four consecutive even numbers is 27. Find the largest of these numbers.***

Sol. Let the four consecutive even numbers be x, $x + 2$, $x + 4$ and $x + 6$.

Then, sum of these numbers $= (27 \times 4) = 108$.

So, $x + (x + 2) + (x + 4) + (x + 6) = 108$ or $4x = 96$ or $x = 24$.

$\therefore$ Largest number $= (x + 6) = 30$.

Ex. 9. ***The sum of the squares of three consecutive odd numbers is 2531. Find the numbers.***

Sol. Let the numbers be x, $x + 2$ and $x + 4$.

Then, $x^2 + (x + 2)^2 + (x + 4)^2 = 2531 \quad \Leftrightarrow \quad 3x^2 + 12x - 2511 = 0$

$\Leftrightarrow \quad x^2 + 4x - 837 = 0 \quad \Leftrightarrow \quad (x - 27)(x + 31) = 0 \quad \Leftrightarrow \quad x = 27$.

Hence, the required numbers are 27, 29 and 31.

Ex. 10. ***Of two numbers, 4 times the smaller one is less than 3 times the larger one by 5. If the sum of the numbers is larger than 6 times their difference by 6, find the two numbers.***

Sol. Let the numbers be x and y, such that $x > y$.

Then, $3x - 4y = 5$ ...(*i*) and $(x + y) - 6(x - y) = 6 \Rightarrow -5x + 7y = 6$ ...(*ii*)

Solving (*i*) and (*ii*), we get : $x = 59$ and $y = 43$.

Hence, the required numbers are 59 and 43.

Ex. 11. ***The ratio between a two-digit number and the sum of the digits of that number is 4 : 1. If the digit in the unit's place is 3 more than the digit in the ten's place, what is the number ?***

Sol. Let the ten's digit be x. Then, unit's digit $= (x + 3)$.

Sum of the digits $= x + (x + 3) = 2x + 3$. Number $= 10x + (x + 3) = 11x + 3$.

$\therefore \quad \dfrac{11x + 3}{2x + 3} = \dfrac{4}{1} \quad \Leftrightarrow \quad 11x + 3 = 4(2x + 3) \quad \Leftrightarrow \quad 3x = 9 \quad \Leftrightarrow \quad x = 3$.

Hence, required number $= 11x + 3 = 36$.

Ex. 12. ***A number consists of two digits. The sum of the digits is 9. If 63 is subtracted from the number, its digits are interchanged. Find the number.***

Sol. Let the ten's digit be x. Then, unit's digit $= (9 - x)$.

Number $= 10x + (9 - x) = 9x + 9$.

Number obtained by reversing the digits $= 10(9 - x) + x = 90 - 9x$.

$\therefore \quad (9x + 9) - 63 = 90 - 9x \quad \Leftrightarrow \quad 18x = 144 \quad \Leftrightarrow \quad x = 8$.

So, ten's digit = 8 and unit's digit = 1.

Hence, the required number is 81.

Ex. 13. ***A fraction becomes $\frac{2}{3}$ when 1 is added to both, its numerator and denominator. And, it becomes $\frac{1}{2}$ when 1 is subtracted from both the numerator and denominator. Find the fraction.***

Sol. Let the required fraction be $\frac{x}{y}$. Then,

$\frac{x+1}{y+1} = \frac{2}{3} \Rightarrow 3x - 2y = -1$ ...(i) and $\frac{x-1}{y-1} = \frac{1}{2} \Rightarrow 2x - y = 1$. ...(ii)

Solving (i) and (ii), we get : $x = 3, y = 5$.

$\therefore$ Required fraction $= \frac{3}{5}$.

Ex. 14. ***50 is divided into two parts such that the sum of their reciprocals is*** $\frac{1}{12}$. ***Find the two parts.***

Sol. Let the two parts be x and $(50 - x)$.

Then, $\frac{1}{x} + \frac{1}{50 - x} = \frac{1}{12} \Leftrightarrow \frac{50 - x + x}{x(50 - x)} = \frac{1}{12} \Rightarrow x^2 - 50x + 600 = 0$

$\Rightarrow (x - 30)(x - 20) = 0 \Rightarrow x = 30$ or $x = 20$.

So, the parts are 30 and 20.

Ex. 15. ***If three numbers are added in pairs, the sums equal 10, 19 and 21. Find the numbers.*** **(S.S.C. 2000)**

Sol. Let the numbers be x, y and z. Then,

$x + y = 10$ ...(i) $y + z = 19$ ...(ii) $x + z = 21$ ...(iii)

Adding (i), (ii) and (iii), we get : $2(x + y + z) = 50$ or $(x + y + z) = 25$.

Thus, $x = (25 - 19) = 6$; $y = (25 - 21) = 4$; $z = (25 - 10) = 15$.

Hence, the required numbers are 6, 4 and 15.

EXERCISE 7A

(OBJECTIVE TYPE QUESTIONS)

Directions : *Mark (✓) against the correct answer :*

1. The difference between a number and its three-fifth is 50. What is the number ?
   (*a*) 75 (*b*) 100 (*c*) 125 (*d*) None of these
   (Bank P.O. 2003)
2. If a number is decreased by 4 and divided by 6, the result is 8. What would be the result if 2 is subtracted from the number and then it is divided by 5 ?
   (*a*) $9\frac{2}{3}$ (*b*) 10 (*c*) $10\frac{1}{5}$ (*d*) $11\frac{1}{5}$ (*e*) None of these
   (Bank P.O. 2000)
3. If one-third of one-fourth of a number is 15, then three-tenth of that number is :
   (*a*) 35 (*b*) 36 (*c*) 45 (*d*) 54
   (N.I.F.T. 2003)
4. A number is doubled and 9 is added. If the resultant is trebled, it becomes 75. What is that number ? **(S.S.C. 1999)**
   (*a*) 3.5 (*b*) 6 (*c*) 8 (*d*) None of these
5. Three-fourth of a number is 60 more than its one-third. The number is :
   (*a*) 84 (*b*) 108 (*c*) 144 (*d*) None of these
6. When 24 is subtracted from a number, it reduces to its four-seventh. What is the sum of the digits of that number ?
   (*a*) 1 (*b*) 9 (*c*) 11
   (*d*) Data inadequate (*e*) None of these

7. Find the number which when multiplied by 15 is increased by 196. **(L.I.C. 2003)**
(*a*) 14 (*b*) 20 (*c*) 26 (*d*) 28

8. If a number, when divided by 4, is reduced by 21, the number is :
(*a*) 18 (*b*) 20 (*c*) 28 (*d*) 38

9. A number whose fifth part increased by 4 is equal to its fourth part diminished by 10, is :
(*a*) 240 (*b*) 260 (*c*) 270 (*d*) 280

10. The difference of two numbers is 20% of the larger number. If the smaller number is 12, the larger one is :
(*a*) 15 (*b*) 16 (*c*) 18 (*d*) 20

11. If one-seventh of a number exceeds its eleventh part by 100, then the number is :
(*a*) 770 (*b*) 1100 (*c*) 1825 (*d*) 1925

12. If the sum of one-half and one-fifth of a number exceeds one-third of that number by $7\frac{1}{3}$, the number is : **(C.B.I. 1998)**
(*a*) 15 (*b*) 18 (*c*) 20 (*d*) 30

13. If doubling a number and adding 20 to the result gives the same answer as multiplying the number by 8 and taking away 4 from the product, the number is :
(*a*) 2 (*b*) 3 (*c*) 4 (*d*) 6
(S.S.C. 2000)

14. If 50 is subtracted from two-third of a number, the result is equal to sum of 40 and one-fourth of that number. What is the number ? **(R.R.B. 2002)**
(*a*) 174 (*b*) 216 (*c*) 246 (*d*) 336

15. If the sum of a number and its square is 182, what is the number ?
(*a*) 15 (*b*) 26 (*c*) 28 (*d*) 91 (*e*) None of these
(Bank P.O. 1999)

16. Twenty times a positive integer is less than its square by 96. What is the integer ?
(*a*) 20 (*b*) 24 (*c*) 30
(*d*) Cannot be determined (*e*) None of these **(Bank P.O. 2003)**

17. Thrice the square of a natural number decreased by 4 times the number is equal to 50 more than the number. The number is : **(S.S.C. 2003)**
(*a*) 4 (*b*) 5 (*c*) 6 (*d*) 10

18. The sum of a number and its reciprocal is one-eighth of 34. What is the product of the number and its square root ? **(Hotel Management, 2001)**
(*a*) 8 (*b*) 27 (*c*) 32 (*d*) None of these

19. Two-third of a positive number and $\frac{25}{216}$ of its reciprocal are equal. The number is :
(*a*) $\frac{5}{12}$ (*b*) $\frac{12}{5}$ (*c*) $\frac{25}{144}$ (*d*) $\frac{144}{25}$
(S.S.C. 1999)

20. Find a positive number which when increased by 17 is equal to 60 times the reciprocal of the number. **(I.M.T. 2002)**
(*a*) 3 (*b*) 10 (*c*) 17 (*d*) 20

21. A positive number when decreased by 4 is equal to 21 times the reciprocal of the number. The number is :
(*a*) 3 (*b*) 5 (*c*) 7 (*d*) 9

22. The sum of a positive number and its reciprocal is thrice the difference of the number and its reciprocal. The number is :

(*a*) $\sqrt{2}$ (*b*) $\frac{1}{\sqrt{2}}$ (*c*) $\sqrt{3}$ (*d*) $\frac{1}{\sqrt{3}}$

23. The product of two natural numbers is 17. Then, the sum of the reciprocals of their squares is : **(S.S.C. 1999)**

(*a*) $\frac{1}{289}$ (*b*) $\frac{289}{290}$ (*c*) $\frac{290}{289}$ (*d*) 289

24. If $2\frac{1}{2}$ is added to a number and the sum multiplied by $4\frac{1}{2}$ and 3 is added to the product and then dividing the sum by $1\frac{1}{5}$, the quotient becomes 25. What is the number ? **(R.R.B. 2002)**

(*a*) $2\frac{1}{2}$ (*b*) $3\frac{1}{2}$ (*c*) $4\frac{1}{2}$ (*d*) $5\frac{1}{2}$

25. Three numbers are in the ratio 4 : 5 : 6 and their average is 25. The largest number is :

(*a*) 30 (*b*) 32 (*c*) 36 (*d*) 42

26. Three numbers are in the ratio of 3 : 4 : 6 and their product is 1944. The largest of these numbers is :

(*a*) 6 (*b*) 12 (*c*) 18 (*d*) None of these

27. Two numbers are such that the square of one is 224 less than 8 times the square of the other. If the numbers be in the ratio of 3 : 4, the numbers are :

(*a*) 6, 8 (*b*) 9, 12 (*c*) 12, 16 (*d*) None of these

28. Two numbers are such that the ratio between them is 4 : 7. If each is increased by 4, the ratio becomes 3 : 5. The larger number is :

(*a*) 36 (*b*) 48 (*c*) 56 (*d*) 64

29. The sum of three numbers is 264. If the first number be twice the second and third number be one-third of the first, then the second number is : **(R.R.B. 2004)**

(*a*) 48 (*b*) 54 (*c*) 72 (*d*) 84

30. The sum of two numbers is 22. Five times one number is equal to 6 times the other. The bigger of the two numbers is : **(C.B.I. 1998)**

(*a*) 10 (*b*) 12 (*c*) 15 (*d*) 16

31. One-fifth of a number is equal to $\frac{5}{8}$ of another number. If 35 is added to the first number, it becomes four times of the second number. The second number is :

(*a*) 25 (*b*) 40 (*c*) 70 (*d*) 125

(Bank P.O. 1999)

32. The sum of two numbers is 25 and their difference is 13. Find their product.

(*a*) 104 (*b*) 114 (*c*) 315 (*d*) 325

(L.I.C. 2003)

33. If the sum of two numbers is 33 and their difference is 15, the smaller number is :

(*a*) 9 (*b*) 12 (*c*) 15 (*d*) 18

(C.B.I. 1997)

34. The sum of two numbers is 40 and their difference is 4. The ratio of the numbers is :

(*a*) 11 : 9 (*b*) 11 : 18 (*c*) 21 : 19 (*d*) 22 : 9

(S.S.C. 2000)

35. The product of two numbers is 192 and the sum of these two numbers is 28. What is the smaller of these two numbers ? **(Bank P.O. 1999)**

(*a*) 12 (*b*) 14 (*c*) 16 (*d*) 18 (*e*) None of these

36. The difference between two integers is 5. Their product is 500. Find the numbers.

(*a*) 15, 20 (*b*) 20, 25 (*c*) 30, 25 (*d*) 21, 26

(Hotel Management, 2003)

37. Two numbers differ by 5. If their product is 336, then the sum of the two numbers is :

(*a*) 21 (*b*) 28 (*c*) 37 (*d*) 51

(S.S.C. 1999)

38. Two different natural numbers are such that their product is less than their sum. One of the numbers must be :

(*a*) 1 (*b*) 2 (*c*) 3 (*d*) None of these

39. The product of two numbers is 9375 and the quotient, when the larger one is divided by the smaller, is 15. The sum of the numbers is : **(S.S.C. 2004)**

(*a*) 380 (*b*) 395 (*c*) 400 (*d*) 425

40. The difference between two numbers is 1365. When the larger number is divided by the smaller one, the quotient is 6 and the remainder is 15. The smaller number is :

(*a*) 240 (*b*) 270 (*c*) 295 (*d*) 360

41. The sum of two numbers is 40 and their product is 375. What will be the sum of their reciprocals ? **(S.S.C. 1999)**

(*a*) $\frac{1}{40}$ (*b*) $\frac{8}{75}$ (*c*) $\frac{75}{4}$ (*d*) $\frac{75}{8}$

42. The sum of two positive integers multiplied by the bigger number is 204, and their difference multiplied by the smaller number is 35. The numbers are :

(*a*) 12, 5 (*b*) 13, 4 (*c*) 14, 3 (*d*) 24, 10

43. If the sum and difference of two numbers are 20 and 8 respectively, then the difference of their squares is : **(S.S.C. 2000)**

(*a*) 12 (*b*) 28 (*c*) 160 (*d*) 180

44. The product of two numbers is 120 and the sum of their squares is 289. The sum of the numbers is : **(R.R.B. 2004)**

(*a*) 20 (*b*) 23 (*c*) 169 (*d*) None of these

45. The product of two numbers is 45 and the sum of their squares is 106. The numbers are : **(R.R.B. 2002)**

(*a*) 3 and 5 (*b*) 5 and 9 (*c*) 5 and 19 (*d*) 45 and 1

46. The sum of the squares of two numbers is 3341 and the difference of their squares is 891. The numbers are :

(*a*) 25, 36 (*b*) 25, 46 (*c*) 35, 46 (*d*) None of these

47. The difference between two positive integers is 3. If the sum of their squares is 369, then the sum of the numbers is : **(S.S.C. 2003)**

(*a*) 25 (*b*) 27 (*c*) 33 (*d*) 81

48. If the sum of two numbers is 22 and the sum of their squares is 404, then the product of the numbers is : **(S.S.C. 2000)**

(*a*) 40 (*b*) 44 (*c*) 80 (*d*) 88

49. The difference between the squares of two numbers is 256000 and the sum of the numbers is 1000. The numbers are :

(*a*) 600, 400 (*b*) 628, 372 (*c*) 640, 360 (*d*) None of these

50. If the difference of two numbers is 3 and the difference of their squares is 39, then the larger number is :

(*a*) 8 (*b*) 9 (*c*) 12 (*d*) 13

51. The sum of three consecutive numbers is 87. The greatest among these three numbers is : **(Hotel Management, 2003)**

(*a*) 26 (*b*) 28 (*c*) 29 (*d*) 30

52. Three times the first of three consecutive odd integers is 3 more than twice the third. The third integer is : **(M.B.A. 1998)**

(*a*) 9 (*b*) 11 (*c*) 13 (*d*) 15

53. The sum of four consecutive even integers is 1284. The greatest of them is :

(*a*) 320 (*b*) 322 (*c*) 324 (*d*) 326

(S.S.C. 2002)

54. The sum of three consecutive odd numbers is 20 more than the first of these numbers. What is the middle number ? **(S.B.I.P.O. 1997)**

(*a*) 7 (*b*) 9 (*c*) 11

(*d*) Data inadequate (*e*) None of these

55. The product of three consecutive even numbers when divided by 8 is 720. The product of their square roots is : **(Hotel Management, 2001)**

(*a*) $12\sqrt{10}$ (*b*) $24\sqrt{10}$ (*c*) 120 (*d*) None of these

56. The sum of three consecutive multiples of 3 is 72. What is the largest number ?

(*a*) 21 (*b*) 24 (*c*) 27 (*d*) 36

(S.S.C. 1999)

57. What is the sum of two consecutive even numbers, the difference of whose squares is 84 ? **(S.S.C. 2003)**

(*a*) 34 (*b*) 38 (*c*) 42 (*d*) 46

58. The sum of the squares of three consecutive natural numbers is 2030. What is the middle number ? **(S.S.C. 2000)**

(*a*) 25 (*b*) 26 (*c*) 27 (*d*) 28

59. There are two numbers such that the sum of twice the first and thrice the second is 39, while the sum of thrice the first and twice the second is 36. The larger of the two is :

(*a*) 6 (*b*) 8 (*c*) 9 (*d*) 12

60. In a two-digit number, the digit in the unit's place is four times the digit in ten's place and sum of the digits is equal to 10. What is the number ? **(Bank P.O. 1999)**

(*a*) 14 (*b*) 41 (*c*) 82

(*d*) Data inadequate (*e*) None of these

61. A number of two digits has 3 for its unit's digit, and the sum of digits is $\frac{1}{7}$ of the number itself. The number is **(L.I.C. 2003)**

(*a*) 43 (*b*) 53 (*c*) 63 (*d*) 73.

62. A two-digit number exceeds the sum of the digits of that number by 18. If the digit at the unit's place is double the digit in the ten's place, what is the number ?

(*a*) 24 (*b*) 42 (*c*) 48 (*d*) Data inadequate

63. The sum of the digits of a two-digit number is 15 and the difference between the digits is 3. What is the two-digit number ? **(B.S.R.B. 2003)**

(*a*) 69 (*b*) 78 (*c*) 96

(*d*) Cannot be determined (*e*) None of these

64. In a two-digit number, if it is known that its unit's digit exceeds its ten's digit by 2 and that the product of the given number and the sum of its digits is equal to 144, then the number is : **(C.B.I. 2003)**

(*a*) 24 (*b*) 26 (*c*) 42 (*d*) 46

65. A number consists of two digits. If the digits interchange places and the new number is added to the original number, then the resulting number will be divisible by :
(*a*) 3 (*b*) 5 (*c*) 9 (*d*) 11
(S.S.C. 2003)

66. The sum of the digits of a two-digit number is 9 less than the number. Which of the following digits is at unit's place of the number ?
(*a*) 1 (*b*) 2 (*c*) 4 (*d*) Data inadequate

67. The difference between a two-digit number and the number obtained by interchanging the positions of its digits is 36. What is the difference between the two digits of that number ? **(Bank P.O. 2003)**
(*a*) 3 (*b*) 4 (*c*) 9
(*d*) Cannot be determined (*e*) None of these

68. The difference between a two-digit number and the number obtained by interchanging the two digits is 63. Which is the smaller of the two numbers ? **(Bank P.O. 2003)**
(*a*) 29 (*b*) 70 (*c*) 92
(*d*) Cannot be determined (*e*) None of these.

69. The sum of the digits of a two-digit number is $\frac{1}{5}$ of the difference between the number and the number obtained by interchanging the positions of the digits. What is definitely the difference between the digits of that number ? **(Bank P.O. 2000)**
(*a*) 5 (*b*) 7 (*c*) 9
(*d*) Data inadequate (*e*) None of these

70. If the digit in the unit's place of a two-digit number is halved and the digit in the ten's place is doubled, the number thus obtained is equal to the number obtained by interchanging the digits. Which of the following is definitely true ? **(Bank P.O. 2003)**
(*a*) Sum of the digits is a two-digit number.
(*b*) Digit in the unit's place is twice the digit in the ten's place.
(*c*) Digits in the unit's place and the ten's place are equal.
(*d*) Digit in the unit's place is half of the digit in the ten's place.
(*e*) None of these

71. If the number obtained on interchanging the digits of a two-digit number is 18 more than the original number and the sum of the digits is 8, then what is the original number ? **(S.B.I.P.O. 2002)**
(*a*) 26 (*b*) 35 (*c*) 53
(*d*) Cannot be determined (*e*) None of these

72. The difference between a two-digit number and the number obtained by interchanging the digits is 36. What is the difference between the sum and the difference of the digits of the number if the ratio between the digits of the number is 1 : 2 ? **(M.A.T. 1999)**
(*a*) 4 (*b*) 8 (*c*) 16 (*d*) None of these

73. A number consists of 3 digits whose sum is 10. The middle digit is equal to the sum of the other two and the number will be increased by 99 if its digits are reversed. The number is : **(Hotel Management, 2003)**
(*a*) 145 (*b*) 253 (*c*) 370 (*d*) 352

74. A two-digit number becomes five-sixth of itself when its digits are reversed. The two digits differ by one. The number is :
(*a*) 45 (*b*) 54 (*c*) 56 (*d*) 65

75. A number consists of two digits such that the digit in the ten's place is less by 2 than the digit in the unit's place. Three times the number added to $\frac{6}{7}$ times the number obtained by reversing the digits equals 108. The sum of the digits in the number is :

(*a*) 6 (*b*) 7 (*c*) 8 (*d*) 9

(S.S.C. 2003)

76. The digit in the unit's place of a number is equal to the digit in the ten's place of half of that number and the digit in the ten's place of that number is less than the digit in unit's place of half of the number by 1. If the sum of the digits of the number is 7, then what is the number ? **(S.B.I.P.O. 2001)**

(*a*) 34 (*b*) 52 (*c*) 162
(*d*) Data inadequate (*e*) None of these

77. In a two-digit number, the digit in the unit's place is more than twice the digit in ten's place by 1. If the digits in the unit's place and the ten's place are interchanged, difference between the newly formed number and the original number is less than the original number by 1. What is the original number ? **(Bank P.O. 1999)**

(*a*) 25 (*b*) 37 (*c*) 49 (*d*) 52 (*e*) 73

78. A certain number of two digits is three times the sum of its digits and if 45 be added to it, the digits are reversed. The number is : **(L.I.C.A.A.O. 2003)**

(*a*) 23 (*b*) 27 (*c*) 32 (*d*) 72

79. A two-digit number is such that the product of the digits is 8. When 18 is added to the number, then the digits are reversed. The number is : **(M.B.A. 2003)**

(*a*) 18 (*b*) 24 (*c*) 42 (*d*) 81

80. The product of two fractions is $\frac{14}{15}$ and their quotient is $\frac{35}{24}$. The greater fraction is :

(*a*) $\frac{4}{5}$ (*b*) $\frac{7}{6}$ (*c*) $\frac{7}{4}$ (*d*) $\frac{7}{3}$

(S.S.C. 2002)

81. In a pair of fractions, fraction A is twice the fraction B and the product of two fractions is $\frac{2}{25}$ What is the value of fraction A ? **(Bank P.O. 1999)**

(*a*) $\frac{1}{5}$ (*b*) $\frac{1}{25}$ (*c*) $\frac{2}{5}$ (*d*) Data inadequate

82. The sum of the numerator and denominator of a fraction is 11. If 1 is added to the numerator and 2 is subtracted from the denominator, it becomes $\frac{2}{3}$. The fraction is :

(*a*) $\frac{5}{6}$ (*b*) $\frac{6}{5}$ (*c*) $\frac{3}{8}$ (*d*) $\frac{8}{3}$

83. The denominator of a fraction is 3 more than the numerator. If the numerator as well as the denominator is increased by 4, the fraction becomes $\frac{4}{5}$. What was the original fraction ? **(S.B.I.P.O. 1999)**

(*a*) $\frac{8}{11}$ (*b*) $\frac{5}{8}$ (*c*) $\frac{10}{13}$ (*d*) $\frac{7}{10}$

84. The difference between the numerator and the denominator of a fraction is 5. If 5 is added to its denominator, the fraction is decreased by $1\frac{1}{4}$. Find the value of the fraction.

(*a*) $\frac{1}{6}$ (*b*) $2\frac{1}{4}$ (*c*) $3\frac{1}{4}$ (*d*) 6

(M.B.A. 1997)

85. The numerator and denominator of a fraction are in the ratio of 2 : 3. If 6 is subtracted from the numerator, the result is a fraction that has a value $\frac{2}{3}$ of the original fraction. The numerator of the original fraction is : **(S.S.C. 1999)**

(*a*) 6 (*b*) 18 (*c*) 27 (*d*) 36

86. If 1 is added to the denominator of a fraction, the fraction becomes $\frac{1}{2}$. If 1 is added to the numerator of the fraction, the fraction becomes 1. The fraction is : **(C.B.I. 1997)**

(*a*) $\frac{1}{3}$ (*b*) $\frac{2}{3}$ (*c*) $\frac{3}{4}$ (*d*) $\frac{3}{2}$

87. If the numerator of a fraction is increased by 2 and the denominator is increased by 3, the fraction becomes $\frac{7}{9}$ and if both the numerator as well as the denominator are decreased by 1, the fraction becomes $\frac{4}{5}$. What is the original fraction ?

(*a*) $\frac{5}{6}$ (*b*) $\frac{9}{11}$ (*c*) $\frac{13}{16}$ (*d*) $\frac{17}{21}$

(S.B.I.P.O. 1999)

88. When the numerator of a fraction increases by 4, the fraction increases by $\frac{2}{3}$. The denominator of the fraction is :

(*a*) 2 (*b*) 3 (*c*) 4 (*d*) 6

89. 54 is to be divided into two parts such that the sum of 10 times the first and 22 times the second is 780. The bigger part is :

(*a*) 24 (*b*) 34 (*c*) 30 (*d*) 32

90. 243 has been divided into three parts such that half of the first part, one-third of the second part and one-fourth of the third part are equal. The largest part is :

(*a*) 74 (*b*) 86 (*c*) 92 (*d*) 108

91. The sum of four numbers is 64. If you add 3 to the first number, 3 is subtracted from the second number, the third is multiplied by 3 and the fourth is divided by 3, then all the results are equal. What is the difference between the largest and the smallest of the original numbers ? **(S.B.I.P.O. 2000)**

(*a*) 21 (*b*) 27 (*c*) 32
(*d*) Cannot be determined (*e*) None of these

92. The sum of the squares of three numbers is 138, while the sum of their products taken two at a time is 131. Their sum is : **(Hotel Management, 1999)**

(*a*) 20 (*b*) 30 (*c*) 40 (*d*) None of these

93. The sum of three numbers is 136. If the ratio between first and second be 2 : 3 and that between second and third is 5 : 3, then the second number is :

(*a*) 40 (*b*) 48 (*c*) 60 (*d*) 72

94. Of the three numbers, the sum of the first two is 45; the sum of the second and the third is 55 and the sum of the third and thrice the first is 90. The third number is :

(*a*) 20 (*b*) 25 (*c*) 30 (*d*) 3

ANSWERS

1. (*c*)	2. (*b*)	3. (*d*)	4. (*c*)	5. (*c*)	6. (*c*)	7. (*a*)	8. (*c*)	9. (*d*)
10. (*a*)	11. (*d*)	12. (*c*)	13. (*c*)	14. (*b*)	15. (*e*)	16. (*b*)	17. (*b*)	18. (*a*)
19. (*a*)	20. (*a*)	21. (*c*)	22. (*a*)	23. (*c*)	24. (*b*)	25. (*a*)	26. (*c*)	27. (*a*)
28. (*c*)	29. (*c*)	30. (*b*)	31. (*b*)	32. (*b*)	33. (*a*)	34. (*a*)	35. (*a*)	36. (*b*)

37. (c)	**38.** (a)	**39.** (c)	**40.** (b)	**41.** (b)	**42.** (a)	**43.** (c)	**44.** (b)	**45.** (b)
46. (c)	**47.** (b)	**48.** (a)	**49.** (b)	**50.** (a)	**51.** (d)	**52.** (d)	**53.** (c)	**54.** (b)
55. (b)	**56.** (c)	**57.** (c)	**58.** (b)	**59.** (c)	**60.** (e)	**61.** (c)	**62.** (a)	**63.** (d)
64. (a)	**65.** (d)	**66.** (d)	**67.** (b)	**68.** (d)	**69.** (d)	**70.** (b)	**71.** (b)	**72.** (b)
73. (b)	**74.** (b)	**75.** (a)	**76.** (b)	**77.** (b)	**78.** (b)	**79.** (b)	**80.** (b)	**81.** (c)
82. (c)	**83.** (a)	**84.** (b)	**85.** (b)	**86.** (b)	**87.** (a)	**88.** (d)	**89.** (b)	**90.** (d)
91. (c)	**92.** (a)	**93.** (c)	**94.** (c)					

SOLUTIONS

1. Let the number be x. Then, $x - \frac{3}{5}x = 50 \Leftrightarrow \frac{2}{5}x = 50 \Leftrightarrow x = \left(\frac{50 \times 5}{2}\right) = 125.$

2. Let the number be x. Then, $\frac{x-4}{6} = 8 \Leftrightarrow x - 4 = 48 \Leftrightarrow x = 52.$

$\therefore \quad \frac{x-2}{5} = \frac{52-2}{5} = \frac{50}{5} = 10.$

3. Let the number be x. Then, $\frac{1}{3}$ of $\frac{1}{4}$ of $x = 15 \Leftrightarrow x = 15 \times 12 = 180.$

So, required number $= \left(\frac{3}{10} \times 180\right) = 54.$

4. Let the number be x. Then, $3(2x + 9) = 75 \Leftrightarrow 2x + 9 = 25 \Leftrightarrow 2x = 16 \Leftrightarrow x = 8.$

5. Let the number be x. Then, $\frac{3}{4}x - \frac{1}{3}x = 60 \Leftrightarrow \frac{5x}{12} = 60 \Leftrightarrow x = \left(\frac{60 \times 12}{5}\right) = 144.$

6. Let the number be x. Then,

$x - 24 = \frac{4}{7}x \Leftrightarrow x - \frac{4}{7}x = 24 \Leftrightarrow \frac{3}{7}x = 24 \Leftrightarrow x = \left(\frac{24 \times 7}{3}\right) = 56.$

$\therefore$ Sum of the digits $= (5 + 6) = 11.$

7. Let the number be x. Then, $15x - x = 196 \Leftrightarrow 14x = 196 \Leftrightarrow x = 14.$

8. Let the number be x. Then, $\frac{x}{4} = x - 21 \Leftrightarrow x = 4x - 84 \Leftrightarrow 3x = 84 \Leftrightarrow x = 28.$

9. Let the number be x. Then, $\left(\frac{1}{5}x + 4\right) = \left(\frac{1}{4}x - 10\right) \Leftrightarrow \frac{x}{20} = 14 \Leftrightarrow x = 14 \times 20 = 280.$

10. Let the larger number be x.

Then, $x - 12 = 20\%$ of $x \Leftrightarrow x - \frac{x}{5} = 12 \Leftrightarrow \frac{4x}{5} = 12 \Leftrightarrow x = \left(\frac{12 \times 5}{4}\right) = 15.$

11. Let the number be x. Then, $\frac{1}{7}x - \frac{1}{11}x = 100 \Leftrightarrow \frac{4x}{77} = 100 \Leftrightarrow x = \frac{7700}{4} = 1925.$

12. Let the number be x.

Then, $\left(\frac{1}{2}x + \frac{1}{5}x\right) - \frac{1}{3}x = \frac{22}{3} \Leftrightarrow \frac{11x}{30} = \frac{22}{3} \Leftrightarrow x = \left(\frac{22 \times 30}{3 \times 11}\right) = 20.$

13. Let the number be x. Then, $2x + 20 = 8x - 4 \Leftrightarrow 6x = 24 \Leftrightarrow x = 4.$

14. Let the number be x.

Then, $\frac{2}{3}x - 50 = \frac{1}{4}x + 40 \Leftrightarrow \frac{2}{3}x - \frac{1}{4}x = 90 \Leftrightarrow \frac{5x}{12} = 90 \Leftrightarrow x = \left(\frac{90 \times 12}{5}\right) = 216.$

15. Let the number be x.
Then, $x + x^2 = 182 \Leftrightarrow x^2 + x - 182 = 0 \Leftrightarrow (x + 14)(x - 13) = 0 \Leftrightarrow x = 13.$

16. Let the integer be x.
Then, $x^2 - 20x = 96 \Leftrightarrow x^2 - 20x - 96 = 0 \Leftrightarrow (x + 4)(x - 24) = 0 \Leftrightarrow x = 24.$

17. Let the number be x.
Then, $3x^2 - 4x = x + 50 \Leftrightarrow 3x^2 - 5x - 50 = 0 \Leftrightarrow (3x + 10)(x - 5) = 0 \Leftrightarrow x = 5.$

18. Let the number be x. Then, $x + \frac{1}{x} = \frac{34}{8} \Leftrightarrow \frac{x^2 + 1}{x} = \frac{34}{8} \Leftrightarrow 8x^2 = 34x + 8 = 0$

$\Leftrightarrow 4x^2 - 17x + 4 = 0 \Leftrightarrow (4x - 1)(x - 4) = 0 \Leftrightarrow x = 4.$

$\left[\text{neglecting } x = \frac{1}{4}, \text{ as } x \text{ is a natural no.}\right]$

$\therefore$ Required number $= 4 \times \sqrt{4} = 4 \times 2 = 8$

19. Let the number be x.

Then, $\frac{2}{3}x = \frac{25}{216} \times \frac{1}{x} \Leftrightarrow x^2 = \frac{25}{216} \times \frac{3}{2} = \frac{25}{144} \Leftrightarrow x = \sqrt{\frac{25}{144}} = \frac{5}{12}.$

20. Let the number be x.

Then, $x + 17 = \frac{60}{x} \Leftrightarrow x^2 + 17x - 60 = 0 \Leftrightarrow (x + 20)(x - 3) = 0 \Leftrightarrow x = 3.$

21. Let the number be x.

Then, $x - 4 = \frac{21}{x} \Leftrightarrow x^2 - 4x - 21 = 0 \Leftrightarrow (x - 7)(x + 3) = 0 \Leftrightarrow x = 7.$

22. Let the number be x. Then, $x + \frac{1}{x} = 3\left(x - \frac{1}{x}\right) \Leftrightarrow \frac{x^2 + 1}{x} = 3\left(\frac{x^2 - 1}{x}\right)$

$\Leftrightarrow x^2 + 1 = 3x^2 - 3 \Leftrightarrow 2x^2 = 4 \Leftrightarrow x^2 = 2 \Leftrightarrow x = \sqrt{2}.$

23. Let the numbers be a and b. Then, $ab = 17 \Rightarrow a = 1$ and $b = 17$.

So, $\frac{1}{a^2} + \frac{1}{b^2} = \frac{a^2 + b^2}{a^2 b^2} = \frac{1^2 + (17)^2}{(1 \times 17)^2} = \frac{290}{289}.$

24. Let the number be x. Then,

$$\frac{4\frac{1}{2}\left(x + 2\frac{1}{2}\right) + 3}{1\frac{1}{5}} = 25 \Leftrightarrow \frac{\frac{9}{2}\left(x + \frac{5}{2}\right) + 3}{\frac{6}{5}} = 25$$

$$\Leftrightarrow \frac{9x}{2} + \frac{45}{4} + 3 = 25 \times \frac{6}{5} = 30 \Leftrightarrow \frac{9x}{2} = 30 - \frac{57}{4} \Leftrightarrow \frac{9x}{2} = \frac{63}{4}$$

$$\Leftrightarrow x = \left(\frac{63}{4} \times \frac{2}{9}\right) = \frac{7}{2} = 3\frac{1}{2}.$$

25. Let the numbers be $4x$, $5x$ and $6x$. Then, $\frac{4x + 5x + 6x}{3} = 25 \Leftrightarrow 5x = 25 \Leftrightarrow x = 5$

$\therefore$ Largest number $= 6x = 30.$

26. Let the numbers be $3x$, $4x$ and $6x$.
Then, $3x \times 4x \times 6x = 1944 \Leftrightarrow 72x^3 = 1944 \Leftrightarrow x^3 = 27 \Leftrightarrow x = 3.$

$\therefore$ Largest number $= 6x = 18.$

27. Let the numbers be $3x$ and $4x$. Then,
$(4x)^2 = 8 \times (3x)^2 - 224 \Leftrightarrow 16x^2 = 72x^2 - 224 \Leftrightarrow 56x^2 = 224 \Leftrightarrow x^2 = 4 \Leftrightarrow x = 2.$
So, the numbers are 6 and 8.

28. Let the numbers be $4x$ and $7x$. Then, $\frac{4x+4}{7x+4} = \frac{3}{5} \Leftrightarrow 5(4x+4) = 3(7x+4) \Leftrightarrow x = 8.$

$\therefore$ Larger number $= 7x = 56.$

29. Let the second number be x. Then, first number $= 2x$ and third number $= \frac{2x}{3}$.

$\therefore \quad 2x + x + \frac{2x}{3} = 264 \Leftrightarrow \frac{11x}{3} = 264 \Leftrightarrow x = \left(\frac{264 \times 3}{11}\right) = 72.$

30. Let the numbers be x and $(22 - x)$. Then, $5x = 6(22 - x) \Leftrightarrow 11x = 132 \Leftrightarrow x = 12.$
So, the numbers are 12 and 10.

31. Let the numbers be x and y. Then, $\frac{1}{5}x = \frac{5}{8}y \Leftrightarrow y = \frac{8}{25}x.$

Now, $x + 35 = 4y \Leftrightarrow x + 35 = \frac{32}{25}x \Leftrightarrow \frac{7}{25}x = 35 \Leftrightarrow x = \left(\frac{35 \times 25}{7}\right) = 125.$

$\therefore$ Second number $= y = \frac{8}{25}x = \left(\frac{8}{25} \times 125\right) = 40.$

32. Let the numbers be x and y. Then, $x + y = 25$ and $x - y = 13.$
$4xy = (x+y)^2 - (x-y)^2 = (25)^2 - (13)^2 = 625 - 169 = 456 \Rightarrow xy = 114.$

33. Let the numbers be x and y.
Then, $x + y = 33$ ...(i) and $x - y = 15$ ...(ii)
Solving (i) and (ii), we get : $x = 24, y = 9.$
$\therefore$ Smaller number $= 9.$

34. Let the numbers be x and y. Then,

$\frac{x+y}{x-y} = \frac{40}{4} = 10 \Leftrightarrow (x+y) = 10(x-y) \Leftrightarrow 9x = 11y \Leftrightarrow \frac{x}{y} = \frac{11}{9}$

35. Let the numbers be x and $(28 - x)$. Then,
$x(28 - x) = 192 \Leftrightarrow x^2 - 28x + 192 = 0 \Leftrightarrow (x - 16)(x - 12) = 0$
$\Leftrightarrow x = 16$ or $x = 12.$

So, the numbers are 16 and 12.

36. Let the integers be x and $(x + 5)$. Then,
$x(x + 5) = 500 \Leftrightarrow x^2 + 5x - 500 = 0 \Leftrightarrow (x + 25)(x - 20) = 0 \Leftrightarrow x = 20.$
So, the numbers are 20 and 25.

37. Let the numbers be x and y. Then, $x - y = 5$ and $xy = 336.$
$(x+y)^2 = (x-y)^2 + 4xy = 25 + 4 \times 336 = 1369 \Rightarrow x + y = \sqrt{1369} = 37.$

38. Since $1.x < 1 + x$, so one of the numbers is 1.

39. Let the numbers be x and y. Then, $xy = 9375$ and $\frac{x}{y} = 15.$

$\frac{xy}{(x/y)} = \frac{9375}{15} \Leftrightarrow y^2 = 625 \Leftrightarrow y = 25 \Rightarrow x = 15y = (15 \times 25) = 375.$

$\therefore$ Sum of the numbers $= 375 + 25 = 400.$

40. Let the numbers be x and $(x + 1365)$.
Then, $x + 1365 = 6x + 15 \Leftrightarrow 5x = 1350 \Leftrightarrow x = 270.$

41. Let the numbers be x and y. Then, $x + y = 40$ and $xy = 375.$

$\therefore \quad \frac{1}{x} + \frac{1}{y} = \frac{x+y}{xy} = \frac{40}{375} = \frac{8}{75}$

42. Let the numbers be x and y such that $x > y$. Then,
$x(x + y) = 204 \Rightarrow x^2 + xy = 204$ ...(i) and $y(x - y) = 35 \Rightarrow xy - y^2 = 35$ ...(ii)
Subtracting (ii) from (i), we get : $x^2 + y^2 = 169$.
The only triplet satisfying this condition is (12, 5, 13). Thus, $x = 12$, $y = 5$.

43. Let the numbers be x and y. Then, $x + y = 20$ and $x - y = 8$.
$\therefore\ x^2 - y^2 = (x + y)(x - y) = 20 \times 8 = 160$.

44. Let the numbers be x and y. Then, $xy = 120$ and $x^2 + y^2 = 289$.
$\therefore\ (x + y)^2 = x^2 + y^2 + 2xy = 289 + 240 = 529$.
$\therefore\ x + y = \sqrt{529} = 23$.

45. Let the numbers be x and y. Then, $xy = 45$ and $x^2 + y^2 = 106$.
$(x + y) = \sqrt{(x^2 + y^2) + 2xy} = \sqrt{106 + 90} = \sqrt{196} \Rightarrow x + y = 14$ ...(i)
$(x - y) = \sqrt{(x^2 + y^2) - 2xy} = \sqrt{106 - 90} = \sqrt{16} \Rightarrow x - y = 4$ ...(ii)
Solving (i) and (ii), we get : $x = 9$ and $y = 5$.

46. Let the numbers be x and y. Then,
$x^2 + y^2 = 3341$ ...(i) and $x^2 - y^2 = 891$ ...(ii)
Adding (i) and (ii), we get : $2x^2 = 4232$ or $x^2 = 2116$ or $x = 46$.
Subtracting (ii) from (i), we get : $2y^2 = 2450$ or $y^2 = 1225$ or $y = 35$.
So, the numbers are 35 and 46.

47. Let the numbers be x and $(x + 3)$. Then,
$x^2 + (x + 3)^2 = 369 \Leftrightarrow x^2 + x^2 + 9 + 6x = 369$
$\Leftrightarrow 2x^2 + 6x - 360 = 0 \Leftrightarrow x^2 + 3x - 180 = 0 \Leftrightarrow (x + 15)(x - 12) = 0 \Leftrightarrow x = 12$.
So, the numbers are 12 and 15.
$\therefore$ Required sum = (12 + 15) = 27.

48. Let the numbers be x and y. Then, $(x + y) = 22$ and $x^2 + y^2 = 404$.
Now, $2xy = (x + y)^2 - (x^2 + y^2) = (22)^2 - 404 = 484 - 404 = 80 \Rightarrow xy = 40$.

49. Let the numbers be x and y. Then, $x^2 - y^2 = 256000$ and $x + y = 1000$.
On dividing, we get : $x - y = 256$.
Solving $x + y = 1000$ and $x - y = 256$, we get : $x = 628$ and $y = 372$.

50. Let the numbers be x and y. Then, $x^2 - y^2 = 39$ and $x - y = 3$.
On dividing, we get : $x + y = 13$.
Solving $x + y = 13$ and $x - y = 3$, we get : $x = 8$ and $y = 5$.
$\therefore$ Larger number = 8.

51. Let the numbers be x, $x + 1$ and $x + 2$.
Then, $x + (x + 1) + (x + 2) = 87 \Leftrightarrow 3x = 84 \Leftrightarrow x = 28$.
$\therefore$ Greatest number = $(x + 2) = 30$.

52. Let the three integers be x, $x + 2$ and $x + 4$ Then, $3x = 2(x + 4) + 3 \Leftrightarrow x = 11$.
$\therefore$ Third integer = $x + 4 = 15$.

53. Let the four integers be x, $x + 2$, $x + 4$ and $x + 6$.
Then, $x + (x + 2) + (x + 4) + (x + 6) = 1284 \Leftrightarrow 4x = 1272 \Leftrightarrow x = 318$.
$\therefore$ Greatest integer = $x + 6 = 324$.

54. Let the numbers be x, $x + 2$ and $x + 4$.
Then, $x + (x + 2) + (x + 4) = x + 20 \Leftrightarrow 2x = 14 \Leftrightarrow x = 7$.
$\therefore$ Middle number = $x + 2 = 9$.

55. Let the numbers be x, $x + 2$ and $x + 4$.

Then, $\frac{x(x+2)(x+4)}{8} = 720 \Rightarrow x(x+2)(x+4) = 5760.$

$\therefore \quad \sqrt{x} \times \sqrt{(x+2)} \times \sqrt{(x+4)} = \sqrt{x(x+2)(x+4)} = \sqrt{5760} = 24\sqrt{10}.$

56. Let the numbers be $3x$, $3x + 3$ and $3x + 6$.

Then, $3x + (3x + 3) + (3x + 6) = 72 \Leftrightarrow 9x = 63 \Leftrightarrow x = 7.$

$\therefore$ Largest number $= 3x + 6 = 27.$

57. Let the numbers be x and $x + 2$.

Then, $(x + 2)^2 - x^2 = 84 \Leftrightarrow 4x + 4 = 84 \Leftrightarrow 4x = 80 \Leftrightarrow x = 20.$

$\therefore$ Required sum $= x + (x + 2) = 2x + 2 = 42.$

58. Let the numbers be x, $x + 1$ and $x + 2$.

Then, $x^2 + (x + 1)^2 + (x + 2)^2 = 2030 \Leftrightarrow 3x^2 + 6x - 2025 = 0$

$\Leftrightarrow \quad x^2 + 2x - 675 = 0 \Leftrightarrow (x + 27)(x - 25) = 0 \Leftrightarrow x = 25.$

$\therefore$ Middle number $= (x + 1) = 26.$

59. Let the numbers be x and y. Then, $2x + 3y = 39$ ...(*i*) and $3x + 2y = 36$ ...(*ii*)

On solving (*i*) and (*ii*), we get : $x = 6$ and $y = 9$.

$\therefore$ Larger number = 9.

60. Let the ten's digits be x. Then, unit's digit $= 4x$.

$\therefore \quad x + 4x = 10 \Leftrightarrow 5x = 10 \Leftrightarrow x = 2.$

So, ten's digit = 2, unit's digit = 8.

Hence, the required number is 28.

61. Let the ten's digit be x. Then, number $= 10x + 3$ and sum of digits $= (x + 3)$.

So, $(x + 3) = \frac{1}{7}(10x + 3) \Leftrightarrow 7x + 21 = 10x + 3 \Leftrightarrow 3x = 18 \Leftrightarrow x = 6.$

Hence, the number is 63.

62. Let the ten's digit be x. Then, unit's digit $= 2x$.

Number $= 10x + 2x = 12x$; Sum of digits $= x + 2x = 3x$.

$\therefore \quad 12x - 3x = 18 \Leftrightarrow 9x = 18 \Leftrightarrow x = 2.$

Hence, required number $= 12x = 24$.

63. Let the ten's digit be x and unit's digit be y.

Then, $x + y = 15$ and $x - y = 3$ or $y - x = 3$.

Solving $x + y = 15$ and $x - y = 3$, we get : $x = 9$, $y = 6$.

Solving $x + y = 15$ and $y - x = 3$, we get : $x = 6$, $y = 9$.

So, the number is either 96 or 69. Hence, the number cannot be determined.

64. Let the ten's digit be x. Then, unit's digit $= x + 2$.

Number $= 10x + (x + 2) = 11x + 2$; Sum of digits $= x + (x + 2) = 2x + 2$.

$\therefore \quad (11x + 2)(2x + 2) = 144 \Leftrightarrow 22x^2 + 26x - 140 = 0 \Leftrightarrow 11x^2 + 13x - 70 = 0$

$\Leftrightarrow (x - 2)(11x + 35) = 0 \Leftrightarrow x = 2.$

Hence, required number $= 11x + 2 = 24$.

65. Let the ten's digit be x and unit's digit be y. Then, number $= 10x + y$.

Number obtained by interchanging the digits $= 10y + x$.

$\therefore \quad (10x + y) + (10y + x) = 11(x + y)$, which is divisible by 11.

66. Let the ten's digit be x and unit's digit be y. Then, $(10x + y) - (x + y) = 9$ or $x = 1$.

From this data, we cannot find y, the unit's digit. So, the data is inadequate.

67. Let the ten's digit be x and unit's digit be y.
Then, $(10x + y) - (10y + x) = 36 \Leftrightarrow 9(x - y) = 36 \Leftrightarrow x - y = 4$.

68. Let the ten's digit be x and unit's digit be y.
Then, $(10x + y) - (10y + x) = 63 \Leftrightarrow 9(x - y) = 63 \Leftrightarrow x - y = 7$.
Thus, none of the numbers can be determined.

69. Let the ten's digit be x and unit's digit be y.
Then, $x + y = \frac{1}{5}[(10x + y) - (10y + x)] \Leftrightarrow 5x + 5y = 9x - 9y \Leftrightarrow 4x = 14y$.
Thus, the value of $(x - y)$ cannot be determined from the given data.

70. Let the ten's digit be x and unit's digit be y.
Then, $10 \times 2x + \frac{1}{2}y = 10y + x \Leftrightarrow 20x - x = 10y - \frac{y}{2} \Leftrightarrow 19x = \frac{19}{2}y \Leftrightarrow y = 2x$.
Thus, the unit's digit is twice the ten's digit.

71. Let ten's digit $= x$. Then, unit's digit $= (8 - x)$.
$\therefore \quad [10(8 - x) + x] - [10x + (8 - x)] = 18 \Leftrightarrow 18x = 54 \Leftrightarrow x = 3$.
So, ten's digit = 3 and unit's digit = 5. Hence, original number = 35.

72. Since the number is greater than the number obtained on reversing the digits, so the ten's digit is greater than the unit's digit.
Let the ten's and unit's digits be $2x$ and x respectively.
Then, $(10 \times 2x + x) - (10x + 2x) = 36 \Leftrightarrow 9x = 36 \Leftrightarrow x = 4$.
$\therefore \quad$ Required difference $= (2x + x) - (2x - x) = 2x = 8$.

73. Let the middle digit be x. Then, $2x = 10$ or $x = 5$. So, the number is either 253 or 352. Since the number increases on reversing the digits, so the hundred's digit is smaller than the unit's digit. Hence, required number = 253.

74. Since the number reduces on reversing the digits, so ten's digit is greater than the unit's digit.
Let the unit's digit be x. Then, ten's digit $= (x + 1)$.
$\therefore \quad 10x + (x + 1) = \frac{5}{6}[10(x + 1) + x] \Leftrightarrow 66x + 6 = 55x + 50 \Leftrightarrow 11x = 44 \Leftrightarrow x = 4$.
Hence, required number = 54.

75. Let the unit's digit be x. Then, ten's digit $= (x - 2)$.
$\therefore \quad 3[10(x - 2) + x] + \frac{6}{7}[10x + (x - 2)] = 108$
$\Leftrightarrow 231x - 420 + 66x - 12 = 756 \Leftrightarrow 297x = 1188 \Leftrightarrow x = 4$.
Hence, sum of the digits $= x + (x - 2) = 2x - 2 = 6$.

76. Let the ten's digit be x and unit's digit be y. Then, $\frac{10x + y}{2} = 10y + (x + 1)$
$\Leftrightarrow 10x + y = 20y + 2x + 2 \Leftrightarrow 8x - 19y = 2$ ...(i) and $x + y = 7$ ...(ii)
Solving, (i) and (ii), we get : $x = 5, y = 2$. Hence, required number = 52.

77. Let the ten's digit be x. Then, unit's digit $= 2x + 1$.
$[10x + (2x + 1)] - [\{10(2x + 1) + x\} - \{10x + (2x + 1)\}] = 1$
$\Leftrightarrow (12x + 1) - (9x + 9) = 1 \Leftrightarrow 3x = 9 \Leftrightarrow x = 3$.
So, ten's digit = 3 and unit's digit = 7. Hence, original number = 37.

78. Let the ten's digit be x and unit's digit be y.
Then, $10x + y = 3(x + y) \Rightarrow 7x - 2y = 0$ ...(i)
$10x + y + 45 = 10y + x \Rightarrow y - x = 5$ ...(ii)
Solving (i) and (ii), we get : $x = 2$ and $y = 7$.
$\therefore$ Required number = 27.

79. Let the ten's and unit's digit be x and $\frac{8}{x}$ respectively.

Then, $\left(10x + \frac{8}{x}\right) + 18 = 10 \times \frac{8}{x} + x \Leftrightarrow 10x^2 + 8 + 18x = 80 + x^2$

$\Leftrightarrow \quad 9x^2 + 18x - 72 = 0 \Leftrightarrow x^2 + 2x - 8 = 0 \Leftrightarrow (x + 4)(x - 2) = 0 \Leftrightarrow x = 2.$

So, ten's digit = 2 and unit's digit = 4. Hence, required number = 24.

80. Let the two fractions be a and b. Then, $ab = \frac{14}{15}$ and $\frac{a}{b} = \frac{35}{24}$.

$\frac{ab}{(a/b)} = \left(\frac{14}{15} \times \frac{24}{35}\right) \Leftrightarrow b^2 = \frac{16}{25} \Leftrightarrow b = \frac{4}{5}.\ ab = \frac{14}{15} \Rightarrow a = \left(\frac{14}{15} \times \frac{5}{4}\right) = \frac{7}{6}$

Since $a > b$, so greater fraction is $\frac{7}{6}$.

81. $A = 2B \Rightarrow B = \frac{1}{2}A$. So, $AB = \frac{2}{25} \Rightarrow \frac{1}{2}A^2 = \frac{2}{25} \Rightarrow A^2 = \frac{4}{25} \Rightarrow A = \frac{2}{5}$.

82. Let the fraction be $\frac{x}{y}$. Then, $x + y = 11$. ...(*i*)

$\frac{x+1}{y-2} = \frac{2}{3} \Rightarrow 3(x+1) = 2(y-2) \Rightarrow 3x - 2y = -7$ ...(*ii*)

Solving (*i*) and (*ii*), we get : $x = 3$ and $y = 8$. So, the fraction is $\frac{3}{8}$.

83. Let the numerator be x. Then, denominator = $x + 3$.

Now, $\frac{x+4}{(x+3)+4} = \frac{4}{5} \Leftrightarrow 5(x+4) = 4(x+7) \Leftrightarrow x = 8.$

$\therefore$ The fraction is $\frac{8}{11}$.

84. Let the denominator be x. Then, numerator = $x + 5$.

Now, $\frac{x+5}{x} - \frac{x+5}{x+5} = \frac{5}{4} \Leftrightarrow \frac{x+5}{x} = \frac{5}{4} + 1 = \frac{9}{4} = 2\frac{1}{4}.$

So, the fraction is $2\frac{1}{4}$.

85. Let the fraction be $\frac{2x}{3x}$. Then, $\frac{2x-6}{3x} = \frac{2}{3} \times \frac{2x}{3x} \Leftrightarrow \frac{2x-6}{3x} = \frac{4x}{9x} \Leftrightarrow 18x^2 - 54x = 12x^2$

$\Leftrightarrow 6x^2 = 54x \Leftrightarrow x = 9.$

Hence, numerator of the original fraction = $2x = 18$.

86. Let the fraction be $\frac{x}{y}$. Then,

$\frac{x}{y+1} = \frac{1}{2} \Leftrightarrow 2x - y = 1$ ...(*i*) and $\frac{x+1}{y} = 1 \Leftrightarrow x - y = -1$ ...(*ii*)

Solving (*i*) and (*ii*), we get : $x = 2$, $y = 3$. Hence, the required fraction is $\frac{2}{3}$.

87. Let the fraction be $\frac{x}{y}$. Then,

$\frac{x+2}{y+3} = \frac{7}{9} \Leftrightarrow 9x - 7y = 3$ ...(*i*) and $\frac{x-1}{y-1} = \frac{4}{5} \Leftrightarrow 5x - 4y = 1$ ...(*ii*)

Solving (*i*) and (*ii*), we get : $x = 5$, $y = 6$. Hence, the original fraction is $\frac{5}{6}$.

88. Let the fraction be $\frac{x}{y}$. Then, $\frac{x+4}{y} - \frac{x}{y} = \frac{2}{3} \Leftrightarrow \frac{4}{y} = \frac{2}{3} \Leftrightarrow y = \left(\frac{4 \times 3}{2}\right) = 6.$

$\therefore$ Denominator = 6.

89. Let the two parts be $(54 - x)$ and x.

Then, $10(54 - x) + 22x = 780 \Leftrightarrow 12x = 240 \Leftrightarrow x = 20.$

$\therefore$ Bigger part = $(54 - x) = 34$.

90. Let the three parts be A, B and C.

Let $\frac{A}{2} = \frac{B}{3} = \frac{C}{4} = x$. Then, $A = 2x$, $B = 3x$ and $C = 4x$. So, $A : B : C = 2 : 3 : 4$.

$\therefore$ Largest part = $\left(243 \times \frac{4}{9}\right) = 108$.

91. Let the four numbers be A, B, C and D. Let $A + 3 = B - 3 = 3C = \frac{D}{3} = x$.

Then, $A = x - 3$, $B = x + 3$, $C = \frac{x}{3}$ and $D = 3x$.

$A + B + C + D = 64 \Rightarrow (x - 3) + (x + 3) + \frac{x}{3} + 3x = 64$

$\Rightarrow 5x + \frac{x}{3} = 64 \Rightarrow 16x = 192 \Rightarrow x = 12.$

Thus, the numbers are 9, 15, 4 and 36.

$\therefore$ Required difference = $(36 - 4) = 32$.

92. Let the numbers be *a*, *b* and *c*. Then, $a^2 + b^2 + c^2 = 138$ and $(ab + bc + ca) = 131$.

$(a + b + c)^2 = a^2 + b^2 + c^2 + 2(ab + bc + ca) = 138 + 2 \times 131 = 400$

$\Rightarrow (a + b + c) = \sqrt{400} = 20.$

93. $A : B = 2 : 3$ and $B : C = 5 : 3 = \frac{3}{5} \times 5 : \frac{3}{5} \times 3 = 3 : \frac{9}{5}$.

So, $A : B : C = 2 : 3 : \frac{9}{5} = 10 : 15 : 9$.

$\therefore$ Second number = $\left(136 \times \frac{15}{34}\right) = 60$.

94. Let the numbers be *x*, *y* and *z*. Then, $x + y = 45$, $y + z = 55$ and $3x + z = 90$

$\Rightarrow y = 45 - x$, $z = 55 - y = 55 - (45 - x) = 10 + x$.

$\therefore$ $3x + 10 + x = 90$ or $x = 20$.

$y = (45 - 20) = 25$ and $z = (10 + 20) = 30$.

$\therefore$ Third number = 30.

EXERCISE 7B

(DATA SUFFICIENCY TYPE QUESTIONS)

Directions (*Questions 1 to 6*) : *Each of the questions given below consists of a statement and/or a question and two statements numbered I and II given below it. You have to decide whether the data provided in the statement(s) is/are sufficient to answer the question. Read both the statements and*

Give answer (a) if the data in Statement I alone are sufficient to answer the question, while the data in Statement II alone are not sufficient to answer the question;

Give answer (b) if the data in Statement II alone are sufficient to answer the question, while the data in Statement I alone are not sufficient to answer the question;

Give answer (c) if the data either in Statement I or in Statement II alone are sufficient to answer the question;

Give answer (d) if the data even in both Statements I and II together are not sufficient to answer the question;

Give answer (e) if the data in both Statements I and II together are necessary to answer the question.

1. What is the two-digit number ? **(S.B.I.P.O. 2003)**
   I. The difference between the two digits is 9.
   II. The sum of the digits is equal to the difference between the two digits.
2. What is the difference between the digits of a two-digit number ? **(Bank P.O. 1999)**
   I. The sum of the digits of that number is 8.
   II. One-fifth of that number is 15 less than half of 44.
3. What is the ratio between the two numbers ?
   I. The sum of two numbers is twice their difference.
   II. The smaller number is 6.
4. What is the two-digit number whose first digit is a and the second digit is b ? The number is greater than 9. **(M.A.T. 2000)**
   I. The number is a multiple of 51.
   II. The sum of the digits a and b is 6.
5. The difference between the digits of a two-digit number is 4. What is the digit in the unit's place ?
   I. The difference between the number and the number obtained by interchanging the positions of the digits is 36.
   II. The sum of the digits of that number is 12.
6. What is the number ? **(Bank P.O. 2000)**
   I. The sum of the two digits is 8. The ratio of the two digits is 1 : 3.
   II. The product of two digits of a number is 12. The quotient of two digits is 3.

Directions (*Questions 7 to 10*) : *Each of the questions given below consists of a question followed by three statements. You have to study the question and the statements and decide which of the statement(s) is/are necessary to answer the given question.*

7. What is the two-digit number ? **(M.B.A. 2002)**
   I. Sum of the digits is 7.
   II. Difference between the number and the number obtained by interchanging the digits is 9.
   III. Digit in the ten's place is bigger than the digit in the unit's place by 1.
   (*a*) I and II only (*b*) II and III only (*c*) I and III only
   (*d*) All I, II and III (*e*) None of these
8. What is the sum of the digits of the two-digit number ?
   I. The ratio between the ten's digit and unit's digit of the number is 3 : 2.
   II. The number obtained on reversing the order of its digits is 18 less than the original number.
   III. The product of the digits is 24.
   (*a*) Any two of the three (*b*) I only or II and III only (*c*) All I, II and III
   (*d*) I and II only (*e*) None of these

9. What will be the sum of two numbers ? **(S.B.I.P.O. 2000)**

I. Among the two numbers, the bigger number is greater than the smaller number by 6.

II. 40% of the smaller number is equal to 30% of the bigger number.

III. The ratio between half of the bigger number and one-third of the smaller number is 2 : 1.

(*a*) I and II only (*b*) II and III only (*c*) All I, II and III
(*d*) Any two of the three (*e*) None of these

10. What is the two-digit number ? **(R.B.I. 2002)**

I. The difference between the two-digit number and the number formed by interchanging the digits is 27.

II. The difference between the two digits is 3.

III. The digit at unit's place is less than that at ten's place by 3.

(*a*) I and II only (*b*) I and III only (*c*) All I, II and III
(*d*) I, and either II or III (*e*) Even with all I, II and III, answer cannot be given.

ANSWERS

1. (*e*) 2. (*e*) 3. (*a*) 4. (*e*) 5. (*b*) 6. (*b*) 7. (*e*) 8. (*a*)
9. (*a*) 10. (*c*)

SOLUTIONS

1. Let the tens and unit digits be x and y respectively. Then,

I. $x - y = 9$.

II. $x + y = x - y$.

From I and II, we get $x - y = 9$ and $x + y = 9$.

On solving, we get $x = 9$ and $y = 0$.

$\therefore$ Required number is 90.

Thus, both I and II are needed to get the answer.

$\therefore$ Correct answer is (*e*).

2. Let the tens and unit digits be x and y respectively. Then,

I. $x + y = 8$ ...(*i*)

II. $\left(\frac{1}{2} \times 44\right) - \frac{1}{5}(10x + y) = 15 \Rightarrow 10x + y = 35$ ...(*ii*)

On solving (*i*) and (*ii*), we get $x = 3$ and $y = 5$.

Thus, I and II together give the answer.

$\therefore$ Correct answer is (*e*).

3. Let the two numbers be x and y.

I gives, $x + y = 2(x - y) \Leftrightarrow x = 3y \Leftrightarrow \frac{x}{y} = \frac{3}{1} \Leftrightarrow x : y = 3 : 1$.

Thus, I only gives the answer.

II does not give the answer.

$\therefore$ Correct answer is (*a*).

4. Number $= 10b + a$.

I. $10b + a = 51 \times c$, where $c = 1, 2, 3$ etc. ...(*i*)

II. $a + b = 6$ ...(*ii*)

Taking $c = 1$, we get $10b + (6 - b) = 51 \Leftrightarrow 9b = 45 \Leftrightarrow b = 5$.

$\therefore$ $a = 1$, $b = 5$. So, number = 51.

Thus, I and II together give the answer.

$\therefore$ Correct answer is (*e*).

5. Let the ten's digit be x and unit's digit be y.

Then, $x - y = \pm 4$ ...(*i*)

I. $(10x + y) - (10y + x) = 36 \Leftrightarrow x - y = 4$ ...(*ii*)

II. $x + y = 12$ ...(*iii*)

Thus, (*i*) and (*iii*) together give the answer.

$\therefore$ II alone gives the answer and I alone does not give the answer.

$\therefore$ Correct answer is (*b*).

6. Let the tens and units digit be x and y respectively. Then,

I. $x + y = 8$ and $\frac{x}{y} = \frac{1}{3}$.

II. $xy = 12$ and $\frac{x}{y} = \frac{3}{1}$.

$\therefore$ II gives, $x^2 = 36 \Leftrightarrow x = 6$. So, $3y = 6 \Leftrightarrow y = 2$.

Thus, II alone gives the number. Clearly, I alone does not give the answer.

$\therefore$ Correct answer is (*b*).

7. Let the tens and units digit be x and y respectively.

I. $x + y = 7$.

II. $(10x + y) - (10y + x) = 9 \Rightarrow x - y = 1$.

III. $x - y = 1$.

Thus, I and II as well as I and III give the answer.

$\therefore$ Correct answer is (*e*).

8. **I.** Let the tens and units digit be $3x$ and $2x$ respectively.

II. $(30x + 2x) - (20x + 3x) = 18 \Leftrightarrow x = 2$.

III. $3x \times 2x = 24 \Leftrightarrow x^2 = 4 \Leftrightarrow x = 2$.

Thus, any two of the three will give the answer.

$\therefore$ Correct answer is (*a*).

9. Let the required numbers be x and y, where $x > y$.

I. $x - y = 6$ ...(*i*)

II. $\frac{30}{100}x = \frac{40}{100}y \Leftrightarrow 3x - 4y = 0$ ...(*ii*)

III. $\frac{\frac{1}{2}x}{\frac{1}{3}y} = \frac{2}{1} \Leftrightarrow \frac{3x}{2y} = \frac{2}{1} \Leftrightarrow \frac{x}{y} = \frac{4}{3}$.

Thus, I and II only give the answer.

$\therefore$ Correct answer is (*a*).

10. Let the tens and units digit be x and y respectively.

I. $(10x + y) - (10y + x) = 27 \Leftrightarrow x - y = 3$.

II. $x - y = 3$.

III. $x - y = 3$.

Thus, even all the given three statements together do not give the answer.

$\therefore$ Correct answer is (*e*).

---

8. PROBLEMS ON AGES

SOLVED EXAMPLES

Ex. 1. ***Rajeev's age after 15 years will be 5 times his age 5 years back. What is the present age of Rajeev ?*** **(Hotel Management, 2002)**

Sol. Let Rajeev's present age be x years. Then,

Rajeev's age after 15 years = $(x + 15)$ years.

Rajeev's age 5 years back = $(x - 5)$ years.

$\therefore \quad x + 15 = 5(x - 5) \Leftrightarrow x + 15 = 5x - 25 \Leftrightarrow 4x = 40 \Leftrightarrow x = 10.$

Hence, Rajeev's present age = 10 years.

Ex. 2. ***The ages of two persons differ by 16 years. If 6 years ago, the elder one be 3 times as old as the younger one, find their present ages.*** **(A.A.O. Exam, 2003)**

Sol. Let the age of the younger person be x years.

Then, age of the elder person = $(x + 16)$ years.

$\therefore \quad 3(x - 6) = (x + 16 - 6) \Leftrightarrow 3x - 18 = x + 10 \Leftrightarrow 2x = 28 \Leftrightarrow x = 14.$

Hence, their present ages are 14 years and 30 years.

Ex. 3. ***The product of the ages of Ankit and Nikita is 240. If twice the age of Nikita is more than Ankit's age by 4 years, what is Nikita's age ?*** **(S.B.I.P.O. 1999)**

Sol. Let Ankit's age be x years. Then, Nikita's age = $\frac{240}{x}$ years.

$$\therefore \quad 2 \times \frac{240}{x} - x = 4 \Leftrightarrow 480 - x^2 = 4x \Leftrightarrow x^2 + 4x - 480 = 0$$

$$\Leftrightarrow (x + 24)(x - 20) = 0 \Leftrightarrow x = 20.$$

Hence, Nikita's age = $\left(\frac{240}{20}\right)$ years = 12 years.

Ex. 4. ***The present age of a father is 3 years more than three times the age of his son. Three years hence, father's age will be 10 years more than twice the age of the son. Find the present age of the father.*** **(S.S.C. 2003)**

Sol. Let the son's present age be x years. Then, father's present age = $(3x + 3)$ years.

$\therefore \quad (3x + 3 + 3) = 2(x + 3) + 10 \Leftrightarrow 3x + 6 = 2x + 16 \Leftrightarrow x = 10.$

Hence, father's present age = $(3x + 3) = (3 \times 10 + 3)$ years = 33 years.

Ex. 5. ***Rohit was 4 times as old as his son 8 years ago. After 8 years, Rohit will be twice as old as his son. What are their present ages ?***

Sol. Let son's age 8 years ago be x years. Then, Rohit's age 8 years ago = $4x$ years.

Son's age after 8 years = $(x + 8) + 8 = (x + 16)$ years.

Rohit's age after 8 years = $(4x + 8) + 8 = (4x + 16)$ years.

$\therefore \quad 2(x + 16) = 4x + 16 \Leftrightarrow 2x = 16 \Leftrightarrow x = 8.$

Hence, son's present age = $(x + 8)$ = 16 years.

Rohit's present age = $(4x + 8)$ = 40 years.

Ex. 6. ***One year ago, the ratio of Gaurav's and Sachin's age was 6 : 7 respectively. Four years hence, this ratio would become 7 : 8. How old is Sachin ?*** **(NABARD, 2002)**

Sol. Let Gaurav's and Sachin's ages one year ago be $6x$ and $7x$ years respectively. Then,

Gaurav's age 4 years hence = $(6x + 1) + 4 = (6x + 5)$ years.

Sachin's age 4 years hence = $(7x + 1) + 4 = (7x + 5)$ years.

$\therefore \quad \dfrac{6x+5}{7x+5} = \dfrac{7}{8} \Leftrightarrow 8(6x+5) = 7(7x+5) \Leftrightarrow 48x + 40 = 49x + 35 \Leftrightarrow x = 5.$

Hence, Sachin's present age = $(7x + 1) = 36$ years.

Ex. 7. ***Abhay's age after six years will be three-seventh of his father's age. Ten years ago, the ratio of their ages was 1 : 5. What is Abhay's father's age at present ?***

Sol. Let the ages of Abhay and his father 10 years ago be x and $5x$ years respectively. Then,

Abhay's age after 6 years = $(x + 10) + 6 = (x + 16)$ years.

Father's age after 6 years = $(5x + 10) + 6 = (5x + 16)$ years.

$\therefore \quad (x+16) = \dfrac{3}{7}(5x+16) \Leftrightarrow 7(x+16) = 3(5x+16) \Leftrightarrow 7x + 112 = 15x + 48$

$\Leftrightarrow 8x = 64 \Leftrightarrow x = 8.$

Hence, Abhay's father's present age = $(5x + 10) = 50$ years.

EXERCISE 8A

(OBJECTIVE TYPE QUESTIONS)

Directions : *Mark (✓) against the correct answer :*

1. Sachin is younger than Rahul by 4 years. If their ages are in the respective ratio of 7 : 9, how old is Sachin ? **(Bank P.O. 2003)**
   (*a*) 16 years (*b*) 18 years (*c*) 28 years
   (*d*) Cannot be determined (*e*) None of these
2. The ratio between the present ages of P and Q is 6 : 7. If Q is 4 years old than P, what will be the ratio of the ages of P and Q after 4 years ? **(S.B.I.P.O. 1998)**
   (*a*) 3 : 4 (*b*) 3 : 5 (*c*) 4 : 3
   (*d*) Data inadequate (*e*) None of these
3. The ratio between the present ages of P and Q is 5 : 7 respectively. If the difference between Q's present age and P's age after 6 years is 2, what is the total of P's and Q's present ages ? **(Bank P.O. 1999)**
   (*a*) 48 years (*b*) 52 years (*c*) 56 years
   (*d*) Cannot be determined (*e*) None of these
4. At present, the ratio between the ages of Arun and Deepak is 4 : 3. After 6 years, Arun's age will be 26 years. What is the age of Deepak at present ? **(R.R.B. 2003)**
   (*a*) 12 years (*b*) 15 years (*c*) $19\frac{1}{2}$ years (*d*) 21 years
5. Present ages of X and Y are in the ratio 5 : 6 respectively. Seven years hence this ratio will become 6 : 7 respectively. What is X's present age in years ? **(Bank P.O. 2003)**
   (*a*) 35 (*b*) 42 (*c*) 49
   (*d*) Cannot be determined (*e*) None of these
6. Present ages of Sameer and Anand are in the ratio of 5 : 4 respectively. Three years hence, the ratio of their ages will become 11 : 9 respectively. What is Anand's present age in years ? **(R.B.I. 2003)**
   (*a*) 24 (*b*) 27 (*c*) 40
   (*d*) Cannot be determined (*e*) None of these

7. Six years ago, the ratio of the ages of Kunal and Sagar was 6 : 5. Four years hence, the ratio of their ages will be 11 : 10. What is Sagar's age at present ? **(Bank P.O. 2004)**
(*a*) 16 years (*b*) 18 years (*c*) 20 years
(*d*) Cannot be determined (*e*) None of these

8. The total of the ages of Jayant, Prem and Saransh is 93 years. Ten years ago, the ratio of their ages was 2 : 3 : 4. What is the present age of Saransh ?
(*a*) 24 years (*b*) 32 years (*c*) 34 years (*d*) 38 years

9. The ratio of the present ages of two brothers is 1 : 2 and 5 years back, the ratio was 1 : 3. What will be the ratio of their ages after 5 years ? **(S.S.C. 2002)**
(*a*) 1 : 4 (*b*) 2 : 3 (*c*) 3 : 5 (*d*) 5 : 6

10. Hitesh is 40 years old and Ronnie is 60 years old. How many years ago was the ratio of their ages 3 : 5 ?
(*a*) 5 years (*b*) 10 years (*c*) 20 years (*d*) 37 years

11. The ratio of the father's age to his son's age is 7 : 3. The product of their ages is 756. The ratio of their ages after 6 years will be :
(*a*) 5 : 2 (*b*) 2 : 1 (*c*) 11 : 7 (*d*) 13 : 9

12. The present ages of three persons are in proportions 4 : 7 : 9. Eight years ago, the sum of their ages was 56. Find their present ages (in years). **(I.M.T. 2002)**
(*a*) 8, 20, 28 (*b*) 16, 28, 36 (*c*) 20, 35, 45 (*d*) None of these

13. The ratio of the ages of a man and his wife is 4 : 3. After 4 years, this ratio will be 9 : 7. If at the time of marriage, the ratio was 5 : 3, then how many years ago were they married ?
(*a*) 8 years (*b*) 10 years (*c*) 12 years (*d*) 15 years

14. The ratio between the school ages of Neelam and Shaan is 5 : 6 respectively. If the ratio between the one-third age of Neelam and half of Shaan's age is 5 : 9, then what is the school age of Shaan ? **(Bank P.O. 2002)**
(*a*) 25 years (*b*) 30 years (*c*) 36 years
(*d*) Cannot be determined (*e*) None of these

15. The ratio between the present ages of A and B is 5 : 3 respectively. The ratio between A's age 4 years ago and B's age 4 years hence is 1 : 1. What is the ratio between A's age 4 years hence and B's age 4 years ago ? **(SIDBI, 2000)**
(*a*) 1 : 3 (*b*) 2 : 1 (*c*) 3 : 1 (*d*) 4 : 1 (*e*) None of these

16. Ten years ago, A was half of B in age. If the ratio of their present ages is 3 : 4, what will be the total of their present ages ?
(*a*) 20 years (*b*) 30 years (*c*) 45 years (*d*) None of these

17. A is two years older than B who is twice as old as C. If the total of the ages of A, B and C be 27, then how old is B ? **(Hotel Management, 2003)**
(*a*) 7 (*b*) 8 (*c*) 9 (*d*) 10 (*e*) 11

18. A man is 24 years older than his son. In two years, his age will be twice the age of his son. The present age of the son is : **(R.R.B. 2003)**
(*a*) 14 years (*b*) 18 years (*c*) 20 years (*d*) 22 years

19. Eighteen years ago, a father was three times as old as his son. Now the father is only twice as old as his son. Then the sum of the present ages of the son and the father is : **(S.S.C. 2003)**
(*a*) 54 (*b*) 72 (*c*) 105 (*d*) 108

20. A person's present age is two-fifth of the age of his mother. After 8 years, he will be one-half of the age of his mother. How old is the mother at present ?
(*a*) 32 years (*b*) 36 years (*c*) 40 years (*d*) 48 years
(IGNOU, 2003)

21. Tanya's grandfather was 8 times older to her 16 years ago. He would be 3 times of her age 8 years from now. Eight years ago, what was the ratio of Tanya's age to that of her grandfather ? **(S.S.C. 2003)**

(*a*) 1 : 2 (*b*) 1 : 5 (*c*) 3 : 8 (*d*) None of these

22. The age of father 10 years ago was thrice the age of his son. Ten years hence, father's age will be twice that of his son. The ratio of their present ages is :

(*a*) 5 : 2 (*b*) 7 : 3 (*c*) 9 : 2 (*d*) 13 : 4

(L.I.C.A.A.O. 2003)

23. Four years ago, the father's age was three times the age of his son. The total of the ages of the father and the son after four years, will be 64 years. What is the father's age at present ?

(*a*) 32 years (*b*) 36 years (*c*) 44 years
(*d*) Data inadequate (*e*) None of these

24. One year ago, Promila was four times as old as her daughter Sakshi. Six years hence, Promila's age will exceed her daughter's age by 9 years. The ratio of the present ages of Promila and her daughter is :

(*a*) 9 : 2 (*b*) 11 : 3 (*c*) 12 : 5 (*d*) 13 : 4

25. The sum of the present ages of a father and his son is 60 years. Six years ago, father's age was five times the age of the son. After 6 years, son's age will be :

(*a*) 12 years (*b*) 14 years (*c*) 18 years (*d*) 20 years

(R.R.B. 2000)

26. The total age of A and B is 12 years more than the total age of B and C. C is how many years younger than A ? **(SIDBI, 2000)**

(*a*) 12 (*b*) 24 (*c*) C is elder than A
(*d*) Data inadequate (*e*) None of these

27. Q is as much younger than R as he is older than T. If the sum of the ages of R and T is 50 years, what is definitely the difference between R and Q's age ?

(*a*) 1 year (*b*) 2 years (*c*) 25 years
(*d*) Data inadequate (*e*) None of these **(Bank P.O. 1999)**

28. The age of a man is three times the sum of the ages of his two sons. Five years hence, his age will be double of the sum of the ages of his sons. The father's present age is :

(*a*) 40 years (*b*) 45 years (*c*) 50 years (*d*) 55 years

29. The sum of the ages of a father and his son is 45 years. Five years ago, the product of their ages was 34. The ages of the son and the father are respectively :

(*a*) 6 and 39 (*b*) 7 and 38 (*c*) 9 and 36 (*d*) 11 and 34

30. Rajan got married 8 years ago. His present age is $\frac{6}{5}$ times his age at the time of his marriage. Rajan's sister was 10 years younger to him at the time of his marriage. The age of Rajan's sister is : **(U.P.S.C. 2003)**

(*a*) 32 years (*b*) 36 years (*c*) 38 years (*d*) 40 years

31. The sum of the ages of 5 children born at the intervals of 3 years each is 50 years. What is the age of the youngest child ? **(S.S.C. 2000)**

(*a*) 4 years (*b*) 8 years (*c*) 10 years (*d*) None of these

32. Father is aged three times more than his son Ronit. After 8 years, he would be two and a half times of Ronit's age. After further 8 years, how many times would he be of Ronit's age ? **(C.B.I. 1998)**

(*a*) 2 times (*b*) $2\frac{1}{2}$ times (*c*) $2\frac{3}{4}$ times (*d*) 3 times

33. The difference between the ages of two persons is 10 years. Fifteen years ago, the elder one was twice as old as the younger one. The present age of the elder person is :
(*a*) 25 years (*b*) 35 years (*c*) 45 years (*d*) 55 years

34. A father said to his son, "I was as old as you are at present at the time of your birth." If the father's age is 38 years now, the son's age five years back was :
(*a*) 14 years (*b*) 19 years (*c*) 33 years (*d*) 38 years
(Assistant Grade, 1998)

35. In 10 years, A will be twice as old as B was 10 years ago. If A is now 9 years older than B, the present age of B is :
(*a*) 19 years (*b*) 29 years (*c*) 39 years (*d*) 49 years

36. Sneh's age is $\frac{1}{6}$th of her father's age. Sneh's father's age will be twice of Vimal's age after 10 years. If Vimal's eighth birthday was celebrated two years before, then what is Sneh's present age ?
(*a*) $6\frac{2}{3}$ years (*b*) 24 years (*c*) 30 years (*d*) None of these

37. If 6 years are subtracted from the present age of Gagan and the remainder is divided by 18, then the present age of his grandson Anup is obtained. If Anup is 2 years younger to Madan whose age is 5 years, then what is Gagan's present age ?
(*a*) 48 years (*b*) 60 years (*c*) 84 years (*d*) 96 years

38. Ayesha's father was 38 years of age when she was born while her mother was 36 years old when her brother four years younger to her was born. What is the difference between the ages of her parents ? **(Hotel Management, 2002)**
(*a*) 2 years (*b*) 4 years (*c*) 6 years (*d*) 8 years

39. My brother is 3 years elder to me. My father was 28 years of age when my sister was born while my mother was 26 years of age when I was born. If my sister was 4 years of age when my brother was born, then, what was the age of my father and mother respectively when my brother was born ?
(*a*) 32 yrs, 23 yrs (*b*) 32 yrs, 29 yrs (*c*) 35 yrs, 29 yrs (*d*) 35 yrs, 33 yrs

40. A person was asked to state his age in years. His reply was, "Take my age three years hence, multiply it by 3 and then subtract three times my age three years ago and you will know how old I am." What was the age of the person ? **(S.S.C. 2004)**
(*a*) 18 years (*b*) 20 years (*c*) 24 years (*d*) 32 years

ANSWERS

1. (*e*)	2. (*e*)	3. (*a*)	4. (*b*)	5. (*a*)	6. (*a*)	7. (*a*)	8. (*d*)
9. (*c*)	10. (*b*)	11. (*b*)	12. (*b*)	13. (*c*)	14. (*d*)	15. (*c*)	16. (*d*)
17. (*d*)	18. (*d*)	19. (*d*)	20. (*c*)	21. (*d*)	22. (*b*)	23. (*e*)	24. (*d*)
25. (*d*)	26. (*a*)	27. (*d*)	28. (*b*)	29. (*a*)	30. (*c*)	31. (*a*)	32. (*a*)
33. (*b*)	34 (*b*)	35. (*c*)	36. (*d*)	37. (*b*)	38. (*c*)	39. (*a*)	40. (*a*)

SOLUTIONS

1. Let Rahul's age be *x* years. Then, Sachin's age = $(x - 7)$ years.

$$\therefore \frac{x-7}{x} = \frac{7}{9} \Leftrightarrow 9x - 63 = 7x \Leftrightarrow 2x = 63 \Leftrightarrow x = 31.5.$$

Hence, Sachin's age = $(x - 7)$ = 24.5 years.

2. Let P's age and Q's age be $6x$ years and $7x$ years respectively.
Then, $7x - 6x = 4 \Leftrightarrow x = 4$.
$\therefore$ Required ratio $= (6x + 4) : (7x + 4) = 28 : 32 = 7 : 8$.

3. Let the present ages of P and Q be $5x$ years and $7x$ years respectively.
Then, $7x - (5x + 6) = 2 \Leftrightarrow 2x = 8 \Leftrightarrow x = 4$.
$\therefore$ Required sum $= 5x + 7x = 12x = 48$ years.

4. Let the present ages of Arun and Deepak be $4x$ years and $3x$ years respectively. Then,
$4x + 6 = 26 \Leftrightarrow 4x = 20 \Leftrightarrow x = 5$.
$\therefore$ Deepak's age $= 3x = 15$ years.

5. Let the present ages of X and Y be $5x$ years and $6x$ years respectively.
Then, $\frac{5x + 7}{6x + 7} = \frac{6}{7} \Leftrightarrow 7(5x + 7) = 6(6x + 7) \Leftrightarrow x = 7$.
$\therefore$ X's present age $= 5x = 35$ years.

6. Let the present ages of Sameer and Anand be $5x$ years and $4x$ years respectively.
Then, $\frac{5x + 3}{4x + 3} = \frac{11}{9} \Leftrightarrow 9(5x + 3) = 11(4x + 3) \Leftrightarrow x = 6$.
$\therefore$ Anand's present age $= 4x = 24$ years.

7. Let the ages of Kunal and Sagar 6 years ago be $6x$ and $5x$ years respectively.
Then, $\frac{(6x + 6) + 4}{(5x + 6) + 4} = \frac{11}{10} \Leftrightarrow 10(6x + 10) = 11(5x + 10) \Leftrightarrow 5x = 10 \Leftrightarrow x = 2$.
$\therefore$ Sagar's present age $= (5x + 6) = 16$ years.

8. Let the ages of Jayant, Prem and Saransh 10 years ago be $2x$, $3x$ and $4x$ years respectively.
Then, $(2x + 10) + (3x + 10) + (4x + 10) = 93 \Leftrightarrow 9x = 63 \Leftrightarrow x = 7$.
$\therefore$ Saransh's present age $= (4x + 10) = 38$ years.

9. Let the present ages of the two brothers be x years and $2x$ years respectively.
Then, $\frac{x - 5}{2x - 5} = \frac{1}{3} \Leftrightarrow 3(x - 5) = (2x - 5) \Leftrightarrow x = 10$.
$\therefore$ Required ratio $= (x + 5) : (2x + 5) = 15 : 25 = 3 : 5$.

10. Suppose, the ratio was $3 : 5$, x years ago.
Then, $\frac{40 - x}{60 - x} = \frac{3}{5} \Leftrightarrow 5(40 - x) = 3(60 - x) \Leftrightarrow 2x = 20 \Leftrightarrow x = 10$.

11. Let the present ages of the father and son be $7x$ and $3x$ years respectively.
Then, $7x \times 3x = 756 \Leftrightarrow 21x^2 = 756 \Leftrightarrow x^2 = 36 \Leftrightarrow x = 6$.
$\therefore$ Required ratio $= (7x + 6) : (3x + 6) = 48 : 24 = 2 : 1$.

12. Let their present ages be $4x$, $7x$ and $9x$ years respectively.
Then, $(4x - 8) + (7x - 8) + (9x - 8) = 56 \Leftrightarrow 20x = 80 \Leftrightarrow x = 4$.
$\therefore$ Their present ages are 16 years, 28 years and 36 years respectively.

13. Let the present ages of the man and his wife be $4x$ and $3x$ years respectively.
Then, $\frac{4x + 4}{3x + 4} = \frac{9}{7} \Leftrightarrow 7(4x + 4) = 9(3x + 4) \Leftrightarrow x = 8$.
So, their present ages are 32 years and 24 years respectively.
Suppose they were married z years ago.
Then, $\frac{32 - z}{24 - z} = \frac{5}{3} \Leftrightarrow 3(32 - z) = 5(24 - z) \Leftrightarrow 2z = 24 \Leftrightarrow z = 12$.

14. Let the school ages of Neelam and Shaan be $5x$ and $6x$ years respectively. Then,

$$\frac{\frac{1}{3} \times 5x}{\frac{1}{2} \times 6x} = \frac{5}{9} \Leftrightarrow \left(\frac{1}{3} \times 9 \times 5x\right) = \left(\frac{5}{2} \times 6x\right) \Leftrightarrow 15 = 15.$$

Thus, Shaan's age cannot be determined.

15. Let the present ages of A and B be $5x$ and $3x$ years respectively.

Then, $\frac{5x - 4}{3x + 4} = \frac{1}{1} \Leftrightarrow 5x - 4 = 3x + 4 \Leftrightarrow 2x = 8 \Leftrightarrow x = 4.$

$\therefore$ Required ratio $= (5x + 4) : (3x - 4) = 24 : 8 = 3 : 1.$

16. Let the ages of A and B 10 years ago be x and $2x$ years respectively.

Then, $\frac{x + 10}{2x + 10} = \frac{3}{4} \Leftrightarrow 4(x + 10) = 3(2x + 10) \Leftrightarrow 2x = 10 \Leftrightarrow x = 5.$

$\therefore$ Sum of their present ages $= (x + 10) + (2x + 10) = (3x + 20) = 35$ years.

17. Let C's age be x years. Then, B's age $= 2x$ years. A's age $= (2x + 2)$ years.

$\therefore$ $(2x + 2) + 2x + x = 27 \Leftrightarrow 5x = 25 \Leftrightarrow x = 5.$

Hence, B's age $= 2x = 10$ years.

18. Let the son's present age be x years. Then, man's present age $= (x + 24)$ years.

$\therefore$ $(x + 24) + 2 = 2(x + 2) \Leftrightarrow x + 26 = 2x + 4 \Leftrightarrow x = 22.$

19. Let the present ages of the father and son be $2x$ and x years respectively.

Then, $(2x - 18) = 3(x - 18) \Leftrightarrow x = 36.$

$\therefore$ Required sum $= (2x + x) = 3x = 108$ years.

20. Let the mother's present age be x years. Then, the person's present age $= \left(\frac{2}{5}x\right)$ years.

$\therefore$ $\left(\frac{2}{5}x + 8\right) = \frac{1}{2}(x + 8) \Leftrightarrow 2(2x + 40) = 5(x + 8) \Leftrightarrow x = 40.$

21. 16 years ago, let T $= x$ years and G $= 8x$ years.

After 8 years from now, T $= (x + 16 + 8)$ years and G $= (8x + 16 + 8)$ years.

$\therefore$ $8x + 24 = 3(x + 24) \Leftrightarrow 5x = 48.$

8 years ago, $\frac{T}{G} = \frac{x + 8}{8x + 8} = \frac{\frac{48}{5} + 8}{8 \times \frac{48}{5} + 8} = \frac{88}{424} = \frac{11}{53}.$

22. Let the ages of father and son 10 years ago be $3x$ and x years respectively.

Then, $(3x + 10) + 10 = 2[(x + 10) + 10] \Leftrightarrow 3x + 20 = 2x + 40 \Leftrightarrow x = 20.$

$\therefore$ Required ratio $= (3x + 10) : (x + 10) = 70 : 30 = 7 : 3.$

23. Let the ages of father and son 4 years ago be $3x$ and x years respectively.

Then, $[(3x + 4) + 4] + [(x + 4) + 4] = 64 \Leftrightarrow 4x = 48 \Leftrightarrow x = 12.$

$\therefore$ Father's present age $= 3x = 36$ years.

24. Let the ages of Promila and Sakshi 1 year ago be $4x$ and x years respectively.

Then, $[(4x + 1) + 6] - [(x + 1) + 6] = 9 \Leftrightarrow 3x = 9 \Leftrightarrow x = 3.$

$\therefore$ Required ratio $= (4x + 1) : (x + 1) = 13 : 4.$

25. Let the present ages of son and father be x and $(60 - x)$ years respectively.

Then, $(60 - x) - 6 = 5(x - 6) \Leftrightarrow 54 - x = 5x - 30 \Leftrightarrow 6x = 84 \Leftrightarrow x = 14.$

$\therefore$ Son's age after 6 years $= (x + 6) = 20$ years.

26. $(A + B) - (B + C) = 12 \Leftrightarrow A - C = 12.$

27. $R - Q = R - T \Rightarrow Q = T.$ Also, $R + T = 50 \Rightarrow R + Q = 50.$

So, $(R - Q)$ cannot be determined.

28. Let the sum of present ages of the two sons be x years.

Then, father's present age = $3x$ years.

$\therefore$ $(3x + 5) = 2(x + 10) \Leftrightarrow 3x + 5 = 2x + 20 \Leftrightarrow x = 15.$

Hence, father's present age = 45 years.

29. Let the ages of father and son be x and $(45 - x)$ years respectively.

Then, $(x - 5)(45 - x - 5) = 34 \Leftrightarrow (x - 5)(40 - x) = 34 \Leftrightarrow x^2 - 45x + 234 = 0$

$\Leftrightarrow (x - 39)(x - 6) = 0 \Leftrightarrow x = 39$ or $x = 6$.

$\therefore$ Father's age = 39 years and son's age = 6 years.

30. Let Rajan's present age be x years. Then, his age at the time of marriage = $(x - 8)$ years.

$\therefore$ $x = \frac{6}{5}(x - 8) \Leftrightarrow 5x = 6x - 48 \Leftrightarrow x = 48.$

Rajan's sister's age at the time of his marriage = $(x - 8) - 10 = (x - 18)$ = 30 years.

$\therefore$ Rajan's sister's present age = $(30 + 8)$ years = 38 years.

31. Let the ages of the children be x, $(x + 3)$, $(x + 6)$, $(x + 9)$ and $(x + 12)$ years.

Then, $x + (x + 3) + (x + 6) + (x + 9) + (x + 12) = 50 \Leftrightarrow 5x = 20 \Leftrightarrow x = 4.$

$\therefore$ Age of the youngest child = x = 4 years.

32. Let Ronit's present age be x years. Then, father's present age = $(x + 3x)$ years = $4x$ years.

$\therefore$ $(4x + 8) = \frac{5}{2}(x + 8) \Leftrightarrow 8x + 16 = 5x + 40 \Leftrightarrow 3x = 24 \Leftrightarrow x = 8.$

Hence, required ratio = $\frac{(4x + 16)}{(x + 16)} = \frac{48}{24} = 2.$

33. Let their ages be x years and $(x + 10)$ years respectively.

Then, $(x + 10) - 15 = 2(x - 15) \Leftrightarrow x - 5 = 2x - 30 \Leftrightarrow x = 25.$

$\therefore$ Present age of the elder person = $(x + 10)$ = 35 years.

34. Let the son's present age be x years. Then, $(38 - x) = x \Leftrightarrow 2x = 38 \Leftrightarrow x = 19.$

$\therefore$ Son's age 5 years back = $(19 - 5)$ years = 14 years.

35. Let B's present age = x years. Then, A's present age = $(x + 9)$ years.

$\therefore$ $(x + 9) + 10 = 2(x - 10) \Leftrightarrow x + 19 = 2x - 20 \Leftrightarrow x = 39.$

36. Vimal's age after 10 years = $(8 + 2 + 10)$ years = 20 years.

Sneh's father's age after 10 years = 40 years. Sneh's father's present age = 30 years.

$\therefore$ Sneh's age = $\left(\frac{1}{6} \times 30\right)$ years = 5 years.

37. Anup's age = $(5 - 2)$ years = 3 years. Let Gagan's age be x years.

Then, $\frac{x - 6}{18} = 3 \Leftrightarrow x - 6 = 54 \Leftrightarrow x = 60.$

38. Mother's age when Ayesha's brother was born = 36 years.

Father's age when Ayesha's brother was born = $(38 + 4)$ years = 42 years.

$\therefore$ Required difference = $(42 - 36)$ years = 6 years.

39. Clearly, my brother was born 3 years before I was born and 4 years after my sister was born.

So, father's age when brother was born = $(28 + 4)$ years = 32 years;

mother's age when brother was born = $(26 - 3)$ years = 23 years.

40. Let the present age of the person be x years.

Then, $3(x + 3) - 3(x - 3) = x \Leftrightarrow (3x + 9) - (3x - 9) = x \Leftrightarrow x = 18.$

EXERCISE 8B

(DATA SUFFICIENCY TYPE QUESTIONS)

Directions (*Questions 1 to 8*) : *Each of the questions given below consists of a statement and/or a question and two statements numbered I and II given below it. You have to decide whether the data provided in the statement(s) is/are sufficient to answer the question. Read both the statements and*

Give answer (a) if the data in Statement I alone are sufficient to answer the question, while the data in Statement II alone are not sufficient to answer the question;

Give answer (b) if the data in Statement II alone are sufficient to answer the question, while the data in Statement I alone are not sufficient to answer the question;

Give answer (c) if the data either in Statement I or in Statement II alone are sufficient to answer the question;

Give answer (d) if the data even in both Statements I and II together are not sufficient to answer the question;

Give answer (e) if the data in both Statements I and II together are necessary to answer the question.

1. The sum of the ages of P, Q and R is 96 years. What is the age of Q ?

I. P is 6 years older than R.

II. The total of the ages of Q and R is 56 years.

2. What is Sonia's present age ? **(Bank P.O. 2003)**

I. Sonia's present age is five times Deepak's present age.

II. Five years ago her age was twenty-five times Deepak's age at that time.

3. How old is C now ?

I. Three years ago, the average of A and B was 18 years.

II. With C joining them now, the average becomes 22 years.

4. What is Reena's present age ? **(Bank P.O. 2003)**

I. Reena's present age is five times her son's present age.

II. Reena's age two years hence will be three times her daughter's age at that time.

5. What is the average age of A and B ?

I. The ratio between one-fifth of A's age and one-fourth of B's age is 1 : 2.

II. The product of their ages is 20 times B's age.

6. Average age of employees working in a department is 30 years. In the next year, ten workers will retire. What will be the average age in the next year ? **(I.M.T. 2002)**

I. Retirement age is 60 years.

II. There are 50 employees in the department.

7. What is the ratio between the ages of the father and the son ?

I. The sum of their ages is 50 years.

II. 3 times the sum of their ages is equal to 5 times the father's age.

8. Divya is twice as old as Shruti. What is the difference in their ages ? **(Bank P.O. 2003)**

I. Five years hence, the ratio of their ages would be 9 : 5.

II. Ten years back, the ratio of their ages was 3 : 1.

Directions (*Questions 9 to 13*) : *Each of the questions given below consists of a question followed by three statements. You have to study the question and the statements and decide which of the statements is/are necessary to answer the question.*

9. What is the present age of A ?

I. The sum of the ages of A and B is 21 years.

II. The difference of the ages of A and B is 5 years.

III. The product of the ages of A and B is 104 years.

(a) I and II only (b) II and III only (c) I and III only

(d) Any two of the three (e) None of these

10. What is the present age of Tanya ? **(Bank P.O. 2004)**

I. The ratio between the present ages of Tanya and her brother Rahul is 3 : 4 respectively.

II. After 5 years the ratio between the ages of Tanya and Rahul will be 4 : 5.

III. Rahul is 5 years older than Tanya.

(a) I and II only (b) II and III only (c) I and III only

(d) All I, II and III (e) Any two of the three

11. What is the difference between the ages of Y and X ?

I. The ratio between the ages of X and Y is 2 : 3.

II. Y's age is 50% more than X's age.

III. One-fourth of X's age is equal to one-sixth of Y's age.

(a) All I, II and III (b) Any two of the three

(c) III, and either I or II (d) Only I and II

(e) Question cannot be answered even with information in all three statements

12. What is Arun's present age ? **(M.B.A. 2002)**

I. Five years ago, Arun's age was double that of his son's age at that time.

II. Present ages of Arun and his son are in the ratio of 11 : 6 respectively.

III. Five years hence, the respective ratio of Arun's age and his son's age will become 12 : 7.

(a) Only I and II (b) Only II and III (c) Only I and III

(d) Any two of the three (e) None of these

13. What is Ravi's present age ? **(R.B.I. 2002)**

I. The present age of Ravi is half of that of his father.

II. After 5 years, the ratio of Ravi's age to that of his father's age will be 6 : 11.

III. Ravi is 5 years younger than his brother.

(a) I and II only (b) II and III only

(c) I and III only (d) All I, II and III

(e) Even with all the three statements answer cannot be given.

Directions (*Questions 14 to 16*) : *Each of these questions is followed by three statements. You have to study the question and all the three statements given to decide whether any information provided in the statement(s) is redundant and can be dispensed with while answering the given question.*

14. What is the ratio of the present ages of Anna and her mother ?

I. The sum of the ages of Anna, her mother and her father is 62.

II. Five years ago, Anna's age was one-fifth of her father's age.

III. Two years ago, the sum of the ages of Anna and her father was 36.

(a) I or II only (b) II or III only (c) III only

(d) I or III only (e) All I, II and III are required.

15. What will be the ratio between ages of Sam and Albert after 5 years ? **(Bank P.O. 1999)**

I. Sam's present age is more than Albert's present age by 4 years.

II. Albert's present age is 20 years.

III. The ratio of Albert's present age to Sam's present age is 5 : 6.

(*a*) I or II or III only (*b*) II only (*c*) III only
(*d*) I or III only (*e*) II or III only.

16. What is the difference between the present ages of Ayush and Deepak ? **(S.B.I.P.O. 1998)**

I. The ratio between Ayush's present age and his age after 8 years is 4 : 5.
II. The ratio between the present ages of Ayush and Deepak is 4 : 3.
III. The ratio between Deepak's present age and his age four years ago is 6 : 5.

(*a*) Any two of I II and III (*b*) I or III only
(*c*) Any one of the three (*d*) All I, II and III are required
(*e*) Even with all I, II and III, the answer cannot be obtained.

ANSWERS

1. (*e*)	**2.** (*e*)	**3.** (*e*)	**4.** (*d*)	**5.** (*e*)	**6.** (*e*)	**7.** (*b*)	**8.** (*c*)
9. (*d*)	**10.** (*e*)	**11.** (*e*)	**12.** (*d*)	**13.** (*a*)	**14.** (*e*)	**15.** (*a*)	**16.** (*c*)

SOLUTIONS

1. Given : $P + Q + R = 96$ ...(*i*)
I. $P = R + 6$ ...(*ii*)
II. $Q + R = 56$ ...(*iii*)
On subtracting (*iii*) from (*i*), we get $P = 40$.
Putting $P = 40$ in (*ii*), we get $R = 34$. Putting $R = 34$ in (*iii*), we get $Q = 22$.
Thus, I and II both together give the answer. So, correct answer is (*e*).

2. I. $S = 5D \Rightarrow D = \frac{S}{5}$ ...(*i*)
II. $S - 5 = 25(D - 5) \Leftrightarrow S = 25D - 120$ ...(*ii*)
Using (*i*) in (*ii*), we get $S = \left(25 \times \frac{S}{5}\right) - 120 \Leftrightarrow 4S = 120 \Leftrightarrow S = 30$.
Thus, I and II both together give the answer. So, correct answer is (*e*).

3. I. 3 years ago, $\frac{1}{2}(A + B) = 18 \Rightarrow$ 3 years ago, $(A + B) = 36$
Now, $(A + B) = (36 + 3 + 3) = 42 \Rightarrow A + B = 42$ ...(*i*)
II. Now, $\frac{1}{3}(A + B + C) = 22 \Rightarrow A + B + C = 66$ ...(*ii*)
From I and II, we get $C = (66 - 42) = 24$.
Thus, I and II both together give the answer. So, correct answer is (*e*).

4. I. Reena's Present age = 5 × (Her son's present age).
II. Reena's age 2 years hence = 3 times her daughter's age at that time.
Clearly, data even in I and II is not sufficient to get Reena's present age.
∴ Correct answer is (*d*).

5. I. $\frac{A}{5} : \frac{B}{4} = 1 : 2 \Leftrightarrow \frac{A}{5} \times \frac{4}{B} = \frac{1}{2} \Leftrightarrow \frac{A}{B} = \left(\frac{1}{2} \times \frac{5}{4}\right) = \frac{5}{8} \Leftrightarrow A : B = 5 : 8$.
II. $20B = AB$.
Let A's age be $5x$ years. Then, B's age is $8x$ years.
∴ $20 \times 8x = 5x \times 8x \Leftrightarrow 40x = 160 \Leftrightarrow x = 4$.
∴ $A = 20$ and $B = 32$.
Thus, I and II together give the answer. So, correct answer is (*e*).

6. I. Retirement age is 60 years.
II. There are 50 employees in the department.
Average age of 50 employees = 30 years.
Total age of 50 employees = (50×30) years = 1500 years.
Number of employees next year = 40.
Total age of 40 employees next year = $(1500 + 40 - 60 \times 10) = 940$.

Average age next year = $\frac{940}{40}$ years = $23\frac{1}{2}$ years.

Thus, I and II together give the answer. So, correct answer is (*e*).

7. I. F + S = 50 ...(*i*) II. 3 (F + S) = 5F ...(*ii*)

From II, we get $2F = 3S \Leftrightarrow \frac{F}{S} = \frac{3}{2}$.

Thus, II alone gives the answer, but I alone does not give the answer.

$\therefore$ Correct answer is (*b*).

8. Let Divya's present age be D years and Shruti's present age be S years.
Then, $D = 2 \times S \Leftrightarrow D - 2S = 0$ ...(*i*)

I. $\frac{D+5}{S+5} = \frac{9}{5}$ ...(*ii*) II. $\frac{D-10}{S-10} = \frac{3}{1}$ ...(*iii*)

From (*ii*), we get $5D + 25 = 9S + 45 \Leftrightarrow 5D - 9S = 20$ ...(*iv*)
From (*iii*), we get $D - 10 = 3S - 30 \Leftrightarrow D - 3S = -20$ ...(*v*)
Thus from (*i*) and (*ii*), we get the answer.
Also, from (*i*) and (*iii*), we get the answer.
$\therefore$ I alone as well as II alone gives the answer. Hence, the correct answer is (*c*).

9. I. A + B = 21. II. A − B = 5. III. AB = 104.
Clearly, any two of three will give the answer. So, correct answer is (*d*).

10. I. Let the present ages of Tanya and Rahul be $3x$ years and $4x$ years.
II. After 5 years, (Tanya's age) : (Rahul's age) = 4 : 5.
III. (Rahul's age) = (Tanya's age) + 5.

From I and II, we get $\frac{3x+5}{4x+5} = \frac{4}{5}$. This gives x.

$\therefore$ Tanya's age = $3x$ can be found. Thus, I and II give the answer.
From I and III, we get $4x = 3x + 5$. This gives x.
$\therefore$ Tanya's age = $3x$ can be found. Thus, I and III give the answer.
From III : Let Tanya's present age be t years.
Then, Rahul's present age = $(t + 5)$ years.

Thus, **from II and III,** we get : $\frac{t}{t+5} = \frac{4}{5}$. This gives t.

Thus, II and III give the answer.
$\therefore$ Correct answer is (*e*).

11. I. $X : Y = 2 : 3 \Rightarrow \frac{X}{Y} = \frac{2}{3} \Rightarrow 3X = 2Y$.

II. $Y = \frac{150}{100} X \Rightarrow Y = \frac{3X}{2} \Rightarrow 3X = 2Y$.

III. $\frac{1}{4} X = \frac{1}{6} Y \Rightarrow 6X = 4Y \Rightarrow 3X = 2Y$.

Thus, even I, II and III together do not give the answer.
$\therefore$ Correct answer is (*e*).

12. **II.** Let the present ages of Arun and his son be $11x$ and $6x$ years respectively.

I. 5 years ago, Arun's age = 2 × His son's age.

III. 5 years hence, $\dfrac{\text{Arun's age}}{\text{Son's age}} = \dfrac{12}{7}$.

Clearly, any two of the above will give Arun's present age.

∴ Correct answer is (*d*).

13. **I.** Let Ravi's present age be x years. Then, his father's present age = $2x$ years.

II. After 5 years, $\dfrac{\text{Ravi's age}}{\text{Father's age}} = \dfrac{6}{11}$.

III. Ravi is younger than his brother.

From I and II, we get $\dfrac{x+5}{2x+5} = \dfrac{6}{11}$. This gives x, the answer.

Thus, I and II together give the answer. Clearly, III is redundant.

∴ Correct answer is (*a*).

14. **I.** A + M + F = 62.

II. $(A - 5) = \dfrac{1}{5}(F - 5)$.

III. $(A - 2) + (F - 2) = 36$.

From II and III, we may get A and F.

Putting these values in I, we get M.

Thus, all I, II and III are required to get the answer.

∴ Correct answer is (*e*).

15. Clearly, any two of the given statements will give the answer and in each case, the third is redundant.

∴ Correct answer is (*a*).

16. Clearly, any two of the given statements will give the answer and in each case, the third is redundant.

∴ Correct answer is (*c*).

---

9. SURDS AND INDICES

IMPORTANT FACTS AND FORMULAE

1. LAWS OF INDICES :

(*i*) $a^m \times a^n = a^{m+n}$ (*ii*) $\dfrac{a^m}{a^n} = a^{m-n}$ (*iii*) $(a^m)^n = a^{mn}$

(*iv*) $(ab)^n = a^n b^n$ (*v*) $\left(\dfrac{a}{b}\right)^n = \dfrac{a^n}{b^n}$ (*vi*) $a^0 = 1$

2. SURDS : *Let a be a rational number and n be a positive integer such that* $a^{\frac{1}{n}} = \sqrt[n]{a}$ *is irrational. Then,* $\sqrt[n]{a}$ *is called a surd of order n.*

3. LAWS OF SURDS :

(*i*) $\sqrt[n]{a} = a^{\frac{1}{n}}$ (*ii*) $\sqrt[n]{ab} = \sqrt[n]{a} \times \sqrt[n]{b}$ (*iii*) $\sqrt[n]{\dfrac{a}{b}} = \dfrac{\sqrt[n]{a}}{\sqrt[n]{b}}$

(*iv*) $(\sqrt[n]{a})^n = a$ (*v*) $\sqrt[m]{\sqrt[n]{a}} = \sqrt[mn]{a}$ (*vi*) $(\sqrt[n]{a})^m = \sqrt[n]{a^m}$.

SOLVED EXAMPLES

Ex. 1. ***Simplify :*** **(*i*)** $(27)^{\frac{2}{3}}$ **(*ii*)** $(1024)^{-\frac{4}{5}}$ **(*iii*)** $\left(\dfrac{8}{125}\right)^{-\frac{4}{3}}$.

Sol. (*i*) $(27)^{\frac{2}{3}} = (3^3)^{\frac{2}{3}} = 3^{\left(3 \times \frac{2}{3}\right)} = 3^2 = 9.$

(*ii*) $(1024)^{-\frac{4}{5}} = (4^5)^{-\frac{4}{5}} = 4^{\left\{5 \times \frac{(-4)}{5}\right\}} = 4^{-4} = \dfrac{1}{4^4} = \dfrac{1}{256}.$

(*iii*) $\left(\dfrac{8}{125}\right)^{-\frac{4}{3}} = \left\{\left(\dfrac{2}{5}\right)^3\right\}^{-\frac{4}{3}} = \left(\dfrac{2}{5}\right)^{\left\{3 \times \frac{(-4)}{3}\right\}} = \left(\dfrac{2}{5}\right)^{-4} = \left(\dfrac{5}{2}\right)^4 = \dfrac{5^4}{2^4} = \dfrac{625}{16}.$

Ex. 2. ***Evaluate :*** **(*i*)** $(.00032)^{\frac{3}{5}}$ **(*ii*)** $(256)^{0.16} \times (16)^{0.18}$.

Sol. (*i*) $(0.00032)^{\frac{3}{5}} = \left(\dfrac{32}{100000}\right)^{\frac{3}{5}} = \left(\dfrac{2^5}{10^5}\right)^{\frac{3}{5}} = \left\{\left(\dfrac{2}{10}\right)^5\right\}^{\frac{3}{5}} = \left(\dfrac{1}{5}\right)^{\left(5 \times \frac{3}{5}\right)} = \left(\dfrac{1}{5}\right)^3 = \dfrac{1}{125}.$

(*ii*) $(256)^{0.16} \times (16)^{0.18} = \{(16)^2\}^{0.16} \times (16)^{0.18} = (16)^{(2 \times 0.16)} \times (16)^{0.18}$

$= (16)^{0.32} \times (16)^{0.18} = (16)^{(0.32 + 0.18)} = (16)^{0.5} = (16)^{\frac{1}{2}} = 4.$

Ex. 3. ***What is the quotient when $(x^{-1} - 1)$ is divided by $(x - 1)$?***

Sol. $\dfrac{x^{-1} - 1}{x - 1} = \dfrac{\frac{1}{x} - 1}{x - 1} = \dfrac{(1 - x)}{x} \times \dfrac{1}{(x - 1)} = -\dfrac{1}{x}.$

Hence, the required quotient is $-\dfrac{1}{x}$.

Ex. 4. ***If $2^{x-1} + 2^{x+1} = 1280$, then find the value of x.***

Sol. $2^{x-1} + 2^{x+1} = 1280 \Leftrightarrow 2^{x-1}(1 + 2^2) = 1280$

$\Leftrightarrow 2^{x-1} = \dfrac{1280}{5} = 256 = 2^8 \Leftrightarrow x - 1 = 8 \Leftrightarrow x = 9.$

Hence, $x = 9$.

Ex. 5. ***Find the value of*** $\left[5\left(8^{\frac{1}{3}} + 27^{\frac{1}{3}}\right)^3\right]^{\frac{1}{4}}$

Sol. $\left[5\left(8^{\frac{1}{3}} + 27^{\frac{1}{3}}\right)^3\right]^{\frac{1}{4}} = \left[5\left\{(2^3)^{\frac{1}{3}} + (3^3)^{\frac{1}{3}}\right\}^3\right]^{\frac{1}{4}} = \left[5\left\{2^{\left(3 \times \frac{1}{3}\right)} + 3^{\left(3 \times \frac{1}{3}\right)}\right\}^3\right]^{\frac{1}{4}}$

$= \{5\,(2 + 3)^3\}^{\frac{1}{4}} = (5 \times 5^3)^{\frac{1}{4}} = (5^4)^{\frac{1}{4}} = 5^{\left(4 \times \frac{1}{4}\right)} = 5^1 = 5$

Ex. 6. ***Find the value of*** $\left\{(16)^{\frac{3}{2}} + (16)^{-\frac{3}{2}}\right\}$.

Sol. $\left[(16)^{\frac{3}{2}} + (16)^{-\frac{3}{2}}\right] = \left[(4^2)^{\frac{3}{2}} + (4^2)^{-\frac{3}{2}}\right] = 4^{\left(2 \times \frac{3}{2}\right)} + 4^{\left\{2 \times \frac{(-3)}{2}\right\}}$

$= 4^3 + 4^{-3} = 4^3 + \dfrac{1}{4^3} = \left(64 + \dfrac{1}{64}\right) = \dfrac{4097}{64}.$

Ex. 7. ***If $\left(\frac{1}{5}\right)^{3y} = 0.008$, then find the value of $(0.25)^y$.***

Sol. $\left(\dfrac{1}{5}\right)^{3y} = 0.008 = \dfrac{8}{1000} = \dfrac{1}{125} = \left(\dfrac{1}{5}\right)^3 \Leftrightarrow 3y = 3 \Leftrightarrow y = 1.$

$\therefore (0.25)^y = (0.25)^1 = 0.25.$

Ex. 8. ***Find the value of*** $\dfrac{(243)^{\frac{n}{5}} \cdot 3^{2n+1}}{9^n \times 3^{n-1}}$.

Sol. $\dfrac{(243)^{\frac{n}{5}} \cdot 3^{2n+1}}{9^n \times 3^{n-1}} = \dfrac{(3^5)^{\frac{n}{5}} \times 3^{2n+1}}{(3^2)^n \times 3^{n-1}} = \dfrac{3^{\left(5 \times \frac{n}{5}\right)} \times 3^{2n+1}}{3^{2n} \times 3^{n-1}} = \dfrac{3^n \times 3^{2n+1}}{3^{2n} \times 3^{n-1}}$

$= \dfrac{3^{n+(2n+1)}}{3^{2n+n-1}} = \dfrac{3^{(3n+1)}}{3^{(3n-1)}} = 3^{(3n+1)-(3n-1)} = 3^2 = 9.$

Ex. 9. ***Find the value of*** $\left(2^{\frac{1}{4}} - 1\right)\left(2^{\frac{3}{4}} + 2^{\frac{1}{2}} + 2^{\frac{1}{4}} + 1\right)$ **(N.I.F.T. 2003)**

Sol. Putting $2^{\frac{1}{4}} = x$, we get :

$$\left(2^{\frac{1}{4}} - 1\right)\left(2^{\frac{3}{4}} + 2^{\frac{1}{2}} + 2^{\frac{1}{4}} + 1\right) = (x-1)(x^3 + x^2 + x + 1), \text{ where } x = 2^{\frac{1}{4}}$$

$$= (x-1)[x^2(x+1) + (x+1)]$$

$$= (x-1)(x+1)(x^2+1) = (x^2-1)(x^2+1)$$

$$= (x^4 - 1) = \left[\left(2^{\frac{1}{4}}\right)^4 - 1\right] = \left[2^{\left(\frac{1}{4}\times 4\right)} - 1\right] = (2-1) = 1.$$

Ex. 10. *Find the value of* $\dfrac{6^{\frac{2}{3}} \times \sqrt[3]{6^7}}{\sqrt[3]{6^6}}$.

Sol. $$\frac{6^{\frac{2}{3}} \times \sqrt[3]{6^7}}{\sqrt[3]{6^6}} = \frac{6^{\frac{2}{3}} \times (6^7)^{\frac{1}{3}}}{(6^6)^{\frac{1}{3}}} = \frac{6^{\frac{2}{3}} \times 6^{\left(7\times\frac{1}{3}\right)}}{6^{\left(6\times\frac{1}{3}\right)}} = \frac{6^{\frac{2}{3}} \times 6^{\left(\frac{7}{3}\right)}}{6^2}$$

$$= 6^{\frac{2}{3}} \times 6^{\left(\frac{7}{3}-2\right)} = 6^{\frac{2}{3}} \times 6^{\frac{1}{3}} = 6^{\left(\frac{2}{3}+\frac{1}{3}\right)} = 6^1 = 6.$$

Ex. 11. *If* $x = y^a$, $y = z^b$ ***and*** $z = x^c$, ***then find the value of abc.***

Sol. $z^1 = x^c = (y^a)^c$ $\quad [\because x = y^a]$

$= y^{(ac)} = (z^b)^{ac}$ $\quad [\because y = z^b]$

$= z^{b(ac)} = z^{abc}$

$\therefore abc = 1.$

Ex. 12. *Simplify :* $\left(\dfrac{x^a}{x^b}\right)^{(a^2+b^2+ab)} \times \left(\dfrac{x^b}{x^c}\right)^{(b^2+c^2+bc)} \times \left(\dfrac{x^c}{x^a}\right)^{(c^2+a^2+ca)}$

Sol. Given Expression $= \{x^{(a-b)}\}^{(a^2+b^2+ab)} . \{x^{(b-c)}\}^{(b^2+c^2+bc)} . \{x^{(c-a)}\}^{(c^2+a^2+ca)}$

$$= x^{(a-b)(a^2+b^2+ab)} . x^{(b-c)(b^2+c^2+bc)} . x^{(c-a)(c^2+a^2+ca)}$$

$$= x^{(a^3-b^3)} . x^{(b^3-c^3)} . x^{(c^3-a^3)} = x^{(a^3-b^3+b^3-c^3+c^3-a^3)} = x^0 = 1.$$

Ex. 13. *Which is larger* $\sqrt{2}$ ***or*** $\sqrt[3]{3}$ **?**

Sol. Given surds are of order 2 and 3. Their L.C.M. is 6.

Changing each to a surd of order 6, we get :

$$\sqrt{2} = 2^{\frac{1}{2}} = 2^{\left(\frac{1}{2}\times\frac{3}{3}\right)} = 2^{\frac{3}{6}} = (2^3)^{\frac{1}{6}} = (8)^{\frac{1}{6}} = \sqrt[6]{8}$$

$$\sqrt[3]{3} = 3^{\frac{1}{3}} = 3^{\left(\frac{1}{3}\times\frac{2}{2}\right)} = 3^{\frac{2}{6}} = (3^2)^{\frac{1}{6}} = (9)^{\frac{1}{6}} = \sqrt[6]{9}.$$

Clearly, $\sqrt[6]{9} > \sqrt[6]{8}$ and hence $\sqrt[3]{3} > \sqrt{2}$.

Ex. 14. *Find the largest from among* $\sqrt[4]{6}$, $\sqrt{2}$ ***and*** $\sqrt[3]{4}$.

Sol. Given surds are of order 4, 2 and 3 respectively. Their L.C.M. is 12.

Changing each to a surd of order 12, we get :

$$\sqrt[4]{6} = 6^{\frac{1}{4}} = 6^{\left(\frac{1}{4}\times\frac{3}{3}\right)} = \left(6^{\frac{3}{12}}\right) = (6^3)^{\frac{1}{12}} = (216)^{\frac{1}{12}}.$$

$$\sqrt{2} = 2^{\frac{1}{2}} = 2^{\left(\frac{1}{2}\times\frac{6}{6}\right)} = \left(2^{\frac{6}{12}}\right) = (2^6)^{\frac{1}{12}} = (64)^{\frac{1}{12}}.$$

$$\sqrt[3]{4} = 4^{\frac{1}{3}} = 4^{\left(\frac{1}{3}\times\frac{4}{4}\right)} = \left(4^{\frac{4}{12}}\right) = (4^4)^{\frac{1}{12}} = (256)^{\frac{1}{12}}.$$

Clearly, $(256)^{\frac{1}{12}} > (216)^{\frac{1}{12}} > (64)^{\frac{1}{12}}$.

$\therefore$ Largest one is $(256)^{\frac{1}{12}}$ *i.e.*, $\sqrt[3]{4}$.

EXERCISE 9

Directions : *Mark (✓) against the correct answer* :

1. The value of $(256)^{\frac{5}{4}}$ is :

(*a*) 512 (*b*) 984 (*c*) 1024 (*d*) 1032

2. The value of $(\sqrt{8})^{\frac{1}{3}}$ is :

(*a*) 2 (*b*) 4 (*c*) $\sqrt{2}$ (*d*) 8

3. The value of $\left(\frac{32}{243}\right)^{-\frac{4}{5}}$ is :

(*a*) $\frac{4}{9}$ (*b*) $\frac{9}{4}$ (*c*) $\frac{16}{81}$ (*d*) $\frac{81}{16}$

4. The value of $\left(-\frac{1}{216}\right)^{-\frac{2}{3}}$ is :

(*a*) 36 (*b*) $-$ 36 (*c*) $\frac{1}{36}$ (*d*) $-\frac{1}{36}$

5. The value of $5^{\frac{1}{4}} \times (125)^{0.25}$ is :

(*a*) $\sqrt{5}$ (*b*) 5 (*c*) $5\sqrt{5}$ (*d*) 25

6. The value of $\frac{1}{(216)^{-\frac{2}{3}}} + \frac{1}{(256)^{-\frac{3}{4}}} + \frac{1}{(32)^{-\frac{1}{5}}}$ is : **(M.B.A. 2003)**

(*a*) 102 (*b*) 105 (*c*) 107 (*d*) 109

7. The value of $[(10)^{150} \div (10)^{146}]$ is : **(Bank P.O. 2002)**

(*a*) 1000 (*b*) 10000 (*c*) 100000 (*d*) 10^6

8. $(2.4 \times 10^3) \div (8 \times 10^{-2}) = ?$

(*a*) 3×10^{-5} (*b*) 3×10^4 (*c*) 3×10^5 (*d*) 30

9. $\left(\frac{1}{216}\right)^{-\frac{2}{3}} \div \left(\frac{1}{27}\right)^{-\frac{4}{3}} = ?$

(*a*) $\frac{3}{4}$ (*b*) $\frac{2}{3}$ (*c*) $\frac{4}{9}$ (*d*) $\frac{1}{8}$

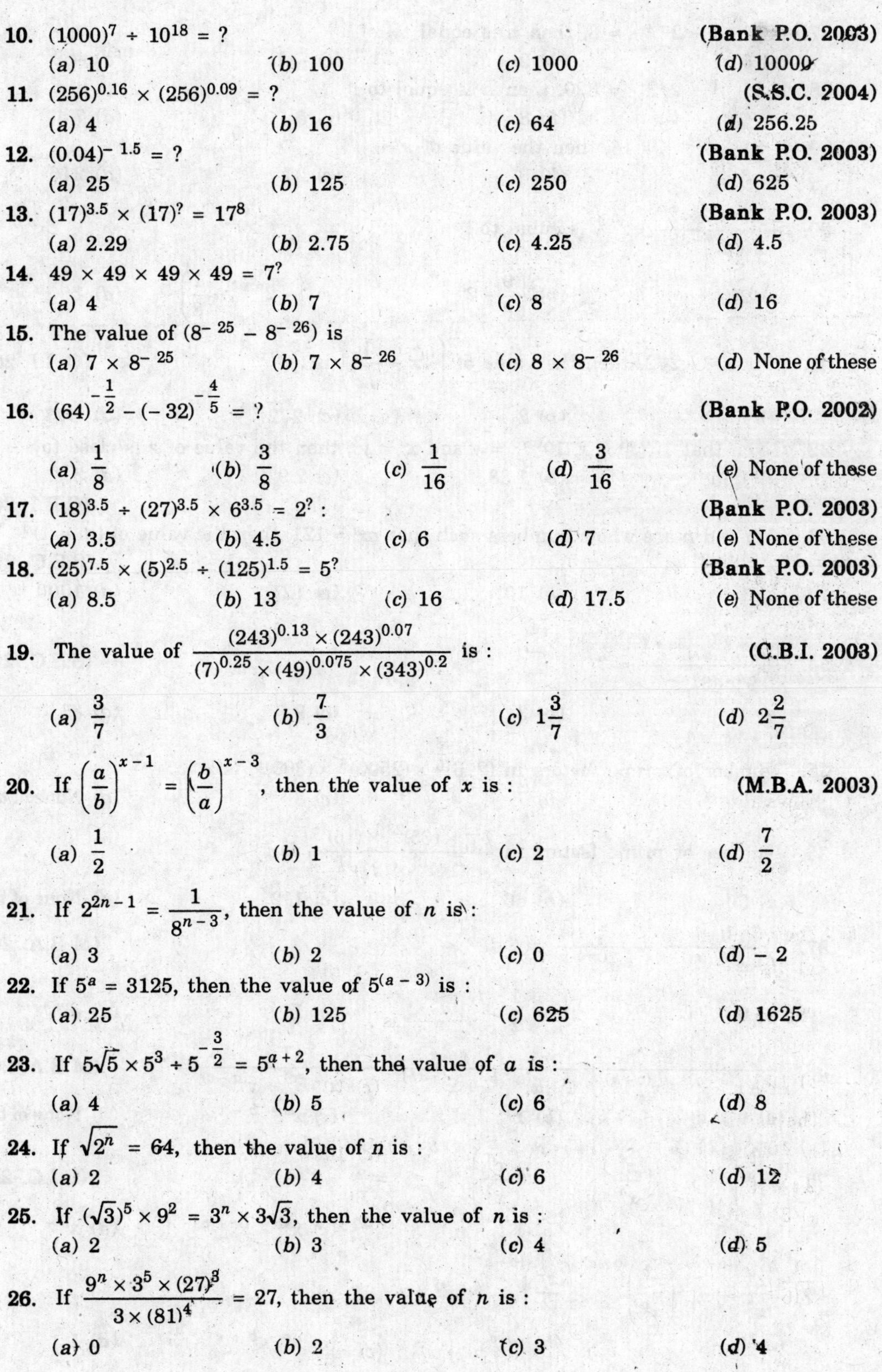

10. $(1000)^7 \div 10^{18} = ?$ **(Bank P.O. 2003)**

(*a*) 10 (*b*) 100 (*c*) 1000 (*d*) 10000

11. $(256)^{0.16} \times (256)^{0.09} = ?$ **(S.S.C. 2004)**

(*a*) 4 (*b*) 16 (*c*) 64 (*d*) 256.25

12. $(0.04)^{-1.5} = ?$ **(Bank P.O. 2003)**

(*a*) 25 (*b*) 125 (*c*) 250 (*d*) 625

13. $(17)^{3.5} \times (17)^? = 17^8$ **(Bank P.O. 2003)**

(*a*) 2.29 (*b*) 2.75 (*c*) 4.25 (*d*) 4.5

14. $49 \times 49 \times 49 \times 49 = 7^?$

(*a*) 4 (*b*) 7 (*c*) 8 (*d*) 16

15. The value of $(8^{-25} - 8^{-26})$ is

(*a*) 7×8^{-25} (*b*) 7×8^{-26} (*c*) 8×8^{-26} (*d*) None of these

16. $(64)^{-\frac{1}{2}} - (-32)^{-\frac{4}{5}} = ?$ **(Bank P.O. 2002)**

(*a*) $\frac{1}{8}$ (*b*) $\frac{3}{8}$ (*c*) $\frac{1}{16}$ (*d*) $\frac{3}{16}$ (*e*) None of these

17. $(18)^{3.5} \div (27)^{3.5} \times 6^{3.5} = 2^?$: **(Bank P.O. 2003)**

(*a*) 3.5 (*b*) 4.5 (*c*) 6 (*d*) 7 (*e*) None of these

18. $(25)^{7.5} \times (5)^{2.5} \div (125)^{1.5} = 5^?$ **(Bank P.O. 2003)**

(*a*) 8.5 (*b*) 13 (*c*) 16 (*d*) 17.5 (*e*) None of these

19. The value of $\dfrac{(243)^{0.13} \times (243)^{0.07}}{(7)^{0.25} \times (49)^{0.075} \times (343)^{0.2}}$ is : **(C.B.I. 2003)**

(*a*) $\frac{3}{7}$ (*b*) $\frac{7}{3}$ (*c*) $1\frac{3}{7}$ (*d*) $2\frac{2}{7}$

20. If $\left(\dfrac{a}{b}\right)^{x-1} = \left(\dfrac{b}{a}\right)^{x-3}$, then the value of x is : **(M.B.A. 2003)**

(*a*) $\frac{1}{2}$ (*b*) 1 (*c*) 2 (*d*) $\frac{7}{2}$

21. If $2^{2n-1} = \dfrac{1}{8^{n-3}}$, then the value of n is :

(*a*) 3 (*b*) 2 (*c*) 0 (*d*) -2

22. If $5^a = 3125$, then the value of $5^{(a-3)}$ is :

(*a*) 25 (*b*) 125 (*c*) 625 (*d*) 1625

23. If $5\sqrt{5} \times 5^3 \div 5^{-\frac{3}{2}} = 5^{a+2}$, then the value of a is :

(*a*) 4 (*b*) 5 (*c*) 6 (*d*) 8

24. If $\sqrt{2^n} = 64$, then the value of n is :

(*a*) 2 (*b*) 4 (*c*) 6 (*d*) 12

25. If $(\sqrt{3})^5 \times 9^2 = 3^n \times 3\sqrt{3}$, then the value of n is :

(*a*) 2 (*b*) 3 (*c*) 4 (*d*) 5

26. If $\dfrac{9^n \times 3^5 \times (27)^3}{3 \times (81)^4} = 27$, then the value of n is :

(*a*) 0 (*b*) 2 (*c*) 3 (*d*) 4

27. If $2^{n+4} - 2^{n+2} = 3$, then n is equal to :
(a) 0 (b) 2 (c) – 1 (d) – 2

28. If $2^{n-1} + 2^{n+1} = 320$, then n is equal to :
(a) 6 (b) 8 (c) 5 (d) 7

29. If $3^x - 3^{x-1} = 18$, then the value of x^x is :
(a) 3 (b) 8 (c) 27 (d) 216

30. $\dfrac{2^{n+4} - 2 \times 2^n}{2 \times 2^{(n+3)}} + 2^{-3}$ is equal to :
(a) 2^{n+1} (b) $\left(\dfrac{9}{8} - 2^n\right)$ (c) $\left(-2^{n+1} + \dfrac{1}{8}\right)$ (d) 1

31. If $x = 3 + 2\sqrt{2}$, then the value of $\left(\sqrt{x} - \dfrac{1}{\sqrt{x}}\right)$ is : **(C.B.I. 2003)**
(a) 1 (b) 2 (c) $2\sqrt{2}$ (d) $3\sqrt{3}$

32. Given that $10^{0.48} = x$, $10^{0.70} = y$ and $x^z = y^2$, then the value of z is close to :
(a) 1.45 (b) 1.88 (c) 2.9 (d) 3.7
(C.B.I. 2003)

33. If m and n are whole numbers such that $m^n = 121$, then the value of $(m-1)^{n+1}$ is :
(S.S.C. 2001)
(a) 1 (b) 10 (c) 121 (d) 1000

34. $\dfrac{(243)^{\frac{n}{5}} \times 3^{2n+1}}{9^n \times 3^{n-1}} = ?$ **(S.S.C. 2004)**
(a) 1 (b) 3 (c) 9 (d) 3^n

35. Number of prime factors in $(216)^{\frac{3}{5}} \times (2500)^{\frac{2}{5}} \times (300)^{\frac{1}{5}}$ is :
(a) 6 (b) 7 (c) 8 (d) None of these

36. Number of prime factors in $\dfrac{6^{12} \times (35)^{28} \times (15)^{16}}{(14)^{12} \times (21)^{11}}$ is :
(a) 56 (b) 66 (c) 112 (d) None of these

37. $\dfrac{1}{1 + a^{(n-m)}} + \dfrac{1}{1 + a^{(m-n)}} = ?$ **(M.B.A. 2003)**
(a) 0 (b) $\dfrac{1}{2}$ (c) 1 (d) a^{m+n}

38. $\dfrac{1}{1 + x^{(b-a)} + x^{(c-a)}} + \dfrac{1}{1 + x^{(a-b)} + x^{(c-b)}} + \dfrac{1}{1 + x^{(b-c)} + x^{(a-c)}} = ?$ **(M.B.A. 2003)**
(a) 0 (b) 1 (c) x^{a-b-c} (d) None of these

39. $\left(\dfrac{x^b}{x^c}\right)^{(b+c-a)} \cdot \left(\dfrac{x^c}{x^a}\right)^{(c+a-b)} \cdot \left(\dfrac{x^a}{x^b}\right)^{(a+b-c)} = ?$ **(L.I.C. 2003)**
(a) x^{abc} (b) 1 (c) $x^{ab+bc+ca}$ (d) x^{a+b+c}

40. $\left(\dfrac{x^a}{x^b}\right)^{(a+b)} \cdot \left(\dfrac{x^b}{x^c}\right)^{(b+c)} \cdot \left(\dfrac{x^c}{x^a}\right)^{(c+a)} = ?$
(a) 0 (b) x^{abc} (c) x^{a+b+c} (d) 1

41. $\left(\frac{x^a}{x^b}\right)^{\frac{1}{ab}} \left(\frac{x^b}{x^c}\right)^{\frac{1}{bc}} \left(\frac{x^c}{x^a}\right)^{\frac{1}{ca}} = ?$

(*a*) 1 (*b*) $x^{\frac{1}{abc}}$ (*c*) $x^{\frac{1}{(ab+bc+ca)}}$ (*d*) None of these

42. If $abc = 1$, then $\left(\frac{1}{1+a+b^{-1}} + \frac{1}{1+b+c^{-1}} + \frac{1}{1+c+a^{-1}}\right) = ?$

(*a*) 0 (*b*) 1 (*c*) $\frac{1}{ab}$ (*d*) ab

43. If *a, b, c* are real numbers, then the value of $\sqrt{a^{-1}b} \cdot \sqrt{b^{-1}c} \cdot \sqrt{c^{-1}a}$ is :

(*a*) abc (*b*) $\sqrt{abc}$ (*c*) $\frac{1}{abc}$ (*d*) 1

44. If $3^{(x-y)} = 27$ and $3^{(x+y)} = 243$, then x is equal to : **(R.R.B. 2003)**

(*a*) 0 (*b*) 2 (*c*) 4 (*d*) 6

45. If $\left(\frac{9}{4}\right)^x \cdot \left(\frac{8}{27}\right)^{x-1} = \frac{2}{3}$, then the value of x is :

(*a*) 1 (*b*) 2 (*c*) 3 (*d*) 4

46. If $2^x = \sqrt[3]{32}$, then x is equal to :

(*a*) 5 (*b*) 3 (*c*) $\frac{3}{5}$ (*d*) $\frac{5}{3}$

47. If $2^x \times 8^{\frac{1}{5}} = 2^{\frac{1}{5}}$, then x is equal to :

(*a*) $\frac{1}{5}$ (*b*) $-\frac{1}{5}$ (*c*) $\frac{2}{5}$ (*d*) $-\frac{2}{5}$

48. If $5^{(x+3)} = (25)^{(3x-4)}$, then the value of x is :

(*a*) $\frac{5}{11}$ (*b*) $\frac{11}{5}$ (*c*) $\frac{11}{3}$ (*d*) $\frac{13}{5}$

49. If $a^x = b^y = c^z$ and $b^2 = ac$, then y equals :

(*a*) $\frac{xz}{x+z}$ (*b*) $\frac{xz}{2(x-z)}$ (*c*) $\frac{xz}{2(z-x)}$ (*d*) $\frac{2xz}{(x+z)}$

50. If $2^x = 3^y = 6^{-z}$, then $\left(\frac{1}{x} + \frac{1}{y} + \frac{1}{z}\right)$ is equal to :

(*a*) 0 (*b*) 1 (*c*) $\frac{3}{2}$ (*d*) $-\frac{1}{2}$

51. If $a^x = b$, $b^y = c$ and $c^z = a$, then the value of xyz is .

(*a*) 0 (*b*) 1 (*c*) $\frac{1}{abc}$ (*d*) abc

52. If $2^x = 4^y = 8^z$ and $\left(\frac{1}{2x} + \frac{1}{4y} + \frac{1}{6z}\right) = \frac{24}{7}$, then the value of z is :

(*a*) $\frac{7}{16}$ (*b*) $\frac{7}{32}$ (*c*) $\frac{7}{48}$ (*d*) $\frac{7}{64}$

53. The largest number from among $\sqrt{2}$, $\sqrt[3]{3}$ and $\sqrt[4]{4}$ is :

(*a*) $\sqrt{2}$ (*b*) $\sqrt[3]{3}$ (*c*) $\sqrt[4]{4}$ (*d*) All are equal

54. If $x = 5 + 2\sqrt{6}$, then $\dfrac{(x-1)}{\sqrt{x}}$ is equal to :

(*a*) $\sqrt{2}$ (*b*) $2\sqrt{2}$ (*c*) $\sqrt{3}$ (*d*) $2\sqrt{3}$

ANSWERS

1. (*c*)	**2.** (*c*)	**3.** (*d*)	**4.** (*a*)	**5.** (*b*)	**6.** (*a*)	**7.** (*b*)	**8.** (*b*)	**9.** (*c*)
10. (*c*)	**11.** (*a*)	**12.** (*b*)	**13.** (*d*)	**14.** (*c*)	**15.** (*b*)	**16.** (*c*)	**17.** (*d*)	**18.** (*b*)
19. (*a*)	**20.** (*c*)	**21.** (*b*)	**22.** (*a*)	**23.** (*a*)	**24.** (*d*)	**25.** (*d*)	**26.** (*c*)	**27.** (*d*)
28. (*d*)	**29.** (*c*)	**30.** (*d*)	**31.** (*b*)	**32.** (*c*)	**33.** (*d*)	**34.** (*c*)	**35.** (*b*)	**36.** (*b*)
37. (*c*)	**38.** (*b*)	**39.** (*b*)	**40.** (*d*)	**41.** (*a*)	**42.** (*b*)	**43.** (*d*)	**44.** (*c*)	**45.** (*d*)
46. (*d*)	**47.** (*d*)	**48.** (*b*)	**49.** (*d*)	**50.** (*a*)	**51.** (*b*)	**52.** (*c*)	**53.** (*b*)	**54.** (*b*)

SOLUTIONS

1. $(256)^{\frac{5}{4}} = (4^4)^{\frac{5}{4}} = 4^{\left(4 \times \frac{5}{4}\right)} = 4^5 = 1024.$

2. $(\sqrt{8})^{\frac{1}{3}} = \left(8^{\frac{1}{2}}\right)^{\frac{1}{3}} = 8^{\left(\frac{1}{2} \times \frac{1}{3}\right)} = 8^{\frac{1}{6}} = (2^3)^{\frac{1}{6}} = 2^{\left(3 \times \frac{1}{6}\right)} = 2^{\frac{1}{2}} = \sqrt{2}.$

3. $\left(\dfrac{32}{243}\right)^{-\frac{4}{5}} = \left\{\left(\dfrac{2}{3}\right)^5\right\}^{-\frac{4}{5}} = \left(\dfrac{2}{3}\right)^{5 \times \frac{(-4)}{5}} = \left(\dfrac{2}{3}\right)^{(-4)} = \left(\dfrac{3}{2}\right)^4 = \dfrac{3^4}{2^4} = \dfrac{81}{16}.$

4. $\left(-\dfrac{1}{216}\right)^{-\frac{2}{3}} = \left[\left(-\dfrac{1}{6}\right)^3\right]^{-\frac{2}{3}} = \left(-\dfrac{1}{6}\right)^{3 \times \frac{(-2)}{3}} = \left(-\dfrac{1}{6}\right)^{-2} = \dfrac{1}{\left(-\dfrac{1}{6}\right)^2} = \dfrac{1}{\left(\dfrac{1}{36}\right)} = 36.$

5. $5^{\frac{1}{4}} \times (125)^{0.25} = 5^{0.25} \times (5^3)^{0.25} = 5^{0.25} \times 5^{(3 \times 0.25)} = 5^{0.25} \times 5^{0.75} = 5^{(0.25 + 0.75)} = 5^1 = 5.$

6. $\dfrac{1}{(216)^{-\frac{2}{3}}} + \dfrac{1}{(256)^{-\frac{3}{4}}} + \dfrac{1}{(32)^{-\frac{1}{5}}} = \dfrac{1}{(6^3)^{-\frac{2}{3}}} + \dfrac{1}{(4^4)^{\left(-\frac{3}{4}\right)}} + \dfrac{1}{(2^5)^{-\frac{1}{5}}}$

$= \dfrac{1}{6^{3 \times \frac{(-2)}{3}}} + \dfrac{1}{4^{4 \times \frac{(-3)}{4}}} + \dfrac{1}{2^{5 \times \frac{(-1)}{5}}} = \dfrac{1}{6^{-2}} + \dfrac{1}{4^{-3}} + \dfrac{1}{2^{-1}}$

$= (6^2 + 4^3 + 2^1) = (36 + 64 + 2) = 102.$

7. $(10)^{150} \div (10)^{146} = \dfrac{(10)^{150}}{(10)^{146}} = (10)^{(150 - 146)} = 10^4 = 10000.$

8. $(2.4 \times 10^3) \div (8 \times 10^{-2}) = \dfrac{2.4 \times 10^3}{8 \times 10^{-2}} = \dfrac{24 \times 10^2}{8 \times 10^{-2}} = (3 \times 10^4).$

9. $\left(\dfrac{1}{216}\right)^{-\frac{2}{3}} \div \left(\dfrac{1}{27}\right)^{-\frac{4}{3}} = (216)^{\frac{2}{3}} \div (27)^{\frac{4}{3}} = \dfrac{(216)^{\frac{2}{3}}}{(27)^{\frac{4}{3}}} = \dfrac{(6^3)^{\frac{2}{3}}}{(3^3)^{\frac{4}{3}}} = \dfrac{6^{\left(3 \times \frac{2}{3}\right)}}{3^{\left(3 \times \frac{4}{3}\right)}} = \dfrac{6^2}{3^4} = \dfrac{36}{81} = \dfrac{4}{9}.$

10. $(1000)^7 \div 10^{18} = \frac{(1000)^7}{10^{18}} = \frac{(10^3)^7}{10^{18}} = \frac{10^{(3\times 7)}}{10^{18}} = \frac{10^{21}}{10^{18}} = (10)^{(21-18)} = 10^3 = 1000.$

11. $(256)^{0.16} \times (256)^{0.09} = (256)^{(0.16+0.09)} = (256)^{0.25} = (256)^{\left(\frac{25}{100}\right)}$

$= (256)^{\frac{1}{4}} = (4^4)^{\frac{1}{4}} = 4^{\left(4\times\frac{1}{4}\right)} = 4^1 = 4$

12. $(0.04)^{-1.5} = \left(\frac{4}{100}\right)^{-1.5} = \left(\frac{1}{25}\right)^{-\frac{3}{2}} = (25)^{\frac{3}{2}} = (5^2)^{\frac{3}{2}} = 5^{\left(2\times\frac{3}{2}\right)} = 5^3 = 125.$

13. Let $(17)^{3.5} \times (17)^x = 17^8$. Then, $(17)^{3.5+x} = (17)^8$.

$\therefore\ 3.5 + x = 8 \Leftrightarrow x = (8 - 3.5) \Leftrightarrow x = 4.5.$

14. $49 \times 49 \times 49 \times 49 = (7^2 \times 7^2 \times 7^2 \times 7^2) = 7^{(2+2+2+2)} = 7^8.$

So, the correct answer is 8.

15. $8^{-25} - 8^{-26} = \left(\frac{1}{8^{25}} - \frac{1}{8^{26}}\right) = \frac{(8-1)}{8^{26}} = 7 \times 8^{-26}.$

16. $(64)^{-\frac{1}{2}} - (-32)^{-\frac{4}{5}} = (8^2)^{-\frac{1}{2}} - \{(-2)^5\}^{-\frac{4}{5}} = 8^{2\times\frac{(-1)}{2}} - (-2)^{5\times\frac{(-4)}{5}} = 8^{-1} - (-2)^{-4}$

$= \frac{1}{8} - \frac{1}{(-2)^4} = \left(\frac{1}{8} - \frac{1}{16}\right) = \frac{1}{16}.$

17. $(18)^{3.5} \div (27)^{3.5} \times 6^{3.5} = 2^x$

$\Leftrightarrow (18)^{3.5} \times \frac{1}{(27)^{3.5}} \times 6^{3.5} = 2^x \Leftrightarrow (3^2 \times 2)^{3.5} \times \frac{1}{(3^3)^{3.5}} \times (2\times 3)^{3.5} = 2^x$

$\Leftrightarrow 3^{(2\times 3.5)} \times 2^{3.5} \times \frac{1}{3^{(3\times 3.5)}} \times 2^{3.5} \times 3^{3.5} = 2^x$

$\Leftrightarrow 3^7 \times 2^{3.5} \times \frac{1}{3^{10.5}} \times 2^{3.5} \times 3^{3.5} = 2^x \Leftrightarrow 2^7 = 2^x \Leftrightarrow x = 7.$

18. Let $(25)^{7.5} \times (5)^{2.5} \div (125)^{1.5} = 5^x$. Then, $\frac{(5^2)^{7.5} \times (5)^{2.5}}{(5^3)^{1.5}} = 5^x \Leftrightarrow \frac{5^{(2\times 7.5)} \times 5^{2.5}}{5^{(3\times 1.5)}} = 5^x$

$\Leftrightarrow \frac{5^{15} \times 5^{2.5}}{5^{4.5}} = 5^x \Leftrightarrow 5^x = 5^{(15+2.5-4.5)} = 5^{13} \Leftrightarrow x = 13.$

19. $\frac{(243)^{0.13} \times (243)^{0.07}}{7^{0.25} \times (49)^{0.075} \times (343)^{0.2}} = \frac{(243)^{(0.13+0.07)}}{7^{0.25} \times (7^2)^{0.075} \times (7^3)^{0.2}}$

$= \frac{(243)^{0.2}}{7^{0.25} \times 7^{(2\times 0.075)} \times 7^{(3\times 0.2)}} = \frac{(3^5)^{0.2}}{7^{0.25} \times 7^{0.15} \times 7^{0.6}}$

$= \frac{3^{(5\times 0.2)}}{7^{(0.25+0.15+0.6)}} = \frac{3^1}{7^1} = \frac{3}{7}.$

20. $\left(\frac{a}{b}\right)^{x-1} = \left(\frac{b}{a}\right)^{x-3} \Leftrightarrow \left(\frac{a}{b}\right)^{x-1} = \left(\frac{a}{b}\right)^{-(x-3)} = \left(\frac{a}{b}\right)^{(3-x)}$

$\Leftrightarrow x - 1 = 3 - x \Leftrightarrow 2x = 4 \Leftrightarrow x = 2.$

21. $2^{2n-1} = \frac{1}{8^{n-3}} \Leftrightarrow 2^{2n-1} = \frac{1}{(2^3)^{n-3}} = \frac{1}{2^{3(n-3)}} = \frac{1}{2^{(3n-9)}} = 2^{(9-3n)}$

$\Leftrightarrow 2n - 1 = 9 - 3n \Leftrightarrow 5n = 10 \Leftrightarrow n = 2.$

22. $5^a = 3125 \Leftrightarrow 5^a = 5^5 \Leftrightarrow a = 5.$

$\therefore \quad 5^{(a-3)} = 5^{(5-3)} = 5^2 = 25.$

23. $5\sqrt{5} \times 5^3 \div 5^{-\frac{3}{2}} = 5^{a+2} \Leftrightarrow \dfrac{5 \times 5^{\frac{1}{2}} \times 5^3}{5^{-\frac{3}{2}}} = 5^{a+2} \Leftrightarrow 5^{\left(1+\frac{1}{2}+3+\frac{3}{2}\right)} = 5^{a+2}$

$\Leftrightarrow 5^6 = 5^{a+2} \Leftrightarrow a + 2 = 6 \Leftrightarrow a = 4.$

24. $\sqrt{2^n} = 64 \Leftrightarrow (2^n)^{\frac{1}{2}} = 2^6 \Leftrightarrow 2^{\frac{n}{2}} = 2^6 \Leftrightarrow \dfrac{n}{2} = 6 \Leftrightarrow n = 12.$

25. $(\sqrt{3})^5 \times 9^2 = 3^n \times 3\sqrt{3} \Leftrightarrow \left(3^{\frac{1}{2}}\right)^5 \times (3^2)^2 = 3^n \times 3 \times 3^{\frac{1}{2}} \Leftrightarrow 3^{\left(\frac{1}{2}\times 5\right)} \times 3^{(2\times 2)} = 3^{\left(n+1+\frac{1}{2}\right)}$

$\Leftrightarrow 3^{\left(\frac{5}{2}+4\right)} = 3^{\left(n+\frac{3}{2}\right)} \Leftrightarrow n + \dfrac{3}{2} = \dfrac{13}{2} \Leftrightarrow n = \left(\dfrac{13}{2} - \dfrac{3}{2}\right) = \dfrac{10}{2} = 5.$

26. $\dfrac{9^n \times 3^5 \times (27)^3}{3 \times (81)^4} = 27 \Leftrightarrow \dfrac{(3^2)^n \times 3^5 \times (3^3)^3}{3 \times (3^4)^4} = 3^3 \Leftrightarrow \dfrac{3^{2n} \times 3^5 \times 3^{(3\times 3)}}{3 \times 3^{(4\times 4)}} = 3^3$

$\Leftrightarrow \dfrac{3^{2n+5+9}}{3 \times 3^{16}} = 3^3 \Leftrightarrow \dfrac{3^{2n+14}}{3^{17}} = 3^3 \Leftrightarrow 3^{(2n+14-17)} = 3^3$

$\Leftrightarrow 3^{2n-3} = 3^3 \Leftrightarrow 2n - 3 = 3 \Leftrightarrow 2n = 6 \Leftrightarrow n = 3.$

27. $2^{n+4} - 2^{n+2} = 3 \Leftrightarrow 2^{n+2}(2^2 - 1) = 3 \Leftrightarrow 2^{n+2} = 1 = 2^0 \Leftrightarrow n + 2 = 0 \Leftrightarrow n = -2.$

28. $2^{n-1} + 2^{n+1} = 320 \Leftrightarrow 2^{n-1}(1 + 2^2) = 320 \Leftrightarrow 5 \times 2^{n-1} = 320$

$\Leftrightarrow 2^{n-1} = \dfrac{320}{5} = 64 = 2^6 \Leftrightarrow n - 1 = 6 \Leftrightarrow n = 7.$

29. $3^x - 3^{x-1} = 18 \Leftrightarrow 3^{x-1}(3-1) = 18 \Leftrightarrow 3^{x-1} = 9 = 3^2 \Leftrightarrow x - 1 = 2 \Leftrightarrow x = 3.$

$\therefore \quad x^x = 3^3 = 27.$

30. $\dfrac{2^{n+4} - 2 \times 2^n}{2 \times 2^{n+3}} + 2^{-3} = \dfrac{2^{n+4} - 2^{n+1}}{2^{n+4}} + \dfrac{1}{2^3} = \dfrac{2^{n+1}(2^3 - 1)}{2^{n+4}} + \dfrac{1}{2^3}$

$= \dfrac{2^{n+1} \times 7}{2^{n+1} \times 2^3} + \dfrac{1}{2^3} = \left(\dfrac{7}{8} + \dfrac{1}{8}\right) = \dfrac{8}{8} = 1.$

31. $\left(\sqrt{x} - \dfrac{1}{\sqrt{x}}\right)^2 = x + \dfrac{1}{x} - 2 = (3 + 2\sqrt{2}) + \dfrac{1}{(3+2\sqrt{2})} - 2$

$= (3 + 2\sqrt{2}) + \dfrac{1}{(3+2\sqrt{2})} \times \dfrac{(3-2\sqrt{2})}{(3-2\sqrt{2})} - 2 = (3 + 2\sqrt{2}) + (3 - 2\sqrt{2}) - 2 = 4.$

$\therefore \quad \left(\sqrt{x} - \dfrac{1}{\sqrt{x}}\right) = 2.$

32. $x^z = y^2 \Leftrightarrow (10^{0.48})^z = (10^{0.70})^2 \Leftrightarrow 10^{(0.48z)} = 10^{(2 \times 0.70)} = 10^{1.40}$

$\Leftrightarrow 0.48z = 1.40 \Leftrightarrow z = \dfrac{140}{48} = \dfrac{35}{12} = 2.9$ (approx.).

33. We know that $11^2 = 121$. Putting $m = 11$ and $n = 2$, we get :

$(m - 1)^{n+1} = (11 - 1)^{(2+1)} = 10^3 = 1000.$

34. Given Expression $= \dfrac{(243)^{\frac{n}{5}} \times 3^{2n+1}}{9^n \times 3^{n-1}} = \dfrac{(3^5)^{\frac{n}{5}} \times 3^{2n+1}}{(3^2)^n \times 3^{n-1}} = \dfrac{3^{\left(5 \times \frac{n}{5}\right)} \times 3^{2n+1}}{3^{2n} \times 3^{n-1}}$

$$= \frac{3^n \times 3^{2n+1}}{3^{2n} \times 3^{n-1}} = \frac{3^{(n+2n+1)}}{3^{(2n+n-1)}} = \frac{3^{3n+1}}{3^{3n-1}} = 3^{(3n+1-3n+1)} = 3^2 = 9.$$

35. $(216)^{\frac{3}{5}} \times (2500)^{\frac{2}{5}} \times (300)^{\frac{1}{5}} = (3^3 \times 2^3)^{\frac{3}{5}} \times (5^4 \times 2^2)^{\frac{2}{5}} \times (5^2 \times 2^2 \times 3)^{\frac{1}{5}}$

$$= 3^{\left(3 \times \frac{3}{5}\right)} \times 2^{\left(3 \times \frac{3}{5}\right)} \times 5^{\left(4 \times \frac{2}{5}\right)} \times 2^{\left(2 \times \frac{2}{5}\right)} \times 5^{\left(2 \times \frac{1}{5}\right)} \times 2^{\left(2 \times \frac{1}{5}\right)} \times 3^{\frac{1}{5}}$$

$$= 3^{\frac{9}{5}} \times 2^{\frac{9}{5}} \times 5^{\frac{8}{5}} \times 2^{\frac{4}{5}} \times 5^{\frac{2}{5}} \times 2^{\frac{2}{5}} \times 3^{\frac{1}{5}}$$

$$= 3^{\left(\frac{9}{5} + \frac{1}{5}\right)} \times 2^{\left(\frac{9}{5} + \frac{4}{5} + \frac{2}{5}\right)} \times 5^{\left(\frac{8}{5} + \frac{2}{5}\right)} = 3^2 \times 2^3 \times 5^2.$$

Hence, the number of prime factors = (2 + 3 + 2) = 7.

36. $\dfrac{6^{12} \times (35)^{28} \times (15)^{16}}{(14)^{12} \times (21)^{11}} = \dfrac{(2 \times 3)^{12} \times (5 \times 7)^{28} \times (3 \times 5)^{16}}{(2 \times 7)^{12} \times (3 \times 7)^{11}} = \dfrac{2^{12} \times 3^{12} \times 5^{28} \times 7^{28} \times 3^{16} \times 5^{16}}{2^{12} \times 7^{12} \times 3^{11} \times 7^{11}}$

$$= 2^{(12-12)} \times 3^{(12+16-11)} \times 5^{(28+16)} \times 7^{(28-12-11)}$$

$$= 2^0 \times 3^{17} \times 5^{44} \times 7^{-5} = \frac{3^{17} \times 5^{44}}{7^5}$$

Number of prime factors = 17 + 44 + 5 = 66.

37. $\dfrac{1}{1 + a^{(n-m)}} + \dfrac{1}{1 + a^{(m-n)}} = \dfrac{1}{\left(1 + \dfrac{a^n}{a^m}\right)} + \dfrac{1}{\left(1 + \dfrac{a^m}{a^n}\right)}$

$$= \frac{a^m}{(a^m + a^n)} + \frac{a^n}{(a^m + a^n)} = \frac{(a^m + a^n)}{(a^m + a^n)} = 1.$$

38. Given Exp. $= \dfrac{1}{\left(1 + \dfrac{x^b}{x^a} + \dfrac{x^c}{x^a}\right)} + \dfrac{1}{\left(1 + \dfrac{x^a}{x^b} + \dfrac{x^c}{x^b}\right)} + \dfrac{1}{\left(1 + \dfrac{x^b}{x^c} + \dfrac{x^a}{x^c}\right)}$

$$= \frac{x^a}{(x^a + x^b + x^c)} + \frac{x^b}{(x^a + x^b + x^c)} + \frac{x^c}{(x^a + x^b + x^c)} = \frac{(x^a + x^b + x^c)}{(x^a + x^b + x^c)} = 1.$$

39. Given Exp. $= x^{(b-c)(b+c-a)} \cdot x^{(c-a)(c+a-b)} \cdot x^{(a-b)(a+b-c)}$

$$= x^{(b-c)(b+c) - a(b-c)} \cdot x^{(c-a)(c+a) - b(c-a)} \cdot x^{(a-b)(a+b) - c(a-b)}$$

$$= x^{(b^2 - c^2 + c^2 - a^2 + a^2 - b^2)} \cdot x^{-a(b-c) - b(c-a) - c(a-b)} = (x^0 \times x^0) = (1 \times 1) = 1.$$

40. Given Exp. $= x^{(a-b)(a+b)} \cdot x^{(b-c)(b+c)} \cdot x^{(c-a)(c+a)}$

$$= x^{(a^2 - b^2)} \cdot x^{(b^2 - c^2)} \cdot x^{(c^2 - a^2)} = x^{(a^2 - b^2 + b^2 - c^2 + c^2 - a^2)} = x^0 = 1.$$

41. Given Exp. $= \{x^{(a-b)}\}^{\frac{1}{ab}} \cdot \{x^{(b-c)}\}^{\frac{1}{bc}} \cdot \{x^{(c-a)}\}^{\frac{1}{ca}} = x^{\frac{(a-b)}{ab}} \cdot x^{\frac{(b-c)}{bc}} \cdot x^{\frac{(c-a)}{ca}}$

$$= x^{\left\{\frac{(a-b)}{ab} + \frac{(b-c)}{bc} + \frac{(c-a)}{ca}\right\}} = x^{\left(\frac{1}{b} - \frac{1}{a}\right) + \left(\frac{1}{c} - \frac{1}{b}\right) + \left(\frac{1}{a} - \frac{1}{c}\right)} = x^0 = 1.$$

42. Given Exp. $= \dfrac{1}{1+a+b^{-1}} + \dfrac{1}{1+b+c^{-1}} + \dfrac{1}{1+c+a^{-1}}$

$= \dfrac{1}{1+a+b^{-1}} + \dfrac{b^{-1}}{b^{-1}+1+b^{-1}c^{-1}} + \dfrac{a}{a+ac+1}$

$= \dfrac{1}{1+a+b^{-1}} + \dfrac{b^{-1}}{1+b^{-1}+a} + \dfrac{a}{a+b^{-1}+1} = \dfrac{1+a+b^{-1}}{1+a+b^{-1}} = 1.$

$[\because\ abc = 1 \Rightarrow (bc)^{-1} = a \Rightarrow b^{-1}c^{-1} = a \text{ and } ac = b^{-1}]$

43. $\sqrt{a^{-1}b}\cdot\sqrt{b^{-1}c}\cdot\sqrt{c^{-1}a} = (a^{-1})^{\frac{1}{2}}\cdot b^{\frac{1}{2}}\cdot(b^{-1})^{\frac{1}{2}}\cdot c^{\frac{1}{2}}\cdot(c^{-1})^{\frac{1}{2}}\cdot a^{\frac{1}{2}}$

$= (a^{-1}a)^{\frac{1}{2}}\cdot(b\cdot b^{-1})^{\frac{1}{2}}\cdot(c\cdot c^{-1})^{\frac{1}{2}} = (1)^{\frac{1}{2}}\cdot(1)^{\frac{1}{2}}\cdot(1)^{\frac{1}{2}} = (1\times1\times1) = 1.$

44. $3^{x-y} = 27 = 3^3 \Leftrightarrow x - y = 3$ ...(*i*)

$3^{x+y} = 243 = 3^5 \Leftrightarrow x + y = 5$ ...(*ii*)

On solving (*i*) and (*ii*), we get $x = 4$.

45. $\left(\dfrac{9}{4}\right)^x\cdot\left(\dfrac{8}{27}\right)^{x-1} = \dfrac{2}{3} \Leftrightarrow \dfrac{9^x}{4^x}\times\dfrac{8^{x-1}}{(27)^{x-1}} = \dfrac{2}{3}$

$\Leftrightarrow \dfrac{(3^2)^x}{(2^2)^x}\times\dfrac{(2^3)^{(x-1)}}{(3^3)^{(x-1)}} = \dfrac{2}{3} \Leftrightarrow \dfrac{3^{2x}\times2^{3(x-1)}}{2^{2x}\times3^{3(x-1)}} = \dfrac{2}{3}$

$\Leftrightarrow \dfrac{2^{(3x-3-2x)}}{3^{(3x-3-2x)}} = \dfrac{2}{3} \Leftrightarrow \dfrac{2^{(x-3)}}{3^{(x-3)}} = \dfrac{2}{3} \Leftrightarrow \left(\dfrac{2}{3}\right)^{(x-3)} = \left(\dfrac{2}{3}\right)^1 \Leftrightarrow x-3 = 1 \Leftrightarrow x = 4.$

46. $2^x = \sqrt[3]{32} \Leftrightarrow 2^x = (32)^{\frac{1}{3}} = (2^5)^{\frac{1}{3}} = 2^{\frac{5}{3}} \Leftrightarrow x = \dfrac{5}{3}.$

47. $2^x\times8^{\frac{1}{5}} = 2^{\frac{1}{5}} \Leftrightarrow 2^x\times(2^3)^{\frac{1}{5}} = 2^{\frac{1}{5}} \Leftrightarrow 2^x\times2^{\frac{3}{5}} = 2^{\frac{1}{5}} \Leftrightarrow 2^{\left(x+\frac{3}{5}\right)} = 2^{\frac{1}{5}}$

$\Leftrightarrow x+\dfrac{3}{5} = \dfrac{1}{5} \Leftrightarrow x = \left(\dfrac{1}{5}-\dfrac{3}{5}\right) = \dfrac{-2}{5}.$

48. $5^{(x+3)} = 25^{(3x-4)} \Leftrightarrow 5^{(x+3)} = (5^2)^{(3x-4)}$

$\Leftrightarrow 5^{(x+3)} = 5^{2(3x-4)} \Leftrightarrow 5^{(x+3)} = 5^{(6x-8)}$

$\Leftrightarrow x+3 = 6x-8 \Leftrightarrow 5x = 11 \Leftrightarrow x = \dfrac{11}{5}.$

49. Let $a^x = b^y = c^z = k$. Then, $a = k^{\frac{1}{x}}$, $b = k^{\frac{1}{y}}$ and $c = k^{\frac{1}{z}}$.

$\therefore\ b^2 = ac \Leftrightarrow \left(k^{\frac{1}{y}}\right)^2 = k^{\frac{1}{x}}\times k^{\frac{1}{z}} \Leftrightarrow k^{\left(\frac{2}{y}\right)} = k^{\left(\frac{1}{x}+\frac{1}{z}\right)}$

$\therefore\ \dfrac{2}{y} = \dfrac{(x+z)}{xz} \Leftrightarrow \dfrac{y}{2} = \dfrac{xz}{(x+z)} \Leftrightarrow y = \dfrac{2xz}{(x+z)}.$

50. Let $2^x = 3^y = 6^{-z} = k \Leftrightarrow 2 = k^{\frac{1}{x}}$, $3 = k^{\frac{1}{y}}$ and $6 = k^{-\frac{1}{z}}$.

Now, $2\times3 = 6 \Leftrightarrow k^{\frac{1}{x}}\times k^{\frac{1}{y}} = k^{-\frac{1}{z}} \Leftrightarrow k^{\left(\frac{1}{x}+\frac{1}{y}\right)} = k^{-\frac{1}{z}}$

$\therefore\ \dfrac{1}{x}+\dfrac{1}{y} = -\dfrac{1}{z} \Leftrightarrow \dfrac{1}{x}+\dfrac{1}{y}+\dfrac{1}{z} = 0.$

51. $a^1 = c^z = (b^y)^z = b^{yz} = (a^x)^{yz} = a^{xyz}$. $\therefore$ $xyz = 1$.

52. $2^x = 4^y = 8^z \Leftrightarrow 2^x = 2^{2y} = 2^{3z} \Leftrightarrow x = 2y = 3z.$

$$\therefore \quad \frac{1}{2x}+\frac{1}{4y}+\frac{1}{6z}=\frac{24}{7} \Leftrightarrow \frac{1}{6z}+\frac{1}{6z}+\frac{1}{6z}=\frac{24}{7} \Leftrightarrow \frac{3}{6z}=\frac{24}{7} \Leftrightarrow z=\left(\frac{3}{6}\times\frac{7}{24}\right)=\frac{7}{48}.$$

53. L.C.M. of 2, 3, 4 is 12.

$$\sqrt{2} = 2^{\frac{1}{2}} = 2^{\left(\frac{1}{2}\times\frac{6}{6}\right)} = 2^{\frac{6}{12}} = (2^6)^{\frac{1}{12}} = (64)^{\frac{1}{12}} = \sqrt[12]{64}$$

$$\sqrt[3]{3} = 3^{\frac{1}{3}} = 3^{\left(\frac{1}{3}\times\frac{4}{4}\right)} = 3^{\frac{4}{12}} = (3^4)^{\frac{1}{12}} = (81)^{\frac{1}{12}} = \sqrt[12]{81}$$

$$\sqrt[4]{4} = 4^{\frac{1}{4}} = 4^{\left(\frac{1}{4}\times\frac{3}{3}\right)} = 4^{\frac{3}{12}} = (4^3)^{\frac{1}{12}} = (64)^{\frac{1}{12}} = \sqrt[12]{64}$$

Clearly, $\sqrt[12]{81}$, *i.e.*, $\sqrt[3]{3}$ is the largest.

54. $x = 5+2\sqrt{6} = 3+2+2\sqrt{6} = (\sqrt{3})^2 + (\sqrt{2})^2 + 2\times\sqrt{3}\times\sqrt{2} = (\sqrt{3}+\sqrt{2})^2.$

Also, $(x-1) = 4+2\sqrt{6} = 2(2+\sqrt{6}) = 2\sqrt{2}(\sqrt{2}+\sqrt{3}).$

$$\therefore \quad \frac{(x-1)}{\sqrt{x}} = \frac{2\sqrt{2}(\sqrt{3}+\sqrt{2})}{(\sqrt{3}+\sqrt{2})} = 2\sqrt{2}.$$

10. PERCENTAGE

IMPORTANT FACTS AND FORMULAE

I. Concept of Percentage : By a certain ***percent***, we mean that many hundredths. Thus, x percent means x hundredths, written as $x\%$.

To express x% as a fraction : We have, $x\% = \frac{x}{100}$.

Thus, $20\% = \frac{20}{100} = \frac{1}{5}$; $48\% = \frac{48}{100} = \frac{12}{25}$, etc.

To express $\frac{a}{b}$ ***as a percent*** : We have, $\frac{a}{b} = \left(\frac{a}{b} \times 100\right)\%$.

Thus, $\frac{1}{4} = \left(\frac{1}{4} \times 100\right)\% = 25\%$; $0.6 = \frac{6}{10} = \frac{3}{5} = \left(\frac{3}{5} \times 100\right)\% = 60\%$.

II. If the price of a commodity increases by R%, then the reduction in consumption so as not to increase the expenditure is

$$\left[\frac{R}{(100+R)} \times 100\right]\%$$

If the price of a commodity decreases by R%, then the increase in consumption so as not to decrease the expenditure is

$$\left[\frac{R}{(100-R)} \times 100\right]\%$$

III. Results on Population : Let the population of a town be P now and suppose it increases at the rate of R% per annum, then :

1. Population after n years $= P\left(1 + \frac{R}{100}\right)^n$.

2. Population n years ago $= \frac{P}{\left(1 + \frac{R}{100}\right)^n}$.

IV. Results on Depreciation : Let the present value of a machine be P. Suppose it depreciates at the rate of R% per annum. Then :

1. Value of the machine after n years $= P\left(1 - \frac{R}{100}\right)^n$.

2. Value of the machine n years ago $= \frac{P}{\left(1 - \frac{R}{100}\right)^n}$.

V. If A is R% more than B, then B is less than A by

$$\left[\frac{R}{(100+R)} \times 100\right]\%.$$

If A is R% less than B, then B is more than A by

$$\left[\frac{R}{(100-R)} \times 100\right]\%.$$

SOLVED EXAMPLES

Ex. 1. *Express each of the following as a fraction :*

(i) 56% *(ii) 4%* *(iii) 0.6%* *(iv) 0.08%*

Sol. (i) $56\% = \frac{56}{100} = \frac{14}{25}$. (ii) $4\% = \frac{4}{100} = \frac{1}{25}$.

(ii) $0.6\% = \frac{0.6}{100} = \frac{6}{1000} = \frac{3}{500}$. (iv) $0.08\% = \frac{0.08}{100} = \frac{8}{10000} = \frac{1}{1250}$.

Ex. 2. *Express each of the following as a decimal :*

(i) 6% *(ii) 28%* *(iii) 0.2%* *(iv) 0.04%*

Sol. (i) $6\% = \frac{6}{100} = 0.06$. (ii) $28\% = \frac{28}{100} = 0.28$.

(iii) $0.2\% = \frac{0.2}{100} = 0.002$. (iv) $0.04\% = \frac{0.04}{100} = 0.0004$.

Ex. 3. *Express each of the following as rate percent :*

(i) $\frac{23}{36}$ *(ii)* $6\frac{3}{4}$ *(iii) 0.004*

Sol. (i) $\frac{23}{36} = \left(\frac{23}{36} \times 100\right)\% = \left(\frac{575}{9}\right)\% = 63\frac{8}{9}\%$.

(ii) $0.004 = \frac{4}{1000} = \left(\frac{4}{1000} \times 100\right)\% = 0.4\%$.

(iii) $6\frac{3}{4} = \frac{27}{4} = \left(\frac{27}{4} \times 100\right)\% = 675\%$.

Ex. 4. *Evaluate :*

(i) 28% of 450 + 45% of 280 **(Bank P.O. 2003)**

(ii) $16\frac{2}{3}\%$ *of 600 gm –* $33\frac{1}{3}\%$ *of 180 gm* **(R.R.B. 1998)**

Sol. (i) $28\% \text{ of } 450 + 45\% \text{ of } 280 = \left(\frac{28}{100} \times 450 + \frac{45}{100} \times 280\right) = (126 + 126) = 252$.

(ii) $16\frac{2}{3}\% \text{ of } 600 \text{ gm} - 33\frac{1}{3}\% \text{ of } 180 \text{ gm}$

$= \left[\left(\frac{50}{3} \times \frac{1}{100} \times 600\right) - \left(\frac{100}{3} \times \frac{1}{100} \times 180\right)\right] \text{ gm} = (100 - 60) \text{ gm} = 40 \text{ gm}.$

Ex. 5. *(i) 2 is what percent of 50 ?* **(S.S.C. 2000)**

(ii) $\frac{1}{2}$ *is what percent of* $\frac{1}{3}$ *?* **(S.S.C. 2002)**

(iii) What percent of 7 is 84 ?

(iv) What percent of 2 metric tonnes is 40 quintals ?

(v) What percent of 6.5 litres is 130 ml ?

Sol. (i) Required percentage $= \left(\frac{2}{50} \times 100\right)\% = 4\%$.

(ii) Required percentage $= \left(\frac{1}{2} \times \frac{3}{1} \times 100\right)\% = 150\%$.

(iii) Required percentage $= \left(\frac{84}{7} \times 100\right)\% = 1200\%$.

(iv) 1 metric tonne = 10 quintals.

$\therefore$ Required percentage $= \left(\frac{40}{2 \times 10} \times 100\right)\% = 200\%$.

(v) Required percentage $= \left(\frac{130}{6.5 \times 1000} \times 100\right)\% = 2\%$.

Ex. 6. ***Find the missing figures :***

(i) ?% of 25 = 2.125 ***(ii) 9% of ? = 63*** ***(iii) 0.25% of ? = 0.04***

Sol. (i) Let x% of 25 = 2.125. Then, $\frac{x}{100} \times 25 = 2.125 \Leftrightarrow x = (2.125 \times 4) = 8.5$.

(ii) Let 9% of x = 6.3. Then, $\frac{9}{100} x = 6.3 \Leftrightarrow x = \left(\frac{6.3 \times 100}{9}\right) = 70$.

(iii) Let 0.25% of x = 0.04. Then, $\frac{0.25}{100} x = 0.04 \Leftrightarrow x = \left(\frac{0.04 \times 100}{0.25}\right) = 16$.

Ex. 7. ***Which is greatest in $16\frac{2}{3}\%$, $\frac{2}{15}$ and 0.17 ?***

Sol. $16\frac{2}{3}\% = \left(\frac{50}{3} \times \frac{1}{100}\right) = \frac{1}{6} = 0.166$, $\frac{2}{15} = 0.133$. Clearly, 0.17 is the greatest.

Ex. 8. ***If the sales tax be reduced from $3\frac{1}{2}\%$ to $3\frac{1}{3}\%$, then what difference does it make to a person who purchases an article with marked price of Rs. 8400 ?*** **(S.S.C. 2002)**

Sol. Required difference $= \left(3\frac{1}{2}\% \text{ of Rs. } 8400\right) - \left(3\frac{1}{3}\% \text{ of Rs. } 8400\right)$

$= \left(\frac{7}{2} - \frac{10}{3}\right)\% \text{ of Rs. } 8400 = \frac{1}{6}\% \text{ of Rs. } 8400$

$= \text{Rs. } \left(\frac{1}{6} \times \frac{1}{100} \times 8400\right) = \text{Rs. } 14$.

Ex. 9. ***An inspector rejects 0.08% of the meters as defective. How many will he examine to reject 2 ?*** **(M.A.T. 2000)**

Sol. Let the number of meters to be examined be x.

Then, 0.08% of $x = 2 \Leftrightarrow \left(\frac{8}{100} \times \frac{1}{100} \times x\right) = 2 \Leftrightarrow x = \left(\frac{2 \times 100 \times 100}{8}\right) = 2500$.

Ex. 10. ***Sixty-five percent of a number is 21 less than four-fifth of that number. What is the number ?***

Sol. Let the number be x.

Then, $\frac{4}{5} x - (65\% \text{ of } x) = 21 \Leftrightarrow \frac{4}{5} x - \frac{65}{100} x = 21 \Leftrightarrow 15x = 2100 \Leftrightarrow x = 140$.

Ex. 11. ***Difference of two numbers is 1660. If 7.5% of one number is 12.5% of the other number, find the two numbers.***

Sol. Let the numbers be x and y. Then, 7.5% of x = 12.5% of $y \Leftrightarrow x = \frac{125}{75} y = \frac{5}{3} y$.

Now, $x - y = 1660 \Leftrightarrow \frac{5}{3} y - y = 1660 \Rightarrow \frac{2}{3} y = 1660 \Rightarrow y = \left(\frac{1660 \times 3}{2}\right) = 2490$.

$\therefore$ One number = 2490, Second number $= \frac{5}{3} y = 4150$.

Ex. 12. ***In expressing a length 81.472 km as nearly as possible with three significant digits, find the percentage error.*** **(S.S.C. 1997)**

Sol. Error = (81.5 – 81.472) km = 0.028.

$\therefore$ Required percentage = $\left(\frac{0.028}{81.472} \times 100\right)\% = 0.034\%$.

Ex. 13. ***In an election between two candidates, 75% of the voters cast their votes, out of which 2% of the votes were declared invalid. A candidate got 9261 votes which were 75% of the total valid votes. Find the total number of votes enrolled in that election.*** **(S.S.C. 2003)**

Sol. Let the total number of votes enrolled be x. Then,

Number of votes cast = 75% of x. Valid votes = 98% of (75% of x).

$\therefore$ 75% of [98% of (75% of x)] = 9261

$\Leftrightarrow \left(\frac{75}{100} \times \frac{98}{100} \times \frac{75}{100} \times x\right) = 9261 \Leftrightarrow x = \left(\frac{9261 \times 100 \times 100 \times 100}{75 \times 98 \times 75}\right) = 16800.$

Ex. 14. ***Shobha's Mathematics Test had 75 problems i.e., 10 arithmetic, 30 algebra and 35 geometry problems. Although she answered 70% of the arithmetic, 40% of the algebra and 60% of the geometry problems correctly, she did not pass the test because she got less than 60% of the problems right. How many more questions she would have needed to answer correctly to earn a 60% passing grade?*** **(C.D.S. 2002)**

Sol. Number of questions attempted correctly = (70% of 10 + 40% of 30 + 60% of 35)

= (7 + 12 + 21) = 40.

Questions to be answered correctly for 60% grade = 60% of 75 = 45.

$\therefore$ Required number of questions = (45 – 40) = 5.

Ex. 15. ***If 50% of (x – y) = 30% of (x + y), then what percent of x is y?*** **(S.S.C. 2003)**

Sol. 50% of $(x - y)$ = 30% of $(x + y)$ $\Leftrightarrow \frac{50}{100}(x - y) = \frac{30}{100}(x + y)$

$\Leftrightarrow 5(x - y) = 3(x + y) \Leftrightarrow 2x = 8y \Leftrightarrow x = 4y.$

$\therefore$ Required percentage = $\left(\frac{y}{x} \times 100\right)\% = \left(\frac{y}{4y} \times 100\right)\% = 25\%$.

Ex. 16. ***Mr. Jones gave 40% of the money he had, to his wife. He also gave 20% of the remaining amount to each of his three sons. Half of the amount now left was spent on miscellaneous items and the remaining amount of Rs. 12,000 was deposited in the bank. How much money did Mr. Jones have initially?***

Sol. Let the initial amount with Mr. Jones be Rs. x. Then

Money given to wife = Rs. $\frac{40}{100}x$ = Rs. $\frac{2x}{5}$. Balance = Rs. $\left(x - \frac{2x}{5}\right)$ = Rs. $\frac{3x}{5}$.

Money given to 3 sons = Rs. $\left[3 \times \left(\frac{20}{100} \times \frac{3x}{5}\right)\right]$ = Rs. $\frac{9x}{25}$.

Balance = Rs. $\left(\frac{3x}{5} - \frac{9x}{25}\right)$ = Rs. $\frac{6x}{25}$.

Amount deposited in bank = Rs. $\left(\frac{1}{2} \times \frac{6x}{25}\right)$ = Rs. $\frac{3x}{25}$.

$\therefore \frac{3x}{25} = 12000 \Leftrightarrow x = \left(\frac{12000 \times 25}{3}\right) = 100000.$

So, Mr. Jones initially had Rs. 1,00,000 with him.

Short-cut Method : Let the initial amount with Mr. Jones be Rs. x.

Then, $\frac{1}{2}$ [100 – (3 × 20)]% of (100 – 40)% of x = 12000.

$\Leftrightarrow \quad \frac{1}{2} \times \frac{40}{100} \times \frac{60}{100} \times x = 12000 \quad \Leftrightarrow \quad \frac{3}{25} x = 12000 \quad \Leftrightarrow \quad x = \left(\frac{12000 \times 25}{3}\right) = 100000.$

Ex. 17. ***10% of the inhabitants of a village having died of cholera, a panic set in, during which 25% of the remaining inhabitants left the village. The population is then reduced to 4050. Find the number of original inhabitants.*** **(S.S.C. 2002)**

Sol. Let the total number of original inhabitants be x.

Then, (100 – 25)% of (100 – 10)% of x = 4050

$\Leftrightarrow \quad \left(\frac{75}{100} \times \frac{90}{100} \times x\right) = 4050 \quad \Leftrightarrow \quad \frac{27}{40} x = 4050 \quad \Leftrightarrow \quad x = \left(\frac{4050 \times 40}{27}\right) = 6000.$

$\therefore$ Number of original inhabitants = 6000.

Ex. 18. ***A salesman's commission is 5% on all sales upto Rs. 10,000 and 4% on all sales exceeding this. He remits Rs. 31,100 to his parent company after deducting his commission. Find the total sales.*** **(R.R.B. 2001)**

Sol. Let his total sales be Rs. x. Now, (Total Sales) – (Commission) = Rs. 31,100.

$\therefore \quad x$ – [5% of 10000 + 4% of (x – 10000)] = 31100

$\Leftrightarrow \quad x - \left[\frac{5}{100} \times 10000 + \frac{4}{100}(x - 10000)\right] = 31100 \quad \Leftrightarrow \quad x - 500 - \frac{(x - 10000)}{25} = 31100$

$\Leftrightarrow \quad x - \frac{x}{25} = 31200 \quad \Leftrightarrow \quad \frac{24x}{25} = 31200 \quad \Leftrightarrow \quad x = \left(\frac{31200 \times 25}{24}\right) = 32500.$

$\therefore$ Total sales = Rs. 32,500.

Ex. 19. ***Raman's salary was decreased by 50% and subsequently increased by 50%. How much percent does he lose ?*** **(Hotel Management, 2003)**

Sol. Let original salary = Rs. 100.

New final salary = 150% of (50% of Rs. 100) = Rs. $\left(\frac{150}{100} \times \frac{50}{100} \times 100\right)$ = Rs. 75.

$\therefore$ Decrease = 25%.

Ex. 20. ***Paulson spends 75% of his income. His income is increased by 20% and he increased his expenditure by 10%. Find the percentage increase in his savings.***

Sol. Let original income = Rs. 100. Then, expenditure = Rs. 75 and savings = Rs. 25.

New income = Rs. 120, New expenditure = Rs. $\left(\frac{110}{100} \times 75\right)$ = Rs. $\frac{165}{2}$.

New savings = Rs. $\left(120 - \frac{165}{2}\right)$ = Rs. $\frac{75}{2}$.

Increase in savings = Rs. $\left(\frac{75}{2} - 25\right)$ = Rs. $\frac{25}{2}$.

$\therefore$ Increase% = $\left(\frac{25}{2} \times \frac{1}{25} \times 100\right)\%$ = 50%.

Ex. 21. ***The salary of a person was reduced by 10%. By what percent should his reduced salary be raised so as to bring it at par with his original salary ?*** **(S.S.C. 2004)**

Sol. Let the original salary be Rs. 100. New salary = Rs. 90.

Increase on 90 = 10. Increase on 100 = $\left(\frac{10}{90} \times 100\right)\% = 11\frac{1}{9}\%$.

Ex. 22. ***When the price of a product was decreased by 10%, the number sold increased by 30%. What was the effect on the total revenue ?*** **(R.B.I. 2003)**

Sol. Let the price of the product be Rs. 100 and let original sale be 100 pieces.

Then, Total Revenue = Rs. (100 × 100) = Rs. 10000.

New revenue = Rs. (90 × 130) = Rs. 11700.

$\therefore$ Increase in revenue $= \left(\frac{1700}{10000} \times 100\right)\% = 17\%.$

Ex. 23. ***If the numerator of a fraction be increased by 15% and its denominator be diminished by 8%, the value of the fraction is $\frac{15}{16}$. Find the original fraction.***

Sol. Let the original fraction be $\frac{x}{y}$.

Then, $\frac{115\% \text{ of } x}{92\% \text{ of } y} = \frac{15}{16} \Rightarrow \frac{115x}{92y} = \frac{15}{16} \Rightarrow \frac{x}{y} = \left(\frac{15}{16} \times \frac{92}{115}\right) = \frac{3}{4}.$

Ex. 24. ***In the new budget, the price of kerosene oil rose by 25%. By how much percent must a person reduce his consumption so that his expenditure on it does not increase?***

Sol. Reduction in consumption $= \left[\frac{R}{(100 + R)} \times 100\right]\% = \left(\frac{25}{125} \times 100\right)\% = 20\%.$

Ex. 25. ***The population of a town is 1,76,400. If it increases at the rate of 5% per annum, what will be its population 2 years hence ? What was it 2 years ago ?***

Sol. Population after 2 years $= 176400 \times \left(1 + \frac{5}{100}\right)^2 = \left(176400 \times \frac{21}{20} \times \frac{21}{40}\right) = 194481$

Population 2 years ago $= \frac{176400}{\left(1 + \frac{5}{100}\right)^2} = \left(176400 \times \frac{20}{21} \times \frac{20}{21}\right) = 160000.$

Ex. 26. ***The value of a machine depreciates at the rate of 10% per annum. If its present value is Rs. 1,62,000, what will be its worth after 2 years ? What was the value of the machine 2 years ago ?***

Sol. Value of the machine after 2 years

$= \text{Rs.} \left[162000 \times \left(1 - \frac{10}{100}\right)^2\right] = \text{Rs.} \left(162000 \times \frac{9}{10} \times \frac{9}{10}\right) = \text{Rs. } 131220.$

Value of the machine 2 years ago

$= \text{Rs.} \left[\frac{162000}{\left(1 - \frac{10}{100}\right)^2}\right] = \text{Rs.} \left(162000 \times \frac{10}{9} \times \frac{10}{9}\right) = \text{Rs. } 200000.$

Ex. 27. ***During one year, the population of a town increased by 5% and during the next year, the population decreased by 5%. If the total population is 9975 at the end of the second year, then what was the population size in the beginning of the first year?*** **(Hotel Management, 2003)**

Sol. Population in the beginning of the first year

$= \frac{9975}{\left(1 + \frac{5}{100}\right)\left(1 - \frac{5}{100}\right)} = \left(9975 \times \frac{20}{21} \times \frac{20}{19}\right) = 10000.$

Ex. 28. ***If A earns $33\frac{1}{3}$% more than B, how much percent does B earn less than A?***

Sol. Required percentage $= \left[\dfrac{\left(\frac{100}{3}\right)}{\left(100+\frac{100}{3}\right)} \times 100\right]\% = \left(\dfrac{100}{400} \times 100\right)\% = 25\%.$

Ex. 29. ***If A's salary is 20% less than B's salary, by how much percent is B's salary more than A's?***

Sol. Required percentage $= \left[\dfrac{20}{(100-20)} \times 100\right]\% = 25\%.$

Ex. 30. ***How many kg of pure salt must be added to 30 kg of 2% solution of salt and water to increase it to a 10% solution?*** **(M.A.T. 2004)**

Sol. Amount of salt in 30 kg solution $= \left(\dfrac{2}{100} \times 30\right)$ kg $= 0.6$ kg.

Let x kg of pure salt be added.

Then, $\dfrac{0.6+x}{30+x} = \dfrac{10}{100} \Leftrightarrow 60 + 100x = 300 + 10x \Leftrightarrow 90x = 240 \Leftrightarrow x = \dfrac{8}{3} = 2\dfrac{2}{3}.$

Ex. 31. ***Due to a reduction of $6\frac{1}{4}$% in the price of sugar, a man is able to buy 1 kg more for Rs. 120. Find the original and reduced rate of sugar.***

Sol. Let original rate be Rs. x per kg.

Reduced rate = Rs. $\left[\left(100 - \dfrac{25}{4}\right) \times \dfrac{1}{100} x\right]$ = Rs. $\dfrac{15x}{16}$ per kg.

$\therefore \quad \dfrac{120}{\frac{15x}{16}} - \dfrac{120}{x} = 1 \Leftrightarrow \dfrac{128}{x} - \dfrac{120}{x} = 1 \Leftrightarrow x = 8.$

So, original rate = Rs. 8 per kg.

Reduced rate = Rs. $\left(\dfrac{15}{16} \times 8\right)$ per kg = Rs. 7.50 per kg.

Ex. 32. ***In an examination, 35% of total students failed in Hindi, 45% failed in English and 20% in both. Find the percentage of those who passed in both the subjects.***

Sol. Let A and B be the sets of students who failed in Hindi and English respectively.

Then, $n(A) = 35$, $n(B) = 45$, $n(A \cap B) = 20$.

So, $n(A \cup B) = n(A) + n(B) - n(A \cap B) = (35 + 45 - 20) = 60.$

$\therefore$ Percentage failed in Hindi or English or both = 60%.

Hence, percentage passed = $(100 - 60)\% = 40\%$.

Ex. 33. ***In an examination, 80% of the students passed in English, 85% in Mathematics and 75% in both English and Mathematics. If 40 students failed in both the subjects, find the total number of students.***

Sol. Let the total number of students be x.

Let A and B represent the sets of students who passed in English and Mathematics respectively.

Then, number of students passed in one or both the subjects

$= n(A \cup B) = n(A) + n(B) - n(A \cap B) = 80\%$ of x + 85% of x − 75% of x

$= \left(\dfrac{80}{100}x + \dfrac{85}{100}x - \dfrac{75}{100}x\right) = \dfrac{90}{100}x = \dfrac{9}{10}x.$

$\therefore$ Students who failed in both the subjects = $\left(x - \frac{9x}{10}\right) = \frac{x}{10}$.

So, $\frac{x}{10} = 40$ or $x = 400$. Hence, total number of students = 400.

EXERCISE 10

(OBJECTIVE TYPE QUESTIONS)

Directions : *Mark (✓) against the correct answer* :

1. The ratio 5 : 4 expressed as a percent equals : **(S.S.C. 2000)**
(*a*) 12.5% (*b*) 40% (*c*) 80% (*d*) 125%

2. 3.5 can be expressed in terms of percentage as : **(R.R.B. 1998)**
(*a*) 0.35% (*b*) 3.5% (*c*) 35% (*d*) 350%

3. Half of 1 percent written as a decimal is : **(S.S.C. 1999)**
(*a*) 0.005 (*b*) 0.05 (*c*) 0.02 (*d*) 0.2

4. What is 15 percent of Rs. 34 ? **(I.M.T. 2002)**
(*a*) Rs. 3.40 (*b*) Rs. 3.75 (*c*) Rs. 4.50 (*d*) Rs. 5.10

5. 63% of $3\frac{4}{7}$ is :
(*a*) 2.25 (*b*) 2.40 (*c*) 2.50 (*d*) 2.75

6. 88% of 370 + 24% of 210 – ? = 118 **(Bank P.O. 2003)**
(*a*) 256 (*b*) 258 (*c*) 268 (*d*) 358

7. 860% of 50 + 50% of 860 = ? **(R.B.I. 2003)**
(*a*) 430 (*b*) 516 (*c*) 860 (*d*) 960

8. 45% of 750 – 25% of 480 = ? **(Bank P.O. 2002)**
(*a*) 216 (*b*) 217.50 (*c*) 236.50 (*d*) 245

9. 40% of 1640 + ? = 35% of 980 + 150% of 850 **(S.B.I.P.O. 1997)**
(*a*) 372 (*b*) 842 (*c*) 962 (*d*) 1052

10. 218% of 1674 = ? × 1800
(*a*) 0.5 (*b*) 4 (*c*) 6 (*d*) None of these

11. 60% of 264 is the same as : **(Hotel Management, 2001)**
(*a*) 10% of 44 (*b*) 15% of 1056 (*c*) 30% of 132 (*d*) None of these

12. 270 candidates appeared for an examination, of which 252 passed. The pass percentage is :
(*a*) 80% (*b*) $83\frac{1}{2}$% (*c*) $90\frac{1}{3}$% (*d*) $93\frac{1}{3}$%

13. 5 out of 2250 parts of earth is sulphur. What is the percentage of sulphur in earth ?
(*a*) $\frac{11}{50}$ (*b*) $\frac{2}{9}$ (*c*) $\frac{1}{45}$ (*d*) $\frac{2}{45}$

14. What percent of 7.2 kg is 18 gms ?
(*a*) .025% (*b*) .25% (*c*) 2.5% (*d*) 25%

15. 0.01 is what percent of 0.1 ? **(S.S.C. 2000)**
(*a*) $\frac{1}{100}$ (*b*) $\frac{1}{10}$ (*c*) 10 (*d*) 100

16. What percent of Rs. 2650 is Rs 1987.50 ? **(Hotel Management, 2002)**
(*a*) 60% (*b*) 75% (*c*) 80% (*d*) 90%

17. What percent of a day is 3 hours ? **(R.R.B. 2003)**
(*a*) $12\frac{1}{2}\%$ (*b*) $16\frac{2}{3}\%$ (*c*) $18\frac{2}{3}\%$ (*d*) $22\frac{1}{2}\%$

18. It costs Re. 1 to photocopy a sheet of paper. However, 2% discount is allowed on all photocopies done after first 1000 sheets. How much will it cost to copy 5000 sheets of paper ? **(IGNOU, 2003)**
(*a*) Rs. 3920 (*b*) Rs. 3980 (*c*) Rs. 4900 (*d*) Rs. 4920

19. A housewife saved Rs. 2.50 in buying an item on sale. If she spent Rs. 25 for the item, approximately how much percent she saved in the transaction ?
(*a*) 8% (*b*) 9% (*c*) 10% (*d*) 11%
(Section Officers', 2003)

20. How many litres of pure acid are there in 8 litres of a 20% solution ?
(*a*) 1.4 (*b*) 1.5 (*c*) 1.6 (*d*) 2.4

21. Rajeev buys goods worth Rs. 6650. He gets a rebate of 6% on it. After getting the rebate, he pays sales tax @ 10%. Find the amount he will have to pay for the goods.
(*a*) Rs. 6876.10 (*b*) Rs. 6999.20 (*c*) Rs. 6654 (*d*) Rs. 7000
(M.A.T. 2002)

22. Which one of the following shows the best percentage ? **(Hotel Management, 1996)**
(*a*) $\frac{384}{540}$ (*b*) $\frac{425}{500}$ (*c*) $\frac{570}{700}$ (*d*) $\frac{480}{660}$

23. 5% of (25% of Rs. 1600) is
(*a*) Rs. 5 (*b*) Rs. 17.50 (*c*) Rs. 20 (*d*) Rs. 25

24. 0.15% of $33\frac{1}{3}\%$ of Rs. 10,000 is **(S.S.C. 2002)**
(*a*) Re. 0.05 (*b*) Rs. 5 (*c*) Rs. 105 (*d*) Rs. 150

25. 30% of 28% of 480 is the same as
(*a*) 15% of 56% of 240 (*b*) 60% of 28% of 240
(*c*) 60% of 56% of 240 (*d*) None of these

26. What is 25% of 25% equal to ?
(*a*) 0.00625 (*b*) 0.0625 (*c*) 0.625 (*d*) 6.25

27. What percent is 3% of 5% ?
(*a*) 15% (*b*) 30% (*c*) 50% (*d*) 60%

28. 4598 is 95% of ?
(*a*) 4800 (*b*) 4840 (*c*) 4850 (*d*) 4880

29. ?% of 360 = 129.6 **(Bank P.O. 2002)**
(*a*) 36 (*b*) 64 (*c*) 72 (*d*) 77

30. ?% of 932 + 30 = 309.6 **(Bank P.O. 2003)**
(*a*) 25 (*b*) 30 (*c*) 35 (*d*) 40

31. 45% of 1500 + 35% of 1700 = ?% of 3175 **(Bank P.O. 2000)**
(*a*) 30 (*b*) 35 (*c*) 45 (*d*) None of these

32. 65% of ? = 20% of 422.50 **(Bank P.O. 2003)**
(*a*) 84.5 (*b*) 130 (*c*) 139.425 (*d*) 200

33. An agent gets a commission of 2.5% on the sales of cloth. If on a certain day, he gets Rs. 12.50 as commission, the cloth sold through him on that day is worth
(*a*) Rs. 250 (*b*) Rs. 500 (*c*) Rs. 750 (*d*) Rs. 1250

34. If Rs. 2800 is $\frac{2}{7}$ percent of the value of a house, the worth of the house (in Rs.) is : **(L.I.C. 2003)**
(*a*) 8,00,000 (*b*) 9,80,000 (*c*) 10,00,000 (*d*) 12,00,000

35. 15% of (?)% of 582 = 17.46

(*a*) 2 (*b*) 10 (*c*) 20 (*d*) None of these

36. $\sqrt{784} + ? = 78\%$ of 500 :

(*a*) 342 (*b*) 352 (*c*) 362 (*d*) 372

37. If 120 is 20% of a number, then 120% of that number will be :

(*a*) 20 (*b*) 120 (*c*) 360 (*d*) 720

(Section Officers', 2003)

38. If 35% of a number is 175, then what percent of 175 is that number ?

(*a*) 35% (*b*) 65% (*c*) 280% (*d*) None of these

39. Two-fifth of one-third of three-seventh of a number is 15. What is 40 percent of that number ? **(Bank P.O. 2002)**

(*a*) 72 (*b*) 84 (*c*) 136 (*d*) 140 (*e*) None of these

40. The difference between a number and its two-fifth is 510. What is 10% of that number ?

(*a*) 12.75 (*b*) 85 (*c*) 204 (*d*) None of these

(Bank P.O. 2003)

41. If 15% of 40 is greater than 25% of a number by 2, then the number is :

(*a*) 12 (*b*) 16 (*c*) 24 (*d*) 32

42. Subtracting 40% of a number from the number, we get the result as 30. The number is :

(*a*) 28 (*b*) 50 (*c*) 52 (*d*) 70

43. If 35% of a number is 12 less than 50% of that number, then the number is :

(*a*) 40 (*b*) 50 (*c*) 60 (*d*) 80

(C.B.I. 1998)

44. The number which exceeds 16% of it by 42 is : **(C.B.I. 1997)**

(*a*) 50 (*b*) 52 (*c*) 58 (*d*) 60

45. What percentage of numbers from 1 to 70 have squares that end in the digit 1 ?

(*a*) 1 (*b*) 14 (*c*) 20 (*d*) 21

(M.B.A. 2002)

46. By how much percent is four-fifth of 70 lesser than five-seventh of 112 ?

(*a*) 24% (*b*) 30% (*c*) 36% (*d*) 42%

47. If a number x is 10% less than another number y and y is 10% more than 125, then x is equal to : **(S.S.C. 2002)**

(*a*) 123.75 (*b*) 140.55 (*c*) 143 (*d*) 150

48. If 75% of a number is added to 75, then the result is the number itself. The number is : **(Section Officers', 2001)**

(*a*) 50 (*b*) 60 (*c*) 300 (*d*) 400

49. A number, when 35 is subtracted from it, reduces to its 80 percent. What is four-fifth of that number ? **(B.S.R.B. 1998)**

(*a*) 70 (*b*) 90 (*c*) 120 (*d*) 140

50. Which of the following multipliers will cause a number to be increased by 29.7% ?

(*a*) 1.297 (*b*) 12.97 (*c*) 129.7 (*d*) 1297

51. The sum of two numbers is 2490. If 6.5% of one number is equal to 8.5% of the other, then the numbers are : **(IGNOU, 2003)**

(*a*) 989, 1501 (*b*) 1011, 1479 (*c*) 1401, 1089 (*d*) 1411, 1079

52. The sum of two numbers is $\frac{28}{25}$ of the first number. The second number is what percent of the first ? **(Hotel Management, 1997)**

(*a*) 12% (*b*) 14% (*c*) 16% (*d*) 18%

53. If 25% of a number is subtracted from a second number, the second number reduces to its five-sixth. What is the ratio of the first number to the second number ?

(*a*) 1 : 3 (*b*) 2 : 3 (*c*) 3 : 2 (*d*) Data inadequate

(S.B.I.P.O. 1999)

54. The difference of two numbers is 20% of the larger number. If the smaller number is 20, then the larger number is : **(S.S.C. 2000)**

(*a*) 25 (*b*) 45 (*c*) 50 (*d*) 80

55. When any number is divided by 12, then dividend becomes $\frac{1}{4}$th of the other number. By how much percent first number is greater than the second number ?

(*a*) 150 (*b*) 200 (*c*) 300 (*d*) Data inadequate

(Bank P.O. 2000)

56. If one number is 80% of the other and 4 times the sum of their squares is 656, then the numbers are : **(Hotel Management, 1998)**

(*a*) 4, 5 (*b*) 8, 10 (*c*) 16, 20 (*d*) None of these

57. Two numbers A and B are such that the sum of 5% of A and 4% of B is two-third of the sum of 6% of A and 8% of B. Find the ratio of A : B. **(M.B.A. 2002)**

(*a*) 2 : 3 (*b*) 1 : 1 (*c*) 3 : 4 (*d*) 4 : 3

58. Three candidates contested an election and received 1136, 7636 and 11628 votes respectively. What percentage of the total votes did the winning candidate get ?

(*a*) 57% (*b*) 60% (*c*) 65% (*d*) 90%

(I.M.T. 2002)

59. The population of a town increased from 1,75,000 to 2,62,500 in a decade. The average percent increase of population per year is : **(C.B.I. 1997)**

(*a*) 4.37% (*b*) 5% (*c*) 6% (*d*) 8.75%

60. A student multiplied a number by $\frac{3}{5}$ instead of $\frac{5}{3}$. What is the percentage error in the calculation ? **(S.S.C. 1999)**

(*a*) 34% (*b*) 44% (*c*) 54% (*d*) 64%

61. A tempo is insured to the extent of $\frac{4}{5}$ of its original value. If the premium on it at the rate of 1.3 percent amounts to Rs. 910, the original value of the tempo is :

(*a*) Rs. 78,500 (*b*) Rs. 80,000 (*c*) Rs. 82,500 (*d*) Rs. 87,500

62. When 15% is lost in grinding wheat, a country can export 30 lakh tons of wheat. On the other hand, if 10% is lost in grinding, it can export 40 lakh tons of wheat. The production of wheat in the country is :

(*a*) 20 lakh tons (*b*) 80 lakh tons (*c*) 200 lakh tons (*d*) 800 lakh tons

63. In a competitive examination in State A, 6% candidates got selected from the total appeared candidates. State B had an equal number of candidates appeared and 7% candidates got selected with 80 more candidates got selected than A. What was the number of candidates appeared from each State ? **(S.B.I.P.O. 2000)**

(*a*) 7600 (*b*) 8000 (*c*) 8400 (*d*) Data inadequate

64. The price of a car is Rs. 3,25,000. It was insured to 85% of its price. The car was damaged completely in an accident and the insurance company paid 90% of the insurance. What was the difference between the price of the car and the amount received ?

(*a*) Rs. 32,500 (*b*) Rs. 48,750 (*c*) Rs. 76,375 (*d*) Rs. 81,250

(Bank P.O. 2003)

65. Gauri went to the stationers and bought things worth Rs. 25, out of which 30 paise went on sales tax on taxable purchases. If the tax rate was 6%, then what was the cost of the tax free items ? **(M.A.T. 2003)**

(*a*) Rs. 15 (*b*) Rs. 15.70 (*c*) Rs. 19.70 (*d*) Rs. 20

66. A batsman scored 110 runs which included 3 boundaries and 8 sixes. What percent of his total score did he make by running between the wickets ? **(S.S.C. 2004)**

(*a*) 45% (*b*) $45\frac{5}{11}\%$ (*c*) $54\frac{6}{11}\%$ (*d*) 55%

67. After deducting a commission of 5%, a T.V. set costs Rs. 9595. Its marked price is :

(*a*) Rs. 10,000 (*b*) Rs. 10,075 (*c*) Rs. 10,100 (*d*) Rs. 10,500

68. A fruit seller had some apples. He sells 40% apples and still has 420 apples. Originally, he had : **(S.S.C. 2003)**

(*a*) 588 apples (*b*) 600 apples (*c*) 672 apples (*d*) 700 apples

69. A person who spends $66\frac{2}{3}\%$ of his income is able to save Rs. 1200 per month. His monthly expenses (in Rs.) are : **(S.S.C. 1999)**

(*a*) Rs. 1200 (*b*) Rs. 2400 (*c*) Rs. 3000 (*d*) Rs. 3200

70. In an examination, 35% of the students passed and 455 failed. How many students appeared for the examination ? **(S.S.C. 2000)**

(*a*) 490 (*b*) 700 (*c*) 845 (*d*) 1300

71. In a market survey, 20% opted for product A whereas 60% opted for product B. The remaining individuals were not certain. If the difference between those who opted for product B and those who were uncertain was 720, how many individuals were covered in the survey ?

(*a*) 1440 (*b*) 1800 (*c*) 3600 (*d*) Data inadequate

72. A student has to obtain 33% of the total marks to pass. He got 125 marks and failed by 40 marks. The maximum marks are : **(C.B.I. 2003)**

(*a*) 300 (*b*) 500 (*c*) 800 (*d*) 1000

73. In an election a candidate who gets 84% of the votes is elected by a majority of 476 votes. What is the total number of votes polled ? **(Hotel Management, 2003)**

(*a*) 672 (*b*) 700 (*c*) 749 (*d*) 848

74. In an election between two candidates, one got 55% of the total valid votes, 20% of the votes were invalid. If the total number of votes was 7500, the number of valid votes that the other candidate got, was : **(R.R.B. 2003)**

(*a*) 2700 (*b*) 2900 (*c*) 3000 (*d*) 3100

75. At an election involving two candidates, 68 votes were declared invalid. The winning candidate secures 52% and wins by 98 votes. The total number of votes polled is :

(*a*) 2382 (*b*) 2450 (*c*) 2518 (*d*) None of these

76. 10% of the voters did not cast their vote in an election between two candidates. 10% of the votes polled were found invalid. The successful candidate got 54% of the valid votes and won by a majority of 1620 votes. The number of voters enrolled on the voters' list was : **(S.S.C. 2003)**

(*a*) 25000 (*b*) 33000 (*c*) 35000 (*d*) 40000

77. 8% of the people eligible to vote are between 18 and 21 years of age. In an election, 85% of those eligible to vote, who were between 18 and 21, actually voted. In that election, the number of persons between 18 and 21, who actually voted, was what percent of those eligible to vote ? **(R.R.B. 1998)**

(*a*) 4.2 (*b*) 6.4 (*c*) 6.8 (*d*) 8

78. In an election, 30% of the voters voted for candidate A whereas 60% of the remaining voted for candidate B. The remaining voters did not vote. If the difference between those who voted for candidate A and those who did not vote was 1200, how many individuals were eligible for casting vote in that election ?

(a) 10,000 (b) 45,000 (c) 60,000 (d) 72,000

79. Two tailors X and Y are paid a total of Rs. 550 per week by their employer. If X is paid 120 percent of the sum paid to Y, how much is Y paid per week ?

(a) Rs. 200 (b) Rs. 250 (c) Rs. 300 (d) None of these

(N.I.F.T. 2000)

80. While purchasing one item costing Rs. 400, I had to pay the sales tax at 7% and on another costing Rs. 6400, the sales tax was 9%. What percent of the sales tax I had to pay, taking the two items together on an average ?

(a) 8% (b) $8\frac{13}{17}\%$ (c) $8\frac{15}{17}\%$ (d) $8\frac{1}{2}\%$

81. A student secures 90%, 60% and 54% marks in test papers with 100, 150 and 200 respectively as maximum marks. The percentage of his aggregate is :

(a) 64 (b) 68 (c) 70 (d) None of these

(Hotel Management, 1999)

82. 1100 boys and 700 girls are examined in a test; 42% of the boys and 30% of the girls pass. The percentage of the total who failed is :

(a) 58% (b) $62\frac{2}{3}\%$ (c) 64% (d) 78%

83. In a certain school, 20% of students are below 8 years of age. The number of students above 8 years of age is $\frac{2}{3}$ of the number of students of 8 years age which is 48. What is the total number of students in the school ? **(Bank P.O. 2003)**

(a) 72 (b) 80 (c) 120 (d) 150 (e) None of these

84. In an examination, 5% of the applicants were found ineligible and 85% of the eligible candidates belonged to the general category. If 4275 eligible candidates belonged to other categories, then how many candidates applied for the examination ?

(a) 30,000 (b) 35,000 (c) 37,000 (d) None of these

(Hotel Management, 1998)

85. Two students appeared at an examination. One of them secured 9 marks more than the other and his marks was 56% of the sum of their marks. The marks obtained by them are : **(S.S.C. 2004)**

(a) 39, 30 (b) 41, 32 (c) 42, 33 (d) 43, 34

86. If x is 90% of y, then what percent of x is y ? **(S.S.C. 1997)**

(a) 90% (b) $101\frac{1}{9}\%$ (c) $111\frac{1}{9}\%$ (d) 190%

87. $x\%$ of y is $y\%$ of :

(a) x (b) $100x$ (c) $\frac{x}{100}$ (d) $\frac{y}{100}$

88. If 20% of $a = b$, then $b\%$ of 20 is the same as : **(Hotel Management, 1998)**

(a) 4% of a (b) 5% of a (c) 20% of a (d) None of these

89. If $x\%$ of y is the same as $\frac{4}{5}$ of 80, then the value of xy is :

(a) 320 (b) 400 (c) 640 (d) None of these

90. If $x\%$ of y is 100 and $y\%$ of z is 200, then find a relation between x and z.

(a) $z = \frac{x}{2}$ (b) $z = 2x$ (c) $z = \frac{x}{4}$ (d) $z = 4x$

(S.S.C. 2002)

91. If $p\%$ of p is 36, then p is equal to : **(S.S.C. 2000)**
(*a*) 15 (*b*) 60 (*c*) 600 (*d*) 3600

92. If $x\%$ of y is equal to z, what percent of z is x ? **(S.S.C. 1999)**
(*a*) $\frac{y^2}{100}$ (*b*) $\frac{y}{100^2}$ (*c*) $\frac{100}{y}$ (*d*) $\frac{100^2}{y}$

93. If x is 80% of y, then what percent of $2x$ is y ? **(C.B.I. 1998)**
(*a*) 40% (*b*) $62\frac{1}{2}\%$ (*c*) $66\frac{2}{3}\%$ (*d*) 80%

94. Subtracting 6% of x from x is equivalent to multiplying x by how much ?
(*a*) 0.094 (*b*) 0.94 (*c*) 9.4 (*d*) 94

95. ($x\%$ of y + $y\%$ of x) = ?
(*a*) $x\%$ of y (*b*) $y\%$ of x (*c*) 2% of xy (*d*) $xy\%$ of 3

96. If A is 150 percent of B, then B is what percent of (A + B) ?
(*a*) $33\frac{1}{3}\%$ (*b*) 40% (*c*) $66\frac{2}{3}\%$ (*d*) 75%

97. If 8% of x = 4% of y, then 20% of x is :
(*a*) 10% of y (*b*) 16% of y (*c*) 80% of y (*d*) None of these

98. If 20% of A = B and 40% of B = C, then 60% of (A + B) is :
(*a*) 30% of C (*b*) 60% of C (*c*) 75% of C (*d*) None of these

99. If $x\%$ of a is the same as $y\%$ of b, then $z\%$ of b is :
(*a*) $\frac{xy}{z}\%$ of a (*b*) $\frac{yz}{x}\%$ of a (*c*) $\frac{xz}{y}\%$ of a (*d*) None of these

100. If A = $x\%$ of y and B = $y\%$ of x, then which of the following is true ?
(*a*) A is smaller than B. (*b*) A is greater than B.
(*c*) Relationship between A and B cannot be determined.
(*d*) If x is smaller than y, then A is greater than B.
(*e*) None of these **(Bank P.O. 2003)**

101. $33\frac{1}{3}\%$ of a man's daily output is equal to 50% of a second man's daily output. If the second man turns out 1500 screws daily, then the first man's output in terms of making screws is :
(*a*) 500 (*b*) 1000 (*c*) 2000 (*d*) 2250

Directions (*Questions 102 to 106*) : *A survey of magazine reading habits of the people living in five cities P, Q, R, S and T is summarised in a table given below. The Column I in the table gives percentage of magazine-readers in each city who read only one magazine a week. The Column II gives the total number of magazine-readers who read two or more magazines a week. Read the table and then answer these questions*: **(S.S.C. 1999)**

City	I	II
P	75	6000
Q	80	3500
R	60	3000
S	55	2700
T	25	4200

102. The city with the lowest number of magazine-readers is :
(a) Q (b) R (c) S (d) T

103. Which city has the highest number of magazine-readers who read only one magazine a week ?
(a) P (b) Q (c) R (d) S

104. The highest number of magazine-readers in any given city is :
(a) 17500 (b) 18000 (c) 24000 (d) 30000

105. How many magazine-readers in city Q read only one magazine a week ?
(a) 14000 (b) 18000 (c) 12500 (d) 16500

106 The total number of all the magazine-readers in the five cities who read only one magazine a week is :
(a) 19400 (b) 24000 (c) 41200 (d) 42000

107. Rohit spends 40% of his salary on food, 20% on house rent, 10% on entertainment and 10% on conveyance. If his savings at the end of a month are Rs. 1500, then his monthly salary is : **(S.S.C. 2003)**
(a) Rs. 6000 (b) Rs. 7500 (c) Rs. 8000 (d) Rs. 10,000

108. Kunal spent Rs. 35,000 in buying raw materials, Rs. 40,000 in buying machinery and 20% of the total amount he had as cash with him. What was the total amount ?
(a) Rs. 80,000 (b) Rs. 85,750 (c) Rs. 90,000 (d) Rs. 93,750

109. Gaurav spends 30% of his monthly income on food articles, 40% of the remaining on conveyance and clothes and saves 50% of the remaining. If his monthly salary is Rs. 18,400, how much money does he save every month ?
(a) Rs. 3624 (b) Rs. 3864 (c) Rs. 4264 (d) Rs. 5888

110. A spider climbed $62\frac{1}{2}\%$ of the height of the pole in one hour and in the next hour it covered $12\frac{1}{2}\%$ of the remaining height. If the height of the pole is 192 m, then distance climbed in second hour is : **(Section Officers', 2003)**
(a) 3 m (b) 5 m (c) 7 m (d) 9 m

111. A man spends 35% of his income on food, 25% on children's education and 80% of the remaining on house rent. What percent of his income he is left with ?
(a) 8% (b) 10% (c) 12% (d) 14%

112. From the salary of an officer, 10% is deducted as house rent, 20% of the rest, he spends on conveyance, 20% of the rest he pays as income tax and 10% of the balance, he spends on clothes. Then, he is left with Rs. 15,552. Find his total salary.
(a) Rs. 25,000 (b) Rs. 30,000 (c) Rs. 35,000 (d) Rs. 40,000
(L.I.C.A.A.O. 2003)

113. Aman gave 40% of the amount he had to Rohan. Rohan in turn gave one-fourth of what he received from Aman to Sahil. After paying Rs. 200 to the taxi driver out of the amount he got from Rohan, Sahil now has Rs. 600 left with him. How much amount did Aman have ? **(Bank P.O. 2000)**
(a) Rs. 4000 (b) Rs. 8000 (c) Rs. 12,000 (d) Data inadequate

114. Sameer spends 24% of his monthly income on food and 15% on the education of his children. Of the remaining salary, he spends 25% on entertainment and 20% on conveyance. He is now left with Rs. 10,736. What is the monthly salary of Sameer ?
(a) Rs. 27,600 (b) Rs. 28,000 (c) Rs. 31,200 (d) Rs. 32,000
(Bank P.O. 2004)

115. 405 sweets were distributed equally among children in such a way that the number of sweets received by each child is 20% of the total number of children. How many sweets did each child receive ? **(Bank P.O. 2003)**
(a) 9 (b) 15 (c) 18 (d) 45

116. The sum of the number of boys and girls in a school is 150. If the number of boys is x, then the number of girls becomes x% of the total number of students. The number of boys is : **(S.S.C. 2002)**

(a) 40 (b) 50 (c) 60 (d) 90

117. In an examination of n questions, a student replied 15 out of the first 20 questions correctly. Of the remaining questions, he answered one-third correctly. All the questions have the same credit. If the student gets 50% marks, the value of n is :

(a) 20 (b) 40 (c) 50 (d) 100

118. The salaries of A and B together amount to Rs. 2000. A spends 95% of his salary and B, 85% of his. If now, their savings are the same, what is A's salary ?

(a) Rs. 750 (b) Rs. 1250 (c) Rs. 1500 (d) Rs. 1600

119. A's marks in Biology are 20 less than 25% of the total marks obtained by him in Biology, Maths and Drawing. If his marks in Drawing be 50, what are his marks in Maths ?

(a) 40 (b) 45
(c) 50 (d) Cannot be determined

120. A salesman is allowed $5\frac{1}{2}$% discount on the total sales made by him plus a bonus of $\frac{1}{2}$% on the sales over Rs. 10,000. If his total earnings were Rs. 1990, then his total sales (in Rs.) were : **(C.B.I. 2003)**

(a) 30,000 (b) 32,000 (c) 34,000 (d) 35,000

121. In an examination, there are three papers and a candidate has to get 35% of the total to pass. In one paper, he gets 62 out of 150 and in the second 35 out of 150. How much must he get, out of 180, in the third paper to just qualify for a pass ?

(a) 60.5 (b) 68 (c) 70 (d) 71 **(R.R.B. 2002)**

122. In a History examination, the average for the entire class was 80 marks. If 10% of the students scored 95 marks and 20% scored 90 marks, what was the average marks of the remaining students of the class ? **(D.M.R.C. 2003)**

(a) 65.5 (b) 72.5 (c) 75 (d) 85

123. A scored 30% marks and failed by 15 marks. B scored 40% marks and obtained 35 marks more than those required to pass. The pass percentage is : **(S.S.C. 2003)**

(a) 33% (b) 38% (c) 43% (d) 46%

124. The price of a table is Rs. 400 more than that of a chair. If 6 tables and 6 chairs together cost Rs. 4800, by what percent is the price of the chair less than that of the table ?

(a) $33\frac{1}{3}$% (b) 50% (c) $66\frac{2}{3}$% (d) None of these

125. In a recent survey, 40% houses contained two or more people. Of those houses containing only one person, 25% were having only a male. What is the percentage of all houses, which contain exactly one female and no males ? **(S.B.I.P.O. 2000)**

(a) 15 (b) 40 (c) 75
(d) Can't be determined (e) None of these

126. In a city, 40% of the people are illiterate and 60% are poor. Among the rich, 10% are illiterate. What percentage of the poor population is illiterate ?

(a) 36% (b) 40% (c) 60% (d) None of these

127. Of the 1000 inhabitants of a town, 60% are males of whom 20% are literate. If, of all the inhabitants, 25% are literate, then what percent of the females of the town are literate ? **(M.A.T. 2003)**

(a) 22.5 (b) 27.5 (c) 32.5 (d) 37.5

128. $37\frac{1}{2}\%$ of the candidates in an examination were girls, 75% of the boys and $62\frac{1}{2}\%$ of the girls passed and 342 girls failed. The number of boys failed was :

(*a*) 350 (*b*) 360 (*c*) 370 (*d*) 380

(S.S.C. 2003)

129. $\frac{5}{9}$ part of the population in a village are males. If 30% of the males are married, the percentage of unmarried females in the total population is :

(*a*) 20% (*b*) $27\frac{7}{9}\%$ (*c*) 40% (*d*) 70%

130. In a city, 35% of the population is composed of migrants, 20% of whom are from rural areas. Of the local population, 48% is female while this figure for rural and urban migrants is 30% and 40% respectively. If the total population of the city is 728400, what is its female population ?

(*a*) 324138 (*b*) 349680 (*c*) 509940 (*d*) None of these

131. The boys and girls in a college are in the ratio 3 : 2. If 20% of the boys and 25% of the girls are adults, the percentage of students who are not adults is :

(*a*) 58% (*b*) 67.5% (*c*) 78% (*d*) 82.5%

132. A man bought a house for Rs. 5 lakhs and rents it. He puts $12\frac{1}{2}\%$ of each month's rent aside for repairs, pays Rs. 1660 as annual taxes and realises 10% on his investment thereafter. The monthly rent of the house is :

(*a*) Rs. 2460 (*b*) Rs. 2500 (*c*) Rs. 4920 (*d*) Rs. 5000

133. A debtor can pay 87 paise in the rupee, but if his creditors would take 20% of his debts, he could pay them and have Rs. 42 left. His debts and assets respectively are :

(*a*) Rs. 400, Rs. 520 (*b*) Rs. 500, Rs. 521

(*c*) Rs. 600, Rs. 522 (*d*) Rs. 1000, Rs. 525

134. If the price of a book is first decreased by 25% and then increased by 20%, then the net change in the price will be : **(S.S.C. 2003)**

(*a*) No change (*b*) 5% increase (*c*) 5% decrease (*d*) 10% decrease

135. The price of a shirt is increased by 15% and then reduced by 15%. The final price of the shirt : **(Hotel Management, 2002)**

(*a*) does not change (*b*) increases by 2.25%

(*c*) decreases by 2.25% (*d*) None of these

136. A number is decreased by 10% and then increased by 10%. The number so obtained is 10 less than the original number. What was the original number ? **(S.S.C. 1999)**

(*a*) 1000 (*b*) 1050 (*c*) 1500 (*d*) 2000

137. The price of an article was increased by $r\%$. Later the new price was decreased by $r\%$. If the latest price was Re. 1, then the original price was : **(S.S.C 2004)**

(*a*) Re. 1 (*b*) Rs. $\left(\frac{1-r^2}{100}\right)$

(*c*) Rs. $\frac{\sqrt{1-r^2}}{100}$ (*d*) Rs. $\left(\frac{10000}{10000-r^2}\right)$

138. Peter could save 10% of his income. But two years later when his income is increased by 20%, he could save the same amount only as before. By how much percent has his expenditure increased ? **(R.R.B. 2003)**

(*a*) 22% (*b*) $22\frac{2}{9}\%$ (*c*) $23\frac{1}{3}\%$ (*d*) 24%

139. Madan pays income tax at the rate of 10%. If his income increased by 10% and his tax rate increases to 15%, his net income would increase by Rs. 350. What is Madan's income ?

(a) Rs. 8000 (b) Rs. 10,000 (c) Rs. 12,000 (d) Rs. 14,000

140. Mr. X, a businessman had the income in the year 2000, such that he earned a profit of 20% on his investment in the business. In the year 2001, his investment was less by Rs. 5000 but still had the same income (Income = Investment + Profit) as that in 2000. Thus, the percent profit earned in 2001 increased by 6%. What was his investment in 2000 ? **(S.B.I.P.O. 2001)**

(a) Rs. 1,02,000 (b) Rs. 1,05,000 (c) Rs. 1,50,500
(d) Data inadequate (e) None of these

141. What percent decrease in salaries would exactly cancel out the 20 percent increase ?

(a) $16\frac{2}{3}$ (b) 18 (c) 20 (d) $33\frac{1}{3}$ **(S.S.C. 2000)**

142. A number is increased by 20% and then again by 20%. By what percent should the increased number be reduced so as to get back the original number ? **(S.S.C. 2004)**

(a) $19\frac{11}{31}\%$ (b) $30\frac{5}{9}\%$ (c) 40% (d) 44%

143. The price of a T.V. set is decreased by 25% as a result of which the sale increased by 20%. What will be the effect on the total revenue of the shop ? **(Bank P.O. 2003)**

(a) No effect (b) 5% decrease (c) 5% increase
(d) 10% increase (e) None of these

144. The price of tea being increased by 20%, a man reduces his consumption by 20%. By how much percent will his expenses for tea be decreased ? **(S.S.C. 2003)**

(a) 2% (b) 4% (c) 6% (d) 8%

145. Entry fee in an exhibition was Re. 1. Later, this was reduced by 25% which increased the sale by 20%. The percentage increase in the number of visitors is

(a) 54 (b) 57 (c) 60 (d) 66

146. The income of a broker remains unchanged though the rate of commission is increased from 4% to 5%. The percentage of slump in business is :

(a) 1% (b) 8% (c) 20% (d) 80%

147. In a fraction, if numerator is increased by 40% and denominator is increased by 80%, then what fraction of the original is the new fraction ? **(S.B.I.P.O. 2000)**

(a) $\frac{1}{2}$ (b) $\frac{7}{9}$ (c) $\frac{7}{18}$ (d) Data inadequate

148. If the price of petrol is increased by 30%, by how much percent a car owner must reduce his consumption in order to maintain the same budget ? **(S.S.C. 2000)**

(a) 21% (b) $21\frac{1}{3}\%$ (c) $23\frac{1}{13}\%$ (d) 33%

149. The price of wheat falls by 16%. By what percentage a person can increase the consumption of wheat so that his overall budget does not change ? **(M.B.A. 2002)**

(a) 16% (b) 18% (c) 18.5% (d) 19%

150. The price of oil is increased by 25%. If the expenditure is not allowed to increase, the ratio between the reduction in consumption and the original consumption is

(a) 1 : 3 (b) 1 : 4 (c) 1 : 5 (d) 1 : 6

151. If the price of sugar rises from Rs. 6 per kg to Rs. 7.50 per kg, a person, to have no increase in his expenditure on sugar, will have to reduce his consumption of sugar by

(a) 15% (b) 20% (c) 25% (d) 30%

152. Prices register an increase of 10% on foodgrains and 15% on other items of expenditure. If the ratio of an employee's expenditure on foodgrains and other items be 2 : 5, by how much should his salary be increased in order that he may maintain the same level of consumption as before, his present salary being Rs. 2590 ?

(*a*) Rs. 323.75 (*b*) Rs. 350 (*c*) Rs. 360.50 (*d*) None of these

153. A district has 64000 inhabitants. If the population increases at the rate of $2\frac{1}{2}\%$ per annum, then the number of inhabitants at the end of 3 years will be **(S.S.C. 2003)**

(*a*) 68911 (*b*) 68921 (*c*) 69200 (*d*) 70000

154. If inflation increases at a rate of 8% p.a., what will a Rs. 20 article cost at the end of two years ? **(Bank P.O. 1999)**

(*a*) Between Rs. 20 and Rs. 21 (*b*) Between Rs. 21 and Rs. 22
(*c*) Between Rs. 22 and Rs. 23 (*d*) Between Rs. 23 and Rs. 24

155. The population of a town was 1,60,000 three years ago. If it increased by 3%, 2.5% and 5% respectively in the last three years, then the present population is :

(*a*) 1,77,000 (*b*) 1,77,366 (*c*) 1,77,461 (*d*) 1,77,596

(IGNOU, 2003)

156. The population of a town 2 years ago was 62,500. Due to migration to big cities, it decreases every year at the rate of 4%. The present population of the town is :

(*a*) 56,700 (*b*) 57,600 (*c*) 58,800 (*d*) 60,000

(S.S.C. 2004)

157. Depreciation applicable to an equipment is 20%. The value of the equipment 3 years from now will be less by : **(M.B.A. 2002)**

(*a*) 45% (*b*) 48.8% (*c*) 51.2% (*d*) 60%

158. The population of a town increases by 5% annually. If its population in 2001 was 1,38,915, what it was in 1998 ? **(R.R.B. 2001)**

(*a*) 1,00,000 (*b*) 1,08,000 (*c*) 1,10,000 (*d*) 1,20,000

159. The value of a machine depreciates at the rate of 10% every year. It was purchased 3 years ago. If its present value is Rs. 8748, its purchase price was :

(*a*) Rs. 10,000 (*b*) Rs. 11,372 (*c*) Rs. 12,000 (*d*) Rs. 12,500

(A.A.O. Exam, 2003)

160. In the month of January, the Railway Police caught 4000 ticketless travellers. In February, the number rose by 5%. However, due to constant vigil by the Police and the Railway staff, the number reduced by 5% and in April it further reduced by 10%. The total number of ticketless travellers caught in the month of April was :

(*a*) 3125 (*b*) 3255 (*c*) 3575 (*d*) 3591

(M.B.A. 1999)

161. The population of a variety of tiny bush in an experimental field increased by 10% in the first year, increased by 8% in the second year but decreased by 10% in the third year. If the present number of bushes in the experimental field is 26730, then the number of bushes in the beginning was : **(M.A.T. 2002)**

(*a*) 25000 (*b*) 27000 (*c*) 28000 (*d*) 24600

162. The production of a company has ups and downs every year. The production increases for two consecutive years consistently by 15% and in the third year it decreases by 10%. Again in the next two years it increases by 15% each year and decreases by 10% in the third year. If we start counting from the year 1998, approximately what will be the effect on production of the company in 2002 ? **(Bank P.O. 2002)**

(*a*) 27% increase (*b*) 32% increase (*c*) 37% increase
(*d*) 42% increase (*e*) 52% increase

163. The present population of a country estimated to be 10 crores is expected to increase to 13.31 crores during the next three years. The uniform rate of growth is :

(a) 8% (b) 10% (c) 12.7% (d) 15%

164. A building worth Rs. 1,33,100 is constructed on land worth Rs. 72,900. After how many years will the value of both be the same if land appreciates at 10% p.a. and building depreciates at 10% p.a. ?

(a) $1\frac{1}{2}$ (b) 2 (c) $2\frac{1}{2}$ (d) 3

165. The population of a town increases 4% annually but is decreased by emigration annually to the extent of (1/2)%. What will be the increase percent in 3 years ?

(a) 9.8 (b) 10 (c) 10.5 (d) 10.8

166. The current birth rate per thousand is 32, whereas corresponding death rate is 11 per thousand. The net growth rate in terms of population increase in percent is given by :

(a) 0.0021% (b) 0.021% (c) 2.1% (d) 21%

167. The total population of a village is 5000. The number of males and females increases by 10% and 15% respectively and consequently the population of the village becomes 5600. What was the number of males in the village ? **(Bank P.O. 2003)**

(a) 2000 (b) 2500 (c) 3000 (d) 4000

168. A's income is 25% more than B's income. B's income in terms of A's income is :

(a) 75% (b) 80% (c) 90% (d) 96%

169. A's salary is 50% more than B's. How much percent is B's salary less than A's ?

(a) 33% (b) $33\frac{1}{4}\%$ (c) $33\frac{1}{3}\%$ (d) $33\frac{1}{2}\%$

(S.S.C. 2002)

170. If A's height is 40% less than that of B, how much percent B's height is more than that of A ? **(S.S.C. 2000)**

(a) $33\frac{1}{3}\%$ (b) 40% (c) 60% (d) $66\frac{2}{3}\%$

171. p is six times as large as q. The percent that q is less than p, is :

(a) $16\frac{2}{3}$ (b) 60 (c) $83\frac{1}{3}$ (d) 90

172. Two numbers are less than a third number by 30% and 37% respectively. How much percent is the second number less than the first ? **(S.S.C. 2002)**

(a) 3% (b) 4% (c) 7% (d) 10%

173. Two numbers are respectively $12\frac{1}{2}\%$ and 25% more than a third number. The first number as a percentage of the second number is : **(C.B.I. 2003)**

(a) 50 (b) 60 (c) 75 (d) 90

174. A's salary is 40% of B's salary which is 25% of C's salary. What percentage of C's salary is A's salary ? **(M.B.A. 2003)**

(a) 5% (b) 10% (c) 15% (d) 20%

175. 5% of income of A is equal to 15% of income of B and 10% of income of B is equal to 20% of income of C. If C's income is Rs. 2000, then the total income of A, B and C is :

(a) Rs. 6000 (b) Rs. 14,000 (c) Rs. 18,000 (d) Rs. 20,000

176. Peter earned 40% more money than Albert. Albert earned 20% less than Michael. Peter earned more than Michael by : **(S.S.C. 2003)**

(a) 10% (b) 12% (c) 20% (d) 25%

177. Amit's monthly income is 30% more than that of Raunaq. Raunaq's monthly income is 20% less than that of Deepak. If the difference between the monthly incomes of Amit and Deepak is Rs. 800, what is the monthly income of Raunaq ? **(Bank P.O. 1999)**
(*a*) Rs. 12,000 (*b*) Rs. 16,000 (*c*) Rs. 20,000
(*d*) Data inadequate (*e*) None of these

178. In an examination in which full marks were 800, A gets 20% more than B, B gets 20% more than C, and C gets 15% less than D. If A got 576, what percentage of full marks did D get (approximately) ? **(R.R.B. 1998)**
(*a*) 45.7 (*b*) 51.2 (*c*) 58.8 (*d*) 61.7

179. In an examination, the percentage of students qualified to the number of students appeared from school A is 70%. In school B, the number of students appeared is 20% more than the students appeared from school A and the number of students qualified from school B is 50% more than the students qualified from school A. What is the percentage of students qualified to the number of students appeared from school B ?
(*a*) 30% (*b*) 70% (*c*) 78.5% (*d*) 87.5% **(Bank P.O. 1999)**

180. Fresh fruit contains 68% water and dry fruit contains 20% water. How much dry fruit can be obtained from 100 kg of fresh fruits ? **(S.S.C. 2004)**
(*a*) 32 kg (*b*) 40 kg (*c*) 52 kg (*d*) 80 kg

181. A large watermelon weighs 20 kg with 96% of its weight being water. It is allowed to stand in the sun and some of the water evaporates so that only 95% of its weight is water. Its reduced weight will be :
(*a*) 16 kg (*b*) 16.5 kg (*c*) 17 kg (*d*) 18 kg

182. How much pure alcohol has to be added to 400 ml of a solution containing 15% alcohol to change the concentration of alcohol in the mixture to 32% ? **(S.S.C. 2003)**
(*a*) 60 ml (*b*) 68 ml (*c*) 100 ml (*d*) 128 ml

183. Milk contains 5% water. What quantity of pure milk should be added to 10 litres of milk to reduce this to 2% ? **(Bank P.O. 2003)**
(*a*) 5 litres (*b*) 7 litres (*c*) 15 litres
(*d*) Cannot be determined (*e*) None of these

184. The quantity of water (in ml) needed to reduce 9 ml shaving lotion containing 50% alcohol to a lotion containing 30% alcohol, is :
(*a*) 4 (*b*) 5 (*c*) 6 (*d*) 7

185. To a sugar solution of 3 litres containing 40% sugar, one litre of water is added. The percentage of sugar in the new solution is :
(*a*) $13\frac{1}{3}\%$ (*b*) 15% (*c*) 30% (*d*) 33%

186. One type of liquid contains 20% water and the second type of liquid contains 35% of water. A glass is filled with 10 parts of first liquid and 4 parts of second liquid. The percentage of water in the new mixture in the glass is : **(C.B.I. 1997)**
(*a*) 20% (*b*) $24\frac{2}{7}\%$ (*c*) 37% (*d*) 40%

187. In some quantity of ghee, 60% is pure ghee and 40% is vanaspati. If 10 kg of pure ghee is added, then the strength of vanaspati ghee becomes 20%. The original quantity was : **(Hotel Management, 2003)**
(*a*) 10 kg (*b*) 15 kg (*c*) 20 kg (*d*) 25 kg

188. The weight of the container alone is 25% of the container filled with a certain fluid. When some fluid is removed, the weight of the container and remaining fluid is 50% of the original total weight. What fractional part of the liquid has been removed ?
(*a*) $\frac{1}{3}$ (*b*) $\frac{1}{2}$ (*c*) $\frac{2}{3}$ (*d*) $\frac{3}{4}$
(D.M.R.C. 2003)

189. From a container having pure milk, 20% is replaced by water and the process is repeated thrice. At the end of the third operation, the milk is : **(S.S.C. 2003)**

(*a*) 40% pure (*b*) 50% pure (*c*) 51.2% pure (*d*) 58.8% pure

190. An empty fuel tank of a car was filled with A type petrol. When the tank was half-empty, it was filled with B type petrol. Again when the tank was half-empty, it was filled with A type petrol. When the tank was half-empty again, it was filled with B type petrol. What is the percentage of A type petrol at present in the tank ?

(*a*) 33.5% (*b*) 37.5% (*c*) 40% (*d*) 50%

(Bank P.O. 2003)

191. A bag contains 600 coins of 25 p denomination and 1200 coins of 50 p denomination. If 12% of 25 p coins and 24% of 50 p coins are removed, the percentage of money removed from the bag is nearly :

(*a*) 15.6% (*b*) 17.8% (*c*) 21.6% (*d*) 30%

192. The price of rice is reduced by 2%. How many kilograms of rice can now be bought for the money which was sufficient to buy 49 kg of rice earlier ? **(S.S.C. 2004)**

(*a*) 48 kg (*b*) 49 kg (*c*) 50 kg (*d*) 51 kg

193. A reduction of 21% in the price of wheat enables a person to buy 10.5 kg more for Rs. 100. What is the reduced price per kg ?

(*a*) Rs. 2 (*b*) Rs. 2.25 (*c*) Rs. 2.30 (*d*) Rs. 2.50

194. Due to an increase of 30% in the price of eggs, 3 eggs less are available for Rs. 7.80. The present rate of eggs per dozen is : **(N.I.F.T. 1997)**

(*a*) Rs. 8.64 (*b*) Rs. 8.88 (*c*) Rs. 9.36 (*d*) Rs. 10.40

195. The price of sugar having gone down by 10%, Sharad can buy 6.2 kg more for Rs. 279. The difference between the original and the reduced price (per kg) is :

(*a*) Re. 0.50 (*b*) Re. 1 (*c*) Rs. 1.50 (*d*) Rs. 4.50

196. In an examination, 34% of the students failed in Mathematics and 42% failed in English. If 20% of the students failed in both the subjects, then the percentage of students who passed in both the subjects was : **(S.S.C. 2003)**

(*a*) 44 (*b*) 50 (*c*) 54 (*d*) 56

197. 40% of the people read newspaper X, 50% read newspaper Y and 10% read both the papers. What percentage of the people read neither newspaper ?

(*a*) 10% (*b*) 15% (*c*) 20% (*d*) 25%

198. Out of 450 students of a school, 325 play football, 175 play cricket and 50 neither play football nor cricket. How many students play both football and cricket ?

(*a*) 50 (*b*) 75 (*c*) 100 (*d*) 225

(S.S.C. 2004)

199. In a hotel, 60% had vegetarian lunch while 30% had non-vegetarian lunch and 15% had both types of lunch. If 96 people were present, how many did not eat either type of lunch ? **(S.S.C. 2000)**

(*a*) 20 (*b*) 24 (*c*) 26 (*d*) 28

200. There are 600 boys in a hostel. Each plays either hockey or football or both. If 75% play hockey and 45% play football, how many play both ?

(*a*) 48 (*b*) 60 (*c*) 80 (*d*) 120

201. In a certain office, 72% of the workers prefer tea and 44% prefer coffee. If each of them prefers tea or coffee and 40 like both, the total number of workers in the office is :

(*a*) 200 (*b*) 240 (*c*) 250 (*d*) 320

202. In an examination, 65% students passed in Civics and 60% in History, 40% passed in both of these subjects. If 90 students failed in History and Civics both, then what is the total number of students ? **(R.R.B. 2003)**

(*a*) 600 (*b*) 650 (*c*) 700 (*d*) 750

203. In an examination, 35% candidates failed in one subject and 42% failed in another subject while 15% failed in both the subjects. If 2500 candidates appeared at the examination, how many passed in either subject but not in both ?
(a) 325 (b) 1175 (c) 2125 (d) None of these

ANSWERS

1. (d)	2. (d)	3. (a)	4. (d)	5. (a)	6. (b)	7. (c)	8. (b)	9. (c)
10. (d)	11. (b)	12. (d)	13. (b)	14. (d)	15. (c)	16. (b)	17. (a)	18. (d)
19. (b)	20. (c)	21. (a)	22. (b)	23. (c)	24. (b)	25. (b)	26. (b)	27. (d)
28. (b)	29. (a)	30. (b)	31. (d)	32. (b)	33. (b)	34 (b)	35. (c)	36. (c)
37. (d)	38. (d)	39. (e)	40. (b)	41. (b)	42. (b)	43. (d)	44. (a)	45. (c)
46. (b)	47. (a)	48. (c)	49. (d)	50. (a)	51. (d)	52. (a)	53. (b)	54. (a)
55. (b)	56. (b)	57. (d)	58. (a)	59. (b)	60. (b)	61. (d)	62. (c)	63. (b)
64. (c)	65. (c)	66. (b)	67. (c)	68. (d)	69. (b)	70. (b)	71. (b)	72. (b)
73. (b)	74. (a)	75. (c)	76. (a)	77. (c)	78. (c)	79. (b)	80. (c)	81. (a)
82. (b)	83. (e)	84. (a)	85. (c)	86. (c)	87. (a)	88. (a)	89. (d)	90. (b)
91. (b)	92. (d)	93. (b)	94. (b)	95. (c)	96. (b)	97. (a)	98. (d)	99. (c)
100. (e)	101. (d)	102. (d)	103. (a)	104. (c)	105. (a)	106. (c)	107. (b)	108. (d)
109. (b)	110. (d)	111. (a)	112. (b)	113. (b)	114. (d)	115. (a)	116. (c)	117. (c)
118. (c)	119. (d)	120. (c)	121. (d)	122. (c)	123. (a)	124. (c)	125. (e)	126. (c)
127. (c)	128. (d)	129. (b)	130. (d)	131. (c)	132. (c)	133. (c)	134. (d)	135. (c)
136. (a)	137. (d)	138. (b)	139. (b)	140. (b)	141. (a)	142. (b)	143. (e)	144. (b)
145. (c)	146. (c)	147. (b)	148. (c)	149. (d)	150. (c)	151. (b)	152. (d)	153. (b)
154. (d)	155. (b)	156. (b)	157. (b)	158. (d)	159. (c)	160. (d)	161. (a)	162. (c)
163. (b)	164. (d)	165. (d)	166. (c)	167. (c)	168. (b)	169. (c)	170. (d)	171. (c)
172. (d)	173. (d)	174. (b)	175. (c)	176. (b)	177. (b)	178. (c)	179. (d)	180. (b)
181. (a)	182. (c)	183. (c)	184. (c)	185. (c)	186. (b)	187. (a)	188. (c)	189. (c)
190. (b)	191. (c)	192. (c)	193. (a)	194. (c)	195. (a)	196. (a)	197. (c)	198. (c)
199. (b)	200. (d)	201. (c)	202. (a)	203. (b)				

SOLUTIONS

1. $5 : 4 = \frac{5}{4} = \left(\frac{5}{4} \times 100\right)\% = 125\%.$

2. $3.5 = \frac{35}{10} = \left(\frac{35}{10} \times 100\right)\% = 350\%.$

3. $\frac{1}{2}\% = \left(\frac{1}{2} \times \frac{1}{100}\right) = \frac{0.5}{100} = 0.005.$

4. 15% of Rs. 34 = Rs. $\left(\frac{15}{100} \times 34\right)$ = Rs. 5.10.

5. 63% of $3\frac{4}{7} = \left(\frac{63}{100} \times \frac{25}{7}\right) = \frac{9}{4} = 2.25.$

6. Let 88% of 370 + 24% of 210 − x = 118.

Then, $x = \left(\frac{88}{100} \times 370\right) + \left(\frac{24}{100} \times 210\right) - 118 = 325.60 + 50.40 - 118 = 376 - 118 = 258.$

7. Given expression $= \left(\frac{860}{100} \times 50 + \frac{50}{100} \times 860\right) = 430 + 430 = 860.$

8. Given expression $= \left(\frac{45}{100} \times 750\right) - \left(\frac{25}{100} \times 480\right) = (337.50 - 120) = 217.50.$

9. Let 40% of 1640 + x = 35% of 980 + 150% of 850

Then, x = 35% of 980 + 150% of 850 − 40% of 1640

$= \left(\frac{35}{100} \times 980 + \frac{150}{100} \times 850\right) - \left(\frac{40}{100} \times 1640\right) = (343 + 1275 - 656)$

$= (1618 - 656) = 962.$

10. Let 218% of 1674 = $x \times 1800$. Then, $x = \left(\frac{218}{100} \times 1674 \times \frac{1}{1800}\right) = 2.0274.$

11. 60% of 264 $= \left(\frac{60}{100} \times 264\right) = 158.40$; 10% of 44 $= \left(\frac{10}{100} \times 44\right) = 4.40$;

15% of 1056 $= \left(\frac{15}{100} \times 1056\right) = 158.40$; 30% of 132 $= \left(\frac{30}{100} \times 132\right) = 39.60.$

$\therefore$ 60% of 264 = 15% of 1056.

12. Pass percentage $= \left(\frac{252}{270} \times 100\right)\% = \frac{280}{3}\% = 93\frac{1}{3}\%.$

13. Required percentage $= \left(\frac{5}{2250} \times 100\right)\% = \frac{2}{9}\%.$

14. Required percentage $= \left(\frac{18}{7200} \times 100\right)\% = \frac{1}{4}\% = 0.25\%.$

15. Required percentage $= \left(\frac{0.01}{0.1} \times 100\right)\% = \left(\frac{1}{10} \times 100\right)\% = 10\%.$

16. Required percentage $= \left(\frac{1987.50}{2650} \times 100\right)\% = \left(\frac{19875}{265} \times \frac{1}{100} \times 100\right)\% = 75\%.$

17. Required percentage $= \left(\frac{3}{24} \times 100\right)\% = \frac{25}{2}\% = 12\frac{1}{2}\%.$

18. Total cost = Rs. $[1 \times 1000 + (100 - 2)\%$ of $1 \times 4000]$

= Rs. $(1000 + 0.98 \times 4000)$ = Rs. $(1000 + 3920)$ = Rs. 4920.

19. Actual price = Rs. (25 + 2.50) = Rs. 27.50.

$\therefore$ Saving $= \left(\frac{2.50}{27.50} \times 100\right)\% = \frac{100}{11}\% = 9\frac{1}{11}\% \approx 9\%.$

20. Quantity of pure acid = 20% of 8 litres $= \left(\frac{20}{100} \times 8\right)$ litres = 1.6 litres.

21. Rebate = 6% of Rs. 6650 = Rs. $\left(\frac{6}{100} \times 6650\right)$ = Rs. 399.

Sales tax = 10% of Rs. (6650 − 399) = Rs. $\left(\frac{10}{100} \times 6251\right)$ = Rs. 625.10.

$\therefore$ Final amount = Rs. (6251 + 625.10) = Rs. 6876.10.

22. $\frac{384}{540} = \left(\frac{384}{540} \times 100\right)\% = 71\frac{1}{9}\%$; $\frac{425}{500} = \left(\frac{425}{500} \times 100\right)\% = 85\%$;

$\frac{570}{700} = \left(\frac{570}{700} \times 100\right)\% = 81\frac{3}{7}\%$; $\frac{480}{660} = \left(\frac{480}{660} \times 100\right)\% = 72\frac{8}{11}\%$.

$\therefore$ $\frac{425}{500}$ shows the best percentage.

23. 5% of (25% of Rs. 1600) = Rs. $\left[\frac{5}{100} \times \left(\frac{25}{100} \times 1600\right)\right]$ = Rs. 20.

24. 0.15% of $33\frac{1}{3}$% of Rs. 10,000 = Rs. $\left[\frac{15}{100} \times \frac{1}{100} \times \left(\frac{100}{3} \times \frac{1}{100} \times 10000\right)\right]$ = Rs 5.

25. Clearly, 60% of 28% of 240 $= \left(\frac{60}{100} \times \frac{28}{100} \times 240\right) = \left(\frac{30}{100} \times \frac{28}{100} \times 2 \times 240\right)$

$= \left(\frac{30}{100} \times \frac{28}{100} \times 480\right)$ = 30% of 28% of 480.

26. 25% of 25% $= \frac{25}{100} \times \frac{25}{100} = \frac{1}{16} = 0.0625$.

27. Required percentage $= \left(\frac{3\%}{5\%} \times 100\right)\% = \left[\frac{(3/100)}{(5/100)} \times 100\right]\% = 60\%$.

28. Let 95% of $x = 4598$. Then, $\frac{95}{100} \times x = 4598$ or $x = \left(4598 \times \frac{100}{95}\right) = 4840$.

29. Let x% of 360 = 129.6. Then, $\frac{x}{100} \times 360 = \frac{1296}{10}$ or $x = \left(\frac{1296}{10} \times \frac{100}{360}\right) = 36$.

30. Let x% of 932 + 30 = 309.6. Then, $\left(\frac{x}{100} \times 932\right) = 279.6$ or $x = \left(\frac{2796}{10} \times \frac{100}{932}\right) = 30$.

31. Let x% of 3175 = 45% of 1500 + 35% of 1700.

Then, $\frac{x}{100} \times 3175 = \left(\frac{45}{100} \times 1500 + \frac{35}{100} \times 1700\right) = 675 + 595 = 1270$.

$\Leftrightarrow \quad x = \left(\frac{1270 \times 100}{3175}\right) = 40$.

32. Let 65% of x = 20% of 422.50.

Then, $\frac{65}{100} \times x = \left(\frac{20}{100} \times \frac{4225}{10}\right) \Leftrightarrow x = \left(\frac{845}{10} \times \frac{100}{65}\right) = 130$.

33. Let the total sale be Rs. x.

Then, 2.5% of $x = 12.50 \Leftrightarrow \left(\frac{25}{100} \times \frac{1}{100} \times x\right) = \frac{125}{10} \Leftrightarrow x = \left(\frac{125}{10} \times \frac{100 \times 10}{25}\right) = 500$.

34. Let the worth of the house be Rs. x.

Then, $\frac{2}{7}$% of $x = 2800 \Leftrightarrow \left(\frac{2}{7} \times \frac{1}{100} \times x\right) = 2800 \Leftrightarrow x = \left(\frac{2800 \times 100 \times 7}{2}\right) = 9{,}80{,}000$.

35. Let 15% of x% of 582 = 17.46.

Then, $\frac{15}{100} \times \frac{x}{100} \times 582 = \frac{1746}{100} \Leftrightarrow x = \left(\frac{1746}{100} \times \frac{100 \times 100}{15 \times 582}\right) = 20$.

36. Let $\sqrt{784} + x = 78\%$ of 500. Then, $x = \left(\frac{78}{100} \times 500\right) - \sqrt{784} = (390 - 28) = 362.$

37. Let the number be x.

Then, 20% of $x = 120 \Leftrightarrow \left(\frac{20}{100} \times x\right) = 120 \Leftrightarrow x = \left(\frac{120 \times 100}{20}\right) = 600.$

$\therefore$ 120% of $x = \left(\frac{120}{100} \times 600\right) = 720.$

38. Let the number be x.

Then, 35% of $x = 175 \Leftrightarrow \left(\frac{35}{100} \times x\right) = 175 \Leftrightarrow x = \left(\frac{175 \times 100}{35}\right) = 500.$

Now, let y% of 175 = 500.

Then, $\left(\frac{y}{100} \times 175\right) = 500 \Leftrightarrow y = \left(\frac{500 \times 100}{175}\right) = \frac{2000}{7} = 285\frac{5}{7}.$

39. Let the number be x. Then, $\frac{2}{5}$ of $\frac{1}{3}$ of $\frac{3}{7}$ of $x = 15 \Leftrightarrow x = \left(15 \times \frac{7}{3} \times 3 \times \frac{5}{2}\right) = \frac{525}{2}.$

$\therefore$ 40% of $\frac{525}{2} = \left(\frac{40}{100} \times \frac{525}{2}\right) = 105.$

40. Let the number be x. Then, $x - \frac{2}{5}x = 510 \Leftrightarrow \frac{3}{5}x = 510 \Leftrightarrow x = \left(\frac{510 \times 5}{3}\right) = 850.$

$\therefore$ 10% of 850 = 85.

41. Let the number be x. Then,

15% of 40 – 25% of $x = 2 \Leftrightarrow \frac{25}{100}x = \left(\frac{15}{100} \times 40\right) - 2 \Leftrightarrow \frac{x}{4} = 4 \Leftrightarrow x = 16.$

42. Let the number be x. Then, x – 40% of x = 30

$\Leftrightarrow x - \frac{40}{100}x = 30 \Leftrightarrow x - \frac{2}{5}x = 30 \Leftrightarrow \frac{3x}{5} = 30 \Leftrightarrow x = \left(\frac{30 \times 5}{3}\right) = 50.$

43. Let the number be x. Then, 50% of x – 35% of x = 12

$\Leftrightarrow \frac{50}{100}x - \frac{35}{100}x = 12 \Leftrightarrow \frac{15}{100}x = 12 \Leftrightarrow x = \left(\frac{12 \times 100}{15}\right) = 80.$

44. Let the number be x. Then, x – 16% of x = 42

$\Leftrightarrow x - \frac{16}{100}x = 42 \Leftrightarrow x - \frac{4}{25}x = 42 \Leftrightarrow \frac{21}{25}x = 42 \Leftrightarrow x = \left(\frac{42 \times 25}{21}\right) = 50.$

45. Clearly, the numbers which have 1 or 9 in the unit's digit, have squares that end in the digit 1. Such numbers from 1 to 70 are 1, 9, 11, 19, 21, 29, 31, 39, 41, 49, 51, 59, 61, 69.

Number of such numbers = 14.

$\therefore$ Required percentage $= \left(\frac{14}{70} \times 100\right)\% = 20\%.$

46. $\frac{4}{5} \times 70 = 56$ and $\frac{5}{7} \times 112 = 80.$

$\therefore$ Required percentage $= \left(\frac{80 - 56}{80} \times 100\right)\% = \left(\frac{24}{80} \times 100\right)\% = 30\%.$

47. y = 125 + 10% of 125 = 125 + 12.50 = 137.50.

$\therefore$ x = 137.50 – 10% of 137.50 = 137.50 – 13.75 = 123.75.

48. Let the number be x. Then,

75% of $x + 75 = x \Leftrightarrow x - \frac{75}{100}x = 75 \Leftrightarrow x - \frac{3}{4}x = 75 \Leftrightarrow \frac{x}{4} = 75 \Leftrightarrow x = 300.$

49. Let the number be x.

Then, $x - 35 = \frac{80}{100}x \Leftrightarrow x - \frac{80}{100}x = 35 \Leftrightarrow x = \frac{35 \times 100}{20} = 175 \Leftrightarrow \frac{4}{5}x = 140.$

50. Let the number be 100 and required multiplier be y.

Then, $100y = 129.7$ or $y = \frac{129.7}{100} = 1.297.$

51. Let the numbers be x and y. Then, 6.5% of $x = 8.5\%$ of $y \Leftrightarrow x = \frac{85}{65}y = \frac{17}{13}y.$

Now, $x + y = 2490 \Rightarrow \frac{17}{13}y + y = 2490 \Rightarrow \frac{30}{13}y = 2490 \Rightarrow y = \left(\frac{2490 \times 13}{30}\right) = 1079.$

$\therefore$ One number $= y = 1079$, other number $= \frac{17}{13}y = 1411.$

52. Let the numbers be x and y. Then,

$x + y = \frac{28}{25}x \Leftrightarrow y = \frac{28}{25}x - x \Leftrightarrow y = \frac{3}{25}x \Leftrightarrow \frac{y}{x} = \left(\frac{3}{25} \times 100\right)\% = 12\%.$

53. Let the numbers be x and y.

Then, $y - 25\%$ of $x = \frac{5}{6}y \Leftrightarrow y - \frac{5}{6}y = \frac{25}{100}x \Leftrightarrow \frac{y}{6} = \frac{x}{4} \Leftrightarrow \frac{x}{y} = \frac{4}{6} = \frac{2}{3}.$

54. Let the larger number be x.

Then, $x - 20 = \frac{20}{100}x \Leftrightarrow x - \frac{1}{5}x = 20 \Leftrightarrow \frac{4}{5}x = 20 \Leftrightarrow x = \left(20 \times \frac{5}{4}\right) = 25.$

55. Let the numbers be x and y. Then, $\frac{x}{12} = \frac{y}{4} \Leftrightarrow x = 3y.$

$\therefore$ Required percentage $= \left(\frac{x - y}{y} \times 100\right)\% = \left(\frac{2y}{y} \times 100\right)\% = 200\%.$

56. Let one number $= x$. Then, other number $= 80\%$ of $x = \frac{4}{5}x.$

$\therefore 4\left[x^2 + \left(\frac{4}{5}x\right)^2\right] = 656 \Leftrightarrow x^2 + \frac{16}{25}x^2 = 164 \Leftrightarrow \frac{41}{25}x^2 = 164$

$\Leftrightarrow x^2 = \left(\frac{164 \times 25}{41}\right) = 100 \Leftrightarrow x = 100.$

So, the numbers are 10 and 8.

57. 5% of A + 4% of B $= \frac{2}{3}$(6% of A + 8% of B)

$\Leftrightarrow \frac{5}{100}A + \frac{4}{100}B = \frac{2}{3}\left(\frac{6}{100}A + \frac{8}{100}B\right)$

$\Leftrightarrow \frac{1}{20}A + \frac{1}{25}B = \frac{1}{25}A + \frac{4}{75}B \Leftrightarrow \left(\frac{1}{20} - \frac{1}{25}\right)A = \left(\frac{4}{75} - \frac{1}{25}\right)B$

$\Leftrightarrow \frac{1}{100}A = \frac{1}{75}B \Leftrightarrow \frac{A}{B} = \frac{100}{75} = \frac{4}{3}.$

58. Total number of votes polled = (1136 + 7636 + 11628) = 20400.

$\therefore$ Required percentage = $\left(\frac{11628}{20400} \times 100\right)\% = 57\%$.

59. Increase in 10 years = (262500 – 175000) = 87500.

Increase% = $\left(\frac{87500}{175000} \times 100\right)\% = 50\%$.

$\therefore$ Required average = $\left(\frac{50}{10}\right)\% = 5\%$.

60. Let the number be x. Then, error = $\frac{5}{3}x - \frac{3}{5}x = \frac{16}{15}x$.

Error% = $\left(\frac{16x}{15} \times \frac{3}{5x} \times 100\right)\% = 64\%$.

61. Let the original value of the tempo be Rs. x. Then,

1.3% of $\frac{4}{5}$ of $x = 910 \Leftrightarrow \frac{13}{10} \times \frac{1}{100} \times \frac{4}{5} \times x = 910$

$\Leftrightarrow x = \left(\frac{910 \times 10 \times 100 \times 5}{13 \times 4}\right) = 87500.$

62. Let the total production be x lakh tons. Then, 15% of x – 10% of x = (40 – 30) lakh tons

$\Leftrightarrow$ 5% of x = 10 lakh tons $\Leftrightarrow x = \left(\frac{10 \times 100}{5}\right)$ = 200 lakh tons.

63. Let the number of candidates appeared from each state be x.

Then, 7% of x – 6% of x = 80 $\Leftrightarrow$ 1% of x = 80 $\Leftrightarrow$ $x = 80 \times 100 = 8000$.

64. Amount paid to car owner = 90% of 85% of Rs. 3,25,000

= Rs. $\left(\frac{90}{100} \times \frac{85}{100} \times 325000\right)$ = Rs. 2,48,625.

$\therefore$ Required difference = Rs. (325000 – 248625) = Rs. 76,375.

65. Let the amount of taxable purchases be Rs. x.

Then, 6% of $x = \frac{30}{100} \Leftrightarrow x = \left(\frac{30}{100} \times \frac{100}{6}\right) = 5.$

$\therefore$ Cost of tax free items = Rs. [25 – (5 + 0.30)] = Rs. 19.70.

66. Number of runs made by running = 110 – (3 × 4 + 8 × 6) = 50.

$\therefore$ Required percentage = $\left(\frac{50}{110} \times 100\right)\% = 45\frac{5}{11}\%$.

67. Let the marked price be x.

Then, x – 5% of x = 9595 $\Leftrightarrow$ 95% of x = 9595 $\Leftrightarrow$ $x = \left(\frac{9595 \times 100}{95}\right) = 10100.$

68. Suppose originally he had x apples.

Then, (100 – 40)% of x = 420 $\Leftrightarrow \frac{60}{100} \times x = 420 \Leftrightarrow x = \left(\frac{420 \times 100}{60}\right) = 700$

69. Let the monthly income be Rs. x.

Then, $\left(100 - 66\frac{2}{3}\right)\%$ of x = 1200 $\Leftrightarrow$ $33\frac{1}{3}\%$ of x = 1200

$\Leftrightarrow \frac{100}{3} \times \frac{1}{100} \times x = 1200 \Leftrightarrow x = 1200 \times 3 = 3600.$

$\therefore$ Monthly expenses = Rs. (3600 – 1200) = Rs. 2400.

70. Let the number of students appeared be x.

Then, 65% of $x = 455 \Leftrightarrow \frac{65}{100}x = 455 \Leftrightarrow x = \left(\frac{455 \times 100}{65}\right) = 700.$

71. Percentage of uncertain individuals = [100 – (20 + 60)]% = 20%.

$\therefore$ 60% of x – 20% of x = 720 $\Leftrightarrow$ 40% of x = 720

$$\Leftrightarrow \frac{40}{100}x = 720 \Leftrightarrow x = \left(\frac{720 \times 100}{40}\right) = 1800.$$

72. Let the maximum marks be x.

Then, 33% of $x = 125 + 40 \Leftrightarrow \frac{33}{100}x = 165 \Leftrightarrow x = \left(\frac{165 \times 100}{33}\right) = 500.$

73. Let the total number of votes polled be x.

Then, votes polled by other candidate = (100 – 84)% of x = 16% of x.

$\therefore$ 84% of x – 16% of x = 476 $\Leftrightarrow \frac{68}{100}x = 476 \Leftrightarrow x = \left(\frac{476 \times 100}{68}\right) = 700.$

74. Number of valid votes = 80% of 7500 = 6000.

Valid votes polled by other candidate = 45% of 6000 = $\left(\frac{45}{100} \times 6000\right) = 2700.$

75. Let the number of valid votes be x.

Then, 52% of x – 48% of x = 98 $\Leftrightarrow$ 4% of x = 98

$$\Leftrightarrow \frac{4}{100}x = 98 \Leftrightarrow x = 98 \times 25 = 2450.$$

$\therefore$ Total number of votes polled = (2450 + 68) = 2518.

76. Let the total number of voters be x. Then, Votes polled = 90% of x.

Valid votes = 90% of (90% of x).

$\therefore$ 54% of [90% of (90% of x)] – 46% of [90% of (90% of x)] = 1620

$\Leftrightarrow$ 8% of [90% of (90% of x)] = 1620

$$\Leftrightarrow \frac{8}{100} \times \frac{90}{100} \times \frac{90}{100} \times x = 1620 \Leftrightarrow x = \left(\frac{1620 \times 100 \times 100 \times 100}{8 \times 90 \times 90}\right) = 25000.$$

77. Let the number of persons eligible to vote be x. Then,

Number of eligible persons between 18 and 21 = 8% of x.

Number of persons between 18 and 21, who voted = 85% of (8% of x)

$$= \left(\frac{85}{100} \times \frac{8}{100} \times x\right) = \frac{68}{1000}x.$$

$\therefore$ Required percentage = $\left(\frac{68x}{1000} \times \frac{1}{x} \times 100\right)\% = 6.8\%.$

78. Let the number of persons eligible to vote be x.

Then, voters who voted for A = 30% of x.

Voters who voted for B = 60% of (70% of x)

$$= \left(\frac{60}{100} \times \frac{70}{100} \times 100\right)\% \text{ of } x = 42\% \text{ of } x.$$

Voters who did not vote = [100 – (30 + 42)]% of x = 28% of x.

$\therefore$ 30% of x – 28% of x = 1200 $\Leftrightarrow$ 2% of x = 1200 $\Leftrightarrow x = \left(\frac{1200 \times 100}{2}\right) = 60000.$

79. Let the sum paid to Y per week be Rs. z. Then, z + 120% of z = 550

$\Leftrightarrow \; z + \frac{120}{100} z = 550 \;\Leftrightarrow\; \frac{11}{5} z = 550 \;\Leftrightarrow\; z = \left(\frac{550 \times 5}{11}\right) = 250.$

80. Total sales tax paid = 7% of Rs. 400 + 9% of Rs. 6400

$= \text{Rs.} \left(\frac{7}{100} \times 400 + \frac{9}{100} \times 6400\right) = \text{Rs.}\ (28 + 576) = \text{Rs.}\ 604.$

Total cost of the items = Rs. (400 + 6400) = Rs. 6800.

$\therefore$ Required percentage $= \left(\frac{604}{6800} \times 100\right)\% = 8\frac{15}{17}\%.$

81. Total marks secured = (90% of 100 + 60% of 150 + 54% of 200)

$= \left(\frac{90}{100} \times 100 + \frac{60}{100} \times 150 + \frac{54}{100} \times 200\right) = (90 + 90 + 108) = 288.$

Total maximum marks = (100 + 150 + 200) = 450.

$\therefore$ Aggregate percentage $= \left(\frac{288}{450} \times 100\right)\% = 64\%.$

82. Total number of students = 1100 + 700 = 1800.

Number of students passed = (42% of 1100 + 30% of 700) = (462 + 210) = 672.

Number of failures = 1800 – 672 = 1128.

$\therefore$ Percentage failure $= \left(\frac{1128}{1800} \times 100\right)\% = 62\frac{2}{3}\%.$

83. Let the number of students be x. Then,

Number of students of or above 8 years = (100 – 20)% of x = 80% of x.

$\therefore$ 80% of $x = 48 + \frac{2}{3}$ of 48 $\Leftrightarrow \frac{80}{100} x = 80 \Leftrightarrow x = 100.$

84. Let the total number of applicants be x. Number of eligible candidates = 95% of x.

Eligible candidates of other categories = 15% of (95% of x)

$= \left(\frac{15}{100} \times \frac{95}{100} \times x\right) = \frac{57}{400} x.$

$\therefore \frac{57}{400} x = 4275 \Leftrightarrow x = \left(\frac{4275 \times 400}{57}\right) = 30000.$

85. Let their marks be $(x + 9)$ and x.

Then, $x + 9 = \frac{56}{100}(x + 9 + x) \Leftrightarrow 25\,(x + 9) = 14\,(2x + 9) \Leftrightarrow 3x = 99 \Leftrightarrow x = 33.$

So, their marks are 42 and 33.

86. $X = \frac{90}{100} Y \Rightarrow X = \frac{9}{10} Y \Rightarrow Y = \frac{10}{9} X \Rightarrow \frac{Y}{X} = \frac{10}{9}.$

$\therefore$ Required percentage $= \left(\frac{Y}{X} \times 100\right)\% = \left(\frac{10}{9} \times 100\right)\% = 111\frac{1}{9}\%.$

87. $x\%$ of $y = \left(\frac{x}{100} \times y\right) = \left(\frac{y}{100} \times x\right) = y\%$ of x.

88. 20% of $a = b \Rightarrow \frac{20}{100} a = b.$

$\therefore$ $b\%$ of $20 = \left(\frac{b}{100} \times 20\right) = \left(\frac{20}{100} a \times \frac{1}{100} \times 20\right) = \frac{4}{100} a = 4\%$ of a.

89. $\frac{x}{100} \times y = \frac{4}{5} \times 80 \Rightarrow xy = 64 \times 100 = 6400.$

90. Clearly, $y\%$ of $z = 2$ ($x\%$ of y) $\Rightarrow \frac{yz}{100} = \frac{2xy}{100} \Rightarrow z = 2x.$

91. $p\%$ of $p = 36 \Leftrightarrow \left(\frac{p}{100} \times p\right) = 36 \Leftrightarrow p^2 = 3600 \Leftrightarrow p = 60.$

92. $x\%$ of $y = z \Rightarrow \frac{x}{100} y = z \Rightarrow \frac{x}{z} = \frac{100}{y}.$

$\therefore$ Required percentage $= \left(\frac{x}{z} \times 100\right)\% = \left(\frac{100}{y} \times 100\right)\% = \left(\frac{100^2}{y}\right)\%.$

93. $x = 80\%$ of $y \Leftrightarrow x = \frac{80}{100} y \Leftrightarrow \frac{y}{x} = \frac{5}{4} \Leftrightarrow \frac{y}{2x} = \frac{5}{8}.$

$\therefore$ Required percentage $= \left(\frac{y}{2x} \times 100\right)\% = \left(\frac{5}{8} \times 100\right)\% = 62\frac{1}{2}\%.$

94. Let $x - 6\%$ of $x = xz$. Then, 94% of $x = xz \Leftrightarrow \frac{94}{100} x \times \frac{1}{x} = z \Leftrightarrow z = 0.94.$

95. $x\%$ of $y + y\%$ of $x = \frac{x}{100} y + \frac{y}{100} x = \frac{2xy}{100} = 2\%$ of xy.

96. $A = 150\%$ of $B \Rightarrow A = \frac{150}{100} B \Rightarrow \frac{A}{B} = \frac{3}{2} \Rightarrow \frac{A}{B} + 1 = \frac{3}{2} + 1$

$\Rightarrow \frac{A+B}{B} = \frac{5}{2} \Rightarrow \frac{B}{A+B} = \frac{2}{5}.$

$\therefore$ Required percentage $= \left(\frac{B}{A+B} \times 100\right)\% = \left(\frac{2}{5} \times 100\right)\% = 40\%.$

97. 8% of $x = 4\%$ of $y \Rightarrow \frac{8}{100} x = \frac{4}{100} y \Rightarrow x = \frac{1}{2} y.$

$\therefore$ 20% of $x = 20\%$ of $\frac{1}{2} y = 10\%$ of y.

98. $\frac{20}{100} A = B$ and $\frac{40}{100} B = C \Rightarrow \frac{1}{5} A = B$ and $\frac{2}{5} B = C \Rightarrow A = 5B$ and $B = \frac{5}{2} C$

$\Rightarrow A = \frac{25}{2} C$ and $B = \frac{5}{2} C.$

$\therefore$ 60% of $(A + B) = \frac{60}{100}\left(\frac{25}{2} C + \frac{5}{2} C\right) = \frac{60 \times 15}{100} C = \frac{900}{100} C = 900\%$ of C.

99. $x\%$ of $a = y\%$ of $b \Rightarrow \frac{x}{100} a = \frac{y}{100} b \Rightarrow b = \left(\frac{x}{y}\right) a.$

$\therefore$ $z\%$ of $b = \left(z\% \text{ of } \frac{x}{y}\right) a = \left(\frac{xz}{y \times 100}\right) a = \left(\frac{xz}{y}\right)\%$ of a.

100. $x\%$ of $y = \left(\frac{x}{100} \times y\right) = \left(\frac{y}{100} \times x\right) = y\%$ of $x \Rightarrow A = B.$

101. Let the first man's output be x.

Then, $33\frac{1}{3}\%$ of $x = 50\%$ of $1500 \Leftrightarrow \left(\frac{100}{3} \times \frac{1}{100} \times x\right) = 750 \Leftrightarrow x = 750 \times 3 = 2250.$

Questions 102-106

Let the number of magazine-readers in city P be x.

Then, $(100 - 75)\%$ of $x = 6000 \Leftrightarrow \frac{25}{100}x = 6000 \Leftrightarrow x = \left(\frac{6000 \times 100}{25}\right) = 24000.$

Number of readers in P, reading only one magazine a week = (24000 − 6000) = 18000.

Similarly, we can find these values in other cases. Thus, we have the following table :

City	No. of magazine-readers	No. of readers reading only one magazine a week
P	24000	18000
Q	17500	14000
R	7500	4500
S	6000	3300
T	5600	1400

102. The lowest number of magazine-readers is 5600 and this is in the case of city T.

103. The highest number of magazine-readers who read only one magazine a week is 18000 and this is in the case of city P.

104. The highest number of magazine-readers is 24000.

105. Number of magazine-readers in city Q reading only one magazine a week = 14000.

106. Total number of magazine-readers reading only one magazine a week

= (18000 + 14000 + 4500 + 3300 + 1400) = 41200.

107. Saving = [100 − (40 + 20 + 10 + 10)]% = 20%. Let the monthly salary be Rs. x.

Then, 20% of $x = 1500 \Leftrightarrow \frac{20}{100}x = 1500 \Leftrightarrow x = 1500 \times 5 = 7500.$

108. Let the total amount be Rs. x. Then, $(100 - 20)\%$ of $x = 35000 + 40000$

$\Leftrightarrow$ 80% of $x = 75000 \Leftrightarrow \frac{80}{100}x = 75000 \Leftrightarrow x = \left(\frac{75000 \times 5}{4}\right) = 93750.$

109. Saving = 50% of (100 − 40)% of (100 − 30)% of Rs. 18,400

$= \text{Rs.}\left(\frac{50}{100} \times \frac{60}{100} \times \frac{70}{100} \times 18400\right) = \text{Rs. } 3864.$

110. Height climbed in second hour $= 12\frac{1}{2}\%$ of $\left(100 - 62\frac{1}{2}\right)\%$ of 192 m

$= \left(\frac{25}{2} \times \frac{1}{100} \times \frac{75}{2} \times \frac{1}{100} \times 192\right) \text{ m} = 9 \text{ m}.$

111. Let the total income be x.

Then, income left = $(100 - 80)\%$ of $[100 - (35 + 25)]\%$ of x = 20% of 40% of x

$= \left(\frac{20}{100} \times \frac{40}{100} \times 100\right)\%$ of x = 8% of x.

112. Let the total salary be Rs. x.

Then, (100 − 10)% of (100 − 20)% of (100 − 20)% of (100 − 10)% of x = 15552

$\Leftrightarrow \left(\frac{90}{100} \times \frac{80}{100} \times \frac{80}{100} \times \frac{90}{100} \times x\right) = 15552 \Leftrightarrow x = \left(\frac{15552 \times 10000}{64 \times 81}\right) = 30000.$

113. Let the amount with Aman be Rs. x.

Then, amount received by Sahil $= \frac{1}{4}$ of 40% of Rs. x = 10% of Rs. x.

$\therefore$ 10% of $x = 600 + 200 \Leftrightarrow \frac{10}{100}x = 800 \Leftrightarrow x = 800 \times 10 = 8000.$

114. Let the monthly salary of Sameer be Rs. x.
Then, $[100 - (25 + 20)]\%$ of $[100 - (24 + 15)]\%$ of $x = 10736 \Leftrightarrow 55\%$ of 61% of $x = 10736$

$\Leftrightarrow \frac{55}{100} \times \frac{61}{100} \times x = 10736 \Leftrightarrow x = \left(\frac{10736 \times 100 \times 100}{55 \times 61}\right) = 32000.$

115. Let the total number of children be x.

Then, $x \times (20\% \text{ of } x) = 405 \Leftrightarrow \frac{1}{5}x^2 = 405 \Leftrightarrow x^2 = 2025 \Leftrightarrow x = 45.$

$\therefore$ Number of sweets received by each child = 20% of 45 = 9.

116. We have : $x + x\%$ of $150 = 150$

$\Leftrightarrow x + \frac{x}{100} \times 150 = 150 \Leftrightarrow \frac{5}{2}x = 150 \Leftrightarrow x = \left(\frac{150 \times 2}{5}\right) = 60.$

117. $15 + \frac{1}{3}(n - 20) = 50\%$ of $n = \frac{50}{100}n = \frac{n}{2} \Leftrightarrow 90 + 2n - 40 = 3n \Leftrightarrow n = 50.$

118. Let A's salary = Rs. x. Then, B's salary = Rs. $(2000 - x)$.

$(100 - 95)\%$ of A = $(100 - 85)\%$ of B $\Leftrightarrow \frac{5}{100}x = \frac{15}{100}(2000 - x) \Leftrightarrow x = 1500.$

119. Let B + M + D = x. Then, B = 25% of $x - 20 = \left(\frac{25}{100}x - 20\right) = \left(\frac{x}{4} - 20\right)$ and D = 50.

$\therefore \frac{x}{4} - 20 + M + 50 = x$ or $M = \left(\frac{3x}{4} - 30\right)$.

So, marks in Maths cannot be determined.

120. Let the total sales be Rs. x. Then, $5\frac{1}{2}\%$ of $x + \frac{1}{2}\%$ of $(x - 10000) = 1990$

$\Leftrightarrow \frac{11}{2} \times \frac{1}{100} \times x + \frac{1}{2} \times \frac{1}{100} \times (x - 10000) = 1990$

$\Leftrightarrow 12x - 10000 = 398000 \Leftrightarrow 12x = 408000 \Leftrightarrow x = 34000.$

121. Let the marks required be x. Then, $(62 + 35 + x) = 35\%$ of $(150 + 150 + 180)$

$\Leftrightarrow 97 + x = \frac{35}{100} \times 480 \Leftrightarrow x = 168 - 97 = 71.$

122. Let the number of students in the class be 100 and let the required average be x.
Then, $(10 \times 95) + (20 \times 90) + (70 \times x) = (100 \times 80)$

$\Leftrightarrow 70x = 8000 - (950 + 1800) = 5250 \Leftrightarrow x = 75.$

123. Let total marks = x. Then, $(30\% \text{ of } x) + 15 = (40\% \text{ of } x) - 35$

$\Leftrightarrow \frac{30}{100}x + 15 = \frac{40}{100}x - 35 \Leftrightarrow \frac{1}{10}x = 50 \Leftrightarrow x = 500.$

So, passing marks = $(30\% \text{ of } 500) + 15 = \left(\frac{30}{100} \times 500 + 15\right) = 165.$

$\therefore$ Pass percentage $= \left(\frac{165}{500} \times 100\right)\% = 33\%.$

124. Let the price of a chair be Rs. x. Then, price of a table = Rs. $(x + 400)$.
So, $6(x + 400) + 6x = 4800 \Leftrightarrow 12x = 2400 \Leftrightarrow x = 200.$

$\therefore$ Price of a table = Rs. 600; Price of a chair = Rs. 200.

Required percentage $= \left(\frac{400}{600} \times 100\right)\% = 66\frac{2}{3}\%.$

125. Let the total number of houses be x. Then,

$\therefore$ Number of houses having one female only $= (100 - 25)\%$ of $(100 - 40)\%$ of x

$$= \left(\frac{75}{100} \times \frac{60}{100} \times x\right) = \frac{9}{20}x.$$

$\therefore$ Required percentage $= \left(\frac{9x}{20} \times \frac{1}{x} \times 100\right)\% = 45\%.$

126. Let the total population be x. Then,

Poor population $= \frac{60}{100}x = \frac{3}{5}x.$ Illiterate population $= \frac{40}{100}x = \frac{2}{5}x.$

Illiterate rich $= 10\%$ of $(100 - 60)\%$ of $x = \left(\frac{10}{100} \times \frac{40}{100} \times x\right) = \frac{x}{25}.$

Illiterate poor $= \left(\frac{2}{5}x - \frac{x}{25}\right) = \frac{9x}{25}.$

$\therefore$ Required percentage $= \left(\frac{9x}{25} \times \frac{5}{3x} \times 100\right)\% = 60\%.$

127. Number of males $= 60\%$ of $1000 = 600$. Number of females $= (1000 - 600) = 400.$
Number of literates $= 25\%$ of $1000 = 250.$
Number of literate males $= 20\%$ of $600 = 120.$
Number of literate females $= (250 - 120) = 130.$

$\therefore$ Required percentage $= \left(\frac{130}{400} \times 100\right)\% = 32.5\%.$

128. Let the total number of candidates be x. Then, $\left(100 - 62\frac{1}{2}\right)\%$ of $37\frac{1}{2}\%$ of $x = 342$

$$\Leftrightarrow \frac{75}{2} \times \frac{1}{100} \times \frac{75}{2} \times \frac{1}{100} \times x = 342 \Leftrightarrow \frac{9x}{64} = 342 \Leftrightarrow x = \left(\frac{342 \times 64}{9}\right) = 2432.$$

Number of boys failed $= (100 - 75)\%$ of $\left(100 - 37\frac{1}{2}\right)\%$ of 2432

$$= \left(\frac{25}{100} \times \frac{125}{2} \times \frac{1}{100} \times 2432\right) = 380.$$

129. Let total population $= x$. Then, number of males $= \frac{5}{9}x.$

Married males $= 30\%$ of $\frac{5}{9}x = \left(\frac{30}{100} \times \frac{5}{9}x\right) = \frac{x}{6}.$

Married females $= \frac{x}{6}$; Number of females $= \left(x - \frac{5}{9}x\right) = \frac{4x}{9}.$

Unmarried females $= \left(\frac{4x}{9} - \frac{x}{6}\right) = \frac{5x}{18}.$

$\therefore$ Required percentage $= \left(\frac{5x}{18} \times \frac{1}{x} \times 100\right)\% = 27\frac{7}{9}\%.$

130. Migrants $= 35\%$ of $728400 = \left(\frac{35x}{100} \times 728400\right) = 254940.$

Local population $= (728400 - 254940) = 473460.$

Rural population = 20% of 473460 = 94692.

Urban population = (254940 − 94692) = 160248.

∴ Female population = 48% of 473460 + 30% of 94692 + 40% of 160248

$$= \left(\frac{48}{100} \times 473460 + \frac{30}{100} \times 94692 + \frac{40}{100} \times 160248\right)$$

$$= 227260.8 + 28407.6 + 64099.2 = 896660.$$

131. Let the number of boys and girls be $3x$ and $2x$ respectively. Then,

No. of students who are not adults $= \left(\frac{80}{100} \times 3x\right) + \left(\frac{75}{100} \times 2x\right) = \left(\frac{12x}{5} + \frac{3x}{2}\right) = \frac{39x}{10}$.

∴ Required percentage $= \left(\frac{39x}{10} \times \frac{1}{5x} \times 100\right)\% = 78\%$.

132. Suppose monthly rent = Rs. x. Then, $12x - \frac{25}{2}\%$ of $12x - 1660$ = 10% of 500000

$$\Leftrightarrow \quad 12x - \frac{25}{200} \times 12x - 1660 = 50000 \Leftrightarrow \frac{21x}{2} = 51660 \Leftrightarrow x = \left(51660 \times \frac{2}{21}\right) = 4920.$$

133. Let total debt = x. Asset $= \frac{87}{100} x$.

After paying 20% of the debt, he is left with 80% of the debt plus Rs. 42.

∴ 80% of $x + 42 = \frac{87}{100} x \Leftrightarrow \frac{87}{100} x - \frac{80}{100} x = 42 \Leftrightarrow x = 600$.

So, debt = Rs. 600 and assets = Rs. $\left(\frac{87}{100} \times 600\right)$ = Rs. 522.

134. Let the original price be Rs. 100.

New final price = 120% of (75% of Rs. 100) = Rs. $\left(\frac{120}{100} \times \frac{75}{100} \times 100\right)$ = Rs. 90.

∴ Decrease = 10%.

135. Let the original price be Rs. 100.

New final price = 85% of (115% of Rs. 100) = Rs. $\left(\frac{85}{100} \times \frac{115}{100} \times 100\right)$ = Rs. 97.75.

∴ Decrease = (100 − 97.75)% = 2.25%.

136. Let the original number be x.

Final numoer obtained = 110% of (90% of x) $= \left(\frac{110}{100} \times \frac{90}{100} \times x\right) = \frac{99}{100} x$.

∴ $x - \frac{99}{100} x = 10 \Leftrightarrow \frac{1}{100} x = 10 \Leftrightarrow x = 10 \times 100 = 1000$.

137. Let the original price be Rs. x.

∴ $(100 - r)\%$ of $(100 + r)\%$ of $x = 1$

$$\Rightarrow \frac{(100 - r)}{100} \times \frac{(100 + r)}{100} \times x = 1 \Rightarrow x = \frac{100 \times 100}{(100 - r)(100 + r)} = \frac{10000}{(10000 - r^2)}.$$

138. Let original income = Rs. 100. Then, saving = Rs. 10 and expenditure = Rs. 90.

New income = Rs. 120, New saving = Rs. 10.

New expenditure = Rs. (120 − 10) = Rs. 110.

Increase in expenditure = Rs. (110 − 90) = Rs. 20.

∴ Increase% $= \left(\frac{20}{90} \times 100\right)\% = 22\frac{2}{9}\%$.

139. Let Madan's income be Rs. x.

Then, Net income = $(100 - 10)\%$ of Rs. x = 90% of Rs. x = Rs. $\frac{9x}{10}$.

New net income = 85% of 110% of Rs. x = Rs. $\left(\frac{85}{100} \times \frac{110}{100} \times x\right)$ = Rs. $\frac{187}{200}x$.

$\therefore \quad \frac{187x}{200} - \frac{9x}{10} = 350 \Leftrightarrow \frac{7x}{200} = 350 \Leftrightarrow x = \left(\frac{350 \times 200}{7}\right) = 10000.$

140. Let his investment in the year 2000 be Rs. x.

Then, income in 2000 = Rs. $[x + 20\%$ of $x]$ = Rs. $\frac{120}{100}x$.

Income in 2001 = Rs. $\left[\frac{126}{100}(x - 5000)\right]$.

$\therefore \quad \frac{120}{100}x = \frac{126}{100}(x - 5000) \Leftrightarrow 120x = 126(x - 5000) \Leftrightarrow 6x = 630000 \Leftrightarrow x = 105000.$

141. Let original salary = Rs. 100. New salary = Rs. 120.

Decrease on 120 = 20. Decrease on 100 = $\left(\frac{20}{120} \times 100\right)\% = 16\frac{2}{3}\%$.

142. Let original number = 100.

New number = 120% of 120% of 100 = $\left(\frac{120}{100} \times \frac{120}{100} \times 100\right) = 144$.

Decrease on 144 = 44. Decrease on 100 = $\left(\frac{44}{144} \times 100\right)\% = 30\frac{5}{9}\%$.

143. Let original price per T.V. = Rs. 100 and original sale = 100 T.V.s.
Then, total revenue = Rs. (100×100) = Rs. 10,000.
New revenue = Rs. (75×120) = Rs. 9000.

$\therefore$ Decrease in revenue = $\left(\frac{1000}{10000} \times 100\right)\% = 10\%$.

144. Let original consumption = 100 units and original price = Rs. 100 per unit.
Original expenditure = Rs. (100×100) = Rs. 10000.
New expenditure = Rs. (120×80) = Rs. 9600.

$\therefore$ Decrease in expenditure = $\left(\frac{400}{10000} \times 100\right)\% = 4\%$.

145. Let the total original sale be Rs. 100. Then, original number of visitors = 100.

New number of visitors = $\frac{120}{0.75} = 160$.

$\therefore$ Increase% = 60%.

146. Suppose the business value changes from x to y.

4% of x = 5% of $y \Rightarrow \frac{4}{100}x = \frac{5}{100}y \Rightarrow y = \frac{4}{5}x$.

$\therefore$ Change in business = $\left(x - \frac{4}{5}x\right) = \frac{x}{5}$.

Percentage slump = $\left(\frac{x}{5} \times \frac{1}{x} \times \frac{1}{100}\right)\% = 20\%$.

147. Let the original fraction be $\frac{x}{y}$. Then, new fraction $= \frac{140\% \text{ of } x}{180\% \text{ of } y} = \frac{140x}{180y} = \frac{7x}{9y}$.

$\therefore \quad \frac{\text{New fraction}}{\text{Original fraction}} = \left(\frac{7x}{9y} \times \frac{y}{x}\right) = \frac{7}{9}$.

148. Decrease in consumption $= \left[\frac{R}{(100+R)} \times 100\right]\% = \left(\frac{30}{130} \times 100\right)\% = 23\frac{1}{13}\%$.

149. Increase in consumption $= \left[\frac{R}{(100-R)} \times 100\right]\% = \left(\frac{16}{84} \times 100\right)\% = \frac{400}{21}\% = 19.04\% \approx 19\%$.

150. Let original consumption be 1 unit costing Rs. 100.

New cost = Rs. 125. New consumption $= \left(\frac{1}{125} \times 100\right) = \frac{4}{5}$ unit.

$\therefore \quad \frac{\text{Reduction in consumption}}{\text{Original consumption}} = \frac{\left(1 - \frac{4}{5}\right)}{1} = \frac{1}{5}$, *i.e.*, 1 : 5.

151. Let original consumption = 100 kg and new consumption = x kg.

So, $100 \times 6 = x \times 7.50 \quad \Leftrightarrow \quad x = 80$ kg.

$\therefore$ Reduction in consumption = 20%.

152. Let expenditures on food and other items be Rs. $2x$ and Rs. $5x$.

Then, $2x + 5x = 2590$ or $x = 370$.

So, expenditure on food = Rs. (2×370) = Rs. 740.

Expenditure on other items = Rs. (5×370) = Rs. 1850.

New expenditure = 110% of Rs. 740 + 115% of Rs. 1850

$$= \text{Rs.} \left(\frac{110}{100} \times 740 + \frac{115}{100} \times 1850\right) = \text{Rs.} (814 + 2127.50) = \text{Rs. } 2941.50.$$

$\therefore$ Desired increase = Rs. (2941.50 − 2590) = Rs. 351.50.

153. Population after 3 years $= 64000 \times \left(1 + \frac{5}{2 \times 100}\right)^3 = \left(64000 \times \frac{41}{40} \times \frac{41}{40} \times \frac{41}{40}\right) = 68921$.

154. Cost after 2 years = Rs. $\left[20 \times \left(1 + \frac{8}{100}\right)^2\right]$ = Rs. $\left(20 \times \frac{27}{25} \times \frac{27}{25}\right)$ = Rs. 23.33.

155. Present population $= 160000 \times \left(1 + \frac{3}{100}\right)\left(1 + \frac{5}{2 \times 100}\right)\left(1 + \frac{5}{100}\right)$

$$= \left(160000 \times \frac{103}{100} \times \frac{41}{40} \times \frac{21}{20}\right) = 177366.$$

156. Present population $= 62500 \times \left(1 - \frac{4}{100}\right)^2 = \left(62500 \times \frac{24}{25} \times \frac{24}{25}\right) = 57600$.

157. Let the present value be Rs. 100.

Value after 3 years = Rs. $\left[100 \times \left(1 - \frac{20}{100}\right)^3\right]$ = Rs. $\left(100 \times \frac{4}{5} \times \frac{4}{5} \times \frac{4}{5}\right)$ = Rs. 51.20.

$\therefore$ Reduction in value = (100 − 51.20)% = 48.8%.

158. Population in 1998 $= \dfrac{138915}{\left(1+\dfrac{5}{100}\right)^3} = \left(138915 \times \dfrac{20}{21} \times \dfrac{20}{21} \times \dfrac{20}{21}\right) = 120000.$

159. Purchase price = Rs. $\left[\dfrac{8748}{\left(1-\dfrac{10}{100}\right)^3}\right]$ = Rs. $\left(8748 \times \dfrac{10}{9} \times \dfrac{10}{9} \times \dfrac{10}{9}\right)$ = Rs. 12000.

160. Number of ticketless travellers in April

$= 4000 \times \left(1+\dfrac{5}{100}\right)\left(1-\dfrac{5}{100}\right)\left(1-\dfrac{10}{100}\right) = \left(4000 \times \dfrac{21}{20} \times \dfrac{19}{20} \times \dfrac{9}{10}\right) = 3591.$

161. Number of bushes in the beginning

$= \dfrac{26730}{\left(1+\dfrac{10}{100}\right)\left(1+\dfrac{8}{100}\right)\left(1-\dfrac{10}{100}\right)} = \left(26730 \times \dfrac{10}{11} \times \dfrac{25}{27} \times \dfrac{10}{9}\right) = 25000.$

162. Let the production in 1998 be 100 units. Then,

Production in 2002 $= 100 \times \left(1+\dfrac{15}{100}\right)^2\left(1-\dfrac{10}{100}\right)\left(1+\dfrac{15}{100}\right)$

$= \left(100 \times \dfrac{23}{20} \times \dfrac{23}{20} \times \dfrac{9}{10} \times \dfrac{23}{20}\right) = 136.88.$

$\therefore$ Increase in production = (136.88 – 100)% = 36.88% ≈ 37%.

163. 10 crores $\times \left(1+\dfrac{R}{100}\right)^3$ = 13.31 crores.

$\therefore \left(1+\dfrac{R}{100}\right)^3 = \dfrac{13.31 \text{ crores}}{10 \text{ crores}} = \dfrac{13.31}{10} = \dfrac{1331}{1000} = \left(\dfrac{11}{10}\right)^3.$

So, $\left(1+\dfrac{R}{100}\right) = \dfrac{11}{10} \Leftrightarrow \left(1+\dfrac{R}{100}\right) = \left(1+\dfrac{1}{10}\right) \Leftrightarrow \dfrac{R}{100} = \dfrac{1}{10} \Leftrightarrow R = 10.$

164. Let the required time be n years. Then, $72900 \times \left(1+\dfrac{10}{100}\right)^n = 133100 \times \left(1-\dfrac{10}{100}\right)^n$

$\Leftrightarrow \left(\dfrac{11}{10}\right)^n \times \left(\dfrac{10}{9}\right)^n = \dfrac{133100}{72900} \Leftrightarrow \left(\dfrac{11}{9}\right)^n = \dfrac{1331}{729} = \left(\dfrac{11}{9}\right)^3 \Leftrightarrow n = 3.$

165. Let original population = 100.

Population after 3 years $= 100 \times \left(1+\dfrac{3\frac{1}{2}}{100}\right)^3 = 100 \times \dfrac{207}{200} \times \dfrac{207}{200} \times \dfrac{207}{200} = 110.87.$

$\therefore$ Increase = (110.87 – 100)% = 10.87% ≈ 10.8%.

166. Net growth on 1000 = (32 – 11) = 21. Net growth on 100 $= \left(\dfrac{21}{1000} \times 100\right)\% = 2.1\%$

167. Let the number of males be x. Then, number of females = $(5000 - x)$.

$\therefore$ 10% of x + 15% of $(5000 - x)$ = (5600 – 5000)

$\Leftrightarrow \dfrac{10}{100}x + \dfrac{15}{100}(5000 - x) = 600 \Leftrightarrow 10x + 75000 - 15x = 60000$

$\Leftrightarrow 5x = 15000 \Leftrightarrow x = 3000.$

168. A = 125% of B $\Rightarrow$ A = $\frac{125}{100}$B $\Rightarrow$ B = $\frac{100}{125}$A = $\left(\frac{4}{5}\times 100\right)$% of A = 80% of A.

169. B's salary is less than A's by $\left[\frac{50}{(100+50)}\times 100\right]$% *i.e.*, $\frac{100}{3}$% = $33\frac{1}{3}$%.

170. Excess of B's height over A's = $\left[\frac{40}{(100-40)}\times 100\right]$% = $\frac{200}{3}$% = $66\frac{2}{3}$%.

171. $p = 6q$. So, q is less than p by $5q$.

$\therefore$ Required percentage = $\left(\frac{5q}{p}\times 100\right)$% = $\left(\frac{5q}{6q}\times 100\right)$% = $83\frac{1}{3}$%.

172. Let third number be x.

Then, first number = 70% of x = $\frac{7x}{10}$; second number = 63% of x = $\frac{63x}{100}$.

Difference = $\left(\frac{7x}{10}-\frac{63x}{100}\right) = \frac{7x}{100}$.

$\therefore$ Required percentage = $\left(\frac{7x}{100}\times\frac{10}{7x}\times 100\right)$% = 10%.

173. Let third number be x.

Then, first number = $112\frac{1}{2}$% of x = $\frac{9x}{8}$; second number = 125% of x = $\frac{5}{4}x$.

$\therefore$ Required percentage = $\left(\frac{9x}{8}\times\frac{4}{5x}\times 100\right)$% = 90%.

174. A = 40% of B = 40% of (25% of C) = $\left(\frac{40}{100}\times\frac{25}{100}\times 100\right)$% of C = 10% of C.

175. $\frac{5}{100}$A = $\frac{15}{100}$B and $\frac{10}{100}$B = $\frac{20}{100}$C $\Rightarrow$ A = 3B and B = 2C = 2×2000 = 4000.

$\therefore$ A = 3 × 4000 = 12000.

Hence, A + B + C = (12000 + 4000 + 2000) = 18000.

176. P = $\frac{140}{100}$A = $\frac{140}{100}\left(\frac{80}{100}\text{M}\right) = \left(\frac{140}{100}\times\frac{80}{100}\times 100\right)$% of M = 112% of M.

177. Let Deepak's monthly income = Rs. 100. Then, Raunaq's monthly income = Rs. 80.

Amit's monthly income = Rs. $\left(\frac{130}{100}\times 80\right)$ = Rs. 104.

If difference between Amit's and Deepak's income is Rs. 4, then Raunaq's income = Rs. 80.

If difference is Rs. 800, Raunaq's income = Rs. $\left(\frac{80}{4}\times 800\right)$ = Rs. 16000.

178. A = $\frac{120}{100}$B, B = $\frac{120}{100}$C and C = $\frac{85}{100}$D.

$\therefore$ B = $\frac{5}{6}$A, C = $\frac{5}{6}$B and D = $\frac{20}{17}$C.

B = $\frac{5}{6}\times 576$ = 480; C = $\frac{5}{6}\times 480$ = 400; D = $\frac{20}{17}\times 400 = \frac{8000}{17}$.

So, required percentage = $\left(\frac{8000}{17}\times\frac{1}{800}\times 100\right)$% = 58.82%.

179. Let number of students appeared from school A = 100.

Then, number of students qualified from school A = 70.

Number of students appeared from school B = 120.

Number of students qualified from school B = $\left(\frac{150}{100} \times 70\right) = 105$.

$\therefore$ Required percentage = $\left(\frac{105}{120} \times 100\right)\% = 87.5\%$.

180. Quantity of pulp in 100 kg of fresh fruits = (100 – 68)% of 100 kg = 32 kg.

Let the quantity of dry fruit obtained be x kg.

Then, $(100 - 20)\%$ of $x = 32 \Leftrightarrow \frac{80}{100}x = 32 \Leftrightarrow x = \left(\frac{32 \times 100}{80}\right) = 40$.

181. Let the reduced weight be x kg.

Clearly, the quantity of pulp remains the same in both the cases.

So, (100 – 96)% of 20 kg = (100 – 95)% of x kg

$\Leftrightarrow$ 4% of 20 kg = 5% of x kg $\Leftrightarrow x = \left(\frac{4}{5} \times 20\right)$ kg = 16 kg.

182. Quantity of alcohol in 400 ml solution = $\left(\frac{15}{100} \times 400\right)$ ml = 60 ml.

Quantity of water = (400 – 60) ml = 340 ml.

Let x ml of alcohol be added.

Then, $\frac{60 + x}{400 + x} = \frac{32}{100} \Leftrightarrow 6000 + 100x = 12800 + 32x \Leftrightarrow 68x = 6800 \Leftrightarrow x = 100$.

183. Quantity of water in 10 litres = 5% of 10 litres = 0.5 litres.

Let x litres of pure milk be added. Then, $\frac{0.5}{10 + x} = \frac{2}{100} \Leftrightarrow 2x = 30 \Leftrightarrow x = 15$.

184. Quantity of alcohol in 9 ml lotion = $\left(\frac{50}{100} \times 9\right)$ ml = 4.5 ml.

Let the water to be added be x ml.

Then, $\frac{4.5}{9 + x} = \frac{30}{100} \Leftrightarrow 270 + 30x = 450 \Leftrightarrow x = 6$ ml.

185. Quantity of sugar = $\left(\frac{40}{100} \times 3\right)$ kg = 1.2 kg.

$\therefore$ New percentage = $\left(\frac{1.2}{4} \times 100\right)\% = 30\%$.

186. Required percentage = $\left(\frac{20\% \text{ of } 10 + 35\% \text{ of } 4}{10 + 4} \times 100\right)\% = \left(\frac{3.4}{14} \times 100\right)\% = 24\frac{2}{7}\%$.

187. Let the original quantity be x kg. Vanaspati ghee in x kg = $\left(\frac{40}{100}x\right)$ kg = $\left(\frac{2x}{5}\right)$ kg.

Now, $\frac{\frac{2x}{5}}{x + 10} = \frac{20}{100} \Leftrightarrow \frac{2x}{5x + 50} = \frac{1}{5} \Leftrightarrow 5x = 50 \Leftrightarrow x = 10$.

188. Let the original total weight be x. Weight of container $= \frac{25}{100}x = \frac{x}{4}$.

Original weight of fluid $= \left(x - \frac{x}{4}\right) = \frac{3x}{4}$.

New weight of (container + fluid) $= \frac{50}{100}x = \frac{x}{2}$. New weight of fluid $= \left(\frac{x}{2} - \frac{x}{4}\right) = \frac{x}{4}$.

$\therefore$ Required fraction $= \frac{\left(\frac{3x}{4} - \frac{x}{4}\right)}{\frac{3x}{4}} = \frac{x}{2} \times \frac{4}{3x} = \frac{2}{3}$.

189. Let total quantity of original milk = 1000 gm.

Milk after first operation = 80% of 1000 = 800 gm.

Milk after second operation = 80% of 800 = 640 gm.

Milk after third operation = 80% of 640 = 512 gm.

$\therefore$ Strength of final mixture = 51.2%.

190. Let the capacity of the tank be 100 litres. Then,

Initially : A type petrol = 100 litres.

After first operation :

A type petrol $= \left(\frac{100}{2}\right)$ = 50 litres; B type petrol = 50 litres.

After second operation :

A type petrol $= \left(\frac{50}{2} + 50\right)$ = 75 litres; B type petrol $= \left(\frac{50}{2}\right)$ = 25 litres.

After third operation :

A type petrol $= \left(\frac{75}{2}\right)$ = 37.5 litres; B type petrol $= \left(\frac{25}{2} + 50\right)$ = 62.5 litres.

$\therefore$ Required percentage = 37.5%.

191. Total money = Rs. $\left(600 \times \frac{25}{100} + 1200 \times \frac{50}{100}\right)$ = Rs. 750.

25 paise coins removed $= \left(\frac{12}{100} \times 600\right) = 72$.

50 paise coins removed $= \left(\frac{24}{100} \times 1200\right) = 288$.

Money removed = Rs. $\left(72 \times \frac{25}{100} + 288 \times \frac{50}{100}\right)$ = Rs. 162.

$\therefore$ Required percentage $= \left(\frac{162}{750} \times 100\right)\% = 21.6\%$.

192. Let the original price be Rs. 100 per kg.

Money required to buy 49 kg of rice = Rs. (100 × 49) = Rs. 4900

New price = Rs. 98 per kg.

$\therefore$ Quantity of rice bought $= \left(\frac{4900}{98}\right)$ kg = 50 kg.

193. Let original price = Rs. x per kg. Reduced price = Rs. $\left(\frac{79x}{100}\right)$ per kg.

$$\therefore \quad \frac{100}{\frac{79x}{100}} - \frac{100}{x} = 10.5 \Leftrightarrow \frac{10000}{79x} - \frac{100}{x} = 10.5$$

$$\Leftrightarrow 10000 - 7900 = 10.5 \times 79x \Leftrightarrow x = \frac{2100}{10.5 \times 79}.$$

$\therefore$ Reduced price = Rs. $\left(\frac{79}{100} \times \frac{2100}{10.5 \times 79}\right)$ per kg = Rs. 2 per kg.

194. Let the original price per egg be Rs. x. Then, increased price = Rs. $\left(\frac{130}{100}x\right)$.

$$\therefore \quad \frac{7.80}{x} - \frac{7.80}{\frac{130}{100}x} = 3 \Leftrightarrow \frac{7.80}{x} - \frac{780}{130x} = 3$$

$$\Leftrightarrow 1014 - 780 = 3 \times 130x \Leftrightarrow 390x = 234 \Leftrightarrow x = 0.6.$$

So, present price per dozen = Rs. $\left(12 \times \frac{130}{100} \times 0.6\right)$ = Rs. 9.36.

195. Let original price = Rs. x per kg. Reduced price = Rs. $\left(\frac{90x}{100}\right)$ per kg.

$$\therefore \quad \frac{279}{\left(\frac{90x}{100}\right)} - \frac{279}{x} = 6.2 \Leftrightarrow \frac{27900}{90x} - \frac{279}{x} = 6.2$$

$$\Leftrightarrow 27900 - 25110 = 6.2 \times 90x$$

$$\Leftrightarrow 558x = 2790 \Leftrightarrow x = 5.$$

$\therefore$ Required difference = 10% of Rs. 5 = Re. 0.50.

196. $n(A) = 34$, $n(B) = 42$, $n(A \cap B) = 20$.

So, $n(A \cup B) = n(A) + n(B) - n(A \cap B) = 34 + 42 - 20 = 56$.

$\therefore$ Percentage failed in either or both the subjects = 56.

Hence, percentage passed = (100 − 56)% = 44%.

197. $n(A) = 40$, $n(B) = 50$, $n(A \cap B) = 10$.

$n(A \cup B) = n(A) + n(B) - n(A \cap B) = 40 + 50 - 10 = 80$.

$\therefore$ Percentage reading either or both newspapers = 80%.

Hence, percentage reading neither newspaper = (100 − 80)% = 20%.

198. $n(A) = 325$, $n(B) = 175$, $n(A \cup B) = 450 - 50 = 400$.

Required number = $n(A \cap B) = n(A) + n(B) - n(A \cup B) = 325 + 175 - 400 = 100$.

199. $n(A) = \left(\frac{60}{100} \times 96\right) = \frac{288}{5}$, $n(B) = \left(\frac{30}{100} \times 96\right) = \frac{144}{5}$, $n(A \cap B) = \left(\frac{15}{100} \times 96\right) = \frac{72}{5}$.

$$\therefore \quad n(A \cup B) = n(A) + n(B) - n(A \cap B) = \frac{288}{5} + \frac{144}{5} - \frac{72}{5} = \frac{360}{5} = 72.$$

So, people who had either or both types of lunch = 72.

Hence, people who had neither type of lunch = (96 − 72) = 24.

200. $n(A) = \left(\frac{75}{100} \times 600\right) = 450$, $n(B) = \left(\frac{45}{100} \times 600\right) = 270$, $n(A \cup B) = 600$.

$\therefore \quad n(A \cap B) = n(A) + n(B) - n(A \cup B) = (450 + 270 - 600) = 120.$

201. Let total number be x. Then,

$n(A) = \frac{72}{100} x = \frac{18x}{25}$, $n(B) = \frac{44}{100} x = \frac{11x}{25}$ and $n(A \cap B) = 40$.

$n(A \cup B) = n(A) + n(B) - n(A \cup B)$

$\Rightarrow \quad x = \frac{18x}{25} + \frac{11x}{25} - 40 \Rightarrow \frac{29x}{25} - x = 40 \Rightarrow \frac{4x}{25} = 40 \Rightarrow x = 250.$

202. Let the total number of students be x.

Number passed in one or both is given by :

$n(A \cup B) = n(A) + n(B) - n(A \cap B) = 65\%$ of $x + 60\%$ of $x - 40\%$ of x

$= \left(\frac{65}{100} x + \frac{60}{100} x - \frac{40}{100} x\right) = \frac{85}{100} x = \frac{17}{20} x.$

Failed in both $= \left(x - \frac{17}{20} x\right) = \frac{3x}{20}$.

$\therefore \quad \frac{3x}{20} = 90 \Leftrightarrow x = \left(\frac{90 \times 20}{3}\right) = 600.$

203. Failed in 1st subject $= \left(\frac{35}{100} \times 2500\right) = 875.$

Failed in 2nd subject $= \left(\frac{42}{100} \times 2500\right) = 1050.$

Failed in both $= \left(\frac{15}{100} \times 2500\right) = 375.$

Failed in 1st subject only $= (875 - 375) = 500.$

Failed in 2nd subject only $= (1050 - 375) = 675.$

$\therefore$ Passed in 2nd only + Passed in 1st only $= (675 + 500) = 1175.$

11. PROFIT AND LOSS

IMPORTANT FACTS

Cost Price : The price at which an article is purchased, is called its ***cost price***, abbreviated as ***C.P.***

Selling Price : The price at which an article is sold, is called its ***selling price***, abbreviated as ***S.P.***

Profit or Gain : If S.P. is greater than C.P., the seller is said to have a ***profit*** or ***gain***.

Loss : If S.P. is less than C.P., the seller is said to have incurred a ***loss***.

FORMULAE

1. Gain = (S.P.) – (C.P.)
2. Loss = (C.P.) – (S.P.)
3. Loss or gain is always reckoned on C.P.
4. $\text{Gain\%} = \left(\dfrac{\text{Gain} \times 100}{\text{C.P.}}\right)$
5. $\text{Loss\%} = \left(\dfrac{\text{Loss} \times 100}{\text{C.P.}}\right)$
6. $\text{S.P.} = \dfrac{(100 + \text{Gain\%})}{100} \times \text{C.P.}$
7. $\text{S.P.} = \dfrac{(100 - \text{Loss\%})}{100} \times \text{C.P.}$
8. $\text{C.P.} = \dfrac{100}{(100 + \text{Gain\%})} \times \text{S.P.}$
9. $\text{C.P.} = \dfrac{100}{(100 - \text{Loss\%})} \times \text{S.P.}$
10. If an article is sold at a gain of say, 35%, then S.P. = 135% of C.P.
11. If an article is sold at a loss of say, 35%, then S.P. = 65% of C.P.
12. When a person sells two similar items, one at a gain of say, *x*%, and the other at a loss of *x*%, then the seller always incurs a loss given by :

$$\text{Loss\%} = \left(\frac{\text{Common Loss and Gain\%}}{10}\right)^2 = \left(\frac{x}{10}\right)^2.$$

13. If a trader professes to sell his goods at cost price, but uses false weights, then

$$\text{Gain\%} = \left[\frac{\text{Error}}{(\text{True Value}) - (\text{Error})} \times 100\right]\%.$$

SOLVED EXAMPLES

Ex. 1. ***A man buys an article for Rs. 27.50 and sells it for Rs. 28.60. Find his gain percent.***

Sol. C.P. = Rs. 27.50, S.P. = Rs. 28.60.

So, Gain = Rs. (28.60 – 27.50) = Rs. 1.10.

$\therefore \quad \text{Gain\%} = \left(\dfrac{1.10}{27.50} \times 100\right)\% = 4\%.$

Ex. 2. ***If a radio is purchased for Rs. 490 and sold for Rs. 465.50, find the loss percent.***

Sol. C.P. = Rs. 490, S.P. = Rs. 465.50.

Loss = Rs. (490 − 465.50) = Rs. 24.50.

$\therefore$ Loss% $= \left(\frac{24.50}{490} \times 100\right)\% = 5\%$.

Ex. 3. ***Find S.P., when***

(i) C.P. = Rs. 56.25, Gain = 20% ***(ii) C.P. = Rs. 80.40, Loss = 5%***

Sol. (*i*) S.P = 120% of Rs. 56.25 = Rs. $\left(\frac{120}{100} \times 56.25\right)$ = Rs. 67.50.

(*ii*) S.P. = 85% of Rs. 80.40 = Rs. $\left(\frac{85}{100} \times 80.40\right)$ = Rs. 68.34.

Ex. 4. ***Find C.P., when***

(i) S.P. = Rs. 40.60, Gain = 16% ***(ii) S.P. = Rs. 51.70, Loss = 12%***

Sol. (*i*) C.P. = Rs. $\left(\frac{100}{116} \times 40.60\right)$ = Rs. 35.

(*ii*) C.P. = Rs. $\left(\frac{100}{88} \times 51.70\right)$ = Rs. 58.75.

Ex. 5. ***A person incurs 5% loss by selling a watch for Rs. 1140. At what price should the watch be sold to earn 5% profit ?*** **(R.R.B. 2002)**

Sol. Let the new S.P. be Rs. *x*. Then,

(100 − loss%) : (1st S.P.) = (100 + gain%) : (2nd S.P.)

$\Rightarrow \left(\frac{100-5}{1140}\right) = \left(\frac{100+5}{x}\right) \Rightarrow x = \left(\frac{105 \times 1140}{95}\right) = 1260.$

$\therefore$ New S.P. = Rs. 1260.

Ex. 6. ***A book was sold for Rs. 27.50 with a profit of 10%. If it were sold for Rs. 25.75, then what would have been the percentage of profit or loss ?***

(Hotel Management, 2003)

Sol. S.P. = Rs. 27.50, Profit = 10%.

So, C.P. = Rs. $\left(\frac{100}{110} \times 27.50\right)$ = Rs. 25.

When S.P. = Rs. 25.75, profit = Rs. (25.75 − 25) = Re. 0.75.

$\therefore$ Profit% $= \left(\frac{0.75}{25} \times 100\right)\% = 3\%$.

Ex. 7. ***If the cost price is 96% of the selling price, then what is the profit percent?***

Sol. Let S.P. = Rs. 100. Then, C.P. = Rs. 96; Profit = Rs. 4.

$\therefore$ Profit% $= \left(\frac{4}{96} \times 100\right)\% = \frac{25}{6}\% = 4.17\%$.

Ex. 8. ***The C.P. of 21 articles is equal to S.P. of 18 articles. Find the gain or loss percent.***

Sol. Let C.P. of each article be Re. 1.

Then, C.P. of 18 articles = Rs. 18, S.P. of 18 articles = Rs. 21.

$\therefore$ Gain% $= \left(\frac{3}{18} \times 100\right)\% = 16\frac{2}{3}\%$.

Ex. 9. ***By selling 33 metres of cloth, one gains the selling price of 11 metres. Find the gain percent.*** **(Section Officers', 2001)**

Sol. (S.P. of 33 m) – (C.P. of 33 m) = Gain = S.P. of 11 m.

$\therefore$ S.P. of 22 m = C.P. of 33 m.

Let C.P. of each metre be Re. 1. Then, C.P. of 22 m = Rs. 22, S.P. of 22 m = Rs. 33.

$\therefore$ Gain% $= \left(\frac{11}{22} \times 100\right)\% = 50\%$.

Ex. 10. ***A vendor bought bananas at 6 for Rs. 10 and sold them at 4 for Rs. 6. Find his gain or loss percent.***

Sol. Suppose, number of bananas bought = L.C.M. of 6 and 4 = 12.

$\therefore$ C.P. = Rs. $\left(\frac{10}{6} \times 12\right)$ = Rs. 20; S.P. = Rs. $\left(\frac{6}{4} \times 12\right)$ = Rs. 18.

$\therefore$ Loss% $= \left(\frac{2}{20} \times 100\right)\% = 10\%$.

Ex. 11. ***A man bought toffees at 3 for a rupee. How many for a rupee must he sell to gain 50% ?***

Sol. C.P. of 3 toffees = Re. 1; S.P. of 3 toffees = 150% of Re. 1 = $\frac{3}{2}$.

For Rs. $\frac{3}{2}$, toffees sold = 3. For Re. 1, toffees sold = $\left(3 \times \frac{2}{3}\right) = 2$.

Ex. 12. ***A grocer purchased 80 kg of sugar at Rs. 13.50 per kg and mixed it with 120 kg sugar at Rs. 16 per kg. At what rate should he sell the mixture to gain 16% ?***

Sol. C.P. of 200 kg of mixture = Rs. (80 × 13.50 + 120 × 16) = Rs. 3000.

S.P. = 116% of Rs. 3000 = Rs. $\left(\frac{116}{100} \times 3000\right)$ = Rs. 3480.

$\therefore$ Rate of S.P. of the mixture = Rs. $\left(\frac{3480}{200}\right)$ per kg = Rs. 17.40 per kg.

Ex. 13. ***Pure ghee costs Rs. 100 per kg. After adulterating it with vegetable oil costing Rs. 50 per kg, a shopkeeper sells the mixture at the rate of Rs. 96 per kg, thereby making a profit of 20%. In what ratio does he mix the two ?***

Sol. Mean cost price = Rs. $\left(\frac{100}{120} \times 96\right)$ = Rs. 80 per kg.

By the rule of alligation

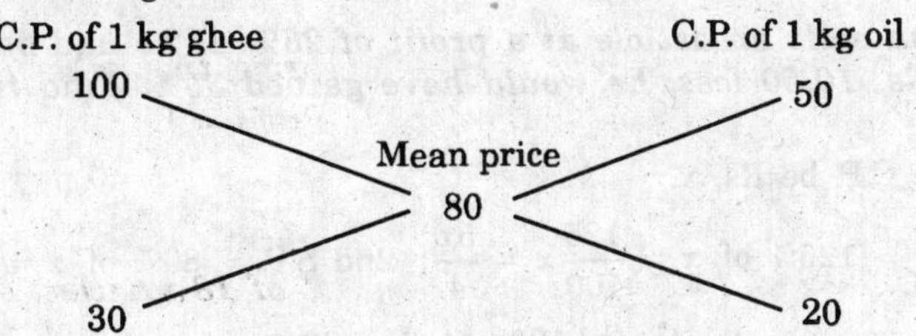

$\therefore$ Required ratio = 30 : 20 = 3 : 2.

Ex. 14. ***A dishonest dealer professes to sell his goods at cost price but uses a weight of 960 gms for a kg. weight. Find his gain percent.***

Sol. Gain% $= \left[\frac{\text{Error}}{(\text{True Value}) - (\text{Error})} \times 100\right]\% = \left(\frac{40}{960} \times 100\right)\% = 4\frac{1}{6}\%$.

Ex. 15. ***If the manufacturer gains 10%, the wholesale dealer 15% and the retailer 25%, then find the cost of production of a table, the retail price of which is Rs. 1265?***

Sol. Let the cost of production of the table be Rs. x.

Then, 125% of 115% of 110% of x = 1265

$$\Rightarrow \frac{125}{100} \times \frac{115}{100} \times \frac{110}{100} \times x = 1265 \Rightarrow \frac{253}{160} x = 1265 \Rightarrow x = \left(\frac{1265 \times 160}{253}\right) = \text{Rs. } 800.$$

Ex. 16. ***Monika purchased a pressure cooker at $\frac{9}{10}$th of its selling price and sold it at 8% more than its S.P. Find her gain percent.***

Sol. Let the S.P. be Rs. x. Then, C.P. = Rs. $\frac{9x}{10}$, Receipt = 108% of Rs. x = Rs. $\frac{27x}{25}$.

$$\text{Gain} = \text{Rs.} \left(\frac{27x}{25} - \frac{9x}{10}\right) = \text{Rs.} \left(\frac{108x - 90x}{100}\right) = \text{Rs. } \frac{18x}{100}.$$

$$\therefore \quad \text{Gain\%} = \left(\frac{18x}{100} \times \frac{10}{9x} \times 100\right)\% = 20\%.$$

Ex. 17. ***An article is sold at a certain price. By selling it at $\frac{2}{3}$ of that price one loses 10%. Find the gain percent at original price.***

Sol. Let the original S.P. be Rs. x. Then, New S.P. = Rs. $\frac{2}{3}x$, Loss = 10%.

$$\text{So, C.P.} = \text{Rs.} \left(\frac{100}{90} \times \frac{2}{3} x\right) = \frac{20x}{27}.$$

$$\text{Now, C.P.} = \text{Rs. } \frac{20x}{27}, \text{ S.P.} = \text{Rs. } x. \text{ Gain} = \text{Rs.} \left(x - \frac{20x}{27}\right) = \text{Rs. } \frac{7x}{27}.$$

$$\therefore \quad \text{Gain\%} = \left(\frac{7x}{27} \times \frac{27}{20x} \times 100\right)\% = 35\%.$$

Ex. 18. ***A tradesman sold an article at a loss of 20%. If the selling price had been increased by Rs. 100, there would have been a gain of 5%. What was the cost price of the article?*** **(S.S.C. 2004)**

Sol. Let C.P. be Rs. x. Then, (105% of x) – (80% of x) = 100 or 25% of x = 100

$$\therefore \quad \frac{x}{4} = 100 \text{ or } x = 400.$$

So, C.P. = Rs. 400.

Ex. 19. ***A man sells an article at a profit of 25%. If he had bought it at 20% less and sold it for Rs. 10.50 less, he would have gained 30%. Find the cost price of the article.***

Sol. Let the C.P. be Rs. x.

$$\text{1st S.P.} = 125\% \text{ of } x = \frac{125}{100} x = \frac{5x}{4}; \text{ 2nd S.P.} = 80\% \text{ of } x = \frac{80}{100} x = \frac{4x}{5}.$$

$$\text{2nd S.P.} = 130\% \text{ of } \frac{4x}{5} = \left(\frac{130}{100} \times \frac{4x}{5}\right) = \frac{26x}{25}.$$

$$\therefore \quad \frac{5x}{4} - \frac{26x}{25} = 10.50 \Leftrightarrow \frac{21x}{100} = 10.50 \Leftrightarrow x = \left(\frac{10.50 \times 100}{21}\right) = 50.$$

Hence, C.P. = Rs. 50.

Ex. 20. ***The price of a jewel, passing through three hands, rises on the whole by 65%. If the first and the second sellers earned 20% and 25% profit respectively, find the percentage profit earned by the third seller.***

Sol. Let the original price of the jewel be Rs. P and let the profit earned by the third seller be x%.

Then, $(100 + x)$% of 125% of 120% of P = 165% of P

$$\Rightarrow \left[\frac{(100+x)}{100} \times \frac{125}{100} \times \frac{120}{100} \times P\right] = \left(\frac{165}{100} \times P\right)$$

$$\Rightarrow (100 + x) = \left(\frac{165 \times 100 \times 100}{125 \times 120}\right) = 110 \Rightarrow x = 10\%.$$

Ex. 21. ***A man sold two flats for Rs. 6,75,958 each. On one he gains 16% while on the other he loses 16%. How much does he gain or lose in the whole transaction ?***

Sol. **Remember** : In such a case, there is always a loss. The selling price is immaterial.

$$\therefore \quad \text{Loss\%} = \left(\frac{\text{Common Loss and Gain\%}}{10}\right)^2 = \left(\frac{16}{10}\right)^2 \% = \left(\frac{64}{25}\right)\% = 2.56\%.$$

Ex. 22. ***A dealer sold three-fourth of his articles at a gain of 20% and the remaining at cost price. Find the gain earned by him in the whole transaction.***

Sol. Let C.P. of whole be Rs. x.

$$\text{C.P. of } \frac{3}{4}\text{th} = \text{Rs. } \frac{3x}{4}, \text{ C.P. of } \frac{1}{4}\text{th} = \text{Rs. } \frac{x}{4}$$

$$\therefore \quad \text{Total S.P.} = \text{Rs. } \left[\left(120\% \text{ of } \frac{3x}{4}\right) + \frac{x}{4}\right] = \text{Rs. } \left(\frac{9x}{10} + \frac{x}{4}\right) = \text{Rs. } \frac{23x}{20}.$$

$$\text{Gain} = \text{Rs. } \left(\frac{23x}{20} - x\right) = \text{Rs. } \frac{3x}{20}.$$

$$\therefore \quad \text{Gain\%} = \left(\frac{3x}{20} \times \frac{1}{x} \times 100\right)\% = 15\%.$$

Ex. 23. ***A man bought a horse and a carriage for Rs. 3000. He sold the horse at a gain of 20% and the carriage at a loss of 10%, thereby gaining 2% on the whole. Find the cost of the horse.*** **(M.B.A. 2002)**

Sol. Let the C.P. of the horse be Rs. x. Then, C.P. of the carriage = Rs. (3000 – x).

$\therefore$ 20% of x – 10% of (3000 – x) = 2% of 3000

$$\Rightarrow \frac{x}{5} - \frac{(3000 - x)}{10} = 60 \Rightarrow 2x - 3000 + x = 600 \Rightarrow 3x = 3600 \Rightarrow x = 1200.$$

Hence, C.P. of the horse = Rs. 1200.

Ex. 24. ***Find the single discount equivalent to a series discount of 20%, 10% and 5%.***

Sol. Let marked price be Rs. 100.

Then, Net S.P. = 95% of 90% of 80% of Rs. 100

$$= \text{Rs. } \left(\frac{95}{100} \times \frac{90}{100} \times \frac{80}{100} \times 100\right) = \text{Rs. } 68.40.$$

$\therefore$ Required discount = (100 – 68.40)% = 31.6%.

Ex. 25. ***After getting two successive discounts, a shirt with a list price of Rs. 150 is available at Rs. 105. If the second discount is 12.5%, find the first discount.***

Sol. Let the first discount be x%.

Then, 87.5% of $(100 - x)$% of 150 = 105

$$\Rightarrow \frac{87.5}{100} \times \frac{(100 - x)}{100} \times 150 = 105 \Rightarrow 100 - x = \left(\frac{105 \times 100 \times 100}{150 \times 87.5}\right) = 80$$

$\Rightarrow$ x = (100 – 80) = 20.

$\therefore$ First discount = 20%.

Ex. 26. ***An uneducated retailer marks all his goods at 50% above the cost price and thinking that he will still make 25% profit, offers a discount of 25% on the marked price. What is his actual profit on the sales ?*** **(IGNOU, 2003)**

Sol. Let C.P. = Rs. 100. Then, marked price = Rs. 150.

S.P. = 75% of Rs. 150 = Rs. 112.50.

$\therefore$ Gain% = 12.50%.

Ex. 27. ***A retailer buys 40 pens at the marked price of 36 pens from a wholesaler. If he sells these pens giving a discount of 1%, what is the profit percent ?*** **(S.S.C. 2003)**

Sol. Let the marked price of each pen be Re. 1.

Then, C.P. of 40 pens = Rs. 36. S.P. of 40 pens = 99% of Rs. 40 = Rs. 39.60.

$\therefore$ Profit% $= \left(\frac{3.60}{36} \times 100\right)\% = 10\%.$

Ex. 28. ***At what percentage above the C.P. must an article be marked so as to gain 33% after allowing a customer a discount of 5% ?*** **(M.B.A. 2003)**

Sol. Let C.P. = Rs. 100. Then, S.P. = Rs. 133.

Let marked price be Rs. x.

Then, 95% of x = 133 $\Rightarrow \frac{95}{100}x = 133 \Rightarrow x = \left(133 \times \frac{100}{95}\right) = 140.$

$\therefore$ Marked price = 40% above C.P.

Ex. 29. ***When a producer allows 36% commission on the retail price of his product, he earns a profit of 8.8%. What would be his profit percent if the commission is reduced by 24% ?*** **(M.B.A. 2002)**

Sol. Let retail price = Rs. 100. Then, commission = Rs. 36.

$\therefore$ S.P. = Rs. (100 − 36) = Rs. 64.

But, profit = 8.8%.

$\therefore$ C.P. = Rs. $\left(\frac{100}{108.8} \times 64\right)$ = Rs. $\frac{1000}{17}$.

New commission = Rs. 12. New S.P. = Rs. (100 − 12) = Rs. 88.

Gain = Rs. $\left(88 - \frac{1000}{17}\right)$ = Rs. $\frac{496}{17}$.

$\therefore$ Gain% $= \left(\frac{496}{17} \times \frac{17}{1000} \times 100\right)\% = 49.6\%.$

EXERCISE 11A

(OBJECTIVE TYPE QUESTIONS)

Directions : ***Mark (✓) against the correct answer :***

1. I gain 70 paise on Rs. 70. My gain percent is :

(a) 0.1% (b) 1% (c) 7% (d) 10%

2. In terms of percentage profit, which is the best transaction ? **(C.B.I. 2003)**

	C.P. (in Rs.)	Profit (in Rs.)
(a)	36	17
(b)	50	24
(c)	40	19
(d)	60	29

3. If books bought at prices ranging from Rs. 200 to Rs. 350 are sold at prices ranging from Rs. 300 to Rs. 425, what is the greatest possible profit that might be made in selling eight books ?
(a) Rs. 400 (b) Rs. 600
(c) Cannot be determined (d) None of these

4. A shopkeeper sold an article for Rs. 2090.42. Approximately, what will be the percentage profit if he sold that article for Rs. 2602.58 ?
(a) 15% (b) 20% (c) 25% (d) 30%

5. Alfred buys an old scooter for Rs. 4700 and spends Rs. 800 on its repairs. If he sells the scooter for Rs. 5800, his gain percent is : **(R.R.B. 2003)**
(a) $4\frac{4}{7}\%$ (b) $5\frac{5}{11}\%$ (c) 10% (d) 12%

6. A shopkeeper purchased 70 kg of potatoes for Rs. 420 and sold the whole lot at the rate of Rs. 6.50 per kg. What will be his gain percent ? **(S.S.C. 2003)**
(a) $4\frac{1}{6}\%$ (b) $6\frac{1}{4}\%$ (c) $8\frac{1}{3}\%$ (d) 20%

7. Sam purchased 20 dozens of toys at the rate of Rs. 375 per dozen. He sold each one of them at the rate of Rs. 33. What was his percentage profit ? **(Bank P.O. 2000)**
(a) 3.5 (b) 4.5 (c) 5.6 (d) 6.5 (e) None of these

8. 100 oranges are bought at the rate of Rs. 350 and sold at the rate of Rs. 48 per dozen. The percentage of profit or loss is : **(S.S.C. 2003)**
(a) $14\frac{2}{7}\%$ gain (b) 15% gain (c) $14\frac{2}{7}\%$ loss (d) 15% loss

9. A man buys a cycle for Rs. 1400 and sells it at a loss of 15%. What is the selling price of the cycle ? **(S.S.C. 2002)**
(a) Rs. 1090 (b) Rs. 1160 (c) Rs. 1190 (d) Rs. 1202

10. A sells an article which costs him Rs. 400 to B at a profit of 20%. B then sells it to C, making a profit of 10% on the price he paid to A. How much does C pay B ?
(a) Rs. 472 (b) Rs. 476 (c) Rs. 528 (d) Rs. 532

11. Peter purchased a machine for Rs. 80,000 and spent Rs. 5000 on repair and Rs. 1000 on transport and sold it with 25% profit. At what price did he sell the machine ?
(a) Rs. 1,05,100 (b) Rs. 1,06,250 (c) Rs. 1,07,500
(d) Rs. 1,17,500 (e) None of these **(Bank P.O. 1998)**

12. By selling an article for Rs. 100, a man gains Rs. 15. Then, his gain% is :
(a) 15% (b) $12\frac{2}{3}\%$ (c) $17\frac{11}{17}\%$ (d) $17\frac{1}{4}\%$

13. When a commodity is sold for Rs. 34.80, there is a loss of 2%. What is the cost price of the commodity ?
(a) Rs. 26.10 (b) Rs. 43 (c) Rs. 43.20 (d) Rs. 46.40

14. A shopkeeper expects a gain of $22\frac{1}{2}\%$ on his cost price. If in a week, his sale was of Rs. 392, what was his profit ? **(Bank P.O. 2003)**
(a) Rs. 18.20 (b) Rs. 70 (c) Rs. 72 (d) Rs. 88.25

15. The sale price of an article including the sales tax is Rs. 616. The rate of sales tax is 10%. If the shopkeeper has made a profit of 12%, then the cost price of the article is :
(a) Rs. 500 (b) Rs. 515 (c) Rs. 550 (d) Rs. 600

16. Saransh purchased 120 reams of paper at Rs. 80 per ream. He spent Rs. 280 on transportation, paid octroi at the rate of 40 paise per ream and paid Rs. 72 to the coolie. If he wants to have a gain of 8%, what must be the selling price per ream ?

(*a*) Rs. 86 (*b*) Rs. 87.48 (*c*) Rs. 89 (*d*) Rs. 90

17. A person bought 20 litres of milk at the rate of Rs. 8 per litre. He got it churned after spending Rs. 10 and 5 kg of cream and 20 litres of toned milk were obtained. If he sold the cream at Rs. 30 per kg and toned milk at Rs. 4 per litre, his profit in the transaction is :

(*a*) 25% (*b*) 35.3% (*c*) 37.5% (*d*) 42.5%

18. Jacob bought a scooter for a certain sum of money. He spent 10% of the cost on repairs and sold the scooter for a profit of Rs. 1100. How much did he spend on repairs if he made a profit of 20% ? **(Assistant Grade, 1997)**

(*a*) Rs. 400 (*b*) Rs. 440 (*c*) Rs. 500 (*d*) Rs. 550

19. A manufacturer undertakes to supply 2000 pieces of a particular component at Rs. 25 per piece. According to his estimates, even if 5% fail to pass the quality tests, then he will make a profit of 25%. However, as it turned out, 50% of the components were rejected. What is the loss to the manufacturer ? **(M.A.T. 2003)**

(*a*) Rs. 12,000 (*b*) Rs. 13,000 (*c*) Rs. 14,000 (*d*) Rs. 15,000

20. A trader buys a chair for Rs. 600 and sells it for Rs. 765 at a credit of 4 months. Reckoning money worth 6% p.a., his gain percent is :

(*a*) 20% (*b*) $22\frac{1}{2}\%$ (*c*) 25% (*d*) $27\frac{1}{2}\%$

21. When a plot is sold for Rs. 18,700, the owner loses 15%. At what price must the plot be sold in order to gain 15% ? **(A.A.O. Exam, 2003)**

(*a*) Rs. 21,000 (*b*) Rs. 22,500 (*c*) Rs. 25,300 (*d*) Rs. 25,800

22. A fruitseller sells mangoes at the rate of Rs. 9 per kg and thereby loses 20%. At what price per kg, he should have sold them to make a profit of 5% ? **(R.R.B. 2002)**

(*a*) Rs. 11.81 (*b*) Rs. 12 (*c*) Rs. 12.25 (*d*) Rs. 12.31

23. A property dealer sells a house for Rs. 6,30,000 and in the bargain makes a profit of 5%. Had he sold it for Rs. 5,00,000, then what percentage of loss or gain he would have made ? **(Hotel Management, 2001)**

(*a*) $2\frac{1}{4}\%$ gain (*b*) 10% loss (*c*) $12\frac{1}{2}\%$ loss (*d*) $16\frac{2}{3}\%$ loss

24. A shopkeeper sells one transistor for Rs. 840 at a gain of 20% and another for Rs. 960 at a loss of 4%. His total gain or loss percent is : **(Hotel Management, 1999)**

(*a*) $5\frac{15}{17}\%$ loss (*b*) $5\frac{15}{17}\%$ gain (*c*) $6\frac{2}{3}\%$ gain (*d*) None of these

25. If selling price of an article is $\frac{4}{3}$ of its cost price, the profit in the transaction is :

(*a*) $16\frac{2}{3}\%$ (*b*) $20\frac{1}{2}\%$ (*c*) $25\frac{1}{2}\%$ (*d*) $33\frac{1}{3}\%$

26. The ratio of the cost price and the selling price is 4 : 5. The profit percent is :

(*a*) 10% (*b*) 20% (*c*) 25% (*d*) 30%

(Hotel Management, 2003)

27. The ratio between the sale price and the cost price of an article is 7 : 5. What is the ratio between the profit and the cost price of that article ? **(Bank P.O. 2000)**

(*a*) 2 : 7 (*b*) 5 : 2 (*c*) 7 : 2

(*d*) Data inadequate (*e*) None of these

28. A man gains 20% by selling an article for a certain price. If he sells it at double the price, the percentage of profit will be : (S.S.C. 2004)
(a) 40 (b) 100 (c) 120 (d) 140

29. If selling price is doubled, the profit triples. Find the profit percent :(M.A.T. 2001)
(a) $66\frac{2}{3}$ (b) 100 (c) $105\frac{1}{3}$ (d) 120

30. At what profit percent must an article be sold so that by selling at half that price, there may be a loss of 30% ?
(a) 25% (b) 36% (c) 40% (d) 42%

31. The C.P. of an article is 40% of the S.P. The percent that the S.P. is of C.P. is :
(a) 250 (b) 240 (c) 60 (d) 40

32. By selling a pen for Rs. 15, a man loses one-sixteenth of what it costs him. The cost price of the pen is :
(a) Rs. 16 (b) Rs. 18 (c) Rs. 20 (d) Rs. 21

33. By selling an article, Michael earned a profit equal to one-fourth of the price he bought it. If he sold it for Rs. 375, what was the cost price ?
(a) Rs. 281.75 (b) Rs. 300 (c) Rs. 312.50 (d) Rs. 350

34. 10% loss on selling price is what percent loss on the cost price ?
(a) $9\frac{1}{11}\%$ (b) $9\frac{2}{11}\%$ (c) 10% (d) 11%

35. If loss is $\frac{1}{3}$ of S.P., the loss percentage is :
(a) $16\frac{2}{3}\%$ (b) 20% (c) 25% (d) $33\frac{1}{3}\%$

36. In a certain store, the profit is 320% of the cost. If the cost increases by 25% but the selling price remains constant, approximately what percentage of the selling price is the profit ? (M.A.T. 1998)
(a) 30% (b) 70% (c) 100% (d) 250%

37. The profit earned by selling an article for Rs. 832 is equal to the loss incurred when the same article is sold for Rs. 448. What should be the sale price for making 50% profit ? (Bank P.O. 2000)
(a) Rs. 920 (b) Rs. 960 (c) Rs. 1060 (d) Rs. 1200 (e) None of these

38. The profit earned by selling an article for Rs. 900 is double the loss incurred when the same article is sold for Rs. 450. At what price should the article be sold to make 25% profit ?
(a) Rs. 600 (b) Rs. 750 (c) Rs. 800 (d) Data inadequate

39. The percentage profit earned by selling an article for Rs. 1920 is equal to the percentage loss incurred by selling the same article for Rs. 1280. At what price should the article be sold to make 25% profit ? (SIDBI, 2000)
(a) Rs. 2000 (b) Rs. 2200 (c) Rs. 2400
(d) Data inadequate (e) None of these

40. Profit earned by selling an article for Rs. 1060 is 20% more than the loss incurred by selling the article for Rs. 950. At what price should the article be sold to earn 20% profit ?
(a) Rs. 980 (b) Rs. 1080 (c) Rs. 1800 (d) None of these

41. If the cost price of 12 pens is equal to the selling price of 8 pens, the gain percent is :
(a) 25% (b) $33\frac{1}{3}\%$ (c) 50% (d) $66\frac{2}{3}\%$
(S.S.C. 2004)

42. The cost price of 19 articles is equal to the selling price of 16 articles. Gain percent is

(a) $3\frac{9}{17}\%$ (b) $15\frac{15}{19}\%$ (c) $18\frac{3}{4}\%$ (d) 20%

43. If the selling price of 50 articles is equal to the cost price of 40 articles, then the loss or gain percent is : **(Hotel Management, 2003)**

(a) 20% loss (b) 20% gain (c) 25% loss (d) 25% gain

44. If by selling 110 mangoes, the C.P. of 120 mangoes is realised, the gain percent is :

(a) $9\frac{1}{11}\%$ (b) $9\frac{1}{9}\%$ (c) $10\frac{10}{11}\%$ (d) $11\frac{1}{9}\%$

45. The cost price of 20 articles is the same as the selling price of x articles. If the profit is 25%, then the value of x is : **(M.A.T. 2004)**

(a) 15 (b) 16 (c) 18 (d) 25

46. On an order of 5 dozen boxes of a consumer product, a retailer receives an extra dozen free. This is equivalent to allowing him a discount of : **(C.B.I. 1997)**

(a) 15% (b) $16\frac{1}{6}\%$ (c) $16\frac{2}{3}\%$ (d) 20%

47. A man sold 18 cots for Rs. 16,800, gaining thereby the cost price of 3 cots. The cost price of a cot is : **(S.S.C. 2000)**

(a) Rs. 650 (b) Rs. 700 (c) Rs. 750 (d) Rs. 800

48. If on selling 12 notebooks, a seller makes a profit equal to the selling price of 4 notebooks, what is his percent profit ? **(Bank P.O. 2000)**

(a) $16\frac{2}{3}$ (b) 25 (c) 50

(d) Data inadequate (e) None of these

49. On selling 17 balls at Rs. 720, there is a loss equal to the cost price of 5 balls. The cost price of a ball is : **(S.S.C. 2004)**

(a) Rs. 45 (b) Rs. 50 (c) Rs. 55 (d) Rs. 60

50. A vendor loses the selling price of 4 oranges on selling 36 oranges. His loss percent is :

(a) 10% (b) $11\frac{1}{9}\%$ (c) $12\frac{1}{2}\%$ (d) None of these

51. A man buys 2 dozen bananas at Rs. 16 per dozen. After selling 18 bananas at the rate of Rs. 12 per dozen, the shopkeeper reduced the rate to Rs. 4 per dozen. The percent loss is : **(Section Officers', 2003)**

(a) 25.2% (b) 32.4% (c) 36.5% (d) 37.5%

52. A man bought apples at the rate of 8 for Rs. 34 and sold them at the rate of 12 for Rs. 57. How many apples should be sold to earn a net profit of Rs. 45 ? **(S.S.C. 2003)**

(a) 90 (b) 100 (c) 135 (d) 150

53. Oranges are bought at the rate of 10 for Rs. 25 and sold at the rate of 9 for Rs. 25. The profit is :

(a) $9\frac{1}{11}\%$ (b) 10% (c) $11\frac{1}{9}\%$ (d) $12\frac{1}{2}\%$

54. Some articles were bought at 6 for Rs. 5 and sold at 5 for Rs. 6. Gain percent is :

(a) 30% (b) $33\frac{1}{3}\%$ (c) 35% (d) 44%

(S.S.C. 2004)

55. A man bought some fruits at the rate of 16 for Rs. 24 and sold them at the rate of 8 for Rs. 18. What is the profit percent ? **(Bank P.O. 2003)**

(a) 25% (b) 40% (c) 50% (d) 60% (e) None of these

56. A man purchased a box full of pencils at the rate of 7 for Rs. 9 and sold all of them at the rate of 8 for Rs. 11. In this transaction, he gained Rs. 10. How many pencils did the box contain ? **(C.B.I. 1997)**

(a) 100 (b) 112 (c) 114 (d) 115

57. A man bought a number of clips at 3 for a rupee and an equal number at 2 for a rupee. At what price per dozen should he sell them to make a profit of 20% ?

(a) Rs. 4 (b) Rs. 5 (c) Rs. 6 (d) Rs. 7

58. A man buys eggs at 2 for Re. 1 and an equal number at 3 for Rs. 2 and sells the whole at 5 for Rs. 3. His gain or loss percent is :

(a) $2\frac{2}{7}$% loss (b) $3\frac{6}{7}$% gain (c) $3\frac{2}{7}$% loss (d) $2\frac{6}{7}$% gain

59. A man bought some oranges at Rs. 10 per dozen and bought the same number of oranges at Rs. 8 per dozen. He sold these oranges at Rs. 11 per dozen and gained Rs. 120. The total number of oranges bought by him was :

(a) 30 dozens (b) 40 dozens (c) 50 dozens (d) 60 dozens

60. A vendor bought toffees at 6 for a rupee. How many for a rupee must he sell to gain 20% ? **(C.B.I. 1998)**

(a) 3 (b) 4 (c) 5 (d) 6

61. By selling 12 toffees for a rupee, a man loses 20%. How many for a rupee should he sell to get a gain of 20% ? **(R.R.B. 2003)**

(a) 5 (b) 8 (c) 10 (d) 15

62. By selling 45 lemons for Rs. 40, a man loses 20%. How many should he sell for Rs. 24 to gain 20% in the transaction ?

(a) 16 (b) 18 (c) 20 (d) 22

63. A trader mixes 26 kg of rice at Rs. 20 per kg with 30 kg of rice of other variety at Rs. 36 per kg and sells the mixture at Rs. 30 per kg. His profit percent is :

(a) No profit, no loss (b) 5% (c) 8% (d) 10% (e) None of these **(Bank P.O. 2003)**

64. Arun purchased 30 kg of wheat at the rate of Rs. 11.50 per kg and 20 kg of wheat at the rate of Rs. 14.25 per kg. He mixed the two and sold the mixture. Approximately what price per kg should he sell the mixture to make 30% profit ? **(Bank P.O. 1999)**

(a) Rs. 14.80 (b) Rs. 15.40 (c) Rs. 15.60 (d) Rs. 16.30 (e) Rs. 18.20

65. Padam purchased 30 kg of rice at the rate of Rs. 17.50 per kg and another 30 kg rice at a certain rate. He mixed the two and sold the entire quantity at the rate of Rs. 18.60 per kg and made 20% overall profit. At what price per kg did he purchase the lot of another 30 kg rice ? **(Bank P.O. 2000)**

(a) Rs. 12.50 (b) Rs. 13.50 (c) Rs. 14.50 (d) Rs. 15.50 (e) None of these

66. A trader mixes three varieties of groundnuts costing Rs. 50, Rs. 20 and Rs. 30 per kg in the ratio 2 : 4 : 3 in terms of weight, and sells the mixture at Rs. 33 per kg. What percentage of profit does he make ? **(Hotel Management, 1998)**

(a) 8% (b) 9% (c) 10% (d) None of these

67. A dairyman pays Rs. 6.40 per litre of milk. He adds water and sells the mixture at Rs. 8 per litre, thereby making 37.5% profit. The proportion of water to milk received by the customers is : **(M.A.T. 2003)**

(a) 1 : 10 (b) 1 : 12 (c) 1 : 15 (d) 1 : 20

68. By mixing two brands of tea and selling the mixture at the rate of Rs. 177 per kg, a shopkeeper makes a profit of 18%. If to every 2 kg of one brand costing Rs. 200 per kg, 3 kg of the other brand is added, then how much per kg does the other brand cost ?

(*a*) Rs. 110 (*b*) Rs. 120 (*c*) Rs. 140 (*d*) None of these

(Hotel Management, 1999)

69. The manufacturer of a certain item can sell all he can produce at the selling price of Rs. 60 each. It costs him Rs. 40 in materials and labour to produce each item and he has overhead expenses of Rs. 3000 per week in order to operate the plant. The number of units he should produce and sell in order to make a profit of at least Rs. 1000 per week, is :

(*a*) 200 (*b*) 250 (*c*) 300 (*d*) 400

70. A dishonest dealer uses a scale of 90 cm instead of a metre scale and claims to sell at cost price. His profit is :

(N.I.F.T. 2000)

(*a*) 9% (*b*) 10% (*c*) 12% (*d*) None of these

71. A shopkeeper professes to sell his goods at cost price but uses a weight of 800 gm instead of kilogram weight. Thus, he makes a profit of :

(C.B.I. 1997)

(*a*) 20% (*b*) $16\frac{2}{3}\%$ (*c*) 25% (*d*) None of these

72. A dishonest dealer professes to sell his goods at cost price. But he uses a false weight and thus gains $6\frac{18}{47}\%$. For a kg, he uses a weight of :

(A.A.O. Exam, 2003)

(*a*) 940 gms (*b*) 947 gms (*c*) 953 gms (*d*) 960 gms

73. A shopkeeper cheats to the extent of 10% while buying as well as selling, by using false weights. His total gain is :

(Bank P.O. 2003)

(*a*) 10% (*b*) 11% (*c*) 20% (*d*) 21% (*e*) $22\frac{2}{9}\%$

74. A grocer sells rice at a profit of 10% and uses weights which are 20% less than the market weight. The total gain earned by him will be :

(*a*) 30% (*b*) 35% (*c*) 37.5% (*d*) None of these

75. A fair price shopkeeper takes 10% profit on his goods. He lost 20% goods during theft. His loss percent is :

(S.S.C. 2000)

(*a*) 8 (*b*) 10 (*c*) 11 (*d*) 12

76. A sells a bicycle to B at a profit of 20%. B sells it to C at a profit of 25%. If C pays Rs. 225 for it, the cost price of the bicycle for A is :

(B.S.F. 2001)

(*a*) Rs. 110 (*b*) Rs. 120 (*c*) Rs. 125 (*d*) Rs. 150

77. A bought a radio set and spent Rs. 110 on its repairs. He then sold it to B at 20% profit, B sold it to C at a loss of 10% and C sold it for Rs. 1188 at a profit of 10%. What is the amount for which A bought the radio set ?

(*a*) Rs. 850 (*b*) Rs. 890 (*c*) Rs. 930 (*d*) Rs. 950

78. A house worth Rs. 1,50,000 is sold by X to Y at 5% profit. Y sells the house back to X at 2% loss. Then, in the entire transaction :

(*a*) X loses Rs. 1350 (*b*) X gains Rs. 3150

(*c*) X loses Rs. 4350 (*d*) X gains Rs. 4350

79. A manufacturer sells a pair of glasses to a wholesale dealer at a profit of 18%. The wholesaler sells the same to a retailer at a profit of 20%. The retailer in turn sells them to a customer for Rs. 30.09, thereby earning a profit of 25%. The cost price for the manufacturer is :

(*a*) Rs. 15 (*b*) Rs. 16 (*c*) Rs. 17 (*d*) Rs. 18

80. An article was sold for Rs. 144. If the percentage of profit was numerically equal to the cost price, the cost of the article was :

(*a*) Rs. 72 (*b*) Rs. 80 (*c*) Rs. 90 (*d*) Rs. 100

81. Rahul purchased a scooter at $\frac{13}{15}$th of its selling price and sold it at 12% more than its selling price. His gain is :

(*a*) 20% (*b*) $29\frac{3}{13}$% (*c*) 30% (*d*) $38\frac{1}{13}$%

82. A man buys an article for 10% less than its value and sells it for 10% more than its value. His gain or loss percent is : **(S.S.C. 1999)**

(*a*) no profit, no loss (*b*) 20% profit
(*c*) less than 20% profit (*d*) more than 20% profit

83. Samant bought a microwave oven and paid 10% less than the original price. He sold it with 30% profit on the price he had paid. What percentage of profit did Samant earn on the original price ? **(Bank P.O. 2002)**

(*a*) 17% (*b*) 20% (*c*) 27% (*d*) 32% (*e*) None of these

84. If 5% more is gained by selling an article for Rs. 350 than by selling it for Rs. 340, the cost of the article is : **(C.B.I. 1997)**

(*a*) Rs. 50 (*b*) Rs. 160 (*c*) Rs. 200 (*d*) Rs. 225

85. If a man reduces the selling price of a fan from Rs. 400 to Rs. 380, his loss increases by 2%. The cost price of the fan is : **(R.R.B. 2001)**

(*a*) Rs. 480 (*b*) Rs. 500 (*c*) Rs. 600 (*d*) None of these

86. An article when sold at a gain of 5% yields Rs. 15 more than when sold at a loss of 5%. Its cost price would be :

(*a*) Rs. 150 (*b*) Rs. 200 (*c*) Rs. 250 (*d*) Rs. 300

87. A shopkeeper sells an article at a loss of $12\frac{1}{2}$%. Had he sold it for Rs. 51.80 more, he would have earned a profit of 6%. The cost price of the article is :

(*a*) Rs. 280 (*b*) Rs. 300 (*c*) Rs. 380 (*d*) Rs. 400

(Section Officers', 2003)

88. The difference between the cost price and sale price of an article is Rs. 240. If the profit is 20%, the selling price is :

(*a*) Rs. 1240 (*b*) Rs. 1400 (*c*) Rs. 1600 (*d*) None of these

89. A dealer sold an article at a loss of $2\frac{1}{2}$%. Had he sold it for Rs. 100 more, he would have gained $7\frac{1}{2}$%. To gain $12\frac{1}{2}$%, he should sell it for :

(*a*) Rs. 850 (*b*) Rs. 925 (*c*) Rs. 1080 (*d*) Rs. 1125

90. The cash difference between the selling prices of an article at a profit of 4% and 6% is Rs. 3. The ratio of the two selling prices is : **(C.B.I. 2003)**

(*a*) 51 : 52 (*b*) 52 : 53 (*c*) 51 : 53 (*d*) 52 : 55

91. A shopkeeper sells two watches for Rs. 308 each. On one he gets 12% profit and on the other 12% loss. His profit or loss in the entire transaction was : **(B.S.F. 2001)**

(*a*) Neither profit, nor loss (*b*) $1\frac{11}{25}$% loss

(*c*) $1\frac{11}{25}$% profit (*d*) $3\frac{2}{25}$% loss

92. A man sells two flats at the rate of Rs. 1.995 lakhs each. On one he gains 5% and on the other, he loses 5%. His gain or loss percent in the whole transaction is :

(*a*) 0.25% loss (*b*) 0.25% gain (*c*) 2.5% loss (*d*) 25% loss

93. A man sells two commodities for Rs. 4000 each, neither losing nor gaining in the deal. If he sold one commodity at a gain of 25%, the other commodity is sold at a loss of :

(a) $16\frac{2}{3}\%$ (b) $18\frac{2}{9}\%$ (c) 25% (d) None of these.

94 A house and a shop were sold for Rs. 1 lakh each. In this transaction, the house sale resulted into 20% loss whereas the shop sale resulted into 20% profit. The entire transaction resulted in :

(a) no loss, no gain (b) loss of Rs. $\frac{1}{12}$ lakh

(c) loss of Rs. $\frac{1}{18}$ lakh (d) gain of Rs. $\frac{1}{24}$ lakh

95. Ranjan purchased 120 tables at a price of Rs. 110 per table. He sold 30 tables at a profit of Rs. 12 per table and 75 tables at a profit of Rs. 14 per table. The remaining tables were sold at a loss of Rs. 7 per table. What is the average profit per table ?

(a) Rs. 10.04 (b) Rs. 10.875 (c) Rs. 12.80 (d) Rs. 12.875

96. Hemant sold 10 sarees for a total profit of Rs. 460 and 12 sarees for a total profit of Rs. 144. At what profit per saree should he sell the remaining 20 sarees so that he gets an average profit of Rs. 18 per saree ?

(a) Rs. 7.40 (b) Rs. 7.60 (c) Rs. 7.80 (d) Rs. 8

97. Sanket purchased 20 dozen notebooks at Rs. 48 per dozen. He sold 8 dozen at 10% profit and the remaining 12 dozen with 20% profit. What is his profit percentage in the transaction ?

(a) 7.68 (b) 15 (c) 16 (d) 19.2

98. A man purchased sugar worth Rs. 400. He sold $\frac{3}{4}$th at a loss of 10% and the remainder at a gain of 10%. On the whole, he gets :

(a) a loss of 5% (b) a gain of $5\frac{1}{2}\%$

(c) a loss of $5\frac{1}{19}\%$ (d) a loss of $5\frac{5}{19}\%$

99. A businessman sold $\frac{2}{3}$ of his stock at a gain of 20% and the rest at a gain of 14%. The overall percentage of gain to the businessman is :

(a) 12% (b) 17% (c) 18% (d) 20%

100. A cloth merchant sold half of his cloth at 20% profit, half of the remaining at 20% loss and the rest was sold at the cost price. In the total transaction, his gain or loss will be : **(S.S.C. 2003)**

(a) Neither loss nor gain (b) 5% loss

(c) 5% gain (d) 10% gain

101. A person purchases 90 clocks and sells 40 clocks at a gain of 10% and 50 clocks at a gain of 20%. If he sold all of them at a uniform profit of 15%, then he would have got Rs. 40 less. The cost price of each clock is : **(Hotel Management, 2003)**

(a) Rs. 50 (b) Rs. 60 (c) Rs. 80 (d) Rs. 90

102. A person earns 15% on an investment but loses 10% on another investment. If the ratio of the two investments be 3 : 5, what is the gain or loss on the two investments taken together ?

(a) $6\frac{1}{4}\%$ loss (b) $13\frac{1}{8}\%$ gain (c) $13\frac{1}{8}\%$ loss (d) None of these

103. A man bought goods worth Rs. 6000 and sold half of them at a gain of 10%. At what gain percent must he sell the remainder so as to get a gain of 25% on the whole ?

(a) 25% (b) 30% (c) 35% (d) 40%

104. A fruitseller has 24 kg of apples. He sells a part of these at a gain of 20% and the balance at a loss of 5%. If on the whole he earns a profit of 10%, the amount of apples sold at a loss is :

(*a*) 4.6 kg (*b*) 6 kg (*c*) 9.6 kg (*d*) 11.4 kg

105. Two-third of a consignment was sold at a profit of 5% and the remainder at a loss of 2%. If the total profit was Rs. 400, the value of the consignment (in Rs.) was

(*a*) 10,000 (*b*) 12,000 (*c*) 15,000 (*d*) 20,000

106. A trader purchases a watch and a wall clock for Rs. 390. He sells them making a profit of 10% on the watch and 15% on the wall clock. He earns a profit of Rs. 51.50. The difference between the original prices of the wall clock and the watch is equal to :

(*a*) Rs. 80 (*b*) Rs. 100 (*c*) Rs. 110 (*d*) Rs. 120

107. Albert buys 4 horses and 9 cows for Rs. 13,400. If he sells the horses at 10% profit and the cows at 20% profit, then he earns a total profit of Rs. 1880. The cost of a horse is : **(C.D.S. 2003)**

(*a*) Rs. 1000 (*b*) Rs. 2000 (*c*) Rs. 2500 (*d*) Rs. 3000

108. A man purchases two clocks A and B at a total cost of Rs. 650. He sells A with 20% profit and B at a loss of 25% and gets the same selling price for both the clocks. What are the purchasing prices of A and B respectively ?

(*a*) Rs. 225, Rs. 425 (*b*) Rs. 250, Rs. 400
(*c*) Rs. 275, Rs. 375 (*d*) Rs. 300, Rs. 350

109. The C.P. of two watches taken together is Rs. 840. If by selling one at a profit of 16% and the other at a loss of 12%, there is no loss or gain in the whole transaction, then the C.P. of the two watches are respectively :

(*a*) Rs. 360, Rs. 480 (*b*) Rs. 480, Rs. 360
(*c*) Rs. 380, Rs. 460 (*d*) Rs. 400, Rs. 440

110. On selling a chair at 7% loss and a table at 17% gain, a man gains Rs. 296. If he sells the chair at 7% gain and the table at 12% gain, then he gains Rs. 400. The actual price of the table is :

(*a*) Rs. 1600 (*b*) Rs. 1800 (*c*) Rs. 2200 (*d*) Rs. 2400

111. A shopkeeper offers 2.5% discount on cash purchases. What cash amount would Rohan pay for a cycle, the marked price of which is Rs. 650 ? **(IGNOU, 2003)**

(*a*) Rs. 633.25 (*b*) Rs. 633.75 (*c*) Rs. 634 (*d*) Rs. 635

112. If a company sells a car with a marked price of Rs. 2,72,000 and gives a discount of 4% on Rs. 2,00,000 and 2.5% on the remaining amount of Rs. 72,000, then the actual price charged by the company for the car is : **(S.S.C. 2003)**

(*a*) Rs. 2,50,000 (*b*) Rs. 2,55,000 (*c*) Rs. 2,60,100 (*d*) Rs. 2,62,200

113. Garima purchased a briefcase with an additional 10% discount on the reduced price after deducting 20% on the labelled price. If the labelled price was Rs. 1400, at what price did she purchase the briefcase ? **(Bank P.O. 2002)**

(*a*) Rs. 980 (*b*) Rs. 1008 (*c*) Rs. 1056 (*d*) Rs. 1120 (*e*) None of these

114. A bag marked at Rs. 80 is sold for Rs. 68. The rate of discount is :

(*a*) 12% (*b*) 15% (*c*) $17\frac{11}{17}\%$ (*d*) 20%

115. A pair of articles was bought for Rs. 37.40 at a discount of 15%. What must be the marked price of each of the articles ? **(A.A.O. Exam, 2003)**

(*a*) Rs. 11 (*b*) Rs. 22 (*c*) Rs. 33 (*d*) Rs. 44

116. A shopkeeper gives 12% additional discount on the discounted price, after giving an initial discount of 20% on the labelled price of a radio. If the final sale price of the radio is Rs. 704, then what is its labelled price ? **(R.R.B. 2002)**

(*a*) Rs. 844.80 (*b*) Rs. 929.28 (*c*) Rs. 1000 (*d*) Rs. 1044.80

117. A fan is listed at Rs. 1500 and a discount of 20% is offered on the list price. What additional discount must be offered to the customer to bring the net price to Rs. 1104 ?
(*a*) 8% (*b*) 10% (*c*) 12% (*d*) 15%
(S.S.C. 2002)

118. A discount of 15% on one article is the same as a discount of 20% on another article. The costs of the two articles can be : **(S.S.C. 1999)**
(*a*) Rs. 40, Rs. 20 (*b*) Rs. 60, Rs. 40 (*c*) Rs. 80, Rs. 60 (*d*) Rs. 60, Rs. 40

119. If the S.P. of Rs. 24 results in a 20% discount on list price, what S.P. would result in a 30% discount on list price ?
(*a*) Rs. 18 (*b*) Rs. 20 (*c*) Rs. 21 (*d*) Rs. 27

120. An article was sold for Rs. y after giving a discount of x%. Then, its list price is :
(*a*) $\frac{100y}{100-x}$ (*b*) $\frac{100y}{1-x}$ (*c*) $\frac{100y}{1-(x/100)}$ (*d*) None of these

121. Jatin bought a refrigerator with 20% discount on the labelled price. Had he bought it with 25% discount, he would have saved Rs. 500. At what price did he buy the refrigerator ?
(*a*) Rs. 5000 (*b*) Rs. 10,000 (*c*) Rs. 12,500 (*d*) Rs. 15,000

122. A manufacturer offers a 20% rebate on the marked price of a product. The retailer offers another 30% rebate on the reduced price. The two reductions are equivalent to a single reduction of :
(*a*) 40% (*b*) 44% (*c*) 46% (*d*) 50%

123. Successive discounts of 10%, 12% and 15% amount to a single discount of :
(*a*) 32.68% (*b*) 35.28% (*c*) 36.68% (*d*) None of these
(R.R.B. 2003)

124. List price of an article at a showroom is Rs. 2000 and it is being sold at successive discounts of 20% and 10%. Its net selling price will be : **(S.S.C. 2004)**
(*a*) Rs. 1400 (*b*) Rs. 1440 (*c*) Rs. 1520 (*d*) Rs. 1700

125. Find the selling price of an article if a shopkeeper allows two successive discounts of 5% each on the marked price of Rs. 80 **(C.B.I. 2003)**
(*a*) Rs. 70.10 (*b*) Rs. 70.20 (*c*) Rs. 72 (*d*) Rs. 72.20

126. The price of a VCR is marked at Rs. 12,000. If successive discounts of 15%, 10% and 5% be allowed, then at what price does a customer buy it ?
(*a*) Rs. 8400 (*b*) Rs. 8721 (*c*) Rs. 8856 (*d*) None of these
(Hotel Management, 2002)

127. After successive discounts of 12% and 5% an article was sold for Rs. 209. What was the original price of the article ?
(*a*) Rs. 226 (*b*) Rs. 250 (*c*) Rs. 252 (*d*) Rs. 269

128. Applied to a bill for Rs. 1,00,000, the difference between a discount of 40% and two successive discounts of 36% and 4% is : **(Section Officers', 2003)**
(*a*) Nil (*b*) Rs. 1440 (*c*) Rs. 2500 (*d*) Rs. 1960

129. The difference between a discount of 35% and two successive discounts of 20% on a certain bill was Rs. 22. Find the amount of the bill. **(Bank P.O. 1999)**
(*a*) Rs. 200 (*b*) Rs. 1100 (*c*) Rs. 2200
(*d*) Data inadequate (*e*) None of these

130. Two shopkeepers announce the same price of Rs. 700 for a sewing machine. The first offers successive discounts of 30% and 6% while the second offers successive discounts of 20% and 16%. The shopkeeper that offers better discount, charges .... less than the other shopkeeper.
(*a*) Rs. 9.80 (*b*) Rs. 16.80 (*c*) Rs. 22.40 (*d*) Rs. 36.40

131. The marked price of a watch was Rs. 720. A man bought the same for Rs. 550.80 after getting two successive discounts, the first being 10%. What was the second discount rate ? **(S.S.C. 2000)**

(*a*) 12% (*b*) 14% (*c*) 15% (*d*) 18%

132. A shopkeeper purchased 150 identical pieces of calculators at the rate of Rs. 250 each. He spent an amount of Rs. 2500 on transport and packing. He fixed the labelled price of each calculator at Rs. 320. However, he decided to give a discount of 5% on the labelled price. What is the percentage profit earned by him ? **(Bank P.O. 1999)**

(*a*) 14% (*b*) 15% (*c*) 16% (*d*) 20% (*e*) None of these

133. A trader marked the price of his commodity so as to include a profit of 25%. He allowed discount of 16% on the marked price. His actual profit was : **(S.S.C. 2004)**

(*a*) 5% (*b*) 9% (*c*) 16% (*d*) 25%

134. A tradesman marks his goods 30% above the C.P. If he allows a discount of $6\frac{1}{4}\%$, then his gain percent is :

(*a*) $21\frac{7}{8}\%$ (*b*) 22% (*c*) $23\frac{3}{4}\%$ (*d*) None of these

135. The price of an article is raised by 30% and then two successive discounts of 10% each are allowed. Ultimately, the price of the article is : **(S.S.C. 2003)**

(*a*) decreased by 5.3% (*b*) increased by 3%
(*c*) increased by 5.3% (*d*) increased by 10%

136. A retailer buys 30 articles from a wholesaler at the price of 27. If he sells them at their marked price, the gain percent in the transaction is :

(*a*) $9\frac{1}{11}\%$ (*b*) 10% (*c*) $11\frac{1}{9}\%$ (*d*) $16\frac{2}{3}\%$

137. By selling an umbrella for Rs. 300, a shopkeeper gains 20%. During a clearance sale, the shopkeeper allows a discount of 10% on the marked price. His gain percent during the sale is : **(M.B.A. 2002)**

(*a*) 7 (*b*) 7.5 (*c*) 8 (*d*) 9

138. The cost price of an article is 64% of the marked price. Calculate the gain percent after allowing a discount of 12%. **(C.B.I. 1998)**

(*a*) 37.5% (*b*) 48% (*c*) 50.5% (*d*) 52%

139. A shopkeeper allows a discount of 10% on the marked price of an item but charges a sales tax of 8% on the discounted price. If the customer pays Rs. 680.40 as the price including the sales tax, then what is the marked price of the item ?

(*a*) Rs. 630 (*b*) Rs. 700 (*c*) Rs. 780 (*d*) None of these

140. At what percent above the cost price must a shopkeeper mark his goods so that he gains 20% even after giving a discount of 10% on the marked price ? **(S.S.C. 2004)**

(*a*) 25% (*b*) 30% (*c*) $33\frac{1}{3}\%$ (*d*) $37\frac{1}{2}\%$

141. At what price should a shopkeeper mark a radio that costs him Rs. 1200 in order that he may offer a discount of 20% on the marked price and still make a profit of 25% ?

(*a*) Rs. 1675 (*b*) Rs. 1875 (*c*) Rs. 1900 (*d*) Rs. 2025 (*e*) None of these

(Bank P.O. 1998)

142. A shopkeeper earns a profit of 12% on selling a book at 10% discount on the printed price. The ratio of the cost price to the printed price of the book is :

(*a*) 45 : 56 (*b*) 50 : 61 (*c*) 55 : 69 (*d*) 99 : 125

143. By selling an article at $\frac{2}{5}$ of the marked price, there is a loss of 25%. The ratio of the marked price and the cost price of the article is : **(S.S.C. 2003)**

(*a*) 2 : 5 (*b*) 5 : 2 (*c*) 8 : 15 (*d*) 15 : 8

144. A tradesman gives 4% discount on the marked price and gives 1 article free for buying every 15 articles and thus gains 35%. The marked price is above the cost price by :

(*a*) 20% (*b*) 39% (*c*) 40% (*d*) 50%

145. A trader marked the selling price of an article at 10% above the cost price. At the time of selling, he allows certain discount and suffers a loss of 1%. He allowed a discount of : **(S.S.C. 2003)**

(*a*) 9% (*b*) 10% (*c*) 10.5% (*d*) 11%

146. A shopkeeper fixes the marked price of an item 35% above its cost price. The percentage of discount allowed to gain 8% is : **(Assistant Grade, 1997)**

(*a*) 20% (*b*) 27% (*c*) 31% (*d*) 43%

147. A trader marked his goods at 20% above the cost price. He sold half the stock at the marked price, one quarter at a discount of 20% on the marked price and the rest at a discount of 40% on the marked price. His total gain is : **(S.S.C. 2004)**

(*a*) 2% (*b*) 4.5% (*c*) 13.5% (*d*) 15%

148. A product when sold with 10% rebate on the listed price gave a profit of Rs. 70. What was its cost price ? **(Bank P.O. 2003)**

(*a*) Rs. 200 (*b*) Rs. 350 (*c*) Rs. 700

(*d*) Cannot be determined (*e*) None of these

149. The labelled price of a cupboard is Rs. 6500. The shopkeeper sold it by giving 5% discount on the labelled price and earned a profit of 15%. What approximately is the cost price of the cupboard ? **(Bank P.O. 1999)**

(*a*) Rs. 5000 (*b*) Rs. 5350 (*c*) Rs. 5600 (*d*) Rs. 5800 (*e*) Rs. 6000

150. Kunal bought a suitcase with 15% discount on the labelled price. He sold the suitcase for Rs. 2880 with 20% profit on the labelled price. At what price did he buy the suitcase? **(S.B.I.P.O. 1997)**

(*a*) Rs. 2040 (*b*) Rs. 2400 (*c*) Rs. 2604 (*d*) Rs. 2640 (*e*) None of these

151. A shopkeeper sells a badminton racket, whose marked price is Rs. 30, at a discount of 15% and gives a shuttle cock costing Rs. 1.50 free with each racket. Even then he makes a profit of 20%. His cost price per racket is : **(S.S.C. 2004)**

(*a*) Rs. 19.75 (*b*) Rs. 20 (*c*) Rs. 21 (*d*) Rs. 21.25

152. If a commission of 10% is given on the written price of an article, the gain is 20%. If the commission is increased to 20%, the gain is :

(*a*) $6\frac{2}{3}\%$ (*b*) $7\frac{1}{4}\%$ (*c*) $12\frac{1}{2}\%$ (*d*) $13\frac{1}{3}\%$

153. A shopkeeper sold a T.V. set for Rs. 17,940 with a discount of 8% and earned a profit of 19.6%. What would have been the percentage of profit earned if no discount was offered ? **(Bank P.O. 2003)**

(*a*) 24.8% (*b*) 25% (*c*) 26.4%

(*d*) Cannot be determined (*e*) None of these

154. A shopkeeper sells 25 articles at Rs. 45 per article after giving 10% discount and earns 50% profit. If the discount is not given, the profit gained is : **(S.B.I.P.O. 2000)**

(*a*) 60% (*b*) $60\frac{2}{3}\%$ (*c*) 66% (*d*) $66\frac{2}{3}\%$ (*e*) None of these

155. A shopkeeper sold sarees at Rs. 266 each after giving 5% discount on labelled price. Had he not given the discount, he would have earned a profit of 12% on the cost price. What was the cost price of each saree ? **(S.B.I.P.O. 1999)**

(*a*) Rs. 240 (*b*) Rs. 260 (*c*) Rs. 280

(*d*) Data inadequate (*e*) None of these

156. Even after reducing the marked price of a transistor by Rs. 32, a shopkeeper makes a profit of 15%. If the cost price be Rs. 320, what percentage of profit would he have made if he had sold the transistor at the marked price ?

(*a*) 10% (*b*) 20% (*c*) 25% (*d*) None of these

157. A shopkeeper sold an article offering a discount of 5% and earned a profit of 23.5%. What would have been the percentage of profit earned if no discount was offered ?

(*a*) 24.5 (*b*) 28.5 (*c*) 30

(*d*) Data inadequate (*e*) None of these **(Bank P.O. 2002)**

158. Komal buys an article at a discount of 25%. At what percentage above the cost price should he sell it to make a profit of 25% over the original list price ?

(*a*) 25 (*b*) 30 (*c*) 40 (*d*) 66.67

159. Peter bought an item at 20% discount on its original price. He sold it with 40% increase on the price he bought it. The new sale price is by what percent more than the original price ? **(Bank P.O. 2003)**

(*a*) 7.5 (*b*) 8 (*c*) 10 (*d*) 12 (*e*) None of these

160. Tarun got 30% concession on the labelled price of an article and sold it for Rs. 8750 with 25% profit on the price he bought. What was the labelled price ?

(*a*) Rs. 10,000 (*b*) Rs. 12,000 (*c*) Rs. 16,000

(*d*) Data inadequate (*e*) None of these

ANSWERS

1. (*b*) **2.** (*d*) **3.** (*d*) **4.** (*c*) **5.** (*b*) **6.** (*c*) **7.** (*c*) **8.** (*a*) **9.** (*c*)
10. (*c*) **11.** (*c*) **12.** (*c*) **13.** (*d*) **14.** (*c*) **15.** (*a*) **16.** (*d*) **17.** (*b*) **18.** (*c*)
19. (*b*) **20.** (*c*) **21.** (*c*) **22.** (*a*) **23.** (*d*) **24.** (*b*) **25.** (*d*) **26.** (*c*) **27.** (*e*)
28. (*d*) **29.** (*b*) **30.** (*c*) **31.** (*a*) **32.** (*a*) **33.** (*b*) **34.** (*a*) **35.** (*c*) **36.** (*b*)
37. (*b*) **38.** (*b*) **39.** (*a*) **40.** (*d*) **41.** (*c*) **42.** (*c*) **43.** (*a*) **44.** (*a*) **45.** (*b*)
46. (*c*) **47.** (*d*) **48.** (*c*) **49.** (*d*) **50.** (*a*) **51.** (*d*) **52.** (*a*) **53.** (*c*) **54.** (*d*)
55. (*c*) **56.** (*b*) **57.** (*c*) **58.** (*d*) **59.** (*d*) **60.** (*c*) **61.** (*b*) **62.** (*b*) **63.** (*b*)
64. (*d*) **65.** (*b*) **66.** (*c*) **67.** (*a*) **68.** (*d*) **69.** (*a*) **70.** (*d*) **71.** (*c*) **72.** (*a*)
73. (*d*) **74.** (*c*) **75.** (*d*) **76.** (*d*) **77.** (*b*) **78.** (*b*) **79.** (*c*) **80.** (*b*) **81.** (*b*)
82. (*d*) **83.** (*a*) **84.** (*c*) **85.** (*d*) **86.** (*a*) **87.** (*a*) **88.** (*d*) **89.** (*d*) **90.** (*b*)
91. (*b*) **92.** (*a*) **93.** (*a*) **94.** (*b*) **95.** (*b*) **96.** (*b*) **97.** (*c*) **98.** (*a*) **99.** (*c*)
100. (*c*) **101.** (*c*) **102.** (*d*) **103.** (*d*) **104.** (*c*) **105.** (*c*) **106.** (*c*) **107.** (*b*) **108.** (*b*)
109. (*a*) **110.** (*d*) **111.** (*b*) **112.** (*d*) **113.** (*b*) **114.** (*b*) **115.** (*b*) **116.** (*c*) **117.** (*a*)
118. (*c*) **119.** (*c*) **120.** (*a*) **121.** (*b*) **122.** (*b*) **123.** (*a*) **124.** (*b*) **125.** (*d*) **126.** (*b*)
127. (*b*) **128.** (*b*) **129.** (*c*) **130.** (*a*) **131.** (*b*) **132.** (*a*) **133.** (*a*) **134.** (*a*) **135.** (*c*)
136. (*c*) **137.** (*c*) **138.** (*a*) **139.** (*b*) **140.** (*c*) **141.** (*b*) **142.** (*a*) **143.** (*d*) **144.** (*d*)
145. (*b*) **146.** (*a*) **147.** (*a*) **148.** (*d*) **149.** (*b*) **150.** (*a*) **151.** (*b*) **152.** (*a*) **153.** (*e*)
154. (*d*) **155.** (*e*) **156.** (*c*) **157.** (*c*) **158.** (*c*) **159.** (*d*) **160.** (*a*)

SOLUTIONS

1. Gain% $= \left(\frac{0.70}{70} \times 100\right)\% = 1\%.$

2. (*a*) Profit% $= \left(\frac{17}{36} \times 100\right)\% = 47\frac{2}{9}\%.$ (*b*) Profit% $= \left(\frac{24}{50} \times 100\right)\% = 48\%.$

(*c*) Profit% $= \left(\frac{19}{40} \times 100\right)\% = 47\frac{1}{2}\%$. (*d*) Profit% $= \left(\frac{29}{60} \times 100\right)\% = 48\frac{1}{3}\%$.

Clearly, (*d*) is the best transaction.

3. Least C.P. = Rs. (200 × 8) = Rs. 1600. Greatest S.P. = Rs. (425 × 8) = Rs. 3400.
Required profit = Rs. (3400 − 1600) = Rs. 1800.

4. Profit = Rs. (2602.58 − 2090.42) = Rs. 512.16.

$$\text{Profit\%} = \left(\frac{512.16}{2090.42} \times 100\right)\% = \left(\frac{512160}{209042} \times 10\right)\% = 24.5\% \approx 25\%.$$

5. C.P. = Rs. (4700 + 800) = Rs. 5500; S.P. = Rs. 5800.

$$\text{Gain\%} = \left(\frac{300}{5500} \times 100\right)\% = 5\frac{5}{11}\%.$$

6. C.P. of 1 kg = Rs. $\left(\frac{420}{70}\right)$ = Rs. 6. S.P. of 1 kg = Rs. 6.50.

$$\therefore \quad \text{Gain\%} = \left(\frac{0.50}{6} \times 100\right)\% = \frac{25}{3}\% = 8\frac{1}{3}\%.$$

7. C.P. of 1 toy = Rs. $\left(\frac{375}{12}\right)$ = Rs. 31.25. S.P. of 1 toy = Rs. 33.

$$\therefore \quad \text{Profit\%} = \left(\frac{1.75}{31.25} \times 100\right)\% = \frac{28}{5}\% = 5.6\%.$$

8. C.P. of 1 orange = Rs. $\left(\frac{350}{100}\right)$ = Rs. 3.50. S.P. of 1 orange = Rs. $\left(\frac{48}{12}\right)$ = Rs. 4.

$$\therefore \quad \text{Gain\%} = \left(\frac{0.50}{3.50} \times 100\right)\% = \frac{100}{7}\% = 14\frac{2}{7}\%.$$

9. S.P. = 85% of Rs. 1400 = Rs. $\left(\frac{85}{100} \times 1400\right)$ = Rs. 1190.

10. C.P. for B = 120% of Rs. 400 = Rs. $\left(\frac{120}{100} \times 400\right)$ = Rs. 480.

C.P. for C = 110% of Rs. 480 = Rs. $\left(\frac{110}{100} \times 480\right)$ = Rs. 528.

11. C.P. = Rs. (80000 + 5000 + 1000) = Rs. 86000, Profit = 25%.

∴ S.P. = 125% of Rs. 86000 = Rs. $\left(\frac{125}{100} \times 86000\right)$ = Rs. 107500.

12. S.P. = Rs. 100, gain = Rs. 15.

∴ C.P. = Rs. (100 − 15) = Rs. 85.

$$\text{Gain\%} = \left(\frac{15}{85} \times 100\right)\% = \frac{300}{17}\% = 17\frac{11}{17}\%$$

13. C.P. = Rs. $\left(\frac{100}{75} \times 34.80\right)$ = Rs. 46.40.

14. C.P. = Rs. $\left(\frac{100}{122.50} \times 392\right)$ = Rs $\left(\frac{1000}{1225} \times 392\right)$ = Rs. 320.

∴ Profit = Rs. (392 − 320) = Rs. 72.

15. 110% of S.P. = 616 $\Rightarrow$ S.P. = Rs. $\left(\frac{616 \times 100}{110}\right)$ = Rs. 560.

$\therefore$ C.P. = Rs. $\left(\frac{100}{112} \times 560\right)$ = Rs. 500.

16. Total investment = Rs. $\left(120 \times 80 + 280 + \frac{40}{100} \times 120 + 72\right)$

= Rs. (9600 + 280 + 48 + 72) = Rs. 10000.

S.P. of 120 reams = 108% of Rs. 10000 = Rs. 10800.

$\therefore$ S.P. per ream = Rs. $\left(\frac{10800}{120}\right)$ = Rs. 90.

17. Investment = Rs. (20 × 8 + 10) = Rs. 170. Receipt = Rs. (30 × 5 + 20 × 4) = Rs. 230.

$\therefore$ Gain% = $\left(\frac{60}{170} \times 100\right)$% = 35.29% ≈ 35.3%.

18. Let the C.P. be Rs. x. Then, 20% of x = 1100 $\Rightarrow$ $\frac{20}{100} \times x = 1100$ $\Rightarrow$ $x = 5500$.

C.P. = Rs. 5500, Expenditure on repairs = 10%.

Actual price = Rs. $\left(\frac{100}{110} \times 5500\right)$ = Rs. 5000.

$\therefore$ Expenditure on repairs = Rs. (5500 − 5000) = Rs. 500.

19. Total cost incurred = Rs. $\left[\frac{100}{125} \times 25 \times (95\% \text{ of } 2000)\right]$

= Rs. $\left(\frac{100}{125} \times 25 \times 1900\right)$ = Rs. 38000.

Loss to the manufacturer = Rs. [38000 − (25 × 1000)] = Rs. 13000.

20. C.P. = Rs. $\left(600 + \frac{600 \times 6 \times 4}{100 \times 12}\right)$ = Rs. 612. Gain = Rs. (765 − 612) = Rs. 153.

$\therefore$ Gain% = $\left(\frac{153}{612} \times 100\right)$% = 25%.

21. 85 : 18700 = 115 : x or $x = \left(\frac{18700 \times 115}{85}\right)$ = 25300.

Hence, S.P. = Rs. 25,300.

22. 80 : 9 = 105 : x or $x = \left(\frac{9 \times 105}{80}\right)$ = 11.81.

Hence, S.P. per kg = Rs. 11.81.

23. C.P. = Rs. $\left(\frac{100}{105} \times 630000\right)$ = Rs. 600000.

$\therefore$ Required loss% = $\left(\frac{100000}{600000} \times 100\right)\% = 16\frac{2}{3}\%$.

24. C.P. of 1st transistor = Rs. $\left(\frac{100}{120} \times 840\right)$ = Rs. 700.

C.P. of 2nd transistor = Rs. $\left(\frac{100}{96} \times 960\right)$ = Rs. 1000.

So, total C.P. = Rs. (700 + 1000) = Rs. 1700.
Total S.P. = Rs. (840 + 960) = Rs. 1800.

$\therefore$ Gain% = $\left(\frac{100}{1700} \times 100\right)\% = 5\frac{15}{17}\%$.

25. Let C.P. = Rs. x. Then, S.P. = Rs. $\frac{4x}{3}$. Gain = Rs. $\left(\frac{4x}{3} - x\right)$ = Rs. $\frac{x}{3}$.

$\therefore$ Gain% = $\left(\frac{x}{3} \times \frac{1}{x} \times 100\right)\% = 33\frac{1}{3}\%$.

26. Let C.P. = Rs. $4x$. Then, S.P. = Rs. $5x$. Gain = Rs. $(5x - 4x)$ = Rs. x.

$\therefore$ Gain% = $\left(\frac{x}{4x} \times 100\right)\% = 25\%$.

27. Let C.P. = Rs. $5x$ and S.P. = Rs. $7x$. Then, Gain = Rs. $2x$.

$\therefore$ Required ratio = $2x : 5x = 2 : 5$.

28. Let C.P. = Rs. x. Then, S.P. = Rs. (120% of x) = Rs. $\frac{6x}{5}$.

New S.P. = Rs. $\left(2 \times \frac{6x}{5}\right)$ = Rs. $\frac{12x}{5}$. Profit = Rs. $\left(\frac{12x}{5} - x\right)$ = Rs. $\frac{7x}{5}$.

$\therefore$ Profit% = $\left(\frac{7x}{5} \times \frac{1}{x} \times 100\right)\% = 140\%$.

29. Let C.P. be Rs. x and S.P. be Rs. y. Then, $3(y - x) = (2y - x) \Rightarrow y = 2x$.
Profit = Rs. $(y - x)$ = Rs. $(2x - x)$ = Rs. x.

$\therefore$ Profit% = $\left(\frac{x}{x} \times 100\right)\% = 100\%$.

30. Let S.P. = Rs x. New S.P. = Rs. $\frac{x}{2}$, Loss = 30%.

So, C.P. = Rs. $\left(\frac{100}{70} \times \frac{x}{2}\right)$ = Rs. $\frac{5x}{7}$. Profit = Rs. $\left(x - \frac{5x}{7}\right)$ = Rs. $\frac{2x}{7}$.

$\therefore$ Profit% = $\left(\frac{2x}{7} \times \frac{7}{5x} \times 100\right)\% = 40\%$.

31. C.P. = $\frac{40}{100} \times$ S.P. $\Rightarrow$ S.P. = $\frac{5}{2}$ C.P. = $\left(\frac{5}{2} \times 100\right)\%$ of C.P. = 250% of C.P.

32. Let the C.P. be Rs. x. Then, $x - 15 = \frac{x}{16} \Rightarrow x - \frac{x}{16} = 15 \Rightarrow \frac{15x}{16} = 15 \Rightarrow x = 16$.

$\therefore$ C.P. = Rs. 16.

33. S.P. = C.P. + $\frac{1}{4}$ C.P. = $\frac{5}{4}$ C.P.

$\therefore$ $\frac{5}{4}$ C.P. = 375 $\Rightarrow$ C.P. = Rs. $\left(375 \times \frac{4}{5}\right)$ = Rs. 300.

34. Let S.P. = Rs. 100. Then, Loss = Rs. 10, C.P. = Rs. (100 + 10) = Rs. 110.

$\therefore$ Loss% = $\left(\frac{10}{110} \times 100\right)\% = 9\frac{1}{11}\%$.

35. Let S.P. = Rs. x. Then, Loss = Rs. $\frac{x}{3}$. C.P. = Rs. $\left(x + \frac{x}{3}\right)$ = Rs. $\frac{4x}{3}$.

$\therefore$ Loss% = $\left(\frac{x}{3} \times \frac{3}{4x} \times 100\right)\% = 25\%$.

36. Let C.P. = Rs. 100. Then, Profit = Rs. 320, S.P. = Rs. 420.
New C.P. = 125% of Rs. 100 = Rs. 125; New S.P. = Rs. 420.
Profit = Rs. (420 − 125) = Rs. 295.

$\therefore$ Required percentage = $\left(\frac{295}{420} \times 100\right)\% = \frac{1475}{21}\% \approx 70\%$.

37. Let C.P. = Rs. x. Then, $832 - x = x - 448 \Rightarrow 2x = 1280 \Rightarrow x = 640$.

$\therefore$ Required S.P. = 150% of Rs. 640 = Rs. $\left(\frac{150}{100} \times 640\right)$ = Rs. 960.

38. Let C.P. = Rs. x. Then, $900 + x = 2(x - 450) \Rightarrow 3x = 1800 \Rightarrow x = 600$.

$\therefore$ Required S.P. = 125% of Rs. 600 = Rs. $\left(\frac{125}{100} \times 600\right)$ = Rs. 750.

39. Let C.P. be Rs. x.

Then, $\frac{1920 - x}{x} \times 100 = \frac{x - 1280}{x} \times 100 \Rightarrow 1920 - x = x - 1280$

$\Rightarrow 2x = 3200 \Rightarrow x = 1600$.

$\therefore$ Required S.P. = 125% of Rs. 1600 = Rs. $\left(\frac{125}{100} \times 1600\right)$ = Rs. 2000.

40. Let C.P. be Rs. x.

Then, $(1060 - x) = \frac{120}{100}(x - 950) \Rightarrow 106000 - 100x = 120x - 120 \times 950$

$\Rightarrow 220x = 220000 \Rightarrow x = 1000$.

$\therefore$ Desired S.P. = Rs. $\left(\frac{120}{100} \times 1000\right)$ = Rs. 1200.

41. Let C.P. of each pen be Re. 1. Then, C.P. of 8 pens = Rs. 8; S.P. of 8 pens = Rs. 12.

$\therefore$ Gain% = $\left(\frac{4}{8} \times 100\right)\% = 50\%$.

42. Let C.P. of each article be Re. 1.
Then, C.P. of 16 articles = Rs. 16; S.P. of 16 articles = Rs. 19.

$\therefore$ Gain% = $\left(\frac{3}{16} \times 100\right)\% = 18\frac{3}{4}\%$.

43. Let C.P. of each article be Re. 1.
Then, C.P. of 50 articles = Rs. 50; S.P. of 50 articles = Rs. 40.

$\therefore$ Loss% = $\left(\frac{10}{50} \times 100\right)\% = 20\%$

44. Let C.P. of each mango be Re. 1.
C.P. of 110 mangoes = Rs. 110; S.P. of 110 mangoes = Rs. 120.

$\therefore$ Gain% = $\left(\frac{10}{110} \times 100\right)\% = 9\frac{1}{11}\%$.

45. Let C.P. of each article be Re. 1. C.P. of x articles = Rs. x; S.P. of x articles = Rs. 20.
Profit = Rs. $(20 - x)$.

$\therefore \frac{20 - x}{x} \times 100 = 25 \Rightarrow 2000 - 100x = 25x \Rightarrow 125x = 2000 \Rightarrow x = 16$.

46. Clearly, the retailer gets 1 dozen out of 6 dozens free.

$\therefore$ Equivalent discount = $\left(\frac{1}{6} \times 100\right)\% = 16\frac{2}{3}\%$.

47. (S.P. of 18 cots) – (C.P. of 18 cots) = (C.P. of 3 cots)

$\Rightarrow$ C.P. of 21 cots = S.P. of 18 cots = Rs. 16800

$\Rightarrow$ C.P. of 1 cot = Rs. $\left(\frac{16800}{21}\right)$ = Rs. 800.

48. (S.P. of 12 notebooks) – (C.P. of 12 notebooks) = (S.P. of 4 notebooks)

$\Rightarrow$ C.P. of 12 notebooks = S.P. of 8 notebooks.

Let C.P. of each notebook be Re. 1.

Then, C.P. of 8 notebooks = Rs. 8; S.P. of 8 notebooks = Rs. 12.

$\therefore$ Gain% = $\left(\frac{4}{8} \times 100\right)\%$ = 50%.

49. (C.P. of 17 balls) – (S.P. of 17 balls) = (C.P. of 5 balls)

$\Rightarrow$ C.P. of 12 balls = S.P. of 17 balls = Rs. 720

$\Rightarrow$ C.P. of 1 ball = Rs. $\left(\frac{720}{12}\right)$ = Rs. 60.

50. (C.P. of 36 mangoes) – (S.P. of 36 mangoes) = Loss = (S.P. of 4 mangoes)

$\Rightarrow$ S.P. of 40 mangoes = C.P. of 36 mangoes.

Let C.P. of each mango be Re. 1.

C.P. of 40 mangoes = Rs. 40; S.P. of 40 mangoes = Rs. 36.

$\therefore$ Loss% = $\left(\frac{4}{40} \times 100\right)\%$ = 10%.

51. C.P. = Rs. (16 × 2) = 32. S.P. = Rs. (12 × 1.5 + 4 × 0.5) = Rs. (18 + 2) = Rs. 20.

$\therefore$ Loss% = $\left(\frac{12}{32} \times 100\right)\%$ = 37.5%.

52. C.P. of 1 apple = Rs. $\left(\frac{34}{8}\right)$ = Rs. 4.25. S.P. of 1 apple = Rs. $\left(\frac{57}{12}\right)$ = Rs. 4.75.

Profit on each apple = Re. 0.50.

$\therefore$ Number of apples required = $\left(\frac{45}{0.50}\right)$ = 90.

53. Suppose, number of oranges bought = L.C.M. of 9 and and 10 = 90.

C.P. of 90 oranges = Rs. $\left(\frac{25}{10} \times 90\right)$ = Rs. 225.

S.P. of 90 oranges = Rs. $\left(\frac{25}{9} \times 90\right)$ = Rs. 250.

$\therefore$ Profit% = $\left(\frac{25}{225} \times 100\right)\% = \frac{100}{9}\% = 11\frac{1}{9}\%$.

54. Suppose, number of articles bought = L.C.M. of 6 and 5 = 30.

C.P. of 30 articles = Rs. $\left(\frac{5}{6} \times 30\right)$ = Rs. 25. S.P. of 30 articles = Rs. $\left(\frac{6}{5} \times 30\right)$ = Rs. 36.

$\therefore$ Gain% = $\left(\frac{11}{25} \times 100\right)\%$ = 44%.

55. Suppose, number of fruits bought = L.C.M. of 16 and 8 = 16.

C.P. of 16 fruits = Rs. 24. S.P. of 16 fruits = Rs. $\left(\frac{18}{8} \times 16\right)$ = Rs. 36.

$\therefore$ Profit% = $\left(\frac{12}{24} \times 100\right)\%$ = 50%.

56. Suppose, number of pencils bought = L.C.M. of 7 and 8 = 56.

C.P. of 56 pencils = Rs. $\left(\frac{9}{7} \times 56\right)$ = Rs. 72. S.P. of 56 pencils = Rs. $\left(\frac{11}{8} \times 56\right)$ = Rs. 77.

Now, Rs. 5 are gained on 56 pencils.

So, Rs. 10 are gained on $\left(\frac{56}{5} \times 10\right)$ = 112 pencils.

57. Suppose he bought 1 dozen clips of each kind.

C.P. of 2 dozens = Rs. $\left(\frac{1}{3} \times 12 + \frac{1}{2} \times 12\right)$ = Rs. 10.

$\therefore$ S.P. of 2 dozens = 120% of Rs. 10 = Rs. $\left(\frac{120}{100} \times 10\right)$ = Rs. 12.

Hence, S.P. per dozen = Rs. 6.

58. Suppose he buys 6 eggs of each kind.

C.P. of 12 eggs = Rs. $\left(\frac{1}{2} \times 6 + \frac{2}{3} \times 6\right)$ = Rs. 7. S.P. of 12 eggs = Rs. $\left(\frac{3}{5} \times 12\right)$ = Rs. 7.20.

$\therefore$ Gain = $\left(\frac{0.20}{7} \times 100\right)\%$ = $2\frac{6}{7}\%$.

59. **C.P. of 2 dozen** oranges = Rs. (10 + 8) = Rs. 18. S.P. of 2 dozen oranges = Rs. 22.
If profit is **Rs. 4, oranges** bought = 2 dozen.

If profit is Rs. 120, oranges bought = $\left(\frac{2}{4} \times 120\right)$ dozens = 60 dozens.

60. C.P. of 6 toffees = Re. 1. S.P. of 6 toffees = 120% of Re. 1 = Rs. $\frac{6}{5}$

For Rs. $\frac{6}{5}$, toffees sold = 6. For Re. 1, toffees sold = $\left(6 \times \frac{5}{6}\right)$ = 5.

61. Let S.P. of 12 toffees be Rs. x. Then, 80 : 1 = 120 : x or $x = \left(\frac{120}{80}\right) = \frac{3}{2}$.

For Rs. $\frac{3}{2}$, toffees sold = 12. For Re. 1, toffees sold = $\left(12 \times \frac{2}{3}\right)$ = 8.

62. Let S.P. of 45 lemons be Rs. x. Then, 80 : 40 = 120 : x or $x = \left(\frac{120 \times 40}{80}\right)$ = 60.

For Rs. 60, lemons sold = 45. For Rs. 24, lemons sold = $\left(\frac{45}{60} \times 24\right)$ = 18.

63. C.P. of 56 kg rice = Rs. (26 × 20 + 30 × 36) = Rs. (520 + 1080) = Rs. 1600.
S.P. of 56 kg rice = Rs. (56 × 30) = Rs. 1680.

$\therefore$ Gain = $\left(\frac{80}{1600} \times 100\right)\%$ = 5%.

64. C.P. of 50 kg wheat = Rs. (30 × 11.50 + 20 × 14.25) = Rs. (345 + 285) = Rs. 630.

S.P. of 50 kg wheat = 130% of Rs. 630 = Rs. $\left(\frac{130}{100} \times 630\right)$ = Rs. 819.

$\therefore$ S.P. per kg = Rs. $\left(\frac{819}{50}\right)$ = Rs. 16.38 ≈ Rs. 16.30.

65. Let the required price per kg be Rs. x. Then,

C.P. of 60 kg rice = Rs. $(30 \times 17.50 + 30 \times x)$ = Rs. $(525 + 30x)$.

S.P. of 60 kg rice = Rs. (60×18.60) = Rs. 1116.

$$\therefore \quad \frac{1116 - (525 + 30x)}{525 + 30x} \times 100 = 20 \Leftrightarrow \frac{591 - 30x}{525 + 30x} = \frac{1}{5}$$

$$\Leftrightarrow 2955 - 150x = 525 + 30x \Leftrightarrow 180x = 2430 \Leftrightarrow x = \left(\frac{2430}{180}\right) = \left(\frac{27}{2}\right) = 13.50.$$

So, the C.P. of second lot is Rs. 13.50 per kg.

66. Suppose he bought 2 kg, 4 kg and 3 kg of the three varieties.

C.P. of 9 kg = Rs. $(2 \times 50 + 4 \times 20 + 3 \times 30)$ = Rs. 270.

S.P. of 9 kg = Rs. (9×33) = Rs. 297.

$$\therefore \quad \text{Profit\%} = \left(\frac{27}{270} \times 100\right)\% = 10\%.$$

67. Mean cost price = Rs. $\left(\frac{100}{137.5} \times 8\right)$ = Rs. $\frac{64}{11}$.

By the rule of alligation :

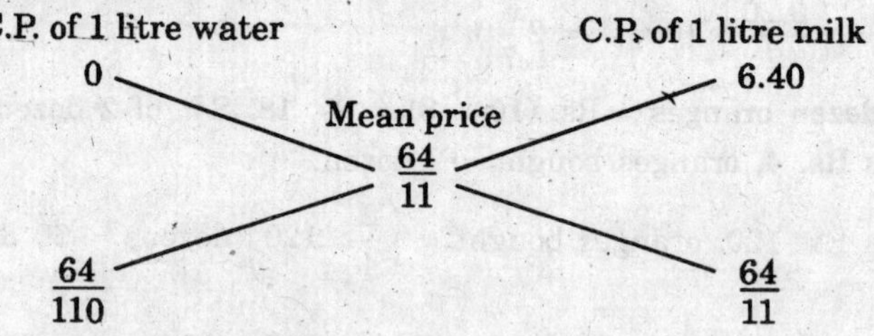

$$\therefore \quad \text{Required ratio} = \frac{64}{110} : \frac{64}{11} = 1 : 10.$$

68. Let the cost of the other brand be Rs. x per kg.

C.P. of 5 kg = Rs. $(2 \times 200 + 3 \times x)$ = Rs. $(400 + 3x)$.

S.P. of 5 kg = Rs. (5×177) = Rs. 885.

$$\therefore \quad \frac{885 - (400 + 3x)}{400 + 3x} \times 100 = 18 \Leftrightarrow \frac{485 - 3x}{400 + 3x} = \frac{9}{50}$$

$$\Leftrightarrow 24250 - 150x = 3600 + 27x \Leftrightarrow 177x = 20650 \Leftrightarrow x = \left(\frac{350}{3}\right) = 116\frac{2}{3}.$$

So, cost of the other brand = Rs. 116.66.

69. Suppose, he must produce x items. Then, C.P. = Rs. $(40x + 300)$, S.P. = Rs. $60x$.

$\therefore \quad 60x - (40x + 300) = 1000$ or $20x = 4000$ or $x = 200$.

70. $$\text{Gain\%} = \left(\frac{10}{90} \times 100\right)\% = 11\frac{1}{9}\%.$$

71. $$\text{Profit\%} = \left(\frac{200}{800} \times 100\right)\% = 25\%.$$

72. Let error = x gms. Then, $\frac{x}{1000 - x} \times 100 = 6\frac{18}{47} \Leftrightarrow \frac{100x}{1000 - x} = \frac{300}{47}$

$\Leftrightarrow 47x = 3(1000 - x) \Leftrightarrow 50x = 3000 \Leftrightarrow x = 60.$

$\therefore$ Weight used = $(1000 - 60)$ = 940 gms.

73. **Rule** : Gain% $= \dfrac{(100 + \text{common gain\%})^2}{100} - 100.$

$\therefore$ Gain% $= \left[\dfrac{(100+10)^2}{100} - 100\right]\% = \left(\dfrac{12100 - 10000}{100}\right)\% = 21\%.$

74. Let us consider a packet of rice marked 1 kg.
Its actual weight is 80% of 1000 gm = 800 gm.
Let C.P. of each gm be Re. 1. Then, C.P. of this packet = Rs. 800.

S.P. of this packet = 110% of C.P. of 1 kg = Rs. $\left(\dfrac{110}{100} \times 1000\right)$ = Rs. 1100.

$\therefore$ Gain% $= \left(\dfrac{300}{800} \times 100\right)\% = 37.5\%.$

75. Suppose he has 100 items. Let C.P. of each item be Re. 1.
Total cost = Rs. 100. Number of items left after theft = 80.
S.P. of each item = Rs. 1.10.
$\therefore$ Total sale = Rs. (1.10 × 80) = Rs. 88.

Hence, Loss% $= \left(\dfrac{12}{100} \times 100\right)\% = 12\%.$

76. 125% of 120% of A = 225 $\Rightarrow \dfrac{125}{100} \times \dfrac{120}{100} \times A = 225 \Rightarrow A = \left(225 \times \dfrac{2}{3}\right) = 150.$

77. 110% of 90% of 120% of A = 1188

$\Rightarrow \dfrac{110}{100} \times \dfrac{90}{100} \times \dfrac{120}{100} A = 1188 \Rightarrow \dfrac{1188}{1000} A = 1188 \Rightarrow A = 1000.$

$\therefore$ A purchased it for Rs. (1000 − 110) = Rs. 890.

78. Money spent by X = Rs. 150000.
Money received by X = 105% of Rs. 150000 = Rs. 157500.
C.P. to X = 98% of Rs. 157500 = Rs. 154350.
$\therefore$ X gains Rs. (157500 − 154350) = Rs. 3150.

79. Let the cost price for the manufacturer be Rs. x.
Then, 125% of 120% of 118% of x = 30.09.

$\Rightarrow \dfrac{125}{100} \times \dfrac{120}{100} \times \dfrac{118}{100} x = \dfrac{3009}{100} \Rightarrow \dfrac{177}{100} x = \dfrac{3009}{100} \Rightarrow x = \left(\dfrac{3009}{177}\right) = 17.$

80. Let C.P. = Rs. x, Profit% = x% and S.P. = Rs. 144.

$\therefore\ x = \left[\dfrac{100}{(100+x)} \times 144\right] \Rightarrow x^2 + 100x = 14400 \Rightarrow x^2 + 100x - 14400 = 0$

$\Rightarrow x^2 + 180x - 80x - 14400 = 0 \Rightarrow (x + 180)(x - 80) = 0 \Rightarrow x = 80.$

81. Let S.P. be Rs. x. Then, C.P. = Rs. $\dfrac{13}{15} x$, Receipt = 112% of Rs. x = Rs. $\dfrac{28}{25} x$.

Gain = Rs. $\left(\dfrac{28x}{25} - \dfrac{13x}{15}\right)$ = Rs. $\dfrac{19x}{75}$.

$\therefore$ Gain% $= \left(\dfrac{19x}{75} \times \dfrac{15}{13x} \times 100\right)\% = \dfrac{380}{13}\% = 29\dfrac{3}{13}\%.$

82. Let the article be worth Rs. x.

C.P. = 90% of Rs. x = Rs. $\frac{9x}{10}$; S.P. = 110% of Rs. x = Rs. $\frac{11x}{10}$.

Gain = Rs. $\left(\frac{11x}{10} - \frac{9x}{10}\right)$ = Rs. $\frac{x}{5}$.

$\therefore$ Gain% = $\left(\frac{x}{5} \times \frac{10}{9x} \times 100\right)\%$ = $22\frac{2}{9}\%$ > 20%.

83. Let original price = Rs. 100.

Then C.P. = Rs. 90, S.P. = 130% of Rs. 90 = Rs. $\left(\frac{130}{100} \times 90\right)$ = Rs. 117.

$\therefore$ Required percentage = (117 − 100)% = 17%.

84. Let C.P. be Rs. x. Then, 5% of x = (350 − 340) = 10 $\Rightarrow$ $\frac{x}{20}$ = 10 $\Rightarrow$ x = 200.

85. Let C.P. be Rs. x. Then, 2% of x = (400 − 380) = 20 $\Rightarrow$ $\frac{x}{50}$ = 20 $\Rightarrow$ x = 1000.

86. Let C.P. be Rs. x. Then, $\frac{105}{100}x - \frac{95}{100}x = 15 \Rightarrow \frac{10x}{100} = 15 \Rightarrow x = 150$.

87. Let C.P. be Rs. x. Then, (106% of x) − $\left(87\frac{1}{2}\% \text{ of } x\right)$ = 51.80

$\Rightarrow$ $18\frac{1}{2}\%$ of x = 51.80 $\Rightarrow$ $x = \left(\frac{51.80 \times 100 \times 2}{37}\right)$ = 280.

88. Let the C.P. be Rs. x.

Then, S.P. = 120% of Rs. x = Rs. $\left(x \times \frac{120}{100}\right)$ = Rs. $\frac{6x}{5}$

$\therefore$ $\frac{6x}{5} - x = 240 \Leftrightarrow x = 1200$.

$\therefore$ S.P. = Rs. $\left(\frac{6}{5} \times 1200\right)$ = Rs. 1200.

89. Let C.P. be Rs. x. Then,

$\left(107\frac{1}{2}\% \text{ of } x\right) - \left(97\frac{1}{2}\% \text{ of } x\right) = 100 \Rightarrow 10\% \text{ of } x = 100 \Rightarrow x = 1000.$

$\therefore$ Desired S.P. = $112\frac{1}{2}\%$ of Rs. 1000 = Rs. $\left(\frac{225}{2} \times \frac{1}{100} \times 1000\right)$ = Rs. 1125.

90. Let C.P. of the article be Rs. x. Then, Required ratio = $\frac{104\% \text{ of } x}{106\% \text{ of } x} = \frac{104}{106} = \frac{52}{53}$ = 52 : 53.

91. Loss% = $\left(\frac{\text{Common Loss and Gain\%}}{10}\right)^2\% = \left(\frac{12}{10}\right)^2\% = \frac{36}{25}\% = 1\frac{11}{25}\%$.

92. Loss% = $\left(\frac{5}{10}\right)^2\% = (0.5)^2\% = 0.25\%$.

93. Total S.P. = Rs. 8000 and Total C.P. = Rs. 8000.
S.P. of 1st commodity = Rs. 4000. Gain on it = 25%.

$\therefore$ C.P. of 1st commodity = Rs. $\left(\frac{100}{125} \times 4000\right)$ = Rs. 3200.

C.P. of 2nd commodity = Rs. (8000 − 3200) = Rs. 4800.
S.P. of 2nd commodity = Rs. 4000.

$\therefore$ Loss on 2nd commodity = $\left(\frac{800}{4800}\times 100\right)\% = 16\frac{2}{3}\%$.

94. Total S.P. = Rs. 2 lakh.

C.P. of house = Rs. $\left(\frac{100}{80}\times 1\right)$ lakh = Rs. $\frac{5}{4}$ lakh.

C.P. of shop = Rs. $\left(\frac{100}{120}\times 1\right)$ lakh = Rs. $\frac{5}{6}$ lakh.

Total C.P. = Rs. $\left(\frac{5}{4}+\frac{5}{6}\right)$ lakh = Rs. $\frac{25}{12}$ lakh.

$\therefore$ Loss = Rs. $\left(\frac{25}{12}-2\right)$ lakh = Rs. $\frac{1}{12}$ lakh.

95. Total C.P. = Rs. (120 × 110) = Rs. 13200.
Total S.P = Rs. [(30 × 110 + 30 × 12) + (75 × 110 + 75 × 14) + (15 × 110 − 15 × 7)]
= Rs. 14505.

Average profit = Rs. $\left(\frac{14505-13200}{120}\right)$ = Rs. $\frac{1305}{120}$ = Rs. 10.875.

96. Total profit required = Rs. (42 × 18) = Rs. 756.
Profit on 22 sarees = Rs. (460 + 144) = Rs. 604.
Profit on 20 sarees = Rs. (756 − 604) = Rs. 152.

Average profit on these sarees = Rs. $\left(\frac{152}{20}\right)$ = Rs. 7.60.

97. C.P. of 20 dozen = Rs. (48 × 20) = Rs. 960.
C.P. of 8 dozen = Rs. (48 × 8) = Rs. 384.
C.P. of 12 dozen = Rs. (960 − 384) = Rs. 576.

Total S.P. = Rs. $\left(\frac{110}{100}\times 384+\frac{120}{100}\times 576\right)$ = Rs. 1113.60.

$\therefore$ Profit% = $\left(\frac{153.60}{960}\times 100\right)\% = 16\%$.

98. C.P. of $\frac{3}{4}$th = Rs. $\left(\frac{3}{4}\times 400\right)$ = Rs. 300, C.P. of $\frac{1}{4}$th = Rs. 100.

$\therefore$ Total S.P. = (90% of Rs. 300 + 110% of Rs. 100) = Rs. 380.

Loss = $\left(\frac{20}{400}\times 100\right)\% = 5\%$.

99. Let C.P. of whole be Rs. x. C.P. of $\frac{2}{3}$rd = Rs. $\frac{2x}{3}$, C.P. of $\frac{1}{3}$rd = Rs. $\frac{x}{3}$.

Total S.P. = Rs. $\left[\left(120\% \text{ of } \frac{2x}{3}\right)+\left(114\% \text{ of } \frac{x}{3}\right)\right]$ = Rs. $\left(\frac{4x}{5}+\frac{19x}{50}\right)$ = Rs. $\frac{59x}{50}$.

Gain = Rs. $\left(\frac{59x}{50}-x\right)$ = Rs. $\frac{9x}{50}$.

$\therefore$ Gain% = $\left(\frac{9x}{50}\times\frac{1}{x}\times 100\right)\% = 18\%$.

100. Let C.P. of whole be Rs. x. C.P. of $\frac{1}{2}$ stock = Rs. $\frac{x}{2}$, C.P. of $\frac{1}{4}$ stock = Rs. $\frac{x}{4}$.

Total S.P. = Rs. $\left[\left(120\% \text{ of } \frac{x}{2}\right) + \left(80\% \text{ of } \frac{x}{4}\right) + \frac{x}{4}\right]$ = Rs. $\left(\frac{3x}{5} + \frac{x}{5} + \frac{x}{4}\right)$ = Rs. $\frac{21x}{20}$.

Gain = Rs. $\left(\frac{21x}{20} - x\right)$ = Rs. $\frac{x}{20}$.

$\therefore$ Gain% = $\left(\frac{x}{20} \times \frac{1}{x} \times 100\right)\%$ = 5%.

101. Let C.P. of each clock be Rs. x. Then, C.P. of 90 clocks = Rs. $90x$.

$\therefore$ $[(110\% \text{ of } 40x) + (120\% \text{ of } 50x)] - (115\% \text{ of } 90x) = 40$

$\Rightarrow$ $44x + 60x - 103.5x = 40 \Rightarrow 0.5x = 40 \Rightarrow x = 80$.

102. Let the investments be $3x$ and $5x$. Then, total investment = $8x$.

Total receipt = $(115\% \text{ of } 3x + 90\% \text{ of } 5x) = (3.45x + 4.5x) = 7.95x$.

$\therefore$ Loss = $\left(\frac{0.05x}{8x} \times 100\right)\%$ = 0.625%.

103. Let the required gain percent be x%.

Then, (110% of 3000) + [(100 + x)% of 3000] = 125% of 6000

$\Rightarrow$ $\left(\frac{110}{100} \times 3000\right) + \left[\frac{(100+x)}{100} \times 3000\right] = \frac{125}{100} \times 6000$

$\Rightarrow$ $30(100 + x) = 4200 \Rightarrow 100 + x = 140 \Rightarrow x = 40\%$.

104. Let the quantity sold at a loss be x kg and let C.P. per kg be Re. 1.

Total C.P. = Rs. 24.

Total S.P. = Rs. [120% of $(24 - x)$ + 95% of x] = Rs. $\left[\frac{6}{5}(24 - x) + \frac{19x}{20}\right]$ = Rs. $\left(\frac{576 - 5x}{20}\right)$.

$\therefore$ $\frac{576 - 5x}{20}$ = 110% of 24 $\Rightarrow \frac{576 - 5x}{20} = \frac{264}{10} \Rightarrow 576 - 5x = 528$

$\Rightarrow 5x = 48 \Rightarrow x = 9.6$ kg.

105. Let the total value be Rs. x. Value of $\frac{2}{3}$rd = Rs. $\frac{2x}{3}$, Value of $\frac{1}{3}$rd = Rs. $\frac{x}{3}$.

Total S.P. = Rs. $\left[\left(105\% \text{ of } \frac{2x}{3}\right) + \left(98\% \text{ of } \frac{x}{3}\right)\right]$ = Rs. $\left(\frac{210x}{300} + \frac{98x}{300}\right)$ = Rs. $\frac{308x}{300}$.

$\therefore$ $\frac{308x}{300} - x = 400 \Rightarrow \frac{8x}{300} = 400 \Rightarrow x = \left(\frac{400 \times 300}{8}\right) = 15000$.

106. Let C.P. of watch be Rs. x. Then, C.P. of wall clock = Rs. $(390 - x)$.

$\therefore$ $(10\% \text{ of } x) + [15\% \text{ of } (390 - x)] = 51.50 \Rightarrow \frac{10}{100} \times x + \frac{15}{100} \times (390 - x) = \frac{515}{10}$

$\Rightarrow$ $10x + 5850 - 15x = 5150 \Rightarrow 5x = 700 \Rightarrow x = 140$.

So, C.P. of watch = Rs. 140, C.P. of wall clock = Rs. 250.

$\therefore$ Difference = Rs. (250 − 140) = Rs. 110.

107. Let C.P. of each horse be Rs. x and C.P. of each cow be Rs. y. Then,

$4x + 9y = 13400$ ...(*i*)

And, 10% of $4x$ + 20% of $9y$ = 1880

$\Rightarrow$ $\frac{2}{5}x + \frac{9}{5}y = 1880 \Rightarrow 2x + 9y = 9400$ ...(*ii*)

Solving (*i*) and (*ii*), we get : $x = 2000$ and $y = 600$.

$\therefore$ Cost price of each horse = Rs. 2000.

108. Let C.P. of clock A be Rs. x and that of clock B be Rs. $(650 - x)$. Then,

$$120\% \text{ of } x = 75\% \text{ of } (650 - x) \Rightarrow 650 - x = \frac{120}{75}x = \frac{8}{5}x$$

$$\Rightarrow \frac{13}{5}x = 650 \Rightarrow x = \left(\frac{650 \times 5}{13}\right) = 250.$$

$\therefore$ C.P. of A = Rs. 250, C.P. of B = Rs. 400.

109. Let the C.P. of the watches be Rs. x and Rs. $(840 - x)$.

$\therefore$ $(116\% \text{ of } x) + [88\% \text{ of } (840 - x)] = 840$

$\Rightarrow 116x + 73920 - 88x = 84000 \Rightarrow 28x = 10080 \Rightarrow x = 360.$

$\therefore$ Their cost prices are Rs. 360 and Rs. 480.

110. Let C.P. of the chair be Rs. x and that of the table be Rs. y.

Then, $17\% \text{ of } y - 7\% \text{ of } x = 296 \Rightarrow 17y - 7x = 29600$ ...(i)

And, $12\% \text{ of } y + 7\% \text{ of } x = 400 \Rightarrow 12y + 7x = 40000$ ...(ii)

Solving (i) and (ii), we get : $y = 2400$ and $x = 1600$.

$\therefore$ C.P. of table = Rs. 2400.

111. S.P. $= 97\frac{1}{2}\%$ of Rs. 650 = Rs. $\left(\frac{195}{2} \times \frac{1}{100} \times 650\right)$ = Rs. 633.75.

112. M.P. = Rs. 272000.

Discount = Rs. [(4% of 200000) + (2.5% of 72000)] = Rs. (8000 + 1800) = Rs. 9800.

$\therefore$ Actual price = Rs. (272000 − 9800) = Rs. 262200.

113. C.P. = 90% of 80% of Rs. 1400 = Rs. $\left(\frac{90}{100} \times \frac{80}{100} \times 1400\right)$ = Rs. 1008.

114. Rate of discount = $\left(\frac{12}{80} \times 100\right)\% = 15\%$.

115. S.P. of each article = Rs. $\left(\frac{37.40}{2}\right)$ = Rs. 18.70.

Let M.P. be Rs. x.

Then, $85\% \text{ of } x = 18.70 \Rightarrow x = \left(\frac{18.70 \times 100}{85}\right) = 22.$

116. Let the labelled price be Rs. x.

$$88\% \text{ of } 80\% \text{ of } x = 704 \Rightarrow x = \left(\frac{704 \times 100 \times 100}{88 \times 80}\right) = 1000.$$

117. S.P. after 1st discount = Rs. $\left(\frac{80}{100} \times 1500\right)$ = Rs. 1200.

Net S.P. = Rs. 1104. Discount on Rs. 1200 = Rs. 96.

$\therefore$ Required discount = $\left(\frac{96}{1200} \times 100\right)\% = 8\%$.

118. Let the costs of the two articles be x and y. Then, 15% of x = 20% of $y \Rightarrow \frac{x}{y} = \frac{20}{15} = \frac{4}{3}$.

So, x and y must be in the ratio of 4 : 3.

119. Let the list price be Rs. x.

$$\Rightarrow \frac{80}{100}x = 24 \Rightarrow x = \frac{24 \times 100}{80} = 30.$$

$\therefore$ Required S.P. = 70% of Rs. 30 = Rs. 21.

120. Let the list price be Rs. z.

$\therefore$ $(100 - x)\%$ of $z = y \Rightarrow \left(\frac{100-x}{100}\right) \times z = y \Rightarrow z = \left(\frac{100y}{100-x}\right)$.

121. Let the labelled price be Rs. x. Then,

$(80\%$ of $x) - (75\%$ of $x) = 500 \Rightarrow 5\%$ of $x = 500 \Rightarrow x = \left(\frac{500 \times 100}{5}\right) = 10000$.

122. Let marked price be Rs. 100.

Then, Final S.P. = 70% of 80% of Rs. 100 = Rs. $\left(\frac{70}{100} \times \frac{80}{100} \times 100\right)$ = Rs. 56.

$\therefore$ Single discount = (100 − 56)% = 44%.

123. Let marked price be Rs. 100.

Then, S.P. = 85% of 88% of 90% of Rs. 100 = Rs. $\left(\frac{85}{100} \times \frac{88}{100} \times \frac{90}{100} \times 100\right)$ = Rs. 67.32.

$\therefore$ Single discount = (100 − 67.32)% = 32.68%.

124. S.P. = 90% of 80% of Rs. 2000 = Rs. $\left(\frac{90}{100} \times \frac{80}{100} \times 2000\right)$ = Rs. 1440.

125. S.P. = 95% of 95% of Rs. 80 = Rs. $\left(\frac{95}{100} \times \frac{95}{100} \times 80\right)$ = Rs. 72.20.

126. Actual price = 95% of 90% of 85% of Rs. 12000

= Rs. $\left(\frac{95}{100} \times \frac{90}{100} \times \frac{85}{100} \times 12000\right)$ = Rs. 8721.

127. Let the original price be Rs. x. Then,

95% of 88% of $x = 209 \Rightarrow x = \left(\frac{209 \times 100 \times 100}{95 \times 88}\right) = 250$.

128. S.P. in 1st case = 60% of Rs. 100000 = Rs. 60000.

S.P. in 2nd case = 96% of 64% of Rs. 100000

= Rs. $\left(\frac{96}{100} \times \frac{64}{100} \times 100000\right)$ = Rs. 61440.

$\therefore$ Difference = Rs. (61440 − 60000) = Rs. 1440.

129. Let the amount of the bill be Rs. x. Then,

$(65\%$ of $x) - (80\%$ of 80% of $x) = 22 \Rightarrow \left(\frac{65}{100} \times x\right) - \left(\frac{80}{100} \times \frac{80}{100} \times x\right) = 22$

$\Rightarrow \frac{65}{100}x - \frac{64}{100}x = 22 \Rightarrow \frac{x}{100} = 22 \Rightarrow x = 2200$.

130. S.P. in 1st case = 94% of 70% of Rs. 700 = Rs. $\left(\frac{94}{100} \times \frac{70}{100} \times 700\right)$ = Rs. 460.60.

S.P. in 2nd case = 84% of 80% of Rs. 700 = Rs. $\left(\frac{84}{100} \times \frac{80}{100} \times 700\right)$ = Rs. 470.40.

$\therefore$ Difference = Rs. (470.40 − 460.60) = Rs. 9.80.

131. Let the second discount rate be $x\%$. Then,

$(100 - x)\%$ of 90% of 720 = 550.80

$\Rightarrow \frac{(100-x)}{100} \times \frac{90}{100} \times 720 = 550.80 \Rightarrow (100 - x) = \left(\frac{55080}{9 \times 72}\right) = 85 \Rightarrow x = 15$.

$\therefore$ Second discount rate = 15%.

132. Cost of each calculator = Rs. $\left(250 + \frac{2500}{150}\right)$ = Rs. $266\frac{2}{3}$.

S.P. of each calculator = Rs. $\left(\frac{95}{100} \times 320\right)$ = Rs. 304.

$\therefore$ Profit% = $\left(\frac{112}{3} \times \frac{3}{800} \times 100\right)\%$ = 14%.

133. Let C.P. be Rs. 100. Then, marked price = Rs. 125.

S.P. = 84% of Rs. 125 = Rs. $\left(\frac{84}{100} \times 125\right)$ = Rs. 105.

$\therefore$ Profit% = (105 − 100)% = 5%.

134. Let C.P. be Rs. 100. Then, marked price = Rs. 130.

S.P. = $\left(100 - \frac{25}{4}\right)\%$ of Rs. 130 = Rs. $\left(\frac{375}{400} \times 130\right)$ = Rs. 121.875.

$\therefore$ Profit% = (121.875 − 100)% = 21.875% = $\frac{21875}{1000}\%$ = $21\frac{7}{8}\%$.

135. Let the original price be Rs. 100. Then, marked price = Rs. 130.

Final price = 90% of 90% of Rs. 130 = Rs. $\left(\frac{90}{100} \times \frac{90}{100} \times 130\right)$ = Rs. 105.30

$\therefore$ Increase in price = (105.30 − 100)% = 5.3%.

136. Let the marked price of each article be Re. 1.
Then, C.P. of 30 = Rs. 27, S.P. of 30 = Rs. 30.

$\therefore$ Gain% = $\left(\frac{3}{27} \times 100\right)\%$ = $11\frac{1}{9}\%$.

137. Marked price = Rs. 300. C.P. = Rs. $\left(\frac{100}{120} \times 300\right)$ = Rs. 250.

Sale price = 90% of Rs. 300 = Rs. 270.

$\therefore$ Required gain% = $\left(\frac{20}{250} \times 100\right)\%$ = 8%.

138. Let marked price = Rs. 100. Then, C.P. = Rs. 64. S.P = Rs. 88.

$\therefore$ Gain% = $\left(\frac{24}{64} \times 100\right)\%$ = 37.5%.

139. Let the marked price be Rs. x. Then, 108% of 90% of x = 680.40

$\Rightarrow \frac{108}{100} \times \frac{90}{100} x = 680.40 \Rightarrow x = \left(\frac{68040 \times 100}{108 \times 90}\right)$ = Rs. 700.

140. Let C.P. = Rs. 100. Then, S.P. = Rs. 120.

Let marked price be Rs. x. Then, 90% of x = 120 $\Rightarrow x = \left(\frac{120 \times 100}{90}\right) = 133\frac{1}{3}$.

$\therefore$ Marked price = $33\frac{1}{3}\%$ above C.P.

141. C.P. = Rs. 1200. S.P. = 125% of Rs. 1200 = Rs. $\left(\frac{125}{100} \times 1200\right)$ = Rs. 1500.

Let marked price be Rs. x. Then, 80% of x = 1500 $\Rightarrow x = \left(\frac{1500 \times 100}{80}\right)$ = 1875.

$\therefore$ Marked price = Rs. 1875.

142. Let cost price be Rs. 100. The, S.P. = Rs. 112.
Let printed price be Rs. x.

$$90\% \text{ of } x = 112 \Rightarrow x = \left(\frac{112 \times 100}{90}\right) = \text{Rs. } \frac{1120}{9}.$$

$$\therefore \text{ Required ratio} = 100 : \frac{1120}{9} = 900 : 1120 = 45 : 56.$$

143. Let cost price = Rs. 100. Then,

$$\frac{2}{5} \text{ of (Marked Price)} = 75 \Rightarrow \text{Marked Price} = \text{Rs. } \left(\frac{75 \times 5}{2}\right) = \text{Rs. } \frac{375}{2}.$$

$$\therefore \text{ Required ratio} = \frac{375}{2} : 100 = 375 : 200 = 15 : 8.$$

144. Let the C.P. of each article be Rs. 100.
Then, C.P. of 16 articles = Rs. (100 × 16) = Rs. 1600.

$$\text{S.P. of 15 articles} = \text{Rs. } \left(1600 \times \frac{135}{100}\right) = \text{Rs. } 2160.$$

$$\text{S.P. of each article} = \text{Rs. } \frac{2160}{15} = \text{Rs. } 144.$$

If S.P. is Rs. 96, marked price = Rs. 100.

$$\text{If S.P. is Rs. 144, marked price} = \text{Rs. } \left(\frac{100}{96} \times 144\right) = \text{Rs. } 150.$$

∴ Marked price = 50% above C.P

145. Let C.P. = Rs. 100. Then, Marked Price = Rs. 110, S.P. = Rs. 99.

$$\therefore \text{ Discount\%} = \left(\frac{11}{110} \times 100\right)\% = 10\%.$$

146. Let C.P. = Rs. 100. Then, Marked Price = Rs. 135, S.P. = Rs. 108.

$$\therefore \text{ Discount\%} = \left(\frac{27}{135} \times 100\right)\% = 20\%.$$

147. Let C.P. of whole stock = Rs. 100. Then, Marked Price of whole stock = Rs. 120.

M.P. of $\frac{1}{2}$ stock = Rs. 60, M.P. of $\frac{1}{4}$ stock = Rs. 30.

∴ Total S.P. = Rs. [60 + (80% of 30) + (60% of 30)] = Rs. (60 + 24 + 18) = Rs. 102.
Hence, gain% = (102 – 100)% = 2%.

148. Since the marked price is not given, so the cost price cannot be determined.

149. S.P. = 95% of Rs. 6500 = Rs. $\left(\frac{95}{100} \times 6500\right)$ = Rs. 6175.

Profit = 15%.

$$\therefore \text{ C.P.} = \text{Rs. } \left(\frac{110}{115} \times 6175\right) = \text{Rs. } 5369.56 \approx \text{Rs. } 5350.$$

150. Let the labelled price be Rs. x. Then, 120% of $x = 2880 \Rightarrow x = \left(\frac{2880 \times 100}{120}\right) = 2400.$

$$\therefore \text{ C.P.} = 85\% \text{ of Rs. } 2400 = \text{Rs. } \left(\frac{85}{100} \times 2400\right) = \text{Rs. } 2040.$$

151. Marked price = Rs. 30. S.P. = Rs. $\left[\left(\frac{85}{100} \times 30\right) - 1.50\right]$ = Rs. (25.50 − 1.50) = Rs. 24.

Let C.P. be Rs. x. Then, 120% of $x = 24 \Rightarrow x = \left(\frac{24 \times 100}{120}\right)$ = Rs. 20.

152. Let the marked price be Rs. 100.

Then, S.P. = Rs. $\left(\frac{90}{100} \times 100\right)$ = Rs. 90. Gain = 20%.

$\therefore$ C.P. = Rs. $\left(\frac{100}{120} \times 90\right)$ = Rs. 75.

New commission = Rs. 20; New S.P. = Rs. 80.

$\therefore$ New Profit = $\left(\frac{5}{75} \times 100\right)\% = 6\frac{2}{3}\%$.

153. S.P. = Rs. 17940. Let marked price be Rs. x.

Then, $\frac{92}{100}x = 17940 \Rightarrow x$ = Rs. $\left(17940 \times \frac{100}{92}\right)$ = Rs. 19500.

C.P. = Rs. $\left(\frac{100}{119.6} \times 17940\right)$ = Rs. $\left(\frac{1000}{1196} \times 17940\right)$ = Rs. 15000.

Now C.P. = Rs. 15000, S.P. = Rs. 19500.

$\therefore$ Required profit% = $\left(\frac{4500}{15000} \times 100\right)\% = 30\%$.

154. S.P. of 1 article = Rs. 45. Let marked price of each article be Rs. x.

Then, $\frac{90}{100}x = 45 \Rightarrow x$ = Rs. $\left(\frac{45 \times 100}{90}\right)$ = Rs. 50.

C.P. = Rs. $\left(\frac{100}{150} \times 45\right)$ = Rs. 30.

Now, C.P. = Rs. 30, S.P. = Rs. 50.

$\therefore$ Required profit% = $\left(\frac{20}{30} \times 100\right)\% = 66\frac{2}{3}\%$.

155. S.P. of 1 saree = Rs. 266. Let the labelled price of each saree be Rs. x.

Then, $\frac{95}{100}x = 266 \Rightarrow x$ = Rs. $\left(\frac{266 \times 100}{95}\right)$ = Rs. 280.

Now, S.P. = Rs. 280, Profit = 12%.

$\therefore$ C.P. of 1 saree = Rs. $\left(\frac{100}{112} \times 280\right)$ = Rs. 250.

156. C.P. = Rs. 320, Profit = 15%.

S.P. = Rs. $\left(\frac{115}{100} \times 320\right)$ = Rs. 368. Marked price = Rs. (368 + 32) = Rs. 400.

$\therefore$ Required profit% = $\left(\frac{80}{320} \times 100\right)\% = 25\%$.

157. Let C.P. be Rs. 100. Then, S.P. = Rs. 123.50.

Let marked price be Rs. x. Then, $\frac{95}{100}x = 123.50 \Rightarrow x$ = Rs. $\left(\frac{12350}{95}\right)$ = Rs. 130.

Now, S.P. = Rs. 130, C.P. = Rs. 100.

$\therefore$ Profit% = 30%.

158. Let original list price = Rs. 100. Then, C.P. = Rs. 75. Desired S.P. = Rs 125.

$\therefore$ Required percentage = $\left(\frac{50}{75} \times 100\right)\%$ = 66.67%.

159. Let the original price be Rs. 100. Then, C.P. = Rs. 80.

S.P. = 140% of Rs. 80 = Rs. $\left(\frac{140}{100} \times 80\right)$ = Rs. 112.

$\therefore$ Required percentage = (112 − 100)% = 12%.

160. C.P. = Rs. $\left(\frac{100}{125} \times 8750\right)$ = Rs. 7000. Let the labelled price be Rs. x.

Then, $\frac{70}{100}x = 7000 \Rightarrow x =$ Rs. $\left(\frac{7000 \times 100}{70}\right)$ = Rs. 10000.

EXERCISE 11B

(DATA SUFFICIENCY TYPE QUESTIONS)

1. A shopkeeper sells some toys at Rs. 250 each. What percent profit does he make ? To find the answer, which of the following information given in Statements I and II is / are necessary ?

I. Number of toys sold. II. Cost price of each toy.

(*a*) Only I is necessary. (*b*) Only II is necessary.

(*c*) Both I and II are necessary. (*d*) Either I or II is necessary.

(*e*) None of these

2. A shopkeeper sells some articles at the profit of 25% on the original price. What is the exact amount of profit ?

To find the answer, which of the following information given in Statements I and II is / are necessary ?

I. Sale price of the article. II. Number of articles sold.

(*a*) Only I is necessary. (*b*) Only II is necessary.

(*c*) Either I or II is necessary. (*d*) Both I and II are necessary.

(*e*) None of these

Directions (*Questions 3 to 13*) : *Each of the questions given below consists of a statement and / or a question and two statements numbered I and II given below it. You have to decide whether the data provided in the statement(s) is / are sufficient to answer the question. Read both the statements and*

Give answer (a) if the data in Statement I alone are sufficient to answer the question, while the data in Statement II alone are not sufficient to answer the question;

Give answer (b) if the data in Statement II alone are sufficient to answer the question, while the data in Statement I alone are not sufficient to answer the question;

Give answer (c) if the data either in Statement I or in Statement II alone are sufficient to answer the question;

Give answer (d) if the data even in both Statements I and II together are not sufficient to answer the question;

Give answer (e) if the data in both Statements I and II together are necessary to answer the question.

3. By selling a product with 20% profit, how much profit was earned ?

I. The difference between cost and selling price is Rs. 40.

II. The selling price is 120 percent of the cost price. **(S.B.I.P.O. 2003)**

4. What is the cost price of the article ?

I. The profit earned on the article is one-third of the cost price.

II. The article is sold for Rs. 400.

5. What would have been the selling price per kg of rice? **(Bank P.O. 1999)**

I. 50 kg of rice was purchased for Rs. 3350 and Rs. 150 were spent on transport.

II. Profit earned was 5%.

6. How much was the loss ?

I. The cost is Rs. 300.

II. The loss is 25% of the selling price.

7. A man mixes two types of rice (X and Y) and sells the mixture at the rate of Rs. 17 per kg. Find his profit percentage. **(M.B.A. 2002)**

I. The rate of X is Rs. 20 per kg.

II. The rate of Y is Rs. 13 per kg.

8. What is the percent profit earned by selling the product ? **(Bank P.O. 2003)**

I. The profit earned was Rs. 50.

II. Had it been sold for Rs. 310, the profit would have been Rs. 70.

9. What is the cost price of the cassette ?

I. The percent profit made when the cassette is sold for Rs. 78 is twice as much as when it is sold for Rs. 69.

II. If the price of the cassette is marked at 20% above the cost price and a discount of 10% is offered on the marked price, the seller gains 8%.

10. What was the cost price of the suitcase purchased by Richard ? **(Bank P.O. 2002)**

I. Richard got 20% concession on the labelled price.

II. Richard sold the suitcase for Rs. 2000 with 25% profit on the labelled price.

11. By selling a product for Rs. 100, how much profit was earned ? **(Bank P.O. 2002)**

I. 20% profit would have been earned if it were sold for Rs. 90.

II. The profit was one-third of the purchase price.

12. What is the price of a banana ?

I. A man can buy 14 bananas and 35 oranges for Rs. 84.

II. With 50% discount on the price of bananas, Rs. 12 would buy 4 bananas and 5 oranges.

13. How much profit did Anand make by selling a bed ? **(S.B.I.P.O. 1998)**

I. He bought the bed with 40% discount on labelled price.

II. He sold it with 20% profit on the labelled price.

Directions (*Questions 14 to 20*) : *Each of the following questions consists of a question followed by three statements I, II and III. You have to study the question and the statements and decide which of the statement(s) is/are necessary to answer the question.*

14. How many articles were sold ? **(Bank P.O. 2002)**

I. Total profit earned was Rs. 1596.

II. Cost price per article was Rs. 632.

III. Selling price per article was Rs. 765.

(*a*) Any two of the three (*b*) I and II only

(*c*) II and III only (*d*) All I, II and III

(*e*) Question cannot be answered even with the information in all the three statements.

15. What was the amount of profit earned ? **(Bank P.O. 2003)**
I. 10% discount was offered on the labelled price.
II. Had there been no discount, profit would have been 30%.
III. Selling price was more than the cost price by 20%.
(a) All I, II and III (b) Any two of the three
(c) III, and either I or II (d) I, and either II or III
(e) Question cannot be answered even with the information in all the three statements.

16. What was the cost price of the watch ?
I. The shopkeeper labelled the price of the watch 20% above the cost price.
II. After allowing a discount of 15% on the labelled price, the shopkeeper charges Rs. 408 for the watch.
III. Had there been no discount, the shopkeeper would have earned 20% profit.
(a) I, and either II or III (b) II, and either I or III
(c) III, and either I or II (d) I and II only
(e) Any two of the three

17. How much profit did Manick earn on the cost price of an article by selling it ?
I. He got 15% discount on the marked price at the time of purchase.
II. He sold it for Rs. 3060.
III. He earned 2% profit on the marked price. **(S.B.I.P.O. 2000)**
(a) I and II only (b) II and III only
(c) I only or II and III together (d) All I, II and III
(e) Even I, II and III together are not sufficient to answer the question.

18. By selling an article what is the profit percent gained ? **(S.B.I.P.O. 2002)**
I. 5% discount is given on list price.
II. If discount is not given, 20% profit is gained.
III. The cost price of the article is Rs. 5000.
(a) Only I and II (b) Only II and III (c) Only I and III
(d) All I, II and III (e) None of these

19. An item costing Rs. 3000 is sold at a certain discount. Find the rate of discount offered.
I. The profit earned after discount is 5%.
II. Had the discount rate been doubled, the seller incurs a loss of 15%.
III. The item is marked at a price 25% above the cost price.
(a) Only I and II (b) Only II and III (c) Only I and III
(d) All I, II and III (e) Any two of the three

20. What was the percentage of discount given ? **(R.B.I. 2003)**
I. 23.5% profit was earned by selling an almirah for Rs. 12,350.
II. If there were no discount, the earned profit would have been 30%.
III. The cost price of the almirah was Rs. 10,000.
(a) Only I and II (b) Only II and III (c) Only I and III
(d) Any two of the three (e) None of these

Directions (*Questions 21 to 22*) : *Each of these questions is followed by three statements. You have to study the question and all the three statements given to decide whether any information provided in the statement(s) is/are redundant and can be dispensed with while answering the given question.*

21. What is the percent profit earned by the shopkeeper on selling the articles in his shop ?
I. Labelled price of the articles sold was 130% of the cost price.
II. Cost price of each article was Rs. 550.
III. A discount of 10% on labelled price was offered. **(S.B.I.P.O. 2001)**

(*a*) Only I (*b*) Only II
(*c*) Only III (*d*) All the three are required
(*e*) Question cannot be answered even with information in all the three statements.

22. What is the marked price of the suitcase ?

I. When a discount of 15% is offered, the profit earned is 10.5%.

II. The cost price of the suitcase is Rs. 1500.

III. The marked price is 30% above the cost price.

(*a*) I only (*b*) Either I or III (*c*) Any one of the three
(*d*) All I, II and III are required (*e*) None of these

ANSWERS

1. (*b*)	**2.** (*d*)	**3.** (*a*)	**4.** (*e*)	**5.** (*e*)	**6.** (*e*)	**7.** (*d*)	**8.** (*b*)
9. (*a*)	**10.** (*e*)	**11.** (*c*)	**12.** (*d*)	**13.** (*d*)	**14.** (*d*)	**15.** (*e*)	**16.** (*b*)
17. (*d*)	**18.** (*a*)	**19.** (*e*)	**20.** (*e*)	**21.** (*b*)	**22.** (*b*)		

SOLUTIONS

1. S.P. = Rs. 250 each. To find gain percent, we must know the C.P. of each.

$\therefore$ Correct answer is (*b*).

2. Gain = 25% of C.P.

In order to find gain, we must know the sale price of each article and the number of articles sold.

$\therefore$ Correct answer is (*d*).

3. Gain = 20%

I. Profit = (S.P.) – (C.P.) = Rs. 40.

Thus, I gives the answer. But, II does not give the answer.

$\therefore$ Correct answer is (*a*).

4. I. Gain = $\frac{1}{3}$ (C.P.).

II. S.P. = Rs. 400.

$$\text{Gain} = (\text{S.P.}) - (\text{C.P.}) \Rightarrow \frac{1}{3}(\text{C.P.}) = (\text{Rs. } 400) - (\text{C.P.}) \Rightarrow \left(1 + \frac{1}{3}\right)(\text{C.P.}) = \text{Rs. } 400$$

$$\Rightarrow \quad \text{C.P.} = \text{Rs.}\left(400 \times \frac{3}{4}\right) = \text{Rs. } 300.$$

Thus, I and II both are needed to get the answer.

$\therefore$ Correct answer is (*e*).

5. I. Total C.P. of 50 kg = Rs. (3350 + 150) = Rs. 3500.

$$\therefore \quad \text{C.P. of 1 kg} = \text{Rs.}\left(\frac{3500}{50}\right) = \text{Rs. } 70.$$

II. Gain = 5%.

$$\therefore \quad \text{S.P. of 1 kg} = 105\% \text{ of Rs. } 70 = \text{Rs.}\left(70 \times \frac{105}{100}\right) = \text{Rs. } 73.50.$$

Thus, both I and II are needed to get the answer.

$\therefore$ Correct answer is (*e*).

6. I. C.P. = Rs. 300.

II. Loss = 25% of S.P.

Let S.P. be Rs. x. Then, loss = 25% of Rs. x = Rs. $\frac{x}{4}$.

Loss = (C.P.) − (S.P.) $\Rightarrow \frac{x}{4} = 300 - x \Rightarrow \left(x + \frac{x}{4}\right) = 300$

$\Rightarrow x = \left(300 \times \frac{4}{5}\right) = 240.$

$\therefore$ Loss = 25% of Rs. 240 = Rs. $\left(\frac{25}{100} \times 240\right)$ = Rs. 60.

Thus, I and II are required to get the answer.

$\therefore$ Correct answer is (*e*).

7. The ratio in which X and Y are mixed, is not given.

So, both I and II together cannot give the answer.

$\therefore$ Correct answer is (*d*).

8. II gives, S.P. = Rs. 310 and gain = Rs. 70.

$\therefore$ C.P = Rs. (310 − 70) = Rs. 240.

$\therefore$ Gain% = $\left(\frac{70}{240} \times 310\right)$%.

Thus, II alone gives the answer.

Clearly, I alone does not give the answer.

$\therefore$ Correct answer is (*b*).

9. Let the C.P. be Rs. x. Then,

I. $\frac{(78 - x)}{x} \times 100 = 2 \times \frac{(69 - x)}{x} \times 100 \Leftrightarrow 78 - x = 138 - 2x \Leftrightarrow x = 60.$

Thus, I only gives the answer.

II. Let the C.P. be Rs. x. Then, M.P. = Rs. $\left(\frac{120}{100} \times x\right)$ = Rs. $\frac{6x}{5}$.

$\therefore$ S.P. = 90% of Rs. $\frac{6x}{5}$ = Rs. $\left(\frac{6x}{5} \times \frac{90}{100}\right)$ = Rs. $\frac{27x}{25}$.

Thus, 108% of $x = \frac{27x}{25}$. This does not give x.

$\therefore$ II does not give the answer.

$\therefore$ Correct answer is (*a*).

10. Let the labelled price be Rs. x.

I. C.P. = 80% of Rs. x = Rs. $\left(x \times \frac{80}{100}\right)$ = Rs. $\frac{4x}{5}$.

II. S.P. = Rs. 2000, S.P. = 125% of Rs. x = Rs. $\left(\frac{125}{100} \times x\right)$ = Rs. $\frac{5x}{4}$.

$\therefore \frac{5x}{4} = 2000 \Rightarrow x = \frac{2000 \times 4}{5} = 1600.$

$\therefore$ C.P. = Rs. $\frac{4x}{5}$ = Rs. $\left(\frac{4}{5} \times 1600\right)$ = Rs. 1280.

Thus, I and II together give the answer.

$\therefore$ Correct answer is (*e*).

11. S.P. = Rs. 100.

I. When S.P. = Rs. 90, Gain = 20%.

$\therefore$ C.P. = Rs. $\left(\frac{100}{120} \times 90\right)$ = Rs. 75.

Now, (C.P. = Rs. 75 and S.P. = Rs. 100) $\Rightarrow$ Profit = Rs. 25.

Thus, I alone gives the answer.

II. Let the C.P. be Rs. x. Then, gain = Rs. $\frac{x}{3}$.

$\therefore$ S.P. = Rs. $\left(x + \frac{x}{3}\right)$ = Rs. $\frac{4x}{3}$.

Thus, $\frac{4x}{3} = 100 \Rightarrow x = \left(\frac{3 \times 100}{4}\right) = 75$ and so C.P. = Rs. 75.

Thus, II alone gives the answer.

$\therefore$ Correct answer is (*c*).

12. Let the price of a banana be Rs. x and that of an orange Rs. y.

I. $14x + 35y = 84 \Rightarrow 2x + 5y = 12$ ...(*i*)

II. $4 \times \frac{x}{2} + 5y = 12 \Rightarrow 2x + 5y = 12$ ...(*ii*)

Thus, even I and II together do not give the answer.

$\therefore$ Correct answer is (*d*).

13. I. Let the labelled price be Rs. x.

C.P. = 60% of Rs. x = Rs. $\left(x \times \frac{60}{100}\right)$ = Rs. $\frac{3x}{5}$.

II. S.P. = 120% of Rs. x = Rs. $\left(x \times \frac{120}{100}\right)$ = Rs. $\frac{6x}{5}$.

Profit = Rs. $\left(\frac{6x}{5} - \frac{3x}{5}\right)$ = Rs. $\frac{3x}{5}$.

Thus, even I and II together do not give the answer.

$\therefore$ Correct answer is (*d*).

14. I. Total gain = Rs. 1596.

II. C.P. of each article = Rs. 632.

III. S.P. of each article = Rs. 765.

Let the number of articles be x.

Then, $765x - 632x = 1596 \Rightarrow x = \frac{1596}{133} = 12$.

Thus, all I, II and III are needed to get the answer.

$\therefore$ Correct answer is (*d*).

15. Let the M.P. be Rs. x.

I. S.P. = 90% of Rs. x = Rs. $\left(x \times \frac{90}{100}\right)$ = Rs. $\frac{9x}{10}$.

II. If S.P. = Rs. x, then gain = 30%.

$\therefore$ C.P. = Rs. $\left(\frac{100}{130} \times x\right)$ = Rs. $\frac{10x}{13}$.

III. Gain = 20%.

Thus, I, II, III do not give the answer.

$\therefore$ Correct answer is (*e*).

16. I. Let the C.P. be Rs. x.

Then, M.P. = 120% of Rs. x = Rs. $\left(\frac{120}{100} \times x\right)$ = Rs. $\frac{6x}{5}$.

II. S.P. = 85% of M.P. = Rs. $\left(\frac{6x}{5} \times \frac{85}{100}\right)$ = Rs. $\frac{51x}{50}$.

$\therefore \quad \frac{51x}{50} = 408 \Rightarrow x = \left(408 \times \frac{50}{51}\right) \Rightarrow x = 400.$

Thus, I and II give the answer.

III. When there is no discount, then S.P. = M.P. = Rs. $\frac{6x}{5}$ [From I]

Thus, II and III give the same answer.

$\therefore$ Correct answer is (*b*).

17. Let the M.P. be Rs. x.

I. C.P. = 85% of Rs. x = Rs. $\left(x \times \frac{85}{100}\right)$ = Rs. $\frac{17x}{20}$.

II. S.P. = Rs. 3060.

III. 102% of $x = 3060 \Rightarrow x = \left(3060 \times \frac{100}{102}\right) = 3000.$

$\therefore$ C.P. = Rs. $\frac{17x}{20}$ = Rs. $\left(\frac{17}{20} \times 3000\right)$ = Rs. 2550.

So, gain = Rs. (3060 − 2550) = Rs. 510.

Thus all I, II and III give the answer.

$\therefore$ Correct answer is (*d*).

18. I. Let the list price be Rs. x.

Then, S.P. = 95% of Rs. x = Rs. $\left(x \times \frac{95}{100}\right)$ = Rs. $\frac{19x}{20}$.

II. When S.P. = Rs. x and gain = 20%.

Then, C.P. = Rs. $\left(\frac{100}{120} \times x\right)$ = Rs. $\frac{5x}{6}$.

$\therefore$ Gain = $\left(\frac{19x}{20} - \frac{5x}{6}\right) = \left(\frac{57x - 50x}{60}\right) = \frac{7x}{60}.$

$\therefore$ Gain% = $\left(\frac{7x}{60} \times \frac{6}{5x} \times 100\right)\% = 14\%.$

Thus, I and II only give the answer.

$\therefore$ Correct answer is (*a*).

19. C.P. = Rs. 3000. Let the rate of discount be x%.

I. S.P. = 105% of Rs. 3000 = Rs. 3150.

II. Let M.P. = Rs. x. Then, $\frac{(x - 3150)}{(x - 85\% \text{ of } 3000)} = \frac{1}{2} \Rightarrow x = 3750$

From I and II, discount = Rs. (3750 − 3150) = Rs. 600.

Discount% = $\left(\frac{600}{3750} \times 100\right)\% = 16\%.$

Thus, I and II give the answer.

III. M.P. = 125% of Rs. 3000 = Rs. 3750.

From I and III, discount = (M.P.) – (S.P.) = Rs. 600.

Thus, Discount% can be calculated.

Thus, I and III give the answer.

From II and III, we get : discount = Rs. $\left(\frac{3750 - 85\% \text{ of } 3000}{2}\right)$ = Rs. 600.

Thus, II and III give the answer.

∴ Correct answer is (*e*).

20. **I.** S.P. = Rs. 12350, Gain = 23.5%.

∴ C.P. = Rs. $\left(\frac{100}{123.5} \times 12350\right)$ = Rs. 10000.

II. M.P. = 130% of C.P. = 130% of Rs. 10000 = Rs. 13000.

From I and II, discount = Rs. (13000 – 12350) = Rs. 650.

Discount% = $\left(\frac{650}{13000} \times 100\right)\%$ = 5%.

Thus, I and II give the answer.

III gives C.P. = Rs. 10000.

So, II and III give the answer.

∴ Correct answer is (*e*).

21. **I.** Let C.P. be Rs. x. Then, M.P. = 130% of x = Rs. $\frac{13x}{10}$.

III. S.P. = 90% of M.P.

Thus, I and III give, S.P. = Rs. $\left(\frac{90}{100} \times \frac{13x}{10}\right)$ = Rs. $\frac{117x}{100}$.

Gain = Rs. $\left(\frac{117x}{100} - x\right)$ = Rs. $\frac{17x}{100}$.

Thus, from I and III, gain% can be obtained.

Clearly, II is redundant.

∴ Correct answer is (*b*).

22. **II.** C.P. = Rs. 1500.

I. Gain = 10.5%.

∴ From I and II, we get

S.P. = 110.5% of C.P. = Rs. $\left(\frac{110.5}{100} \times 1500\right)$ = Rs. 1657.50.

Discount = 15%.

∴ M.P. = Rs. $\left(\frac{100}{85} \times 1657.50\right)$ = Rs. 1950.

Thus, I and II give the answer and so III is redundant.

III. M.P. = 130% of C.P.

From II and III, we get : M.P. = Rs. $\left(\frac{130}{100} \times 1500\right)$ = Rs. 1950.

∴ II and III give the answer and so I is redundant.

So, either I or III is redundant.

∴ Correct answer is (*b*).

---

12. RATIO AND PROPORTION

IMPORTANT FACTS AND FORMULAE

I. **RATIO** : The ratio of two quantities a and b in the same units, is the fraction $\frac{a}{b}$ and we write it as $a : b$.

In the ratio $a : b$, we call a as the **first term** or **antecedent** and b, the **second term** or **consequent**.

Ex. The ratio 5 : 9 represents $\frac{5}{9}$ with antecedent = 5, consequent = 9.

Rule : The multiplication or division of each term of a ratio by the same non-zero number does not affect the ratio.

Ex. 4 : 5 = 8 : 10 = 12 : 15 etc. Also, 4 : 6 = 2 : 3.

2. **PROPORTION** : *The equality of two ratios is called proportion.*

If $a : b = c : d$, we write, $a : b :: c : d$ and we say that a, b, c, d are in proportion. Here a and d are called **extremes**, while b and c are called **mean terms.**

Product of means = Product of extremes.

Thus, $a : b :: c : d \Leftrightarrow (b \times c) = (a \times d)$.

3. (*i*) **Fourth Proportional** : If $a : b = c : d$, then d is called the fourth proportional to a, b, c.

(*ii*) **Third Proportional** : If $a : b = b : c$, then c is called the third proportional to a and b.

(*iii*) **Mean Proportional** : Mean proportional between a and b is $\sqrt{ab}$.

4. (*i*) **COMPARISON OF RATIOS** :

We say that $(a : b) > (c : d) \Leftrightarrow \frac{a}{b} > \frac{c}{d}$.

(*ii*) **COMPOUNDED RATIO** :

The compounded ratio of the ratios $(a : b)$, $(c : d)$, $(e : f)$ is $(ace : bdf)$.

5. (*i*) ***Duplicate ratio*** of $(a : b)$ is $(a^2 : b^2)$.

(*ii*) ***Sub-duplicate ratio*** of $(a : b)$ is $(\sqrt{a} : \sqrt{b})$

(*iii*) ***Triplicate ratio*** of $(a : b)$ is $(a^3 : b^3)$.

(*iv*) **Sub-triplicate ratio** of $(a : b)$ is $\left(a^{\frac{1}{3}} : b^{\frac{1}{3}}\right)$.

(*v*) If $\frac{a}{b} = \frac{c}{d}$, then $\frac{a+b}{a-b} = \frac{c+d}{c-d}$. **(componendo and dividendo)**

6. **VARIATION** :

(*i*) We say that x is directly proportional to y, if $x = ky$ for some constant k and we write, $x \propto y$.

(*ii*) We say that x is inversely proportional to y, if $xy = k$ for some constant k and we write, $x \propto \frac{1}{y}$.

SOLVED PROBLEMS

Ex. 1. ***If a : b = 5 : 9 and b : c = 4 : 7, find a : b : c.***

Sol. $a : b = 5 : 9$ and $b : c = 4 : 7 = \left(4 \times \frac{9}{4}\right) : \left(7 \times \frac{9}{4}\right) = 9 : \frac{63}{4}$

$\Rightarrow$ $a : b : c = 5 : 9 : \frac{63}{4} = 20 : 36 : 63.$

Ex. 2. ***Find :***

(i) the fourth proportional to 4, 9, 12;
(ii) the third proportional to 16 and 36;
(iii) the mean proportional between 0.08 and 0.18.

Sol. (*i*) Let the fourth proportional to 4, 9, 12 be *x*.

Then, $4 : 9 :: 12 : x \Leftrightarrow 4 \times x = 9 \times 12 \Leftrightarrow x = \frac{9 \times 12}{4} = 27.$

$\therefore$ Fourth proportional to 4, 9, 12 is 27.

(*ii*) Let the third proportional to 16 and 36 be *x*.

Then, $16 : 36 :: 36 : x \Leftrightarrow 16 \times x = 36 \times 36 \Leftrightarrow x = \frac{36 \times 36}{16} = 81.$

$\therefore$ Third proportional to 16 and 36 is 81.

(*iii*) Mean proportional between 0.08 and 0.18

$= \sqrt{0.08 \times 0.18} = \sqrt{\frac{8}{100} \times \frac{18}{100}} = \sqrt{\frac{144}{100 \times 100}} = \frac{12}{100} = 0.12.$

Ex. 3. ***If x : y = 3 : 4, find (4x + 5y) : (5x – 2y).***

Sol. $\frac{x}{y} = \frac{3}{4} \Rightarrow \frac{4x + 5y}{5x - 2y} = \frac{4\left(\frac{x}{y}\right) + 5}{5\left(\frac{x}{y}\right) - 2} = \frac{\left(4 \times \frac{3}{4} + 5\right)}{\left(5 \times \frac{3}{4} - 2\right)} = \frac{(3+5)}{\left(\frac{7}{4}\right)} = \frac{32}{7}.$

Ex. 4. ***Divide Rs. 672 in the ratio 5 : 3.***

Sol. Sum of ratio terms = (5 + 3) = 8.

$\therefore$ First part = Rs. $\left(672 \times \frac{5}{8}\right)$ = Rs. 420; Second part = Rs. $\left(672 \times \frac{3}{8}\right)$ = Rs. 252.

Ex. 5. ***Divide Rs. 1162 among A, B, C in the ratio 35 : 28 : 20.***

Sol. Sum of ratio terms = (35 + 28 + 20) = 83.

A's share = Rs. $\left(1162 \times \frac{35}{83}\right)$ = Rs. 490; B's share = Rs. $\left(1162 \times \frac{28}{83}\right)$ = Rs. 392;

C's share = Rs. $\left(1162 \times \frac{20}{83}\right)$ = Rs. 280.

Ex. 6. ***A bag contains 50 p, 25 p and 10 p coins in the ratio 5 : 9 : 4, amounting to Rs. 206. Find the number of coins of each type.***

Sol. Let the number of 50 p, 25 p and 10 p coins be 5*x*, 9*x* and 4*x* respectively.

Then, $\frac{5x}{2} + \frac{9x}{4} + \frac{4x}{10} = 206$

$\Leftrightarrow$ $50x + 45x + 8x = 4120 \Leftrightarrow 103x = 4120 \Leftrightarrow x = 40.$

$\therefore$ Number of 50 p coins = (5 × 40) = 200; Number of 25 p coins = (9 × 40) = 360;
Number of 10 p coins = (4 × 40) = 160.

Ex. 7. A mixture contains alcohol and water in the ratio 4 : 3. If 5 litres of water is added to the mixture, the ratio becomes 4 : 5. Find the quantity of alcohol in the given mixture.

Sol. Let the quantity of alcohol and water be $4x$ litres and $3x$ litres respectively. Then,

$$\frac{4x}{3x+5} = \frac{4}{5} \Leftrightarrow 20x = 4(3x+5) \Leftrightarrow 8x = 20 \Leftrightarrow x = 2.5.$$

$\therefore$ Quantity of alcohol = (4×2.5) litres = 10 litres.

EXERCISE 12

(OBJECTIVE TYPE QUESTIONS)

Directions : *Mark (✓) against the correct answer* :

1. If A : B = 5 : 7 and B : C = 6 : 11, then A : B : C is :
(*a*) 55 : 77 : 66 (*b*) 30 : 42 : 77 (*c*) 35 : 49 : 42 (*d*) None of these

2. If A : B = 3 : 4 and B : C = 8 : 9, then A : C is :
(*a*) 1 : 3 (*b*) 3 : 2 (*c*) 2 : 3 (*d*) 1 : 2

3. If A : B = 8 : 15, B : C = 5 : 8 and C : D = 4 : 5, then A : D is equal to :
(*a*) 2 : 7 (*b*) 4 : 15 (*c*) 8 : 15 (*d*) 15 : 4

4. If A : B : C = 2 : 3 : 4, then $\frac{A}{B} : \frac{B}{C} : \frac{C}{A}$ is equal to : **(S.S.C. 2002)**
(*a*) 4 : 9 : 16 (*b*) 8 : 9 : 12 (*c*) 8 : 9 : 16 (*d*) 8 : 9 : 24

5. If $A : B = \frac{1}{2} : \frac{3}{8}$, $B : C = \frac{1}{3} : \frac{5}{9}$ and $C : D = \frac{5}{6} : \frac{3}{4}$, then the ratio A : B : C : D is :
(*a*) 4 : 6 : 8 : 10 (*b*) 6 : 4 : 8 : 10 (*c*) 6 : 8 : 9 : 10 (*d*) 8 : 6 : 10 : 9

6. If A : B = 2 : 3, B : C = 4 : 5 and C : D = 6 : 7, then A : B : C : D is :
(*a*) 16 : 22 : 30 : 35 (*b*) 16 : 24 : 15 : 35
(*c*) 16 : 24 : 30 : 35 (*d*) 18 : 24 : 30 : 35 **(S.S.C. 2002)**

7. If 2A = 3B = 4C, then A : B : C is :
(*a*) 2 : 3 : 4 (*b*) 4 : 3 : 2 (*c*) 6 : 4 : 3 (*d*) 20 : 15 : 2

8. If $\frac{A}{3} = \frac{B}{4} = \frac{C}{5}$, then A : B : C is :
(*a*) 4 : 3 : 5 (*b*) 5 : 4 : 3 (*c*) 3 : 4 : 5 (*d*) 20 : 15 : 2

9. If 2A = 3B and 4B = 5C, then A : C is :
(*a*) 4 : 3 (*b*) 8 : 15 (*c*) 15 : 8 (*d*) 3 : 4

10. The ratio of $4^{3.5} : 2^5$ is same as :
(*a*) 2 : 1 (*b*) 4 : 1 (*c*) 7 : 5 (*d*) 7 : 10

11. If $\frac{1}{5} : \frac{1}{x} = \frac{1}{x} : \frac{1}{1.25}$, then the value of x is :
(*a*) 1.5 (*b*) 2 (*c*) 2.5 (*d*) 3.5

12. If 0.75 : x :: 5 : 8, then x is equal to : **(L.I.C. 2003)**
(*a*) 1.12 (*b*) 1.20 (*c*) 1.25 (*d*) 1.30

13. If $x : y = 5 : 2$, then $(8x + 9y) : (8x + 2y)$ is : **(S.S.C. 2001)**
(*a*) 22 : 29 (*b*) 26 : 61 (*c*) 29 : 22 (*d*) 61 : 26

14. If 15% of x = 20% of y, then $x : y$ is :
(*a*) 3 : 4 (*b*) 4 : 3 (*c*) 17 : 16 (*d*) 16 : 17

15. If $(x : y) = 2 : 1$, then $(x^2 - y^2) : (x^2 + y^2)$ is :
(a) 3 : 5 (b) 5 : 3 (c) 1 : 3 (d) 3 : 1

16. If $(4x^2 - 3y^2) : (2x^2 + 5y^2) = 12 : 19$, then $(x : y)$ is :
(a) 2 : 3 (b) 1 : 2 (c) 3 : 2 (d) 2 : 1

17. If $x^2 + 4y^2 = 4xy$, then $x : y$ is :
(a) 2 : 1 (b) 1 : 2 (c) 1 : 1 (d) 1 : 4

18. If $5x^2 - 13xy + 6y^2 = 0$, then $x : y$ is :
(a) (2 : 1) only (b) (3 : 5) only
(c) (5 : 3) or (1 : 2) (d) (3 : 5) or (2 : 1)

19. If $\frac{x}{5} = \frac{y}{8}$, then $(x + 5) : (y + 8)$ is equal to :
(a) 3 : 5 (b) 13 : 8 (c) 8 : 5 (d) 5 : 8

20. If $\frac{a}{3} = \frac{b}{4} = \frac{c}{7}$, then $\frac{a+b+c}{c}$ is equal to :
(a) 7 (b) 2 (c) $\frac{1}{2}$ (d) $\frac{1}{7}$

21. If $(a + b) : (b + c) : (c + a) = 6 : 7 : 8$ and $(a + b + c) = 14$, then the value of c is :
(a) 6 (b) 7 (c) 8 (d) 14

22. The salaries of A, B, C are in the ratio 2 : 3 : 5. If the increments of 15%, 10% and 20% are allowed respectively in their salaries, then what will be the new ratio of their salaries ? **(Bank P.O. 2002)**
(a) 3 : 3 : 10 (b) 10 : 11 : 20
(c) 23 : 33 : 60 (d) Cannot be determined

23. If Rs. 782 be divided into three parts, proportional to $\frac{1}{2} : \frac{2}{3} : \frac{3}{4}$, then the first part is : **(C.B.I. 2003)**
(a) Rs. 182 (b) Rs. 190 (c) Rs. 196 (d) Rs. 204

24. If 76 is divided into four parts proportional to 7, 5, 3, 4, then the smallest part is :
(a) 12 (b) 15 (c) 16 (d) 19

25. Two numbers are in the ratio 3 : 5. If 9 is subtracted from each, the new numbers are in the ratio 12 : 23. The smaller number is : **(S.S.C. 2003)**
(a) 27 (b) 33 (c) 49 (d) 55

26. Two numbers are in the ratio 1 : 2. If 7 is added to both, their ratio changes to 3 : 5. The greatest number is : **(Hotel Management, 2003)**
(a) 24 (b) 26 (c) 28 (d) 32

27. Rs. 1210 were divided among A, B, C so that A : B = 5 : 4 and B : C = 9 : 10. Then, C gets :
(a) Rs. 340 (b) Rs. 400 (c) Rs. 450 (d) Rs. 475

28. In a bag, there are coins of 25 p, 10 p and 5 p in the ratio of 1 : 2 : 3. If there are Rs. 30 in all, how many 5 p coins are there ? **(Hotel Management, 2003)**
(a) 50 (b) 100 (c) 150 (d) 200

29. The ratio of three numbers is 3 : 4 : 5 and the sum of their squares is 1250. The sum of the numbers is :
(a) 30 (b) 50 (c) 60 (d) 90

30. The ratio of three numbers is 3 : 4 : 7 and their product is 18144. The numbers are :
(a) 9, 12, 21 (b) 15, 20, 25 (c) 18, 24, 42 (d) None of these

31. Salaries of Ravi and Sumit are in the ratio 2 : 3. If the salary of each is increased by Rs. 4000, the new ratio becomes 40 : 57. What is Sumit's present salary ?
(a) Rs. 17,000 (b) Rs. 20,000 (c) Rs. 25,500 (d) None of these
(Bank P.O. 2003)

32. If Rs. 510 be divided among A, B, C in such a way that A gets $\frac{2}{3}$ of what B gets and B gets $\frac{1}{4}$ of what C gets, then their shares are respectively : **(I.M.T. 2002)**

(*a*) Rs. 120, Rs. 240, Rs. 150 (*b*) Rs. 60, Rs. 90, Rs. 360
(*c*) Rs. 150, Rs. 300, Rs. 60 (*d*) None of these

33. The sum of three numbers is 98. If the ratio of the first to the second is 2 : 3 and that of the second to the third is 5 : 8, then the second number is : **(S.S.C. 2001)**

(*a*) 20 (*b*) 30 (*c*) 48 (*d*) 58

34. A fraction which bears the same ratio to $\frac{1}{27}$ that $\frac{3}{11}$ does to $\frac{5}{9}$, is equal to :

(*a*) $\frac{1}{55}$ (*b*) $\frac{1}{11}$ (*c*) $\frac{3}{11}$ (*d*) 55 **(S.S.C. 2001)**

35. Rs. 366 are divided amongst A, B and C so that A may get $\frac{1}{2}$ as much as B and C together, B may get $\frac{2}{3}$ as much as A and C together, then the share of A is :

(*a*) Rs. 122 (*b*) Rs. 129.60 (*c*) Rs. 146.60 (*d*) Rs. 183

36. A sum of Rs. 1300 is divided amongst P, Q, R and S such that

$\frac{\text{P's share}}{\text{Q's share}} = \frac{\text{Q's share}}{\text{R's share}} = \frac{\text{R's share}}{\text{S's share}} = \frac{2}{3}$. Then, P's share is : **(L.I.C. 2003)**

(*a*) Rs. 140 (*b*) Rs. 160 (*c*) Rs. 240 (*d*) Rs. 320

37. A and B together have Rs. 1210. If $\frac{4}{15}$ of A's amount is equal to $\frac{2}{5}$ of B's amount, how much amount does B have ? **(A.A.O. 2003)**

(*a*) Rs. 460 (*b*) Rs. 484 (*c*) Rs. 550 (*d*) Rs. 664

38. Two numbers are respectively 20% and 50% more than a third number. The ratio of the two numbers is : **(S.S.C. 2003)**

(*a*) 2 : 5 (*b*) 3 : 5 (*c*) 4 : 5 (*d*) 6 : 7

39. Two whole numbers whose sum is 72 cannot be in the ratio :

(*a*) 5 : 7 (*b*) 3 : 5 (*c*) 3 : 4 (*d*) 4 : 5

40. If a carton containing a dozen mirrors is dropped, which of the following cannot be the ratio of broken mirrors to unbroken mirrors ?

(*a*) 2 : 1 (*b*) 3 : 1 (*c*) 3 : 2 (*d*) 7 : 5

41. Seats for Mathematics, Physics and Biology in a school are in the ratio 5 : 7 : 8. There is a proposal to increase these seats by 40%, 50% and 75% respectively. What will be the ratio of increased seats ? **(Bank P.O. 2003)**

(*a*) 2 : 3 : 4 (*b*) 6 : 7 : 8 (*c*) 6 : 8 : 9 (*d*) None of these

42. The ratio of the number of boys and girls in a college is 7 : 8. If the percentage increase in the number of boys and girls be 20% and 10% respectively, what will be the new ratio ? **(R.B.I. 2003)**

(*a*) 8 : 9 (*b*) 17 : 18
(*c*) 21 : 22 (*d*) Cannot be determined

43. A sum of money is to be distributed among A, B, C, D in the proportion of 5 : 2 : 4 : 3. If C gets Rs. 1000 more than D, what is B's share ? **(R.B.I. 2003)**

(*a*) Rs. 500 (*b*) Rs. 1500 (*c*) Rs. 2000 (*d*) None of these

44. If 40% of a number is equal to two-third of another number, what is the ratio of first number to the second number ? **(Bank P.O. 2002)**

(*a*) 2 : 5 (*b*) 3 : 7 (*c*) 5 : 3 (*d*) 7 : 3

45. Ratio of the earnings of A and B is 4 : 7. If the earnings of A increase by 50% and those of B decrease by 25%, the new ratio of their earnings becomes 8 : 7. What are A's earnings ? **(Bank P.O. 2002)**

(*a*) Rs. 21,000 (*b*) Rs. 26,000 (*c*) Rs. 28,000 (*d*) Data inadequate

46. What least number must be subtracted from each of the numbers 14, 17, 34 and 42 so that the remainders may be proportional ?

(*a*) 0 (*b*) 1 (*c*) 2 (*d*) 7

47. In a mixture of 60 litres, the ratio of milk and water is 2 : 1. If this ratio is to be 1 : 2, then the quantity of water to be further added is :

(*a*) 20 litres (*b*) 30 litres (*c*) 40 litres (*d*) 60 litres

48. The fourth proportional to 5, 8, 15 is : **(R.R.B. 2002)**

(*a*) 18 (*b*) 24 (*c*) 19 (*d*) 20 (*e*) 21

49. The mean proportional between 234 and 104 is :

(*a*) 12 (*b*) 39 (*c*) 54 (*d*) None of these

50. The third proportional to 0.36 and 0.48 is :

(*a*) 0.64 (*b*) 0.1728 (*c*) 0.42 (*d*) 0.94

51. The third proportional to $(x^2 - y^2)$ and $(x - y)$ is :

(*a*) $(x + y)$ (*b*) $(x - y)$ (*c*) $\frac{x+y}{x-y}$ (*d*) $\frac{x-y}{x+y}$

52. The ratio of third proportional to 12 and 30 and the mean proportional between 9 and 25 is :

(*a*) 2 : 1 (*b*) 5 : 1 (*c*) 7 : 15 (*d*) 9 : 14

53. In a ratio, which is equal to 3 : 4, if the antecedent is 12, then the consequent is :

(*a*) 9 (*b*) 16 (*c*) 20 (*d*) 24

54. The prices of a scooter and a T.V. are in the ratio 7 : 5. If the scooter costs Rs. 8000 more than a T.V. set, then the price of a T.V. set is :

(*a*) Rs. 20,000 (*b*) Rs. 24,000 (*c*) Rs. 28,000 (*d*) Rs. 32,000

55. An amount of Rs. 735 was divided between A, B and C. If each of them had received Rs. 25 less, their shares would have been in the ratio of 1 : 3 : 2. The money received by C was :

(*a*) Rs. 195 (*b*) Rs. 200 (*c*) Rs. 225 (*d*) Rs. 245

56. An amount of Rs. 2430 is divided among A, B and C such that if their shares be reduced by Rs. 5, Rs. 10 and Rs. 15 respectively, the remainders shall be in the ratio of 3 : 4 : 5. Then, B's share was :

(*a*) Rs. 605 (*b*) Rs. 790 (*c*) Rs. 800 (*d*) Rs. 810

57. The ratio between two numbers is 3 : 4 and their L.C.M. is 180. The first number is :

(*a*) 60 (*b*) 45 (*c*) 20 (*d*) 15

58. An alloy is to contain copper and zinc in the ratio 9 : 4. The zinc required to be melted with 24 kg of copper is :

(*a*) $10\frac{2}{3}$ kg (*b*) $10\frac{1}{3}$ kg (*c*) $9\frac{2}{3}$ kg (*d*) 9 kg

59. 60 kg of an alloy A is mixed with 100 kg of alloy B. If alloy A has lead and tin in the ratio 3 : 2 and alloy B has tin and copper in the ratio 1 : 4, then the amount of tin in the new alloy is :

(*a*) 36 kg (*b*) 44 kg (*c*) 53 kg (*d*) 80 kg

60. Gold is 19 times as heavy as water and copper is 9 times as heavy as water. In what ratio should these be mixed to get an alloy 15 times as heavy as water ?

(*a*) 1 : 1 (*b*) 2 : 3 (*c*) 1 : 2 (*d*) 3 : 2

61. 15 litres of mixture contains 20% alcohol and the rest water. If 3 litres of water be mixed with it, the percentage of alcohol in the new mixture would be :

(a) 15% (b) $16\frac{2}{3}\%$ (c) 17% (d) $18\frac{1}{2}\%$

62. 20 litres of a mixture contains milk and water in the ratio 5 : 3. If 4 litres of this mixture be replaced by 4 litres of milk, the ratio of milk to water in the new mixture would be :

(a) 2 : 1 (b) 7 : 3 (c) 8 : 3 (d) 4 : 3

63. 85 kg of a mixture contains milk and water in the ratio 27 : 7. How much more water is to be added to get a new mixture containing milk and water in the ratio 3 : 1 ?

(a) 5 kg (b) 6.5 kg (c) 7.25 kg (d) 8 kg

64. The ages of A and B are in the ratio 3 : 1. Fifteen years hence, the ratio will be 2 : 1. Their present ages are :

(a) 30 years, 10 years (b) 45 years, 15 years
(c) 21 years, 7 years (d) 60 years, 20 years

65. The average age of three boys is 25 years and their ages are in the proportion 3 : 5 : 7. The age of the youngest boy is :

(a) 21 years (b) 18 years (c) 15 years (d) 9 years

66. The speeds of three cars are in the ratio 5 : 4 : 6. The ratio between the time taken by them to travel the same distance is :

(a) 5 : 4 : 6 (b) 6 : 4 : 5 (c) 10 : 12 : 15 (d) 12 : 15 : 10

67. In a college, the ratio of the number of boys to girls is 8 : 5. If there are 160 girls, the total number of students in the college is :

(a) 100 (b) 250 (c) 260 (d) 416

68. The sides of a triangle are in the ratio $\frac{1}{2} : \frac{1}{3} : \frac{1}{4}$ and its perimeter is 104 cm. The length of the longest side is :

(a) 52 cm (b) 48 cm (c) 32 cm (d) 26 cm

69. The ratio of the number of boys and girls in a school is 3 : 2. If 20% of the boys and 25% of the girls are scholarship holders, what percentage of the students does not get the scholarship ?

(a) 56 (b) 70 (c) 78 (d) 80

70. In a school, 10% of the boys are same in number as $\frac{1}{4}$th of the girls. What is the ratio of boys to girls in that school ?

(a) 3 : 2 (b) 5 : 2 (c) 2 : 1 (d) 4 : 3

71. Three containers have their volumes in the ratio 3 : 4 : 5. They are full of mixtures of milk and water. The mixtures contain milk and water in the ratio of (4 : 1), (3 : 1) and (5 : 2) respectively. The contents of all these three containers are poured into a fourth container. The ratio of milk and water in the fourth container is :

(a) 4 : 1 (b) 151 : 48 (c) 157 : 53 (d) 5 : 2

72. x varies inversely as square of y. Given that $y = 2$ for $x = 1$. The value of x for $y = 6$ will be equal to : **(C.D.S. 2003)**

(a) 3 (b) 9 (c) $\frac{1}{3}$ (d) $\frac{1}{9}$

73. If 10% of x = 20% of y, then $x : y$ is equal to : **(C.D.S. 2003)**

(a) 1 : 2 (b) 2 : 1 (c) 5 : 1 (d) 10 : 1

74. The electricity bill of a certain establishment is partly fixed and partly varies as the number of units of electricity consumed. When in a certain month 540 units are consumed, the bill is Rs. 1800. In another month 620 units are consumed and the bill is Rs. 2040. In yet another month 500 units are consumed. The bill for that month would be :

(*a*) Rs. 1560 (*b*) Rs. 1680 (*c*) Rs. 1840 (*d*) Rs. 1950

75. The ratio of the incomes of A and B is 5 : 4 and the ratio of their expenditures is 3 : 2. If at the end of the year, each saves Rs. 1600, then the income of A is :

(*a*) Rs. 3400 (*b*) Rs. 3600 (*c*) Rs. 4000 (*d*) Rs. 4400

76. Zinc and copper are melted together in the ratio 9 : 11. What is the weight of melted mixture, if 28.8 kg of zinc has been consumed in it ?

(*a*) 58 kg (*b*) 60 kg (*c*) 64 kg (*d*) 70 kg

77. The compounded ratio of (2 : 3), (6 : 11) and (11 : 2) is :

(*a*) 1 : 2 (*b*) 2 : 1 (*c*) 11 : 24 (*d*) 36 : 121

78. If 0.4 of a number is equal to 0.06 of another number, the ratio of the numbers is :

(*a*) 2 : 3 (*b*) 3 : 4 (*c*) 3 : 20 (*d*) 20 : 3

79. The least whole number which when subtracted from both the terms of the ratio 6 : 7 gives a ratio less than 16 : 21 is :

(*a*) 2 (*b*) 3 (*c*) 4 (*d*) 6

80. A and B are two alloys of gold and copper prepared by mixing metals in the ratio 7 : 2 and 7 : 11 respectively. If equal quantities of the alloys are melted to form a third alloy C, the ratio of gold and copper in C will be :

(*a*) 5 : 7 (*b*) 5 : 9 (*c*) 7 : 5 (*d*) 9 : 5

81. Which of the following ratios is greatest ?

(*a*) 7 : 15 (*b*) 15 : 23 (*c*) 17 : 25 (*d*) 21 : 29

82. A certain amount was divided between A and B in the ratio 4 : 3. If B's share was Rs. 4800, the total amount was :

(*a*) Rs. 11,200 (*b*) Rs. 6400 (*c*) Rs. 19,200 (*d*) Rs. 39,200

83. A sum of Rs. 53 is divided among A, B, C in such a way that A gets Rs. 7 more than what B gets and B gets Rs. 8 more than what C gets. The ratio of their shares is :

(*a*) 16 : 9 : 18 (*b*) 25 : 18 : 10 (*c*) 18 : 25 : 10 (*d*) 15 : 8 : 30

84. What is the ratio whose terms differ by 40 and the measure of which is $\frac{2}{7}$?

(*a*) 16 : 56 (*b*) 14 : 56 (*c*) 15 : 56 (*d*) 16 : 72

ANSWERS

1. (*b*)	**2.** (*c*)	**3.** (*b*)	**4.** (*d*)	**5.** (*d*)	**6.** (*c*)	**7.** (*c*)	**8.** (*c*)
9. (*c*)	**10.** (*b*)	**11.** (*c*)	**12.** (*b*)	**13.** (*c*)	**14.** (*b*)	**15.** (*a*)	**16.** (*c*)
17. (*a*)	**18.** (*d*)	**19.** (*d*)	**20.** (*b*)	**21.** (*a*)	**22.** (*c*)	**23.** (*d*)	**24.** (*a*)
25. (*b*)	**26.** (*c*)	**27.** (*b*)	**28.** (*c*)	**29.** (*c*)	**30.** (*c*)	**31.** (*d*)	**32.** (*b*)
33. (*b*)	**34.** (*a*)	**35.** (*a*)	**36.** (*b*)	**37.** (*b*)	**38.** (*c*)	**39.** (*c*)	**40.** (*c*)
41. (*a*)	**42.** (*c*)	**43.** (*c*)	**44.** (*c*)	**45.** (*d*)	**46.** (*c*)	**47.** (*d*)	**48.** (*b*)
49. (*d*)	**50.** (*a*)	**51.** (*d*)	**52.** (*b*)	**53.** (*b*)	**54.** (*c*)	**55.** (*c*)	**56.** (*d*)
57. (*b*)	**58.** (*a*)	**59.** (*b*)	**60.** (*d*)	**61.** (*b*)	**62.** (*b*)	**63.** (*a*)	**64.** (*b*)
65. (*c*)	**66.** (*d*)	**67.** (*d*)	**68.** (*b*)	**69.** (*c*)	**70.** (*b*)	**71.** (*c*)	**72.** (*d*)
73. (*b*)	**74.** (*b*)	**75.** (*c*)	**76.** (*c*)	**77.** (*b*)	**78.** (*c*)	**79.** (*b*)	**80.** (*c*)
81. (*d*)	**82.** (*a*)	**83.** (*b*)	**84.** (*a*)				

SOLUTIONS

1. A : B = 5 : 7, B : C = 6 : 11 = $\left(6 \times \frac{7}{6}\right) : \left(11 \times \frac{7}{6}\right) = 7 : \frac{77}{6}$.

$\therefore$ A : B : C = $5 : 7 : \frac{77}{6} = 30 : 42 : 77$.

2. $\left(\frac{A}{B} = \frac{3}{4}, \frac{B}{C} = \frac{8}{9}\right) \Rightarrow \frac{A}{C} = \left(\frac{A}{B} \times \frac{B}{C}\right) = \left(\frac{3}{4} \times \frac{8}{9}\right) = \frac{2}{3} \Rightarrow A : C = 2 : 3.$

3. $\frac{A}{B} = \frac{8}{15}, \frac{B}{C} = \frac{5}{8}$ and $\frac{C}{D} = \frac{4}{5} \Rightarrow \frac{A}{D} = \left(\frac{A}{B} \times \frac{B}{C} \times \frac{C}{D}\right) = \left(\frac{8}{15} \times \frac{5}{8} \times \frac{4}{5}\right) = \frac{4}{15}$

$\Rightarrow$ A : D = 4 : 15.

4. Let A = 2x, B = 3x and C = 4x. Then, $\frac{A}{B} = \frac{2x}{3x} = \frac{2}{3}, \frac{B}{C} = \frac{3x}{4x} = \frac{3}{4}$ and $\frac{C}{A} = \frac{4x}{2x} = \frac{2}{1}$

$\Rightarrow \frac{A}{B} : \frac{B}{C} : \frac{C}{A} = \frac{2}{3} : \frac{3}{4} : \frac{2}{1} = 8 : 9 : 24.$

5. $A : B = \frac{1}{2} : \frac{3}{8} = 4 : 3, B : C = \frac{1}{3} : \frac{5}{9} = 3 : 5, C : D = \frac{5}{6} : \frac{3}{4} = 10 : 9$

$\Rightarrow$ A : B = 4 : 3, B : C = 3 : 5 and C : D = $5 : \frac{9}{2}$

$\Rightarrow A : B : C : D = 4 : 3 : 5 : \frac{9}{2} = 8 : 6 : 10 : 9.$

6. A : B = 2 : 3, B : C = 4 : 5 = $\left(4 \times \frac{3}{4}\right) : \left(5 \times \frac{3}{4}\right) = 3 : \frac{15}{4}$

and C : D = 6 : 7 = $\left(6 \times \frac{15}{24}\right) : \left(7 \times \frac{15}{24}\right) = \frac{15}{4} : \frac{35}{8}$

$\Rightarrow A : B : C : D = 2 : 3 : \frac{15}{4} : \frac{35}{8} = 16 : 24 : 30 : 35.$

7. Let 2A = 3B = 4C = k. Then, A = $\frac{k}{2}$, B = $\frac{k}{3}$ and C = $\frac{k}{4}$

$\Rightarrow A : B : C = \frac{k}{2} : \frac{k}{3} : \frac{k}{4} = 6 : 4 : 3.$

8. Let $\frac{A}{3} = \frac{B}{4} = \frac{C}{5} = k$. Then, A = 3$k$, B = 4$k$ and C = 5k

$\Rightarrow$ A : B : C = 3k : 4k : 5k = 3 : 4 : 5.

9. 2A = 3B and 4B = 5C $\Rightarrow \frac{A}{B} = \frac{3}{2}$ and $\frac{B}{C} = \frac{5}{4}$

$\Rightarrow \frac{A}{C} = \left(\frac{A}{B} \times \frac{B}{C}\right) = \left(\frac{3}{2} \times \frac{5}{4}\right) = \frac{15}{8} \Rightarrow A : C = 15 : 8.$

10. $\frac{4^{3.5}}{2^5} = \frac{(2^2)^{3.5}}{2^5} = \frac{2^{(2 \times 3.5)}}{2^5} = \frac{2^7}{2^5} = 2^2 = 4.$

$\therefore$ Required ratio is 4 : 1.

11. $\frac{1}{5} : \frac{1}{x} = \frac{1}{x} : \frac{100}{125} \Rightarrow \left(\frac{1}{x} \times \frac{1}{x}\right) = \left(\frac{1}{5} \times \frac{100}{125}\right) = \frac{4}{25}$

$\Rightarrow \frac{1}{x^2} = \frac{4}{25} \Rightarrow x^2 = \frac{25}{4} \Rightarrow x = \frac{5}{2} = 2.5.$

12. $(x \times 5) = (0.75 \times 8) \Rightarrow x = \frac{6}{5} = 1.20.$

13. Let $x = 5k$ and $y = 2k$. Then, $\frac{8x + 9y}{8x + 2y} = \frac{(8 \times 5k) + (9 \times 2k)}{(8 \times 5k) + (2 \times 2k)} = \frac{58k}{44k} = \frac{29}{22}.$

$\Rightarrow (8x + 9y) : (8x + 2y) = 29 : 22.$

14. 15% of x = 20% of $y \Rightarrow \frac{15x}{100} = \frac{20y}{100} \Rightarrow \frac{x}{y} = \left(\frac{20}{100} \times \frac{100}{15}\right) = \frac{4}{3}$

$\Rightarrow x : y = 4 : 3.$

15. $\frac{x}{y} = \frac{2}{1} \Leftrightarrow \frac{x^2}{y^2} = \frac{4}{1} \Leftrightarrow \frac{x^2 + y^2}{x^2 - y^2} = \frac{4 + 1}{4 - 1}$ [*By componendo and dividendo*]

$\Leftrightarrow \frac{x^2 - y^2}{x^2 + y^2} = \frac{3}{5} \Leftrightarrow (x^2 - y^2) : (x^2 + y^2) = 3 : 5.$

16. $\frac{4x^2 - 3y^2}{2x^2 + 5y^2} = \frac{12}{19} \Leftrightarrow 19\,(4x^2 - 3y^2) = 12\,(2x^2 + 5y^2)$

$\Leftrightarrow 52x^2 = 117y^2 \Leftrightarrow 4x^2 = 9y^2 \Leftrightarrow \frac{x^2}{y^2} = \frac{9}{4} \Leftrightarrow \frac{x}{y} = \frac{3}{2}.$

$\therefore$ Required ratio is 3 : 2.

17. $x^2 + 4y^2 = 4xy \Leftrightarrow x^2 - 4xy + 4y^2 = 0 \Leftrightarrow (x - 2y)^2 = 0$

$\Leftrightarrow (x - 2y) = 0 \Leftrightarrow x = 2y \Leftrightarrow \frac{x}{y} = \frac{2}{1}.$

$\therefore x : y = 2 : 1.$

18. $5x^2 - 13xy + 6y^2 = 0 \Leftrightarrow 5x^2 - 10xy - 3xy + 6y^2 = 0$

$\Leftrightarrow 5x\,(x - 2y) - 3y\,(x - 2y) = 0 \Leftrightarrow (x - 2y)\,(5x - 3y) = 0$

$\Leftrightarrow x = 2y$ or $5x = 3y \Leftrightarrow \frac{x}{y} = \frac{2}{1}$ or $\frac{x}{y} = \frac{3}{5}$

$\therefore (x : y) = (2 : 1)$ or $(3 : 5)$.

19. Let $\frac{x}{5} = \frac{y}{8} = k$. Then, $x = 5k$ and $y = 8k$.

$\therefore \frac{x + 5}{y + 8} = \frac{5k + 5}{8k + 8} = \frac{5\,(k + 1)}{8\,(k + 1)} = \frac{5}{8} \Rightarrow (x + 5) : (y + 8) = 5 : 8.$

20. Let $\frac{a}{3} = \frac{b}{4} = \frac{c}{7} = k$. Then, $a = 3k$, $b = 4k$, $c = 7k$.

$\therefore \frac{a + b + c}{c} = \frac{3k + 4k + 7k}{7k} = \frac{14k}{7k} = 2.$

21. Let $(a + b) = 6k$, $(b + c) = 7k$ and $(c + a) = 8k$.

Then, $2\,(a + b + c) = 21k \Leftrightarrow 2 \times 14 = 21k \Leftrightarrow k = \frac{28}{21} = \frac{4}{3}.$

$\therefore (a + b) = \left(6 \times \frac{4}{3}\right) = 8 \Rightarrow c = (a + b + c) - (a + b) = (14 - 8) = 6.$

22. Let A = $2k$, B = $3k$ and C = $5k$.

A's new salary $= \frac{115}{100}$ of $2k = \left(\frac{115}{100} \times 2k\right) = \frac{23}{10}k$

B's new salary $= \frac{110}{100}$ of $3k = \left(\frac{110}{100} \times 3k\right) = \frac{33}{10}k$

C's new salary $= \frac{120}{100}$ of $5k = \left(\frac{120}{100} \times 5k\right) = 6k$.

$\therefore$ New ratio $= \frac{23k}{10} : \frac{33k}{10} : 6k = 23 : 33 : 60$.

23. Given ratio $= \frac{1}{2} : \frac{2}{3} : \frac{3}{4} = 6 : 8 : 9$.

$\therefore$ 1st part = Rs. $\left(782 \times \frac{6}{23}\right)$ = Rs. 204.

24. Given ratio = 7 : 5 : 3 : 4, Sum of ratio terms = 19.

$\therefore$ Smallest part $= \left(76 \times \frac{3}{19}\right) = 12$.

25. Let the numbers be $3x$ and $5x$. Then, $\frac{3x - 9}{5x - 9} = \frac{12}{23} \Leftrightarrow 23(3x - 9) = 12(5x - 9)$

$\Leftrightarrow 9x = 99 \Leftrightarrow x = 11$.

$\therefore$ The smaller number $= (3 \times 11) = 33$.

26. Let the numbers be x and $2x$. Then, $\frac{x + 7}{2x + 7} = \frac{3}{5} \Leftrightarrow 5(x + 7) = 3(2x + 7) \Leftrightarrow x = 14$.

$\therefore$ Greatest number = 28.

27. A : B = 5 : 4, B : C = 9 : 10 $= \left(9 \times \frac{4}{9}\right) : \left(10 \times \frac{4}{9}\right) = 4 : \frac{40}{9}$.

$\therefore$ A : B : C $= 5 : 4 : \frac{40}{9} = 45 : 36 : 40$.

Sum of ratio terms $= (45 + 36 + 40) = 121$.

$\therefore$ C's share = Rs. $\left(1210 \times \frac{40}{121}\right)$ = Rs. 400.

28. Let the number of 25 p, 10 p and 5 p coins be x, $2x$ and $3x$ respectively.

Then, sum of their values = Rs. $\left(\frac{25x}{100} + \frac{10 \times 2x}{100} + \frac{5 \times 3x}{100}\right)$ = Rs. $\frac{60x}{100}$.

$\therefore \frac{60x}{100} = 30 \Leftrightarrow x = \frac{30 \times 100}{60} = 50$.

Hence, the number of 5 p coins $= (3 \times 50) = 150$.

29. Let the numbers be $3x$, $4x$ and $5x$. Then,

$9x^2 + 16x^2 + 25x^2 = 1250 \Leftrightarrow 50x^2 = 1250 \Leftrightarrow x^2 = 25 \Leftrightarrow x = 5$.

$\therefore$ Sum of numbers $= (3x + 4x + 5x) = 12x = (12 \times 5) = 60$.

30. Let the numbers be $3x$, $4x$ and $7x$. Then,

$3x \times 4x \times 7x = 18144 \Leftrightarrow x^3 = 216 \Leftrightarrow x^3 = 6^3 \Leftrightarrow x = 6$.

$\therefore$ The numbers are 18, 24 and 42.

31. Let the original salaries of Ravi and Sumit be Rs. $2x$ and Rs. $3x$ respectively. Then,

$\frac{2x + 4000}{3x + 4000} = \frac{40}{57} \Leftrightarrow 57(2x + 4000) = 40(3x + 4000) \Leftrightarrow 6x = 68000 \Leftrightarrow 3x = 34000$

Sumit's present salary $= (3x + 4000)$ = Rs. $(34000 + 4000)$ = Rs. 38,000.

32. $\left(A = \frac{2}{3}B \text{ and } B = \frac{1}{4}C\right) \Leftrightarrow \frac{A}{B} = \frac{2}{3}$ and $\frac{B}{C} = \frac{1}{4}$

$\Rightarrow$ A : B = 2 : 3 and B : C = 1 : 4 = 3 : 12 $\Rightarrow$ A : B : C = 2 : 3 : 12.

$\therefore$ A's share = Rs. $\left(510 \times \frac{2}{17}\right)$ = Rs. 60; B's share = Rs. $\left(510 \times \frac{3}{17}\right)$ = Rs. 90;

C's share = Rs. $\left(510 \times \frac{12}{17}\right)$ = Rs. 360.

33. Let the three parts be A, B, C. Then,

A : B = 2 : 3 and B : C = 5 : 8 = $\left(5 \times \frac{3}{5}\right) : \left(8 \times \frac{3}{5}\right) = 3 : \frac{24}{5}$

$\Rightarrow$ A : B : C = $2 : 3 : \frac{24}{5}$ = 10 : 15 : 24 $\Rightarrow$ B = $\left(98 \times \frac{15}{49}\right)$ = 30.

34. Let $x : \frac{1}{27} :: \frac{3}{11} : \frac{5}{9}$. Then, $x \times \frac{5}{9} = \frac{1}{27} \times \frac{3}{11} \Leftrightarrow x = \left(\frac{1}{27} \times \frac{3}{11} \times \frac{9}{5}\right) = \frac{1}{55}$.

35. A : (B + C) = 1 : 2 $\Rightarrow$ A's share = Rs. $\left(366 \times \frac{1}{3}\right)$ = Rs. 122.

36. Let P = $2x$ and Q = $3x$. Then, $\frac{Q}{R} = \frac{2}{3} \Rightarrow R = \frac{3}{2}Q = \left(\frac{3}{2} \times 3x\right) = \frac{9x}{2}$.

Also, $\frac{R}{S} = \frac{2}{3} \Rightarrow S = \frac{3}{2}R = \left(\frac{3}{2} \times \frac{9x}{2}\right) = \frac{27x}{4}$.

Thus, P = $2x$, Q = $3x$, R = $\frac{9x}{2}$ and S = $\frac{27x}{4}$.

Now, P + Q + R + S = 1300 $\Leftrightarrow \left(2x + 3x + \frac{9x}{2} + \frac{27x}{4}\right) = 1300$

$\Leftrightarrow (8x + 12x + 18x + 27x) = 5200$

$\Leftrightarrow 65x = 5200 \Leftrightarrow x = \frac{5200}{65} = 80$.

$\therefore$ P's share = Rs. (2 × 80) = Rs. 160.

37. $\frac{4}{15}A = \frac{2}{5}B \Leftrightarrow A = \left(\frac{2}{5} \times \frac{15}{4}\right)B \Leftrightarrow A = \frac{3}{2}B \Leftrightarrow \frac{A}{B} = \frac{3}{2} \Leftrightarrow$ A : B = 3 : 2

$\therefore$ B's share = Rs. $\left(1210 \times \frac{2}{5}\right)$ = Rs. 484.

38. Let the third number be x.

Then, first number = 120% of $x = \frac{120x}{100} = \frac{6x}{5}$;

second number = 150% of $x = \frac{150x}{100} = \frac{3x}{2}$.

$\therefore$ Ratio of first two numbers = $\frac{6x}{5} : \frac{3x}{2} = 12x : 15x = 4 : 5$.

39. The sum of the ratio terms must divide 72. So, the ratio cannot be 3 : 4.

40. For dividing 12 into two whole numbers, the sum of the ratio terms must be a factor of 12. So, they cannot be in the ratio 3 : 2.

41. Originally, let the number of seats for Mathematics, Physics and Biology be $5x$, $7x$ and $8x$ respectively.

Number of increased seats are (140% of $5x$), (150% of $7x$) and (175% of $8x$)

i.e. $\left(\frac{140}{100} \times 5x\right), \left(\frac{150}{100} \times 7x\right)$ and $\left(\frac{175}{100} \times 8x\right)$ *i.e.* $7x$, $\frac{21x}{2}$ and $14x$.

$\therefore$ Required ratio = $7x : \frac{21x}{2} : 14x = 14x : 21x : 28x = 2 : 3 : 4$.

42. Originally, let the number of boys and girls in the college be $7x$ and $8x$ respectively. Their increased number is (120% of $7x$) and (110% of $8x$)

i.e. $\left(\frac{120}{100} \times 7x\right)$ and $\left(\frac{110}{100} \times 8x\right)$ *i.e.* $\frac{42x}{5}$ and $\frac{44x}{5}$.

$\therefore$ Required ratio $= \frac{42x}{5} : \frac{44x}{5} = 21 : 22.$

43. Let the shares of A, B, C and D be Rs. $5x$, Rs. $2x$, Rs. $4x$ and Rs. $3x$ respectively.
Then, $4x - 3x = 1000 \Leftrightarrow x = 1000$.

$\therefore$ B's share = Rs. $2x$ = Rs. (2×1000) = Rs. 2000.

44. Let 40% of A $= \frac{2}{3}$B. Then, $\frac{40A}{100} = \frac{2B}{3} \Leftrightarrow \frac{2A}{5} = \frac{2B}{3} \Leftrightarrow \frac{A}{B} = \left(\frac{2}{3} \times \frac{5}{2}\right) = \frac{5}{3}$.

$\therefore$ A : B = 5 : 3.

45. Let the original earnings of A and B be Rs. $4x$ and Rs. $7x$.

New earnings of A = 150% of Rs. $4x$ = Rs. $\left(\frac{150}{100} \times 4x\right)$ = Rs. $6x$.

New earnings of B = 75% of Rs. $7x$ = Rs. $\left(\frac{75}{100} \times 7x\right)$ = Rs. $\frac{21x}{4}$.

$\therefore \quad 6x : \frac{21x}{4} = 8 : 7 \Leftrightarrow \frac{6x \times 4}{21x} = \frac{8}{7}$.

This does not give x. So, the given data is inadequate.

46. Let the required number be x. Then, $(14 - x) : (17 - x) :: (34 - x) : (42 - x)$.

$\therefore \quad \frac{14-x}{17-x} = \frac{34-x}{42-x} \Leftrightarrow (14-x)(42-x) = (17-x)(34-x)$

$\Leftrightarrow x^2 - 56x + 588 = x^2 - 51x + 578 \Leftrightarrow 5x = 10 \Leftrightarrow x = 2.$

$\therefore$ Required number = 2.

47. Quantity of milk $= \left(60 \times \frac{2}{3}\right)$ litres = 40 litres.

Quantity of water in it = (60 – 40) litres = 20 litres.
New Ratio required = 1 : 2.

Let quantity of water to be added further be x litres. Then, milk : water $= \frac{40}{(20+x)}$.

Now, $\frac{40}{(20+x)} = \frac{1}{2} \Leftrightarrow 20 + x = 80 \Leftrightarrow x = 60.$

Quantity of water to be further added = 60 litres.

48. Let the fourth proportional to 5, 8, 15 be x.

Then, $5 : 8 :: 15 : x \Leftrightarrow 5x = (8 \times 15) \Leftrightarrow x = \frac{(8 \times 15)}{5} = 24.$

49. Required mean proportional $= \sqrt{234 \times 104} = \sqrt{13 \times 9 \times 2 \times 13 \times 8} = (13 \times 3 \times 4) = 156.$

50. Let the third proportional to 0.36 and 0.48 be x.

Then, $0.36 : 0.48 :: 0.48 : x \Leftrightarrow x = \left(\frac{0.48 \times 0.48}{0.36}\right) = 0.64.$

51. Let the third proportional to $(x^2 - y^2)$ and $(x - y)$ be z. Then,

$(x^2 - y^2) : (x - y) :: (x - y) : z \Leftrightarrow (x^2 - y^2) \times z = (x - y)^2 \Leftrightarrow z = \frac{(x-y)^2}{(x^2 - y^2)} = \frac{(x-y)}{(x+y)}.$

52. Let the third proportional to 12 and 30 be x.

Then, $12 : 30 :: 30 : x \Leftrightarrow 12x = 30 \times 30 \Leftrightarrow x = \frac{(30 \times 30)}{12} = 75.$

$\therefore$ Third proportional to 12 and 30 = 75.

Mean proportional between 9 and 25 = $\sqrt{9 \times 25} = 15.$

$\therefore$ Required ratio = 75 : 15 = 5 : 1.

53. We have $\frac{3}{4} = \frac{12}{x} \Leftrightarrow 3x = 48 \Leftrightarrow x = 16.$

$\therefore$ Consequent = 16.

54. Let the prices of a scooter and a T.V. set be Rs. $7x$ and Rs. $5x$ respectively. Then, $7x - 5x = 8000 \Leftrightarrow 2x = 8000 \Leftrightarrow x = 4000.$

$\therefore$ Price of a T.V. set = Rs. (7×4000) = Rs. 28000.

55. Remainder = Rs. $[735 - (25 \times 3)]$ = Rs. 660.

$\therefore$ Money received by C = Rs. $\left[\left(660 \times \frac{2}{6}\right) + 25\right]$ = Rs. 225.

56. Remainder = Rs. $[2430 - (5 + 10 + 15)]$ = Rs. 2400.

$\therefore$ B's share = Rs. $\left[\left(2400 \times \frac{4}{12}\right) + 10\right]$ = Rs. 810.

57. Let the required numbers be $3x$ and $4x$. Then, their L.C.M. is $12x$.

$\therefore$ $12x = 180 \Leftrightarrow x = 15$. Hence, the first number is 45.

58. Let the required quantity of copper be x kg.

Then, $9 : 4 :: 24 : x \Leftrightarrow 9x = 4 \times 24 \Leftrightarrow x = \frac{4 \times 24}{9} = 10\frac{2}{3}.$

Hence, the required quantity of copper is $10\frac{2}{3}$ kg.

59. Quantity of tin in 60 kg of A = $\left(60 \times \frac{2}{5}\right)$ kg = 24 kg.

Quantity of tin in 100 kg of B = $\left(100 \times \frac{1}{5}\right)$ kg = 20 kg.

Quantity of tin in the new alloy = (24 + 20) kg = 44 kg.

60. G = 19W and C = 9W.

Let 1 gm of gold be mixed with x gm of copper to get $(1 + x)$ gm of the alloy.

(1 gm gold) + (x gm copper) = $(x + 1)$ gm of alloy

$\Leftrightarrow 19W + 9Wx = (x + 1) \times 15W \Leftrightarrow 19 + 9x = 15(x + 1) \Leftrightarrow 6x = 4 \Leftrightarrow x = \frac{2}{3}.$

$\therefore$ Ratio of gold with copper = $1 : \frac{2}{3} = 3 : 2.$

61. Alcohol in 15 litres of mix. = 20% of 15 litres = $\left(\frac{20}{100} \times 15\right)$ litres = 3 litres.

Water in it = (15 − 3) litres = 12 litres.

New quantity of mix. = (15 + 3) litres = 18 litres.

Quantity of alcohol in it = 3 litres.

Percentage of alcohol in new mix. = $\left(\frac{3}{18} \times 100\right)\% = 16\frac{2}{3}\%.$

62. Quantity of milk in 16 litres of mix. = $\left(16 \times \frac{5}{8}\right)$ litres = 10 litres.

Quantity of milk in 20 litres of new mix. = (10 + 4) litres.

Quantity of water in it = (20 – 14) litres = 6 litres.

$\therefore$ Ratio of milk and water in the new mix. = 14 : 6 = 7 : 3.

63. Milk in 85 kg of mix. = $\left(85 \times \frac{27}{34}\right)$ kg = $\frac{135}{2}$ kg.

Water in it = $\left(85 - \frac{135}{2}\right)$ kg = $\frac{35}{2}$ kg.

Let x kg of water be added to it.

Then, $\frac{\left(\frac{135}{2}\right)}{\left(\frac{35}{2} + x\right)} = \frac{3}{1} \Leftrightarrow \frac{135}{35 + 2x} = \frac{3}{1} \Leftrightarrow 105 + 6x = 135 \Leftrightarrow 6x = 30 \Leftrightarrow x = 5.$

$\therefore$ Quantity of water to be added = 5 kg.

64. Let the ages of A and B be $3x$ years and x years respectively.

Then, $\frac{3x + 15}{x + 15} = \frac{2}{1} \Leftrightarrow 2x + 30 = 3x + 15 \Leftrightarrow x = 15.$

So, A's age = (3 × 15) years = 45 years and B's age = 15 years.

65. Total age of 3 boys = (25 × 3) years = 75 years. Ratio of their ages = 3 : 5 : 7.

Age of the youngest = $\left(75 \times \frac{3}{15}\right)$ years = 15 years.

66. Ratio of time taken = $\frac{1}{5} : \frac{1}{4} : \frac{1}{6}$ = 12 : 15 : 10.

67. Let the number of boys and girls be $8x$ and $5x$ respectively. Then, $5x = 160 \Leftrightarrow x = 32$.

$\therefore$ Total number of students = $13x$ = (13 × 32) = 416.

68. Ratio of sides = $\frac{1}{2} : \frac{1}{3} : \frac{1}{4}$ = 6 : 4 : 3.

Largest side = $\left(104 \times \frac{6}{13}\right)$ cm = 48 cm.

69. Let boys = $3x$ and girls = $2x$.

Number of those who do not get scholarship

$$= (80\% \text{ of } 3x) + (75\% \text{ of } 2x) = \left(\frac{80}{100} \times 3x\right) + \left(\frac{75}{100} \times 2x\right) = \frac{39x}{10}.$$

Required percentage = $\left(\frac{39x}{10} \times \frac{1}{5x} \times 100\right)\%$ = 78%.

70. 10% of B = $\frac{1}{4}$ G $\Leftrightarrow \frac{10B}{100} = \frac{1}{4} G \Leftrightarrow B = \frac{5}{2} G$

$\therefore \frac{B}{G} = \frac{5}{2} \Leftrightarrow$ B : G = 5 : 2.

71. Let the three containers contain $3x$, $4x$ and $5x$ litres of mixtures respectively.

Milk in 1st mix. = $\left(3x \times \frac{4}{5}\right)$ litres = $\frac{12x}{5}$ litres.

Water in 1st mix. $= \left(3x - \frac{12x}{5}\right)$ litres $= \frac{3x}{5}$ litres.

Milk in 2nd mix. $= \left(4x \times \frac{3}{4}\right)$ litres $= 3x$ litres.

Water in 2nd mix. $= (4x - 3x)$ litres $= x$ litres.

Milk in 3rd mix. $= \left(5x \times \frac{5}{7}\right)$ litres $= \frac{25x}{7}$ litres.

Water in 3rd mix. $= \left(5x - \frac{25x}{7}\right)$ litres $= \frac{10x}{7}$ litres.

Total milk in final mix. $= \left(\frac{12x}{5} + 3x + \frac{25x}{7}\right)$ litres $= \frac{314x}{35}$ litres.

Total water in final mix. $= \left(\frac{3x}{5} + x + \frac{10x}{7}\right)$ litres $= \frac{106x}{35}$ litres.

Required ratio of milk and water $= \frac{314x}{35} : \frac{106x}{35} = 157 : 53$.

72. Given $x = \frac{k}{y^2}$, where k is a constant.

Now, $y = 2$ and $x = 1$ gives $k = 4$.

$\therefore \quad x = \frac{4}{y^2} \Rightarrow x = \frac{4}{6^2}$, when $y = 6 \Rightarrow x = \frac{4}{36} = \frac{1}{9}$.

73. 10% of x = 20% of $y \Leftrightarrow \frac{10x}{100} = \frac{20y}{100} \Leftrightarrow \frac{x}{10} = \frac{y}{5} \Leftrightarrow \frac{x}{y} = \frac{10}{5} = \frac{2}{1}$.

$\therefore \quad x : y = 2 : 1$.

74. Let the fixed amount be Rs. x and the cost of each unit be Rs. y. Then,

$540y + x = 1800$ ...(*i*) and $620y + x = 2040$ ...(*ii*)

On subtracting (*i*) from (*ii*), we get $80y = 240 \Leftrightarrow y = 3$.

Putting $y = 3$ in (*i*), we get :

$540 \times 3 + x = 1800 \Leftrightarrow x = (1800 - 1620) = 180$.

$\therefore$ Fixed charges = Rs. 180, Charge per unit = Rs. 3.

Total charges for consuming 500 units = Rs. $(180 + 500 \times 3)$ = Rs. 1680.

75. Let the incomes of A and B be Rs. $5x$ and Rs. $4x$ respectively and let their expenditures be Rs. $3y$ and Rs. $2y$ respectively.

Then, $5x - 3y = 1600$ ...(*i*) and $4x - 2y = 1600$ ...(*ii*)

On multiplying (*i*) by 2, (*ii*) by 3 and subtracting, we get : $2x = 1600 \Leftrightarrow x = 800$.

$\therefore$ A's income = Rs. $5x$ = Rs. (5×800) = Rs. 4000.

76. For 9 kg zinc, mixture melted = $(9 + 11)$ kg.

For 28.8 kg zinc, mixture melted $= \left(\frac{20}{9} \times 28.8\right)$ kg = 64 kg.

77. Required ratio $= \left(\frac{2}{3} \times \frac{6}{11} \times \frac{11}{2}\right) = \frac{2}{1} = 2 : 1$.

78. $0.4A = 0.06B \Leftrightarrow \frac{A}{B} = \frac{0.06}{0.40} = \frac{6}{40} = \frac{3}{20}$.

$\therefore \quad A : B = 3 : 20$.

79. Let x be subtracted. Then,

$$\frac{6-x}{7-x} < \frac{16}{21} \Leftrightarrow 21(6-x) < 16(7-x) \Leftrightarrow 5x > 14 \Leftrightarrow x > 2.8.$$

$\therefore$ Least such whole number is 3.

80. Gold in C = $\left(\frac{7}{9}+\frac{7}{18}\right)$ units = $\frac{7}{6}$ units. Copper in C = $\left(\frac{2}{9}+\frac{11}{18}\right)$ units = $\frac{5}{6}$ units.

$\therefore$ Gold : Copper = $\frac{7}{6} : \frac{5}{6} = 7 : 5$.

81 $\frac{7}{15} = 0.466$, $\frac{15}{23} = 0.652$, $\frac{17}{25} = 0.68$ and $\frac{21}{29} = 0.724$.

Clearly, 0.724 is greatest and therefore, 21 : 29 is greatest.

82. If B's share is Rs. 3, total amount = Rs. 7.

If B's share is Rs. 4800, total amount = Rs. $\left(\frac{7}{3} \times 4800\right)$ = Rs. 11200.

83. Suppose C gets Rs. x. Then, B gets Rs. $(x + 8)$ and A gets Rs. $(x + 15)$.

Then, $x + (x + 8) + (x + 15) = 53 \Leftrightarrow x = 10$.

$\therefore$ A : B : C = (10 + 15) : (10 + 8) : 10 = 25 : 18 : 10.

84. Let the ratio be $x : (x + 40)$. Then,

$$\frac{x}{(x+40)} = \frac{2}{7} \Leftrightarrow 7x = 2x + 80 \Leftrightarrow 5x = 80 \Leftrightarrow x = 16.$$

$\therefore$ Required ratio = 16 : 56.

---

13. PARTNERSHIP

IMPORTANT FACTS AND FORMULAE

1. **Partnership** : When two or more than two persons run a business jointly, they are called ***partners*** and the deal is known as ***partnership.***
2. **Ratio of Division of Gains** :
   (*i*) *When investments of all the partners are for the same time*, the gain or loss is distributed among the partners in the ratio of their investments.
   Suppose A and B invest Rs. x and Rs. y respectively for a year in a business, then at the end of the year :
   (A's share of profit) : (B's share of profit) = $x : y$.
   (*ii*) *When investments are for different time periods*, then equivalent capitals are calculated for a unit of time by taking (capital × number of units of time). Now, gain or loss is divided in the ratio of these capitals.
   Suppose A invests Rs. x for p months and B invests Rs. y for q months, then (A's share of profit) : (B's share of profit) = $xp : yq$.
3. **Working and Sleeping Partners** : A partner who manages the business is known as a ***working partner*** and the one who simply invests the money is a ***sleeping partner.***

SOLVED EXAMPLES

Ex. 1. ***A, B and C started a business by investing Rs. 1,20,000, Rs. 1,35,000 and Rs. 1,50,000 respectively. Find the share of each, out of an annual profit of Rs. 56,700.***

Sol. Ratio of shares of A, B and C = Ratio of their investments

$= 120000 : 135000 : 150000 = 8 : 9 : 10.$

$\therefore$ A's share = Rs. $\left(56700 \times \frac{8}{27}\right)$ = Rs. 16800.

B's share = Rs. $\left(56700 \times \frac{9}{27}\right)$ = Rs. 18900.

C's share = Rs. $\left(56700 \times \frac{10}{27}\right)$ = Rs. 21000.

Ex. 2. ***Alfred started a business investing Rs. 45,000. After 3 months, Peter joined him with a capital of Rs. 60,000. After another 6 months, Ronald joined them with a capital of Rs. 90,000. At the end of the year, they made a profit of Rs. 16,500. Find the share of each.***

Sol. Clearly, Alfred invested his capital for 12 months, Peter for 9 months and Ronald for 3 months.

So, ratio of their capitals = $(45000 \times 12) : (60000 \times 9) : (90000 \times 3)$

$= 540000 : 540000 : 270000 = 2 : 2 : 1.$

$\therefore$ Alfred's share = Rs. $\left(16500 \times \frac{2}{5}\right)$ = Rs. 6600;

Peter's share $= \text{Rs.}\left(16500 \times \frac{2}{5}\right) = \text{Rs. } 6600;$

Ronald's share $= \text{Rs.}\left(16500 \times \frac{1}{5}\right) = \text{Rs. } 3300.$

Ex. 3. *A, B and C start a business each investing Rs. 20,000. After 5 months A withdrew Rs. 5000, B withdrew Rs. 4000 and C invests Rs. 6000 more. At the end of the year, a total profit of Rs. 69,900 was recorded. Find the share of each.*

Sol. Ratio of the capitals of A, B and C

$= 20000 \times 5 + 15000 \times 7 : 20000 \times 5 + 16000 \times 7 : 20000 \times 5 + 26000 \times 7$

$= 205000 : 212000 : 282000 = 205 : 212 : 282.$

$\therefore$ A's share $= \text{Rs.}\left(69900 \times \frac{205}{699}\right) = \text{Rs. } 20500;$

B's share $= \text{Rs.}\left(69900 \times \frac{212}{699}\right) = \text{Rs. } 21200;$

C's share $= \text{Rs.}\left(69900 \times \frac{282}{699}\right) = \text{Rs. } 28200.$

Ex. 4. *A, B and C enter into partnership. A invests 3 times as much as B invests and B invests two-third of what C invests. At the end of the year, the profit earned is Rs. 6600. What is the share of B ?*

Sol. Let C's capital = Rs. x. Then, B's capital = Rs. $\frac{2}{3}x$.

A's capital $= \text{Rs.}\left(3 \times \frac{2}{3}x\right) = \text{Rs. } 2x.$

$\therefore$ Ratio of their capitals $= 2x : \frac{2}{3}x : x = 6 : 2 : 3.$

Hence, B's share $= \text{Rs.}\left(6600 \times \frac{2}{11}\right) = \text{Rs. } 1200.$

Ex. 5. *Four milkmen rented a pasture. A grazed 24 cows for 3 months; B 10 cows for 5 months; C 35 cows for 4 months and D 21 cows for 3 months. If A's share of rent is Rs. 720, find the total rent of the field.*

Sol. Ratio of shares of A, B, C, D $= (24 \times 3) : (10 \times 5) : (35 \times 4) : (21 \times 3)$

$= 72 : 50 : 140 : 63.$

Let total rent be Rs. x. Then, A's share = Rs. $\frac{72x}{325}$.

$\therefore \frac{72x}{325} = 720 \Leftrightarrow x = \frac{720 \times 325}{72} = 3250.$

Hence, total rent of the field is Rs. 3250.

Ex. 6. *A invested Rs. 76,000 in a business. After few months, B joined him with Rs. 57,000. At the end of the year, the total profit was divided between them in the ratio 2 : 1. After how many months did B join ?*

Sol. Suppose B joined after x months. Then, B's money was invested for $(12 - x)$ months.

$\therefore \frac{76000 \times 12}{57000 \times (12 - x)} = \frac{2}{1} \Leftrightarrow 912000 = 114000\ (12 - x)$

$\Leftrightarrow 114\ (12 - x) = 912 \Leftrightarrow (12 - x) = 8 \Leftrightarrow x = 4.$

Hence, B joined after 4 months.

Ex. 7. *A, B and C enter into a partnership by investing in the ratio of 3 : 2 : 4. After one year, B invests another Rs. 2,70,000 and C, at the end of 2 years, also invests Rs. 2,70,000. At the end of three years, profits are shared in the ratio of 3 : 4 : 5. Find the initial investment of each.*

Sol. Let the initial investments of A, B and C be Rs. $3x$, Rs. $2x$ and Rs. $4x$ respectively. Then,

$$(3x \times 36) : [(2x \times 12) + (2x + 270000) \times 24] : [(4x \times 24) + (4x + 270000) \times 12] = 3 : 4 : 5.$$

$$\Leftrightarrow \quad 108x : (72x + 6480000) : (144x + 3240000) = 3 : 4 : 5$$

$$\therefore \quad \frac{108x}{72x + 6480000} = \frac{3}{4} \quad \Leftrightarrow \quad 432x = 216x + 19440000$$

$$\Leftrightarrow \quad 216x = 19440000 \quad \Leftrightarrow \quad x = 90000.$$

Hence, A's initial investment = $3x$ = Rs. 2,70,000;
B's initial investment = $2x$ = Rs. 1,80,000;
C's initial investment = $4x$ = Rs. 3,60,000.

EXERCISE 13A

(OBJECTIVE TYPE QUESTIONS)

Directions : *Mark (✓) against the correct answer :*

1. P and Q started a business investing Rs. 85,000 and Rs. 15,000 respectively. In what ratio the profit earned after 2 years be divided between P and Q respectively ?
(a) 3 : 4 (b) 3 : 5 (c) 15 : 23 (d) 17 : 23 (e) None of these
(B.S.R.B. 2003)

2. Anand and Deepak started a business investing Rs. 22,500 and Rs. 35,000 respectively. Out of a total profit of Rs. 13,800, Deepak's share is :
(a) Rs. 5400 (b) Rs. 7200 (c) Rs. 8400 (d) Rs. 9600

3. A, B, C enter into a partnership investing Rs. 35,000, Rs. 45,000 and Rs. 55,000 respectively. The respective shares of A, B, C in an annual profit of Rs. 40,500 are :
(a) Rs. 10,500, Rs. 13,500, Rs. 16,500 (b) Rs. 11,500, Rs. 13,000, Rs. 16,000
(c) Rs. 11,000, Rs. 14,000, Rs. 15,500 (d) Rs. 11,500, Rs. 12,500, Rs. 16,500
(C.B.I. 1997)

4. Reena and Shaloo are partners in a business. Reena invests Rs. 35,000 for 8 months and Shaloo invests Rs. 42,000 for 10 months. Out of a profit of Rs. 31,570, Reena's share is :
(a) Rs. 9471 (b) Rs. 12,628 (c) Rs. 18,040 (d) Rs. 18,942

5. Kamal started a business investing Rs. 9000. After five months, Sameer joined with a capital of Rs. 8000. If at the end of the year, they earn a profit of Rs. 6970, then what will be the share of Sameer in the profit ? **(R.R.B. 2003)**
(a) Rs. 1883.78 (b) Rs. 2380 (c) Rs. 3690 (d) Rs. 3864

6. Simran started a software business by investing Rs. 50,000. After six months, Nanda joined her with a capital of Rs. 80,000. After 3 years, they earned a profit of Rs. 24,500. What was Simran's share in the profit ? **(Bank P.O. 2004)**
(a) Rs. 9423 (b) Rs. 10,250 (c) Rs. 12,500 (d) Rs. 14,000 (e) None of these

7. A and B started a business in partnership investing Rs. 20,000 and Rs. 15,000 respectively. After six months, C joined them with Rs. 20,000. What will be B's share in the total profit of Rs. 25,000 earned at the end of 2 years from the starting of the business ? **(S.B.I.P.O. 2000)**

(*a*) Rs. 7500 (*b*) Rs. 9000 (*c*) Rs. 9500 (*d*) Rs. 10,000 (*e*) None of these

8. Aman started a business investing Rs. 70,000. Rakhi joined him after six months with an amount of Rs. 1,05,000 and Sagar joined them with Rs. 1.4 lakhs after another six months. The amount of profit earned should be distributed in what ratio among Aman, Rakhi and Sagar respectively, 3 years after Aman started the business ?

(*a*) 7 : 6 : 10 (*b*) 12 : 15 : 16 (*c*) 42 : 45 : 56
(*d*) Cannot be determined (*e*) None of these **(Bank P.O. 2003)**

9. Arun, Kamal and Vinay invested Rs. 8000, Rs. 4000 and Rs. 8000 respectively in a business. Arun left after six months. If after eight months, there was a gain of Rs. 4005, then what will be the share of Kamal ? **(R.R.B. 1998)**

(*a*) Rs. 890 (*b*) Rs. 1335 (*c*) Rs. 1602 (*d*) Rs. 1780

10. A, B and C enter into a partnership. They invest Rs. 40,000, Rs. 80,000 and Rs. 1,20,000 respectively. At the end of the first year, B withdraws Rs. 40,000, while at the end of the second year, C withdraws Rs. 80,000. In what ratio will the profit be shared at the end of 3 years ? **(Hotel Management, 1997)**

(*a*) 2 : 3 : 5 (*b*) 3 : 4 : 7 (*c*) 4 : 5 : 9 (*d*) None of these

11. A, B and C enter into a partnership. A initially invests Rs. 25 lakhs and adds another Rs. 10 lakhs after one year. B initially invests Rs. 35 lakhs and withdraws Rs. 10 lakhs after 2 years and C invests Rs. 30 lakhs. In what ratio should the profits be divided at the end of 3 years ?

(*a*) 10 : 10 : 9 (*b*) 20 : 20 : 19 (*c*) 20 : 19 : 18 (*d*) None of these

12. Shekhar started a business investing Rs. 25,000 in 1999. In 2000, he invested an additional amount of Rs. 10,000 and Rajeev joined him with an amount of Rs. 35,000. In 2001, Shekhar invested another additional amount of Rs. 10,000 and Jatin joined them with an amount of Rs. 35,000. What will be Rajeev's share in the profit of Rs. 1,50,000 earned at the end of 3 years from the start of the business in 1999 ?

(*a*) Rs. 45,000 (*b*) Rs. 50,000 (*c*) Rs. 70,000 (*d*) Rs. 75,000 (*e*) None of these **(S.B.I.P.O. 2001)**

13. A and B entered into a partnership investing Rs. 16,000 and Rs. 12,000 respectively. After 3 months, A withdrew Rs. 5000 while B invested Rs. 5000 more. After 3 more months, C joins the business with a capital of Rs. 21,000. The share of B exceeds that of C, out of a total profit of Rs. 26,400 after one year by :

(*a*) Rs. 2400 (*b*) Rs. 3000 (*c*) Rs. 3600 (*d*) Rs. 4800

14. A and B start a business with investments of Rs. 5000 and Rs. 4500 respectively. After 4 months, A takes out half of his capital. After two more months, B takes out one-third of his capital while C joins them with a capital of Rs. 7000. At the end of a year, they earn a profit of Rs. 5080. Find the share of each member in the profit.

(*a*) A – Rs. 1400, B – Rs. 1900, C – Rs. 1780
(*b*) A – Rs. 1600, B – Rs. 1800, C – Rs. 1680
(*c*) A – Rs. 1800, B – Rs. 1500, C – Rs. 1780
(*d*) A – Rs. 1680, B – Rs. 1600, C – Rs. 1800
(*e*) None of these **(Bank P.O. 2003)**

15. A, B, C subscribe Rs. 50,000 for a business. A subscribes Rs. 4000 more than B and B Rs. 5000 more than C. Out of a total profit of Rs. 35,000, A receives :

(*a*) Rs. 8400 (*b*) Rs. 11,900 (*c*) Rs. 13,600 (*d*) Rs. 14,700

16. Three partners A, B, C start a business. Twice A's capital is equal to thrice B's capital and B's capital is four times C's capital. Out of a total profit of Rs. 16,500 at the end of the year, B's share is :
(*a*) Rs. 4000 (*b*) Rs. 6000 (*c*) Rs. 7500 (*d*) Rs. 6600

17. If 4 (A's capital) = 6 (B's capital) = 10 (C's capital), then out of a profit of Rs. 4650, C will receive :
(*a*) Rs. 465 (*b*) Rs. 900 (*c*) Rs. 1550 (*d*) Rs. 2250

18. A, B and C enter into partnership. A invests some money at the beginning, B invests double the amount after 6 months and C invests thrice the amount after 8 months. If the annual profit be Rs. 27,000, C's share is :
(*a*) Rs. 8625 (*b*) Rs. 9000 (*c*) Rs. 10,800 (*d*) Rs. 11,250

19. A, B, C hired a car for Rs. 520 and used it for 7, 8 and 11 hours respectively. Hire charges paid by B were :
(*a*) Rs. 140 (*b*) Rs. 160 (*c*) Rs. 180 (*d*) Rs. 220

20. A, B and C rent a pasture. A puts 10 oxen for 7 months, B puts 12 oxen for 5 months and C puts 15 oxen for 3 months for grazing. If the rent of the pasture is Rs. 175, how much must C pay as his share of rent ? **(S.S.C. 2000)**
(*a*) Rs. 45 (*b*) Rs. 50 (*c*) Rs. 55 (*d*) Rs. 60

21. In a business, A and C invested amounts in the ratio 2 : 1, whereas the ratio between amounts invested by A and B was 3 : 2. If Rs. 1,57,300 was their profit, how much amount did B receive ? **(Bank P.O. 1999)**
(*a*) Rs. 24,200 (*b*) Rs. 36,300 (*c*) Rs. 48,400 (*d*) Rs. 72,600

22. A and B started a partnership business investing some amount in the ratio of 3 : 5. C joined them after six months with an amount equal to that of B. In what proportion should the profit at the end of one year be distributed among A, B and C ?
(*a*) 3 : 5 : 2 (*b*) 3 : 5 : 5 (*c*) 6 : 10 : 5
(*d*) Data inadequate (*e*) None of these **(Bank P.O. 2000)**

23. A, B and C enter into a partnership and their shares are in the ratio $\frac{1}{2} : \frac{1}{3} : \frac{1}{4}$. After 2 months, A withdraws half of his capital and after 10 months, a profit of Rs. 378 is divided among them. What is B's share ? **(S.S.C. 2000)**
(*a*) Rs. 129 (*b*) Rs. 144 (*c*) Rs. 156 (*d*) Rs. 168

24. A, B and C enter into a partnership in the ratio $\frac{7}{2} : \frac{4}{3} : \frac{6}{5}$. After 4 months, A increases his share by 50%. If the total profit at the end of one year be Rs. 21,600, then B's share in the profit is : **(L.I.C.A.A.O. 2003)**
(*a*) Rs. 2100 (*b*) Rs. 2400 (*c*) Rs. 3600 (*d*) Rs. 4000

25. A, B, C started a business with their investments in the ratio 1 : 3 : 5. After 4 months, A invested the same amount as before and B as well as C withdrew half of their investments. The ratio of their profits at the end of the year is :
(*a*) 4 : 3 : 5 (*b*) 5 : 6 : 10 (*c*) 6 : 5 : 10 (*d*) 10 : 5 : 6

26. A and B entered into partnership with capitals in the ratio 4 : 5. After 3 months, A withdrew $\frac{1}{4}$ of his capital and B withdrew $\frac{1}{5}$ of his capital. The gain at the end of 10 months was Rs. 760. A's share in this profit is : **(A.A.O. Exam, 2003)**
(*a*) Rs. 330 (*b*) Rs. 360 (*c*) Rs. 380 (*d*) Rs. 430

27. In a partnership, A invests $\frac{1}{6}$ of the capital for $\frac{1}{6}$ of the time, B invests $\frac{1}{3}$ of the capital for $\frac{1}{3}$ of the time and C, the rest of the capital for the whole time. Out of a profit of Rs. 4600, B's share is :
(*a*) Rs. 650 (*b*) Rs. 800 (*c*) Rs. 960 (*d*) Rs. 1000

28. A, B and C jointly thought of engaging themselves in a business venture. It was agreed that A would invest Rs. 6500 for 6 months, B, Rs. 8400 for 5 months and C, Rs. 10,000 for 3 months. A wants to be the working member for which he was to receive 5% of the profits. The profit earned was Rs. 7400. Calculate the share of B in the profit.
(*a*) Rs. 1900 (*b*) Rs. 2660 (*c*) Rs. 2800 (*d*) Rs. 2840
(M.B.A. 2002)

29. X and Y invested in a business. They earned some profit which they divided in the ratio of 2 : 3. If X invested Rs. 40,000, the amount invested by Y is :
(*a*) Rs. 45,000 (*b*) Rs. 50,000 (*c*) Rs. 60,000 (*d*) Rs. 80,000

30. Manick received Rs. 6000 as his share out of the total profit of Rs. 9000 which he and Raunaq earned at the end of one year. If Manick invested Rs. 20,000 for 6 months, whereas Raunaq invested his amount for the whole year, what was the amount invested by Raunaq ?
(*a*) Rs. 4000 (*b*) Rs. 5000 (*c*) Rs. 6000 (*d*) Rs. 10,000

31. A, B and C enter into a partnership with a capital in which A's contribution is Rs. 10,000. If out of a total profit of Rs. 1000, A gets Rs. 500 and B gets Rs. 300, then C's capital is :
(*a*) Rs. 4000 (*b*) Rs. 5000 (*c*) Rs. 6000 (*d*) Rs. 9000

32. A, B and C started a shop by investing Rs. 27,000, Rs. 72,000 and Rs. 81,000 respectively. At the end of the year, the profits were distributed among them. If C's share of profit be Rs. 36,000, then the total profit was :
(*a*) Rs. 80,000 (*b*) Rs. 95,600 (*c*) Rs. 1,08,000 (*d*) Rs. 1,16,000

33. A and B started a business jointly. A's investment was thrice the investment of B and the period of his investment was two times the period of investment of B. If B received Rs. 4000 as profit, then their total profit is :
(*a*) Rs. 16,000 (*b*) Rs. 20,000 (*c*) Rs. 24,000 (*d*) Rs. 28,000

34. A started a business with Rs. 21,000 and is joined afterwards by B with Rs. 36,000. After how many months did B join if the profits at the end of the year are divided equally ?
(*a*) 3 (*b*) 4 (*c*) 5 (*d*) 6

35. A began a business with Rs. 85,000. He was joined afterwards by B with Rs. 42,500. For how much period does B join, if the profits at the end of the year are divided in the ratio of 3 : 1 ?
(N.I.F.T. 2003)
(*a*) 4 months (*b*) 5 months (*c*) 6 months (*d*) 8 months.

36. A starts business with Rs. 3500 and after 5 months, B joins with A as his partner. After a year, the profit is divided in the ratio 2 : 3. What is B's contribution in the capital ?
(S.S.C. 2000)
(*a*) Rs. 7500 (*b*) Rs. 8000 (*c*) Rs. 8500 (*d*) Rs. 9000

37. A and B start a business jointly. A invests Rs. 16,000 for 8 months and B remains in the business for 4 months. Out of total profit, B claims $\frac{2}{7}$ of the profit. How much money was contributed by B ?
(*a*) Rs. 10,500 (*b*) Rs. 11,900 (*c*) Rs. 12,800 (*d*) Rs. 13,600

38. Two friends P and Q started a business investing in the ratio of 5 : 6. R joined them after six months investing an amount equal to that of Q's. At the end of the year, 20% profit was earned which was equal to Rs. 98,000. What was the amount invested by R ?
(S.B.I.P.O. 1999)
(*a*) Rs. 1,05,000 (*b*) Rs. 1,75,000 (*c*) Rs. 2,10,000
(*d*) Data inadequate (*e*) None of these

39. Three partners shared the profit in a business in the ratio 5 : 7 : 8. They had partnered for 14 months, 8 months and 7 months respectively. What was the ratio of their investments ?
(Hotel Management, 1998)
(*a*) 5 : 7 : 8 (*b*) 28 : 49 : 64 (*c*) 38 : 28 : 21 (*d*) None of these

40. A and B invest in a business in the ratio 3 : 2. If 5% of the total profit goes to charity and A's share is Rs. 855, the total profit is :

(*a*) Rs. 1425 (*b*) Rs. 1500 (*c*) Rs. 1537.50 (*d*) Rs. 1576

41. A and B started a business with initial investments in the ratio 14 : 15 and their annual profits were in the ratio 7 : 6. If A invested the money for 10 months, for how many months did B invest his money ?

(*a*) 6 (*b*) 7 (*c*) 8 (*d*) 9

42. A and B are partners in a business. A contributes $\frac{1}{4}$ of the capital for 15 months and B received $\frac{2}{3}$ of the profit. For how long B's money was used ? **(S.S.C. 2000)**

(*a*) 6 months (*b*) 9 months (*c*) 10 months (*d*) 1 year

ANSWERS

1. (*e*)	**2.** (*c*)	**3.** (*a*)	**4.** (*b*)	**5.** (*b*)	**6.** (*e*)	**7.** (*a*)	**8.** (*b*)	**9.** (*a*)
10. (*b*)	**11.** (*d*)	**12.** (*b*)	**13.** (*c*)	**14.** (*b*)	**15.** (*d*)	**16.** (*b*)	**17.** (*b*)	**18.** (*b*)
19. (*b*)	**20.** (*a*)	**21.** (*c*)	**22.** (*c*)	**23.** (*b*)	**24.** (*d*)	**25.** (*b*)	**26.** (*a*)	**27.** (*b*)
28. (*b*)	**29.** (*c*)	**30.** (*b*)	**31.** (*b*)	**32.** (*a*)	**33.** (*d*)	**34.** (*c*)	**35.** (*d*)	**36.** (*d*)
37. (*c*)	**38.** (*c*)	**39.** (*d*)	**40.** (*b*)	**41.** (*c*)	**42.** (*c*)			

SOLUTIONS

1. P : Q = 85000 : 15000 = 85 : 15 = 17 : 3.

2. Ratio of their shares = 22500 : 35000 = 9 : 14.

Deepak's share = Rs. $\left(13800 \times \frac{14}{23}\right)$ = Rs. 8400.

3. A : B : C = 35000 : 45000 : 55000 = 7 : 9 : 11.

A's share = Rs. $\left(40500 \times \frac{7}{27}\right)$ = Rs. 10500.

B's share = Rs. $\left(40500 \times \frac{9}{27}\right)$ = Rs. 13500.

C's share = Rs. $\left(40500 \times \frac{11}{27}\right)$ = Rs. 16500.

4. Ratio of their shares = (35000 × 8) : (42000 × 10) = 2 : 3.

Reena's share = Rs. $\left(31570 \times \frac{2}{5}\right)$ = Rs. 12628.

5. Kamal : Sameer = (9000 × 12) : (8000 × 7) = 108 : 56 = 27 : 14.

∴ Sameer's share = Rs. $\left(6970 \times \frac{14}{41}\right)$ = Rs. 2380.

6. Simran : Nanda = (50000 × 36) : (80000 × 30) = 3 : 4.

∴ Simran's share = Rs. $\left(24500 \times \frac{3}{7}\right)$ = Rs. 10500.

7. A : B : C = (20000 × 24) : (15000 × 24) : (20000 × 18) = 4 : 3 : 3.

∴ B's share = Rs. $\left(25000 \times \frac{3}{10}\right)$ = Rs. 7500.

8. Aman : Rakhi : Sagar $= (70000 \times 36) : (105000 \times 30) : (140000 \times 24) = 12 : 15 : 16.$

9. Arun : Kamal : Vinay $= (8000 \times 6) : (4000 \times 8) : (8000 \times 8) = 48 : 32 : 64 = 3 : 2 : 4.$

$\therefore$ Kamal's share = Rs. $\left(4005 \times \frac{2}{9}\right)$ = Rs. 890.

10. A : B : C $= (40000 \times 36) : (80000 \times 12 + 40000 \times 24) : (120000 \times 24 + 40000 \times 12)$
$= 144 : 192 : 336 = 3 : 4 : 7.$

11. A : B : C = (25 lakhs × 1) + (35 lakhs × 2) : (35 lakhs × 2 + 25 lakhs × 1) : (30 lakhs × 3)
= 95 lakhs : 95 lakhs : 90 lakhs = 19 : 19 : 18.

12. Shekhar : Rajeev : Jatin
$= (25000 \times 12 + 35000 \times 12 + 45000 \times 12) : (35000 \times 24) : (35000 \times 12)$
$= 1260000 : 840000 : 420000 = 3 : 2 : 1.$

$\therefore$ Rajeev's share = Rs. $\left(150000 \times \frac{2}{6}\right)$ = Rs. 50000.

13. A : B : C $= (16000 \times 3 + 11000 \times 9) : (12000 \times 3 + 17000 \times 9) : (21000 \times 6)$
$= 147 : 189 : 126 = 7 : 9 : 6.$

$\therefore$ Difference of B and C's shares = Rs. $\left(26400 \times \frac{9}{22} - 26400 \times \frac{6}{22}\right)$ = Rs. 3600.

14. A : B : C $= (5000 \times 4 + 2500 \times 8) : (4500 \times 6 + 3000 \times 6) : (7000 \times 6)$
$= 40000 : 45000 : 42000 = 40 : 45 : 42.$

$\therefore$ A's share = Rs. $\left(5080 \times \frac{40}{127}\right)$ = Rs. 1600;

B's share = Rs. $\left(5080 \times \frac{45}{127}\right)$ = Rs. 1800;

C's share = Rs. $\left(5080 \times \frac{42}{127}\right)$ = Rs. 1680.

15. Let C = x. Then, B = x + 5000 and A = x + 5000 + 4000 = x + 9000.
So, $x + x + 5000 + x + 9000 = 50000 \Leftrightarrow 3x = 36000 \Leftrightarrow x = 12000.$
A : B : C = 21000 : 17000 : 12000 = 21 : 17 : 12.

$\therefore$ A's share = Rs. $\left(35000 \times \frac{21}{50}\right)$ = Rs. 14,700.

16. Let C = x. Then, B = $4x$ and 2A = 3 × $4x$ = $12x$ or A = $6x$.
$\therefore$ A : B : C = $6x : 4x : x$ = 6 : 4 : 1.

So, B's capital = Rs. $\left(16500 \times \frac{4}{11}\right)$ = Rs. 6000.

17. Let 4A = 6B = 10C = k. Then, A = $\frac{k}{4}$, B = $\frac{k}{6}$ and C = $\frac{k}{10}$.

$\therefore$ A : B : C = $\frac{k}{4} : \frac{k}{6} : \frac{k}{10}$ = 15 : 10 : 6.

Hence, C's share = Rs. $\left(4650 \times \frac{6}{31}\right)$ = Rs. 900.

18. Let A's investment be Rs. x.
Then, Ratio of capitals = $(x \times 12) : (2x \times 6) : (3x \times 4) = 12x : 12x : 12x = 1 : 1 : 1.$

$\therefore$ C's share = Rs. $\left(27000 \times \frac{1}{3}\right)$ = Rs. 9000.

19. A : B : C = 7 : 8 : 11.

Hire charges paid by B = Rs. $\left(520 \times \frac{8}{26}\right)$ = Rs. 160.

20. A : B : C = 10 × 7 : 12 × 5 : 15 × 3 = 70 : 60 : 45 = 14 : 12 : 9.

∴ C's rent = Rs. $\left(175 \times \frac{9}{35}\right)$ = Rs. 45.

21. A : B = 3 : 2 ⇒ B : A = 2 : 3 = 4 : 6 and A : C = 2 : 1 = 6 : 3.
So, B : A : C = 4 : 6 : 3 or A : B : C = 6 : 4 : 3.

∴ B's share = Rs. $\left(157300 \times \frac{4}{13}\right)$ = Rs. 48400.

22. Let the initial investments of A and B be $3x$ and $5x$.
A : B : C = $(3x \times 12) : (5x \times 12) : (5x \times 6)$ = 36 : 60 : 30 = 6 : 10 : 5.

23. Ratio of initial investments = $\frac{1}{2} : \frac{1}{3} : \frac{1}{4}$ = 6 : 4 : 3.

Let their initial investments be $6x$, $2x$ and $3x$ respectively.

A : B : C = $(6x \times 2 + 3x \times 10) : (4x \times 12) : (3x \times 12)$ = 42 : 48 : 36 = 7 : 8 : 6.

∴ B's share = Rs. $\left(378 \times \frac{8}{21}\right)$ = Rs. 144.

24. Ratio of initial investments = $\frac{7}{2} : \frac{4}{3} : \frac{6}{5}$ = 105 : 40 : 36.

Let the initial investments be $105x$, $40x$ and $36x$.

∴ A : B : C = $\left(105x \times 4 + \frac{150}{100} \times 105x \times 8\right) : (40x \times 12) : (36x \times 12)$

= $1680x : 480x : 432x$ = 35 : 10 : 9.

Hence, B's share = Rs. $\left(21600 \times \frac{10}{54}\right)$ = Rs. 4000.

25. Let their initial investments be x, $3x$ and $5x$ respectively. Then,

A : B : C = $(x \times 4 + 2x \times 8) : \left(3x \times 4 + \frac{3x}{2} \times 8\right) : \left(5x \times 4 + \frac{5x}{2} \times 8\right)$

= $20x : 24x : 40x$ = 5 : 6 : 10.

26. A : B = $\left[4x \times 3 + \left(4x - \frac{1}{4} \times 4x\right) \times 7\right] : \left[5x \times 3 + \left(5x - \frac{1}{5} \times 5x\right) \times 7\right]$

= $(12x + 21x) : (15x + 28x)$ = $33x : 43x$ = 33 : 43.

∴ A's share = Rs. $\left(760 \times \frac{33}{76}\right)$ = Rs. 330.

27. Suppose A invests Rs. $\frac{x}{6}$ for $\frac{y}{6}$ months. Then, B invests Rs. $\frac{x}{3}$ for $\frac{y}{3}$ months.

C invests $\left[x - \left(\frac{x}{6} + \frac{x}{3}\right)\right]$ *i.e.*, Rs. $\frac{x}{2}$ for y months.

∴ A : B : C = $\left(\frac{x}{6} \times \frac{y}{6}\right) : \left(\frac{x}{3} \times \frac{y}{3}\right) : \left(\frac{x}{2} \times y\right) = \frac{1}{36} : \frac{1}{9} : \frac{1}{2}$ = 1 : 4 : 18.

Hence, B's share = Rs. $\left(4600 \times \frac{4}{23}\right)$ = Rs. 800.

28. For managing, A receives = 5% of Rs. 7400 = Rs. 370.

Balance = Rs. (7400 − 370) = Rs. 7030.

Ratio of their investments $= (6500 \times 6) : (8400 \times 5) : (10000 \times 3)$

$= 39000 : 42000 : 30000 = 13 : 14 : 10.$

$\therefore$ B's share = Rs. $\left(7030 \times \frac{14}{37}\right)$ = Rs. 2660.

29. Suppose Y invested Rs. y. Then, $\frac{40000}{y} = \frac{2}{3}$ or $y = \left(\frac{40000 \times 3}{2}\right) = 60000.$

30. Suppose Raunaq invested Rs. x. Then, Manick : Raunaq = $(20000 \times 6) : (x \times 12)$

$\therefore \frac{120000}{12x} = \frac{6000}{3000}$ or $x = \frac{120000}{24} = 5000.$

31. A : B : C = 500 : 300 : 200 = 5 : 3 : 2.

Let their capitals be $5x$, $3x$ and $2x$ respectively. Then, $5x = 10000 \Leftrightarrow x = 2000.$

$\therefore$ C's capital $= 2x$ = Rs. 4000.

32. A : B : C = 27000 : 72000 : 81000 = 3 : 8 : 9. So, C's share : Total Profit = 9 : 20.

Let the total profit be Rs. x. Then, $\frac{9}{20} = \frac{36000}{x}$ or $x = \frac{36000 \times 20}{9} = 80000.$

33. Suppose B invested Rs. x for y months. Then, A invested Rs. $3x$ for $2y$ months.

So, A : B = $(3x \times 2y) : (x \times y) = 6xy : xy = 6 : 1.$

$\therefore$ B's profit : Total profit = 1 : 7.

Let the total profit be Rs. x. Then, $\frac{1}{7} = \frac{4000}{x}$ or $x = 28000.$

34. Suppose B joined after x months.

Then, $21000 \times 12 = 36000 \times (12 - x) \Leftrightarrow 36x = 180 \Leftrightarrow x = 5.$

Hence, B joined after 5 months.

35. Suppose B joined for x months. Then, $\frac{85000 \times 12}{42500 \times x} = \frac{3}{1}$ or $x = \frac{85000 \times 12}{42500 \times 3} = 8.$

So, B joined for 8 months.

36. Let B's capital be Rs. x. Then, $\frac{3500 \times 12}{7x} = \frac{2}{3} \Leftrightarrow 14x = 126000 \Leftrightarrow x = 9000.$

37. Let the total profit be Rs. x. Then, B $= \frac{2x}{7}$ and A $= \left(x - \frac{2x}{7}\right) = \frac{5x}{7}.$

So, A : B $= \frac{5x}{7} : \frac{2x}{7} = 5 : 2.$

Let B's capital be Rs. y. Then, $\frac{16000 \times 8}{y \times 4} = \frac{5}{2} \Leftrightarrow y = \left(\frac{16000 \times 8 \times 2}{5 \times 4}\right) = 12800.$

38. Let the total profit be Rs. z.

Then, 20% of $x = 98000 \Leftrightarrow x = \left(\frac{98000 \times 100}{20}\right) = 490000.$

Let the capitals of P, Q and R be Rs. $5x$, Rs. $6x$ and Rs. $6x$ respectively. Then,

$(5x \times 12) + (6x \times 12) + (6x \times 6) = 490000 \times 12$

$\Leftrightarrow 168x = 490000 \times 12 \Leftrightarrow x = \left(\frac{490000 \times 12}{168}\right) = 35000.$

$\therefore$ R's investment $= 6x$ = Rs. (6×35000) = Rs. 210000.

39. Let their investments be Rs. x for 14 months; Rs. y for 8 months and Rs. z for 7 months respectively.

Then, $14x : 8y : 7z = 5 : 7 : 8$.

Now, $\frac{14x}{8y} = \frac{5}{7} \Leftrightarrow 70x = 40y \Leftrightarrow y = \frac{7}{4}x$.

And, $\frac{14x}{7z} = \frac{5}{8} \Leftrightarrow 112x = 35z \Leftrightarrow z = \frac{112}{35}x = \frac{16}{5}x$.

$\therefore \quad x : y : z = x : \frac{7}{4}x : \frac{16}{5}x = 20 : 35 : 64$.

40. Let the total profit be Rs. 100.

After paying to charity, A's share = Rs. $\left(95 \times \frac{3}{5}\right)$ = Rs. 57.

If A's share is Rs. 57, total profit = Rs. 100.

If A's share is Rs. 855, total profit = $\left(\frac{100}{57} \times 855\right) = 1500$.

41. Suppose A invested Rs. $14x$ for 10 months and B invested Rs. $15x$ for y months. Then,

$\frac{14x \times 10}{15x \times y} = \frac{7}{6} \Leftrightarrow y = \frac{840}{105} = 8$.

Hence, B invested the money for 8 months.

42. Let the total profit be Rs. z. Then,

B's share = Rs. $\frac{2z}{3}$, A's share = Rs. $\left(z - \frac{2z}{3}\right)$ = Rs. $\frac{z}{3}$.

$\therefore \quad A : B = \frac{z}{3} : \frac{2z}{3} = 1 : 2$.

Let the total capital be Rs. x and suppose B's money was used for x months. Then,

$\frac{\frac{1}{4}x \times 15}{\frac{3}{4}x \times y} = \frac{1}{2} \Leftrightarrow y = \left(\frac{15 \times 2}{3}\right) = 10$.

Thus, B's money was used for 10 months.

EXERCISE 13B

(DATA SUFFICIENCY TYPE QUESTIONS)

Directions (***Questions 1 to 4***) : ***Each of the questions given below consists of a statement and/or a question and two statements numbered I and II given below it. You have to decide whether the data provided in the statement(s) is/are sufficient to answer the question. Read both the statements and***

Give answer (a) if the data in Statement I alone are sufficient to answer the question, while the data in Statement II alone are not sufficient to answer the question;

Give answer (b) if the data in Statement II alone are sufficient to answer the question, while the data in Statement I alone are not sufficient to answer the question;

Give answer (c) if the data either in Statement I or in Statement II alone are sufficient to answer the question;

Give answer (d) if the data even in both Statements I and II together are not sufficient to answer the question;

Give answer (e) if the data in both Statements I and II together are necessary to answer the question.

1. Ravi, Gagan and Nitin are running a business firm in partnership. What is Gagan's share in the profit earned by them ? **(M.B.A. 2002)**
   I. Ravi, Gagan and Nitin invested the amounts in the ratio of 2 : 4 : 7.
   II. Nitin's share in the profit is Rs. 8750.
2. A and B start a business jointly. What is A's share out of an annual profit of Rs. 23,800 ?
   I. B's investment is $12\frac{1}{2}\%$ more than A's investment.
   II. A's investment is Rs. 1,20,000.
3. A and B are in a partnership business of one year. At the end of the year, a profit of Rs. 20,000 was earned. What is A's share ?
   I. A invested Rs. 50,000.
   II. B withdrew his capital after 8 months.
4. Rahul, Anurag and Vivek started a business together. In what proportion would the annual profit be distributed among them ? **(Bank P.O. 1999)**
   I. Rahul got one-fourth of the profit.
   II. Rahul and Vivek contributed 75% of the total investment.

Directions (*Questions 5 to 8*) : *Each of the questions given below consists of a question followed by three statements. You have to study the question and the statements and decide which of the statement(s) is/are necessary to answer the given question.*

5. What is R's share of profit in a joint venture ? **(S.B.I.P.O. 2000)**
   I. Q started business investing Rs. 80,000.
   II. R joined him after 3 months.
   III. P joined after 4 months with a capital of Rs. 1,20,000 and got Rs. 6000 as his share of profit.
   (*a*) All I, II and III (*b*) I and III only (*c*) II and III only
   (*d*) Even with all I, II, and III, the answer cannot be arrived at
   (*e*) None of these
6. What is the difference in the shares of profit between P and Q in a joint business at the end of one year ?
   I. P invested Rs. 80,000 and withdrew Rs. 20,000 after 6 months.
   II. Q joined four months after the start of business.
   III. Q's amount was 80% of P's amount during the last six months.
   (*a*) I and II only (*b*) II and III only (*c*) All I, II and III
   (*d*) Even with all I, II and III together, the answer cannot be arrived at.
   (*e*) None of these.
7. A, B and C together start a business with a total investment of Rs. 15,000. At the end of the year, the total profit is Rs. 3000. What is A's share in the profit ?
   I. A's contribution is $\frac{3}{2}$ times B's.
   II. B's contribution is twice that of C.
   III. A's contribution is thrice that of C.
   (*a*) I and II only (*b*) II and III only (*c*) All I, II and III
   (*d*) Any two of the three (*e*) None of these
8. How much did Rohit get as profit at the year-end in the business done by Nitin, Rohit and Kunal ? **(S.B.I.P.O. 1999)**
   I. Kunal invested Rs. 8000 for nine months, his profit was $\frac{3}{2}$ times that of Rohit's and his investment was four times that of Nitin.

II. Nitin and Rohit invested for one year in the proportion 1 : 2 respectively.

III. The three together got Rs. 1000 as profit at the year end.

(*a*) Only I and II (*b*) Only I and III

(*c*) Question cannot be answered even with the information in all the three statements.

(*d*) All I, II and III (*e*) None of these

Directions (*Questions 9-10*) : *Each of these questions is followed by three statements. You have to study the question and all the three statements given to decide whether any information provided in the statement(s) is redundant and can be dispensed with while answering the given question.*

9. Three friends, P, Q and R started a partnership business investing money in the ratio of 5 : 4 : 2 respectively for a period of 3 years. What is the amount received by P as his share in the total profit ? **(S.B.I.P.O. 2000)**

I. Total amount invested in the business in Rs. 22,000.

II. Profit earned at the end of 3 years is $\frac{3}{8}$ of the total investment.

III. The average amount of profit earned per year is Rs. 2750.

(*a*) I or II or III (*b*) Either III only, or I and II together

(*c*) Any two of the three (*d*) All I, II and III are required

(*e*) None of these

10. What will be the percentage share of Y in the profit earned by X, Y and Z together ?

I. X, Y and Z invested a total amount of Rs. 25,000 for a period of two years.

II. The profit earned at the end of 2 years is 30%.

III. The amount invested by Y is equal to the amount invested by X and Z together.

(*a*) I and II only (*b*) II and III only

(*c*) Any two of the three (*d*) All I, II and III are required

(*e*) Question cannot be answered even with information in all the three statements.

ANSWERS

1. (*e*) **2.** (*a*) **3.** (*d*) **4.** (*e*) **5.** (*d*) **6.** (*d*) **7.** (*d*)
8. (*d*) **9.** (*b*) **10.** (*a*)

SOLUTIONS

1. Let us name Ravi, Gagan and Nitin by R, G and N respectively.

I. R : G : N = 2 : 4 : 7.

II. N = 8750.

From I and II, we get :

When N = 7, then G = 4. When N = 8750, then $G = \left(\frac{4}{7} \times 8750\right) = 5000$.

Thus, both I and II are needed to get the answer.

∴ Correct answer is (*e*).

2. Annual profit = Rs. 23800.

I. Let A's investment = Rs. x. Then, B's investment = $112\frac{1}{2}\%$ of Rs. x = Rs. $\left(\frac{9x}{8}\right)$.

$\therefore\quad A : B = x : \frac{9x}{8} = 8 : 9.$

A's share = Rs. $\left(23800 \times \frac{8}{17}\right)$ = Rs. 11200.

Thus, I only gives the answer.

II. A's investment = Rs. 120000.

This is not sufficient to get the answer.

Thus, I gives the answer but II is not sufficient to get the answer.

$\therefore$ Correct answer is (*a*).

3. Since B's investment is not given, both the statements even do not give the answer.

$\therefore$ Correct answer is (*d*).

4. Let the total investment be Rs. x. Then, $R = \frac{x}{4}$.

$$R + V = \left(\frac{75}{100} \times x\right) = \frac{3x}{4} \Rightarrow V = \left(\frac{3x}{4} - \frac{x}{4}\right) = \frac{x}{2}.$$

$$\therefore A = x - \left(\frac{x}{4} + \frac{x}{2}\right) = \frac{x}{4}.$$

$$R : A : V = \frac{x}{4} : \frac{x}{4} : \frac{x}{2} = 1 : 1 : 2.$$

Thus, both I and II are needed to get the answer.

$\therefore$ Correct answer is (*e*).

5. From I, II and III, we get P : Q : R = (120000 × 8) : (80000 × 12) : (x × 9).

Since R's investment is not given, the above ratio cannot be given.

$\therefore$ Given data is inadequate.

$\therefore$ Correct answer is (*d*).

6. I. P's investment = (80000 × 6 + 60000 × 6) = 840000 for 1 month.

II & III. Q's investment = 80% of Rs. 60000 for 8 months

= Rs. (48000 × 8) for 1 month = 384000 for 1 month

P : Q = 840000 : 384000 = 35 : 16.

But, the total profit is not given, so data is inadequate.

$\therefore$ Correct answer is (*d*).

7. Let C's contribution be Rs. x.

From I and II, we get : C = Rs. x, B = Rs. $2x$ and A = Rs. $\left(\frac{3}{2} \times 2x\right)$ = Rs. $3x$.

From II and III, we get C = Rs. x, B = Rs. $2x$ and A = Rs. $3x$.

From I and III, we get C = Rs. x, A = Rs. $3x$ and B = Rs. $\left(\frac{2}{3} \times 3x\right)$ = Rs. $2x$.

Thus, A : B : C = $3x : 2x : x$ = 3 : 2 : 1.

A's share = Rs. $\left(3000 \times \frac{3}{6}\right)$ = Rs. 1500.

Thus, any two of three give the answer.

$\therefore$ Correct answer is (*d*).

8. I and II give, K = Rs. (8000 × 9) for 1 month = Rs. 72000 for 1 month.

$N = \text{Rs.}\left(\frac{1}{4} \times 8000 \times 12\right)$ for 1 month = Rs. 24000 for 1 month.

R = Rs. 48000 for 1 month.

∴ K : N : R = 72000 : 24000 : 48000 = 3 : 1 : 2.

III gives, total profit = Rs. 1000.

∴ Rohit's share = $\text{Rs.}\left(1000 \times \frac{2}{6}\right) = \text{Rs. } 333\frac{1}{3}$.

∴ Correct answer is (*d*).

9. I and II give, profit after 3 years = $\text{Rs.}\left(\frac{3}{8} \times 22000\right)$ = Rs. 8250.

From III also, profit after 3 years = Rs. (2750 × 3) = Rs. 8250

∴ P's share = $\text{Rs.}\left(8250 \times \frac{5}{11}\right)$ = Rs. 3750.

Thus, (either III is redundant) or (I and II are redundant).

∴ Correct answer is (*b*).

10. From III, Y = X + Z ⇒ Y's investment is 50%.

∴ Share of Y is 50%.

Thus, I and II are redundant.

∴ Correct answer is (*a*).

14. CHAIN RULE

IMPORTANT FACTS AND FORMULAE

1. **Direct Proportion** : *Two quantities are said to be directly proportional, if on the increase (or decrease) of the one, the other increases (or decreases) to the same extent.*

   Ex. 1. ***Cost is directly proportional to the number of articles.***
   (*More Articles, More Cost*)

   Ex. 2. ***Work done is directly proportional to the number of men working on it.***
   (*More Men, More Work*)

2. **Indirect Proportion** : *Two quantities are said to be indirectly proportional, if on the increase of the one, the other decreases to the same extent and vice-versa.*

   Ex. 1. ***The time taken by a car in covering a certain distance is inversely proportional to the speed of the car.***
   (*More speed, Less is the time taken to cover a distance*)

   Ex. 2. ***Time taken to finish a work is inversely proportional to the number of persons working at it.***
   (*More persons, Less is the time taken to finish a job*)

   Remark : In solving questions by chain rule, we compare every item with the term to be found out.

SOLVED EXAMPLES

Ex. 1. ***If 15 toys cost Rs. 234, what do 35 toys cost ?***

Sol. Let the required cost be Rs. x. Then,

More toys, More cost (***Direct Proportion***)

$\therefore$ $15 : 35 :: 234 : x \Leftrightarrow (15 \times x) = (35 \times 234) \Leftrightarrow x = \left(\frac{35 \times 234}{15}\right) = 546.$

Hence, the cost of 35 toys is Rs. 546.

Ex. 2. ***If 36 men can do a piece of work in 25 hours, in how many hours will 15 men do it ?***

Sol. Let the required number of hours be x. Then,

Less men, More hours (***Indirect Proportion***)

$\therefore$ $15 : 36 :: 25 : x \Leftrightarrow (15 \times x) = (36 \times 25) \Leftrightarrow x = \frac{36 \times 25}{15} = 60.$

Hence, 15 men can do it in 60 hours.

Ex. 3. ***If the wages of 6 men for 15 days be Rs. 2100, then find the wages of 9 men for 12 days.***

Sol. Let the required wages be Rs. x.

More men, More wages (***Direct Proportion***)

Less days, Less wages (***Direct Proportion***)

$$\left.\begin{array}{l}\text{Men } 6 : 9\\ \text{Days } 15 : 12\end{array}\right\} :: 2100 : x$$

$\therefore \quad (6 \times 15 \times x) = (9 \times 12 \times 2100) \Leftrightarrow x = \left(\frac{9 \times 12 \times 2100}{6 \times 15}\right) = 2520.$

Hence, the required wages are Rs. 2520.

Ex. 4. ***If 20 men can build a wall 56 metres long in 6 days, what length of a similar wall can be built by 35 men in 3 days ?***

Sol. Let the required length be x metres.

More men, More length built (*Direct Proportion*)

Less days, Less length built (*Direct Proportion*)

$$\left.\begin{array}{ll}\text{Men} & 20 : 35 \\ \text{Days} & 6 : 3\end{array}\right\} :: 56 : x$$

$\therefore \quad (20 \times 6 \times x) = (35 \times 3 \times 56) \Leftrightarrow x = \frac{(35 \times 3 \times 56)}{120} = 49.$

Hence, the required length is 49 m.

Ex. 5. ***If 15 men, working 9 hours a day, can reap a field in 16 days, in how many days will 18 men reap the field, working 8 hours a day ?***

Sol. Let the required number of days be x.

More men, Less days (*Indirect Proportion*)

Less hours per day, More days (*Indirect Proportion*)

$$\left.\begin{array}{ll}\text{Men} & 18 : 15 \\ \text{Hours per day} & 8 : 9\end{array}\right\} :: 16 : x$$

$\therefore \quad (18 \times 8 \times x) = (15 \times 9 \times 16) \Leftrightarrow x = \left(\frac{15 \times 144}{144}\right) = 15.$

Hence, required number of days = 15.

Ex. 6. ***If 9 engines consume 24 metric tonnes of coal, when each is working 8 hours a day, how much coal will be required for 8 engines, each running 13 hours a day, it being given that 3 engines of former type consume as much as 4 engines of latter type?***

Sol. Let 3 engines of former type consume 1 unit in 1 hour.

Then, 4 engines of latter type consume 1 unit in 1 hour.

$\therefore$ 1 engine of former type consumes $\frac{1}{3}$ unit in 1 hour.

1 engine of latter type consumes $\frac{1}{4}$ unit in 1 hour.

Let the required consumption of coal be x units.

Less engines, Less coal consumed (*Direct Proportion*)

More working hours, More coal consumed (*Direct Proportion*)

Less rate of consumption, Less coal consumed (*Direct Proportion*)

$$\left.\begin{array}{ll}\text{Number of engines} & 9 : 8 \\ \text{Working hours} & 8 : 13 \\ \text{Rate of consumption} & \frac{1}{3} : \frac{1}{4}\end{array}\right\} :: 24 : x$$

$\therefore \quad \left(9 \times 8 \times \frac{1}{3} \times x\right) = \left(8 \times 13 \times \frac{1}{4} \times 24\right) \Leftrightarrow 24x = 624 \Leftrightarrow x = 26.$

Hence, the required consumption of coal = 26 metric tonnes.

Ex. 7. ***A contract is to be completed in 46 days and 117 men were set to work, each working 8 hours a day. After 33 days,*** $\frac{4}{7}$ ***of the work is completed. How many additional men may be employed so that the work may be completed in time, each man now working 9 hours a day ?***

Sol. Remaining work $= \left(1 - \frac{4}{7}\right) = \frac{3}{7}$. Remaining period = (46 – 33) days = 13 days.

Let the total men working at it be x.

Less work, Less men **(*Direct Proportion*)**

Less days, More men **(*Indirect Proportion*)**

More Hrs/Day, Less men **(*Indirect Proportion*)**

$$\left.\begin{array}{ll}\text{Work} & \frac{4}{7} : \frac{3}{7} \\ \text{Days} & 13 : 33 \\ \text{Hrs/Day} & 9 : 8\end{array}\right\} :: 117 : x$$

$\therefore \quad \frac{4}{7} \times 13 \times 9 \times x = \frac{3}{7} \times 33 \times 8 \times 117$ or $x = \left(\frac{3 \times 33 \times 8 \times 117}{4 \times 13 \times 9}\right) = 198.$

$\therefore$ Additional men to be employed = (198 – 117) = 81.

Ex. 8. ***A garrison of 3300 men had provisions for 32 days, when given at the rate of 850 gms per head. At the end of 7 days, a reinforcement arrives and it was found that the provisions will last 17 days more, when given at the rate of 825 gms per head. What is the strength of the reinforcement ?***

Sol. ***The problem becomes :***

3300 men taking 850 gms per head have provisions for (32 – 7) or 25 days. How many men taking 825 gms each have provisions for 17 days ?

Less ration per head, more men **(*Indirect Proportion*)**

Less days, More men **(*Indirect Proportion*)**

$$\left.\begin{array}{ll}\text{Ration} & 825 : 850 \\ \text{Days} & 17 : 25\end{array}\right\} :: 3300 : x$$

$\therefore \quad 825 \times 17 \times x = 850 \times 25 \times 3300$ or $x = \frac{850 \times 25 \times 3300}{825 \times 17} = 5000.$

$\therefore$ Strength of reinforcement = (5500 – 3300) = 1700.

EXERCISE 14

(OBJECTIVE TYPE QUESTIONS)

Directions : *Mark (✓) against the correct answer* :

1. If the cost of x metres of wire is d rupees, then what is the cost of y metres of wire at the same rate ? **(M.B.A. 2002)**

   (a) Rs. $\left(\frac{xy}{d}\right)$ (b) Rs. (xd) (c) Rs. (yd) (d) Rs. $\left(\frac{yd}{x}\right)$

2. If the price of 6 toys is Rs. 264.37, what will be the approximate price of 5 toys ?

   (a) Rs. 140 (b) Rs. 100 (c) Rs. 200 (d) Rs. 220 (e) Rs. 240 **(Bank P.O. 2000)**

3. The price of 357 mangoes is Rs. 1517.25. What will be the approximate price of 9 dozens of such mangoes ?

(*a*) Rs. 3000 (*b*) Rs. 3500 (*c*) Rs. 4000 (*d*) Rs. 2500

4. If a quarter kg of potato costs 60 paise, how many paise will 200 gm cost ?

(*a*) 48 paise (*b*) 54 paise (*c*) 56 paise (*d*) 72 paise

(C.B.I. 2001)

5. If 11.25 m of a uniform iron rod weighs 42.75 kg, what will be the weight of 6 m of the same rod ?

(*a*) 22.8 kg (*b*) 25.6 kg (*c*) 28 kg (*d*) 26.5 kg

6. On a scale of map, 0.6 cm represents 6.6 km. If the distance between the points on the map is 80.5 cm, the actual distance between these points is :

(*a*) 9 km (*b*) 72.5 km (*c*) 190.75 km (*d*) 885.5 km

7. An industrial loom weaves 0.128 metres of cloth every second. Approximately, how many seconds will it take for the loom to weave 25 metres of cloth ?

(*a*) 178 (*b*) 195 (*c*) 204 (*d*) 488

(M.B.A. 2003)

8. A flagstaff 17.5 m high casts a shadow of length 40.25 m. The height of the building, which casts a shadow of length 28.75 m under similar conditions will be : **(M.B.A. 2002)**

(*a*) 10 m (*b*) 12.5 m (*c*) 17.5 m (*d*) 21.25 m

9. A man completes $\frac{5}{8}$ of a job in 10 days. At this rate, how many more days will it take him to finish the job ? **(M.B.A. 2003)**

(*a*) 5 (*b*) 6 (*c*) 7 (*d*) $7\frac{1}{2}$

10. 36 men can complete a piece of work in 18 days. In how many days will 27 men complete the same work ? **(Bank P.O. 1998)**

(*a*) 12 (*b*) 18 (*c*) 22 (*d*) 24 (*e*) None of these

11. A fort had provision of food for 150 men for 45 days. After 10 days, 25 men left the fort. The number of days for which the remaining food will last, is : **(S.S.C. 2001)**

(*a*) $29\frac{1}{5}$ (*b*) $37\frac{1}{4}$ (*c*) 42 (*d*) 54

12. A wheel that has 6 cogs is meshed with a larger wheel of 14 cogs. When the smaller wheel has made 21 revolutions, then the number of revolutions made by the larger wheel is : **(M.A.T. 2000)**

(*a*) 4 (*b*) 9 (*c*) 12 (*d*) 49

13. In a camp, there is a meal for 120 men or 200 children. If 150 children have taken the meal, how many men will be catered to with the remaining meal ?

(*a*) 20 (*b*) 30 (*c*) 40 (*d*) 50

(Railways, 2003)

14. The cost of 16 packets of salt, each weighing 900 grams is Rs. 28. What will be the cost of 27 packets, if each packet weighs 1 kg ?

(*a*) Rs. 52.50 (*b*) Rs. 56 (*c*) Rs. 58.50 (*d*) Rs. 64.75

15. 4 mat-weavers can weave 4 mats in 4 days. At the same rate, how many mats would be woven by 8 mat-weavers in 8 days ? **(S.S.C. 2004)**

(*a*) 4 (*b*) 8 (*c*) 12 (*d*) 16

16. Running at the same constant rate, 6 identical machines can produce a total of 270 bottles per minute. At this rate, how many bottles could 10 such machines produce in 4 minutes ? **(M.A.T. 2004)**

(*a*) 648 (*b*) 1800 (*c*) 2700 (*d*) 10800

17. In a dairy farm, 40 cows eat 40 bags of husk in 40 days. In how many days one cow will eat one bag of husk ? **(Railways, 2003)**

(*a*) 1 (*b*) $\frac{1}{40}$ (*c*) 40 (*d*) 80

18. 12 men working 8 hours per day complete a piece of work in 10 days. To complete the same work in 8 days, working 15 hours a day, the number of men required, is :

(*a*) 4 (*b*) 5 (*c*) 6 (*d*) 8

19. 10 men, working 6 hours a day can complete a work in 18 days. How many hours a day must 15 men work to complete the same work in 12 days ? **(S.S.C. 2004)**

(*a*) 6 (*b*) 10 (*c*) 12 (*d*) 15

20. 39 persons can repair a road in 12 days, working 5 hours a day. In how many days will 30 persons, working 6 hours a day, complete the work ? **(C.B.I. 2003)**

(*a*) 10 (*b*) 13 (*c*) 14 (*d*) 15

21. 3 pumps, working 8 hours a day, can empty a tank in 2 days. How many hours a day must 4 pumps work to empty the tank in 1 day ? **(M.B.A. 2002)**

(*a*) 9 (*b*) 10 (*c*) 11 (*d*) 12

22. If 8 men can reap 80 hectares in 24 days, then how many hectares can 36 men reap in 30 days ? **(C.B.I. 2001)**

(*a*) 350 (*b*) 400 (*c*) 425 (*d*) 450

23. A certain number of persons can dig a trench 100 m long, 50 m broad and 10 m deep in 10 days. The same number of persons can dig another trench 20 m broad and 15 m deep in 30 days. The length of the second trench is :

(*a*) 400 m (*b*) 500 m (*c*) 800 m (*d*) 900 m

24. If 5 men or 9 women can do a piece of work in 19 days, then in how many days will 3 men and 6 women do the same work ?

(*a*) 12 (*b*) 15 (*c*) 18 (*d*) 21

25. 49 pumps can empty a reservoir in $6\frac{1}{2}$ days, working 8 hours a day. If 196 pumps are used for 5 hours each day, then the same work will be completed in :

(*a*) 2 days (*b*) $2\frac{1}{2}$ days (*c*) $2\frac{3}{5}$ days (*d*) 3 days

26. 30 labourers, working 7 hours a day can finish a piece of work in 18 days. If the labourers work 6 hours a day, then the number of labourers to finish the same piece of work in 30 days, will be :

(*a*) 15 (*b*) 21 (*c*) 22 (*d*) 25

27. If 7 spiders make 7 webs in 7 days, then 1 spider will make 1 web in how many days ?

(*a*) 1 (*b*) $\frac{7}{2}$ (*c*) 7 (*d*) 49

(Railways, 2003)

28. If 18 pumps can raise 2170 tonnes of water in 10 days, working 7 hours a day; in how many days will 16 pumps raise 1736 tonnes of water, working 9 hours a day ?

(*a*) 6 (*b*) 7 (*c*) 8 (*d*) 9

29. If 80 lamps can be lighted, 5 hours per day for 10 days for Rs. 21.25, then the number of lamps, which can be lighted 4 hours daily for 30 days, for Rs. 76.50, is :

(*a*) 100 (*b*) 120 (*c*) 150 (*d*) 160

30. If 12 carpenters, working 6 hours a day, can make 460 chairs in 24 days, how many chairs will 18 carpenters make in 36 days, each working 8 hours a day ?

(*a*) 1260 (*b*) 1320 (*c*) 920 (*d*) 1380

31. 400 persons, working 9 hours per day complete $\frac{1}{4}$th of the work in 10 days The number of additional persons, working 8 hours per day, required to complete the remaining work in 20 days, is :

(*a*) 675 (*b*) 275 (*c*) 250 (*d*) 225

32. If 9 examiners can examine a certain number of answer books in 12 days, working 5 hours a day; for how many hours a day would 4 examiners have to work in order to examine twice the number of answer books in 30 days ?

(*a*) 6 (*b*) 8 (*c*) 9 (*d*) 10

33. If 17 labourers can dig a ditch 20 m long in 18 days, working 8 hours a day; how many more labourers should be engaged to dig a similar ditch 39 m long in 6 days, each labourer working 9 hours a day ?

(*a*) 34 (*b*) 51 (*c*) 68 (*d*) 85

34. 20 men complete one-third of a piece of work in 20 days. How many more men should be employed to finish the rest of the work in 25 more days ?

(*a*) 10 (*b*) 12 (*c*) 15 (*d*) 20

35. If 18 binders bind 900 books in 10 days, how many binders will be required to bind 660 books in 12 days ?

(*a*) 22 (*b*) 14 (*c*) 13 (*d*) 11

36. If $\frac{3}{5}$ of a cistern is filled in 1 minute, how much more time will be required to fill the rest of it ?

(*a*) 30 sec (*b*) 40 sec (*c*) 36 sec (*d*) 24 sec

37. If x men, working x hours per day, can do x units of work in x days, then y men, working y hours per day would be able to complete how many units of work in y days ?

(*a*) $\frac{x^2}{y^3}$ (*b*) $\frac{x^3}{y^2}$ (*c*) $\frac{y^2}{x^3}$ (*d*) $\frac{y^3}{x^2}$

38. A rope makes 70 rounds of the circumference of a cylinder whose radius of the base is 14 cm. How many times can it go round a cylinder with radius 20 cm ?

(*a*) 40 (*b*) 49 (*c*) 100 (*d*) None of these

39. If 5 engines consume 6 metric tonnes of coal when each is running 9 hours a day, how many metric tonnes of coal will be needed for 8 engines, each running 10 hours a day, it being given that 3 engines of the former type consume as much as 4 engines of the latter type ?

(*a*) $3\frac{1}{8}$ (*b*) 8 (*c*) $8\frac{8}{9}$ (*d*) $6\frac{12}{25}$

40. If a certain number of workmen can do a piece of work in 25 hours, in how many hours will another set of an equal number of men, do a piece of work, twice as great, supposing that 2 men of the first set can do as much work in an hour, as 3 men of the second set do in an hour ?

(*a*) 60 (*b*) 75 (*c*) 90 (*d*) 105

41. Some persons can do a piece of work in 12 days. Two times the number of such persons will do half of that work in :

(*a*) 6 days (*b*) 4 days (*c*) 3 days (*d*) 12 days

42. A certain number of men can finish a piece of work in 100 days. If, there were 10 men less, it would take 10 days more for the work to be finished. How many men were there originally ?

(*a*) 75 (*b*) 82 (*c*) 100 (*d*) 110

43. In a camp, 95 men had provisions for 200 days. After 5 days, 30 men left the camp. For how many days will the remaining food last now ?

(*a*) 180 (*b*) 285 (*c*) $139\frac{16}{19}$ (*d*) None of these

44. A garrison of 500 men had provisions for 27 days. After 3 days a reinforcement of 300 men arrived. For how many more days will the remaining food last now ?

(*a*) 15 (*b*) 16 (*c*) $17\frac{1}{2}$ (*d*) 18

45. A garrison had provisions for a certain number of days. After 10 days, $\frac{1}{5}$ of the men desert and it is found that the provisions will now last just as long as before. How long was that ?

(*a*) 15 days (*b*) 25 days (*c*) 35 days (*d*) 50 days

46. 15 men take 21 days of 8 hours each to do a piece of work. How many days of 6 hours each would 21 women take, if 3 women do as much work as 2 men ?

(*a*) 18 (*b*) 20 (*c*) 25 (*d*) 30

47. A contractor undertook to do a certain piece of work in 9 days. He employed certain number of men, but 6 of them being absent from the very first day, the rest could finish the work in 15 days. The number of men originally employed were :

(*a*) 12 (*b*) 15 (*c*) 18 (*d*) 24

48. A contractor undertakes to do a piece of work in 40 days. He engages 100 men at the beginning and 100 more after 35 days and completes the work in stipulated time. If he had not engaged the additional men, how many days behind schedule would it be finished ?

(*a*) 3 (*b*) 5 (*c*) 6 (*d*) 9

49. A contractor employed 30 men to do a piece of work in 38 days. After 25 days, he employed 5 men more and the work was finished one day earlier. How many days he would have been behind, if he had not employed additional men ?

(*a*) 1 (*b*) $1\frac{1}{4}$ (*c*) $1\frac{3}{4}$ (*d*) $1\frac{1}{2}$

50. 12 men and 18 boys, working $7\frac{1}{2}$ hours a day, can do a piece of work in 60 days. If a man works equal to 2 boys, then how many boys will be required to help 21 men to do twice the work in 50 days, working 9 hours a day ?

(*a*) 30 (*b*) 42 (*c*) 48 (*d*) 90

51. If 3 men or 6 boys can do a piece of work in 10 days, working 7 hours a day; how many days will it take to compete a piece of work twice as large with 6 men and 2 boys working together for 8 hours a day ?

(*a*) 6 (*b*) $7\frac{1}{2}$ (*c*) $8\frac{1}{2}$ (*d*) 9

52. 2 men and 7 boys can do a piece of work in 14 days; 3 men and 8 boys can do the same in 11 days, Then, 8 men and 6 boys can do three times the amount of this work in :

(*a*) 18 days (*b*) 21 days (*c*) 24 days (*d*) 30 days

ANSWERS

1. (*d*)	**2.** (*d*)	**3.** (*d*)	**4.** (*a*)	**5.** (*a*)	**6.** (*d*)	**7.** (*b*)	**8.** (*b*)	**9.** (*b*)
10. (*d*)	**11.** (*c*)	**12.** (*b*)	**13.** (*b*)	**14.** (*a*)	**15.** (*d*)	**16.** (*b*)	**17.** (*c*)	**18.** (*d*)
19. (*a*)	**20.** (*b*)	**21.** (*d*)	**22.** (*d*)	**23.** (*b*)	**24.** (*b*)	**25.** (*c*)	**26.** (*b*)	**27.** (*c*)

28. (b) 29. (b) 30. (d) 31. (b) 32. (c) 33. (b) 34. (b) 35. (d) 36. (b)
37. (d) 38. (b) 39. (b) 40. (b) 41. (c) 42. (d) 43. (b) 44. (a) 45. (d)
46. (d) 47. (b) 48. (b) 49. (a) 50. (b) 51. (b) 52. (b)

SOLUTIONS

1. Cost of x metres = Rs. d. Cost of 1 metre = Rs. $\left(\frac{d}{x}\right)$.

   Cost of y metres = Rs. $\left(\frac{d}{x} \times y\right)$ = Rs. $\left(\frac{yd}{x}\right)$.

2. Let the required price be Rs. x. Then, ***Less toys, Less cost*** **(*Direct Proportion*)**

   $\therefore$ $6 : 5 :: 264.37 : x \Leftrightarrow 6x = (5 \times 264.37) \Leftrightarrow x = \frac{(5 \times 264.37)}{6} \Leftrightarrow x = 220.308.$

   $\therefore$ Approximate price of 5 toys = Rs. 220.

3. Let the required price be Rs. x. Then, ***More mangoes, More price*** **(*Direct Proportion*)**

   $\therefore$ $357 : (49 \times 12) :: 1517.25 : x$

   $\Leftrightarrow 357x = (49 \times 12 \times 1517.25) \Leftrightarrow x = \frac{(49 \times 12 \times 1517.25)}{357} \Leftrightarrow x = 2499.$

   Hence, the approximate price is Rs. 2500.

4. Let the required cost be x paise. ***Less weight, Less cost*** **(*Direct Proportion*)**

   $\therefore$ $250 : 200 :: 60 : x \Leftrightarrow 250 \times x = (200 \times 60) \Leftrightarrow x = \frac{(200 \times 60)}{250} \Leftrightarrow x = 48.$

5. Let the required weight be x kg. Then, ***Less length, Less weight*** **(*Direct Proportion*)**

   $\therefore$ $11.25 : 6 :: 42.75 : x \Leftrightarrow 11.25 \times x = 6 \times 42.75 \Leftrightarrow x = \frac{(6 \times 42.75)}{11.25} \Leftrightarrow x = 22.8.$

6. Let the actual distance be x km. Then,

   More distance on the map, More is the actual distance **(*Direct Proportion*)**

   $\therefore$ $0.6 : 80.5 :: 6.6 : x \Leftrightarrow 0.6x = 80.5 \times 6.6 \Leftrightarrow x = \frac{80.5 \times 6.6}{0.6} \Leftrightarrow x = 885.5.$

7. Let the required time be x seconds. Then, ***More metres, more time*** **(*Direct Proportion*)**

   $\therefore$ $0.128 : 25 :: 1 : x$

   $\Leftrightarrow 0.128 \times x = 25 \times 1 \Leftrightarrow x = \frac{25}{0.128} = \frac{25 \times 1000}{128} \Leftrightarrow x = 195.31.$

   $\therefore$ Required time = 195 sec (approximately).

8. Let the height of the building be x metres.

   Less lengthy shadow, Less is the height **(*Direct Proportion*)**

   $\therefore$ $40.25 : 28.75 :: 17.5 : x \Leftrightarrow 40.25 \times x = 28.75 \times 17.5$

   $\Leftrightarrow x = \frac{(28.75 \times 17.5)}{40.25} \Leftrightarrow x = 12.5.$

9. Work done = $\frac{5}{8}$. Balance work = $\left(1 - \frac{5}{8}\right) = \frac{3}{8}$.

   Less work, Less days **(*Direct Proportion*)**

   Let the required number of days be x.

   Then, $\frac{5}{8} : \frac{3}{8} :: 10 : x \Leftrightarrow \frac{5}{8} \times x = \frac{3}{8} \times 10 \Leftrightarrow x = \left(\frac{3}{8} \times 10 \times \frac{8}{5}\right) = 6.$

10. Let the required number of days be x.

Then, ***Less men, More days*** (***Indirect Proportion***)

$\therefore\ 27 : 36 :: 18 : x \Leftrightarrow 27 \times x = 36 \times 18 \Leftrightarrow x = \frac{36 \times 18}{27} \Leftrightarrow x = 24.$

11. After 10 days : 150 men had food for 35 days.

Suppose 125 men had food for x days. Now, ***Less men, More days*** (***Indirect Proportion***)

$\therefore\ 125 : 150 :: 35 : x \Leftrightarrow 125 \times x = 150 \times 35 \Leftrightarrow x = \frac{150 \times 35}{125} \Leftrightarrow x = 42.$

Hence, the remaining food will last for 42 days.

12. Let the required number of revolutions made by larger wheel be x.

Then, ***More cogs, Less revolutions*** (***Indirect Proportion***)

$\therefore\ 14 : 6 :: 21 : x \Leftrightarrow 14 \times x = 6 \times 21 \Leftrightarrow x = \left(\frac{6 \times 21}{14}\right) = 9.$

13. There is a meal for 200 children. 150 children have taken the meal. Remaining meal is to be catered to 50 children.

Now, 200 children ≡ 120 men

$50 \text{ children} \equiv \left(\frac{120}{200} \times 50\right) \text{ men} = 30 \text{ men}.$

14. Let the required cost be Rs. x. Then,

More packets, More cost (***Direct Proportion***)

More weight, More cost (***Direct Proportion***)

$\left.\begin{array}{l}\text{Packets } 16 : 27\\ \text{Weight } 900 : 1000\end{array}\right\} :: 28 : x$

$\therefore\ (16 \times 900 \times x) = (27 \times 1000 \times 28) \Leftrightarrow x = \frac{(27 \times 1000 \times 28)}{16 \times 900} = \frac{105}{2} = 52.50.$

15. Let the required number of mats be x.

More weavers, More mats (***Direct Proportion***)

More days, More mats (***Direct Proportion***)

$\left.\begin{array}{l}\text{Weavers } 4 : 8\\ \text{Days } 4 : 8\end{array}\right\} :: 4 : x$

$\therefore\ 4 \times 4 \times x = 8 \times 8 \times 4 \Leftrightarrow x = \frac{(8 \times 8 \times 4)}{(4 \times 4)} = 16.$

16. Let the required number of bottles be x.

More machines, More bottles (***Direct Proportion***)

More minutes, More bottles (***Direct Proportion***)

$\left.\begin{array}{l}\text{Machines } 6 : 10\\ \text{Time (in Minutes) } 1 : 4\end{array}\right\} :: 270 : x$

$\therefore\ 6 \times 1 \times x = 10 \times 4 \times 270 \Leftrightarrow x = \frac{10 \times 4 \times 270}{6} \Leftrightarrow x = 1800.$

17. Let the required number of days be x.

Less cows, More days (***Indirect Proportion***)

Less bags, Less days (***Direct Proportion***)

$\left.\begin{array}{l}\text{Cows } 1 : 40\\ \text{Bags } 40 : 1\end{array}\right\} :: 40 : x$

$\therefore\ 1 \times 40 \times x = 40 \times 1 \times 40 \Leftrightarrow x = 40.$

18. Let the required number of men be x.

Less days, More men (*Indirect Proportion*)

More working hrs per day, Less men (*Indirect Proportion*)

$$\left.\begin{array}{ll}\text{Days} & 8 : 10 \\ \text{Working Hrs} & 15 : 8\end{array}\right\} :: 12 : x$$

$\therefore \quad 8 \times 15 \times x = 10 \times 8 \times 12 \Leftrightarrow x = \dfrac{10 \times 8 \times 12}{8 \times 15} \Leftrightarrow x = 8.$

19. Let the required number of hours per day be x.

More men, Less hours per day (*Indirect Proportion*)

Less days, More hours per day (*Indirect Proportion*)

$$\left.\begin{array}{ll}\text{Men} & 15 : 10 \\ \text{Days} & 12 : 18\end{array}\right\} :: 6 : x$$

$\therefore \quad 15 \times 12 \times x = 10 \times 18 \times 6 \Leftrightarrow x = \dfrac{10 \times 18 \times 6}{15 \times 12} \Leftrightarrow x = 6.$

20. Let the required number of days be x.

Less persons, More days (*Indirect Proportion*)

More working hrs per day, Less days (*Indirect Proportion*)

$$\left.\begin{array}{ll}\text{Persons} & 30 : 39 \\ \text{Working hrs / day} & 6 : 5\end{array}\right\} :: 12 : x$$

$\therefore \quad 30 \times 6 \times x = 39 \times 5 \times 12 \Leftrightarrow x = \dfrac{39 \times 5 \times 12}{30 \times 6} \Leftrightarrow x = 13.$

21. Let the required number of working hours per day be x.

More pumps, Less working hours per day (*Indirect Proportion*)

Less days, More working hours per day (*Indirect Proportion*)

$$\left.\begin{array}{ll}\text{Pumps} & 4 : 3 \\ \text{Days} & 1 : 2\end{array}\right\} :: 8 : x$$

$\therefore \quad 4 \times 1 \times x = 3 \times 2 \times 8 \Leftrightarrow x = \dfrac{3 \times 2 \times 8}{4} \Leftrightarrow x = 12.$

22. Let the required number of hectares be x. Then,

More men, More hectares (*Direct Proportion*)

More days, More hectares (*Direct Proportion*)

$$\left.\begin{array}{ll}\text{Men} & 8 : 36 \\ \text{Days} & 24 : 30\end{array}\right\} :: 80 : x$$

$\therefore \quad 8 \times 24 \times x = 36 \times 30 \times 80 \Leftrightarrow x = \dfrac{(36 \times 30 \times 80)}{(8 \times 24)} \Leftrightarrow x = 450.$

23. Let the required length be x metres.

More breadth, Less length (*Indirect Proportion*)

More depth, Less length (*Indirect Proportion*)

More days, More length (*Direct Proportion*)

$$\left.\begin{array}{ll}\text{Breadth} & 20 : 50 \\ \text{Depth} & 15 : 10 \\ \text{Days} & 10 : 30\end{array}\right\} :: 100 : x$$

$\therefore \quad 20 \times 15 \times 10 \times x = 50 \times 10 \times 30 \times 100 \Leftrightarrow x = \dfrac{(50 \times 10 \times 30 \times 100)}{(20 \times 15 \times 10)} \Leftrightarrow x = 500.$

24. Let the required number of days be x.

5 men ≡ 9 women ⇔ 3 men ≡ $\left(\frac{9}{5}\times 3\right)$ women = $\frac{27}{5}$ women.

∴ (3 men and 6 women) ≡ $\left(\frac{27}{5}+6\right)$ women = $\frac{57}{5}$ women.

Now, ***More women, Less days (Indirect Proportion)***

$$\therefore \quad \frac{57}{5} : 9 :: 19 : x \Leftrightarrow \frac{57}{5}\times x = 9\times 19 \Leftrightarrow x = \left(9\times 19\times \frac{5}{57}\right) = 15.$$

25. Let the required number of days be x. Then,

More pumps, Less days ***(Indirect Proportion)***

Less working hrs / day, More days ***(Indirect Proportion)***

$$\left.\begin{array}{lr}\text{Pumps} & 196 : 49\\ \text{Working Hrs/Day} & 5 : 8\end{array}\right\} :: \frac{13}{2} : x$$

$$\therefore \quad 196\times 5\times x = 49\times 8\times \frac{13}{2} \Leftrightarrow x = \left(49\times 8\times \frac{13}{2}\times \frac{1}{196\times 5}\right) \Leftrightarrow x = \frac{13}{5} = 2\frac{3}{5}.$$

26. Let the required number of labourers be x. Then,

Less working hrs / day, More labourers ***(Indirect Proportion)***

More days, Less labourers ***(Indirect Proportion)***

$$\left.\begin{array}{lr}\text{Working Hrs/Day} & 6 : 7\\ \text{Days} & 30 : 18\end{array}\right\} :: 30 : x$$

$$\therefore \quad 6 \times 30 \times x = 7 \times 18 \times 30 \Leftrightarrow 6x = 126 \Leftrightarrow x = 21.$$

27. Let the required number of days be x. Then,

Less spiders, More days ***(Indirect Proportion)***

Less webs, Less days ***(Direct Proportion)***

$$\therefore \quad \left.\begin{array}{lr}\text{Spiders} & 1 : 7\\ \text{Webs} & 7 : 1\end{array}\right\} :: 7 : x$$

$$\therefore \quad 1 \times 7 \times x = 7 \times 1 \times 7 \Leftrightarrow x = 7.$$

28. Let the required number of days be x. Then,

Less pumps, More days ***(Indirect Proportion)***

Less weight, Less days ***(Direct Proportion)***

More hours / day, Less days ***(Indirect Proportion)***

$$\left.\begin{array}{lr}\text{Pumps} & 16 : 18\\ \text{Weight} & 2170 : 1736\\ \text{Hours/Day} & 9 : 7\end{array}\right\} :: 10 : x$$

$$\therefore \quad (16 \times 2170 \times 9 \times x) = (18 \times 1736 \times 7 \times 10) \Leftrightarrow x = \frac{18\times 1736\times 7\times 10}{16\times 2170\times 9} = 7.$$

29. Let the required number of lamps be x.

Less hours per day, More lamps ***(Indirect Proportion)***

More money, More lamps ***(Direct Proportion)***

More days, Less lamps ***(Indirect Proportion)***

$$\left.\begin{array}{lr}\text{Hours per day} & 4 : 5\\ \text{Money} & 21.25 : 76.50\\ \text{Number of days} & 30 : 10\end{array}\right\} :: 80 : x$$

$$\therefore \quad 4 \times 21.25 \times 30 \times x = 5 \times 76.50 \times 10 \times 80 \Leftrightarrow$$

$$x = \frac{5 \times 76.50 \times 10 \times 80}{4 \times 21.25 \times 30} \Leftrightarrow x = 120.$$

30. Let the required number of chairs be x. Then,

More carpenters, More chairs **(*Direct Proportion*)**
More hours per day, More chairs **(*Direct Proportion*)**
More days, More chairs **(*Direct Proportion*)**

$$\left.\begin{array}{lr} \text{Carpenters} & 12 : 18 \\ \text{Hours per day} & 6 : 8 \\ \text{Days} & 24 : 36 \end{array}\right\} :: 460 : x$$

$\therefore \quad (12 \times 6 \times 24 \times x) = (18 \times 8 \times 36 \times 460) \Leftrightarrow x = \dfrac{(18 \times 8 \times 36 \times 460)}{(12 \times 6 \times 24)} = 1380.$

$\therefore$ Required number of chairs = 1380.

31. Let the number of persons completing the work in 20 days be x.

Work done $= \dfrac{1}{4}$, Remaining work $= \left(1 - \dfrac{1}{4}\right) = \dfrac{3}{4}$.

Less hours per day, More men required **(*Indirect Proportion*)**
More work, More men required **(*Direct Proportion*)**
More days, Less men required **(*Indirect Proportion*)**

$$\left.\begin{array}{lr} \text{Hours per day} & 8 : 9 \\ \text{Work} & \frac{1}{4} : \frac{3}{4} \\ \text{Days} & 20 : 10 \end{array}\right\} :: 400 : x$$

$\therefore \quad 8 \times \dfrac{1}{4} \times 20 \times x = 9 \times \dfrac{3}{4} \times 10 \times 400 \Leftrightarrow 40x = 27000 \Leftrightarrow x = 675.$

$\therefore$ Additional men = (675 − 400) = 275.

32. Let the required number of working hours per day be x.

Less examiners, More working hours per day **(*Indirect Proportion*)**
More days, Less working hours per day **(*Indirect Proportion*)**
More answer books, More working hours per day **(*Direct Proportion*)**

$$\left.\begin{array}{lr} \text{Examiners} & 4 : 9 \\ \text{Days} & 30 : 12 \\ \text{Answer books} & 1 : 2 \end{array}\right\} :: 5 : x$$

$\therefore \quad (4 \times 30 \times 1 \times x) = (9 \times 12 \times 2 \times 5) \Leftrightarrow 120x = 1080 \Leftrightarrow x = 9.$

33. Let the total number of men to be engaged be x.

More length, More labourers **(*Direct Proportion*)**
Less days, More labourers **(*Indirect Proportion*)**
More hours per day, Less labourers **(*Indirect Proportion*)**

$$\left.\begin{array}{lr} \text{Length} & 26 : 39 \\ \text{Days} & 6 : 18 \\ \text{Hours per day} & 9 : 8 \end{array}\right\} :: 17 : x$$

$\therefore \quad (26 \times 6 \times 9 \times x) = (39 \times 18 \times 8 \times 17) \Leftrightarrow x = \dfrac{(39 \times 18 \times 8 \times 17)}{(26 \times 6 \times 9)} = 68.$

$\therefore$ Number of more labourers = (68 − 17) = 51.

34. Let the total number of men be x. Work done $= \dfrac{1}{3}$, Remaining work $= \left(1 - \dfrac{1}{3}\right) = \dfrac{2}{3}$

More work, More men (Direct Proportion)
More days, Less men (Indirect Proportion)

$$\left.\begin{array}{ll}\text{Work} & \frac{1}{3} : \frac{2}{3} \\ \text{Days} & 25 : 20\end{array}\right\} :: 20 : x$$

$$\therefore \left(\frac{1}{3} \times 25 \times x\right) = \left(\frac{2}{3} \times 20 \times 20\right) \Leftrightarrow x = \frac{800}{25} = 32.$$

$\therefore$ More men to be employed = (32 − 20) = 12.

35. Let the required number of binders be x.
Less books, Less binders (Direct Proportion)
More days, Less binders (Indirect Proportion)

$$\left.\begin{array}{ll}\text{Books} & 900 : 600 \\ \text{Days} & 12 : 10\end{array}\right\} :: 18 : x$$

$$\therefore (900 \times 12 \times x) = (600 \times 10 \times 18) \Leftrightarrow x = \frac{600 \times 10 \times 18}{900 \times 12} = 11.$$

36. Let the required time be x seconds.

Part filled = $\frac{3}{5}$, Remaining part = $\left(1 - \frac{3}{5}\right) = \frac{2}{5}$.

Less part, Less time (Direct Proportion)

$$\therefore \frac{3}{5} : \frac{2}{5} :: 60 : x \Leftrightarrow \left(\frac{3}{5} \times x\right) = \left(\frac{2}{5} \times 60\right) \Leftrightarrow x = 40.$$

37. Let the required number of units of work be z.
More men, More work (Direct Proportion)
More working hours, More work (Direct Proportion)
More days, More work (Direct Proportion)

$$\left.\begin{array}{ll}\text{Men} & x : y \\ \text{Hours per day} & x : y \\ \text{Days} & x : y\end{array}\right\} :: x : z$$

$$\therefore (x \times x \times x \times z) = (y \times y \times y \times x) \Leftrightarrow z = \frac{y^3}{x^2}.$$

38. Let the required number of rounds be x.
More radius, Less rounds (Indirect Proportion)

$$\therefore 20 : 14 :: 70 : x \Leftrightarrow (20 \times x) = (14 \times 70) \Leftrightarrow x = \frac{14 \times 70}{20} \Leftrightarrow x = 49.$$

Hence, the required number of rounds = 49.

39. Let the required quantity of coal be x metric tonnes.
More engines, More coal (Direct Proportion)
More hours per day, More coal (Direct Proportion)
More rate, More coal (Direct Proportion)

$$\left.\begin{array}{ll}\text{Engines} & 5 : 8 \\ \text{Hours per day} & 9 : 10 \\ \text{Rate} & \frac{1}{3} : \frac{1}{4}\end{array}\right\} :: 6 : x$$

$\therefore \left(5 \times 9 \times \frac{1}{3} \times x\right) = \left(8 \times 10 \times \frac{1}{4} \times 6\right) \Leftrightarrow 15x = 120 \Leftrightarrow x = 8$

40. Let the required number of hours be x.

Speeds of working of first and second type of men are $\frac{1}{2}$ and $\frac{1}{3}$.

More work, More time **(*Direct Proportion*)**
Less speed, More time **(*Indirect Proportion*)**

$$\left.\begin{array}{l} \text{Work} \quad 1 : 2 \\ \text{Speed} \quad \frac{1}{3} : \frac{1}{2} \end{array}\right\} :: 25 : x$$

$\therefore \left(1 \times \frac{1}{3} \times x\right) = \left(2 \times \frac{1}{2} \times 25\right) \Leftrightarrow x = 75.$

41. Let x men can do the work in 12 days and the required number of days be z.

More men, Less days **(*Indirect Proportion*)**
Less work, Less days **(*Direct Proportion*)**

$$\left.\begin{array}{l} \text{Men} \quad 2x : x \\ \text{Work} \quad 1 : \frac{1}{2} \end{array}\right\} :: 12 : z$$

$\therefore (2x \times 1 \times z) = \left(x \times \frac{1}{2} \times 12\right) \Leftrightarrow 2xz = 6x \Leftrightarrow z = 3.$

42. Originally, let there be x men.

Less men, More days **(*Indirect Proportion*)**

$\therefore (x - 10) : x :: 100 : 110 \Leftrightarrow (x - 10) \times 110 = x \times 100 \Leftrightarrow 10x = 1100 \Leftrightarrow x = 110.$

43. Let the remaining food will last for x days.

95 men had provisions for 195 days. 65 men had provisions for x days.

Less men, More days **(*Indirect Proportion*)**

$\therefore 65 : 95 :: 195 : x \Leftrightarrow (65 \times x) = (95 \times 195) \Leftrightarrow x = \frac{95 \times 195}{65} = 285.$

44. Let the remaining food will last for x days.

500 men had provisions for $(27 - 3) = 24$ days.

$(500 + 300)$ men had provisions for x days.

More men, Less days **(*Indirect Proportion*)**

$\therefore 800 : 500 :: 24 : x \Leftrightarrow (800 \times x) = (500 \times 24) \Leftrightarrow x = \left(\frac{500 \times 24}{800}\right) = 15.$

45. Initially, let there be x men having food for y days.

After 10 days, x men had food for $(y - 10)$ days. Also, $\left(x - \frac{x}{5}\right)$ men had food for y days.

$\therefore x(y - 10) = \frac{4x}{5} \times y \Leftrightarrow 5xy - 50x = 4xy \Leftrightarrow xy - 50x = 0$

$\Leftrightarrow x(y - 50) = 0 \Leftrightarrow y - 50 = 0 \Leftrightarrow y = 50.$

46. 3 women ≡ 2 men. So, 21 women ≡ 14 men.

Less men, More days **(*Indirect Proportion*)**
Less hours per day, More days **(*Indirect Proportion*)**

$$\left.\begin{array}{l} \text{Men} \quad 14 : 15 \\ \text{Hours per day} \quad 6 : 8 \end{array}\right\} :: 21 : x$$

$\therefore$ $(14 \times 6 \times x) = (15 \times 8 \times 21) \Leftrightarrow x = \frac{(15 \times 8 \times 21)}{(14 \times 6)} = 30.$

$\therefore$ Required number of days = 30.

47. Let there be x men at the beginning.

Less men, More days **(*Indirect Proportion*)**

$\therefore$ $15 : 9 :: x : (x - 6) \Leftrightarrow 15(x - 6) = 9x \Leftrightarrow 6x = 90 \Leftrightarrow x = 15.$

48. $[(100 \times 35) + (200 \times 5)]$ men can finish the work in 1 day.

$\therefore$ 4500 men can finish the work in 1 day. 100 men can finish it in $\frac{4500}{100} = 45$ days.

This is 5 days behind schedule.

49. After 25 days, 35 men complete the work in 12 days.

Thus, 35 men can finish the remaining work in 12 days.

$\therefore$ 30 men can do it in $\frac{(12 \times 35)}{30} = 14$ days, which is **1 day behind.**

50. 1 man ≡ 2 boys $\Leftrightarrow$ (12 men + 18 boys) ≡ $(12 \times 2 + 18)$ boys = 42 boys.

Let required number of boys = x. 21 men + x boys ≡ $(21 \times 2 + x)$ boys = $(42 + x)$ boys.

Less days, More boys **(*Indirect Proportion*)**

More hrs per day, Less boys **(*Indirect Proportion*)**

$$\left.\begin{array}{ll}\text{Days} & 50 : 60 \\ \text{Hours per day} & 9 : \frac{15}{2} \\ \text{Work} & 1 : 2\end{array}\right\} :: 42 : (42 + x)$$

$\therefore$ $[50 \times 9 \times 1 \times (42 + x)] = \left(60 \times \frac{15}{2} \times 2 \times 42\right)$

$\Leftrightarrow (42 + x) = \frac{37800}{450} \Leftrightarrow 42 + x = 84 \Leftrightarrow x = 42.$

51. 3 men ≡ 6 boys $\Leftrightarrow$ (6 men + 2 boys) ≡ 14 boys.

More work, More days **(*Direct Proportion*)**

More boys, Less days **(*Indirect Proportion*)**

More hours per day, Less days **(*Indirect Proportion*)**

$$\left.\begin{array}{ll}\text{Work} & 1 : 2 \\ \text{Boys} & 14 : 6 \\ \text{Hours per day} & 8 : 7\end{array}\right\} :: 10 : x$$

$\therefore$ $(1 \times 14 \times 8 \times x) = (2 \times 6 \times 7 \times 10) \Leftrightarrow x = \frac{840}{112} = 7\frac{1}{2}.$

52. (2×14) men + (7×14) boys ≡ (3×11) men + (8×11) boys.

$\Leftrightarrow$ 5 men ≡ 10 boys $\Leftrightarrow$ 1 man ≡ 2 boys.

$\therefore$ (2 men + 7 boys) ≡ $(2 \times 2 + 7)$ boys = 11 boys.

(8 men + 6 boys) ≡ $(8 \times 2 + 6)$ boys = 22 boys.

Let the required number of days be x.

Now, ***More boys, Less days*** **(*Indirect Proportion*)**

More work, More days **(*Direct Proportion*)**

$$\left.\begin{array}{ll}\text{Boys} & 22 : 11 \\ \text{Work} & 1 : 3\end{array}\right\} :: 14 : x$$

$\therefore$ $(22 \times 1 \times x) = (11 \times 3 \times 14) \quad \therefore \quad x = \frac{462}{22} = 21.$

Hence, the required number of days = 21.

15. TIME AND WORK

IMPORTANT FACTS AND FORMULAE

1. If A can do a piece of work in n days, then A's 1 day's work $= \frac{1}{n}$.
2. If A's 1 day's work $= \frac{1}{n}$, then A can finish the work in n days.
3. If A is thrice as good a workman as B, then :
   Ratio of work done by A and B = 3 : 1.
   Ratio of times taken by A and B to finish a work = 1 : 3.

SOLVED EXAMPLES

Ex. 1. ***Worker A takes 8 hours to do a job. Worker B takes 10 hours to do the same job. How long should it take both A and B, working together but independently, to do the same job ?*** **(IGNOU, 2003)**

Sol. A's 1 hour's work $= \frac{1}{8}$, B's 1 hour's work $= \frac{1}{10}$.

(A + B)'s 1 hour's work $= \left(\frac{1}{8} + \frac{1}{10}\right) = \frac{9}{40}$.

$\therefore$ Both A and B will finish the work in $\frac{40}{9} = 4\frac{4}{9}$ days.

Ex. 2. ***A and B together can complete a piece of work in 4 days. If A alone can complete the same work in 12 days, in how many days can B alone complete that work?*** **(Bank P.O. 2003)**

Sol. (A + B)'s 1 day's work $= \frac{1}{4}$, A's 1 day's work $= \frac{1}{12}$.

$\therefore$ B's 1 day's work $= \left(\frac{1}{4} - \frac{1}{12}\right) = \frac{1}{6}$.

Hence, B alone can complete the work in 6 days.

Ex. 3. ***A can do a piece of work in 7 days of 9 hours each and B can do it in 6 days of 7 hours each. How long will they take to do it, working together $8\frac{2}{5}$ hours a day?***

Sol. A can complete the work in $(7 \times 9) = 63$ hours.
B can complete the work in $(6 \times 7) = 42$ hours.

$\therefore$ A's 1 hour's work $= \frac{1}{63}$ and B's 1 hour's work $= \frac{1}{42}$.

(A + B)'s 1 hour's work $= \left(\frac{1}{63} + \frac{1}{42}\right) = \frac{5}{126}$.

$\therefore$ Both will finish the work in $\left(\frac{126}{5}\right)$ hrs.

Number of days of $8\frac{2}{5}$ hrs each $= \left(\frac{126}{5} \times \frac{5}{42}\right) = 3$ days.

Ex. 4. ***A and B can do a piece of work in 18 days; B and C can do it in 24 days; A and C can do it in 36 days. In how many days will A, B and C finish it, working together and separately ?***

Sol. (A + B)'s 1 day's work $= \frac{1}{18}$, (B + C)'s 1 day's work $= \frac{1}{24}$,

and (A + C)'s 1 day's work $= \frac{1}{36}$.

Adding, we get : 2 (A + B + C)'s 1 day's work $= \left(\frac{1}{18} + \frac{1}{24} + \frac{1}{36}\right) = \frac{9}{72} = \frac{1}{8}$.

$\therefore$ (A + B + C)'s 1 day's work $= \frac{1}{16}$.

Thus, A, B and C together can finish the work in 16 days.

Now, A's 1 day's work = [(A + B + C)'s 1 day's work] – [(B + C)'s 1 day's work]

$$= \left(\frac{1}{16} - \frac{1}{24}\right) = \frac{1}{48}.$$

$\therefore$ A alone can finish the work in 48 days.

Similarly, B's 1 day's work $= \left(\frac{1}{16} - \frac{1}{36}\right) = \frac{5}{144}$.

$\therefore$ B alone can finish the work in $\frac{144}{5} = 28\frac{4}{5}$ days.

And, C's 1 day's work $= \left(\frac{1}{16} - \frac{1}{18}\right) = \frac{1}{144}$.

$\therefore$ C alone can finish the work in 144 days.

Ex. 5. ***A is twice as good a workman as B and together they finish a piece of work in 18 days. In how many days will A alone finish the work ?***

Sol. (A's 1 day's work) : (B's 1 day's work) = 2 : 1.

(A + B)'s 1 day's work $= \frac{1}{18}$.

Divide $\frac{1}{18}$ in the ratio 2 : 1.

$\therefore$ A's 1 day's work $= \left(\frac{1}{18} \times \frac{2}{3}\right) = \frac{1}{27}$.

Hence, A alone can finish the work in 27 days.

Ex. 6. ***A can do a certain job in 12 days. B is 60% more efficient than A. How many days does B alone take to do the same job ?***

Sol. Ratio of times taken by A and B = 160 : 100 = 8 : 5.

Suppose B alone takes x days to do the job.

Then, $8 : 5 :: 12 : x \Rightarrow 8x = 5 \times 12 \Rightarrow x = 7\frac{1}{2}$ days.

Ex. 7. ***A can do a piece of work in 80 days. He works at it for 10 days and then B alone finishes the remaining work in 42 days. In how much time will A and B, working together, finish the work ?***

Sol. Work done by A in 10 days $= \left(\frac{1}{80} \times 10\right) = \frac{1}{8}$.

Remaining work $= \left(1 - \frac{1}{8}\right) = \frac{7}{8}$.

Now, $\frac{7}{8}$ work is done by B in 42 days.

Whole work will be done by B in $\left(42 \times \frac{8}{7}\right) = 48$ days.

$\therefore$ A's 1 day's work $= \frac{1}{80}$ and B's 1 day's work $= \frac{1}{48}$.

$\therefore$ (A + B)'s 1 day's work $= \left(\frac{1}{80} + \frac{1}{48}\right) = \frac{8}{240} = \frac{1}{30}$.

Hence, both will finish the work in 30 days.

Ex. 8. ***A and B undertake to do a piece of work for Rs. 600. A alone can do it in 6 days while B alone can do it in 8 days. With the help of C, they finish it in 3 days. Find the share of each.***

Sol. C's 1 day's work $= \frac{1}{3} - \left(\frac{1}{6} + \frac{1}{8}\right) = \frac{1}{24}$.

$\therefore$ A : B : C = Ratio of their 1 day's work $= \frac{1}{6} : \frac{1}{8} : \frac{1}{24} = 4 : 3 : 1$.

$\therefore$ A's share = Rs. $\left(600 \times \frac{4}{8}\right)$ = Rs. 300, B's share = Rs. $\left(600 \times \frac{3}{8}\right)$ = Rs. 225.

C's share = Rs. [600 − (300 + 225)] = Rs. 75.

Ex. 9. ***A and B working separately can do a piece of work in 9 and 12 days respectively. If they work for a day alternately, A beginning, in how many days, the work will be completed ?***

Sol. (A + B)'s 2 days' work $= \left(\frac{1}{9} + \frac{1}{12}\right) = \frac{7}{36}$.

Work done in 5 pairs of days $= \left(5 \times \frac{7}{36}\right) = \frac{35}{36}$.

Remaining work $= \left(1 - \frac{35}{36}\right) = \frac{1}{36}$.

On 11th day, it is A's turn. $\frac{1}{9}$ work is done by him in 1 day.

$\frac{1}{36}$ work is done by him in $\left(9 \times \frac{1}{36}\right) = \frac{1}{4}$ day.

$\therefore$ Total time taken $= \left(10 + \frac{1}{4}\right)$ days $= 10\frac{1}{4}$ days.

Ex. 10. ***45 men can complete a work in 16 days. Six days after they started working, 30 more men joined them. How many days will they now take to complete the remaining work ?***

Sol. (45 × 16) men can complete the work in 1 day.

$\therefore$ 1 man's 1 day's work $= \frac{1}{720}$.

45 men's 6 days' work $= \left(\frac{1}{16} \times 6\right) = \frac{3}{8}$. Remaining work $= \left(1 - \frac{3}{8}\right) = \frac{5}{8}$.

75 men's 1 day's work $= \frac{75}{720} = \frac{5}{48}$.

Now, $\frac{5}{48}$ work is done by them in 1 day.

$\therefore$ $\frac{5}{8}$ work is done by them in $\left(\frac{48}{5} \times \frac{5}{8}\right) = 6$ days.

Ex. 11. ***2 men and 3 boys can do a piece of work in 10 days while 3 men and 2 boys can do the same work in 8 days. In how many days can 2 men and 1 boy do the work?***

Sol. Let 1 man's 1 day's work = x and 1 boy's 1 day's work = y.

Then. $2x + 3y = \frac{1}{10}$ and $3x + 2y = \frac{1}{8}$.

Solving, we get : $x = \frac{7}{200}$ and $y = \frac{1}{100}$.

$\therefore$ (2 men + 1 boy)'s 1 day's work $= \left(2 \times \frac{7}{200} + 1 \times \frac{1}{100}\right) = \frac{16}{200} = \frac{2}{25}$.

So, 2 men and 1 boy together can finish the work in $\frac{25}{2} = 12\frac{1}{2}$ days.

EXERCISE 15A

(OBJECTIVE TYPE QUESTIONS)

Directions : *Mark (✓) against the correct answer* :

1. A does a work in 10 days and B does the same work in 15 days. In how many days they together will do the same work ? **(R.R.B. 2003)**

   (a) 5 days (b) 6 days (c) 8 days (d) 9 days

2. A can finish a work in 18 days and B can do the same work in half the time taken by A. Then, working together, what part of the same work they can finish in a day ?

   (a) $\frac{1}{6}$ (b) $\frac{1}{9}$ (c) $\frac{2}{5}$ (d) $\frac{2}{7}$

   (S.S.C. 2002)

3. A tyre has two punctures. The first puncture alone would have made the tyre flat in 9 minutes and the second alone would have done it in 6 minutes. If air leaks out at a constant rate, how long does it take both the punctures together to make it flat ?

   (a) $1\frac{1}{2}$ minutes (b) $3\frac{1}{2}$ minutes (c) $3\frac{3}{5}$ minutes (d) $4\frac{1}{4}$ minutes

   (D.M.R.C. 2003)

4. A, B and C can complete a piece of work in 24, 6 and 12 days respectively. Working together, they will complete the same work in : **(C.B.I. 2003)**

   (a) $\frac{1}{24}$ day (b) $\frac{7}{24}$ day (c) $3\frac{3}{7}$ days (d) 4 days

5. A man can do a job in 15 days. His father takes 20 days and his son finishes it in 25 days. How long will they take to complete the job if they all work together ?

   (a) Less than 6 days (b) Exactly 6 days
   (c) Approximately 6.4 days (d) More than 10 days

   (Hotel Management, 2003)

6. A man can do a piece of work in 5 days, but with the help of his son, he can do it in 3 days. In what time can the son do it alone ? **(S.S.C. 2004)**

   (a) $6\frac{1}{2}$ days (b) 7 days (c) $7\frac{1}{2}$ days (d) 8 days

7. A can lay railway track between two given stations in 16 days and B can do the same job in 12 days. With the help of C, they did the job in 4 days only. Then, C alone can do the job in : **(S.S.C. 2003)**

(*a*) $9\frac{1}{5}$ days (*b*) $9\frac{2}{5}$ days (*c*) $9\frac{3}{5}$ days (*d*) 10 days

8. A takes twice as much time as B or thrice as much time to finish a piece of work. Working together, they can finish the work in 2 days. B can do the work alone in : **(S.S.C. 2002)**

(*a*) 4 days (*b*) 6 days (*c*) 8 days (*d*) 12 days

9. X can do $\frac{1}{4}$ of a work in 10 days, Y can do 40% of the work in 40 days and Z can do $\frac{1}{3}$ of the work in 13 days. Who will complete the work first ?

(*a*) X (*b*) Y (*c*) Z (*d*) X and Z both

10. P, Q and R are three typists who working simultaneously can type 216 pages in 4 hours. In one hour, R can type as many pages more than Q as Q can type more than P. During a period of five hours, R can type as many pages as P can during seven hours. How many pages does each of them type per hour ?

(*a*) 14, 17, 20 (*b*) 15, 17, 22 (*c*) 15, 18, 21 (*d*) 16, 18, 22

11. Ronald and Elan are working on an assignment. Ronald takes 6 hours to type 32 pages on a computer, while Elan takes 5 hours to type 40 pages. How much time will they take, working together on two different computers to type an assignment of 110 pages ?

(*a*) 7 hours 30 minutes (*b*) 8 hours

(*c*) 8 hours 15 minutes (*d*) 8 hours 25 minutes

(SCMHRD, 2002)

12. Two workers A and B are engaged to do a work. A working alone takes 8 hours more to complete the job than if both worked together. If B worked alone, he would need $4\frac{1}{2}$ hours more to complete the job than they both working together. What time would they take to do the work together ?

(*a*) 4 hours (*b*) 5 hours (*c*) 6 hours (*d*) 7 hours

13. P can complete a work in 12 days working 8 hours a day. Q can complete the same work in 8 days working 10 hours a day. If both P and Q work together, working 8 hours a day, in how many days can they complete the work ? **(Bank P.O. 1999)**

(*a*) $5\frac{5}{11}$ (*b*) $5\frac{6}{11}$ (*c*) $6\frac{5}{11}$ (*d*) $6\frac{6}{11}$

14. A and B can do a work in 12 days, B and C in 15 days, C and A in 20 days. If A, B and C work together, they will complete the work in : **(S.S.C. 1999)**

(*a*) 5 days (*b*) $7\frac{5}{6}$ days (*c*) 10 days (*d*) $15\frac{2}{3}$ days

15. A and B can do a work in 8 days, B and C can do the same work in 12 days. A, B and C together can finish it in 6 days. A and C together will do it in :

(*a*) 4 days (*b*) 6 days (*c*) 8 days (*d*) 12 days

(R.R.B. 2001)

16. A and B can do a piece of work in 72 days; B and C can do it in 120 days; A and C can do it in 90 days. In what time can A alone do it ?

(*a*) 80 days (*b*) 100 days (*c*) 120 days (*d*) 150 days

17. A and B can do a piece of work in 5 days; B and C can do it in 7 days; A and C can do it in 4 days. Who among these will take the least time if put to do it alone ?

(*a*) A (*b*) B (*c*) C (*d*) Data inadequate

18. A can do a piece of work in 4 hours; B and C together can do it in 3 hours, while A and C together can do it in 2 hours. How long will B alone take to do it ?
(*a*) 8 hours (*b*) 10 hours (*c*) 12 hours (*d*) 24 hours
(S.S.C. 2002)

19. A can do a certain work in the same time in which B and C together can do it. If A and B together could do it in 10 days and C alone in 50 days, then B alone could do it in : **(S.S.C. 2003)**
(*a*) 15 days (*b*) 20 days (*c*) 25 days (*d*) 30 days

20. A works twice as fast as B. If B can complete a work in 12 days independently, the number of days in which A and B can together finish the work is :
(*a*) 4 days (*b*) 6 days (*c*) 8 days (*d*) 18 days
(Asstt. Grade, 1997)

21. A is twice as good a workman as B and together they finish a piece of work in 14 days. The number of days taken by A alone to finish the work is :
(*a*) 11 (*b*) 21 (*c*) 28 (*d*) 42

22. A is thrice as good a workman as B and therefore is able to finish a job in 60 days less than B. Working together, they can do it in : **(S.S.C. 1999)**
(*a*) 20 days (*b*) $22\frac{1}{2}$ days (*c*) 25 days (*d*) 30 days

23. A and B can do a job together in 7 days. A is $1\frac{3}{4}$ times as efficient as B. The same job can be done by A alone in : **(S.S.C. 2003)**
(*a*) $9\frac{1}{3}$ days (*b*) 11 days (*c*) $12\frac{1}{4}$ days (*d*) $16\frac{1}{3}$ days

24. Sakshi can do a piece of work in 20 days. Tanya is 25% more efficient than Sakshi. The number of days taken by Tanya to do the same piece of work is :
(*a*) 15 (*b*) 16 (*c*) 18 (*d*) 25
(Hotel Management, 2003)

25. A is 30% more efficient than B. How much time will they, working together, take to complete a job which A alone could have done in 23 days ?
(*a*) 11 days (*b*) 13 days (*c*) $20\frac{3}{17}$ days (*d*) None of these
(Hotel Management, 1998)

26. A does half as much work as B in three-fourth of the time. If together they take 18 days to complete the work, how much time shall B take to do it ?
(*a*) 30 days (*b*) 35 days (*c*) 40 days (*d*) None of these

27. A is 50% as efficient as B. C does half of the work done by A and B together. If C alone does the work in 40 days, then A, B and C together can do the work in :
(*a*) $13\frac{1}{3}$ days (*b*) 15 days (*c*) 20 days (*d*) 30 days

28. Two workers A and B working together completed a job in 5 days. If A worked twice as efficiently as he actually did and B worked $\frac{1}{3}$ as efficiently as he actually did, the work would have been completed in 3 days. A alone could complete the work in :
(*a*) $5\frac{1}{4}$ days (*b*) $6\frac{1}{4}$ days (*c*) $7\frac{1}{2}$ days (*d*) None of these

29. A can do a work in 15 days and B in 20 days. If they work on it together for 4 days, then the fraction of the work that is left is : **(S.S.C. 2000)**
(*a*) $\frac{1}{4}$ (*b*) $\frac{1}{10}$ (*c*) $\frac{7}{15}$ (*d*) $\frac{8}{15}$

30. A can finish a work in 18 days and B can do the same work in 15 days. B worked for 10 days and left the job. In how many days, A alone can finish the remaining work ?

(*a*) 5 (*b*) $5\frac{1}{2}$ (*c*) 6 (*d*) 8

(Bank P.O. 2002)

31. A and B can complete a work in 15 days and 10 days respectively. They started doing the work together but after 2 days B had to leave and A alone completed the remaining work. The whole work was completed in : **(S.S.C. 2004)**

(*a*) 8 days (*b*) 10 days (*c*) 12 days (*d*) 15 days

32. A can finish a work in 24 days, B in 9 days and C in 12 days. B and C start the work but are forced to leave after 3 days. The remaining work was done by A in :

(*a*) 5 days (*b*) 6 days (*c*) 10 days (*d*) $10\frac{1}{2}$ days

(S.S.C. 2003)

33. A machine P can print one lakh books in 8 hours, machine Q can print the same number of books in 10 hours while machine R can print them in 12 hours. All the machines are started at 9 a.m. while machine P is closed at 11 a.m. and the remaining two machines complete the work. Approximately at what time will the work be finished ? **(Bank P.O. 2003)**

(*a*) 11:30 a.m. (*b*) 12 noon (*c*) 12:30 p.m. (*d*) 1 p.m.

34. A and B can do a piece of work in 30 days, while B and C can do the same work in 24 days and C and A in 20 days. They all work together for 10 days when B and C leave. How many days more will A take to finish the work ? **(C.B.I. 2003)**

(*a*) 18 days (*b*) 24 days (*c*) 30 days (*d*) 36 days

35. X and Y can do a piece of work in 20 days and 12 days respectively. X started the work alone and then after 4 days Y joined him till the completion of the work. How long did the work last ? **(Bank P.O. 2004)**

(*a*) 6 days (*b*) 10 days (*c*) 15 days (*d*) 20 days

36. A and B can together finish a work in 30 days. They worked together for 20 days and then B left. After another 20 days, A finished the remaining work. In how many days A alone can finish the job ? **(S.S.C. 2003)**

(*a*) 40 (*b*) 50 (*c*) 54 (*d*) 60

37. X can do a piece of work in 40 days. He works at it for 8 days and then Y finished it in 16 days. How long will they together take to complete the work ?

(*a*) $13\frac{1}{3}$ days (*b*) 15 days (*c*) 20 days (*d*) 56 days

(Hotel Management, 1999)

38. A, B and C together can complete a piece of work in 10 days. All the three started working at it together and after 4 days A left. Then B and C together completed the work in 10 more days. A alone could complete the work in :

(*a*) 15 days (*b*) 16 days (*c*) 25 days (*d*) 50 days

39. A does $\frac{4}{5}$ of a work in 20 days. He then calls in B and they together finish the remaining work in 3 days. How long B alone would take to do the whole work ?

(*a*) 23 days (*b*) 37 days (*c*) $37\frac{1}{2}$ days (*d*) 40 days

(S.S.C. 2002)

40. A and B together can do a piece of work in 30 days. A having worked for 16 days, B finishes the remaining work alone in 44 days. In how many days shall B finish the whole work alone ? **(C.B.I. 1997)**

(*a*) 30 days (*b*) 40 days (*c*) 60 days (*d*) 70 days

41. A and B together can do a piece of work in 12 days, which B and C together can do in 16 days. After A has been working at it for 5 days and B for 7 days, C finishes it in 13 days. In how many days C alone will do the work ?

(*a*) 16 (*b*) 24 (*c*) 36 (*d*) 48

42. A and B can do a piece of work in 45 days and 40 days respectively. They began to do the work together but A leaves after some days and then B completed the remaining work in 23 days. The number of days after which A left the work was :

(*a*) 6 (*b*) 8 (*c*) 9 (*d*) 12

(Bank P.O. 1998)

43. A can do a piece of work in 14 days which B can do in 21 days. They begin together but 3 days before the completion of the work, A leaves off. The total number of days to complete the work is : **(R.R.B. 2002)**

(*a*) $6\frac{3}{5}$ (*b*) $8\frac{1}{2}$ (*c*) $10\frac{1}{5}$ (*d*) $13\frac{1}{2}$

44. A, B and C can complete a work separately in 24, 36 and 48 days respectively. They started together but C left after 4 days of start and A left 3 days before the completion of the work. In how many days will the work be completed ?

(*a*) 15 days (*b*) 22 days (*c*) 25 days (*d*) 35 days

45. A, B and C together earn Rs. 300 per day, while A and C together earn Rs. 188 and B and C together earn Rs. 152. The daily earning of C is :

(*a*) Rs. 40 (*b*) Rs. 68 (*c*) Rs. 112 (*d*) Rs. 150

46. A, B and C are employed to do a piece of work for Rs. 529. A and B together are supposed to do $\frac{19}{23}$ of the work and B and C together $\frac{8}{23}$ of the work. What amount should A be paid ? **(C.B.I. 1997)**

(*a*) Rs. 315 (*b*) Rs. 345 (*c*) Rs. 355 (*d*) Rs. 375

47. Kim can do a work in 3 days while David can do the same work in 2 days. Both of them finish the work together and get Rs. 150. What is the share of Kim ?

(*a*) Rs. 30 (*b*) Rs. 60 (*c*) Rs. 70 (*d*) Rs. 75

(S.S.C. 1999)

48. If A can do $\frac{1}{4}$ of a work in 3 days and B can do $\frac{1}{6}$ of the same work in 4 days, how much will A get if both work together and are paid Rs. 180 in all ?

(*a*) Rs. 36 (*b*) Rs. 60 (*c*) Rs. 108 (*d*) Rs. 120

49. A alone can do a piece of work in 6 days and B alone in 8 days. A and B undertook to do it for Rs. 3200. With the help of C, they completed the work in 3 days. How much is to be paid to C ? **(S.S.C. 2004)**

(*a*) Rs. 375 (*b*) Rs. 400 (*c*) Rs. 600 (*d*) Rs. 800

50. A sum of money is sufficient to pay A's wages for 21 days and B's wages for 28 days. The same money is sufficient to pay the wages of both for :

(*a*) 12 days (*b*) $12\frac{1}{4}$ days (*c*) 14 days (*d*) $24\frac{1}{2}$ days

51. A can do a piece of work in 10 days; B in 15 days. They work for 5 days. The rest of the work was finished by C in 2 days. If they get Rs. 1500 for the whole work, the daily wages of B and C are :

(*a*) Rs. 150 (*b*) Rs. 225 (*c*) Rs. 250 (*d*) Rs. 300

52. A and B together can complete a work in 12 days. A alone can complete it in 20 days. If B does the work only for half a day daily, then in how many days A and B together will complete the work ? **(R.R.B. 2003)**

(*a*) 10 days (*b*) 11 days (*c*) 15 days (*d*) 20 days

53. A alone can complete a work in 16 days and B alone in 12 days. Starting with A, they work on alternate days. The total work will be completed in : **(S.S.C. 2004)**

(*a*) 12 days (*b*) 13 days (*c*) $13\frac{5}{7}$ days (*d*) $13\frac{3}{4}$ days

54. A, B and C can do a piece of work in 11 days, 20 days and 55 days respectively, working alone. How soon can the work be done if A is assisted by B and C on alternate days ?

(*a*) 7 days (*b*) 8 days (*c*) 9 days (*d*) 10 days

55. A, B and C can do a piece of work in 20, 30 and 60 days respectively. In how many days can A do the work if he is assisted by B and C on every third day ?

(*a*) 12 days (*b*) 15 days (*c*) 16 days (*d*) 18 days

(R.R.B. 2002)

56. A and B can separately do a piece of work in 20 and 15 days respectively. They worked together for 6 days, after which B was replaced by C. If the work was finished in next 4 days, then the number of days in which C alone could do the work will be :

(*a*) 30 (*b*) 35 (*c*) 40 (*d*) 60

57. A, B and C can do a piece of work in 36, 54 and 72 days respectively. They started the work but A left 8 days before the completion of the work while B left 12 days before the completion. The number of days for which C worked is :

(*a*) 4 (*b*) 8 (*c*) 12 (*d*) 24

58. Twenty women can do a work in sixteen days. Sixteen men can complete the same work in fifteen days. What is the ratio between the capacity of a man and a woman ?

(*a*) 3 : 4 (*b*) 4 : 3 (*c*) 5 : 3 (*d*) Data inadequate

(B.S.R.B. 1998)

59. 10 men can complete a piece of work in 15 days and 15 women can complete the same work in 12 days. If all the 10 men and 15 women work together, in how many days will the work get completed ? **(S.B.I.P.O. 1999)**

(*a*) 6 (*b*) $6\frac{1}{3}$ (*c*) $6\frac{2}{3}$ (*d*) $7\frac{2}{3}$

60. Seven men can complete a work in 12 days. They started the work and after 5 days, two men left. In how many days will the work be completed by the remaining men ?

(*a*) 5 (*b*) 6 (*c*) 7 (*d*) 8 (*e*) None of these

61. 12 men complete a work in 9 days. After they have worked for 6 days, 6 more men join them. How many days will they take to complete the remaining work ?

(*a*) 2 days (*b*) 3 days (*c*) 4 days (*d*) 5 days (*e*) None of these

(R.R.B. 2002)

62. Three men, four women and six children can complete a work in seven days. A woman does double the work a man does and a child does half the work a man does. How many women alone can complete this work in 7 days ? **(S.B.I.P.O. 2003)**

(*a*) 7 (*b*) 8 (*c*) 12
(*d*) Cannot be determined (*e*) None of these

63. A man, a woman and a boy can complete a job in 3, 4 and 12 days respectively. How many boys must assist 1 man and 1 woman to complete the job in $\frac{1}{4}$ of a day ?

(*a*) 1 (*b*) 4 (*c*) 19 (*d*) 41

(S.S.C. 2000)

64. 10 men and 15 women together can complete a work in 6 days. It takes 100 days for one man alone to complete the same work. How many days will be required for one woman alone to complete the same work ? **(Bank P.O. 1999)**

(*a*) 90 (*b*) 125 (*c*) 145 (*d*) 150 (*e*) None of these

65. 12 men can complete a piece of work in 4 days, while 15 women can complete the same work in 4 days. 6 men start working on the job and after working for 2 days, all of them stopped working. How many women should be put on the job to complete the remaining work, if it is to be completed in 3 days ? **(S.B.I.P.O. 2000)**

(*a*) 15 (*b*) 18 (*c*) 22
(*d*) Data inadequate (*e*) None of these

66. Twelve children take sixteen days to complete a work which can be completed by eight adults in twelve days. Sixteen adults started working and after three days ten adults left and four children joined them. How many days will they take to complete the remaining work ?

(*a*) 3 (*b*) 4 (*c*) 6 (*d*) 8 (*e*) None of these

67. 10 women can complete a work in 7 days and 10 children take 14 days to complete the work. How many days will 5 women and 10 children take to complete the work?

(*a*) 3 (*b*) 5 (*c*) 7
(*d*) Cannot be determined (*e*) None of these **(Bank P.O. 2003)**

68. Sixteen men can complete a work in twelve days. Twenty-four children can complete the same work in eighteen days. Twelve men and eight children started working and after eight days three more children joined them. How many days will they now take to complete the remaining work ?

(*a*) 2 days (*b*) 4 days (*c*) 6 days (*d*) 8 days (*e*) None of these

69. Twenty-four men can complete a work in sixteen days. Thirty-two women can complete the same work in twenty-four days. Sixteen men and sixteen women started working and worked for twelve days. How many more men are to be added to complete the remaining work in 2 days ? **(Bank P.O. 1999)**

(*a*) 16 (*b*) 24 (*c*) 36 (*d*) 48 (*e*) None of these

70. 5 men and 2 boys working together can do four times as much work as a man and a boy. Working capacities of a woman and a boy are in the ratio :

(*a*) 1 : 2 (*b*) 2 : 1 (*c*) 1 : 3 (*d*) 3 : 1

71. If 12 men and 16 boys can do a piece of work in 5 days; 13 men and 24 boys can do it in 4 days, then the ratio of the daily work done by a man to that of a boy is :

(*a*) 2 : 1 (*b*) 3 : 1 (*c*) 3 : 2 (*d*) 5 : 4

(S.S.C. 1999)

72. 4 men and 6 women can complete a work in 8 days, while 3 men and 7 women can complete it in 10 days. In how many days will 10 women complete it ?

(*a*) 35 (*b*) 40 (*c*) 45 (*d*) 50

(S.S.C. 2004)

73. One man, 3 women and 4 boys can do a piece of work in 96 hours, 2 men and 8 boys can do it in 80 hours, 2 men and 3 women can do it in 120 hours. 5 men and 12 boys can do it in :

(*a*) $39\frac{1}{11}$ hours (*b*) $42\frac{7}{11}$ hours (*c*) $43\frac{7}{11}$ hours (*d*) 44 hours

74. If 6 men and 8 boys can do a piece of work in 10 days while 26 men and 48 boys can do the same in 2 days, the time taken by 15 men and 20 boys in doing the same type of work will be : **(S.S.C. 1999)**

(*a*) 4 days (*b*) 5 days (*c*) 6 days (*d*) 7 days

ANSWERS

1. (*b*)	**2.** (*a*)	**3.** (*c*)	**4.** (*c*)	**5.** (*c*)	**6.** (*c*)	**7.** (*c*)	**8.** (*b*)	**9.** (*c*)
10. (*c*)	**11.** (*c*)	**12.** (*c*)	**13.** (*a*)	**14.** (*c*)	**15.** (*c*)	**16.** (*c*)	**17.** (*a*)	**18.** (*c*)
19. (*c*)	**20.** (*a*)	**21.** (*b*)	**22.** (*b*)	**23.** (*b*)	**24.** (*b*)	**25.** (*b*)	**26.** (*a*)	**27.** (*a*)
28. (*b*)	**29.** (*d*)	**30.** (*c*)	**31.** (*c*)	**32.** (*c*)	**33.** (*d*)	**34.** (*a*)	**35.** (*b*)	**36.** (*d*)
37. (*a*)	**38.** (*c*)	**39.** (*c*)	**40.** (*c*)	**41.** (*b*)	**42.** (*e*)	**43.** (*c*)	**44.** (*a*)	**45.** (*a*)
46. (*b*)	**47.** (*b*)	**48.** (*d*)	**49.** (*b*)	**50.** (*a*)	**51.** (*b*)	**52.** (*c*)	**53.** (*d*)	**54.** (*b*)
55. (*b*)	**56.** (*c*)	**57.** (*d*)	**58.** (*b*)	**59.** (*c*)	**60.** (*e*)	**61.** (*a*)	**62.** (*a*)	**63.** (*d*)
64. (*e*)	**65.** (*a*)	**66.** (*e*)	**67.** (*c*)	**68.** (*b*)	**69.** (*b*)	**70.** (*b*)	**71.** (*a*)	**72.** (*b*)
73. (*c*)	**74.** (*a*)							

SOLUTIONS

1. A's 1 day's work $= \frac{1}{10}$ and B's 1 day's work $= \frac{1}{15}$.

$\therefore$ (A + B)'s 1 day's work $= \left(\frac{1}{10} + \frac{1}{15}\right) = \frac{1}{6}$.

So, both together will finish the work in 6 days.

2. A's 1 day's work $= \frac{1}{18}$ and B's 1 day's work $= \frac{1}{9}$.

$\therefore$ (A + B)'s 1 day's work $= \left(\frac{1}{18} + \frac{1}{9}\right) = \frac{1}{6}$.

3. 1 minute's work of both the punctures $= \left(\frac{1}{9} + \frac{1}{6}\right) = \frac{5}{18}$.

So, both the punctures will make the tyre flat in $\frac{18}{5} = 3\frac{3}{5}$ min.

4. (A + B + C)'s 1 day's work $= \left(\frac{1}{24} + \frac{1}{6} + \frac{1}{12}\right) = \frac{7}{24}$.

So, A, B and C together will complete the job in $\frac{24}{7} = 3\frac{3}{7}$ days.

5. 1 day's work of the three persons $= \left(\frac{1}{15} + \frac{1}{20} + \frac{1}{25}\right) = \frac{47}{300}$.

So, all the three together will complete the work in $\frac{300}{47} \simeq 6.4$ days.

6. Son's 1 day's work $= \left(\frac{1}{3} - \frac{1}{5}\right) = \frac{2}{15}$.

$\therefore$ The son alone can do the work in $\frac{15}{2} = 7\frac{1}{2}$ days.

7. (A + B + C)'s 1 day's work $= \frac{1}{4}$, A's 1 day's work $= \frac{1}{16}$, B's 1 day's work $= \frac{1}{12}$

$\therefore$ C's 1 day's work $= \frac{1}{4} - \left(\frac{1}{16} + \frac{1}{12}\right) = \left(\frac{1}{4} - \frac{7}{48}\right) = \frac{5}{48}$.

So, C alone can do the work in $\frac{48}{5} = 9\frac{3}{5}$ days.

8. Suppose A, B and C take x, $\frac{x}{2}$ and $\frac{x}{3}$ hours respectively to finish the work.

Then, $\left(\frac{1}{x}+\frac{2}{x}+\frac{3}{x}\right)=\frac{1}{2} \Rightarrow \frac{6}{x}=\frac{1}{2} \Rightarrow x = 12.$

So, B takes 6 hours to finish the work.

9. Whole work will be done by X in $(10 \times 4) = 40$ days.

Whole work will be done by Y in $\left(40 \times \frac{100}{40}\right) = 100$ days.

Whole work will be done by Z in $(13 \times 3) = 39$ days.

$\therefore$ Z will complete the work first.

10. Let the number of pages typed in one hour by P, Q and R be x, y and z respectively. Then,

$x+y+z=\frac{216}{4} \Rightarrow x+y+z=54$ ...(*i*)

$z-y=y-x \Rightarrow 2y=x+z$ ...(*ii*)

$5z=7x \Rightarrow x=\frac{5}{7}z$ ...(*iii*)

Solving (*i*), (*ii*) and (*iii*), we get $x = 15$, $y = 18$, $z = 21$.

11. Number of pages typed by Ronald in 1 hour $=\frac{32}{6}=\frac{16}{3}$.

Number of pages typed by Elan in 1 hour $=\frac{40}{5}=8$.

Number of pages typed by both in 1 hour $=\left(\frac{16}{3}+8\right)=\frac{40}{3}$.

$\therefore$ Time taken by both to type 110 pages $=\left(110 \times \frac{3}{40}\right)$ hrs $= 8\frac{1}{4}$ hrs = 8 hrs 15 min.

12. Let A and B together take x hours to complete the work. Then,

A alone takes $(x + 8)$ hrs and B alone takes $\left(x+\frac{9}{2}\right)$ hrs to complete the work. Then,

$$\frac{1}{(x+8)}+\frac{1}{\left(x+\frac{9}{2}\right)}=\frac{1}{x} \Rightarrow \frac{1}{(x+8)}+\frac{2}{(2x+9)}=\frac{1}{x} \Rightarrow x(4x+25)=(x+8)(2x+9)$$

$$\Rightarrow 2x^2 = 72 \Rightarrow x^2 = 36 \Rightarrow x = 6.$$

13. P can complete the work in (12×8) hrs. = 96 hrs.

Q can complete the work in (8×10) hrs. = 80 hrs.

$\therefore$ P's 1 hour's work $=\frac{1}{96}$ and Q's 1 hour's work $=\frac{1}{80}$.

(P + Q)'s 1 hour's work $=\left(\frac{1}{96}+\frac{1}{80}\right)=\frac{11}{480}$.

So, both P and Q will finish the work in $\left(\frac{480}{11}\right)$ hrs.

$\therefore$ Number of days of 8 hours each $=\left(\frac{480}{11}\times\frac{1}{8}\right)=\frac{60}{11}$ days $=5\frac{5}{11}$ days.

14. (A + B)'s 1 day's work $= \frac{1}{12}$; (B + C)'s 1 day's work $= \frac{1}{15}$; (A + C)'s 1 day's work $= \frac{1}{20}$.

Adding, we get : 2 (A + B + C)'s 1 day's work $= \left(\frac{1}{12} + \frac{1}{15} + \frac{1}{20}\right) = \frac{12}{60} = \frac{1}{5}$.

$\therefore$ (A + B + C)'s 1 day's work $= \frac{1}{10}$.

So, A, B and C together can complete the work in 10 days.

15. (A + B + C)'s 1 day's work $= \frac{1}{6}$; (A + B)'s 1 day's work $= \frac{1}{8}$;

(B + C)'s 1 day's work $= \frac{1}{12}$.

$\therefore$ (A + C)'s 1 day's work $= \left(2 \times \frac{1}{6}\right) - \left(\frac{1}{8} + \frac{1}{12}\right) = \left(\frac{1}{3} - \frac{5}{24}\right) = \frac{3}{24} = \frac{1}{8}$.

So, A and C together will do the work in 8 days.

16. (A + B)'s 1 day's work $= \frac{1}{72}$; (B + C)'s 1 day's work $= \frac{1}{120}$; (A + C)'s 1 day's work $= \frac{1}{90}$.

Adding, we get : 2 (A + B + C)'s 1 day's work $= \left(\frac{1}{72} + \frac{1}{120} + \frac{1}{90}\right) = \frac{12}{360} = \frac{1}{30}$.

$\Rightarrow$ (A + B + C)'s 1 day's work $= \frac{1}{60}$.

So, A's 1 day's work $= \left(\frac{1}{60} - \frac{1}{120}\right) = \frac{1}{120}$.

$\therefore$ A alone can do the work in 120 days.

17. (A + B)'s 1 day's work $= \frac{1}{5}$; (B + C)'s 1 day's work $= \frac{1}{7}$; (A + C)'s 1 day's work $= \frac{1}{4}$.

Adding, we get : 2 (A + B + C)'s 1 day's work $= \left(\frac{1}{5} + \frac{1}{7} + \frac{1}{4}\right) = \frac{83}{140}$.

(A + B + C)'s 1 day's work $= \frac{83}{280}$.

A's 1 day's work $= \left(\frac{83}{280} - \frac{1}{7}\right) = \frac{43}{280}$; B's 1 day's work $= \left(\frac{83}{280} - \frac{1}{4}\right) = \frac{13}{280}$;

C's 1 day's work $= \left(\frac{83}{280} - \frac{1}{5}\right) = \frac{27}{280}$.

Thus time taken by A, B, C is $\frac{280}{43}$ days, $\frac{280}{13}$ days, $\frac{280}{27}$ days respectively.

Clearly, the time taken by A is least.

18. A's 1 hour's work $= \frac{1}{4}$; (B + C)'s 1 hour's work $= \frac{1}{3}$; (A + C)'s 1 hour's work $= \frac{1}{2}$.

(A + B + C)'s 1 hour's work $= \left(\frac{1}{4} + \frac{1}{3}\right) = \frac{7}{12}$.

B's 1 hour's work $= \left(\frac{7}{12} - \frac{1}{2}\right) = \frac{1}{12}$.

$\therefore$ B alone will take 12 hours to do the work.

19. (A + B)'s 1 day's work $= \frac{1}{10}$; C's 1 day's work $= \frac{1}{50}$.

(A + B + C)'s 1 day's work $= \left(\frac{1}{10} + \frac{1}{50}\right) = \frac{6}{50} = \frac{3}{25}$ ...(*i*)

Also, A's 1 day's work = (B + C)'s 1 day's work ...(*ii*)

From (*i*) and (*ii*), we get : 2 × (A's 1 day's work) $= \frac{3}{25}$.

$\Rightarrow$ A's 1 day's work $= \frac{3}{50}$.

$\therefore$ B's 1 day's work $= \left(\frac{1}{10} - \frac{3}{50}\right) = \frac{2}{50} = \frac{1}{25}$.

So, B alone could do the work in 25 days.

20. Ratio of rates of working of A and B = 2 : 1. So, ratio of times taken = 1 : 2.

$\therefore$ A's 1 day's work $= \frac{1}{6}$; B's 1 day's work $= \frac{1}{12}$.

(A + B)'s 1 day's work $= \left(\frac{1}{6} + \frac{1}{12}\right) = \frac{3}{12} = \frac{1}{4}$.

So, A and B together can finish the work in 4 days.

21. (A's 1 day's work) : (B's 1 day's work) = 2 : 1.

(A + B)'s 1 day's work $= \frac{1}{14}$.

Divide $\frac{1}{14}$ in the ratio 2 : 1.

$\therefore$ A's 1 day's work $= \left(\frac{1}{14} \times \frac{2}{3}\right) = \frac{1}{21}$.

Hence, A alone can finish the work in 21 days.

22. Ratio of times taken by A and B = 1 : 3.

If difference of time is 2 days, B takes 3 days.

If difference of time is 60 days, B takes $\left(\frac{3}{2} \times 60\right) = 90$ days.

So, A takes 30 days to do the work.

A's 1 day's work $= \frac{1}{30}$, B's 1 day's work $= \frac{1}{90}$.

(A + B)'s 1 day's work $= \left(\frac{1}{30} + \frac{1}{90}\right) = \frac{4}{90} = \frac{2}{45}$.

$\therefore$ A and B together can do the work in $\frac{45}{2} = 22\frac{1}{2}$ days.

23. (A's 1 day's work) : (B's 1 day's work) $= \frac{7}{4} : 1 = 7 : 4$.

Let A's and B's 1 day's work be $7x$ and $4x$ respectively.

Then, $7x + 4x = \frac{1}{7} \Rightarrow 11x = \frac{1}{7} \Rightarrow x = \frac{1}{77}$.

$\therefore$ A's 1 day's work $= \left(\frac{1}{77} \times 7\right) = \frac{1}{11}$.

24. Ratio of times taken by Sakshi and Tanya = 125 : 100 = 5 : 4.

Suppose Tanya takes x days to do the work.

$5 : 4 :: 20 : x \Rightarrow x = \left(\frac{4 \times 20}{5}\right) \Rightarrow x = 16$ days.

Hence, Tanya takes 16 days to complete the work.

25. Ratio of times taken by A and B = 100 : 130 = 10 : 13.

Suppose B takes x days to do the work.

Then, $10 : 13 :: 23 : x \Rightarrow x = \left(\frac{23 \times 13}{10}\right) \Rightarrow x = \frac{299}{10}$.

A's 1 day's work $= \frac{1}{23}$; B's 1 days work $= \frac{10}{299}$.

(A + B)'s 1 day's work $= \left(\frac{1}{23} + \frac{10}{299}\right) = \frac{23}{299} = \frac{1}{13}$.

$\therefore$ A and B together can complete the job in 13 days.

26. Suppose B takes x days to do the work.

$\therefore$ A takes $\left(2 \times \frac{3}{4} x\right) = \frac{3x}{2}$ days to do it.

(A + B)'s 1 day's work $= \frac{1}{18}$.

$\therefore \quad \frac{1}{x} + \frac{2}{3x} = \frac{1}{18}$ or $x = 30$.

27. (A's 1 day's work) : (B's 1 day's work) = 150 : 100 = 3 : 2.

Let A's and B's 1 day's work be $3x$ and $2x$ respectively.

Then, C's 1 day's work $= \left(\frac{3x + 2x}{2}\right) = \frac{5x}{2}$.

$\therefore \quad \frac{5x}{2} = \frac{1}{40}$ or $x = \left(\frac{1}{40} \times \frac{2}{5}\right) = \frac{1}{100}$.

A's 1 day's work $= \frac{3}{100}$; B's 1 day's work $= \frac{1}{50}$; C's 1 day's work $= \frac{1}{40}$.

(A + B + C)'s 1 day's work $= \left(\frac{3}{100} + \frac{1}{50} + \frac{1}{40}\right) = \frac{15}{200} = \frac{3}{40}$.

So, A, B and C together can do the work in $\frac{40}{3} = 13\frac{1}{3}$ days.

28. Let A's 1 day's work = x and B's 1 day's work = y.

Then, $x + y = \frac{1}{5}$ and $2x + \frac{1}{3}y = \frac{1}{3}$.

Solving, we get : $x = \frac{4}{25}$ and $y = \frac{1}{25}$.

$\therefore$ A's 1 day's work $= \frac{4}{25}$.

So, A alone could complete the work in $\frac{25}{4} = 6\frac{1}{4}$ days.

29. A's 1 day's work $= \frac{1}{15}$; B's 1 day's work $= \frac{1}{20}$.

(A + B)'s 1 day's work $= \left(\frac{1}{15} + \frac{1}{20}\right) = \frac{7}{60}$.

(A + B)'s 4 days' work $= \left(\frac{7}{60} \times 4\right) = \frac{7}{15}$.

$\therefore$ Remaining work $= \left(1 - \frac{7}{15}\right) = \frac{8}{15}$.

30. B's 10 days' work $= \left(\frac{1}{15} \times 10\right) = \frac{2}{3}$. Remaining work $= \left(1 - \frac{2}{3}\right) = \frac{1}{3}$.

Now, $\frac{1}{18}$ work is done by A in 1 day.

$\therefore$ $\frac{1}{3}$ work is done by A in $\left(18 \times \frac{1}{3}\right) = 6$ days.

31. (A + B)'s 1 day's work $= \left(\frac{1}{15} + \frac{1}{10}\right) = \frac{1}{6}$.

Work done by A and B in 2 days $= \left(\frac{1}{6} \times 2\right) = \frac{1}{3}$. Remaining work $= \left(1 - \frac{1}{3}\right) = \frac{2}{3}$.

Now, $\frac{1}{15}$ work is done by A in 1 day.

$\therefore$ $\frac{2}{3}$ work will be done by A in $\left(15 \times \frac{2}{3}\right) = 10$ days.

Hence, total time taken = (10 + 2) = 12 days.

32. (B + C)'s 1 day's work $= \left(\frac{1}{9} + \frac{1}{12}\right) = \frac{7}{36}$.

Work done by B and C in 3 days $= \left(\frac{7}{36} \times 3\right) = \frac{7}{12}$.

Remaining work $= \left(1 - \frac{7}{12}\right) = \frac{5}{12}$.

Now, $\frac{1}{24}$ work is done by A in 1 day.

So, $\frac{5}{12}$ work is done by A in $\left(24 \times \frac{5}{12}\right) = 10$ days.

33. (P + Q + R)'s 1 hour's work $= \left(\frac{1}{8} + \frac{1}{10} + \frac{1}{12}\right) = \frac{37}{120}$.

Work done by P, Q and R in 2 hours $= \left(\frac{37}{120} \times 2\right) = \frac{37}{60}$.

Remaining work $= \left(1 - \frac{37}{60}\right) = \frac{23}{60}$.

(Q + R)'s 1 hour's work $= \left(\frac{1}{10} + \frac{1}{12}\right) = \frac{11}{60}$.

Now, $\frac{11}{60}$ work is done by Q and R in 1 hour.

So, $\frac{23}{60}$ work will be done by Q and R in $\left(\frac{60}{11} \times \frac{23}{60}\right) = \frac{23}{11}$ hours ≈ 2 hours.

So, the work will be finished approximately 2 hours after 11 a.m., *i.e.*, around 1 p.m.

34. 2 (A + B + C)'s 1 day's work $= \left(\frac{1}{30} + \frac{1}{24} + \frac{1}{20}\right) = \frac{15}{120} = \frac{1}{8}$.

$\Rightarrow$ (A + B + C)'s 1 day's work $= \frac{1}{16}$.

Work done by A, B and C in 10 days $= \frac{10}{16} = \frac{5}{8}$. Remaining work $= \left(1 - \frac{5}{8}\right) = \frac{3}{8}$.

A's 1 day's work $= \left(\frac{1}{16} - \frac{1}{24}\right) = \frac{1}{48}$.

Now, $\frac{1}{48}$ work is done by A in 1 day.

So, $\frac{3}{8}$ work will be done by A in $\left(48 \times \frac{3}{8}\right) = 18$ days.

35. Work done by X in 4 days $= \left(\frac{1}{20} \times 4\right) = \frac{1}{5}$. Remaining work $= \left(1 - \frac{1}{5}\right) = \frac{4}{5}$.

(X + Y)'s 1 day's work $= \left(\frac{1}{20} + \frac{1}{12}\right) = \frac{8}{60} = \frac{2}{15}$.

Now, $\frac{2}{15}$ work is done by X and Y in 1 day.

So, $\frac{4}{5}$ work will be done by X and Y in $\left(\frac{15}{2} \times \frac{4}{5}\right) = 6$ days.

Hence, total time taken = (6 + 4) days = 10 days.

36. (A + B)'s 20 days' work $= \left(\frac{1}{30} \times 20\right) = \frac{2}{3}$. Remaining work $= \left(1 - \frac{2}{3}\right) = \frac{1}{3}$.

Now, $\frac{1}{3}$ work is done by A in 20 days.

Whole work will be done by A in (20 × 3) = 60 days.

37. Work done by X in 8 days $= \left(\frac{1}{40} \times 8\right) = \frac{1}{5}$. Remaining work $= \left(1 - \frac{1}{5}\right) = \frac{4}{5}$.

Now, $\frac{4}{5}$ work is done by Y in 16 days.

Whole work will be done by Y in $\left(16 \times \frac{5}{4}\right) = 20$ days.

$\therefore$ X's 1 day's work $= \frac{1}{40}$, Y's 1 day's work $= \frac{1}{20}$.

(X + Y)'s 1 day's work $= \left(\frac{1}{40} + \frac{1}{20}\right) = \frac{3}{40}$.

Hence, X and Y will together complete the work in $\frac{40}{3} = 13\frac{1}{3}$ days.

38. Work done by A, B and C in 4 days $= \left(\frac{1}{10} \times 4\right) = \frac{2}{5}$. Remaining work $= \left(1 - \frac{2}{5}\right) = \frac{3}{5}$.

Now, $\frac{3}{5}$ work is done by B and C in 10 days.

Whole work will be done by B and C in $\left(10 \times \frac{5}{3}\right) = \frac{50}{3}$ days.

$(A + B + C)$'s 1 day's work $= \frac{1}{10}$, $(B + C)$'s 1 day's work $= \frac{3}{50}$.

A's 1 day's work $= \left(\frac{1}{10} - \frac{3}{50}\right) = \frac{2}{50} = \frac{1}{25}$.

$\therefore$ A alone could complete the work in 25 days.

39. Whole work is done by A in $\left(20 \times \frac{5}{4}\right) = 25$ days.

Now, $\left(1 - \frac{4}{5}\right)$ *i.e.*, $\frac{1}{5}$ work is done by A and B in 3 days.

Whole work will be done by A and B in $(3 \times 5) = 15$ days.

A's 1 day's work $= \frac{1}{25}$, $(A + B)$'s 1 day's work $= \frac{1}{15}$.

$\therefore$ B's 1 day's work $= \left(\frac{1}{15} - \frac{1}{25}\right) = \frac{4}{150} = \frac{2}{75}$.

So, B alone would do the work in $\frac{75}{2} = 37\frac{1}{2}$ days.

40. Let A's 1 day's work $= x$ and B's 1 day's work $= y$.

Then, $x + y = \frac{1}{30}$ and $16x + 44y = 1$.

Solving these two equations, we get : $x = \frac{1}{60}$ and $y = \frac{1}{60}$.

$\therefore$ B's 1 day's work $= \frac{1}{60}$.

Hence, B alone shall finish the whole work in 60 days.

41. A's 5 days' work + B's 7 days' work + C's 13 days' work = 1

$\Rightarrow$ $(A + B)$'s 5 days' work + $(B + C)$'s 2 days' work + C's 11 days' work = 1

$\Rightarrow$ $\frac{5}{12} + \frac{2}{16}$ + C's 11 days' work = 1

$\Rightarrow$ C's 11 days' work $= 1 - \left(\frac{5}{12} + \frac{2}{16}\right) = \frac{11}{24}$.

$\Rightarrow$ C's 1 day's work $= \left(\frac{11}{24} \times \frac{1}{11}\right) = \frac{1}{24}$.

$\therefore$ C alone can finish the work in 24 days.

42. $(A + B)$'s 1 day's work $= \left(\frac{1}{45} + \frac{1}{40}\right) = \frac{17}{360}$.

Work done by B in 23 days $= \left(\frac{1}{40} \times 23\right) = \frac{23}{40}$. Remaining work $= \left(1 - \frac{23}{40}\right) = \frac{17}{40}$

Now, $\frac{17}{360}$ work was done by $(A + B)$ in 1 day.

$\frac{17}{40}$ work was done by $(A + B)$ in $\left(1 \times \frac{360}{17} \times \frac{17}{40}\right) = 9$ days.

$\therefore$ A left after 9 days.

43. B's 3 days' work $= \left(\frac{1}{21} \times 3\right) = \frac{1}{7}$. Remaining work $= \left(1 - \frac{1}{7}\right) = \frac{6}{7}$.

(A + B)'s 1 day's work $= \left(\frac{1}{14} + \frac{1}{21}\right) = \frac{5}{42}$.

Now, $\frac{5}{42}$ work is done by A and B in 1 day.

$\therefore$ $\frac{6}{7}$ work is done by A and B in $\left(\frac{42}{5} \times \frac{6}{7}\right) = \frac{36}{5}$ days.

Hence, total time taken $= \left(3 + \frac{36}{5}\right)$ days $= 10\frac{1}{5}$ days.

44. (A + B + C)'s 1 day's work $= \left(\frac{1}{24} + \frac{1}{36} + \frac{1}{48}\right) = \frac{13}{144}$.

Work done by (A + B + C) in 4 days $= \left(\frac{13}{144} \times 4\right) = \frac{13}{36}$.

Work done by B in 3 days $= \left(\frac{1}{36} \times 3\right) = \frac{1}{12}$. Remaining work $= \left[1 - \left(\frac{13}{36} + \frac{1}{12}\right)\right] = \frac{5}{9}$.

(A + B)'s 1 day's work $= \left(\frac{1}{24} + \frac{1}{36}\right) = \frac{5}{72}$.

Now, $\frac{5}{72}$ work is done by A and B in $\left(\frac{72}{5} \times \frac{5}{9}\right) = 8$ days.

Hence, total time taken = (4 + 3 + 8) days = 15 days.

45. B's daily earning = Rs. (300 − 188) = Rs. 112.

A's daily earning = Rs. (300 − 152) = Rs. 148.

C's daily earning = Rs. [300 − (112 + 148)] = Rs. 40.

46. Work done by A $= \left(1 - \frac{8}{23}\right) = \frac{15}{23}$.

$\therefore$ $A : (B + C) = \frac{15}{23} : \frac{8}{23} = 15 : 8$.

So, A's share = Rs. $\left(\frac{15}{23} \times 529\right)$ = Rs. 345.

47. Kim's wages : David's wages = Kim's 1 day's work : David's 1 day's work

$= \frac{1}{3} : \frac{1}{2} = 2 : 3$.

$\therefore$ Kim's share = Rs. $\left(\frac{2}{5} \times 150\right)$ = Rs. 60.

48. Whole work is done by A in (3 × 4) = 12 days.

Whole work is done by B in (4 × 6) = 24 days.

A's wages : B's wages = A's 1 day's work : B's 1 day's work $= \frac{1}{12} : \frac{1}{24} = 2 : 1$.

$\therefore$ A's share = Rs. $\left(\frac{2}{3} \times 180\right)$ = Rs. 120

49. C's 1 day's work $= \frac{1}{3} - \left(\frac{1}{6} + \frac{1}{8}\right) = \frac{1}{3} - \frac{7}{24} = \frac{1}{24}$.

A's wages : B's wages : C's wages $= \frac{1}{6} : \frac{1}{8} : \frac{1}{24} = 4 : 3 : 1$.

$\therefore$ C's share = Rs. $\left(\frac{1}{8} \times 3200\right)$ = Rs. 400.

50. Let total money be Rs. x.

A's 1 day's wages = Rs $\frac{x}{21}$, B's 1 day's wages = Rs. $\frac{x}{28}$.

$\therefore$ (A + B)'s 1 day's wages = Rs. $\left(\frac{x}{21} + \frac{x}{28}\right)$ = Rs. $\frac{x}{12}$.

$\therefore$ Money is sufficient to pay the wages of both for 12 days.

51. Part of the work done by A $= \left(\frac{1}{10} \times 5\right) = \frac{1}{2}$.

Part of the work done by B $= \left(\frac{1}{15} \times 5\right) = \frac{1}{3}$.

Part of the work done by C $= 1 - \left(\frac{1}{2} + \frac{1}{3}\right) = \frac{1}{6}$.

So, (A's share) : (B's share) : (C's share) $= \frac{1}{2} : \frac{1}{3} : \frac{1}{6} = 3 : 2 : 1$.

$\therefore$ A's share = Rs. $\left(\frac{3}{6} \times 1500\right)$ = Rs. 750, B's share = Rs. $\left(\frac{2}{6} \times 1500\right)$ = Rs. 500,

C's share = Rs. $\left(\frac{1}{6} \times 1500\right)$ = Rs. 250.

A's daily wages = Rs. $\left(\frac{750}{5}\right)$ = Rs. 150; B's daily wages = Rs. $\left(\frac{500}{5}\right)$ = Rs. 100;

C's daily wages = Rs. $\left(\frac{250}{2}\right)$ = Rs. 125.

$\therefore$ Daily wages of B and C = Rs. (100 + 125) = Rs. 225.

52. B's 1 day's work $= \left(\frac{1}{12} - \frac{1}{20}\right) = \frac{2}{60} = \frac{1}{30}$.

Now, (A + B)'s 1 day's work $= \left(\frac{1}{20} + \frac{1}{60}\right) = \frac{4}{60} = \frac{1}{15}$. [$\because$ B works for half day only]

So, A and B together will complete the work in 15 days.

53. (A + B)'s 2 days' work $= \left(\frac{1}{16} + \frac{1}{12}\right) = \frac{7}{48}$.

Work done in 6 pairs of days $= \left(\frac{7}{48} \times 6\right) = \frac{7}{8}$. Remaining work $= \left(1 - \frac{7}{8}\right) = \frac{1}{8}$.

Work done by A on 13th day $= \frac{1}{16}$. Remaining work $= \left(\frac{1}{8} - \frac{1}{16}\right) = \frac{1}{16}$.

On 14th day, it is B's turn.

$\frac{1}{12}$ work is done by B in 1 day. $\frac{1}{16}$ work is done by B in $\left(12 \times \frac{1}{16}\right) = \frac{3}{4}$ day.

$\therefore$ Total time taken $= 13\frac{3}{4}$ days.

54. (A + B)'s 1 day's work $= \left(\frac{1}{11} + \frac{1}{20}\right) = \frac{31}{220}$. (A + C)'s 1 day's work $= \left(\frac{1}{11} + \frac{1}{55}\right) = \frac{6}{55}$.

Work done in 2 days $= \left(\frac{31}{220} + \frac{6}{55}\right) = \frac{55}{220} = \frac{1}{4}$.

Now, $\frac{1}{4}$ work is done by A in 2 days.

$\therefore$ Whole work will be done in $(2 \times 4) = 8$ days.

55. A's 2 days' work $= \left(\frac{1}{20} \times 2\right) = \frac{1}{10}$.

(A + B + C)'s 1 day's work $= \left(\frac{1}{20} + \frac{1}{30} + \frac{1}{60}\right) = \frac{6}{60} = \frac{1}{10}$.

Work done in 3 days $= \left(\frac{1}{10} + \frac{1}{10}\right) = \frac{1}{5}$.

Now, $\frac{1}{5}$ work is done in 3 days.

$\therefore$ Whole work will be done in $(3 \times 5) = 15$ days.

56. (A + B)'s 6 days' work $= 6\left(\frac{1}{20} + \frac{1}{15}\right) = \frac{7}{10}$; (A + C)'s 4 days' work $= \frac{3}{10}$;

(A + C)'s 1 day's work $= \frac{3}{40}$. A's 1 day's work $= \frac{1}{20}$.

$\therefore$ C's 1 day's work $= \left(\frac{3}{40} - \frac{1}{20}\right) = \frac{1}{40}$.

Hence, C alone can finish the work in 40 days.

57. Suppose the work was finished in x days.

Then, A's $(x - 8)$ days' work + B's $(x - 12)$ days' work + C's x days' work = 1

$\Rightarrow \frac{(x-8)}{36} + \frac{(x-12)}{54} + \frac{x}{72} = 1 \Leftrightarrow 6(x-8) + 4(x-12) + 3x = 216$

$\therefore$ $13x = 312$ or $x = 24$.

58. (20×16) women can complete the work in 1 day.

$\therefore$ 1 woman's 1 day's work $= \frac{1}{320}$.

(16×15) men can complete the work in 1 day.

$\therefore$ 1 man's 1 day's work $= \frac{1}{240}$.

So, required ratio $= \frac{1}{240} : \frac{1}{320} = 4 : 3$.

59. 10 men's 1 day's work $= \frac{1}{15}$; 15 women's 1 day's work $= \frac{1}{12}$.

(10 men + 15 women)'s 1 day's work $= \left(\frac{1}{15} + \frac{1}{12}\right) = \frac{9}{60} = \frac{3}{20}$.

$\therefore$ 10 men and 15 women will complete the work in $\frac{20}{3} = 6\frac{2}{3}$ days.

60. (7 × 12) men can complete the work in 1 day.

$\therefore$ 1 man's 1 day's work $= \frac{1}{84}$.

7 men's 5 days' work $= \left(\frac{1}{12} \times 5\right) = \frac{5}{12}$. Remaining work $= \left(1 - \frac{5}{12}\right) = \frac{7}{12}$.

5 men's 1 day's work $= \left(\frac{1}{84} \times 5\right) = \frac{5}{84}$.

$\frac{5}{84}$ work is done by them in 1 day.

$\frac{7}{12}$ work is done by them in $\left(\frac{84}{5} \times \frac{7}{12}\right) = \frac{49}{5}$ days $= 9\frac{4}{5}$ days.

61. 1 man's 1 day's work $= \frac{1}{108}$.

12 men's 6 days' work $= \left(\frac{1}{9} \times 6\right) = \frac{2}{3}$. Remaining work $= \left(1 - \frac{2}{3}\right) = \frac{1}{3}$.

18 men's 1 day's work $= \left(\frac{1}{108} \times 18\right) = \frac{1}{6}$.

$\frac{1}{6}$ work is done by them in 1 day.

$\therefore$ $\frac{1}{3}$ work is done by them in $\left(6 \times \frac{1}{3}\right) = 2$ days.

62. Let 1 woman's 1 day's work $= x$.

Then, 1 man's 1 day's work $= \frac{x}{2}$ and 1 child's 1 day's work $= \frac{x}{4}$.

So, $\left(\frac{3x}{2} + 4x + \frac{6x}{4}\right) = \frac{1}{7} \Rightarrow \frac{28x}{4} = \frac{1}{7} \Rightarrow x = \left(\frac{1}{7} \times \frac{4}{28}\right) = \frac{1}{49}$.

$\therefore$ 1 woman alone can complete the work in 49 days.

So, to complete the work in 7 days, number of women required $= \left(\frac{49}{7}\right) = 7$.

63. (1 man + 1 woman)'s 1 day's work $= \left(\frac{1}{3} + \frac{1}{4}\right) = \frac{7}{12}$.

Work done by 1 man and 1 woman in $\frac{1}{4}$ day $= \left(\frac{7}{12} \times \frac{1}{4}\right) = \frac{7}{48}$.

Remaining work $= \left(1 - \frac{7}{48}\right) = \frac{41}{48}$.

Work done by 1 boy in $\frac{1}{4}$ day $= \left(\frac{1}{12} \times \frac{1}{4}\right) = \frac{1}{48}$.

$\therefore$ Number of boys required $= \left(\frac{41}{48} \times 48\right) = 41$.

64. 1 man's 1 day's work $= \frac{1}{100}$. (10 men + 15 women)'s 1 day's work $= \frac{1}{6}$.

15 women's 1 day's work $= \left(\frac{1}{6} - \frac{10}{100}\right) = \left(\frac{1}{6} - \frac{1}{10}\right) = \frac{1}{15}$.

1 woman's 1 day's work $= \frac{1}{225}$.

$\therefore$ 1 woman alone can complete the work in 225 days.

65. 1 man's 1 day's work $= \frac{1}{48}$; 1 woman's 1 day's work $= \frac{1}{60}$.

6 men's 2 days' work $= \left(\frac{6}{48} \times 2\right) = \frac{1}{4}$. Remaining work $= \left(1 - \frac{1}{4}\right) = \frac{3}{4}$.

Now, $\frac{1}{60}$ work is done in 1 day by 1 woman.

So, $\frac{3}{4}$ work will be done in 3 days by $\left(60 \times \frac{3}{4} \times \frac{1}{3}\right) = 15$ women.

66. 1 child's 1 day's work $= \frac{1}{192}$; 1 adult's 1 day's work $= \frac{1}{96}$.

Work done in 3 days $= \left(\frac{1}{96} \times 16 \times 3\right) = \frac{1}{2}$. Remaining work $= \left(1 - \frac{1}{2}\right) = \frac{1}{2}$.

(6 adults + 4 children)'s 1 day's work $= \left(\frac{6}{96} + \frac{4}{192}\right) = \frac{1}{12}$.

$\frac{1}{12}$ work is done by them in 1 day.

$\frac{1}{2}$ work is done by them $\left(12 \times \frac{1}{2}\right) = 6$ days.

67. 1 woman's 1 day's work $= \frac{1}{70}$; 1 child's 1 day's work $= \frac{1}{140}$.

(5 women + 10 children)'s 1 day's work $= \left(\frac{5}{70} + \frac{10}{140}\right) = \left(\frac{1}{14} + \frac{1}{14}\right) = \frac{1}{7}$.

$\therefore$ 5 women and 10 children will complete the work in 7 days.

68. 1 man's 1 day's work $= \frac{1}{192}$; 1 child's 1 day's work $= \frac{1}{432}$.

Work done in 8 days $= 8\left(\frac{12}{192} + \frac{8}{432}\right) = 8\left(\frac{1}{16} + \frac{1}{54}\right) = \frac{35}{54}$.

Remaining work $= \left(1 - \frac{35}{54}\right) = \frac{19}{54}$.

(12 men + 11 children)'s 1 day's work $= \left(\frac{12}{192} + \frac{11}{432}\right) = \frac{19}{216}$.

Now, $\frac{19}{216}$ work is done by them in 1 day.

$\therefore$ $\frac{19}{54}$ work will be done by them in $\left(\frac{216}{19} \times \frac{19}{54}\right) = 4$ days.

69. 1 man's 1 day's work $= \frac{1}{384}$; 1 woman's 1 day's work $= \frac{1}{768}$.

Work done in 12 days $= 12\left(\frac{16}{384} + \frac{16}{768}\right) = \left(12 \times \frac{3}{48}\right) = \frac{3}{4}$.

Remaining work $= \left(1 - \frac{3}{4}\right) = \frac{1}{4}$.

(16 men + 16 women)'s 2 days' work $= 2\left(\frac{16}{384} + \frac{16}{768}\right) = \left(2 \times \frac{1}{16}\right) = \frac{1}{8}.$

Remaining work $= \left(\frac{1}{4} - \frac{1}{8}\right) = \frac{1}{8}.$

$\frac{1}{384}$ work is done in 1 day by 1 man.

$\therefore$ $\frac{1}{8}$ work will be done in 2 days by $\left(384 \times \frac{1}{8} \times \frac{1}{2}\right) = 24$ men.

70. Let 1 man's 1 day's work = x and 1 boy's 1 day's work = y.

Then, $5x + 2y = 4(x + y) \Rightarrow x = 2y \Rightarrow \frac{x}{y} = \frac{2}{1}.$

71. Let 1 man's 1 day's work = x and 1 boy's 1 day's work = y.

Then, $12x + 16y = \frac{1}{5}$ and $13x + 24y = \frac{1}{4}.$

Solving these two equations, we get : $x = \frac{1}{100}$ and $y = \frac{1}{200}.$

$\therefore$ Required ratio $= x : y = \frac{1}{100} : \frac{1}{200} = 2 : 1.$

72. Let 1 man's 1 day's work = x and 1 woman's 1 day's work = y.

Then, $4x + 6y = \frac{1}{8}$ and $3x + 7y = \frac{1}{10}.$

Solving these two equations, we get : $x = \frac{11}{400}, y = \frac{1}{400}.$

$\therefore$ 1 woman's 1 day's work $= \frac{1}{400}.$

$\Rightarrow$ 10 women's 1 day's work $= \left(\frac{1}{400} \times 10\right) = \frac{1}{40}.$

Hence, 10 women will complete the work in 40 days.

73. Let 1 man's 1 hour's work = x; 1 woman's 1 hour's work = y and 1 boy's 1 hour's work = z. Then,

$x + 3y + 4z = \frac{1}{96}$ ...(*i*) $2x + 8z = \frac{1}{80}$ ...(*ii*) $2x + 3y = \frac{1}{120}$ ...(*iii*)

Adding (*ii*) and (*iii*) and subtracting (*i*) from it, we get : $3x + 4z = \frac{1}{96}$ ...(*iv*)

From (*ii*) and (*iv*), we get $x = \frac{1}{480}$. Substituting, we get : $y = \frac{1}{720}, z = \frac{1}{960}.$

(5 men + 12 boys)'s 1 hour's work $= \left(\frac{5}{480} + \frac{12}{960}\right) = \left(\frac{1}{96} + \frac{1}{80}\right) = \frac{11}{480}.$

$\therefore$ 5 men and 12 boys can do the work in $\frac{480}{11}$ *i.e.*, $43\frac{7}{11}$ hours.

74. Let 1 man's 1 day's work = x and 1 boy's 1 day's work = y.

Then, $6x + 8y = \frac{1}{10}$ and $26x + 48y = \frac{1}{2}.$

Solving these two equations, we get : $x = \frac{1}{100}$ and $y = \frac{1}{200}$.

(15 men + 20 boys)'s 1 day's work $= \left(\frac{15}{100} + \frac{20}{200}\right) = \frac{1}{4}$.

$\therefore$ 15 men and 20 boys can do the work in 4 days.

EXERCISE 15B

(DATA SUFFICIENCY TYPE QUESTIONS)

Directions (*Questions 1 to 4*) : *Each of the questions given below consists of a statement and/or a question followed by two statements labelled I and II. Read both the statements and*

Give answer (a) if the data in Statement I alone are sufficient to answer the question, while the data in Statement II alone are not sufficient to answer the question;

Give answer (b) if the data in Statement II alone are sufficient to answer the question, while the data in Statement I alone are not sufficient to answer the question;

Give answer (c) if the data either in Statement I or in Statement II alone are sufficient to answer the question;

Give answer (d) if the data even in both Statements I and II together are not sufficient to answer the question;

Give answer (e) if the data in both Statements I and II together are necessary to answer the question.

1. How long will Machine Y, working alone, take to produce *x* candles ? **(M.B.A. 2002)**

I. Machine X produces *x* candles in 5 minutes.

II. Machine X and Machine Y working at the same time produce *x* candles in 2 minutes.

2. B alone can complete a work in 12 days. How many days will A, B and C together take to complete the work ?

I. A and B together can complete the work in 3 days.

II. B and C together can complete the work in 6 days.

3. Is it cheaper to employ X to do a certain job than to employ Y ?

I. X is paid 20% more per hour than Y, but Y takes 2 hours longer to complete the job.

II. X is paid Rs. 80 per hour.

4. A and B together can complete a task in 7 days. B alone can do it in 20 days. What part of the work was carried out by A ? **(M.B.A. 1998)**

I. A completed the job alone after A and B worked together for 5 days.

II. Part of the work done by A could have been done by B and C together in 6 days.

Directions (*Questions 5 to 9*) : *Each of the following questions consists of a question followed by three statements I, II and III. You have to study the question and the statements and decide which of the statement(s) is/are necessary to answer the question.*

5. In how many days can A and B working together complete a job ?

I. A alone can complete the job in 30 days.

II. B alone can complete the job in 40 days.

III. B takes 10 days more than A to complete the job.

(*a*) I and II only (*b*) II and III only (*c*) I and III only

(*d*) Any two of the three (*e*) All I, II and III

6. In how many days can the work be completed by A and B together ?

I. A alone can complete the work in 8 days.

II. If A alone works for 5 days and B alone works for 6 days, the work gets completed.

III. B alone can complete the work in 16 days. **(Bank P.O. 2003)**

(*a*) I and II only (*b*) II and III only (*c*) Any two of the three

(*d*) II and either I or III (*e*) None of these

7. How many workers are required for completing the construction work in 10 days ?

I. 20% of the work can be completed by 8 workers in 8 days.

II. 20 workers can complete the work in 16 days.

III. One-eighth of the work can be completed by 8 workers in 5 days. **(Bank P.O. 2003)**

(*a*) I only (*b*) II and III only (*c*) III only

(*d*) I and III only (*e*) Any one of the three

8. In how many days can the work be done by 9 men and 15 women ?

I. 6 men and 5 women can complete the work in 6 days.

II. 3 men and 4 women can complete the work in 10 days.

III. 18 men and 15 women can complete the work in 2 days.

(*a*) III only (*b*) All I, II and III (*c*) Any two of the three

(*d*) Any one of the three (*e*) None of these

9. In how many days can 10 women finish a work ? **(R.B.I. 2002)**

I. 10 men can complete the work in 6 days.

II. 10 men and 10 women together can complete the work in $3\frac{3}{7}$ days.

III. If 10 men work for 3 days and thereafter 10 women replace them, the remaining work is completed in 4 days.

(*a*) Any two of the three (*b*) I and II only (*c*) II and III only

(*d*) I and III only (*e*) None of these

Directions (*Questions 10-11*) : *Each of these questions is followed by three statements. You have to study the question and all the three statements given to decide whether any information provided in the statement(s) is/are redundant and can be dispensed with while answering the given question.*

10. In how many days can the work be completed by A, B and C together ?

I. A and B together can complete the work in 6 days.

II. B and C together can complete the work in $3\frac{3}{4}$ days.

III. A and C together can complete the work in $3\frac{1}{3}$ days. **(S.B.I.P.O. 2001)**

(*a*) Any one of the three (*b*) I only

(*c*) II only (*d*) III only

(*e*) Information in all the three statements is necessary to answer the question.

11. 8 men and 14 women are working together in a field. After working for 3 days, 5 men and 8 women leave the work. How many more days will be required to complete the work ? **(S.B.I.P.O. 1999)**

I. 19 men and 12 women together can complete the work in 18 days.

II. 16 men can complete two-third of the work in 16 days.

III. In a day, the work done by three men is equal to the work done by four women.

(*a*) I only (*b*) II only (*c*) III only

(*d*) I or II or III (*e*) II or III only

ANSWERS

1. (*e*) **2.** (*e*) **3.** (*d*) **4.** (*a*) **5.** (*d*) **6.** (*c*) **7.** (*e*) **8.** (*c*)
9. (*a*) **10.** (*e*) **11.** (*d*)

SOLUTIONS

1. I gives, Machine X produces $\frac{x}{5}$ candles in 1 min.

II gives, Machines X and Y produce $\frac{x}{2}$ candles in 1 min.

From I and II, Y produces $\left(\frac{x}{2}-\frac{x}{5}\right)=\frac{3x}{10}$ candles in 1 min.

$\frac{3x}{10}$ candles are produced by Y in 1 min.

x candles will be produced by Y in $\left(\frac{10}{3x}\times x\right)$ min $=\frac{10}{3}$ min.

Thus, I and II both are necessary to get the answer.

$\therefore$ Correct answer is (*e*).

2. Given : B's 1 day's work $=\frac{1}{12}$.

I gives, (A + B)'s 1 day's work $=\frac{1}{3}$.

$\Rightarrow$ A's 1 day's work $=\left(\frac{1}{3}-\frac{1}{12}\right)=\frac{3}{12}=\frac{1}{4}$.

II gives, (B + C)'s 1 day's work $=\frac{1}{6}$ $\Rightarrow$ C's 1 day's work $=\left(\frac{1}{6}-\frac{1}{12}\right)=\frac{1}{12}$.

$\therefore$ (A + B + C)'s 1 day's work $=\left(\frac{1}{4}+\frac{1}{12}+\frac{1}{12}\right)=\frac{5}{12}$.

Hence, they all finish the work in $\frac{12}{5}=2\frac{2}{5}$ days.

Thus, I and II both are necessary to get the answer.

$\therefore$ Correct answer is (*e*).

3. Suppose X takes x hours and Y takes $(x+2)$ hours to complete the job.

II. X is paid Rs. 80 per hour.

Total payment to X = Rs. $(80x)$.

I. X = 120% of Y $=\frac{120}{100}$ Y $=\frac{6}{5}$ Y $\Rightarrow$ Y $=\frac{5}{6}$ X.

$\therefore$ Y is paid Rs. $\left(\frac{5}{6}\times 80\right)$ per hour $\Rightarrow$ Y is paid Rs. $\left[\frac{200}{3}(x+2)\right]$

We cannot compare $(80x)$ and $\frac{200}{3}(x+2)$.

$\therefore$ Correct answer is (*d*).

4. B's 1 day's work $= \frac{1}{20}$. (A + B)'s 1 day's work $= \frac{1}{7}$.

I. (A + B)'s 5 day's work $= \frac{5}{7}$. Remaining work $= \left(1 - \frac{5}{7}\right) = \frac{2}{7}$.

$\therefore$ $\frac{2}{7}$ work was carried by A.

II. is irrelevant.

$\therefore$ Correct answer is (*a*).

5. I. A can complete the job in 30 days.

$\therefore$ A's 1 day's work $= \frac{1}{30}$. Remaining work $= \left(1 - \frac{5}{7}\right) = \frac{2}{7}$.

II. B can complete the job in 40 days.

$\therefore$ B's 1 day's work $= \frac{1}{40}$.

III. B takes 10 days more than A to complete the job.

I and II gives, (A + B)'s 1 day's work $= \left(\frac{1}{30} + \frac{1}{40}\right) = \frac{7}{120}$.

$\therefore$ I and III also give the same answer.
II and III also give the same answer.

$\therefore$ Correct answer is (*d*).

6. I. A can complete the job in 8 days. So, A's 1 day's work $= \frac{1}{8}$.

II. A works for 5 days, B works for 6 days and the work is completed.

III. B can complete the job in 16 days. So, B's 1 day's work $= \frac{1}{16}$.

I and III : (A + B)'s 1 day's work $= \left(\frac{1}{8} + \frac{1}{16}\right) = \frac{3}{16}$.

$\therefore$ Both can finish the work in $\frac{16}{3}$ days.

II and III : Suppose A takes x days to finish the work.

Then, $\frac{5}{x} + \frac{6}{16} = 1 \Rightarrow \frac{5}{x} = \left(1 - \frac{3}{8}\right) = \frac{5}{8} \Rightarrow x = 8$.

$\therefore$ (A + B)'s 1 day's work $= \left(\frac{1}{8} + \frac{1}{16}\right) = \frac{3}{16}$.

$\therefore$ Both can finish it in $\frac{16}{3}$ days.

I and II : A's 1 day's work $= \frac{1}{8}$. Suppose B takes x days to finish the work.

Then from II, $\left(5 \times \frac{1}{8} + 6 \times \frac{1}{x} = 1\right) \Rightarrow \frac{6}{x} = \left(1 - \frac{5}{8}\right) = \frac{3}{8} \Rightarrow x = \left(\frac{8 \times 6}{3}\right) = 16$.

$\therefore$ (A + B)'s 1 day's work $= \left(\frac{1}{8} + \frac{1}{16}\right) = \frac{3}{16}$.

$\therefore$ Both can finish it in $\frac{16}{3}$ days.

Hence, the correct answer is (*c*).

7. I. $\frac{20}{100}$ work can be completed by (8×8) workers in 1 day.

$\Rightarrow$ Whole work can be completed by $(8 \times 8 \times 5)$ workers in 1 day

$= \frac{8 \times 8 \times 5}{10}$ workers in 10 days = 32 workers in 10 days.

II. (20×16) workers can finish it in 1 day.

$\Rightarrow \frac{(20 \times 16)}{10}$ workers can finish it in 10 days.

$\Rightarrow$ 32 workers can finish it in 10 days.

III. $\frac{1}{8}$ work can be completed by (8×5) workers in 1 day.

$\Rightarrow$ Whole work can be completed by $(8 \times 5 \times 8)$ workers in 1 day

$= \frac{8 \times 5 \times 8}{10}$ workers in 10 days = 32 workers in 10 days.

$\therefore$ Any one of the three gives the answer.

$\therefore$ Correct answer is (*e*).

8. Clearly, any two of the three will give two equations in *x* and *y*, which can be solved simultaneously.

$\therefore$ Correct answer is (*c*).

$\left[\text{For example I and II together give } \left(6x + 5y = \frac{1}{6},\ 3x + 4y = \frac{1}{10}\right)\right]$.

9. I. (10×6) men can complete the work in 1 day.

$\Rightarrow$ 1 man's 1 day's work $= \frac{1}{60}$.

II. $\left(10 \times \frac{24}{7}\right)$ men + $\left(10 \times \frac{24}{7}\right)$ women can complete the work in 1 day.

$\Rightarrow \left(\frac{240}{7}\right)$ men's 1 day work + $\left(\frac{240}{7}\right)$ women's 1 day work = 1

$\Rightarrow \left(\frac{240}{7} \times \frac{1}{60}\right) + \left(\frac{240}{7}\right)$ women's 1 day's work = 1.

$\Rightarrow \left(\frac{240}{7}\right)$ women's 1 day's work $= \left(1 - \frac{4}{7}\right) = \frac{3}{7}$

$\Rightarrow$ 10 women's 1 day's work $= \left(\frac{3}{7} \times \frac{7}{240} \times 10\right) = \frac{1}{8}$.

So, 10 women can finish the work in 8 days.

III. (10 men's work for 3 days) + (10 women's work for 4 days) = 1

$\Rightarrow$ (10×3) men's 1 day's work + (10×4) women's 1 day's work = 1

$\Rightarrow$ 30 men's 1 day's work + 40 women's 1 day's work = 1.

Thus, I and III will give us the answer.

And, II and III will give us the answer.

$\therefore$ Correct answer is (*a*).

10. I. (A + B)'s 1 day's work $= \frac{1}{6}$.

II. (B + C)'s 1 day's work $= \frac{4}{15}$.

III. (A + C)'s 1 day's work $= \frac{3}{10}$.

Adding, we get 2 (A + B + C)'s 1 day's work $= \left(\frac{1}{6} + \frac{4}{15} + \frac{3}{10}\right) = \frac{22}{30}$

$\Rightarrow$ (A + B + C)'s 1 day's work $= \left(\frac{1}{2} \times \frac{22}{30}\right) = \frac{11}{30}$.

Thus, A, B and C together can finish the work in $\frac{30}{11}$ days.

Hence I, II and III are necessary to answer the question.

$\therefore$ Correct answer is (*e*).

11. Clearly, I only gives the answer.

Similarly, II only gives the answer.

And, III only gives the answer.

$\therefore$ Correct answer is (*d*).

16. PIPES AND CISTERNS

IMPORTANT FACTS AND FORMULAE

1. **Inlet :** A pipe connected with a tank or a cistern or a reservoir, that fills it, is known as an inlet.

   Outlet : A pipe connected with a tank or a cistern or a reservoir, emptying it, is known as an outlet.

2. (*i*) If a pipe can fill a tank in x hours, then :

   part filled in 1 hour $= \frac{1}{x}$.

   (*ii*) If a pipe can empty a full tank in y hours, then :

   part emptied in 1 hour $= \frac{1}{y}$.

   (*iii*) If a pipe can fill a tank in x hours and another pipe can empty the full tank in y hours (where $y > x$), then on opening both the pipes, the net part filled in 1 hour $= \left(\frac{1}{x} - \frac{1}{y}\right)$.

   (*iv*) If a pipe can fill a tank in x hours and another pipe can empty the full tank in y hours (where $x > y$), then on opening both the pipes, the net part emptied in 1 hour $= \left(\frac{1}{y} - \frac{1}{x}\right)$.

SOLVED EXAMPLES

Ex. 1. ***Two pipes A and B can fill a tank in 36 hours and 45 hours respectively. If both the pipes are opened simultaneously, how much time will be taken to fill the tank?***

Sol. Part filled by A in 1 hour $= \frac{1}{36}$; Part filled by B in 1 hour $= \frac{1}{45}$.

Part filled by (A + B) in 1 hour $= \left(\frac{1}{36} + \frac{1}{45}\right) = \frac{9}{180} = \frac{1}{20}$.

Hence, both the pipes together will fill the tank in 20 hours.

Ex. 2. ***Two pipes can fill a tank in 10 hours and 12 hours respectively while a third pipe empties the full tank in 20 hours. If all the three pipes operate simultaneously, in how much time will the tank be filled ?***

Sol. Net part filled in 1 hour $= \left(\frac{1}{10} + \frac{1}{12} - \frac{1}{20}\right) = \frac{8}{60} = \frac{2}{15}$.

$\therefore$ The tank will be full in $\frac{15}{2}$ hrs = 7 hrs 30 min.

Ex. 3. ***If two pipes function simultaneously, the reservoir will be filled in 12 hours. One pipe fills the reservoir 10 hours faster than the other. How many hours does it take the second pipe to fill the reservoir ?***

Sol. Let the reservoir be filled by first pipe in x hours.

Then, second pipe will fill it in $(x + 10)$ hours.

$\therefore \quad \frac{1}{x} + \frac{1}{(x+10)} = \frac{1}{12} \quad \Leftrightarrow \quad \frac{x+10+x}{x(x+10)} = \frac{1}{12}$

$\Leftrightarrow \quad x^2 - 14x - 120 = 0 \quad \Leftrightarrow \quad (x-20)(x+6) = 0$

$\Leftrightarrow \quad x = 20.$ [*neglecting the – ve value of x*]

So, the second pipe will take (20 + 10) hrs *i.e.*, 30 hrs to fill the reservoir.

Ex. 4. ***A cistern has two taps which fill it in 12 minutes and 15 minutes respectively. There is also a waste pipe in the cistern. When all the three are opened, the empty cistern is full in 20 minutes. How long will the waste pipe take to empty the full cistern?***

Sol. Work done by the waste pipe in 1 minute

$$= \frac{1}{20} - \left(\frac{1}{12} + \frac{1}{15}\right) = -\frac{1}{10}$$ [*– ve sign means emptying*]

$\therefore$ Waste pipe will empty the full cistern in 10 minutes.

Ex. 5. ***An electric pump can fill a tank in 3 hours. Because of a leak in the tank, it took $3\frac{1}{2}$ hours to fill the tank. If the tank is full, how much time will the leak take to empty it?***

Sol. Work done by the leak in 1 hour $= \left[\frac{1}{3} - \frac{1}{\left(\frac{7}{2}\right)}\right] = \left(\frac{1}{3} - \frac{2}{7}\right) = \frac{1}{21}.$

$\therefore$ The leak will empty the tank in 21 hours.

Ex. 6. ***Two pipes can fill a cistern in 14 hours and 16 hours respectively. The pipes are opened simultaneously and it is found that due to leakage in the bottom it took 32 minutes more to fill the cistern. When the cistern is full, in what time will the leak empty it?***

Sol. Work done by the two pipes in 1 hour $= \left(\frac{1}{14} + \frac{1}{16}\right) = \frac{15}{112}.$

$\therefore$ Time taken by these pipes to fill the tank $= \frac{112}{15}$ hrs $= 7$ hrs 28 min.

Due to leakage, time taken = 7 hrs 28 min + 32 min = 8 hrs

$\therefore$ Work done by (two pipes + leak) in 1 hour $= \frac{1}{8}.$

Work done by the leak in 1 hour $= \left(\frac{15}{112} - \frac{1}{8}\right) = \frac{1}{112}.$

$\therefore$ Leak will empty the full cistern in 112 hours.

Ex. 7. ***Two pipes A and B can fill a tank in 36 min. and 45 min. respectively. A water pipe C can empty the tank in 30 min. First A and B are opened. After 7 minutes, C is also opened. In how much time, the tank is full?***

Sol. Part filled in 7 min. $= 7\left(\frac{1}{36} + \frac{1}{45}\right) = \frac{7}{20}.$

Remaining part $= \left(1 - \frac{7}{20}\right) = \frac{13}{20}.$

Net part filled in 1 min. when A, B and C are opened $= \left(\frac{1}{36}+\frac{1}{45}-\frac{1}{30}\right) = \frac{1}{60}$.

Now, $\frac{1}{60}$ part is filled in 1 min.,

$\frac{13}{20}$ part is filled in $\left(60 \times \frac{13}{20}\right) = 39$ min.

Total time taken to fill the tank = (39 + 7) min. = 46 min.

Ex. 8. ***Two pipes A and B can fill a tank in 24 min. and 32 min. respectively. If both the pipes are opened simultaneously, after how much time B should be closed so that the tank is full in 18 minutes ?***

Sol. Let B be closed after x minutes. Then,

part filled by (A + B) in x min. + part filled by A in $(18 - x)$ min. = 1

$\therefore \quad x\left(\frac{1}{24}+\frac{1}{32}\right) + (18-x) \times \frac{1}{24} = 1 \quad \Leftrightarrow \quad \frac{7x}{96} + \frac{18-x}{24} = 1$

$\Leftrightarrow \quad 7x + 4(18 - x) = 96 \quad \Leftrightarrow \quad x = 8.$

Hence, B must be closed after 8 minutes.

EXERCISE 16A

(OBJECTIVE TYPE QUESTIONS)

Directions : *Mark (✓) against the correct answer* :

1. Two pipes A and B can fill a tank in 20 and 30 minutes respectively. If both the pipes are used together, then how long will it take to fill the tank ? **(M.A.T 2003)**

(*a*) 12 min (*b*) 15 min (*c*) 25 min (*d*) 50 min

2. A cistern can be filled by a tap in 4 hours while it can be emptied by another tap in 9 hours. If both the taps are opened simultaneously then after how much time will the cistern get filled ? **(Hotel Management, 1997)**

(*a*) 4.5 hrs (*b*) 5 hrs (*c*) 6.5 hrs (*d*) 7.2 hrs

3. A tap can fill a tank in 6 hours. After half the tank is filled, three more similar taps are opened. What is the total time taken to fill the tank completely ?

(*a*) 3 hrs 15 min (*b*) 3 hrs 45 min (*c*) 4 hrs (*d*) 4 hrs 15 min

(S.S.C. 2003)

4. A water tank is two-fifth full. Pipe A can fill a tank in 10 minutes and pipe B can empty it in 6 minutes. If both the pipes are open, how long will it take to empty or fill the tank completely ? **(Bank P.O. 1999)**

(*a*) 6 min, to empty (*b*) 6 min. to fill (*c*) 9 min. to empty

(*d*) 9 min. to fill (*e*) None of these

5. Pipe A can fill a tank in 5 hours, pipe B in 10 hours and pipe C in 30 hours. If all the pipes are open, in how many hours will the tank be filled ? **(C.B.I. 1997)**

(*a*) 2 (*b*) 2.5 (*c*) 3 (*d*) 3.5

6. Pipes A and B can fill a tank in 5 and 6 hours respectively. Pipe C can empty it in 12 hours. If all the three pipes are opened together, then the tank will be filled in :

(*a*) $1\frac{13}{17}$ hours (*b*) $2\frac{8}{11}$ hours (*c*) $3\frac{9}{17}$ hours (*d*) $4\frac{1}{2}$ hours

(Bank P.O. 2002)

7. Three pipes A, B and C can fill a tank from empty to full in 30 minutes, 20 minutes and 10 minutes respectively. When the tank is empty, all the three pipes are opened. A, B and C discharge chemical solutions P, Q and R respectively. What is the proportion of solution R in the liquid in the tank after 3 minutes ? **(D.M.R.C. 2003)**

(*a*) $\frac{5}{11}$ (*b*) $\frac{6}{11}$ (*c*) $\frac{7}{11}$ (*d*) $\frac{8}{11}$

8. Two pipes A and B can separately fill a cistern in 60 minutes and 75 minutes respectively. There is a third pipe in the bottom of the cistern to empty it. If all the three pipes are simultaneously opened, then the cistern is full in 50 minutes. In how much time the third pipe alone can empty the cistern ? **(S.S.C. 2003)**

(*a*) 90 min (*b*) 100 min (*c*) 110 min (*d*) 120 min

9. A pump can fill a tank with water in 2 hours. Because of a leak, it took $2\frac{1}{3}$ hours to fill the tank. The leak can drain all the water of the tank in : **(S.S.C. 2002)**

(*a*) $4\frac{1}{3}$ hrs (*b*) 7 hrs (*c*) 8 hrs (*d*) 14 hrs

10. Two taps A and B can fill a tank in 5 hours and 20 hours respectively. If both the taps are open then due to a leakage, it took 30 minutes more to fill the tank. If the tank is full, how long will it take for the leakage alone to empty the tank ?

(*a*) $4\frac{1}{2}$ hrs (*b*) 9 hrs (*c*) 18 hrs (*d*) 36 hrs

11. Two pipes A and B together can fill a cistern in 4 hours. Had they been opened separately, then B would have taken 6 hours more than A to fill the cistern. How much time will be taken by A to fill the cistern separately ? **(NABARD, 2001)**

(*a*) 1 hr (*b*) 2 hrs (*c*) 6 hrs (*d*) 8 hrs.

12. One pipe can fill a tank three times as fast as another pipe. If together the two pipes can fill the tank in 36 minutes, then the slower pipe alone will be able to fill the tank in : **(C.B.I. 2003)**

(*a*) 81 min (*b*) 108 min (*c*) 144 min (*d*) 192 min

13. A tank is filled in 5 hours by three pipes A, B and C. The pipe C is twice as fast as B and B is twice as fast as A. How much time will pipe A alone take to fill the tank ?

(*a*) 20 hrs (*b*) 25 hrs (*c*) 35 hrs
(*d*) Cannot be determined (*e*) None of these **(Bank P.O. 2003)**

14. A tank is filled by three pipes with uniform flow. The first two pipes operating simultaneously fill the tank in the same time during which the tank is filled by the third pipe alone. The second pipe fills the tank 5 hours faster than the first pipe and 4 hours slower than the third pipe. The time required by the first pipe is :

(*a*) 6 hrs (*b*) 10 hrs (*c*) 15 hrs (*d*) 30 hrs **(M.B.A. 2002)**

15. 12 buckets of water fill a tank when the capacity of each tank is 13.5 litres. How many buckets will be needed to fill the same tank, if the capacity of each bucket is 9 litres ?

(*a*) 8 (*b*) 15 (*c*) 16 (*d*) 18

16. Bucket P has thrice the capacity as bucket Q. It takes 60 turns for bucket P to fill the empty drum. How many turns it will take for both the buckets P and Q, having each turn together to fill the empty drum ?

(*a*) 30 (*b*) 40 (*c*) 45 (*d*) 90

17. Two pipes A and B can fill a tank in 12 minutes and 15 minutes respectively. If both the taps are opened simultaneously, and the tap A is closed after 3 minutes, then how much more time will it take to fill the tank by tap B ?

(*a*) 7 min 15 sec (*b*) 7 min 45 sec (*c*) 8 min 5 sec (*d*) 8 min 15 sec

18. Two pipes A and B can fill a tank in 15 minutes and 20 minutes respectively. Both the pipes are opened together but after 4 minutes, pipe A is turned off. What is the total time required to fill the tank ? **(U.P.S.C. 2002)**
(*a*) 10 min 20 sec (*b*) 11 min 45 sec (*c*) 12 min 30 sec (*d*) 14 min 40 sec

19. Two pipes A and B can fill a tank in 15 hours and 20 hours respectively while a third pipe C can empty the full tank in 25 hours. All the three pipes are opened in the beginning. After 10 hours, C is closed. In how much time, will the tank be full ?
(*a*) 12 hrs (*b*) 13 hrs (*c*) 16 hrs (*d*) 18 hrs

20. A large tanker can be filled by two pipes A and B in 60 minutes and 40 minutes respectively. How many minutes will it take to fill the tanker from empty state if B is used for half the time and A and B fill it together for the other half ?
(*a*) 15 min (*b*) 20 min (*c*) 27.5 min (*d*) 30 min
(D.M.R.C. 2003)

21. Two pipes A and B can fill a cistern in 12 minutes and 15 minutes respectively while a third pipe C can empty the full tank in 6 minutes. A and B are kept open for 5 minutes in the beginning and then C is also opened. In what time is the cistern emptied ?
(*a*) 30 min (*b*) 33 min (*c*) $37\frac{1}{2}$ min (*d*) 45 min

22. Two pipes A and B can fill a tank in 6 hours and 4 hours respectively. If they are opened on alternate hours and if pipe A is opened first, in how many hours, the tank shall be full ?
(*a*) 4 (*b*) $4\frac{1}{2}$ (*c*) 5 (*d*) $5\frac{1}{2}$

23. Three taps A, B and C can fill a tank in 12, 15 and 20 hours respectively. If A is open all the time and B and C are open for one hour each alternately, the tank will be full in : **(S.S.C. 1999)**
(*a*) 6 hrs (*b*) $6\frac{2}{3}$ hrs (*c*) 5 (*d*) $7\frac{1}{2}$ hrs

24. A booster pump can be used for filling as well as for emptying a tank. The capacity of the tank is 2400 m^3. The emptying capacity of the tank is 10 m^3 per minute higher than its filling capacity and the pump needs 8 minutes lesser to empty the tank than it needs to fill it. What is the filling capacity of the pump ?
(*a*) 50 m^3/min (*b*) 60 m^3/min (*c*) 72 m^3/min (*d*) None of these

25. A leak in the bottom of a tank can empty the full tank in 8 hours. An inlet pipe fills water at the rate of 6 litres a minute. When the tank is full, the inlet is opened and due to the leak, the tank is empty in 12 hours. How many litres does the cistern hold ?
(*a*) 7580 (*b*) 7960 (*c*) 8290 (*d*) 8640

26. Two pipes can fill a tank in 20 and 24 minutes respectively and a waste pipe can empty 3 gallons per minute. All the three pipes working together can fill the tank in 15 minutes. The capacity of the tank is : **(Bank P.O. 2001)**
(*a*) 60 gallons (*b*) 100 gallons (*c*) 120 gallons (*d*) 180 gallons

27. Two pipes A and B can fill a cistern in $37\frac{1}{2}$ minutes and 45 minutes respectively. Both pipes are opened. The cistern will be filled in just half an hour, if the pipe B is turned off after : **(S.S.C. 2004)**
(*a*) 5 min (*b*) 9 min (*c*) 10 min (*d*) 15 min

28. Three pipes A, B and C can fill a tank in 6 hours. After working at it together for 2 hours, C is closed and A and B can fill the remaining part in 7 hours. The number of hours taken by C alone to fill the tank is : **(L.I.C.A.A.O. 2003)**
(*a*) 10 (*b*) 12 (*c*) 14 (*d*) 16

ANSWERS

1. (*a*)	**2.** (*d*)	**3.** (*b*)	**4.** (*a*)	**5.** (*c*)	**6.** (*c*)	**7.** (*b*)	**8.** (*b*)
9. (*d*)	**10.** (*d*)	**11.** (*c*)	**12.** (*c*)	**13.** (*c*)	**14.** (*c*)	**15.** (*d*)	**16.** (*c*)
17. (*d*)	**18.** (*d*)	**19.** (*a*)	**20.** (*d*)	**21.** (*d*)	**22.** (*c*)	**23.** (*c*)	**24.** (*a*)
25. (*d*)	**26.** (*c*)	**27.** (*b*)	**28.** (*c*)				

SOLUTIONS

1. Part filled by A in 1 min. $= \frac{1}{20}$; Part filled by B in 1 min. $= \frac{1}{30}$.

Part filled by (A + B) in 1 min. $= \left(\frac{1}{20} + \frac{1}{30}\right) = \frac{1}{12}$.

$\therefore$ Both the pipes can fill the tank in 12 minutes.

2. Net part filled in 1 hour $= \left(\frac{1}{4} - \frac{1}{9}\right) = \frac{5}{36}$.

$\therefore$ The cistern will be filled in $\frac{36}{5}$ hrs *i.e.,* 7.2 hrs.

3. Time taken by one tap to fill half the tank = 3 hrs.

Part filled by the four taps in 1 hour $= \left(4 \times \frac{1}{6}\right) = \frac{2}{3}$.

Remaining part $= \left(1 - \frac{1}{2}\right) = \frac{1}{2}$.

$\therefore \frac{2}{3} : \frac{1}{2} :: 1 : x$ or $x = \left(\frac{1}{2} \times 1 \times \frac{3}{2}\right) = \frac{3}{4}$ hrs *i.e.,* 45 mins.

So, total time taken = 3 hrs 45 min.

4. Clearly, pipe B is faster than pipe A and so, the tank will be emptied.

Part to be emptied $= \frac{2}{5}$.

Part emptied by (A + B) in 1 minute $= \left(\frac{1}{6} - \frac{1}{10}\right) = \frac{1}{15}$.

$\therefore \frac{1}{15} : \frac{2}{5} :: 1 : x$ or $x = \left(\frac{2}{5} \times 1 \times 15\right) = 6$ min.

So, the tank will be emptied in 6 min.

5. Part filled by (A + B + C) in 1 hour $= \left(\frac{1}{5} + \frac{1}{10} + \frac{1}{30}\right) = \frac{1}{3}$.

$\therefore$ All the three pipes together will fill the tank in 3 hours.

6. Net part filled in 1 hour $= \left(\frac{1}{5} + \frac{1}{6} - \frac{1}{12}\right) = \frac{17}{60}$.

$\therefore$ The tank will be full in $\frac{60}{17}$ hrs *i.e.,* $3\frac{9}{17}$ hrs.

7. Part filled by (A + B + C) in 3 minutes $= 3\left(\frac{1}{30} + \frac{1}{20} + \frac{1}{10}\right) = \left(3 \times \frac{11}{60}\right) = \frac{11}{20}$.

Part filled by C in 3 minutes $= \frac{3}{10}$.

$\therefore$ Required ratio $= \left(\frac{3}{10} \times \frac{20}{11}\right) = \frac{6}{11}$.

8. Work done by the third pipe in 1 min.

$$= \frac{1}{50} - \left(\frac{1}{60} + \frac{1}{75}\right) = \left(\frac{1}{50} - \frac{3}{100}\right) = -\frac{1}{100}. \quad \text{[– ve sign means emptying]}$$

$\therefore$ The third pipe alone can empty the cistern in 100 min.

9. Work done by the leak in 1 hour $= \left(\frac{1}{2} - \frac{3}{7}\right) = \frac{1}{14}$.

$\therefore$ Leak will empty the tank in 14 hrs.

10. Part filled by (A + B) in 1 hour $= \left(\frac{1}{5} + \frac{1}{20}\right) = \frac{1}{4}$.

So, A and B together can fill the tank in 4 hours.

Work done by the leak in 1 hour $= \left(\frac{1}{4} - \frac{2}{9}\right) = \frac{1}{36}$.

$\therefore$ Leak will empty the tank in 36 hrs.

11. Let the cistern be filled by pipe A alone in x hours.

Then, pipe B will fill it in $(x + 6)$ hours.

$\therefore \frac{1}{x} + \frac{1}{(x+6)} = \frac{1}{4} \Leftrightarrow \frac{x+6+x}{x(x+6)} = \frac{1}{4}$

$\Leftrightarrow x^2 - 2x - 24 = 0 \Leftrightarrow (x-6)(x+4) = 0$

$\Leftrightarrow x = 6$. *[neglecting the – ve value of x]*

12. Let the slower pipe alone fill the tank in x minutes.

Then, faster pipe will fill it in $\frac{x}{3}$ minutes.

$\therefore \frac{1}{x} + \frac{3}{x} = \frac{1}{36} \Leftrightarrow \frac{4}{x} = \frac{1}{36} \Leftrightarrow x = 144$ min.

13. Suppose pipe A alone takes x hours to fill the tank.

Then, pipes B and C will take $\frac{x}{2}$ and $\frac{x}{4}$ hours respectively to fill the tank.

$\therefore \frac{1}{x} + \frac{2}{x} + \frac{4}{x} = \frac{1}{5} \Leftrightarrow \frac{7}{x} = \frac{1}{5} \Leftrightarrow x = 35$ hrs.

14. Suppose, first pipe alone takes x hours to fill the tank. Then, second and third pipes will take $(x - 5)$ and $(x - 9)$ hours respectively to fill the tank.

$\therefore \frac{1}{x} + \frac{1}{(x-5)} = \frac{1}{(x-9)} \Leftrightarrow \frac{x-5+x}{x(x-5)} = \frac{1}{(x-9)}$

$\Leftrightarrow (2x-5)(x-9) = x(x-5) \Leftrightarrow x^2 - 18x + 45 = 0$

$\Leftrightarrow (x-15)(x-3) = 0 \Leftrightarrow x = 15$. *[neglecting x = 3]*

15. Capacity of the tank = (12 × 13.5) litres = 162 litres.

Capacity of each bucket = 9 litres.

Number of buckets needed $= \left(\frac{162}{9}\right) = 18$.

16. Let capacity of P be x litres. Then, capacity of Q = $\frac{x}{3}$ litres.

Capacity of the drum = $60x$ litres.

Required number of turns = $\dfrac{60x}{\left(x + \frac{x}{3}\right)} = \left(60x \times \frac{3}{4x}\right) = 45.$

17. Part filled in 3 min. = $3\left(\frac{1}{12} + \frac{1}{15}\right) = \left(3 \times \frac{9}{60}\right) = \frac{9}{20}.$

Remaining part = $\left(1 - \frac{9}{20}\right) = \frac{11}{20}.$

Part filled by B in 1 min. = $\frac{1}{15}.$

$\frac{1}{15} : \frac{11}{20} :: 1 : x$ or $x = \left(\frac{11}{20} \times 1 \times 15\right) = 8\frac{1}{4}$ min. = 8 min. 15 sec.

$\therefore$ Remaining part is filled by B in 8 min. 15 sec.

18. Part filled in 4 minutes = $4\left(\frac{1}{15} + \frac{1}{20}\right) = \frac{7}{15}.$

Remaining part = $\left(1 - \frac{7}{15}\right) = \frac{8}{15}.$

Part filled by B in 1 minute = $\frac{1}{20}.$

$\frac{1}{20} : \frac{8}{15} :: 1 : x$ or $x = \left(\frac{8}{15} \times 1 \times 20\right) = 10\frac{2}{3}$ min. = 10 min. 40 sec.

$\therefore$ The tank will be full in (4 min. + 10 min. 40 sec) = 14 min. 40 sec.

19. Part filled in 10 hours = $10\left(\frac{1}{15} + \frac{1}{20} - \frac{1}{25}\right) = \frac{23}{30}.$

Remaining part = $\left(1 - \frac{23}{30}\right) = \frac{7}{30}.$

(A + B)'s 1 hour's work = $\left(\frac{1}{15} + \frac{1}{20}\right) = \frac{7}{60}.$

$\frac{7}{60} : \frac{7}{30} :: 1 : x$ or $x = \left(\frac{7}{30} \times 1 \times \frac{60}{7}\right) = 2$ hours.

$\therefore$ The tank will be full in (10 + 2) hrs = 12 hrs.

20. Part filled by (A + B) in 1 minute = $\left(\frac{1}{60} + \frac{1}{40}\right) = \frac{1}{24}.$

Suppose the tank is filled in x minutes.

Then, $\frac{x}{2}\left(\frac{1}{24} + \frac{1}{40}\right) = 1 \Leftrightarrow \frac{x}{2} \times \frac{1}{15} = 1 \Leftrightarrow x = 30$ min.

21. Part filled in 5 min. = $5\left(\frac{1}{12} + \frac{1}{15}\right) = \left(5 \times \frac{9}{60}\right) = \frac{3}{4}.$

Part emptied in 1 min. when all the pipes are opened

$$= \frac{1}{6} - \left(\frac{1}{12} + \frac{1}{15}\right) = \left(\frac{1}{6} - \frac{3}{20}\right) = \frac{1}{60}.$$

Now, $\frac{1}{60}$ part is emptied in 1 min.

$\therefore$ $\frac{3}{4}$ part will be emptied in $\left(60 \times \frac{3}{4}\right) = 45$ min.

22. A's work in 1 hour $= \frac{1}{6}$, B's work in 1 hour $= \frac{1}{4}$.

(A + B)'s 2 hour's work when opened alternately $= \left(\frac{1}{6} + \frac{1}{4}\right) = \frac{5}{12}$.

(A + B)'s 4 hour's work when opened alternately $= \frac{10}{12} = \frac{5}{6}$.

Remaining part $= \left(1 - \frac{5}{6}\right) = \frac{1}{6}$.

Now, it is A's turn and $\frac{1}{6}$ part is filled by A in 1 hour.

$\therefore$ Total time taken to fill the tank = (4 + 1) hrs = 5 hrs.

23. (A + B)'s 1 hour's work $= \left(\frac{1}{12} + \frac{1}{15}\right) = \frac{9}{60} = \frac{3}{20}$.

(A + C)'s 1 hour's work $= \left(\frac{1}{12} + \frac{1}{20}\right) = \frac{8}{60} = \frac{2}{15}$.

Part filled in 2 hrs $= \left(\frac{3}{20} + \frac{2}{15}\right) = \frac{17}{60}$; Part filled in 6 hrs $= \left(3 \times \frac{17}{60}\right) = \frac{17}{20}$.

Remaining part $= \left(1 - \frac{17}{20}\right) = \frac{3}{20}$.

Now, it is the turn of A and B and $\frac{3}{20}$ part is filled by A and B in 1 hour.

$\therefore$ Total time taken to fill the tank = (6 + 1) hrs = 7 hrs.

24. Let the filling capacity of the pump be x m^3/min.
Then, emptying capacity of the pump = $(x + 10)$ m^3/min.

So, $\frac{2400}{x} - \frac{2400}{(x + 10)} = 8 \quad \Leftrightarrow \quad x^2 + 10x - 3000 = 0$

$\Leftrightarrow \quad (x - 50)(x + 60) = 0 \quad \Leftrightarrow \quad x = 50.$ *[neglecting the – ve value of x]*

25. Work done by the inlet in 1 hour $= \left(\frac{1}{8} - \frac{1}{12}\right) = \frac{1}{24}$.

Work done by the inlet in 1 min. $= \left(\frac{1}{24} \times \frac{1}{60}\right) = \frac{1}{1440}$.

$\therefore$ Volume of $\frac{1}{1440}$ part = 6 litres.

$\therefore$ Volume of whole = (1440 × 6) litres = 8640 litres.

26. Work done by the waste pipe in 1 minute

$= \frac{1}{15} - \left(\frac{1}{20} + \frac{1}{24}\right) = \left(\frac{1}{15} - \frac{11}{120}\right) = -\frac{1}{40}$. *[– ve sign means emptying]*

$\therefore$ Volume of $\frac{1}{40}$ part = 3 gallons.

Volume of whole = (3 × 40) gallons = 120 gallons.

27. Let B be turned off after x minutes. Then,

Part filled by (A + B) in x min. + Part filled by A in $(30 - x)$ min. = 1.

$$\therefore \quad x\left(\frac{2}{75}+\frac{1}{45}\right)+(30-x)\cdot\frac{2}{75}=1$$

$$\Leftrightarrow \quad \frac{11x}{225}+\frac{(60-2x)}{75}=1 \quad \Leftrightarrow \quad 11x+180-6x=225 \quad \Leftrightarrow \quad x=9.$$

28. Part filled in 2 hours $= \frac{2}{6} = \frac{1}{3}$, Remaining part $= \left(1-\frac{1}{3}\right) = \frac{2}{3}$.

$\therefore$ (A + B)'s 7 hour's work $= \frac{2}{3}$; (A + B)'s 1 hour's work $= \frac{2}{21}$.

$\therefore$ C's 1 hour's work = [(A + B + C)'s 1 hour's work − (A + B)'s 1 hour's work]

$$= \left(\frac{1}{6}-\frac{2}{21}\right)=\frac{1}{14}.$$

$\therefore$ C alone can fill the tank in 14 hours.

EXERCISE 16B

(DATA SUFFICIENCY TYPE QUESTIONS)

Directions (*Questions 1 to 4*) : ***Each of the questions given below consists of a statement and / or a question and two statements numbered I and II given below it. You have to decide whether the data provided in the statement(s) is / are sufficient to answer the given question. Read both the statements and***

Give answer (a) if the data in Statement I alone are sufficient to answer the question, while the data in Statement II alone are not sufficient to answer the question;

Give answer (b) if the data in Statement II alone are sufficient to answer the question, while the data in Statement I alone are not sufficient to answer the question;

Give answer (c) if the data either in Statement I or in Statement II alone are sufficient to answer the question;

Give answer (d) if the data even in both Statements I and II together are not sufficient to answer the question;

Give answer (e) if the data in both Statements I and II together are necessary to answer the question.

1. How long will it take to empty the tank if both the inlet pipe A and the outlet pipe B are opened simultaneously ?

I. A can fill the tank in 16 minutes.

II. B can empty the full tank in 8 minutes.

2. Two taps A and B, when opened together, can fill a tank in 6 hours. How long will it take for the pipe A alone to fill the tank ?

I. B alone takes 5 hours more than A to fill the tank.

II. The ratio of the time taken by A to that taken by B to fill the tank is 2 : 3.

3. A tank is fitted with two inlet pipes A and B. Both the pipes are kept open for 10 minutes so that the tank is two-thirds full and then pipe A is closed. How much time will B take to fill the remaining part of the tank ?

I. Pipe A is thrice as fast as pipe B.

II. Pipe B alone can fill the tank in 60 minutes.

4. How much time will the leak take to empty the full cistern ?

I. The cistern is normally filled in 9 hours.

II. It takes one hour more than the usual time to fill the cistern because of a leak in the bottom.

Directions (*Questions 5-6*) : *Each of the questions below consists of a question followed by three statements. You have to study the question and the statements and decide which of the statement(s) is/are necessary to answer the question*:

5. A tank is fitted with two taps A and B. In how much time will the tank be full if both the taps are opened together ?

I. A is 50% more efficient than B.

II. A alone takes 16 hours to fill the tank.

III. B alone takes 24 hours to fill the tank.

(*a*) II and III only (*b*) All I, II and III

(*c*) I and II only (*d*) I and III only

(*e*) Any two of the three

6. If both the pipes are opened, how many hours will be taken to fill the tank ?

I. The capacity of the tank is 400 litres.

II. The pipe A fills the tank in 4 hours.

III. The pipe B fills the tank in 6 hours. **(R.B.I. 2003)**

(*a*) Only I and II (*b*) Only II and III

(*c*) All I, II and III (*d*) Any two of the three

(*e*) Even with all the three statements, answer cannot be given.

ANSWERS

1. (*e*) **2.** (*c*) **3.** (*c*) **4.** (*e*) **5.** (*e*) **6.** (*b*)

SOLUTIONS

1. I. A's 1 minute's filling work $= \frac{1}{16}$.

II. B's 1 minute's emptying work $= \frac{1}{8}$.

(A + B)'s 1 minute's emptying work $= \left(\frac{1}{8} - \frac{1}{16}\right) = \frac{1}{16}$.

$\therefore$ Tank will be emptied in 16 minutes.

Thus, both I and II are necessary to answer the question.

$\therefore$ Correct answer is (*e*).

2. (A + B)'s 1 hour filling work $= \frac{1}{6}$.

I. Suppose A takes x hours to fill the tank.

Then, B takes $(x + 5)$ hours to fill the tank.

$\therefore$ (A's 1 hour work) + (B's 1 hour work) = (A + B)'s 1 hour work

$\Leftrightarrow \frac{1}{x} + \frac{1}{(x+5)} = \frac{1}{6}$ $\Leftrightarrow \frac{(x+5)+x}{x(x+5)} = \frac{1}{6}$

$\Leftrightarrow x^2 + 5x = 12x + 30$ $\Leftrightarrow x^2 - 7x - 30 = 0$

$\Leftrightarrow x^2 - 10x + 3x - 30 = 0$ $\Leftrightarrow x(x - 10) + 3(x - 10) = 0$

$\Leftrightarrow (x - 10)(x + 3) = 0$ $\Leftrightarrow x = 10$.

So, A alone takes 10 hours to fill the tank.

II. Suppose A takes $2x$ hours and B takes $3x$ hours to fill the tank. Then,

$$\frac{1}{2x}+\frac{1}{3x}=\frac{1}{6} \Leftrightarrow \left(\frac{1}{2}+\frac{1}{3}\right)\frac{1}{x}=\frac{1}{6} \Leftrightarrow \frac{5}{6x}=\frac{1}{6} \Leftrightarrow x=5.$$

So, A alone takes $(2 \times 5) = 10$ hours to fill the tank.

Thus, each one of I and II gives the answer.

$\therefore$ Correct answer is (*c*).

3. I. Let B's 1 min. work $= \frac{1}{x}$. Then, A's 1 min. work $= \frac{3}{x}$.

(A + B)'s 1 min. work $= \left(\frac{1}{x}+\frac{3}{x}\right) = \frac{4}{x}$.

(A + B)'s 10 min. work $= \left(\frac{4}{x} \times 10\right) = \frac{40}{x}$.

$\therefore \quad \frac{40}{x} = \frac{2}{3} \Leftrightarrow x = 60.$

$\therefore$ B's 1 min. work $= \frac{1}{60}$.

$\frac{1}{60}$ part is filled by B in 1 min.

$\frac{1}{3}$ part is filled by B in $\left(60 \times \frac{1}{3}\right)$ min. = 20 min.

II. B's 1 min. work $= \frac{1}{60}$.

$\frac{1}{60}$ part is filled by B in 1 min.

$\frac{1}{3}$ part is filled by B in $\left(60 \times \frac{1}{3}\right)$ min. = 20 min.

Hence, the correct answer is (*c*).

4. I. Time taken to fill the cistern without leak = 9 hours.

Part of cistern filled without leak in 1 hour $= \frac{1}{9}$.

II. Time taken to fill the cistern in presence of leak = 10 hours.

Net filling in 1 hour $= \frac{1}{10}$.

Work done by leak in 1 hour $= \left(\frac{1}{9}-\frac{1}{10}\right) = \frac{1}{90}$.

$\therefore$ Leak will empty the full cistern in 90 hours.

Clearly, both I and II are necessary to answer the question.

$\therefore$ Correct answer is (*e*).

5. II. A's 1 hour work $= \frac{1}{16}$.

Suppose B fills the tank in x hours. Then, B's 1 hour work $= \frac{1}{x}$.

I. Work done by A in 1 hour = 150% of $\frac{1}{x} = \left(\frac{1}{x} \times \frac{150}{100}\right) = \frac{3}{2x}$.

$\therefore \quad \dfrac{3}{2x} = \dfrac{1}{16} \Leftrightarrow x = 24.$

So, B can fill the tank in 24 hours.

(A + B)'s 1 hour work $= \left(\dfrac{1}{16} + \dfrac{1}{24}\right) = \dfrac{5}{48}.$

$\therefore$ (A + B) can fill the tank in $\dfrac{48}{5}$ hrs.

Thus, I & II give the answer.

III. Work done by B in 1 hour $= \dfrac{1}{24}.$

From II & III, we get the same answer.

From III & I, we get :

A's 1 hour work = 150% of $\dfrac{1}{24} = \left(\dfrac{1}{24} \times \dfrac{150}{100}\right) = \dfrac{1}{16}.$

Thus, from III & I, we get the same answer.

$\therefore$ Correct answer is (*e*).

6. **II.** Part of the tank filled by A in 1 hour $= \dfrac{1}{4}.$

III. Part of the tank filled by B in 1 hour $= \dfrac{1}{6}.$

(A + B)'s 1 hour's work $= \left(\dfrac{1}{4} + \dfrac{1}{6}\right) = \dfrac{5}{12}.$

$\therefore$ When both A and B are opened together, they will fill the tank in $\dfrac{12}{5}$ hrs = 2 hrs 24 min.

So, II and III are needed.

$\therefore$ Correct answer is (*b*).

17. TIME AND DISTANCE

IMPORTANT FACTS AND FORMULAE

1. Speed $= \left(\dfrac{\text{Distance}}{\text{Time}}\right)$, Time $= \left(\dfrac{\text{Distance}}{\text{Speed}}\right)$, Distance = (Speed × Time)

2. x km / hr $= \left(x \times \dfrac{5}{18}\right)$ m / sec
3. x m / sec $= \left(x \times \dfrac{18}{5}\right)$ km / hr

4. If the ratio of the speeds of A and B is $a : b$, then the ratio of the times taken by them to cover the same distance is $\dfrac{1}{a} : \dfrac{1}{b}$ or $b : a$.

5. Suppose a man covers a certain distance at x km / hr and an equal distance at y km / hr. Then, the average speed during the whole journey is $\left(\dfrac{2xy}{x+y}\right)$ km / hr

SOLVED EXAMPLES

Ex. 1. ***How many minutes does Aditya take to cover a distance of 400 m, if he runs at a speed of 20 km/hr ?*** **(Bank P.O. 2000)**

Sol. Aditya's speed = 20 km / hr $= \left(20 \times \dfrac{5}{18}\right)$ m / sec $= \dfrac{50}{9}$ m / sec.

$\therefore$ Time taken to cover 400 m $= \left(400 \times \dfrac{9}{50}\right)$ sec = 72 sec $= 1\dfrac{12}{60}$ min $= 1\dfrac{1}{5}$ min.

Ex. 2. ***A cyclist covers a distance of 750 m in 2 min 30 sec. What is the speed in km/hr of the cyclist ?*** **(R.R.B. 2002)**

Sol. Speed $= \left(\dfrac{750}{150}\right)$ m / sec = 5m / sec $= \left(5 \times \dfrac{18}{5}\right)$ km / hr = 18 km / hr.

Ex. 3. ***A dog takes 4 leaps for every 5 leaps of a hare but 3 leaps of a dog are equal to 4 leaps of the hare. Compare their speeds.***

Sol. Let the distance covered in 1 leap of the dog be x and that covered in 1 leap of the hare be y.

Then, $3x = 4y \Rightarrow x = \dfrac{4}{3}y \Rightarrow 4x = \dfrac{16}{3}y$.

$\therefore$ Ratio of speeds of dog and hare = Ratio of distances covered by them in the same time

$$= 4x : 5y = \frac{16}{3}y : 5y = \frac{16}{3} : 5 = 16 : 15.$$

Ex. 4. ***While covering a distance of 24 km, a man noticed that after walking for 1 hour and 40 minutes, the distance covered by him was $\dfrac{5}{7}$ of the remaining distance. What was his speed in metres per second ?*** **(R.R.B. 2002)**

Sol. Let the speed be x km / hr.

Then, distance covered in 1 hr. 40 min. *i.e.*, $1\dfrac{2}{3}$ hrs $= \dfrac{5x}{3}$ km.

Remaining distance $= \left(24 - \frac{5x}{3}\right)$ km.

$$\therefore \quad \frac{5x}{3} = \frac{5}{7}\left(24 - \frac{5x}{3}\right) \Leftrightarrow \frac{5x}{3} = \frac{5}{7}\left(\frac{72-5x}{3}\right) \Leftrightarrow 7x = 72 - 5x$$

$$\Leftrightarrow 12x = 72 \quad \Leftrightarrow \quad x = 6$$

Hence, speed $= 6$ km/hr $= \left(6 \times \frac{5}{18}\right)$ m/sec $= \frac{5}{3}$ m/sec $= 1\frac{2}{3}$ m/sec.

Ex. 5. ***Peter can cover a certain distance in 1 hr. 24 min. by covering two-third of the distance at 4 kmph and the rest at 5 kmph. Find the total distance.***

Sol. Let the total distance be x km. Then,

$$\frac{\frac{2}{3}x}{4} + \frac{\frac{1}{3}x}{5} = \frac{7}{5} \Leftrightarrow \frac{x}{6} + \frac{x}{15} = \frac{7}{5} \Leftrightarrow 7x = 42 \Leftrightarrow x = 6.$$

$\therefore$ Total distance $= 6$ km.

Ex. 6. ***A man travelled from the village to the post-office at the rate of 25 kmph and walked back at the rate of 4 kmph. If the whole journey took 5 hours 48 minutes, find the distance of the post-office from the village.*** **(S.S.C. 2004)**

Sol. Average speed $= \left(\frac{2xy}{x+y}\right)$ km/hr $= \left(\frac{2 \times 25 \times 4}{25+4}\right)$ km/hr $= \frac{200}{29}$ km/hr.

Distance travelled in 5 hours 48 minutes *i.e.,* $5\frac{4}{5}$ hrs $= \left(\frac{200}{29} \times \frac{29}{5}\right)$ km $= 40$ km.

$\therefore$ Distance of the post-office from the village $= \left(\frac{40}{2}\right) = 20$ km.

Ex. 7. ***An aeroplane flies along the four sides of a square at the speeds of 200, 400, 600 and 800 km/hr. Find the average speed of the plane around the field.***

Sol. Let each side of the square be x km and let the average speed of the plane around the field be y km/hr. Then,

$$\frac{x}{200} + \frac{x}{400} + \frac{x}{600} + \frac{x}{800} = \frac{4x}{y} \Leftrightarrow \frac{25x}{2400} = \frac{4x}{y} \Leftrightarrow y = \left(\frac{2400 \times 4}{25}\right) = 384.$$

$\therefore$ Average speed $= 384$ km/hr.

Ex. 8. ***Walking at $\frac{5}{6}$ of its usual speed, a train is 10 minutes too late. Find its usual time to cover the journey.***

Sol. New speed $= \frac{5}{6}$ of the usual speed

$\therefore$ New time taken $= \frac{6}{5}$ of the usual time

So, $\left(\frac{6}{5}\text{ of the usual time}\right) - (\text{usual time}) = 10$ min.

$\Rightarrow \frac{1}{5}$ of the usual time $= 10$ min $\Rightarrow$ usual time $= 50$ min.

Ex. 9. ***If a man walks at the rate of 5 kmph, he misses a train by 7 minutes. However, if he walks at the rate of 6 kmph, he reaches the station 5 minutes before the arrival of the train. Find the distance covered by him to reach the station.***

Sol. Let the required distance be x km.

Difference in the times taken at two speeds $= 12$ min $= \frac{1}{5}$ hr.

$\therefore \quad \frac{x}{5} - \frac{x}{6} = \frac{1}{5} \Leftrightarrow 6x - 5x = 6 \Leftrightarrow x = 6.$

Hence, the required distance is 6 km.

Ex. 10. ***A and B are two stations 390 km apart. A train starts from A at 10 a.m. and travels towards B at 65 kmph. Another train starts from B at 11 a.m. and travels towards A at 35 kmph. At what time do they meet ?***

Sol. Suppose they meet x hours after 10 a.m. Then,

(Distance moved by first in x hrs) + [Distance moved by second in $(x - 1)$ hrs] = 390.

$\therefore \quad 65x + 35(x - 1) = 390 \Rightarrow 100x = 425 \Rightarrow x = 4\frac{1}{4}.$

So, they meet 4 hrs. 15 min. after 10 a.m. *i.e.*, at 2.15 p.m.

Ex. 11. ***A goods train leaves a station at a certain time and at a fixed speed. After 6 hours, an express train leaves the same station and moves in the same direction at a uniform speed of 90 kmph. This train catches up the goods train in 4 hours. Find the speed of the goods train.***

Sol. Let the speed of the goods train be x kmph.

Distance covered by goods train in 10 hours

= Distance covered by express train in 4 hours

$\therefore \quad 10x = 4 \times 90$ or $x = 36$.

So, speed of goods train = 36 kmph.

Ex. 12. ***A thief is spotted by a policeman from a distance of 100 metres. When the policeman starts the chase, the thief also starts running. If the speed of the thief be 8 km/hr and that of the policeman 10 km/hr, how far the thief will have run before he is overtaken ?***

Sol. Relative speed of the policeman = (10 – 8) km / hr = 2 km / hr.

Time taken by policeman to cover 100 m $= \left(\frac{100}{1000} \times \frac{1}{2}\right)$ hr $= \frac{1}{20}$ hr.

In $\frac{1}{20}$ hrs, the thief covers a distance of $\left(8 \times \frac{1}{20}\right)$ km $= \frac{2}{5}$ km = 400 m.

Ex. 13. ***I walk a certain distance and ride back taking a total time of 37 minutes. I could walk both ways in 55 minutes. How long would it take me to ride both ways?***

Sol. Let the distance be x km. Then,

(Time taken to walk x km) + (Time taken to ride x km) = 37 min.

$\Rightarrow$ (Time taken to walk $2x$ km) + (Time taken to ride $2x$ km) = 74 min.

But, time taken to walk $2x$ km = 55 min.

$\therefore$ Time taken to ride $2x$ km = (74 – 55) min = 19 min.

EXERCISE 17

(OBJECTIVE TYPE QUESTIONS)

Directions : *Mark (✓) against the correct answer :*

1. A car moves at the speed of 80 km / hr. What is the speed of the car in metres per second ? **(Hotel Management, 2002)**

   (*a*) 8 m / sec (*b*) $20\frac{1}{9}$ m / sec (*c*) $22\frac{2}{9}$ m / sec (*d*) None of these

2. An athlete runs 200 metres race in 24 seconds. His speed is : **(S.S.C. 2002)**

   (*a*) 20 km / hr (*b*) 24 km / hr (*c*) 28.5 km / hr (*d*) 30 km / hr

3. Which of the following trains is the fastest ?
(a) 25 m / sec (b) 1500 m / min (c) 90 km / hr (d) None of these

4. A person crosses a 600 m long street in 5 minutes. What is his speed in km per hour ?
(a) 3.6 (b) 7.2 (c) 8.4 (d) 10
(R.R.B. 2003)

5. A man walking at the rate of 5 km / hr crosses a bridge in 15 minutes. The length of the bridge (in metres) is : **(S.S.C. 2000)**
(a) 600 (b) 750 (c) 1000 (d) 1250

6. How long will a boy take to run round a square field of side 35 metres, if he runs at the rate of 9 km / hr ? **(S.S.C. 1999)**
(a) 50 sec (b) 52 sec (c) 54 sec (d) 56 sec

7. A car is running at a speed of 108 kmph. What distance will it cover in 15 seconds ?
(a) 45 metres (b) 55 metres (c) 450 metres
(d) Cannot be determined (e) None of these **(R.B.I. 2003)**

8. One of the two buses completes a journey of 300 km in $7\frac{1}{2}$ hours and the other a journey of 450 km in 9 hours. The ratio of their average speeds is : **(R.R.B. 2001)**
(a) 2 : 3 (b) 3 : 4 (c) 4 : 5 (d) 8 : 9

9. A truck covers a distance of 550 metres in 1 minute whereas a bus covers a distance of 33 kms in 45 minutes. The ratio of their speeds is : **(S.S.C. 2004)**
(a) 3 : 4 (b) 4 : 3 (c) 3 : 5 (d) 50 : 3

10. The ratio between the speeds of two trains is 7 : 8. If the second train runs 400 kms in 4 hours, then the speed of the first train is : **(I.M.T. 2002)**
(a) 70 km / hr (b) 75 km / hr (c) 84 km / hr (d) 87.5 km / hr

11. A train travels at an average of 50 miles per hour for $2\frac{1}{2}$ hours and then travels at a speed of 70 miles per hour for $1\frac{1}{2}$ hours. How far did the train travel in the entire 4 hours ? **(IGNOU, 2003)**
(a) 120 miles (b) 150 miles (c) 200 miles (d) 230 miles

12. A man in a train notices that he can count 21 telephone posts in one minute. If they are known to be 50 metres apart, then at what speed is the train travelling ?
(a) 55 km / hr (b) 57 km / hr (c) 60 km / hr (d) 63 km / hr

13. Sound is said to travel in air at about 1100 feet per second. A man hears the axe striking the tree, $\frac{11}{5}$ seconds after he sees it strike the tree. How far is the man from the wood chopper ? **(M.B.A. 2002)**
(a) 2197 ft (b) 2420 ft (c) 2500 ft (d) 2629 ft

14. An express train travelled at an average speed of 100 km / hr, stopping for 3 minutes after every 75 km. How long did it take to reach its destination 600 km from the starting point ? **(M.A.T. 2003)**
(a) 6 hrs 21 min (b) 6 hrs 24 min (c) 6 hrs 27 min (d) 6 hrs 30 min

15. A certain distance is covered by a cyclist at a certain speed. If a jogger covers half the distance in double the time, the ratio of the speed of the jogger to that of the cyclist is :
(a) 1 : 2 (b) 2 : 1 (c) 1 : 4 (d) 4 : 1

16. A motor car starts with the speed of 70 km / hr with its speed increasing every two hours by 10 kmph. In how many hours will it cover 345 kms ? **(Bank P.O. 2003)**
(a) $2\frac{1}{4}$ hrs (b) 4 hrs 5 min (c) $4\frac{1}{2}$ hrs
(d) Cannot be determined (e) None of these

17. The speed of a car increases by 2 kms after every one hour. If the distance travelled in the first one hour was 35 kms, what was the total distance travelled in 12 hours ?
(a) 456 kms (b) 482 kms (c) 552 kms
(d) 556 kms (e) None of these **(Bank P.O. 2003)**

18. A train covers a distance of 10 km in 12 minutes. If its speed is decreased by 5 km / hr, the time taken by it to cover the same distance will be : **(S.S.C. 1999)**
(a) 10 min (b) 11 min 20 sec (c) 13 min (d) 13 min 20 sec

19. Anna left for city A from city B at 5.20 a.m. She travelled at the speed of 80 km / hr for 2 hours 15 minutes. After that the speed was reduced to 60 km / hr. If the distance between two cities is 350 kms, at what time did Anna reach city A ?
(a) 9.20 a.m. (b) 9.25 a.m. (c) 9.35 a.m.
(d) 10.05 a.m. (e) None of these **(Bank P.O. 1999)**

20. An aeroplane covers a certain distance at a speed of 240 kmph in 5 hours. To cover the same distance in $1\frac{2}{3}$ hours, it must travel at a speed of : **(S.S.C. 2000)**
(a) 300 kmph (b) 360 kmph (c) 600 kmph (d) 720 kmph

21. A salesman travels a distance of 50 km in 2 hours and 30 minutes. How much faster, in kilometres per hour, on an average, must he travel to make such a trip in $\frac{5}{6}$ hour less time ? **(Hotel Management, 2002)**
(a) 10 (b) 20 (c) 30 (d) None of these

22. A person has to cover a distance of 6 km in 45 minutes. If he covers one-half of the distance in two-thirds of the total time; to cover the remaining distance in the remaining time, his speed (in km / hr) must be : **(S.S.C. 1999)**
(a) 6 (b) 8 (c) 12 (d) 15

23. A man performs $\frac{3}{5}$ of the total journey by rail, $\frac{17}{20}$ by bus and the remaining 6.5 km on foot. His total journey is :
(a) 65 km (b) 100 km (c) 120 km (d) 130 km

24. A can complete a journey in 10 hours. He travels first half of the journey at the rate of 21 km / hr and second half at the rate of 24 km / hr. Find the total journey in km.
(a) 220 km (b) 224 km (c) 230 km (d) 234 km
(Assistant Grade, 1997)

25. A person travels equal distances with speeds of 3 km / hr, 4 km / hr and 5 km / hr and takes a total time of 47 minutes. The total distance (in km) is : **(R.R.B. 2001)**
(a) 2 (b) 3 (c) 4 (d) 5

26. A farmer travelled a distance of 61 km in 9 hours. He travelled partly on foot @ 4 km / hr and partly on bicycle @ 9 km / hr. The distance travelled on foot is :
(a) 14 km (b) 15 km (c) 16 km (d) 17 km
(U.P.S.C. 2002)

27. A is faster than B. A and B each walk 24 km. The sum of their speeds is 7 km / hr and the sum of times taken by them is 14 hours. Then, A's speed is equal to :
(a) 3 km / hr (b) 4 km / hr (c) 5 km / hr (d) 7 km / hr
(I.A.F. 2002)

28. A person travels from P to Q at a speed of 40 kmph and returns by increasing his speed by 50%. What is his average speed for both the trips ? **(M.B.A. 2003)**
(a) 36 kmph (b) 45 kmph (c) 48 kmph (d) 50 kmph

29. A car driver travels from the plains to the hill station, which are 200 km apart at an average speed of 40 km / hr. In the return trip, he covers the same distance at an average speed of 20 km / hr. The average speed of the car over the entire distance of 400 km is :

(*a*) 25 km / hr (*b*) 26.67 km / hr (*c*) 28.56 km / hr (*d*) 30 km / hr

30. Mac travels from A to B a distance of 250 miles in $5\frac{1}{2}$ hours. He returns to A in 4 hours 30 minutes. His average speed is :

(*a*) 44 mph (*b*) 46 mph (*c*) 48 mph (*d*) 50 mph

31. A boy goes to his school from his house at a speed of 3 km / hr and returns at a speed of 2 km / hr. If he takes 5 hours in going and coming, the distance between his house and school is : **(S.S.C. 2004)**

(*a*) 5 km (*b*) 5.5 km (*c*) 6 km (*d*) 6.5 km

32. The average speed of a train in the onward journey is 25% more than that in the return journey. The train halts for one hour on reaching the destination. The total time taken for the complete to and fro journey is 17 hours, covering a distance of 800 km. The speed of the train in the onward journey is :

(*a*) 45 km / hr (*b*) 47.5 km / hr (*c*) 52 km / hr (*d*) 56.25 km / hr

33. I started on my bicycle at 7 a.m. to reach a certain place. After going a certain distance, my bicycle went out of order. Consequently, I rested for 35 minutes and came back to my house walking all the way. I reached my house at 1 p.m. If my cycling speed is 10 kmph and my walking speed is 1 kmph, then on my bicycle I covered a distance of :

(*a*) $4\frac{61}{66}$ km (*b*) $13\frac{4}{9}$ km (*c*) $14\frac{3}{8}$ km (*d*) $15\frac{10}{21}$ km

34. A, B and C are on a trip by a car. A drives during the first hour at an average speed of 50 km / hr. B drives during the next 2 hours at an average speed of 48 km / hr. C drives for the next 3 hours at an average speed of 52 km / hr. They reached their destination after exactly 6 hours. Their mean speed was :

(*a*) 50 km / hr (*b*) $50\frac{1}{3}$ km / hr (*c*) $51\frac{1}{3}$ km / hr (*d*) 52 km / hr

35. A man on tour travels first 160 km at 64 km / hr and the next 160 km at 80 km / hr. The average speed for the first 320 km of the tour is : **(R.R.B. 2003)**

(*a*) 35.55 km / hr (*b*) 36 km / hr (*c*) 71.11 km / hr (*d*) 71 km hr

36 A boy rides his bicycle 10 km at an average speed of 12 km / hr and again travels 12 km at an average speed of 10 km / hr. His average speed for the entire trip is approximately : **(S.S.C. 1999)**

(*a*) 10.4 km / hr (*b*) 10.8 km / hr (*c*) 11 km / hr (*d*) 12.2 km / hr

37. A man travels 600 km by train at 80 km / hr, 800 km by ship at 40 km / hr, 500 km by aeroplane at 400 km / hr and 100 km by car at 50 km / hr. What is the average speed for the entire distance ? **(S.S.C. 2000)**

(*a*) 60 km / hr (*b*) $60\frac{5}{123}$ km / hr (*c*) 62 km / hr (*d*) $65\frac{5}{123}$ km / hr

38. A car travels the first one-third of a certain distance with a speed of 10 km / hr, the next one-third distance with a speed of 20 km / hr, and the last one-third distance with a speed of 60 km / hr. The average speed of the car for the whole journey is :

(*a*) 18 km / hr (*b*) 24 km / hr (*c*) 30 km / hr (*d*) 36 km / hr

(Civil Services, 2003)

39. A motorist covers a distance of 39 km in 45 minutes by moving at a speed of x kmph for the first 15 minutes, then moving at double the speed for the next 20 minutes and then again moving at his original speed for the rest of the journey. Then, x is equal to :

(a) 31.2 (b) 36 (c) 40 (d) 52

40. Mary jogs 9 km at a speed of 6 km per hour. At what speed would she need to jog during the next 1.5 hours to have an average of 9 km per hour for the entire jogging session ?

(a) 9 kmph (b) 10 kmph (c) 12 kmph (d) 14 kmph

41. A car travelling with $\frac{5}{7}$ of its actual speed covers 42 km in 1 hr 40 min 48 sec. Find the actual speed of the car. **(S.S.C. 2002)**

(a) $17\frac{6}{7}$ km / hr (b) 25 km / hr (c) 30 km / hr (d) 35 km / hr

42. A train running at $\frac{7}{11}$ of its own speed reached a place in 22 hours. How much time could be saved if the train would have run at its own speed ?

(a) 7 hours (b) 8 hours (c) 14 hours (d) 16 hours

43. A man can reach a certain place in 30 hours. If he reduces his speed by $\frac{1}{15}$ th, he goes 10 km less in that time. Find his speed. **(S.S.C. 2002)**

(a) 4 km / hr (b) 5 km / hr (c) $5\frac{1}{2}$ km / hr (d) 6 km / hr

44. Walking $\frac{6}{7}$ th of his usual speed, a man is 12 minutes too late. The usual time taken by him to cover that distance is : **(R.R.B. 2001)**

(a) 1 hour (b) 1 hr 12 min. (c) 1 hr 15 min. (d) 1 hr 20 min

45. Starting from his house one day, a student walks at a speed of $2\frac{1}{2}$ kmph and reaches his school 6 minutes late. Next day he increases his speed by 1 kmph and reaches the school 6 minutes early. How far is the school from his house ? **(S.S.C. 2004)**

(a) 1 km (b) $1\frac{1}{2}$ km (c) $1\frac{3}{4}$ km (d) 2 km

46. A train when moves at an average speed of 40 kmph, reaches its destination on time. When its average speed becomes 35 kmph, then it reaches its destination 15 minutes late. Find the length of journey. **(Bank P.O. 2003)**

(a) 30 km (b) 40 km (c) 70 km (d) 80 km

47. Robert is travelling on his cycle and has calculated to reach point A at 2 P.M. if he travels at 10 kmph; he will reach there at 12 noon if he travels at 15 kmph. At what speed must he travel to reach A at 1 P.M. ? **(D.M.R.C. 2003)**

(a) 8 kmph (b) 11 kmph (c) 12 kmph (d) 14 kmph

48. If a train runs at 40 kmph, it reaches its destination late by 11 minutes but if it runs at 50 kmph, it is late by 5 minutes only. The correct time for the train to complete its journey is :

(a) 13 min. (b) 15 min. (c) 19 min. (d) 21 min

49. A man covered a certain distance at some speed. Had he moved 3 kmph faster, he would have taken 40 minutes less. If he had moved 2 kmph slower, he would have taken 40 minutes more. The distance (in km) is : **(S.S.C. 2003)**

(a) 35 (b) $36\frac{2}{3}$ (c) $37\frac{1}{2}$ (d) 40

50. A car travels from P to Q at a constant speed. If its speed were increased by 10 km / hr, it would have taken one hour lesser to cover the distance. It would have taken further 45 minutes lesser if the speed was further increased by 10 km / hr. What is the distance between the two cities ?

(*a*) 420 km (*b*) 540 km (*c*) 600 km (*d*) 650 km

51. A train can travel 50% faster than a car. Both start from point A at the same time and reach point B 75 kms away from A at the same time. On the way, however, the train lost about 12.5 minutes while stopping at the stations. The speed of the car is :

(*a*) 100 kmph (*b*) 110 kmph (*c*) 120 kmph (*d*) 130 kmph

(M.A.T. 2003)

52. Excluding stoppages, the speed of a bus is 54 kmph and including stoppages, it is 45 kmph. For how many minutes does the bus stop per hour ? **(N.I.F.T. 2002)**

(*a*) 9 (*b*) 10 (*c*) 12 (*d*) 20

53. A car covers a distance of 715 km at a constant speed. If the speed of the car would have been 10 km / hr more, then it would have taken 2 hours less to cover the same distance. What is the original speed of the car ?

(*a*) 45 km / hr (*b*) 50 km / hr (*c*) 55 km / hr (*d*) 65 km / hr

54. In covering a certain distance, the speeds of A and B are in the ratio of 3 : 4. A takes 30 minutes more than B to reach the destination. The time taken by A to reach the destination is : **(S.S.C. 1999)**

(*a*) 1 hour (*b*) $1\frac{1}{2}$ hours (*c*) 2 hours (*d*) $2\frac{1}{2}$ hours

55. In covering a distance of 30 km, Abhay takes 2 hours more than Sameer. If Abhay doubles his speed, then he would take 1 hour less than Sameer. Abhay's speed is :

(*a*) 5 kmph (*b*) 6 kmph (*c*) 6.25 kmph (*d*) 7.5 kmph

(M.A.T. 2003)

56. Three persons are walking from a place A to another place B. Their speeds are in the ratio of 4 : 3 : 5. The time ratio to reach B by these persons will be :

(*a*) 4 : 3 : 5 (*b*) 5 : 3 : 4 (*c*) 15 : 9 : 20 (*d*) 15 : 20 : 12

57. With a uniform speed a car covers the distance in 8 hours. Had the speed been increased by 4 km / hr, the same distance could have been covered in $7\frac{1}{2}$ hours. What is the distance covered ? **(Bank P.O. 2003)**

(*a*) 420 km (*b*) 480 km (*c*) 640 km

(*d*) Cannot be determined (*e*) None of these

58. Two men start together to walk to a certain destination, one at 3 kmph and another at 3.75 kmph. The latter arrives half an hour before the former. The distance is :

(*a*) 6 km (*b*) 7.5 km (*c*) 8 km (*d*) 9.5 km

59. If a person walks at 14 km / hr instead of 10 km / hr, he would have walked 20 km more. The actual distance travelled by him is : **(R.R.B. 2000)**

(*a*) 50 km (*b*) 56 km (*c*) 70 km (*d*) 80 km

60. In a flight of 600 km, an aircraft was slowed down due to bad weather. Its average speed for the trip was reduced by 200 km / hr and the time of flight increased by 30 minutes. The duration of the flight is : **(M.A.T. 2002)**

(*a*) 1 hour (*b*) 2 hours (*c*) 3 hours (*d*) 4 hours

61. It takes eight hours for a 600 km journey, if 120 km is done by train and the rest by car. It takes 20 minutes more, if 200 km is done by train and the rest by car. The ratio of the speed of the train to that of the car is : **(M.B.A 2001)**

(*a*) 2 : 3 (*b*) 3 : 2 (*c*) 3 : 4 (*d*) 4 : 3

62. A is twice as fast as B and B is thrice as fast as C is. The journey covered by C in 54 minutes will be covered by B in :
(a) 18 min (b) 27 min (c) 38 min (d) 9 min

63. Two men starting from the same place walk at the rate of 5 kmph and 5.5 kmph respectively. What time will they take to be 8.5 km apart, if they walk in the same direction ?
(a) 4 hrs 15 min (b) 8 hrs 30 min (c) 16 hrs (d) 17 hrs

64. A walks around a circular field at the rate of one round per hour while B runs around it at the rate of six rounds per hour. They start in the same direction from the same point at 7.30 a.m. They shall first cross each other at : **(Civil Services, 2003)**
(a) 7.42 a.m. (b) 7.48 a.m. (c) 8.10 a.m. (d) 8.30 a.m.

65. A walks at 4 kmph and 4 hours after his start, B cycles after him at 10 kmph. How far from the start does B catch up with A ?
(a) 16.7 km (b) 18.6 km (c) 21.5 km (d) 26.7 km

66. A thief is noticed by a policeman from a distance of 200 m. The thief starts running and the policeman chases him. The thief and the policeman run at the rate of 10 km and 11 km per hour respectively. What is the distance between them after 6 minutes ?
(a) 100 m (b) 150 m (c) 190 m (d) 200 m
(S.S.C. 2000)

67. A thief steals a car at 2.30 p.m. and drives it at 60 kmph. The theft is discovered at 3 p.m. and the owner sets off in another car at 75 kmph. When will he overtake the thief ? **(R.R.B. 2002)**
(a) 4.30 p.m. (b) 4.45 p.m. (c) 5 p.m. (d) 5.15 p.m.

68. Two guns were fired from the same place at an interval of 10 minutes and 30 seconds, but a person in the train approaching the place hears the second shot 10 minutes after the first. The speed of the train (in km / hr), supposing that speed travels at 330 metres per second, is :
(a) 19.8 (b) 58.6 (c) 59.4 (d) 111.80

69. Two cyclists start from the same place in opposite directions. One goes towards north at 18 kmph and the other goes towards south at 20 kmph. What time will they take to be 47.5 km apart ?
(a) $1\frac{1}{4}$ hrs (b) $2\frac{1}{4}$ hrs (c) 2 hrs. 23 min. (d) $2\frac{1}{2}$ hrs

70. The distance between two cities A and B is 330 km. A train starts from A at 8 a.m. and travels towards B at 60 km / hr. Another train starts from B at 9 a.m. and travels towards A at 75 km / hr. At what time do they meet ? **(L.I.C.A.A.O. 2003)**
(a) 10 a.m. (b) 10.30 a.m. (c) 11 a.m. (d) 11.30 a.m.

71. The jogging track in a sports complex is 726 metres in circumference. Deepak and his wife start from the same point and walk in opposite directions at 4.5 km / hr and 3.75 km / hr respectively. They will meet for the first time in : **(M.A.T. 2003)**
(a) 4.9 min (b) 5.28 min (c) 5.5 min (d) 6 min

72. A and B walk around a circular track. They start at 8 a.m. from the same point in the opposite directions. A and B walk at a speed of 2 rounds per hour and 3 rounds per hour respectively. How many times shall they cross each other before 9.30 a.m. ?
(a) 5 (b) 6 (c) 7 (d) 8
(U.P.S.C. 2002)

73. Two cars P and Q start at the same time from A and B which are 120 km apart. If the two cars travel in opposite directions, they meet after one hour and if they travel in same direction (from A towards B), then P meets Q after 6 hours. What is the speed of car P ? **(S.B.I.P.O. 2000)**
(a) 60 kmph (b) 70 kmph (c) 120 kmph
(d) Data inadequate (e) None of these

74. Two trains starting at the same time from two stations 200 km apart and going in opposite directions cross each other at a distance of 110 km from one of the stations. What is the ratio of their speeds ?

(*a*) 9 : 20 (*b*) 11 : 9 (*c*) 11 : 20 (*d*) None of these

75. Two trains start from P and Q respectively and travel towards each other at a speed of 50 km / hr and 40 km / hr respectively. By the time they meet, the first train has travelled 100 km more than the second. The distance between P and Q is :

(*a*) 500 km (*b*) 630 km (*c*) 660 km (*d*) 900 km

(S.S.C. 2000)

76. Bombay Express left Delhi for Bombay at 14.30 hrs, travelling at a speed of 60 kmph and Rajdhani Express left Delhi for Bombay on the same day at 16.30 hrs, travelling at a speed of 80 kmph. How far away from Delhi will the two trains meet ?

(*a*) 120 km (*b*) 360 km (*c*) 480 km (*d*) 500 km

77. A train M leaves Meerut at 5 a.m. and reaches Delhi at 9 a.m. Another train leaves Delhi at 7 a.m. and reaches Meerut at 10.30 a.m. At what time do the two trains cross each other ?

(*a*) 7.36 a.m. (*b*) 7.56 a.m. (*c*) 8 a.m. (*d*) 8.26 a.m.

78. A man takes 5 hours 45 min. in walking to a certain place and riding back. He would have gained 2 hours by riding both ways. The time he would take to walk both ways, is :

(*a*) 3 hrs 45 min (*b*) 7 hrs 30 min
(*c*) 7 hrs 45 min (*d*) 11 hrs 45 min

ANSWERS

1. (*c*)	2. (*d*)	3. (*d*)	4. (*b*)	5. (*d*)	6. (*d*)	7. (*c*)	8. (*c*)
9. (*a*)	10. (*a*)	11. (*d*)	12. (*c*)	13. (*b*)	14. (*a*)	15. (*c*)	16. (*c*)
17. (*c*)	18. (*d*)	19. (*e*)	20. (*d*)	21. (*a*)	22. (*c*)	23. (*d*)	24. (*b*)
25. (*b*)	26. (*c*)	27. (*b*)	28. (*c*)	29. (*b*)	30. (*d*)	31. (*c*)	32. (*d*)
33. (*a*)	34. (*b*)	35. (*c*)	36. (*b*)	37. (*d*)	38. (*a*)	39. (*d*)	40. (*c*)
41. (*d*)	42. (*b*)	43. (*c*)	44. (*b*)	45. (*c*)	46. (*c*)	47. (*c*)	48. (*c*)
49. (*d*)	50. (*a*)	51. (*c*)	52. (*b*)	53. (*c*)	54. (*c*)	55. (*a*)	56. (*d*)
57. (*b*)	58. (*a*)	59. (*a*)	60. (*a*)	61. (*c*)	62. (*a*)	63. (*d*)	64. (*a*)
65. (*d*)	66. (*a*)	67. (*e*)	68. (*c*)	69. (*a*)	70. (*c*)	71. (*b*)	72. (*c*)
73. (*b*)	74. (*b*)	75. (*d*)	76. (*c*)	77. (*e*)	78. (*d*)		

SOLUTIONS

1. Speed $= \left(80 \times \frac{5}{18}\right)$ m/sec $= \frac{200}{9}$ m/sec $= 22\frac{2}{9}$ m/sec.

2. Speed $= \frac{200}{24}$ m/sec $= \frac{25}{3}$ m/sec $= \left(\frac{25}{3} \times \frac{18}{5}\right)$ km/hr $= 30$ km/hr.

3. 25 m/sec $= \left(25 \times \frac{18}{5}\right)$ km/hr $= 90$ km/hr.

And, 25 m/sec = (25 × 60) m/min = 1500 m/min.

So, all the three speeds are equal.

4. Speed $= \left(\frac{600}{5 \times 60}\right)$ m/sec $= 2$ m/sec $= \left(2 \times \frac{18}{5}\right)$ km/hr $= 7.2$ km/hr.

5. Speed $= \left(5 \times \frac{5}{18}\right)$ m/sec $= \frac{25}{18}$ m/sec.

Distance covered in 15 minutes $= \left(\frac{25}{18} \times 15 \times 60\right)$ m $= 1250$ m.

6. Speed = 9 km/hr $= \left(9 \times \frac{5}{18}\right)$ m/sec $= \frac{5}{2}$ m/sec.

Distance = (35×4) m = 140 m.

$\therefore$ Time taken $= \left(140 \times \frac{2}{5}\right)$ sec = 56 sec.

7. Speed = 108 kmph $= \left(108 \times \frac{5}{18}\right)$ m/sec = 30 m/sec.

$\therefore$ Distance covered in 15 sec. = (30×15) m = 450 m.

8. Ratio of speeds $= \left(300 \times \frac{2}{15}\right) : \left(\frac{450}{9}\right) = 40 : 50 = 4 : 5.$

9. Ratio of speeds $= \left(\frac{550}{60} \times \frac{18}{5}\right) : \left(\frac{33}{45} \times 60\right) = 33 : 44 = 3 : 4.$

10. Let the speeds of two trains be $7x$ and $8x$ km/hr.

Then, $8x = \frac{400}{4} = 100 \Rightarrow x = \left(\frac{100}{8}\right) = 12.5.$

$\therefore$ Speed of first train = (7×12.5) km/hr = 87.5 km/hr.

11. Total distance travelled $= \left[\left(50 \times 2\frac{1}{2}\right) + \left(70 \times 1\frac{1}{2}\right)\right]$ miles = (125 + 105) miles = 230 miles.

12. Number of gaps between 21 telephone posts = 20.
Distance travelled in 1 minute = (50×20) m = 1000 m = 1 km.
$\therefore$ Speed = 60 km/hr.

13. Distance $= \left(1100 \times \frac{11}{5}\right)$ feet = 2420 feet.

14. Time taken to cover 600 km $= \left(\frac{600}{100}\right)$ hrs = 6 hrs.

Number of stoppages $= \frac{600}{75} - 1 = 7.$

Total time of stoppage = (3×7) min = 21 min.
Hence, total time taken = 6 hrs 21 min.

15. Let the distance covered by the cyclist be x and the time taken be y. Then,

Required ratio $= \frac{\frac{1}{2}x}{2y} : \frac{x}{y} = \frac{1}{4} : 1 = 1 : 4.$

16. Distance covered in first 2 hours = (70×2) km = 140 km.
Distance covered in next 2 hours = (80×2) km = 160 km.
Remaining distance = 345 − (140 + 160) = 45 km.
Speed in the fifth hour = 90 km/hr.

Time taken to cover 45 km $= \left(\frac{45}{90}\right)$ hr $= \frac{1}{2}$ hr.

$\therefore$ Total time taken $= \left(2 + 2 + \frac{1}{2}\right) = 4\frac{1}{2}$ hrs.

17. Total distance travelled in 12 hours = (35 + 37 + 39 + ... upto 12 terms).
This is an A.P. with first term, a = 35, number of terms, n = 12, common difference, d = 2.

$\therefore$ Required distance $= \frac{12}{2}[2 \times 35 + (12 - 1) \times 2] = 6\,(70 + 22) = 552$ km.

18. Speed $= \left(10 \times \frac{60}{12}\right)$ km / hr = 50 km / hr.

New speed = (50 − 5) km / hr = 45 km / hr.

$\therefore$ Time taken $= \left(\frac{10}{45}\right)$ hr $= \left(\frac{2}{9} \times 60\right)$ min $= 13\frac{1}{3}$ min = 13 min 20 sec.

19. Distance covered in 2 hrs 15 min *i.e.*, $2\frac{1}{4}$ hrs $= \left(80 \times \frac{9}{4}\right)$ hrs = 180 hrs.

Time taken to cover remaining distance $= \left(\frac{350 - 180}{60}\right)$ hrs $= \frac{17}{6}$ hrs

$= 2\frac{5}{6}$ hrs = 2 hrs 50 min.

Total time taken = (2 hrs 15 min + 2 hrs 50 min) = 5 hrs 5 min.
So, Anna reached city A at 10.25 a.m.

20. Distance = (240 × 5) km = 1200 km.

$\therefore$ Required speed $= \left(1200 \times \frac{3}{5}\right)$ km / hr = 720 km / hr.

21. Time required = (2 hrs 30 min − 50 min) = 1 hr 40 min $= 1\frac{2}{3}$ hrs

$\therefore$ Required speed $= \left(50 \times \frac{3}{5}\right)$ km / hr = 30 km / hr.

Original speed $= \left(50 \times \frac{2}{5}\right)$ km / hr = 20 km / hr.

$\therefore$ Difference in speed = (30 − 20) km / hr = 10 km / hr.

22. Remaining distance = 3 km and Remaining time $= \left(\frac{1}{3} \times 45\right)$ min = 15 min $= \frac{1}{4}$ hour.

$\therefore$ Required speed = (3 × 4) km / hr = 12 km / hr.

23. Let the total journey be x km.

Then, $\frac{3x}{5} + \frac{7x}{20} + 6.5 = x \Leftrightarrow 12x + 7x + 20 \times 6.5 = 20x \Leftrightarrow x = 130$ km.

24. Let the total distance be x km. Then,

$$\frac{\frac{1}{2}x}{21} + \frac{\frac{1}{2}x}{24} = 10 \Rightarrow \frac{x}{21} + \frac{x}{24} = 20$$

$$\Rightarrow 15x = 168 \times 20 \Rightarrow x = \left(\frac{168 \times 20}{15}\right) = 224 \text{ km.}$$

25. Let the total distance be $3x$ km.

Then, $\frac{x}{3} + \frac{x}{4} + \frac{x}{5} = \frac{47}{60} \Leftrightarrow \frac{47x}{60} = \frac{47}{60} \Leftrightarrow x = 1.$

$\therefore$ Total distance = (3 × 1) km = 3 km.

26. Let the distance travelled on foot be x km.

Then, distance travelled on bicycle = $(61 - x)$ km.

So, $\frac{x}{4} + \frac{(61-x)}{9} = 9 \Leftrightarrow 9x + 4(61 - x) = 9 \times 36 \Leftrightarrow 5x = 80 \Leftrightarrow x = 16$ km.

27. Let A's speed = x km / hr. Then, B's speed = $(7 - x)$ km / hr.

So, $\frac{24}{x} + \frac{24}{(7-x)} = 14 \Leftrightarrow 24(7 - x) + 24x = 14x(7 - x)$

$\Leftrightarrow 14x^2 - 98x + 168 = 0 \Leftrightarrow x^2 - 7x + 12 = 0$

$\Leftrightarrow (x - 3)(x - 4) = 0 \Leftrightarrow x = 3$ or $x = 4$.

Since, A is faster than B, so A's speed = 4 km / hr and B's speed = 3 km / hr.

28. Speed on return trip = 150% of 40 = 60 kmph.

$\therefore$ Average speed $= \left(\frac{2 \times 40 \times 60}{40 + 60}\right)$ km / hr $= \left(\frac{4800}{100}\right)$ km / hr = 48 km / hr.

29. Average speed $= \left(\frac{2 \times 40 \times 20}{40 + 60}\right)$ km / hr $= \left(\frac{80}{3}\right)$ km / hr = 26.67 km / hr.

30. Speed from A to B $= \left(250 \times \frac{2}{11}\right)$ mph $= \left(\frac{500}{11}\right)$ mph.

Speed from B to A $= \left(250 \times \frac{2}{9}\right)$ mph $= \left(\frac{500}{9}\right)$ mph.

$\therefore$ Average speed $= \left(\frac{2 \times \frac{500}{11} \times \frac{500}{9}}{\frac{500}{11} + \frac{500}{9}}\right)$ mph $= \left(\frac{500000}{4500 + 5500}\right)$ mph = 50 mph.

31. Average speed $= \left(\frac{2 \times 3 \times 2}{3 + 2}\right)$ km / hr $= \frac{12}{5}$ km / hr.

Distance travelled $= \left(\frac{12}{5} \times 5\right)$ km = 12 km.

$\therefore$ Distance between house and school $= \left(\frac{12}{2}\right)$ km = 6 km.

32. Let the speed in return journey be x km / hr.

Then, speed in onward journey $= \frac{125}{100} x = \left(\frac{5}{4} x\right)$ km / hr.

Average speed $= \left(\frac{2 \times \frac{5}{4} x \times x}{\frac{5}{4} x + x}\right)$ km / hr $= \frac{10x}{9}$ km / hr.

$\therefore \left(800 \times \frac{9}{10x}\right) = 16 \Leftrightarrow x = \left(\frac{800 \times 9}{16 \times 10}\right) = 45.$

So, speed in onward journey $= \left(\frac{5}{4} \times 45\right)$ km / hr = 56.25 km / hr.

33. Time taken = 5 hrs 25 min $= \frac{65}{12}$ hrs.

Let the required distance be x km.

Then, $\frac{x}{10} + \frac{x}{1} = \frac{65}{12} \Leftrightarrow 11x = \frac{650}{12} \Leftrightarrow x = \frac{325}{66} = 4\frac{61}{66}$ km.

34. Total distance travelled = $(50 \times 1 + 48 \times 2 + 52 \times 3)$ km = 302 km.

Total time taken = 6 hrs.

$\therefore$ Mean speed = $\left(\frac{302}{6}\right)$ km/hr = $50\frac{1}{3}$ km/hr.

35. Total time taken = $\left(\frac{160}{64} + \frac{160}{8}\right)$ hrs = $\frac{9}{2}$ hrs.

$\therefore$ Average speed = $\left(320 \times \frac{2}{9}\right)$ km/hr = 71.11 km/hr.

36. Total distance travelled = $(10 + 12)$ km/hr = 22 km/hr.

Total time taken = $\left(\frac{10}{12} + \frac{12}{10}\right)$ hrs = $\frac{61}{30}$ hrs.

$\therefore$ Average speed = $\left(22 \times \frac{30}{61}\right)$ km/hr = 10.8 km/hr.

37. Total distance travelled = $(600 + 800 + 500 + 100)$ km = 2000 km.

Total time taken = $\left(\frac{600}{80} + \frac{800}{40} + \frac{500}{400} + \frac{100}{50}\right)$ hrs = $\frac{123}{4}$ hrs.

$\therefore$ Average speed = $\left(2000 \times \frac{4}{123}\right)$ km/hr = $\left(\frac{8000}{123}\right)$ km/hr = $65\frac{5}{123}$ km/hr.

38. Let the whole distance travelled be x km and the average speed of the car for the whole journey be y km/hr.

Then, $\frac{(x/3)}{10} + \frac{(x/3)}{20} + \frac{(x/3)}{60} = \frac{x}{y} \Leftrightarrow \frac{x}{30} + \frac{x}{60} + \frac{x}{180} = \frac{x}{y}$

$\Leftrightarrow \frac{1}{18}y = 1 \Leftrightarrow y = 18$ km/hr.

39. $x \times \frac{15}{60} + 2x \times \frac{20}{60} + x \times \frac{10}{60} = 39 \Rightarrow \frac{x}{4} + \frac{2x}{3} + \frac{x}{6} = 39$

$\Rightarrow 3x + 8x + 2x = 468 \Rightarrow x = 36.$

40. Let speed of jogging be x km/hr.

Total time taken = $\left(\frac{9}{6}\text{ hrs} + 1.5\text{ hrs}\right)$ = 3 hrs.

Total distance covered = $(9 + 1.5x)$ km.

$\therefore \frac{9 + 1.5x}{3} = 9 \Leftrightarrow 9 + 1.5x = 27 \Leftrightarrow \frac{3}{2}x = 18 \Leftrightarrow x = \left(18 \times \frac{2}{3}\right) = 12$ kmph.

41. Time taken = 1 hr 40 min 48 sec = 1 hr $40\frac{4}{5}$ min = $1\frac{51}{75}$ hrs = $\frac{126}{75}$ hrs.

Let the actual speed be x km/hr.

Then, $\frac{5}{7}x \times \frac{126}{75} = 42$ or $x = \left(\frac{42 \times 7 \times 75}{5 \times 126}\right) = 35$ km/hr.

42. New speed = $\frac{7}{11}$ of usual speed.

$\therefore$ New time = $\frac{11}{7}$ of usual time.

So $\frac{11}{7}$ of usual time = 22 hrs $\Rightarrow$ usual time = $\left(\frac{22 \times 7}{11}\right)$ = 14 hrs.

Hence, time saved = $(22 - 14)$ = 8 hrs.

43. Let the speed be x km/hr. Then,

$30x - 30 \times \frac{14}{15}x = 10 \Leftrightarrow 2x = 10 \Leftrightarrow x = 5$ km/hr.

44. New speed $= \frac{6}{7}$ of usual speed.

New time $= \frac{7}{6}$ of usual time

$\therefore \left(\frac{7}{6} \text{ of usual time}\right) - (\text{usual time}) = \frac{1}{5}$ hr.

$\Rightarrow \frac{1}{6}$ of usual time $= \frac{1}{5}$ hr $\Rightarrow$ usual time $= \frac{6}{5}$ hr = 1 hr 12 min.

45. Let the distance be x km.

Difference in timings = 12 min $= \frac{12}{60}$ hr $= \frac{1}{5}$ hr.

$\therefore \frac{2x}{5} - \frac{2x}{7} = \frac{1}{5} \Leftrightarrow 14x - 10x = 7 \Leftrightarrow x = 1\frac{3}{4}$ km.

46. Difference between timings = 15 min $= \frac{1}{4}$ hr.

Let the length of journey be x km.

Then, $\frac{x}{35} - \frac{x}{40} = \frac{1}{4} \Leftrightarrow 8x - 7x = 70 \Leftrightarrow x = 70$ km.

47. Let the distance travelled be x km.

Then, $\frac{x}{10} - \frac{x}{15} = 2 \Leftrightarrow 3x - 2x = 60 \Leftrightarrow x = 60$ km.

Time taken to travel 60 km at 10 km/hr $= \left(\frac{60}{10}\right)$ hrs = 6 hrs.

So, Robert started 6 hours before 2 P.M. *i.e.*, at 8 A.M.

$\therefore$ Required speed $= \left(\frac{60}{5}\right)$ kmph = 12 kmph.

48. Let the correct time to complete the journey be x min.
Distance covered in $(x + 11)$ min. at 40 kmph

= Distance covered in $(x + 5)$ min. at 50 kmph

$\therefore \frac{(x+11)}{60} \times 40 = \frac{(x+5)}{60} \times 50 \Leftrightarrow x = 19$ min.

49. Let distance = x km and usual rate = y kmph.

$\frac{x}{y} - \frac{x}{y+3} = \frac{40}{60}$ or $2y(y+3) = 9x$ ...(*i*)

And, $\frac{x}{y-2} - \frac{x}{y} = \frac{40}{60}$ or $y(y-2) = 3x$ ...(*ii*)

On dividing (*i*) by (*ii*), we get $x = 40$ km.

50. Let distance = x km and usual rate = y kmph. Then,

$\frac{x}{y} - \frac{x}{y+10} = 1$ or $y(y+10) = 10x$ ...(*i*)

And, $\frac{x}{y} - \frac{x}{y+20} = \frac{7}{4}$ or $y(y+20) = \frac{80x}{7}$ ...(*ii*)

On dividing (*i*) by (*ii*), we get $y = 60$.
Substituting $y = 60$ in (*i*), we get : $x = 420$ km.

51. Let speed of the car be x kmph.

Then, speed of the train $= \frac{150}{100}x = \left(\frac{3}{2}x\right)$ kmph.

$\therefore \quad \frac{75}{x} - \frac{75}{\frac{3}{2}x} = \frac{125}{10 \times 60} \Leftrightarrow \frac{75}{x} - \frac{50}{x} = \frac{5}{24} \Leftrightarrow x = \left(\frac{25 \times 24}{5}\right) = 120$ kmph.

52. Due to stoppages, it covers 9 km less.

Time taken to cover 9 km $= \left(\frac{9}{54} \times 60\right)$ min $= 10$ min.

53. Let the original speed be x km / hr. Then,

$\frac{715}{x} - \frac{715}{x+10} = 2 \Leftrightarrow 2x(x + 10) = 7150 \Leftrightarrow x^2 + 10x - 3575 = 0$

$\Leftrightarrow (x + 65)(x - 55) = 0 \Leftrightarrow x = 55$ km / hr.

54. Ratio of speeds = 3 : 4. Ratio of times taken = 4 : 3.

Suppose A takes $4x$ hrs and B takes $3x$ hrs to reach the destination. Then,

$4x - 3x = \frac{30}{60} = \frac{1}{2}$ or $x = \frac{1}{2}$.

$\therefore$ Time taken by A = $4x$ hrs $= \left(4 \times \frac{1}{2}\right)$ hrs = 2 hrs.

55. Let Abhay's speed be x km / hr.

Then, $\frac{30}{x} - \frac{30}{2x} = 3 \Leftrightarrow 6x = 30 \Leftrightarrow x = 5$ km / hr.

56. Ratio of speeds = 4 : 3 : 5.

$\therefore$ Ratio of times taken $= \frac{1}{4} : \frac{1}{3} : \frac{1}{5} = 15 : 20 : 12$.

57. Let the distance be x km. Then,

$\frac{x}{7\frac{1}{2}} - \frac{x}{8} = 4 \Leftrightarrow \frac{2x}{15} - \frac{x}{8} = 4 \Leftrightarrow x = 480$ km.

58. Let the distance be x km. Then,

$\frac{x}{3} - \frac{x}{3.75} = \frac{1}{2} \Leftrightarrow 2.5x - 2x = 3.75 \Leftrightarrow x = \frac{3.75}{0.50} = \frac{15}{2} = 7.5$ km.

59. Let the actual distance travelled be x km. Then,

$\frac{x}{10} = \frac{x + 20}{14} \Leftrightarrow 14x = 10x + 200 \Leftrightarrow 4x = 200 \Leftrightarrow x = 50$ km.

60. Let the duration of the flight be x hours. Then,

$\frac{600}{x} - \frac{600}{x + \frac{1}{2}} = 200 \Leftrightarrow \frac{600}{x} - \frac{1200}{2x+1} = 200 \Leftrightarrow x(2x + 1) = 3$

$\Leftrightarrow 2x^2 + x - 3 = 0 \Leftrightarrow (2x + 3)(x - 1) = 0$

$\Leftrightarrow x = 1$ hr. [*neglecting the – ve value of x*]

61. Let the speed of the train be x km / hr and that of the car be y km / hr.

Then, $\frac{120}{x} + \frac{480}{y} = 8$ or $\frac{1}{x} + \frac{4}{y} = \frac{1}{15}$ ...(*i*)

And, $\frac{200}{x} + \frac{400}{y} = \frac{25}{3}$ or $\frac{1}{x} + \frac{2}{y} = \frac{1}{24}$ ...(*ii*)

Solving (*i*) and (*ii*), we get $x = 60$ and $y = 80$.

$\therefore$ Ratio of speeds = 60 : 80 = 3 : 4.

62. Let C's speed = x km / hr. Then, B's speed = $3x$ km / hr and A's speed = $6x$ km / hr.

$\therefore$ Ratio of speeds of A, B, C = $6x : 3x : x = 6 : 3 : 1$.

Ratio of times taken $= \frac{1}{6} : \frac{1}{3} : 1 = 1 : 2 : 6$.

If C takes 6 min., then B takes 2 min.

If C takes 54 min., then B takes $\left(\frac{2}{6} \times 54\right)$ min. = 18 min.

63. To be 0.5 km apart, they take 1 hour.

To be 8.5 km apart, they take $\left(\frac{1}{0.5} \times 8.5\right)$ hrs = 17 hrs.

64. Since A and B move in the same direction along the circle, so they will first meet each other when there is a difference of one round between the two.

Relative speed of A and B = (6 – 1) = 5 rounds per hour.

Time taken to complete one round at this speed $= \frac{1}{5}$ hr = 12 min.

65. Suppose after x km from the start B catches up with A. Then, the difference in the time taken by A to cover x km and that taken by B to cover x km is 4 hours.

$\therefore \frac{x}{4} - \frac{x}{10} = 4$ or $x = 26.7$ km.

66. Relative speed of the thief and p\
oliceman = (11 – 10) km / hr = 1 km / hr.

Distance covered in 6 minutes $= \left(\frac{1}{60} \times 6\right)$ km $= \frac{1}{10}$ km = 100 m.

$\therefore$ Distance between the thief and policeman = (200 – 100) m = 100 m.

67. Suppose the thief is overtaken x hrs after 2.30 p.m.

Then, distance covered by the thief in x hrs

= distance covered by the owner in $\left(x - \frac{1}{2}\right)$ hrs.

$\therefore \quad 60x = 75\left(x - \frac{1}{2}\right) \Leftrightarrow 15x = \frac{75}{2} \Leftrightarrow x = \frac{5}{2}$ hrs.

So, the thief is overtaken at 5 p.m.

68. Let the speed of the train be x m / sec. Then,

Distance travelled by the train in 10 min. = Distance travelled by sound in 30 sec.

$\Leftrightarrow x \times 10 \times 60 = 330 \times 30 \Leftrightarrow x = 16.5$.

$\therefore$ Speed of the train = 16.5 m/sec $= \left(16.5 \times \frac{18}{5}\right)$ km/hr = 59.4 km/hr

69. To be (18 + 20) km apart, they take 1 hour.

To be 47.5 km apart, they take $\left(\frac{1}{38} \times 47.5\right)$ hrs $= 1\frac{1}{4}$ hrs.

70. Suppose they meet x hrs after 8 a.m. Then,

(Distance moved by first in x hrs) + [Distance moved by second in $(x - 1)$ hrs] = 330

$\therefore \quad 60x + 75(x - 1) = 330 \Rightarrow x = 3$.

So, they meet at (8 + 3), *i.e.* 11 a.m.

71. Clearly, the two will meet when they are 726 m apart.

To be (4.5 + 3.75) = 8.25 km apart, they take 1 hour.

To be 726 m apart, they take $\left(\frac{100}{825} \times \frac{726}{1000}\right)$ hrs $= \left(\frac{242}{2750} \times 60\right)$ min = 5.28 min.

72. Relative speed = (2 + 3) = 5 rounds per hour.

So, they cross each other 5 times in an hour and 2 times in half an hour.

Hence, they cross each other 7 times before 9.30 a.m.

73. Let their speeds be x kmph and y kmph respectively.

Then, $\frac{120}{x+y} = 1 \Rightarrow x + y = 120$ ...(i)

Now, when they move in same direction :

(Distance travelled by P in 6 hrs) – (Distance travelled by Q in 6 hrs) = 120 km

$\Rightarrow 6x - 6y = 120 \quad \Rightarrow \quad x - y = 20$ ...(ii)

Solving (i) and (ii), $x = 70$, $y = 50$.

$\therefore$ P's speed = 70 kmph.

74. In the same time, they cover 110 km and 90 km respectively.

$\therefore$ Ratio of their speeds = 110 : 90 = 11 : 9.

75. At the time of meeting, let the distance travelled by the second train be x km.

Then, distance covered by the first train is $(x + 100)$ km.

$\therefore \quad \frac{x}{40} = \frac{x+100}{50} \Leftrightarrow 50x = 40x + 4000 \Leftrightarrow x = 400.$

So, distance between P and Q = $(x + x + 100)$ km = 900 km.

76. Suppose they meet x hours after 14.30 hrs.

Then, $60x = 80(x - 2)$ or $x = 8$.

$\therefore$ Required distance = (60×8) km = 480 km.

77. Let the distance between Meerut and Delhi be x km and let the trains meet y hours after 7 a.m.

Clearly, M covers x km in 4 hrs and N covers x km in $(7/2)$ hrs.

$\therefore$ Speed of M = $\frac{x}{4}$ kmph, Speed of N = $\frac{2x}{7}$ kmph.

Distance covered by M in $(y + 2)$ hrs + Distance covered in y hrs = x.

$\therefore \quad \frac{x}{4}(y+2) + \frac{2x}{7} \times y = x \Leftrightarrow \frac{(y+2)}{4} + \frac{2y}{7} = 1$

$\Leftrightarrow \quad y = \frac{14}{15}$ hrs $= \left(\frac{14}{15} \times 60\right)$ min. = 56 min.

Hence, the trains meet at 7.56 a.m.

78. Let the distance be x km. Then,

(Time taken to walk x km) + (Time taken to ride x km) = $\frac{23}{4}$ hrs.

$\Rightarrow$ (Time taken to walk $2x$ km) + (Time taken to ride $2x$ km) = $\frac{23}{2}$ hrs.

But, time taken to ride $2x$ km = $\frac{15}{4}$ hrs.

$\therefore$ Time taken to walk $2x$ km = $\left(\frac{23}{2} - \frac{15}{4}\right)$ hrs = $\frac{31}{4}$ hrs = 7 hrs 45 min.

EXERCISE 17B

(DATA SUFFICIENCY TYPE QUESTIONS)

Directions (*Questions 1 to 7*) : *Each of the questions below consists of a statement and/or a question and two statements numbered I and II given below it. You have to decide whether the data provided in the statements is/are sufficient to answer the question. Read both the statements and*

Give answer (a) if the data in Statement I alone are sufficient to answer the question, while the data in Statement II alone are not sufficient to answer the question;

Give answer (b) if the data in Statement II alone are sufficient to answer the question, while the data in Statement I alone are not sufficient to answer the question;

Give answer (c) if the data either in Statement I or in Statement II alone are sufficient to answer the question;

Give answer (d) if the data even in both Statements I and II together are not sufficient to answer the question; and

Give answer (e) if the data in both Statements I and II together are necessary to answer the question.

1. How much time did X take to reach the destination ?
   I. The ratio between the speeds of X and Y is 3 : 4.
   II. Y takes 36 minutes to reach the same destination.
2. What is the usual speed of the train ? **(M.B.A. 2002)**
   I. The speed of the train is increased by 25 km/hr to reach the destination 150 km away in time.
   II. The train is late by 30 minutes.
3. Two towns are connected by railway. Can you find the distance between them ?
   I. The speed of mail train is 12 km/hr more than that of an express train.
   II. A mail train takes 40 minutes less than an express train to cover the distance. **(M.B.A. 2001)**
4. The towns A, B and C are on a straight line. Town C is between A and B. The distance from A to B is 100 km. How far is A from C ? **(M.B.A. 2003)**
   I. The distance from A to B is 25% more than the distance from C to B.
   II. The distance from A to C is $\frac{1}{4}$ of the distance from C to B.
5. What is the average speed of the car over the entire distance ?
   I. The car covers the whole distance in four equal stretches at speeds of 10 kmph, 20 kmph, 30 kmph and 60 kmph respectively.
   II. The total time taken is 36 minutes.
6. A car and a bus start from city A at the same time. How far is the city B from city A ?
   I. The car travelling at an average speed of 40 km/hr reaches city B at 4:35 p.m.
   II. The bus reaches city B at 6:15 p.m. at an average speed of 60 km/hr.
7. Two cars pass each other in opposite direction. How long would they take to be 500 km apart ? **(M.A.T. 1998)**
   I. The sum of their speeds is 135 km/hr.
   II. The difference of their speeds is 25 km/hr.

ANSWERS

1. (*e*) 2. (*e*) 3. (*d*) 4. (*c*) 5. (*a*) 6. (*e*) 7. (*a*)

SOLUTIONS

1. I. If Y takes 4 min., then X takes 3 min.

II. If Y takes 36 min., then X takes $\left(\frac{3}{4} \times 36\right)$ min = 27 min.

Thus, I and II together give the answer.

$\therefore$ Correct answer is (*e*).

2. Let the usual speed of the train be x kmph.

Time taken to cover 150 km at usual speed $= \frac{150}{x}$ hrs.

I. Time taken at increased speed $= \frac{150}{(x+25)}$ hrs.

II. $\frac{150}{x} - \frac{150}{(x+25)} = \frac{30}{60}$

$\Leftrightarrow \frac{1}{x} - \frac{1}{(x+25)} = \frac{1}{300} \Leftrightarrow [(x+25) - x] \times 300 = x(x+25)$

$\Leftrightarrow x^2 + 25x - 7500 = 0 \Leftrightarrow (x+100)(x-75) = 0 \Leftrightarrow x = 75.$

Thus, I and II together give the answer.

$\therefore$ Correct answer is (*e*).

3. Let the distance between the two stations be x km.

I. Let the speed of the express train be y km/hr.

Then, speed of the mail train = $(y + 12)$ km/hr.

II. $\frac{x}{y} - \frac{x}{(y+12)} = \frac{40}{60}$.

Thus, even I and II together do not give x.

$\therefore$ Correct answer is (*d*).

4. Let AC = x km. Then, CB = $(100 - x)$ km.

A x C (100 − x) B

I. AB = 125% of CB

$\Leftrightarrow 100 = \frac{125}{100} \times (100 - x) \Leftrightarrow 100 - x = \frac{100 \times 100}{125} = 80 \Leftrightarrow x = 20$ km.

$\therefore$ AC = 20 km.

Thus, I alone gives the answer.

II. AC $= \frac{1}{4}$ CB $\Leftrightarrow x = \frac{1}{4}(100 - x) \Leftrightarrow 5x = 100 \Leftrightarrow x = 20.$

$\therefore$ AC = 20 km.

Thus, II alone gives the answer.

$\therefore$ Correct answer is (*c*).

5. Let the whole distance be $4x$ km.

I. Total time taken $= \left(\frac{x}{10} + \frac{x}{20} + \frac{x}{30} + \frac{x}{60}\right) = \frac{(6x + 3x + 2x + x)}{60} = \frac{12x}{60} = \frac{x}{5}$.

$\therefore$ Speed $= \frac{\text{Distance}}{\text{Time}} = \frac{4x}{(x/5)}$ kmph = 20 km/hr.

$\therefore$ I alone is sufficient to answer the question.

II alone does not give the answer.

$\therefore$ Correct answer is (*a*).

6. Let AB = x km. From I and II, we get :

$$\frac{x}{40} - \frac{x}{60} = 1\frac{40}{60} \qquad [(6{:}15 \text{ p.m.}) - (4{:}35 \text{ p.m.}) = 1 \text{ hr } 40 \text{ min}]$$

$\Leftrightarrow \frac{x}{40} - \frac{x}{60} = \frac{100}{60}$. This gives x.

$\therefore$ Correct answer is (*e*).

7. I gives, relative speed = 135 km/hr.

$\therefore$ Time taken $= \frac{500}{135}$ hrs.

II does not give the relative speed.

$\therefore$ I alone gives the answer and II is irrelevant.

$\therefore$ Correct answer is (*a*).

---

18. PROBLEMS ON TRAINS

IMPORTANT FACTS AND FORMULAE

1. a km/hr $= \left(a \times \frac{5}{18}\right)$ m/s.
2. a m/s $= \left(a \times \frac{18}{5}\right)$ km/hr.
3. Time taken by a train of length l metres to pass a pole or a standing man or a signal post is equal to the time taken by the train to cover l metres.
4. Time taken by a train of length l metres to pass a stationary object of length b metres is the time taken by the train to cover $(l + b)$ metres.
5. Suppose two trains or two bodies are moving in the same direction at u m/s and v m/s, where $u > v$, then their relatives speed $= (u - v)$ m/s.
6. Suppose two trains or two bodies are moving in opposite directions at u m/s and v m/s, then their relative speed is $= (u + v)$ m/s.
7. If two trains of length a metres and b metres are moving in opposite directions at u m/s and v m/s, then time taken by the trains to cross each other $= \frac{(a+b)}{(u+v)}$ sec.
8. If two trains of length a metres and b metres are moving in the same direction at u m/s and v m/s, then the time taken by the faster train to cross the slower train $= \frac{(a+b)}{(u-v)}$ sec.
9. If two trains (or bodies) start at the same time from points A and B towards each other and after crossing they take a and b sec in reaching B and A respectively, then ***(A's speed) : (B's speed)*** $= (\sqrt{b} : \sqrt{a})$.

SOLVED EXAMPLES

Ex. 1. ***A train 100 m long is running at the speed of 30 km/hr. Find the time taken by it to pass a man standing near the railway line.*** **(S.S.C. 2001)**

Sol. Speed of the train $= \left(30 \times \frac{5}{18}\right)$ m/sec $= \left(\frac{25}{3}\right)$ m/sec.

Distance moved in passing the standing man = 100 m.

Required time taken $= \frac{100}{\left(\frac{25}{3}\right)} = \left(100 \times \frac{3}{25}\right)$ sec = 12 sec.

Ex. 2. ***A train is moving at a speed of 132 km/hr. If the length of the train is 110 metres, how long will it take to cross a railway platform 165 metres long?*** **(Section-Officers', 2003)**

Sol. Speed of train $= \left(132 \times \frac{5}{18}\right)$ m/sec $= \left(\frac{110}{3}\right)$ m/sec.

Distance covered in passing the platform = (110 + 165) m = 275 m.

$\therefore$ Time taken $= \left(275 \times \frac{3}{110}\right)$ sec $= \frac{15}{2}$ sec $= 7\frac{1}{2}$ sec.

Ex. 3. ***A man is standing on a railway bridge which is 180 m long. He finds that a train crosses the bridge in 20 seconds but himself in 8 seconds. Find the length of the train and its speed.***

Sol. Let the length of the train be x metres.

Then, the train covers x metres in 8 seconds and $(x + 180)$ metres in 20 seconds.

$\therefore \quad \dfrac{x}{8} = \dfrac{x+180}{20} \Leftrightarrow 20x = 8(x + 180) \Leftrightarrow x = 120.$

$\therefore$ Length of the train = 120 m.

Speed of the train $= \left(\dfrac{120}{8}\right)$ m/sec = m/sec $= \left(15 \times \dfrac{18}{5}\right)$ kmph = 54 kmph.

Ex 4. ***A train 150 m long is running with a speed of 68 kmph. In what time will it pass a man who is running at 8 kmph in the same direction in which the train is going ?***

Sol. Speed of the train relative to man = (68 – 8) kmph

$= \left(60 \times \dfrac{5}{18}\right)$ m/sec $= \left(\dfrac{50}{3}\right)$ m/sec.

Time taken by the train to cross the man

= Time taken by it to cover 150 m at $\left(\dfrac{50}{3}\right)$ m/sec $= \left(150 \times \dfrac{3}{50}\right)$ sec = 9 sec.

Ex. 5. ***A train 220 m long is running with a speed of 59 kmph. In what time will it pass a man who is running at 7 kmph in the direction opposite to that in which the train is going ?***

Sol. Speed of the train relative to man = (59 + 7) kmph

$= \left(66 \times \dfrac{5}{18}\right)$ m/sec $= \left(\dfrac{55}{3}\right)$ m/sec.

Time taken by the train to cross the man

= Time taken by it to cover 220 m at $\left(\dfrac{55}{3}\right)$ m/sec $= \left(220 \times \dfrac{3}{55}\right)$ sec = 12 sec.

Ex. 6. ***Two trains 137 metres and 163 metres in length are running towards each other on parallel lines, one at the rate of 42 kmph and another at 48 kmph. In what time will they be clear of each other from the moment they meet ?***

Sol. Relative speed of the trains = (42 + 48) kmph = 90 kmph

$= \left(90 \times \dfrac{5}{18}\right)$ m/sec = 25 m/sec.

Time taken by the trains to pass each other

= Time taken to cover (137 + 163) m at 25 m/sec $= \left(\dfrac{300}{25}\right)$ sec = 12 seconds.

Ex. 7. ***Two trains 100 metres and 120 metres long are running in the same direction with speeds of 72 km/hr and 54 km/hr. In how much time will the first train cross the second ?*** **(C.B.I. 1997)**

Sol. Relative speed of the trains = (72 – 54) km/hr = 18 km/hr

$= \left(18 \times \dfrac{5}{18}\right)$ m/sec = 5 m/sec.

Time taken by the trains to cross each other

= Time taken to cover (100 + 120) m at 5 m/sec $= \left(\dfrac{220}{5}\right)$ sec = 44 sec.

Ex. 8. ***A train 100 metres long takes 6 seconds to cross a man walking at 5 kmph in a direction opposite to that of the train. Find the speed of the train.***

Sol. Let the speed of the train be x kmph.

Speed of the train relative to man = $(x + 5)$ kmph $= (x+5) \times \frac{5}{18}$ m/sec.

$\therefore \quad \frac{100}{(x+5) \times \frac{5}{18}} = 6 \Leftrightarrow 30(x+5) = 1800 \Leftrightarrow x = 55.$

$\therefore$ Speed of the train is 55 kmph.

Ex. 9. ***A train running at 54 kmph takes 20 seconds to pass a platform. Next it takes 12 seconds to pass a man walking at 6 kmph in the same direction in which the train is going. Find the length of the train and the length of the platform.***

Sol. Let the length of train be x metres and length of platform be y metres.

Speed of the train relative to man = (54 – 6) kmph = 48 kmph

$= \left(48 \times \frac{5}{18}\right)$ m/sec $= \frac{40}{3}$ m/sec.

In passing a man, the train covers its own length with relative speed.

$\therefore$ Length of train = (Relative speed × Time) $= \left(\frac{40}{3} \times 12\right)$ m = 160 m.

Also, speed of the train $= \left(54 \times \frac{5}{18}\right)$ m/sec = 15 m/sec.

$\therefore \quad \frac{x+y}{15} = 20 \Leftrightarrow x + y = 300 \Leftrightarrow y = (300 - 160)$ m = 140 m.

Ex. 10. ***A man sitting in a train which is travelling at 50 kmph observes that a goods train, travelling in opposite direction, takes 9 seconds to pass him. If the goods train is 280 m long, find its speed.***

Sol. Relative speed $= \left(\frac{280}{9}\right)$ m/sec $= \left(\frac{280}{9} \times \frac{18}{5}\right)$ kmph = 112 kmph.

$\therefore$ Speed of goods train = (112 – 50) kmph = 62 kmph.

EXERCISE 18A

(OBJECTIVE TYPE QUESTIONS)

Directions : *Mark (✓) against the correct answer :*

1. A train moves with a speed of 108 kmph. Its speed in metres per second is :
   (*a*) 10.8 (*b*) 18 (*c*) 30 (*d*) 38.8
2. A speed of 14 metres per second is the same as :
   (*a*) 28 km / hr (*b*) 46.6 km / hr (*c*) 50.4 km / hr (*d*) 70 km / hr
3. In what time will a train 100 metres long cross an electric pole, if its speed be 144 km / hr ? **(S.S.C. 2003)**
   (*a*) 2.5 seconds (*b*) 4.25 seconds (*c*) 5 seconds (*d*) 12.5 seconds
4. A train 280 m long, running with a speed of 63 km / hr will pass a tree in :
   (*a*) 15 sec (*b*) 16 sec (*c*) 18 sec (*d*) 20 sec
   (S.S.C. 2003)
5. How long does a train 110 metres long running at the speed of 72 km / hr take to cross a bridge 132 metres in length ? **(R.R.B. 1998)**
   (*a*) 9.8 sec (*b*) 12.1 sec (*c*) 12.42 sec (*d*) 14.3 sec

6. A train 360 m long is running at a speed of 45 km/hr. In what time will it pass a bridge 140 m long ? **(B.S.F. 2001)**
(*a*) 40 sec (*b*) 42 sec (*c*) 45 sec (*d*) 48 sec

7. A train travelling at a speed of 75 mph enters a tunnel $3\frac{1}{2}$ miles long. The train is $\frac{1}{4}$ mile long. How long does it take for the train to pass through the tunnel from the moment the front enters to the moment the rear emerges ?
(*a*) 2.5 min (*b*) 3 min (*c*) 3.2 min (*d*) 3.5 min

8. A train running at the speed of 60 km/hr crosses a pole in 9 seconds. What is the length of the train ? **(Bank P.O. 2003)**
(*a*) 120 metres (*b*) 180 metres (*c*) 324 metres
(*d*) Cannot be determined (*e*) None of these

9. A train 132 m long passes a telegraph pole in 6 seconds. Find the speed of the train.
(*a*) 70 km/hr (*b*) 72 km/hr (*c*) 79.2 km/hr (*d*) 80 km/hr

10. A train covers a distance of 12 km in 10 minutes. If it takes 6 seconds to pass a telegraph post, then the length of the train is : **(Bank P.O. 2000)**
(*a*) 90 m (*b*) 100 m (*c*) 120 m (*d*) 140 m

11. A train 240 m long passed a pole in 24 seconds. How long will it take to pass a platform 650 m long ? **(R.R.B. 1998)**
(*a*) 65 sec (*b*) 89 sec (*c*) 100 sec (*d*) 150 sec

12. The length of the bridge, which a train 130 metres long and travelling at 45 km/hr can cross in 30 seconds, is : **(Section Officers', 2001)**
(*a*) 200 m (*b*) 225 m (*c*) 245 m (*d*) 250 m

13. A train 800 metres long is running at a speed of 78 km/hr. If it crosses a tunnel in 1 minute, then the length of the tunnel (in metres) is : **(S.S.C. 2003)**
(*a*) 130 (*b*) 360 (*c*) 500 (*d*) 540

14. A goods train runs at the speed of 72 kmph and crosses a 250 m long platform in 26 seconds. What is the length of the goods train ? **(Bank P.O. 2003)**
(*a*) 230 m (*b*) 240 m (*c*) 260 m (*d*) 270 m

15. The length of a train and that of a platform are equal. If with a speed of 90 km/hr, the train crosses the platform in one minute, then the length of the train (in metres) is :
(*a*) 500 (*b*) 600 (*c*) 750 (*d*) 900

16. A train of length 150 metres takes 40.5 seconds to cross a tunnel of length 300 metres. What is the speed of the train in km/hr ?
(*a*) 13.33 (*b*) 26.67 (*c*) 40 (*d*) 66.67

17. A train crosses a platform 100 m long in 60 seconds at a speed of 45 km/hr. The time taken by the train to cross an electric pole is :
(*a*) 8 sec (*b*) 52 sec (*c*) 1 minute (*d*) Data inadequate

18. A train passes a station platform in 36 seconds and a man standing on the platform in 20 seconds. If the speed of the train is 54 km/hr, what is the length of the platform ? **(G.INDOMAT, 1997)**
(*a*) 120 m (*b*) 240 m (*c*) 300 m (*d*) None of these

19. A 300 metre long train crosses a platform in 39 seconds while it crosses a signal pole in 18 seconds. What is the length of the platform ?
(*a*) 320 m (*b*) 350 m (*c*) 650 m
(*d*) Data inadequate (*e*) None of these **(Bank P.O. 2002)**

20. A train speeds past a pole in 15 seconds and a platform 100 m long in 25 seconds. Its length is : **(R.R.B 2003)**
(*a*) 50 m (*b*) 150 m (*c*) 200 m (*d*) Data inadequate

21. A train moves past a telegraph post and a bridge 264 m long in 8 seconds and 20 seconds respectively. What is the speed of the train ? **(S.S.C. 2004)**

(*a*) 69.5 km / hr (*b*) 70 km / hr (*c*) 79 km / hr (*d*) 79.2 km / hr

22. A train takes 18 seconds to pass completely through a station 162 m long and 15 seconds through another station 120 m long. The length of the train is :

(*a*) 70 m (*b*) 80 m (*c*) 90 m (*d*) 100 m

23. How many seconds will a 500 metre long train take to cross a man walking with a speed of 3 km / hr in the direction of the moving train if the speed of the train is 63 km / hr ? **(S.S.C. 2000)**

(*a*) 25 (*b*) 30 (*c*) 40 (*d*) 45

24. A jogger running at 9 kmph alongside a railway track is 240 metres ahead of the engine of a 120 metre long train running at 45 kmph in the same direction. In how much time will the train pass the jogger ? **(IGNOU, 2003)**

(*a*) 3.6 sec (*b*) 18 sec (*c*) 36 sec (*d*) 72 sec

25. A train 110 metres long is running with a speed of 60 kmph. In what time will it pass a man who is running at 6 kmph in the direction opposite to that in which the train is going ? **(M.A.T. 2002)**

(*a*) 5 sec (*b*) 6 sec (*c*) 7 sec (*d*) 10 sec

26. Two trains 200 m and 150 m long are running on parallel rails at the rate of 40 kmph and 45 kmph respectively. In how much time will they cross each other, if they are running in the same direction ?

(*a*) 72 sec (*b*) 132 sec (*c*) 192 sec (*d*) 252 sec

27. Two trains 140 m and 160 m long run at the speed of 60 km / hr and 40 km / hr respectively in opposite directions on parallel tracks. The time (in seconds) which they take to cross each other, is : **(S.S.C. 2004)**

(*a*) 9 (*b*) 9.6 (*c*) 10 (*d*) 10.8

28. Two trains are moving in opposite directions @ 60 km / hr and 90 km / hr. Their lengths are 1.10 km and 0.9 km respectively. The time taken by the slower train to cross the faster train in seconds is : **(M.B.A. 2002)**

(*a*) 36 (*b*) 45 (*c*) 48 (*d*) 49

29. A train 125 m long passes a man, running at 5 kmph in the same direction in which the train is going, in 10 seconds. The speed of the train is : **(A.A.O. Exam, 2003)**

(*a*) 45 km / hr (*b*) 50 km / hr (*c*) 54 km / hr (*d*) 55 km / hr

30. A train 110 m long passes a man, running at 6 kmph in the direction opposite to that of the train, in 6 seconds. The speed of the train is :

(*a*) 54 km / hr (*b*) 60 km / hr (*c*) 66 km / hr (*d*) 72 km / hr

31. Two goods train each 500 m long, are running in opposite directions on parallel tracks. Their speeds are 45 km / hr and 30 km / hr respectively. Find the time taken by the slower train to pass the driver of the faster one. **(M.A.T. 2000)**

(*a*) 12 sec (*b*) 24 sec (*c*) 48 sec (*d*) 60 sec

32. Two trains of equal length are running on parallel lines in the same direction at 46 km / hr and 36 km / hr. The faster train passes the slower train in 36 seconds. The length of each train is : **(M.A.T. 2003)**

(*a*) 50 m (*b*) 72 m (*c*) 80 m (*d*) 82 m

33. A 270 metres long train running at the speed of 120 kmph crosses another train running in opposite direction at the speed of 80 kmph in 9 seconds. What is the length of the other train ? **(S.B.I.P.O. 1999)**

(*a*) 230 m (*b*) 240 m (*c*) 260 m
(*d*) 320 m (*e*) None of these

34. Two trains are running in opposite directions with the same speed. If the length of each train is 120 metres and they cross each other in 12 seconds, then the speed of each train (in km / hr) is : **(S.S.C. 2003)**

(*a*) 10 (*b*) 18 (*c*) 36 (*d*) 72

35. Two trains of equal lengths take 10 seconds and 15 seconds respectively to cross a telegraph post. If the length of each train be 120 metres, in what time (in seconds) will they cross each other travelling in opposite direction ? **(S.S.C. 2004)**
(*a*) 10 (*b*) 12 (*c*) 15 (*d*) 20

36. A train 108 m long moving at a speed of 50 km / hr crosses a train 112 m long coming from opposite direction in 6 seconds. The speed of the second train is
(*a*) 48 km / hr (*b*) 54 km / hr (*c*) 66 km / hr (*d*) 82 km / hr

37. A train X speeding with 120 kmph crosses another train Y, running in the same direction, in 2 minutes. If the lengths of the trains X and Y be 100 m and 200 m respectively, what is the speed of train Y ?
(*a*) 111 km / hr (*b*) 123 km / hr (*c*) 127 km / hr (*d*) 129 km / hr

38. Two trains travel in opposite directions at 36 kmph and 45 kmph and a man sitting in slower train passes the faster train in 8 seconds. The length of the faster train is :
(*a*) 80 m (*b*) 100 m (*c*) 120 m (*d*) 180 m

39. Two trains are running at 40 km / hr and 20 km / hr respectively in the same direction. Fast train completely passes a man sitting in the slower train in 5 seconds. What is the length of the fast train ? **(R.R.B. 2001)**
(*a*) 23 m (*b*) $23\frac{2}{9}$ m (*c*) 27 m (*d*) $27\frac{7}{9}$ m

40. A train overtakes two persons who are walking in the same direction in which the train is going, at the rate of 2 kmph and 4 kmph and passes them completely in 9 and 10 seconds respectively. The length of the train is :
(*a*) 45 m (*b*) 50 m (*c*) 54 m (*d*) 72 m

41. A train overtakes two persons walking along a railway track. The first one walks at 4.5 km / hr. The other one walks at 5.4 km / hr. The train needs 8.4 and 8.5 seconds respectively to overtake them. What is the speed of the train if both the persons are walking in the same direction as the train ?
(*a*) 66 km / hr (*b*) 72 km / hr (*c*) 78 km / hr (*d*) 81 km / hr

42. Two trains, each 100 m long, moving in opposite directions, cross each other in 8 seconds. If one is moving twice as fast the other, then the speed of the faster train is :
(*a*) 30 km / hr (*b*) 45 km / hr (*c*) 60 km / hr (*d*) 75 km / hr
(C.D.S. 2001)

43. A train 150 m long passes a km stone in 15 seconds and another train of the same length travelling in opposite direction in 8 seconds. The speed of the second train is :
(*a*) 60 km / hr (*b*) 66 km / hr (*c*) 72 km / hr (*d*) 99 km / hr

44. A train travelling at 48 kmph completely crosses another train having half its length and travelling in opposite direction at 42 kmph, in 12 seconds. It also passes a railway platform in 45 seconds. The length of the platform is
(*a*) 400 m (*b*) 450 m (*c*) 560 m (*d*) 600 m

45. Two trains running in opposite directions cross a man standing on the platform in 27 seconds and 17 seconds respectively and they cross each other in 23 seconds. The ratio of their speeds is : **(Hotel Management, 1997)**
(*a*) 1 : 3 (*b*) 3 : 2 (*c*) 3 : 4 (*d*) None of these

46. Two stations A and B are 110 km apart on a straight line. One train starts from A at 7 a.m. and travels towards B at 20 kmph. Another train starts from B at 8 a.m. and travels towards A at a speed of 25 kmph. At what time will they meet ?
(*a*) 9 a.m. (*b*) 10 a.m. (*c*) 10.30 a.m. (*d*) 11 a.m.

47. A train X starts from Meerut at 4 p.m. and reaches Ghaziabad at 5 p.m. while another train Y starts from Ghaziabad at 4 p.m. and reaches Meerut at 5.30 p.m. The two trains will cross each other at :
(*a*) 4.36 p.m. (*b*) 4.42 p.m. (*c*) 4.48 p.m. (*d*) 4.50 p.m.

48. Two trains, one from Howrah to Patna and the other from Patna to Howrah, start simultaneously. After they meet, the trains reach their destinations after 9 hours and 16 hours respectively. The ratio of their speeds is : **(R.R.B. 2001)**

(*a*) 2 : 3 (*b*) 4 : 3 (*c*) 6 : 7 (*d*) 9 : 16

ANSWERS

1. (*c*)	**2.** (*c*)	**3.** (*a*)	**4.** (*b*)	**5.** (*b*)	**6.** (*a*)	**7.** (*b*)	**8.** (*c*)
9. (*c*)	**10.** (*c*)	**11.** (*b*)	**12.** (*c*)	**13.** (*c*)	**14.** (*d*)	**15.** (*c*)	**16.** (*c*)
17. (*b*)	**18.** (*b*)	**19.** (*b*)	**20.** (*b*)	**21.** (*d*)	**22.** (*c*)	**23.** (*b*)	**24.** (*c*)
25. (*b*)	**26.** (*d*)	**27.** (*d*)	**28.** (*c*)	**29.** (*b*)	**30.** (*b*)	**31.** (*c*)	**32.** (*a*)
33. (*a*)	**34.** (*c*)	**35.** (*b*)	**36.** (*d*)	**37.** (*a*)	**38.** (*d*)	**39.** (*d*)	**40.** (*b*)
41. (*d*)	**42.** (*c*)	**43.** (*d*)	**44.** (*a*)	**45.** (*b*)	**46.** (*b*)	**47.** (*a*)	**48.** (*b*)

SOLUTIONS

1. 108 kmph $= \left(108 \times \frac{5}{18}\right)$ m/sec = 30 m/sec.

2. 14 m/sec $= \left(14 \times \frac{18}{5}\right)$ km/hr = 50.4 km/hr.

3. Speed $= \left(144 \times \frac{5}{18}\right)$ m/sec = 40 m/sec.

Time taken $= \left(\frac{100}{40}\right)$ sec = 2.5 sec.

4. Speed $= \left(63 \times \frac{5}{18}\right)$ m/sec $= \frac{35}{2}$ m/sec.

Time taken $= \left(280 \times \frac{2}{35}\right)$ sec = 16 sec.

5. Speed $= \left(72 \times \frac{5}{18}\right)$ m/sec = 20 m/sec.

Total distance covered = (110 + 132) m = 242 m.

∴ Required time $= \left(\frac{242}{20}\right)$ sec = 12.1 sec.

6. Speed $= \left(45 \times \frac{5}{18}\right)$ m/sec $= \frac{25}{2}$ m/sec.

Total distance covered = (360 + 140) m = 500 m.

∴ Required time $= \left(500 \times \frac{2}{25}\right)$ sec = 40 sec.

7. Total distance covered $= \left(\frac{7}{2} + \frac{1}{4}\right)$ miles $= \frac{15}{4}$ miles.

∴ Time taken $= \left(\frac{15}{4 \times 75}\right)$ hrs $= \frac{1}{20}$ hrs $= \left(\frac{1}{20} \times 60\right)$ min. = 3 min.

8. Speed $= \left(60 \times \frac{5}{18}\right)$ m/sec $= \left(\frac{50}{3}\right)$ m/sec.

Length of the train = (Speed × Time) $= \left(\frac{50}{3} \times 9\right)$ m = 150 m.

9. Speed $= \left(\frac{132}{6}\right)$ m/sec $= \left(22 \times \frac{18}{5}\right)$ km/hr = 79.2 km/hr.

10. Speed $= \left(\frac{12}{10} \times 60\right)$ km/hr $= \left(72 \times \frac{5}{18}\right)$ m/sec = 20 m/sec.

Length of the train = (Speed × Time) = (20 × 6) m = 120 m.

11. Speed $= \left(\frac{240}{24}\right)$ m/sec = 10 m/sec.

$\therefore$ Required time $= \left(\frac{240 + 650}{10}\right)$ sec = 89 sec.

12. Speed $= \left(45 \times \frac{5}{18}\right)$ m/sec $= \left(\frac{25}{2}\right)$ m/sec; Time = 30 sec.

Let the length of bridge be x metres.

Then, $\frac{130 + x}{30} = \frac{25}{2} \Leftrightarrow 2(130 + x) = 750 \Leftrightarrow x = 245$ m.

13. Speed $= \left(78 \times \frac{5}{18}\right)$ m/sec $= \left(\frac{65}{3}\right)$ m/sec.

Time = 1 minute = 60 sec.

Let the length of the tunnel be x metres.

Then, $\frac{800 + x}{60} = \frac{65}{3} \Leftrightarrow 3(800 + x) = 3900 \Leftrightarrow x = 500$.

14. Speed $= \left(72 \times \frac{5}{18}\right)$ m/sec = 20 m/sec; Time = 26 sec.

Let the length of the train be x metres.

Then, $\frac{x + 250}{26} = 20 \Leftrightarrow x + 250 = 520 \Leftrightarrow x = 270$.

15. Speed $= \left(90 \times \frac{5}{18}\right)$ m/sec = 25 m/sec; Time = 1 min. = 60 sec.

Let the length of the train and that of the platform be x metres.

Then, $\frac{2x}{60} = 25 \Leftrightarrow x = \frac{25 \times 60}{2} = 750$.

16. Speed $= \left(\frac{150 + 300}{40.5}\right)$ m/sec $= \left(\frac{450}{40.5} \times \frac{18}{5}\right)$ km/hr = 40 km/hr.

17. Speed $= \left(45 \times \frac{5}{18}\right)$ m/sec $= \left(\frac{25}{2}\right)$ m/sec.

Let the length of the train be x metres.

Then, $\frac{x + 100}{\left(\frac{25}{2}\right)} = 60$ or $x = 650$ m

$\therefore$ Time taken by the train to cross an electric pole $= \left(650 \times \frac{2}{25}\right)$ sec = 52 sec.

18. Speed $= \left(54 \times \frac{5}{18}\right)$ m/sec = 15 m/sec.

Length of the train = (15 × 20) m = 300 m.

Let the length of the platform be x metres.

Then, $\frac{x + 300}{36} = 15 \Leftrightarrow x + 300 = 540 \Leftrightarrow x = 240$ m.

19. Speed $= \left(\frac{300}{18}\right)$ m/sec $= \frac{50}{3}$ m/sec.

Let the length of the platform be x metres.

Then, $\frac{x + 300}{39} = \frac{50}{3} \Leftrightarrow 3(x + 300) = 1950 \Leftrightarrow x = 350$ m.

20. Let the length of the train be x metres and its speed be y m/sec.

They, $\frac{x}{y} = 15 \Rightarrow y = \frac{x}{15}$.

$\therefore \frac{x + 100}{25} = \frac{x}{15} \Leftrightarrow x = 150$ m.

21. Let the length of the train be x metres and its speed by y m/sec.

They, $\frac{x}{y} = 8 \Rightarrow x = 8y$

Now, $\frac{x + 264}{20} = y \Leftrightarrow 8y + 264 = 20y \Leftrightarrow y = 22$.

$\therefore$ Speed = 22 m/sec $= \left(22 \times \frac{18}{5}\right)$ km/hr = 79.2 km/hr.

22. Let the length of the train be x metres.

$\therefore \frac{x + 162}{18} = \frac{x + 120}{15} \Leftrightarrow 15(x + 162) = 18(x + 120) \Leftrightarrow x = 90$ m.

23. Speed of train relative to man = (63 – 3) km/hr = 60 km/hr

$= \left(60 \times \frac{5}{18}\right)$ m/sec $= \frac{50}{3}$ m/sec.

$\therefore$ Time taken to pass the man $= \left(500 \times \frac{3}{50}\right)$ sec = 30 sec.

24. Speed of train relative to jogger = (45 – 9) km/hr = 36 km/hr

$= \left(36 \times \frac{5}{18}\right)$ m/sec = 10 m/sec.

Distance to be covered = (240 + 120) m = 360 m.

$\therefore$ Time taken $= \left(\frac{360}{10}\right)$ sec = 36 sec.

25. Speed of train relative to man = (60 + 6) km/hr = 66 km/hr

$= \left(66 \times \frac{5}{18}\right)$ m/sec $= \left(\frac{55}{3}\right)$ m/sec.

$\therefore$ Time taken to pass the man $= \left(110 \times \frac{3}{55}\right)$ sec = 6 sec.

26. Relative speed = (45 – 40) kmph = 5 kmph $= \left(5 \times \frac{5}{18}\right)$ m/sec $= \left(\frac{25}{18}\right)$ m/sec.

Total distance covered = Sum of lengths of trains = 350 m.

$\therefore$ Time taken $= \left(350 \times \frac{18}{25}\right)$ sec = 252 sec.

27. Relative speed = (60 + 40) km/hr $= \left(100 \times \frac{5}{18}\right)$ m/sec $= \left(\frac{250}{9}\right)$ m/sec.

Distance covered in crossing each other = (140 + 160) m = 300 m

Required time $= \left(300 \times \frac{9}{250}\right)$ sec $= \frac{54}{5}$ sec = 10.8 sec.

28. Relative speed = (60 + 90) km/hr

$= \left(150 \times \frac{5}{18}\right)$ m/sec $= \left(\frac{125}{3}\right)$ m/sec.

Distance covered = (1.10 + 0.9) km = 2 km = 2000 m.

Required time $= \left(2000 \times \frac{3}{125}\right)$ sec = 48 sec.

29. Speed of the train relative to man $= \left(\frac{125}{10}\right)$ m/sec $= \left(\frac{25}{2}\right)$ m/sec.

$= \left(\frac{25}{2} \times \frac{18}{5}\right)$ km/hr = 45 km/hr.

Let the speed of the train be x kmph. Then, relative speed = $(x - 5)$ kmph.

$\therefore$ $x - 5 = 45$ or $x = 50$ kmph.

30. Speed of the train relative to man

$= \left(\frac{110}{6}\right)$ m/sec $= \left(\frac{110}{6} \times \frac{18}{5}\right)$ km/hr = 66 km/hr.

Let the speed of the train be x kmph. Then, relative speed = $(x + 6)$ = kmph.

$\therefore$ $x + 6 = 66$ or $x = 60$ kmph.

31. Relative speed = (45 + 30) km/hr $= \left(75 \times \frac{5}{18}\right)$ m/sec $= \left(\frac{125}{6}\right)$ m/sec.

Distance covered = (500 + 500) m = 1000 m.

Required time $= \left(1000 \times \frac{6}{125}\right)$ sec = 48 sec.

32. Let the length of each train be x metres.

Then, distance covered = $2x$ metres.

Relative speed = (46 − 36) km/hr $= \left(10 \times \frac{5}{18}\right)$ m/sec $= \left(\frac{25}{9}\right)$ m/sec.

$\therefore$ $\frac{2x}{36} = \frac{25}{9} \Leftrightarrow 2x = 100 \Leftrightarrow x = 50.$

33. Relative speed = (120 + 80) km/hr $= \left(200 \times \frac{5}{18}\right)$ m/sec $= \left(\frac{500}{9}\right)$ m/sec.

Let the length of the other train be x metres.

Then, $\frac{x + 270}{9} = \frac{500}{9} \Leftrightarrow x + 270 = 500 \Leftrightarrow x = 230.$

34. Let the speed of each train be x m/sec.

Then, relative speed of the two trains = $2x$ m/sec.

So, $2x = \frac{(120+120)}{12} \Leftrightarrow 2x = 20 \Leftrightarrow x = 10.$

$\therefore$ Speed of each train = 10 m/sec = $\left(10 \times \frac{18}{5}\right)$ km/hr = 36 km/hr.

35. Speed of the first train = $\left(\frac{120}{10}\right)$ m/sec = 12 m/sec.

Speed of the second train = $\left(\frac{120}{15}\right)$ m/sec = 8 m/sec.

Relative speed = (12 + 8) = m/sec = 20 m/sec.

$\therefore$ Required time = $\frac{(120+120)}{20}$ sec = 12 sec.

36. Let the speed of the second train be x km/hr.

Relative speed = $(x + 50)$ km/hr = $\left[(x+50) \times \frac{5}{18}\right]$ m/sec = $\left(\frac{250+5x}{18}\right)$ m/sec.

Distance covered = (108 + 112) = 220 m.

$\therefore \frac{220}{\left(\frac{250+5x}{18}\right)} = 6 \Leftrightarrow 250 + 5x = 660 \Leftrightarrow x = 82$ km/hr.

37. Let the speed of train Y be x km/hr.

Speed of X relative to Y = $(120 - x)$ km/hr

$= \left[(120-x) \times \frac{5}{18}\right]$ m/sec = $\left(\frac{600-5x}{18}\right)$ m/sec.

$\therefore \frac{300}{\left(\frac{600-5x}{18}\right)} = 120 \Leftrightarrow 5400 = 120\,(600 - 5x) \Leftrightarrow x = 111.$

38. Relative speed = (36 + 45) km/hr = $\left(81 \times \frac{5}{18}\right)$ m/sec = $\left(\frac{45}{2}\right)$ m/sec.

Length of train = $\left(\frac{45}{2} \times 8\right)$ m = 180 m.

39. Relative speed = (40 − 20) km/hr = $\left(20 \times \frac{5}{18}\right)$ m/sec = $\left(\frac{50}{9}\right)$ m/sec.

Length of faster train = $\left(\frac{50}{9} \times 5\right)$ m = $\frac{250}{9}$ m = $27\frac{7}{9}$ m.

40. 2 kmph = $\left(2 \times \frac{5}{18}\right)$ m/sec = $\frac{5}{9}$ m/sec and 4 kmph = $\frac{10}{9}$ m/sec.

Let the length of the train be x metres and its speed be y m/sec.

Then, $\frac{x}{\left(y - \frac{5}{9}\right)} = 9$ and $\frac{x}{\left(y - \frac{10}{9}\right)} = 10.$

$\therefore$ $9y - 5 = x$ and $10\,(9y - 10) = 9x \Rightarrow 9y - x = 5$ and $90y - 9x = 100.$

On solving, we get : $x = 50$

$\therefore$ Length of the train is 50 m.

41. $4.5 \text{ km/hr} = \left(4.5 \times \frac{5}{18}\right) \text{ m/sec} = \frac{5}{4} \text{ m/sec} = 1.25 \text{ m/sec}$, and

$5.4 \text{ km/hr} = \left(5.4 \times \frac{5}{18}\right) \text{ m/sec} = \frac{3}{2} \text{ m/sec} = 1.5 \text{ m/sec}$.

Let the speed of the train be x m/sec.

Then, $(x - 1.25) \times 84 = (x - 1.5) \times 8.5$

$\Leftrightarrow 8.4x - 10.5 = 8.5x - 12.75 \Leftrightarrow 0.1x = 2.25 \Leftrightarrow x = 22.5.$

$\therefore$ Speed of the train $= \left(22.5 \times \frac{18}{5}\right)$ km/hr $= 81$ km/hr.

42. Let the speed of the slower train be x m/sec.

Then, speed of the faster train $= 2x$ m/sec.

Relative speed $= (x + 2x)$ m/sec $= 3x$ m/sec.

$\therefore \frac{(100 + 100)}{8} = 3x \Leftrightarrow 24x = 200 \Leftrightarrow x = \frac{25}{3}.$

So, speed of the faster train $= \frac{50}{3}$ m/sec $= \left(\frac{50}{3} \times \frac{18}{5}\right)$ km/hr $= 60$ km/hr.

43. Speed of first train $= \left(\frac{150}{15}\right)$ m/sec $= 10$ m/sec.

Let the speed of second train be x m/sec.

Relative speed $= (10 + x)$ m/sec.

$\therefore \frac{300}{10 + x} = 8 \Leftrightarrow 300 = 80 + 8x \Leftrightarrow x = \frac{220}{8} = \frac{55}{2}$ m/sec.

So, speed of second train $= \left(\frac{55}{2} \times \frac{18}{5}\right)$ kmph $= 99$ kmph.

44. Let the length of the first train be x metres.

Then, the length of second train is $\left(\frac{x}{2}\right)$ metres.

Relative speed $= (48 + 42)$ kmph $= \left(90 \times \frac{5}{18}\right)$ m/sec $= 25$ m/sec.

$\therefore \frac{\left(x + \frac{x}{2}\right)}{25} = 12$ or $\frac{3x}{2} = 300$ or $x = 200$.

$\therefore$ Length of first train $= 200$ m.

Let the length of platform be y metres.

Speed of the first train $= \left(48 \times \frac{5}{18}\right)$ m/sec $= \frac{40}{3}$ m/sec.

$\therefore (200 + y) \times \frac{3}{40} = 45 \Leftrightarrow 600 + 3y = 1800 \Leftrightarrow y = 400$ m.

45. Let the speeds of the two trains be x m/sec and y m/sec respectively. Then, length of the first train $= 27x$ metres, and length of the second train $= 17y$ metres.

$\therefore \frac{27x + 17y}{x + y} = 23 \Leftrightarrow 27x + 17y = 23x + 23y \Leftrightarrow 4x = 6y \Leftrightarrow \frac{x}{y} = \frac{3}{2}.$

46. Suppose they meet x hours after 7 a.m.

Distance covered by A in x hours = $20x$ km.

Distance covered by B in $(x - 1)$ hours = $25\,(x - 1)$ km.

$\therefore\quad 20x + 25\,(x - 1) = 110 \;\Leftrightarrow\; 45x = 135 \;\Leftrightarrow\; x = 3.$

So, they meet at 10 a.m.

47. Suppose, the distance between Meerut and Ghaziabad is x km.

Time taken by X to cover x km = 1 hour.

Time taken by Y to cover x km = $\frac{3}{2}$ hours.

$\therefore$ Speed of X = x kmph, Speed of Y = $\left(\frac{2x}{3}\right)$ kmph.

Let them meet y hours after 4 p.m. Then,

$$xy + \frac{2xy}{3} = x \;\Leftrightarrow\; y\left(1 + \frac{2}{3}\right) = 1 \;\Leftrightarrow\; y = \frac{3}{5} \text{ hours} = \left(\frac{3}{5} \times 60\right) \text{ min} = 36 \text{ min.}$$

So, the two trains meet at 4.36 p.m.

48. Let us name the trains as A and B. Then,

(A's speed) : (B's speed) = $\sqrt{b} : \sqrt{a} = \sqrt{16} : \sqrt{9} = 4 : 3.$

EXERCISE 18B

(DATA SUFFICIENCY TYPE QUESTIONS)

1. A train running at a certain speed crosses a stationary engine in 20 seconds. To find out the speed of the train, which of the following information is necessary ?

(a) Only the length of the train

(b) Only the length of the engine

(c) Either the length of the train or the length of the engine

(d) Both the length of the train and the length of the engine

2. A train running at a certain speed crosses another train running in the opposite direction in 4.8 seconds. To find out the speed of the first train, which of the following information P and Q is sufficient ?

P : The length of the first train Q : The length of the second train

(a) Only P is sufficient (b) Only Q is sufficient

(c) Either P or Q is sufficient (d) Both P and Q are needed

(e) Both P and Q are not sufficient

Directions (*Questions 3 to 12*) : ***Each of the questions given below consists of a statement and / or a question and two statements numbered I and II given below it. You have to decide whether the data provided in the statement(s) is /are sufficient to answer the given question. Read both the statements and***

Give answer (a) if the data in Statement I alone are sufficient to answer the question, while the data in Statement II alone are not sufficient to answer the question;

Give answer (b) if the data in Statement II alone are sufficient to answer the question, while the data in Statement I alone are not sufficient to answer the question;

Give answer (c) if the data either in Statement I or in Statement II alone are sufficient to answer the question;

Give answer (d) if the data even in both Statements I and II together are not sufficient to answer the question;

Give answer (e) if the data in both Statements I and II together are necessary to answer the question.

3. A train crosses a signal post in x seconds. What is the length of the train ?
   I. The train crosses a platform of 100 metres in y seconds.
   II. The train is running at the speed of 80 km / hr. **(NABARD, 2002)**

4. What was the speed of the running train ? **(Bank P.O. 2000)**
   I. Length of the train was 120 metres.
   II. The train crossed the other stationary train whose length was 180 m in 4 seconds.

5. What is the speed of a running train which takes 9 seconds to cross a signal post ?
   I. The length of the train is 90 metres.
   II. The train takes 27 seconds to cross a platform of 180 metres. **(Bank P.O. 1999)**

6. What is the length of a running train ? **(S.B.I.P.O. 1998)**
   I. The train crosses a man in 9 seconds.
   II. The train crosses a 240 metre long platform in 24 seconds.

7. What is the speed of the train ? **(Bank P.O. 2003)**
   I. 280 metres long train crosses a signal pole in 18 seconds.
   II. 280 metres long train crosses a platform in 45 seconds.

8. What was the speed of a running train X ?
   I. The relative speed of train X and another train Y running in opposite direction is 160 kmph.
   II. The train Y crosses a signal post in 9 seconds.

9. What was the length of a running train crossing another 180 metre long train running in the opposite direction ? **(Bank P.O. 1998)**
   I. The relative speed of the two trains was 150 kmph.
   II. The trains took 9 seconds to cross each other.

10. A train crosses another train running in the opposite direction in x seconds. What is the speed of the train ? **(S.B.I.P.O. 2003)**
    I. Both the trains have the same length and are running at the same speed.
    II. One train crosses a pole in 5 seconds.

11. A train crosses a pole in 10 seconds. What is the length of the train ?
    I. The train crosses another train running in opposite direction with a speed of 80 km / hr in 22 seconds.
    II. The speed of the train is 108 km / hr. **(Bank P.O. 2003)**

12. What is the speed of the train whose length is 210 metres ? **(Bank P.O. 2003)**
    I. The train crosses another train of 300 metres length running in opposite direction in 10 seconds.
    II. The train crosses another train running in the same direction at the speed of 60 km / hr in 30 seconds.

Directions (*Questions 13 to 17*) : *Each of the questions given below consists of a question followed by three statements. You have to study the question and the statements and decide which of the statement(s) is/are necessary to answer the question.*

13. What is the speed of the train ? **(S.B.I.P.O. 2002)**
    I. The train crosses a tree in 13 seconds.
    II. The train crosses a platform of length 250 metres in 27 seconds.
    III. The train crosses another train running in the same direction in 32 seconds.

    (*a*) I and II only (*b*) II and III only (*c*) I and III only
    (*d*) Any two of the three (*e*) None of these

14. What is the speed of the train ? (M.B.A. 2002)

I. The train crosses 300 metres long platform in 21 seconds.

II. The train crosses another stationary train of equal length in $19\frac{1}{2}$ seconds.

III. The train crosses a signal pole in $9\frac{3}{4}$ seconds.

(a) I and II only (b) I and either II or III only
(c) II and either I or II only (d) III and either I or II only
(e) None of these

15. What is the speed of the train ? (Bank P.O. 2003)

I. The train crosses a signal pole in 18 seconds.
II. The train crosses a platform of equal length in 36 seconds.
III. Length of the train is 330 metres.

(a) I and II only (b) II and III only (c) I and III only
(d) III and either I or II only (e) Any two of the three

16. What is the length of the train X ?

I. Train X crosses a telegraph post in 20 seconds.
II. Train X crosses a platform of length 800 m in 100 seconds.
III. Train X passes through a tunnel 400 m long in 60 seconds.

(a) I and either II or III only (b) II and III only
(c) II and either I or III only (d) III and either I or II only
(e) Any two of the three

17. What is the speed of the train ?

I. The train passes a man walking at the rate of 3 kmph in 9 seconds.
II. The train passes a man walking at the rate of 6 kmph in 10 seconds.
III. The train is moving in the same direction in which the two men are moving.

(a) I and III only (b) II and III only
(c) I and II only (d) All I, II and III
(e) Question cannot be answered even with information in all the three statements.

Directions (*Questions 18 to 20*) : *Each of these questions is followed by three statements. You have to study the question and all the three statements given to decide whether any information provided in the statement(s) is redundant and can be dispensed with while answering the given question.*

18. How much time will the train A take to cross another train B running in opposite direction ?

I. Train A crosses a signal pole in 6 seconds.
II. Ratio of the speeds of trains A and B is 3 : 2.
III. Length of the two trains together is 500 metres.

(a) I only (b) II only
(c) III only (d) I or II only
(e) Question cannot be answered even with the information in all the three statements.

19. What is the length of a running train P crossing another running train Q ?

I. These two trains take 18 seconds to cross each other.
II. These trains are running in opposite directions.
III. The length of train Q is 180 metres. (S.B.I.P.O. 1997)

(a) I only (b) II only
(c) III only (d) All I, II and III are required
(e) Even with I, II and III, the answer cannot be obtained.

20. At what time will the train reach city X from city Y ? **(S.B.I.P.O. 1999)**

I. The train crosses another train of equal length of 200 metres and running in opposite direction in 15 seconds.

II. The train leaves city Y at 7.15 a.m. for city X situated at a distance of 558 km.

III. The 200 metres long train crosses a signal pole in 10 seconds.

(*a*) I only (*b*) II only (*c*) III only
(*d*) I or III only (*e*) All I, II and III are required.

ANSWERS

1. (*d*)	**2.** (*e*)	**3.** (*c*)	**4.** (*e*)	**5.** (*a*)	**6.** (*e*)	**7.** (*a*)	**8.** (*d*)
9. (*e*)	**10.** (*d*)	**11.** (*b*)	**12.** (*e*)	**13.** (*a*)	**14.** (*b*)	**15.** (*d*)	**16.** (*e*)
17. (*d*)	**18.** (*e*)	**19.** (*e*)	**20.** (*a*)				

SOLUTIONS

1. Time taken by the train to cross a stationary engine

$$= \frac{\text{(Length of train + Length of engine)}}{\text{(Speed of the train)}}$$

$$\Rightarrow \frac{\text{(Length of train + Length of engine)}}{\text{(Speed of the train)}} = 20 \text{ (given)}$$

Hence, to find the speed of the train, the length of the train and the length of the engine both must be known.

∴ The correct answer is (*d*).

2. Let two trains of lengths *a* and *b* metres be moving in opposite directions at *u* m / s and *v* m / s.

Time taken by the trains to cross each other $= \frac{(a+b)}{(u+v)}$ sec.

$$\therefore \frac{a+b}{u+v} = 4.8.$$

In order to find *u*, we must know *a*, *b* and *v*,

i.e., length of first train, length of second train and the speed of the second train.

Thus, P and Q are not sufficient.

∴ The correct answer is (*e*).

3. Let the length of the train be *a* metres.

Time taken to cross a singal post $= \frac{\text{Length of the train}}{\text{Speed of the train}} \Rightarrow x = \frac{l}{\text{Speed.}}$ ...(*i*)

Time taken to cross the platform $= \frac{(l+100)}{\text{Speed}} \Rightarrow y = \frac{l+100}{\text{Speed}}$ ...(*ii*)

Thus, from (*i*) and (*ii*), we can find *l*.

Also, II gives, speed $= \left(80 \times \frac{5}{18}\right)$ m/s $= \frac{200}{9}$ m/s.

Thus, the data in I or II alone are sufficient to answer the question.

∴ The correct answer is (*c*).

4. Speed of the first train $= \dfrac{\text{(sum of the lengths of the two trains)}}{\text{Time taken}}$

$= \dfrac{(120+180)}{4}$ m/s = 75 m/s.

So, both the statements are necessary to get the answer.

∴ The correct answer is (*e*).

5. Speed of the train $= \dfrac{\text{Length of the train}}{\text{Time taken to cross the post}} = \dfrac{90}{9}$ m/s = 10 m/s.

Thus, I alone gives the answer.

Time taken to cross a platform $= \dfrac{\text{(Length of train + Length of platform)}}{\text{Speed of the train}}$

$\Rightarrow$ Speed $= \dfrac{(l+180)}{27}$

But, l is not given. So, speed cannot be obtained.

So, II alone does not give the answer.

∴ The correct answer is (*a*).

6. Time taken by train to cross a man $= \dfrac{\text{Length of train}}{\text{Speed of train}} \Rightarrow$ Speed $= \dfrac{l}{9}$ ...(*i*)

Time taken by train to cross a platform $= \dfrac{\text{(Length of train + Length of platform)}}{\text{Speed of the train}}$

$\Rightarrow$ Speed $= \dfrac{l+240}{24}$ ...(*ii*)

From (*i*) and (*ii*), we get $\dfrac{l}{9} = \dfrac{l+240}{24}$.

Thus, l can be obtained. So both I and II are necessary to get the answer.

∴ The correct answer is (*e*).

7. Speed $= \dfrac{\text{Length of the train}}{\text{Time taken to cross the pole}} = \dfrac{280}{18}$ m/s $= \dfrac{140}{9}$ m/s.

∴ I alone gives the answer.

Time taken to cross the platform $= \dfrac{\text{(Length of train + Length of platform)}}{\text{Speed of the train}}$

$\Rightarrow$ Speed $= \dfrac{(280+p)}{45}$ m/s.

But, p = length of platform, is not given.

∴ II is not sufficient to give the answer.

∴ The correct answer is (*a*).

8. Let the two trains of length *a* metres and *b* metres be moving in opposite directions at *u* m/s and *v* m/s. Then,

I gives, $u + v = 160$.

II gives, $v = \dfrac{b}{9}$.

From these equations, we cannot obtain *u*.

∴ The correct answer is (*d*).

9. Let the two trains of length *a* metres and *b* metres be moving in opposite directions at *u* m/s and *v* m/s.

Time taken to cross each other $= \frac{(a+b)}{(u+v)}$ sec.

Now, $b = 180,\ u + v = \left(150 \times \frac{5}{18}\right)$ m/sec $= \frac{125}{3}$ m/sec.

$\Rightarrow\ 9 = \frac{a+180}{(125/3)}\ \Rightarrow\ a = (375 - 180) = 195$ m.

Thus, both I and II are necessary to get the answer.

$\therefore$ The correct answer is (*e*).

10. Let the two trains of length *a* metres and *b* metres be moving in opposite directions at *u* m/s and *v* m/s.

Time taken to cross each other $= \frac{(a+b)}{(u+v)}$ m/sec. $\Rightarrow\ x = \frac{(a+a)}{(u+u)} = \frac{a}{u}$. ...(*i*)

Time taken to cross the pole $= \frac{\text{Length of the train}}{\text{Speed of the train}} = \frac{a}{u} \Rightarrow \frac{a}{u} = 5$ ...(*ii*)

From (*i*) and (*ii*) also, we cannot find *u*.

$\therefore$ The correct answer is (*d*).

11. Time taken to cross a pole $= \frac{\text{Length of train}}{\text{Speed of train}}\ \Rightarrow\ 10 = \frac{\text{Length of train}}{\left(108 \times \frac{5}{18}\right)}$

$\Rightarrow$ Length of the train = 300 m.

Clearly, II is sufficient to get the answer.

Also, I is not sufficient to get the answer.

$\therefore$ The correct answer is (*b*).

12. Time taken to cross the train, running in opposite directions $= \frac{(l_1 + l_2)}{(u+v)}$ sec.

$\Rightarrow\ 10 = \frac{(210+300)}{(u+v)}\ \Rightarrow\ u + v = 51.$

Time taken to cross the train, running in same direction $= \frac{(l_1 + l_2)}{(u-v)}$ sec.

$\Rightarrow\ 30 = \frac{(210+300)}{\left(u - 60 \times \frac{5}{18}\right)}\ \Rightarrow\ u = \left(17 + \frac{50}{3}\right)$ m/sec.

Thus, *u* and *v* can be obtained.

$\therefore$ Correct answer is (*e*).

13. Let the speed of the train be *x* metres / sec.

Time taken to cross a tree $= \frac{\text{Length of the train}}{\text{Speed of the train}}$

Time taken to cross a platform $= \frac{(\text{Length of train} + \text{Length of platform})}{\text{Speed of the train}}$ ...(*ii*)

I gives, $13 = \frac{l}{x}\ \Rightarrow\ 13x.$

II gives $27 = \frac{l + 250}{x}\ \Rightarrow\ \frac{13x + 250}{x} = 24\ \Rightarrow\ x = \frac{125}{7}$ m/sec.

Thus I and II give the speed of the train.

$\therefore$ The correct answer is (*a*).

14. Let the speed of the train be x m / sec.

Time taken to cross a platform $= \dfrac{\text{(Length of train + Length of platform)}}{\text{Speed of the train}}$

Time taken by the train to cross a stationary train

$$= \frac{\text{(Sum of the lengths of the trains)}}{\text{Speed of moving train}}$$

Time taken to cross a signal pole $= \dfrac{\text{Length of train}}{\text{Speed of train}}$

I gives, $21 = \dfrac{(l + 300)}{x}$; II gives, $\dfrac{39}{2} = \dfrac{2l}{x}$; III gives, $\dfrac{39}{4} = \dfrac{l}{x}$.

Thus, (I and II) or (I and III) give x.

$\therefore$ Correct answer is (*b*).

15. Let the speed of the train be x m / sec.

Time taken to cross a signal pole $= \dfrac{\text{Length of train}}{\text{Speed of train}}$.

Time taken to cross a platform $= \dfrac{\text{(Length of train + Length of platform)}}{\text{Speed of the train}}$

Length of train = 330 m.

I and III give, $18 = \dfrac{330}{x} \Rightarrow x = \dfrac{330}{18}$ m/s $= \dfrac{55}{3}$ m/s.

II and III give, $36 = \dfrac{2 \times 330}{x} \Rightarrow x = \dfrac{660}{36}$ m/s $= \dfrac{55}{3}$ m/s.

$\therefore$ Correct answer is (*d*).

16. Time taken to cross a pole $= \dfrac{\text{Length of train}}{\text{Its speed}} \Rightarrow 20 = \dfrac{l}{\text{speed}} \Rightarrow \text{speed} = \dfrac{l}{20}$ ...(*i*)

Time taken to cross a platform $= \dfrac{(l + 800)}{\text{speed}}$

$\Rightarrow 100 = \dfrac{(l + 800)}{\text{speed}} \Rightarrow \text{speed} = \dfrac{(l + 800)}{100}$ ...(*ii*)

Time taken to pass through a tunnel $= \dfrac{(l + 400)}{60}$

$\Rightarrow 60 = \dfrac{(l + 400)}{\text{speed}} \Rightarrow \text{speed} = \dfrac{(l + 400)}{60}$ ...(*iii*)

Equating any two out of three will give us l.

$\therefore$ Correct answer is (*e*).

17. Let the speed of the train be x m / sec.

III gives that the men are moving in the same direction.

I gives, time taken to pass a man $= \dfrac{l}{\left(x - 3 \times \dfrac{5}{18}\right)} = \left(\dfrac{6l}{6x - 5}\right)$ sec.

$\therefore \quad \dfrac{6l}{6x - 5} = 9 \Rightarrow 54x - 6l = 45 \Rightarrow 18x - 2l = 15$ ...(*i*)

II gives, time taken to pass another man $= \frac{l}{\left(x - 6 \times \frac{5}{18}\right)}$ sec $= \frac{3l}{(3x-5)}$ sec.

$\therefore \frac{3l}{(3x-5)} = 10 \Rightarrow 30x - 3l = 50$ ...(*ii*)

On solving (*i*) and (*ii*), we get : $x = \frac{55}{6}$ m/sec.

Thus, all I, II, III are needed to get the answer.

$\therefore$ (*d*) is correct.

18. II. Let the speeds of A and B be $3x$ m/sec and $2x$ m/sec.

I Length of train A $= (3x \times 6)$ m $= 18x$ metres.

III. Length of train B $= (500 - 18x)$ m.

Relative speed $= (3x + 2x)$ m/sec $= 5x$ m/sec.

Time taken by A to cross B $= \frac{\text{Sum of their lengths}}{\text{Relative speed}} = \frac{500}{5x}$ sec.

Thus, even with the information in all the three statements, question cannot be answered.

$\therefore$ Correct answer is (*e*).

19. Let the length of train P be x metres.

II. These trains are running in opposite directions.

III. Length of train Q is 180 m.

I. Time taken by P to cross Q $= \frac{(180 + x)}{\text{Relative speed}} \Rightarrow 18 = \frac{(180 + x)}{\text{Relative speed}}$

Thus, even with I, II and III, the answer cannot be obtained.

$\therefore$ Correct answer is (*e*).

20. III gives, speed $= \frac{200}{10}$ m/s $= 20$ m/s $= \left(20 \times \frac{18}{5}\right)$ km/hr $= 72$ km/hr.

II gives, time taken $= \left(\frac{558}{72}\right)$ hrs $= \frac{31}{4}$ hrs $= 7\frac{3}{4}$ hrs $= 7$ hrs 45 min.

So, the train will reach city X at 3 p.m.

Hence, I is redundant.

19. BOATS AND STREAMS

IMPORTANT FACTS AND FORMULAE

1. In water, the direction along the stream is called ***downstream.*** And, the direction against the stream is called ***upstream.***
2. If the speed of a boat in still water is u km / hr and the speed of the stream is v km / hr, then :

$$\textit{Speed downstream} = (u + v) \text{ km/hr}$$
$$\textit{Speed upstream} = (u - v) \text{ km/hr.}$$

3. If the speed downstream is a km / hr and the speed upstream is b km / hr, then :

$$\textit{Speed in still water} = \frac{1}{2}(a + b) \text{ km/hr}$$
$$\textit{Rate of stream} = \frac{1}{2}(a - b) \text{ km/hr}$$

SOLVED EXAMPLES

Ex. 1. *A man can row upstream at 7 kmph and downstream at 10 kmph. Find man's rate in still water and the rate of current.*

Sol. Rate in still water $= \frac{1}{2}(10 + 7)$ km / hr $= 8.5$ km / hr.

Rate of current $= \frac{1}{2}(10 - 7)$ km / hr $= 1.5$ km / hr.

Ex. 2. *A man takes 3 hours 45 minutes to row a boat 15 km downstream of a river and 2 hours 30 minutes to cover a distance of 5 km upstream. Find the speed of the river current in km / hr.*

Sol. Rate downstream $= \left(\frac{15}{3\frac{3}{4}}\right)$ km / hr $= \left(15 \times \frac{4}{15}\right)$ km / hr $= 4$ km / hr.

Rate upstream $= \left(\frac{5}{2\frac{1}{2}}\right)$ km / hr $= \left(5 \times \frac{2}{5}\right)$ km / hr $= 2$ km / hr.

$\therefore$ Speed of current $= \frac{1}{2}(4 - 2)$ km / hr $= 1$ km / hr.

Ex. 3. *A man can row 18 kmph in still water. It takes him thrice as long to row up as to row down the river. Find the rate of stream.*

Sol. Let man's rate upstream be x kmph. Then, his rate downstream $= 3x$ kmph.

$\therefore$ Rate in still water $= \frac{1}{2}(3x + x)$ kmph $= 2x$ kmph.

So, $2x = 18$ or $x = 9$.

$\therefore$ Rate upstream $= 9$ km / hr, Rate downstream $= 27$ km / hr.

Hence, rate of stream $= \frac{1}{2}(27 - 9)$ km / hr $= 9$ km / hr.

Ex. 4. ***There is a road beside a river. Two friends started from a place A, moved to a temple situated at another place B and then returned to A again. One of them moves on a cycle at a speed of 12 km/hr, while the other sails on a boat at a speed of 10 km/hr. If the river flows at the speed of 4 km/hr, which of the two friends will return to place A first ?*** (R.R.B. 2001)

Sol. Clearly, the cyclist moves both ways at a speed of 12 km / hr.

So, average speed of the cyclist = 12 km / hr.

The boat sailor moves downstream @ (10 + 4) *i.e.*, 14 km / hr and upstream @ (10 − 4) *i.e.*, 6 km / hr.

So, average speed of the boat sailor $= \left(\frac{2 \times 14 \times 6}{14 + 6}\right)$ km / hr

$= \frac{42}{5}$ km / hr = 8.4 km / hr.

Since the average speed of the cyclist is greater, he will return to A first.

Ex. 5 ***A man can row $7\frac{1}{2}$ kmph in still water. If in a river running at 1.5 km an hour, it takes him 50 minutes to row to a place and back, how far off is the place ?*** (R.R.B. 2002)

Sol. Speed downstream = (7.5 + 1.5) kmph = 9 kmph;

Speed upstream = (7.5 − 1.5) kmph = 6 kmph.

Let the required distance be x km. Then,

$$\frac{x}{9} + \frac{x}{6} = \frac{50}{60} \Leftrightarrow 2x + 3x = \left(\frac{5}{6} \times 18\right) \Leftrightarrow 5x = 15 \Leftrightarrow x = 3.$$

Hence, the required distance is 3 km.

Ex. 6. ***In a stream running at 2 kmph, a motorboat goes 6 km upstream and back again to the starting point in 33 minutes. Find the speed of the motorboat in still water.***

Sol. Let the speed of the motorboat in still water be x kmph. Then,

Speed downstream = $(x + 2)$ kmph; Speed upstream = $(x - 2)$ kmph.

$$\therefore \frac{6}{x+2} + \frac{6}{x-2} = \frac{33}{60} \Leftrightarrow 11x^2 - 240x - 44 = 0 \Leftrightarrow 11x^2 - 242x + 2x - 44 = 0$$

$$\Leftrightarrow (x - 22)(11x + 2) = 0 \Leftrightarrow x = 22.$$

Hence, speed of motorboat in still water = 22 kmph.

Ex. 7. ***A man can row 40 km upstream and 55 km downstream in 13 hours. Also, he can row 30 km upstream and 44 km downstream in 10 hours. Find the speed of the man in still water and the speed of the current.***

Sol. Let rate upstream = x km / hr and rate downstream = y km / hr.

Then, $\frac{40}{x} + \frac{55}{y} = 13$ ...(*i*) and $\frac{30}{x} + \frac{44}{y} = 10$ ...(*ii*)

Multiplying (*ii*) by 4 and (*i*) by 3 and subtracting, we get : $\frac{11}{y} = 1$ or $y = 11$.

Substituting $y = 11$ in (*i*), we get : $x = 5$.

$\therefore$ Rate in still water $= \frac{1}{2}(11 + 5)$ kmph = 8 kmph.

Rate of current $= \frac{1}{2}(11 - 5)$ kmph = 3 kmph.

EXERCISE 19A

(OBJECTIVE TYPE QUESTIONS)

Directions : *Mark (✓) against the correct answer* :

1. In one hour, a boat goes 11 km along the stream and 5 km against the stream. The speed of the boat in still water (in km / hr) is : **(S.S.C. 2000)**
(*a*) 3 (*b*) 5 (*c*) 8 (*d*) 9

2. A man can row upstream at 8 kmph and downstream at 13 kmph. The speed of the stream is :
(*a*) 2.5 km / hr (*b*) 4.2 km / hr (*c*) 5 km / hr (*d*) 10.5 km / hr

3. A man rows downstream 32 km and 14 km upstream. If he takes 6 hours to cover each distance, then the velocity (in kmph) of the current is :
(*a*) $\frac{1}{2}$ (*b*) 1 (*c*) $1\frac{1}{2}$ (*d*) 2

4. A boat running downstream covers a distance of 16 km in 2 hours while for covering the same distance upstream, it takes 4 hours. What is the speed of the boat in still water ? **(S.B.I.P.O. 2002)**
(*a*) 4 km / hr (*b*) 6 km / hr (*c*) 8 km / hr (*d*) Data inadequate

5. A boatman goes 2 km against the current of the stream in 1 hour and goes 1 km along the current in 10 minutes. How long will it take to go 5 km in stationary water ?
(*a*) 40 minutes (*b*) 1 hour (*c*) 1 hr 15 min (*d*) 1 hr 30 min **(R.R.B. 2002)**

6. A man can row three-quarters of a kilometre against the stream in $11\frac{1}{4}$ minutes. The speed (in km / hr) of the man in still water is : **(L.I.C.A.A.O. 2003)**
(*a*) 2 (*b*) 3 (*c*) 4 (*d*) 5

7. A man takes twice as long to row a distance against the stream as to row the same distance in favour of the stream. The ratio of the speed of the boat (in still water) and the stream is : **(S.S.C. 1998)**
(*a*) 2 : 1 (*b*) 3 : 1 (*c*) 3 : 2 (*d*) 4 : 3

8. A boat running upstream takes 8 hours 48 minutes to cover a certain distance, while it takes 4 hours to cover the same distance running downstream. What is the ratio between the speed of the boat and speed of the water current respectively ?
(*a*) 2 : 1 (*b*) 3 : 2 (*c*) 8 : 3
(*d*) Cannot be determined (*e*) None of these **(Bank P.O. 2003)**

9. If a boat goes 7 km upstream in 42 minutes and the speed of the stream is 3 kmph, then the speed of the boat in still water is :
(*a*) 4.2 km / hr (*b*) 9 km / hr (*c*) 13 km / hr (*d*) 21 km / hr

10. A man's speed with the current is 15 km / hr and the speed of the current is 2.5 km / hr. The man's speed against the current is : **(M.A.T. 1997)**
(*a*) 8.5 km / hr (*b*) 9 km / hr (*c*) 10 km / hr (*d*) 12.5 km / hr

11. If a man rows at the rate of 5 kmph in still water and his rate against the current is 3.5 kmph, then the man's rate along the current is :
(*a*) 4.25 kmph (*b*) 6 kmph (*c*) 6.5 kmph (*d*) 8.5 kmph

12 A boat can travel with a speed of 13 km / hr in still water. If the speed of the stream is 4 km / hr, find the time taken by the boat to go 68 km downstream. **(R.R.B. 2003)**
(*a*) 2 hours (*b*) 3 hours (*c*) 4 hours (*d*) 5 hours

13. Speed of a boat in standing water is 9 kmph and the speed of the stream is 1.5 kmph. A man rows to a place at a distance of 105 km and comes back to the starting point. The total time taken by him is :

(*a*) 16 hours (*b*) 18 hours (*c*) 20 hours (*d*) 24 hours

14 The speed of a boat in still water is 15 km / hr and the rate of current is 3 km / hr. The distance travelled downstream in 12 minutes is :

(*a*) 1.2 km (*b*) 1.8 km (*c*) 2.4 km (*d*) 3.6 km

15. A man can row at 5 kmph in still water. If the velocity of current is 1 kmph and it takes him 1 hour to row to a place and come back, how far is the place ?

(*a*) 2.4 km (*b*) 2.5 km (*c*) 3 km (*d*) 3.6 km

(S.S.C. 2004)

16. A boat takes 19 hours for travelling downstream from point A to point B and coming back to a point C midway between A and B. If the velocity of the stream is 4 kmph and the speed of the boat in still water is 14 kmph, what is the distance between A and B ?

(*a*) 160 km (*b*) 180 km (*c*) 200 km (*d*) 220 km

17. A man can row $9\frac{1}{3}$ kmph in still water and finds that it takes him thrice as much time to row up than as to row down the same distance in the river. The speed of the current is :

(*a*) $3\frac{1}{3}$ km / hr (*b*) $3\frac{1}{9}$ km / hr (*c*) $4\frac{2}{3}$ km / hr (*d*) $4\frac{1}{2}$ km / hr

18. A boat covers a certain distance downstream in 1 hour, while it comes back in $1\frac{1}{2}$ hours. If the speed of the stream be 3 kmph, what is the speed of the boat in still water ? **(Bank P.O. 2003)**

(*a*) 12 kmph (*b*) 13 kmph (*c*) 14 kmph

(*d*) 15 kmph (*e*) None of these

19. A motorboat, whose speed is 15 km / hr in still water goes 30 km downstream and comes back in a total of 4 hours 30 minutes. The speed of the stream (in km / hr) is :

(*a*) 4 (*b*) 5 (*c*) 6 (*d*) 10

(R.R.B. 2002)

20. The speed of a boat in still water is 10 km / hr. If it can travel 26 km downstream and 14 km upstream in the same time, the speed of the stream is :

(*a*) 2 km / hr (*b*) 2.5 km / hr (*c*) 3 km / hr (*d*) 4 km / hr

21. A boat takes 90 minutes less to travel 36 miles downstream than to travel the same distance upstream. If the speed of the boat in still water is 10 mph, the speed of the stream is : **(M.A.T. 1997)**

(*a*) 2 mph (*b*) 2.5 mph (*c*) 3 mph (*d*) 4 mph

22. A man rows to a place 48 km distant and back in 14 hours. He finds that he can row 4 km with the stream in the same time as 3 km against the stream. The rate of the stream is :

(*a*) 1 km / hr (*b*) 1.5 km / hr (*c*) 1.8 km / hr (*d*) 3.5 km / hr

23. A boat covers 24 km upstream and 36 km downstream in 6 hours while it covers 36 km upstream and 24 km downstream in $6\frac{1}{2}$ hours. The velocity of the current is :

(*a*) 1 km / hr (*b*) 1.5 km / hr (*c*) 2 km / hr (*d*) 2.5 km / hr

24. At his usual rowing rate, Rahul can travel 12 miles downstream in a certain river in 6 hours less than it takes him to travel the same distance upstream. But if he could double his usual rowing rate for his 24-mile round trip, the downstream 12 miles would then take only one hour less than the upstream 12 miles. What is the speed of the current in miles per hour ? **(M.A.T. 2001)**

(*a*) $1\frac{1}{3}$ (*b*) $1\frac{2}{3}$ (*c*) $2\frac{1}{3}$ (*d*) $2\frac{2}{3}$

ANSWERS

1. (*c*)	**2.** (*a*)	**3.** (*c*)	**4.** (*b*)	**5.** (*c*)	**6.** (*d*)	**7.** (*b*)	**8.** (*c*)
9. (*c*)	**10.** (*c*)	**11.** (*c*)	**12.** (*c*)	**13.** (*d*)	**14.** (*d*)	**15.** (*a*)	**16.** (*b*)
17. (*c*)	**18.** (*d*)	**19.** (*b*)	**20.** (*c*)	**21.** (*a*)	**22.** (*a*)	**23.** (*c*)	**24.** (*d*)

SOLUTIONS

1. Speed in still water $= \frac{1}{2}(11+5)$ kmph $= 8$ kmph.

2. Speed of stream $= \frac{1}{2}(13-8)$ kmph $= 2.5$ kmph.

3. Rate downstream $= \left(\frac{32}{6}\right)$ kmph; Rate upstream $= \left(\frac{14}{6}\right)$ kmph.

$\therefore$ Velocity of current $= \frac{1}{2}\left(\frac{32}{6}-\frac{14}{6}\right)$ kmph $= \frac{3}{2}$ kmph $= 1.5$ kmph

4. Rate downstream $= \left(\frac{16}{2}\right)$ kmph $= 8$ kmph; Rate upstream $= \left(\frac{16}{4}\right)$ kmph $= 4$ kmph

$\therefore$ Speed in still water $= \frac{1}{2}(8+4)$ kmph $= 6$ kmph.

5. Rate downstream $= \left(\frac{1}{10}\times 60\right)$ km/hr $= 6$ km/hr; Rate upstream $= 2$ km/hr.

Speed in still water $= \frac{1}{2}(6+2)$ km/hr $= 4$ km/hr.

$\therefore$ Required time $= \left(\frac{5}{4}\right)$ hrs $= 1\frac{1}{4}$ hrs $= 1$ hr 15 min

6. Rate upstream $= \left(\frac{750}{675}\right)$ m/sec $= \frac{10}{9}$ m/sec;

Rate downstream $= \left(\frac{750}{450}\right)$ m/sec $= \frac{5}{3}$ m/sec.

$\therefore$ Rate in still water $= \frac{1}{2}\left(\frac{10}{9}+\frac{5}{3}\right)$ m/sec $= \frac{25}{18}$ m/sec $= \left(\frac{25}{18}\times\frac{18}{5}\right)$ km/hr $= 5$ km/hr.

7. Let man's rate upstream be x kmph. Then, his rate downstream $= 2x$ kmph.

$\therefore$ (Speed in still water) : (Speed of stream) $= \left(\frac{2x+x}{2}\right) : \left(\frac{2x-x}{2}\right) = \frac{3x}{2} : \frac{x}{2} = 3:1.$

8. Let the man' rate upstream be x kmph and that downstream be y kmph. Then,
Distance covered upstream in 8 hrs 48 min. = Distance covered downstream in 4 hrs.

$$\Rightarrow \left(x \times 8\frac{4}{5}\right) = (y \times 4) \Rightarrow \frac{44}{5}x = 4y \Rightarrow y = \frac{11}{5}x.$$

$$\therefore \text{ Required ratio} = \left(\frac{y+x}{2}\right) : \left(\frac{y-x}{2}\right) = \left(\frac{16x}{5} \times \frac{1}{2}\right) : \left(\frac{6x}{5} \times \frac{1}{2}\right) = \frac{8}{5} : \frac{3}{5} = 8 : 3.$$

9. Rate upstream $= \left(\frac{7}{42} \times 60\right)$ kmph = 10 kmph.

Speed of stream = 3 kmph.

Let speed in still water be x km/hr. Then, speed upstream = $(x - 3)$ km/hr.

$\therefore \quad x - 3 = 10 \quad$ or $\quad x = 13$ km/hr.

10. Man's rate in still water = (15 – 2.5) km/hr = 12.5 km/hr.

Man's rate against the current = (12.5 – 2.5) km/hr = 10 km/hr.

11. Let the rate along the current be x kmph. Then, $\frac{1}{2}(x + 3.5) = 5$ or $x = 6.5$ kmph.

12. Speed downstream = (13 + 4) km/hr = 17 km/hr.

Time taken to travel 68 km downstream $= \left(\frac{68}{17}\right)$ hrs = 4 hrs.

13. Speed upstream = 7.5 kmph; Speed downstream = 10.5 kmph.

$\therefore$ Total time taken $= \left(\frac{105}{7.5} + \frac{105}{10.5}\right)$ hours = 24 hours.

14. Speed downstream = (15 + 3) kmph = 18 kmph

Distance travelled $= \left(18 \times \frac{12}{60}\right)$ km = 3.6 km.

15. Speed downstream = (5 + 1) kmph = 6 kmph; Speed upstream = (5 – 1) kmph = 4 kmph.

Let the required distance be x km.

Then, $\frac{x}{6} + \frac{x}{4} = 1 \Leftrightarrow 2x + 3x = 12 \Leftrightarrow 5x = 12 \Leftrightarrow x = 2.4$ km.

16. Speed downstream = (14 + 4) km/hr = 18 km/hr;

Speed upstream = (14 – 4) km/hr = 10 km/hr.

Let the distance between A and B be x km. Then,

$$\frac{x}{18} + \frac{(x/2)}{10} = 19 \Leftrightarrow \frac{x}{18} + \frac{x}{20} = 19 \Leftrightarrow \frac{19x}{180} = 19 \Leftrightarrow x = 180 \text{ km}.$$

17. Let speed upstream be x kmph. Then, speed downstream = $3x$ kmph.

Speed in still water $= \frac{1}{2}(3x + x)$ kmph $= 2x$ kmph.

$\therefore \quad 2x = \frac{28}{3} \Rightarrow x = \frac{14}{3}.$

So, Speed upstream $= \frac{14}{3}$ km/hr; Speed downstream = 14 km/hr

Hence, speed of the current $= \frac{1}{2}\left(14 - \frac{14}{3}\right)$ km/hr $= \frac{14}{3}$ km/hr $= 4\frac{2}{3}$ km/hr.

18. Let the speed of the boat in still water be x kmph. Then,

Speed downstream = $(x + 3)$ kmph, Speed upstream = $(x - 3)$ kmph.

$$\therefore \quad (x+3) \times 1 = (x-3) \times \frac{3}{2} \Leftrightarrow 2x + 6 = 3x - 9 \Leftrightarrow x = 15 \text{ kmph}.$$

19. Let the speed of the stream be x km / hr. Then,

Speed downstream = $(15 + x)$ km / hr, Speed upstream = $(15 - x)$ km / hr.

$$\therefore \quad \frac{30}{(15+x)} + \frac{30}{(15-x)} = 4\frac{1}{2} \Leftrightarrow \frac{900}{225-x^2} = \frac{9}{2} \Leftrightarrow 9x^2 = 225$$

$$\Leftrightarrow x^2 = 25 \Leftrightarrow x = 5 \text{ km / hr.}$$

20. Let the speed of the stream be x km / hr. Then,

Speed downstream = $(10 + x)$ km / hr, Speed upstream = $(10 - x)$ km / hr.

$$\therefore \quad \frac{26}{(10+x)} = \frac{14}{(10-x)} \Leftrightarrow 260 - 26x = 140 + 14x \Leftrightarrow 40x = 120 \Leftrightarrow x = 3 \text{ km / hr.}$$

21. Let the speed of the stream be x mph. Then,

Speed downstream = $(10 + x)$ mph, Speed upstream = $(10 - x)$ mph.

$$\therefore \quad \frac{36}{(10-x)} - \frac{36}{(10+x)} = \frac{90}{60} \Leftrightarrow 72x \times 60 = 90\,(100 - x^2) \Leftrightarrow x^2 + 48x + 100 = 0$$

$$\Leftrightarrow (x + 50)\,(x - 2) = 0 \Leftrightarrow x = 2 \text{ mph.}$$

22. Suppose he moves 4 km downstream in x hours. Then,

Speed downstream = $\left(\frac{4}{x}\right)$ km / hr, Speed upstream = $\left(\frac{3}{x}\right)$ km / hr.

$$\therefore \quad \frac{48}{(4/x)} + \frac{48}{(3/x)} = 14 \text{ or } x = \frac{1}{2}.$$

So, Speed downstream = 8 km / hr, Speed upstream = 6 km / hr.

Rate of the stream = $\frac{1}{2}(8 - 6)$ km / hr = 1 km / hr.

23. Let rate upstream = x kmph and rate downstream = y kmph.

Then, $\frac{24}{x} + \frac{36}{y} = 36$ ...(*i*) and $\frac{36}{x} + \frac{24}{y} = \frac{13}{2}$ ...(*ii*)

Adding (*i*) and (*ii*), we get : $60\left(\frac{1}{x} + \frac{1}{y}\right) = \frac{25}{2}$ or $\frac{1}{x} + \frac{1}{y} = \frac{5}{24}$ ...(*iii*)

Subtracting (*i*) from (*ii*), we get : $12\left(\frac{1}{x} - \frac{1}{y}\right) = \frac{1}{2}$ or $\frac{1}{x} - \frac{1}{y} = \frac{1}{24}$ ...(*iv*)

Adding (*iii*) and (*iv*), we get : $\frac{2}{x} = \frac{6}{24}$ or $x = 8$.

So, $\frac{1}{8} + \frac{1}{y} = \frac{5}{24} \Leftrightarrow \frac{1}{y} = \left(\frac{5}{24} - \frac{1}{8}\right) = \frac{1}{12} \Leftrightarrow y = 12.$

$\therefore$ Speed upstream = 8 kmph, Speed downstream = 12 kmph.

Hence, rate of current = $\frac{1}{2}(12 - 8)$ kmph = 2 kmph.

24. Let the speed in still water be x mph and the speed of the current be y mph. Then,

Speed upstream = $(x - y)$; Speed downstream = $(x + y)$

$$\therefore \quad \frac{12}{(x-y)} - \frac{12}{(x+y)} = 6 \Leftrightarrow 6\,(x^2 - y^2) = 24y \Leftrightarrow x^2 - y^2 = 4y$$

$$\Leftrightarrow x^2 = (4y + y^2) \qquad ...(i)$$

And, $\frac{12}{(2x-y)} - \frac{12}{(2x+y)} = 1 \Leftrightarrow 4x^2 - y^2 = 24y \Leftrightarrow x^2 = \frac{24y + y^2}{4}$ ...(*ii*)

From (*i*) and (*ii*), we have :

$$4y + y^2 = \frac{24y + y^2}{4} \Leftrightarrow 16y + 4y^2 = 24y + y^2 \Leftrightarrow 3y^2 = 8y \Leftrightarrow y = \frac{8}{3}.$$

$\therefore$ Speed of the current $= \frac{8}{3}$ mph $= 2\frac{2}{3}$ mph.

EXERCISE 19B

(DATA SUFFICIENCY TYPE QUESTIONS)

Directions (*Questions 1 to 6*) : *Each of the questions given below consists of a statement and / or a question and two statements numbered I and II given below it. You have to decide whether the data provided in the statement(s) is / are sufficient to answer the question. Read both the statements and*

Give answer (a) if the data in Statement I alone are sufficient to answer the question, while the data in Statement II alone are not sufficient to answer the question;

Give answer (b) if the data in Statement II alone are sufficient to answer the question while the data in statement I alone are not sufficient to answer the question;

Give answer (c) if the data either in Statement I or in Statement II alone are sufficient to answer the question;

Give answer (d) if the data even in both Statements I and II together are not sufficient to answer the question;

Give answer (e) if the data in both Statements I and II together are necessary to answer the question.

1. What is the speed of the boat in still water ? **(Bank P.O. 2003)**

I. It takes 2 hours to cover the distance between A and B downstream.

II. It takes 4 hours to cover the distance between A and B upstream.

2. What is the speed of the stream ?

I. The ratio of the speed upstream to the speed downstream of a boat is 2 : 3.

II. The distance travelled upstream in 2 hours by the boat is more than the distance travelled by it downstream in 1 hour by 4 km.

3. What is the speed of the boat in still water ? **(Bank P.O. 2003)**

I. The boat covers a distance of 48 kms in 6 hours while running upstream.

II. The boat covers the same distance in 4 hours while running downstream.

4. What is the man's speed in still water ?

I. The speed of the stream is one-third of the man's speed in still water.

II. In a given time, the man can swim twice as far with the stream as he can against it.

5. A boat takes a total time of three hours to travel downstream from P to Q and upstream back from Q to P. What is the speed of the boat in still water ?

I. The speed of the river current is 1 km per hour.

II. The distance between P and Q is 4 km. **(S.B.I.P.O. 1997)**

6. What is the speed of the boat in still water ?

I. The speed downstream of the boat is thrice the speed upstream.

II. The sum of the speeds of the boat, upstream and downstream is 12 kmph.

Directions (*Questions 7-8*) : *Each of the questions given below consists of a question followed by three statements. You have to study the question and the statements and decide which of the statements(s) is / are necessary to answer the questions.*

7. What is the speed of the boat in still water ?
   I. The speed downstream is 12 kmph.
   II. The speed upstream is 4 kmph.
   III. In a to and fro journey between two points, the average speed of the boat was 6 kmph
   (*a*) I and II only (*b*) All I, II and III (*c*) III, and either I or II
   (*d*) Any two of the three (*e*) None of these

8. What is the speed of stream ? **(Bank P.O. 2004)**
   I. The boat covers 24 km in 6 hours moving upstream.
   II. The boat covers 24 km in 3 hours moving downstream.
   III. The ratio between the speed of boat and stream is 3 : 1 respectively.
   (*a*) Any two of the three (*b*) I and II only (*c*) II and III only
   (*d*) I and III only (*e*) All I, II and III

ANSWERS

1. (*d*)	2. (*e*)	3. (*e*)	4. (*d*)	5. (*e*)	6. (*b*)	7. (*d*)	8. (*a*)

SOLUTIONS

1. Let AB = x km.

   I. Speed downstream = $\frac{x}{2}$ km/hr. II. Speed upstream = $\frac{x}{4}$ km/hr.

   Speed of boat in still water = $\frac{1}{2}\left(\frac{x}{2}+\frac{x}{4}\right)$ km/hr.

   Thus, I and II both even do not give the answer.

   ∴ Correct answer is (*d*).

2. I. Let speed upstream = $2x$ km/hr and speed downstream = $3x$ km/hr.

   II. $(2 \times 3x) - (1 \times 2x) = 4 \Leftrightarrow 4x = 4 \Leftrightarrow x = 1$.

   ∴ Speed upstream = 2 km/hr, speed downstream = 3 km/hr.

   Speed of the stream = $\frac{1}{2}(3-2)$ km/hr = $\frac{1}{2}$ km/hr.

   Thus, I and II together give the answer.

   ∴ Correct answer is (*e*).

3. I. Speed upstream = $\frac{48}{6}$ km/hr = 8 km/hr.

   II. Speed downstream = $\frac{48}{4}$ km/hr = 12 km/hr.

   Speed of the boat = $\frac{1}{2}(8+12)$ km/hr = 10 km/hr.

   Thus, I and II together give the answer.

   ∴ Correct answer is (*e*).

4. Let man's speed in still water be x km/hr.

   I. Speed of the stream = $\frac{x}{3}$ km/hr.

   Speed downstream = $\left(x+\frac{x}{3}\right)$ km/hr = $\frac{4x}{3}$ km/hr.

   Speed upstream = $\left(x-\frac{x}{3}\right)$ km/hr = $\frac{2x}{3}$ km/hr.

Suppose that the fixed time is t hrs.

II gives $2\left(\frac{4x}{3} \times t\right) = \left(\frac{2x}{3} \times t\right)$, which does not give x.

$\therefore$ Correct answer is (*d*).

5. I. Speed of the current = 1 km / hr.

II. PQ = 4 km.

Let the speed of the boat in still water be x km / hr. Then,

$\frac{4}{(x+1)} + \frac{4}{(x-1)} = 3$. This gives x.

$\therefore$ Correct answer is (*e*).

6. Let the speed upstream be x km / hr. Then,

I. Speed downstream = $3x$ km / hr.

II gives, speed of the boat in still water = $\left(\frac{1}{2} \times 12\right)$ km / hr = 6 km / hr.

So, II only gives the answer.

$\therefore$ Correct answer is (*b*).

7. From **I and** II, speed of boat in still water = $\frac{1}{2}(12 + 4)$ km / hr = 8 km / hr.

From II **and** III, we get :

Using average speed = $\frac{2xy}{x + y}$, we get :

$\frac{2 \times 4 \times y}{4 + y} = 6 \Leftrightarrow 8y = 24 + 6y \Leftrightarrow y = 12.$

$\therefore$ Required speed = $\frac{1}{2}(12 + 4)$ km / hr = 8 km / hr.

Similarly, I and III also give the answer.

$\therefore$ Correct answer is (*d*).

8. I. Speed upstream = $\frac{24}{6}$ km / hr = 4 km / hr.

II. Speed downstream = $\frac{24}{3}$ km / hr = 8 km / hr.

III. Let the speed of the boat in still water be $3x$ km / hr.

Then, speed of the stream is x km / hr.

$\therefore$ Speed downstream = $2x$ km / hr, Speed upstream = x km / hr.

From I **and** II, we get speed of stream = $\frac{1}{2}(8 - 4)$ km / hr = 2 km / hr.

From II **and** III, we get $2x = 8 \Leftrightarrow x = 4$.

$\therefore$ Speed downstream = 8 km / hr.

$\therefore$ Speed of stream = $\frac{1}{2}(8 - 4)$ km / hr = 2 km / hr.

From I **and** III, we get $x = 4$ and $2x = 8$.

$\therefore$ Speed of stream = $\frac{1}{2}(8 - 4)$ km / hr = 2 km / hr.

Thus, any two of the three will give the answer.

$\therefore$ Correct answer is (*a*).

---

20. ALLIGATION OR MIXTURE

IMPORTANT FACTS AND FORMULAE

1. **Alligation** : It is the rule that enables us to find the ratio in which two or more ingredients at the given price must be mixed to produce a mixture of a desired price.
2. **Mean Price** : The cost price of a unit quantity of the mixture is called the mean price.
3. **Rule of Alligation** : If two ingredients are mixed, then

$$\left(\frac{\text{Quantity of cheaper}}{\text{Quantity of dearer}}\right) = \frac{(\text{C.P. of dearer}) - (\text{Mean price})}{(\text{Mean price}) - (\text{C.P. of cheaper})}.$$

We present as under :

C.P. of a unit quantity of cheaper (c) — C.P. of a unit quantity of dearer (d)

Mean price (m)

$(d - m)$ — $(m - c)$

$\therefore$ (Cheaper quantity) : (Dearer quantity) = $(d - m) : (m - c)$.

4. Suppose a container contains x units of liquid from which y units are taken out and replaced by water. After n operations, the quantity of pure liquid $= \left[x\left(1 - \frac{y}{x}\right)^n\right]$ units.

SOLVED EXAMPLES

Ex. 1. ***In what ratio must rice at Rs. 9.30 per kg be mixed with rice at Rs. 10.80 per kg so that the mixture be worth Rs. 10 per kg ?***

Sol. By the rule of alligation, we have :

C.P. of 1 kg rice of 1st kind (in paise) — C.P. of 1 kg rice of 2nd kind (in paise)

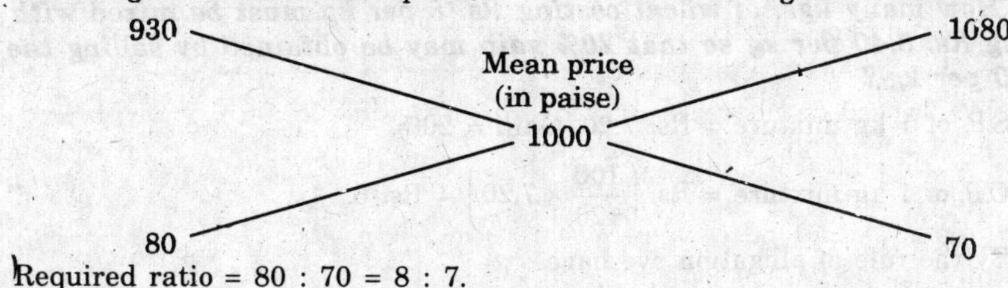

$\therefore$ Required ratio = 80 : 70 = 8 : 7.

Ex. 2. ***How much water must be added to 60 litres of milk at $1\frac{1}{2}$ litres for Rs. 20 so as to have a mixture worth Rs. $10\frac{2}{3}$ a litre ?***

Sol. C.P. of 1 litre of milk = Rs. $\left(20 \times \frac{2}{3}\right)$ = Rs. $\frac{40}{3}$.

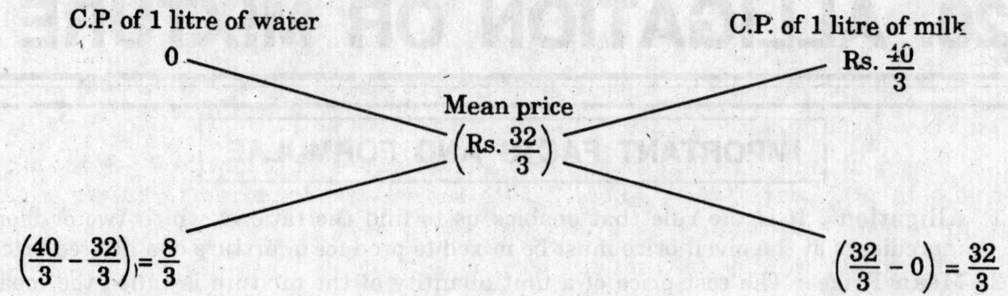

$\therefore$ Ratio of water and milk $= \frac{8}{3} : \frac{32}{3} = 8 : 32 = 1 : 4.$

$\therefore$ Quantity of water to be added to 60 litres of milk $= \left(\frac{1}{4} \times 60\right)$ litres = 15 litres.

Ex. 3. ***In what ratio must water be mixed with milk to gain 20% by selling the mixture at cost price ?***

Sol. Let C.P. of milk be Re. 1 per litre.

Then; S.P. of 1 litre of mixture = Re. 1.

Gain obtained = 20%.

$\therefore$ C.P. of 1 litre of mixture = Rs. $\left(\frac{100}{120} \times 1\right)$ = Re. $\frac{5}{6}$.

By the rule of alligation, we have

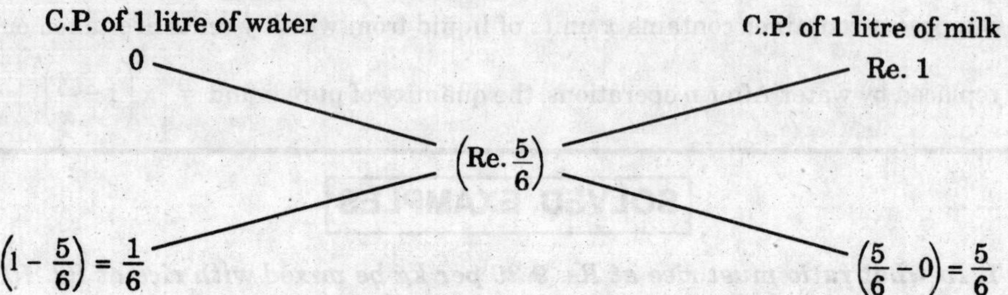

$\therefore$ Ratio of water and milk $= \frac{1}{6} : \frac{5}{6} = 1 : 5.$

Ex. 4. ***How many kgs. of wheat costing Rs. 8 per kg must be mixed with 36 kg of rice costing Rs. 5.40 per kg so that 20% gain may be obtained by selling the mixture at Rs. 7.20 per kg ?***

Sol. S.P. of 1 kg mixture = Rs. 7.20, Gain = 20%.

$\therefore$ C.P. of 1 kg mixture = Rs. $\left(\frac{100}{120} \times 7.20\right)$ = Rs. 6.

By the rule of alligation, we have :

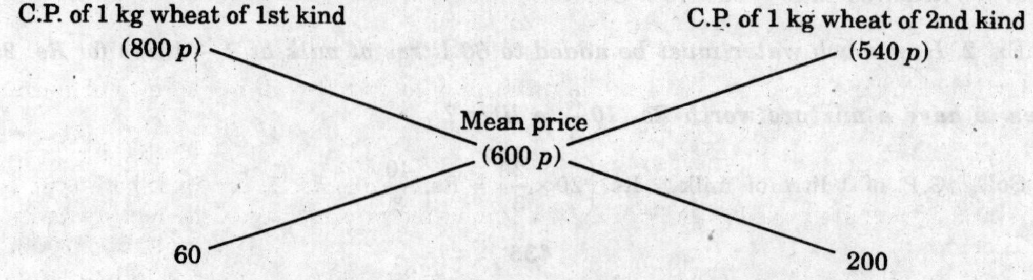

Wheat of 1st kind : Wheat of 2nd kind = 60 : 200 = 3 : 10.

Let x kg of wheat of 1st kind be mixed with 36 kg of wheat of 2nd kind.

Then, 3 : 10 = x : 36 or $10x = 3 \times 36$ or $x = 10.8$ kg.

Ex. 5. ***The milk and water in two vessels A and B are in the ratio 4 : 3 and 2 : 3 respectively. In what ratio, the liquids in both the vessels be mixed to obtain a new mixture in vessel C containing half milk and half water ?***

Sol. Let the C.P. of milk be Re. 1 per litre.

Milk in 1 litre mixture of A = $\frac{4}{7}$ litre; Milk in 1 litre mixture of B = $\frac{2}{5}$ litre;

Milk in 1 litre mixture of C = $\frac{1}{2}$ litre.

$\therefore$ C.P. of 1 litre mixture in A = Re. $\frac{4}{7}$; C.P. of 1 litre mixture in B = Re. $\frac{2}{5}$.

Mean price = Re. $\frac{1}{2}$.

By the rule of alligation, we have :

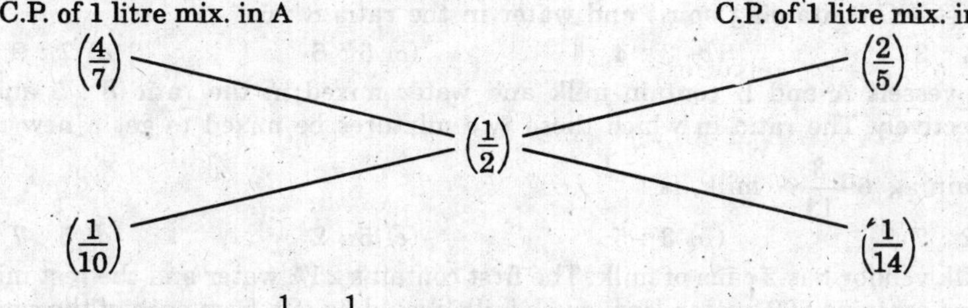

$\therefore$ Required ratio = $\frac{1}{10} : \frac{1}{14} = 7 : 5$.

EXERCISE 20

(OBJECTIVE TYPE QUESTIONS)

Directions : *Mark (✓) against the correct answer :*

1. In what ratio must a grocer mix two varieties of pulses costing Rs. 15 and Rs. 20 per kg respectively so as to get a mixture worth Rs. 16.50 per kg ? **(R.R.B. 2003)**

(*a*) 3 : 7 (*b*) 5 : 7 (*c*) 7 : 3 (*d*) 7 : 5

2. Find the ratio in which rice at Rs. 7.20 a kg be mixed with rice at Rs. 5.70 a kg to produce a mixture worth Rs. 6.30 a kg. **(IGNOU, 2003)**

(*a*) 1 : 3 (*b*) 2 : 3 (*c*) 3 : 4 (*d*) 4 : 5

3. In what ratio must tea at Rs. 62 per kg be mixed with tea at Rs. 72 per kg so that the mixture must be worth Rs. 64.50 per kg ?

(*a*) 3 : 1 (*b*) 3 : 2 (*c*) 4 : 3 (*d*) 5 : 3

4. In what ratio must water be mixed with milk costing Rs. 12 per litre to obtain a mixture worth of Rs. 8 per litre ?

(*a*) 1 : 2 (*b*) 2 : 1 (*c*) 2 : 3 (*d*) 3 : 2

5. The cost of Type 1 rice is Rs. 15 per kg and Type 2 rice is Rs. 20 per kg. If both Type 1 and Type 2 are mixed in the ratio of 2 : 3, then the price per kg of the mixed variety of rice is : **(M.B.A. 2002)**

(*a*) Rs. 18 (*b*) Rs. 18.50 (*c*) Rs. 19 (*d*) Rs. 19.50

6. In what ratio must a grocer mix two varieties of tea worth Rs. 60 a kg and Rs. 65 a kg so that by selling the mixture at Rs. 68.20 a kg he may gain 10% ?
(*a*) 3 : 2 (*b*) 3 : 4 (*c*) 3 : 5 (*d*) 4 : 5
(S.S.C. 2004)

7. How many kilograms of sugar costing Rs. 9 per kg must be mixed with 27 kg of sugar costing Rs. 7 per kg so that there may be a gain of 10% by selling the mixture at Rs. 9.24 per kg ?
(*a*) 36 kg (*b*) 42 kg (*c*) 54 kg (*d*) 63 kg

8. In what ratio must water be mixed with milk to gain $16\frac{2}{3}\%$ on selling the mixture at cost price ? **(L.I.C.A.A.O. 2003)**
(*a*) 1 : 6 (*b*) 6 : 1 (*c*) 2 : 3 (*d*) 4 : 3

9. A dishonest milkman professes to sell his milk at cost price but he mixes it with water and thereby gains 25%. The percentage of water in the mixture is :
(*a*) 4% (*b*) $6\frac{1}{4}\%$ (*c*) 20% (*d*) 25%

10. Two vessels A and B contain spirit and water mixed in the ratio 5 : 2 and 7 : 6 respectively. Find the ratio in which these mixture be mixed to obtain a new mixture in vessel C containing spirit and water in the ratio 8 : 5 ?
(*a*) 4 : 3 (*b*) 3 : 4 (*c*) 5 : 6 (*d*) 7 : 9

11. Two vessels A and B contain milk and water mixed in the ratio 8 : 5 and 5 : 2 respectively. The ratio in which these two mixtures be mixed to get a new mixture containing $69\frac{3}{13}\%$ milk, is :
(*a*) 2 : 7 (*b*) 3 : 5 (*c*) 5 : 2 (*d*) 5 : 7

12. A milk vendor has 2 cans of milk. The first contains 25% water and the rest milk. The second contains 50% water. How much milk should he mix from each of the containers so as to get 12 litres of milk such that the ratio of water to milk is 3 : 5 ?
(*a*) 4 litres, 8 litres (*b*) 6 litres, 6 litres
(*c*) 5 litres, 7 litres (*d*) 7 litres, 5 litres

13. One quality of wheat at Rs. 9.30 per kg is mixed with another quality at a certain rate in the ratio 8 : 7. If the mixture so formed be worth Rs. 10 per kg, what is the rate per kg of the second quality of wheat ?
(*a*) Rs. 10.30 (*b*) Rs. 10.60 (*c*) Rs. 10.80 (*d*) Rs. 11

14. Tea worth Rs. 126 per kg and Rs. 135 per kg are mixed with a third variety in the ratio 1 : 1 : 2. If the mixture is worth Rs. 153 per kg, the price of the third variety per kg will be : **(S.S.C. 1999)**
(*a*) Rs. 169.50 (*b*) Rs. 170 (*c*) Rs. 175.50 (*d*) Rs. 180

15. A merchant has 1000 kg of sugar, part of which he sells at 8% profit and the rest at 18% profit. He gains 14% on the whole. The quantity sold at 18% profit is :
(*a*) 400 kg (*b*) 560 kg (*c*) 600 kg (*d*) 640 kg

16. A jar full of whisky contains 40% alcohol. A part of this whisky is replaced by another containing 19% alcohol and now the percentage of alcohol was found to be 26%. The quantity of whisky replaced is :
(*a*) $\frac{1}{3}$ (*b*) $\frac{2}{3}$ (*c*) $\frac{2}{5}$ (*d*) $\frac{3}{5}$

17. A container contains 40 litres of milk. From this container 4 litres of milk was taken out and replaced by water. This process was repeated further two times. How much milk is now contained by the container ?
(*a*) 26.34 litres (*b*) 27.36 litres (*c*) 28 litres (*d*) 29.16 litres

18. 8 litres are drawn from a cask full of wine and is then filled with water. This operation is performed three more times. The ratio of the quantity of wine now left in cask to that of the water is 16 : 65. How much wine did the cask hold originally ?

(N.I.F.T. 2003)

(*a*) 18 litres (*b*) 24 litres (*c*) 32 litres (*d*) 42 litres

19. A can contains a mixture of two liquids A and B in the ratio 7 : 5. When 9 litres of mixture are drawn off and the can is filled with B, the ratio of A and B becomes 7 : 9. How many litres of liquid A was contained by the can initially ?

(*a*) 10 (*b*) 20 (*c*) 21 (*d*) 25

20. A vessel is filled with liquid, 3 parts of which are water and 5 parts syrup. How much of the mixture must be drawn off and replaced with water so that the mixture may be half water and half syrup ?

(*a*) $\frac{1}{3}$ (*b*) $\frac{1}{4}$ (*c*) $\frac{1}{5}$ (*d*) $\frac{1}{7}$

ANSWERS

1. (*c*) **2.** (*b*) **3.** (*a*) **4.** (*a*) **5.** (*a*) **6.** (*a*) **7.** (*d*) **8.** (*a*) **9.** (*c*) **10.** (*d*)
11. (*a*) **12.** (*b*) **13.** (*c*) **14.** (*c*) **15.** (*c*) **16.** (*b*) **17.** (*d*) **18.** (*b*) **19.** (*c*) **20.** (*c*)

SOLUTIONS

1. By the rule of alligation :

Cost of 1 kg pulses of 1st kind		Cost of 1 kg pulses of 2nd kind
Rs. 15		Rs. 20
	Mean price Rs. 16.50	
3.50		1.50

∴ Required rate = 3.50 : 1.50 = 35 : 15 = 7 : 3.

2. By the rule of alligation :

Cost of 1 kg rice of 1st kind		Cost of 1 kg rice of 2nd kind
720 *p*		570 *p*
	Mean price 630 *p*	
60		90

∴ Required ratio = 60 : 90 = 2 : 3.

3. By the rule of alligation :

Cost of 1 kg tea of 1st kind		Cost of 1 kg tea of 2nd kind
6200 *p*		7200 *p*
	Mean price 6450 *p*	
750		250

∴ Required ratio = 750 : 250 = 3 : 1.

4. By the rule of alligation :

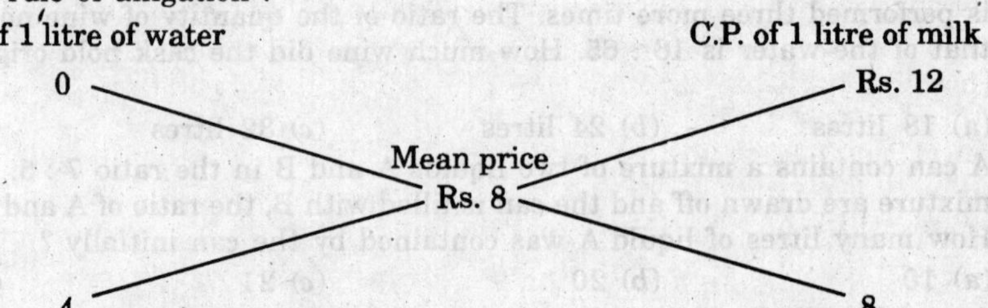

Ratio of water to milk = 4 : 8 = 1 : 2.

5. Let the price of the mixed variety be Rs. x per kg.

By the rule of alligation, we have :

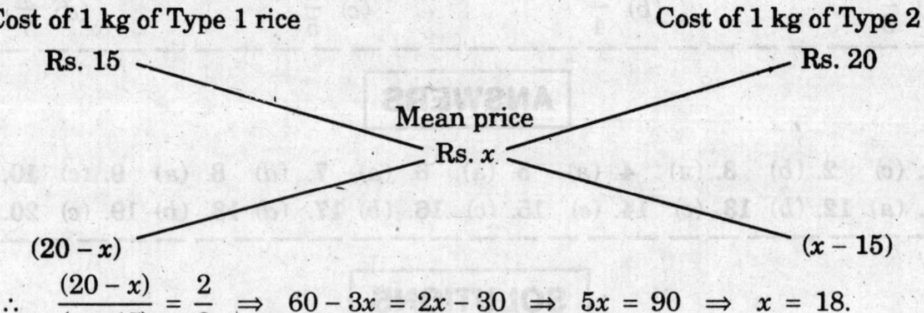

$\therefore \quad \dfrac{(20-x)}{(x-15)} = \dfrac{2}{3} \Rightarrow 60 - 3x = 2x - 30 \Rightarrow 5x = 90 \Rightarrow x = 18.$

So, price of the mixture is Rs. 18 per kg.

6. S.P. of 1 kg of the mixture = Rs. 68.20, Gain = 10 %.

C.P. of 1 kg of the mixture = Rs. $\left(\dfrac{100}{110} \times 68.20\right)$ = Rs. 62.

By the rule of alligation, we have :

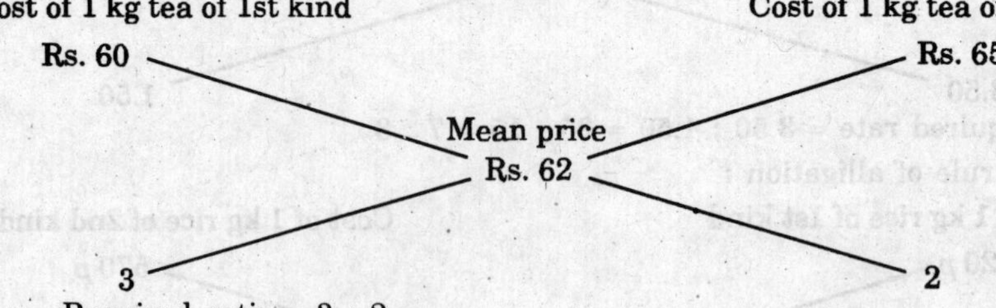

$\therefore$ Required ratio = 3 : 2.

7. S.P. of 1 kg of mixture = Rs. 9.24, Gain = 10%.

$\therefore$ C.P. of 1 kg of mixture = Rs. $\left(\dfrac{100}{110} \times 9.24\right)$ = Rs. 8.40.

By the rule of alligation, we have :

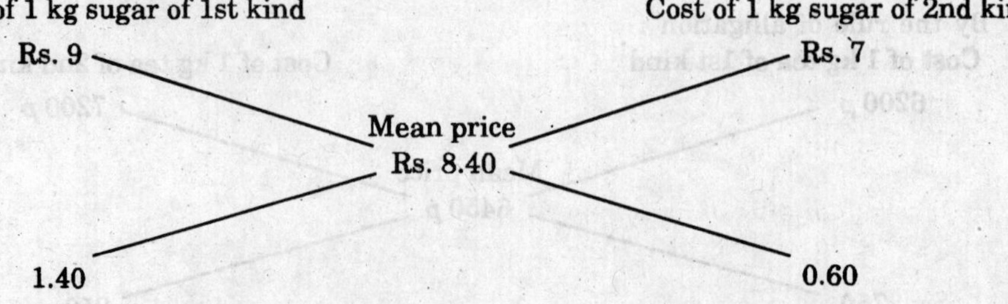

$\therefore$ Ratio of quantities of 1st and 2nd kind = 14 : 6 = 7 : 3.

Let x kg of sugar of 1st kind be mixed with 27 kg of 2nd kind.

Then, 7 : 3 = x : 27 or $x = \left(\frac{7 \times 27}{3}\right) = 63$ kg.

8. Let C.P. of 1 litre milk be Re. 1.

S.P. of 1 litre of mixture = Re. 1, Gain $= \frac{50}{3}\%$.

$\therefore$ C.P. of 1 litre of mixture $= \left(100 \times \frac{3}{350} \times 1\right) =$ Re. $\frac{6}{7}$.

By the rule of alligation, we have :

C.P. of 1 litre of water **C.P. of 1 litre of milk**

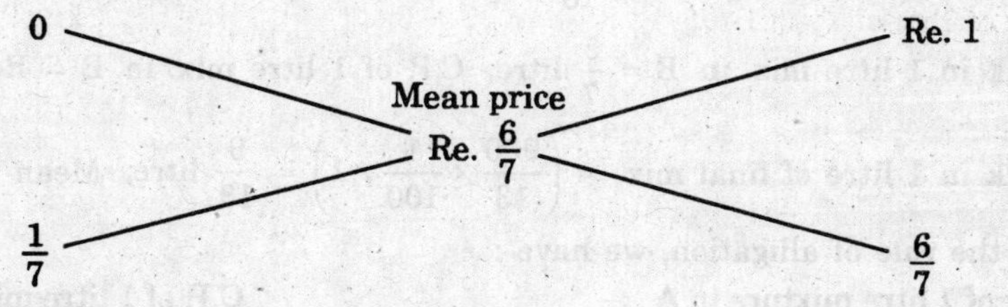

$\therefore$ Ratio of water and milk $= \frac{1}{7} : \frac{6}{7} = 1 : 6$.

9. Let C.P. of 1 litre milk be Re. 1.

Then, S.P. of 1 litre of mixture = Re. 1, Gain = 25%.

C.P. of 1 litre mixture = Re. $\left(\frac{100}{125} \times 1\right) =$ Re. $\frac{4}{5}$.

C.P. of 1 litre milk **C.P. of 1 litre of water**

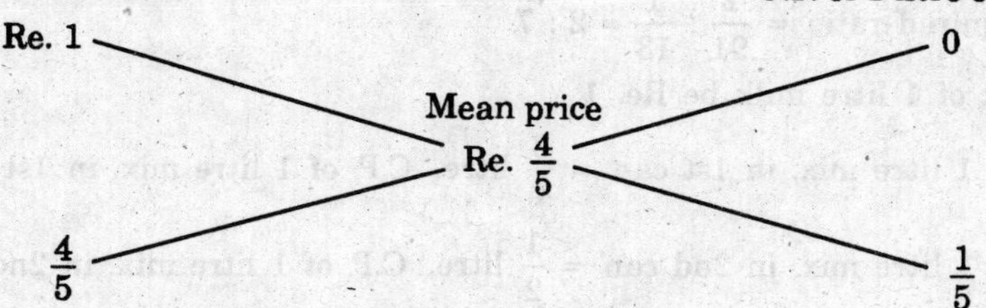

$\therefore$ Ratio of milk to water $= \frac{4}{5} : \frac{1}{5} = 4 : 1$.

Hence, percentage of water in the mixture $= \left(\frac{1}{5} \times 100\right)\% = 20\%$.

10. Let the C.P. of spirit be Re. 1 per litre.

Spirit in 1 litre mix. of A $= \frac{5}{7}$ litre; C.P. of 1 litre mix. in A = Re. $\frac{5}{7}$.

Spirit in 1 litre mix. of B $= \frac{7}{13}$ litre; C.P. of 1 litre mix. in B = Re. $\frac{7}{13}$.

Spirit in 1 litre mix. of C $= \frac{8}{13}$ litre; Mean price = Re. $\frac{8}{13}$.

By the rule of alligation, we have :

C.P. of 1 litre mixture in A C.P. of 1 litre mixture in B

$\left(\frac{5}{7}\right)$ $\left(\frac{7}{13}\right)$

Mean price

$\left(\frac{8}{13}\right)$

$\left(\frac{1}{13}\right)$ $\frac{9}{91}$

$\therefore$ Required ratio $= \frac{1}{13} : \frac{9}{91} = 7 : 9.$

11. Let cost of 1 litre milk be Re. 1.

Milk in 1 litre mix. in A $= \frac{8}{13}$ litre, C.P. of 1 litre mix. in A = Re. $\frac{8}{13}$.

Milk in 1 litre mix. in B $= \frac{5}{7}$ litre, C.P. of 1 litre mix. in B = Re. $\frac{5}{7}$.

Milk in 1 litre of final mix. $= \left(\frac{900}{13} \times \frac{1}{100} \times 1\right) = \frac{9}{13}$ litre; Mean price = Re. $\frac{9}{13}$.

By the rule of alligation, we have :

C.P. of 1 litre mixture in A C.P. of 1 litre mixture in B

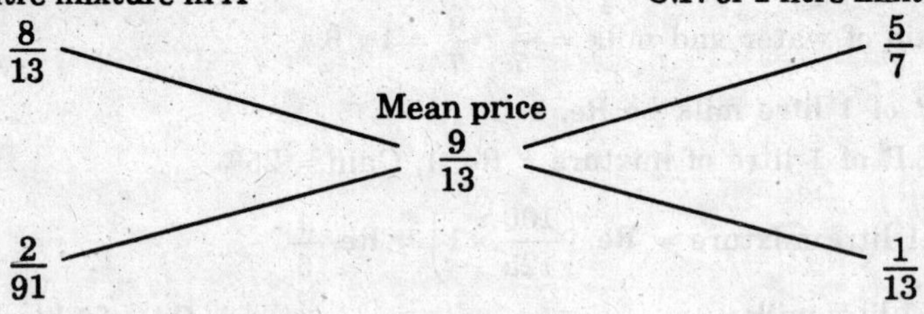

$\therefore$ Required ratio $= \frac{2}{91} : \frac{1}{13} = 2 : 7.$

12. Let cost of 1 litre milk be Re. 1.

Milk in 1 litre mix. in 1st can $= \frac{3}{4}$ litre, C.P. of 1 litre mix. in 1st can = Re. $\frac{3}{4}$.

Milk in 1 litre mix. in 2nd can $= \frac{1}{2}$ litre, C.P. of 1 litre mix. in 2nd can = Re. $\frac{1}{2}$.

Milk in 1 litre of final mix. $= \frac{5}{8}$ litre, Mean price = Re. $\frac{5}{8}$.

By the rule of alligation, we have :

C.P. of 1 litre mixture in 1st can C.P. of 1 litre mixture in 2nd can

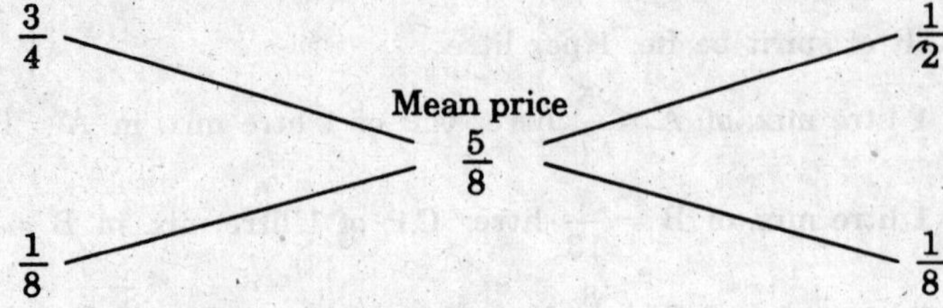

$\therefore$ Ratio of two mixtures $= \frac{1}{8} : \frac{1}{8} = 1 : 1.$

So, quantity of mixture taken from each can $= \left(\frac{1}{2} \times 12\right) = 6$ litres.

13. Let the rate of the second quality be Rs. x per kg.

By the rule of alligation, we have :

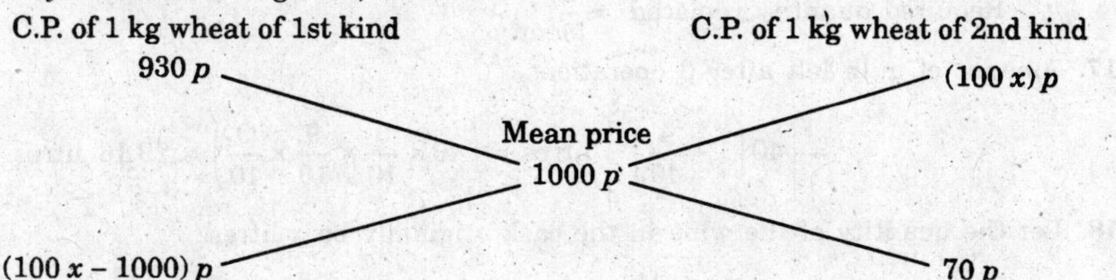

$\therefore \quad \dfrac{100x - 1000}{70} = \dfrac{8}{7} \Rightarrow 700x - 7000 = 560 \Rightarrow 700x = 7560 \Rightarrow x = \text{Rs. } 10.80.$

14. Since first and second varieties are mixed in equal proportions, so their average price

$= \text{Rs. } \left(\dfrac{126 + 135}{2}\right) = \text{Rs. } 130.50.$

So, the mixture is formed by mixing two varieties, one at Rs. 130.50 per kg and the other at say, Rs. x per kg in the ratio 2 : 2, *i.e.*, 1 : 1. We have to find x.

By the rule of alligation, we have :

Cost of 1 kg tea of 1st kind **Cost of 1 kg tea of 2nd kind**

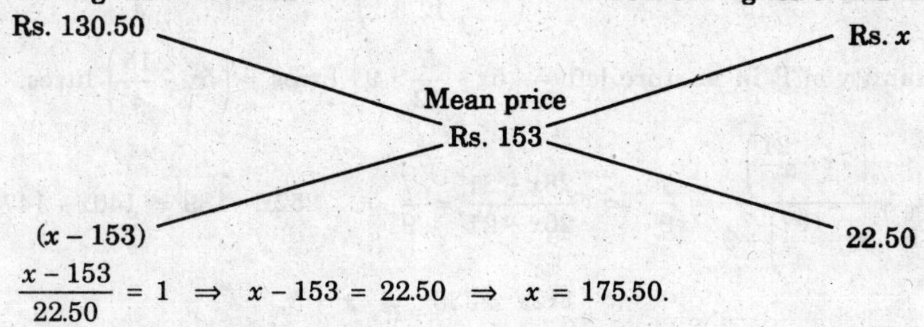

$\therefore \quad \dfrac{x - 153}{22.50} = 1 \Rightarrow x - 153 = 22.50 \Rightarrow x = 175.50.$

Hence, price of the third variety = Rs. 175.50 per kg.

15. By the rule of alligation, we have :

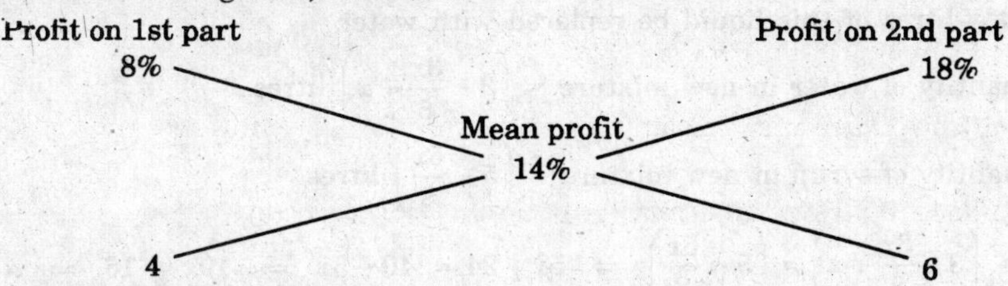

Ratio of 1st and 2nd parts = 4 : 6 = 2 : 3.

$\therefore \quad$ Quantity of 2nd kind $= \left(\dfrac{3}{5} \times 1000\right)$ kg $= 600$ kg.

16. By the rule of alligation, we have :

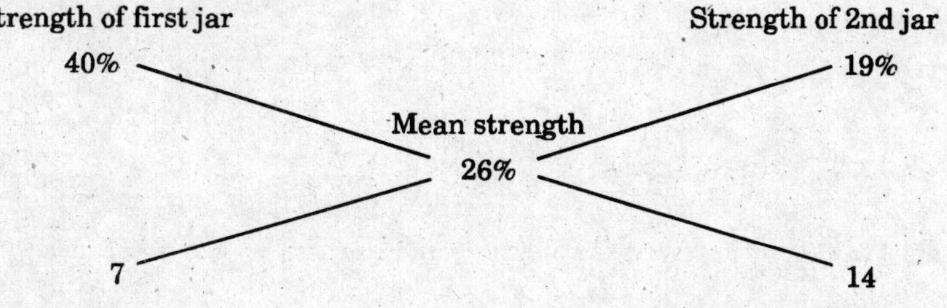

So, ratio of 1st and 2nd quantities = 7 : 14 = 1 : 2.

$\therefore$ Required quantity replaced $= \frac{2}{3}$.

17. Amount of milk left after 3 operations

$$= \left[40\left(1-\frac{4}{40}\right)^3\right] \text{litres} = \left(40 \times \frac{9}{10} \times \frac{9}{10} \times \frac{9}{10}\right) = 29.16 \text{ litres.}$$

18. Let the quantity of the wine in the cask originally be x litres.

Then, quantity of wine left in cask after 4 operations $= \left[x\left(1-\frac{8}{x}\right)^4\right]$ litres.

$$\therefore \frac{x\left(1-\frac{8}{x}\right)^4}{x} = \frac{16}{81} \Rightarrow \left(1-\frac{8}{x}\right)^4 = \left(\frac{2}{3}\right)^2 \Rightarrow \left(\frac{x-8}{x}\right) = \frac{2}{3}$$

$$\Rightarrow 3x - 24 = 2x \Rightarrow x = 24.$$

19. Suppose the can initially contains $7x$ and $5x$ litres of mixtures A and B respectively.

Quantity of A in mixture left $= \left(7x - \frac{7}{12} \times 9\right)$ litres $= \left(7x - \frac{21}{4}\right)$ litres.

Quantity of B in mixture left $= \left(5x - \frac{5}{12} \times 9\right)$ litres $= \left(5x - \frac{15}{4}\right)$ litres.

$$\therefore \frac{\left(7x - \frac{21}{4}\right)}{\left(5x - \frac{15}{4}\right) + 9} = \frac{7}{9} \Rightarrow \frac{28x - 21}{20x + 21} = \frac{7}{9} \Rightarrow 252x - 189 = 140x + 147$$

$$\Rightarrow 112x = 336 \Rightarrow x = 3.$$

So, the can contained 21 litres of A.

20. Suppose the vessel initially contains 8 litres of liquid.

Let x litres of this liquid be replaced with water.

Quantity of water in new mixture $= \left(3 - \frac{3x}{8} + x\right)$ litres.

Quantity of syrup in new mixture $= \left(5 - \frac{5x}{8}\right)$ litres.

$$\therefore \left(3 - \frac{3x}{8} + x\right) = \left(5 - \frac{5x}{8}\right) \Rightarrow 5x + 24 = 40 - 5x \Rightarrow 10x = 16 \Rightarrow x = \frac{8}{5}.$$

So, part of the mixture replaced $= \left(\frac{8}{5} \times \frac{1}{8}\right) = \frac{1}{5}$.

---

21. SIMPLE INTEREST

IMPORTANT FACTS AND FORMULAE

1. **Principal** : The money borrowed or lent out for a certain period is called the ***principal*** or the ***sum***.
2. **Interest** : Extra money paid for using other's money is called ***interest.***
3. **Simple Interest (S.I.)** : If the interest on a sum borrowed for a certain period is reckoned uniformly, then it is called ***simple interest.***

Let Principal = P, Rate = R% per annum (p.a.) and Time = T years. Then,

(*i*) $\text{S.I.} = \left(\frac{P \times R \times T}{100}\right)$.

(*ii*) $P = \left(\frac{100 \times \text{S.I.}}{R \times T}\right)$; $R = \left(\frac{100 \times \text{S.I.}}{P \times T}\right)$ and $T = \left(\frac{100 \times \text{S.I.}}{P \times R}\right)$.

SOLVED EXAMPLES

Ex. 1. ***Find the simple interest on Rs. 68,000 at $16\frac{2}{3}$% per annum for 9 months.***

Sol. P = Rs. 68000, $R = \frac{50}{3}\%$ p.a and $T = \frac{9}{12}$ years $= \frac{3}{4}$ years.

$\therefore$ $\text{S.I.} = \left(\frac{P \times R \times T}{100}\right) = \text{Rs.}\left(68000 \times \frac{50}{3} \times \frac{3}{4} \times \frac{1}{100}\right) = \text{Rs. } 8500.$

Ex. 2. ***Find the simple interest on Rs. 3000 at $6\frac{1}{4}$% per annum for the period from 4th Feb., 2005 to 18th April, 2005.***

Sol. Time = (24 + 31 + 18) days = 73 days $= \frac{73}{365}$ year $= \frac{1}{5}$ year.

P = Rs. 3000 and $R = 6\frac{1}{4}\%$ p.a. $= \frac{25}{4}\%$ p.a.

$\therefore$ $\text{S.I.} = \text{Rs.}\left(3000 \times \frac{25}{4} \times \frac{1}{5} \times \frac{1}{100}\right) = \text{Rs. } 37.50.$

Remark : The day on which money is deposited is not counted while the day on which money is withdrawn is counted.

Ex. 3. ***A sum at simple interest at $13\frac{1}{2}$% per annum amounts to Rs. 2502.50 after 4 years. Find the sum.***

Sol. Let sum be Rs. x. Then, $\text{S.I.} = \text{Rs.}\left(x \times \frac{27}{2} \times 4 \times \frac{1}{100}\right) = \text{Rs. } \frac{27x}{50}$.

$\therefore$ Amount $= \text{Rs.}\left(x + \frac{27x}{50}\right) = \text{Rs. } \frac{77x}{50}$.

$\therefore \quad \frac{77x}{50} = 2502.50 \Leftrightarrow x = \frac{2502.50 \times 50}{77} = 1625.$

Hence, sum = Rs. 1625.

Ex. 4. ***A sum of Rs. 800 amounts to Rs. 920 in 3 years at simple interest. If the interest rate is increased by 3%, it would amount to how much ?***

Sol. S.I. = Rs. (920 − 800) = Rs. 120; P = Rs. 800, T = 3 yrs.

$\therefore \quad R = \left(\frac{100 \times 120}{800 \times 3}\right)\% = 5\%.$

New rate = (5 + 3)% = 8%.

New S.I. = Rs. $\left(\frac{800 \times 8 \times 3}{100}\right)$ = Rs. 192.

$\therefore$ New amount = Rs. (800 + 192) = Rs. 992.

Ex. 5. ***Adam borrowed some money at the rate of 6% p.a. for the first two years, at the rate of 9% p.a. for the next three years, and at the rate of 14% p.a. for the period beyond five years. If he pays a total interest of Rs. 11, 400 at the end of nine years, how much money did he borrow ?*** **(Bank P.O. 1999)**

Sol. Let the sum borrowed be x. Then,

$$\left(\frac{x \times 6 \times 2}{100}\right) + \left(\frac{x \times 9 \times 3}{100}\right) + \left(\frac{x \times 14 \times 4}{100}\right) = 11400$$

$$\Leftrightarrow \left(\frac{3x}{25} + \frac{27x}{100} + \frac{14x}{25}\right) = 11400 \Leftrightarrow \frac{95x}{100} = 11400 \Leftrightarrow x = \left(\frac{11400 \times 100}{95}\right) = 12000.$$

Hence, sum borrowed = Rs. 12,000.

Ex. 6. ***A certain sum of money amounts to Rs. 1008 in 2 years and to Rs. 1164 in $3\frac{1}{2}$ years. Find the sum and the rate of interest.***

Sol. S.I. for $1\frac{1}{2}$ years = Rs. (1164 − 1008) = Rs. 156.

S.I. for 2 years = Rs. $\left(156 \times \frac{2}{3} \times 2\right)$ = Rs. 208.

$\therefore$ Principal = Rs. (1008 − 208) = Rs. 800.

Now, P = 800, T = 2 and S.I. = 208.

$\therefore \quad \text{Rate} = \left(\frac{100 \times 208}{800 \times 2}\right)\% = 13\%.$

Ex. 7. ***At what rate percent per annum will a sum of money double in 16 years ?*** **(R.R.B. 2003)**

Sol. Let principal = P. Then, S.I. = P and T = 16 yrs.

$\therefore \quad \text{Rate} = \left(\frac{100 \times P}{P \times 16}\right)\% = 6\frac{1}{4}\%$ p.a.

Ex. 8. ***The simple interest on a sum of money is $\frac{4}{9}$ of the principal. Find the rate percent and time, if both are numerically equal.*** **(S.S.C. 2000)**

Sol. Let sum = Rs. x. Then, S.I. = Rs. $\frac{4x}{9}$.

Let rate = R% and time = R years.

Then, $\left(\dfrac{x \times R \times R}{100}\right) = \dfrac{4x}{9}$ or $R^2 = \dfrac{400}{9}$ or $R = \dfrac{20}{3} = 6\dfrac{2}{3}$.

$\therefore$ Rate $= 6\dfrac{2}{3}\%$ and Time $= 6\dfrac{2}{3}$ yrs = 6 yrs 8 months.

Ex. 9. ***The simple interest on a certain sum of money for $2\frac{1}{2}$ years at 12% per annum is Rs. 40 less than the simple interest on the same sum for $3\frac{1}{2}$ years at 10% per annum. Find the sum.***

Sol. Let the sum be Rs. x. Then, $\left(\dfrac{x \times 10 \times 7}{100 \times 2}\right) - \left(\dfrac{x \times 12 \times 5}{100 \times 2}\right) = 40$

$\Leftrightarrow \quad \dfrac{7x}{20} - \dfrac{3x}{10} = 40 \Leftrightarrow x = (40 \times 20) = 800.$

Hence, the sum is Rs. 800.

Ex. 10. ***A sum was put at simple interest at a certain rate for 3 years. Had it been put at 2% higher rate, it would have fetched Rs. 360 more. Find the sum.***

Sol. Let sum = P and original rate = R. Then, $\left[\dfrac{P \times (R+2) \times 3}{100}\right] - \left[\dfrac{P \times R \times 3}{100}\right] = 360$

$\Leftrightarrow \quad 3PR + 6P - 3PR = 36000 \quad \Leftrightarrow \quad 6P = 36000 \quad \Leftrightarrow \quad P = 6000.$

Hence, sum = Rs. 6000.

Ex. 11. ***What annual instalment will discharge a debt of Rs. 1092 due in 3 years at 12% simple interest ?***

Sol. Let each instalment be Rs. x. Then, $\left(x + \dfrac{x \times 12 \times 1}{100}\right) + \left(x + \dfrac{x \times 12 \times 2}{100}\right) + x = 1092$

$\Leftrightarrow \quad \dfrac{28x}{25} + \dfrac{31x}{25} + x = 1092 \quad \Leftrightarrow \quad (28x + 31x + 25x) = (1092 \times 25)$

$\Leftrightarrow \quad x = \left(\dfrac{1092 \times 25}{84}\right) = 325.$

$\therefore$ Each instalment = Rs. 325.

Ex. 12. ***A sum of Rs. 1550 is lent out into two parts, one at 8% and another one at 6%. If the total annual income is Rs. 106, find the money lent at each rate.***

(L.I.C. A.A.O. 2003)

Sol. Let the sum lent at 8% be Rs. x and that at 6% be Rs. $(1550 - x)$.

$\therefore \quad \left[\dfrac{x \times 8 \times 1}{100}\right] + \left[\dfrac{(1550 - x) \times 6 \times 1}{100}\right] = 106$

$\Leftrightarrow \quad 8x + 9300 - 6x = 10600 \quad \Leftrightarrow \quad 2x = 1300 \quad \Leftrightarrow \quad x = 650.$

$\therefore$ Money lent at 8% = Rs. 650. Money lent at 6% = Rs. (1550 − 650) = Rs. 900.

EXERCISE 21A

(OBJECTIVE TYPE QUESTIONS)

Directions : *Mark (✓) against the correct answer :*

1. At the rate of $8\frac{1}{2}\%$ p.a. simple interest, a sum of Rs. 4800 will earn how much interest in 2 years 3 months ?

   (*a*) Rs. 796 (*b*) Rs. 816 (*c*) Rs. 918 (*d*) Rs. 956

2. What will be the simple interest earned on an amount of Rs. 16,800 in 9 months at the rate of $6\frac{1}{4}\%$ p.a. ?

(a) Rs. 787.50 (b) Rs. 812.50 (c) Rs. 860 (d) Rs. 887.50

3. The simple interest on Rs. 1820 from March 9, 2003 to May 21, 2003 at $7\frac{1}{2}\%$ rate will be :

(a) Rs. 22.50 (b) Rs. 27.30 (c) Rs. 28.80 (d) Rs. 29

4. A person borrows Rs. 5000 for 2 years at 4% p.a. simple interest. He immediately lends it to another person at $6\frac{1}{4}\%$ p.a. for 2 years. Find his gain in the transaction per year. **(S.S.C. 2000)**

(a) Rs. 112.50 (b) Rs. 125 (c) Rs. 150 (d) Rs. 167.50

5. How much time will it take for an amount of Rs. 450 to yield Rs. 81 as interest at 4.5% per annum of simple interest ? **(IGNOU, 2003)**

(a) 3.5 years (b) 4 years (c) 4.5 years (d) 5 years

6. A sum of Rs. 12,500 amounts to Rs. 15,500 in 4 years at the rate of simple interest. What is the rate of interest ? **(Bank P.O. 2003)**

(a) 3% (b) 4% (c) 5% (d) 6% (e) None of these

7. A sum of Rs. 1600 gives a simple interest of Rs. 252 in 2 years and 4 months. The rate of interest per annum is :

(a) 6% (b) $6\frac{1}{4}\%$ (c) $6\frac{1}{2}\%$ (d) $6\frac{3}{4}\%$

8. Reena took a loan of Rs. 1200 with simple interest for as many years as the rate of interest. If she paid Rs. 432 as interest at the end of the loan period, what was the rate of interest ? **(R.B.I. 2003)**

(a) 3.6 (b) 6 (c) 18 (d) Cannot be determined (e) None of these

9. A man took a loan from a bank at the rate of 12% p.a. simple interest. After 3 years he had to pay Rs. 5400 interest only for the period. The principal amount borrowed by him was : **(S.S.C. 2004)**

(a) Rs. 2000 (b) Rs. 10,000 (c) Rs. 15,000 (d) Rs. 20,000

10. What is the present worth of Rs. 132 due in 2 years at 5% simple interest per annum ?

(a) Rs. 112 (b) Rs. 118.80 (c) Rs. 120 (d) Rs. 122 **(C.B.I. 1997)**

11. A sum fetched a total simple interest of Rs. 4016.25 at the rate of 9 p.c.p.a. in 5 years. What is the sum ? **(NABARD, 2002)**

(a) Rs. 4462.50 (b) Rs. 8032.50 (c) Rs. 8900 (d) Rs. 8925 (e) None of these

12. The simple interest at $x\%$ for x years will be Rs. x on a sum of :

(a) Rs. x (b) Rs. $\left(\frac{100}{x}\right)$ (c) Rs. $100x$ (d) Rs. $\left(\frac{100}{x^2}\right)$

13. Rs. 800 becomes Rs. 956 in 3 years at a certain rate of simple interest. If the rate of interest is increased by 4%, what amount will Rs. 800 become in 3 years ?

(a) Rs. 1020.80 (b) Rs. 1025 (c) Rs. 1052 (d) Data inadequate (e) None of these **(Bank P.O. 2000)**

14. A certain amount earns simple interest of Rs. 1750 after 7 years. Had the interest been 2% more, how much more interest would it have earned ? **(Bank P.O. 2003)**

(a) Rs. 35 (b) Rs. 245 (c) Rs. 350 (d) Cannot be determined (e) None of these

15. In how many years, Rs. 150 will produce the same interest @ 8% as Rs. 800 produce in 3 years @ $4\frac{1}{2}$% ? **(R.R.B. 2001)**

(a) 6 (b) 8 (c) 9 (d) 12

16. If Rs. 64 amounts to Rs. 83.20 in 2 years, what will Rs. 86 amount to in 4 years at the same rate percent per annum ?

(a) Rs. 114.80 (b) Rs. 124.70 (c) Rs. 127.40 (d) Rs. 137.60

17. The simple interest on a certain sum of money at the rate of 5% p.a. for 8 years is Rs. 840. At what rate of interest the same amount of interest can be received on the same sum after 5 years ?

(a) 6% (b) 8% (c) 9% (d) 10%

18. The interest on a certain deposit at 4.5% p.a. is Rs. 202.50 in one year. How much will the additional interest in one year be on the same deposit at 5% p.a. ?

(a) Rs. 20.25 (b) Rs. 22.50 (c) Rs. 25 (d) Rs. 42.75

19. A sum invested at 5% simple interest per annum grows to Rs. 504 in 4 years. The same amount at 10% simple interest per annum in $2\frac{1}{2}$ years will grow to :

(a) Rs. 420 (b) Rs. 450 (c) Rs. 525 (d) Rs. 550 **(C.D.S. 2003)**

20. What will be the ratio of simple interest earned by certain amount at the same rate of interest for 6 years and that for 9 years ? **(Bank P.O. 1998)**

(a) 1 : 3 (b) 1 : 4 (c) 2 : 3 (d) Data inadequate (e) None of these

21. Nitin borrowed some money at the rate of 6% p.a. for the first three years, 9% p.a. for the next five years and 13% p.a. for the period beyond eight years. If the total interest paid by him at the end of eleven years is Rs. 8160, how much money did he borrow ? **(Bank P.O. 2000)**

(a) Rs. 8000 (b) Rs. 10,000 (c) Rs. 12,000 (d) Data inadequate (e) None of these

22. The simple interest on a sum of money will be Rs. 600 after 10 years. If the principal is trebled after 5 years, what will be the total interest at the end of the tenth year ?

(a) Rs. 600 (b) Rs. 900 (c) Rs. 1200 (d) Rs. 1500 (e) Data inadequate

23. The simple interest on Rs. 10 for 4 months at the rate of 3 paise per rupee per month is :

(a) Rs. 1.20 (b) Rs. 1.60 (c) Rs. 2.40 (d) Rs. 3.60

24. An automobile financier claims to be lending money at simple interest, but he includes the interest every six months for calculating the principal. If he is charging an interest of 10%, the effective rate of interest becomes : **(N.I.F.T. 2000)**

(a) 10% (b) 10.25% (c) 10.5% (d) None of these

25. A sum of money at simple interest amounts to Rs. 815 in 3 years and to Rs. 854 in 4 years. The sum is : **(Section Officers', 2001)**

(a) Rs. 650 (b) Rs. 690 (c) Rs. 698 (d) Rs. 700

26. A sum of money lent out at simple interest amounts to Rs. 720 after 2 years and to Rs. 1020 after a further period of 5 years. The sum is : **(S.S.C. 2004)**

(a) Rs. 500 (b) Rs. 600 (c) Rs. 700 (d) Rs. 710

27. A sum of money amounts to Rs. 9800 after 5 years and Rs. 12005 after 8 years at the same rate of simple interest. The rate of interest per annum is : **(S.S.C. 2003)**

(a) 5% (b) 8% (c) 12% (d) 15%

28. A certain sum of money at simple interest amounts to Rs. 1012 in $2\frac{1}{2}$ years and to Rs. 1067.20 in 4 years. The rate of interest per annum is :

(*a*) 2.5% (*b*) 3% (*c*) 4% (*d*) 5%

29. In how many years will a sum of money double itself at 12% per annum ?

(*a*) 6 years 9 months (*b*) 7 years 6 months
(*c*) 8 years 3 months (*d*) 8 years 4 months

30. At what rate percent of simple interest will a sum of money double itself in 12 years ?

(*a*) $8\frac{1}{4}\%$ (*b*) $8\frac{1}{3}\%$ (*c*) $8\frac{1}{2}\%$ (*d*) $9\frac{1}{2}\%$

(S.S.C. 2000)

31. The rate at which a sum becomes four times of itself in 15 years at S.I., will be :

(*a*) 15% (*b*) $17\frac{1}{2}\%$ (*c*) 20% (*d*) 25%

32. If a sum of money at simple interest doubles in 6 years, it will become 4 times in :

(*a*) 12 years (*b*) 14 years (*c*) 16 years (*d*) 18 years

33. A sum of money trebles itself in 15 years 6 months. In how many years would it double itself ?

(*a*) 6 years 3 months (*b*) 7 years 9 months
(*c*) 8 years 3 months (*d*) 9 years 6 months.

34. Consider the following statements :
If a sum of money is lent at simple interest, then the

1. money gets doubled in 5 years if the rate of interest is $16\frac{2}{3}\%$.
2. money gets doubled in 5 years if the rate of interest is 20%.
3. money becomes four times in 10 years if it gets doubled in 5 years.

Of these statements,

(*a*) 1 and 3 are correct (*b*) 2 alone is correct
(*c*) 3 alone is correct (*d*) 2 and 3 are correct

35. The simple interest on a sum of money at 8% per annum for 6 years is half the sum. The sum is :

(*a*) Rs. 4800 (*b*) Rs. 6000 (*c*) Rs. 8000 (*d*) Data inadequate

36. At what rate percent per annum will the simple interest on a sum of money be $\frac{2}{5}$ of the amount in 10 years ? **(S.S.C. 2002)**

(*a*) 4% (*b*) $5\frac{2}{3}\%$ (*c*) 6% (*d*) $6\frac{2}{3}\%$

37. In how much time would the simple interest on a certain sum be 0.125 times the principal at 10% per annum ? **(Assistant Grade, 1997)**

(*a*) $1\frac{1}{4}$ years (*b*) $1\frac{3}{4}$ years (*c*) $2\frac{1}{4}$ years (*d*) $2\frac{3}{4}$ years

38. How long will it take a sum of money invested at 5% p.a. S.I. to increase its value by 40% ?

(*a*) 5 years (*b*) 6 years (*c*) 7 years (*d*) 8 years

39. A sum of money becomes $\frac{7}{6}$ of itself in 3 years at a certain rate of simple interest. The rate per annum is : **(S.S.C. 1999)**

(*a*) $5\frac{5}{9}\%$ (*b*) $6\frac{5}{9}\%$ (*c*) 18% (*d*) 25%

40. Simple interest on a certain sum at a certain annual rate of interest is $\frac{1}{9}$ of the sum. If the numbers representing rate percent and time in years be equal, then the rate of interest is :

(a) $3\frac{1}{3}\%$ (b) 5% (c) $6\frac{2}{3}\%$ (d) 10%

41. Simple interest on a certain amount is $\frac{9}{16}$ of the principal. If the numbers representing the rate of interest in percent and time in years be equal, then time, for which the principal is lent out, is : **(R.R.B. 2003)**

(a) $5\frac{1}{2}$ years (b) $6\frac{1}{2}$ years (c) 7 years (d) $7\frac{1}{2}$ years

42. A lends Rs. 2500 to B and a certain sum to C at the same time at 7% p.a. simple interest. If after 4 years, A altogether receives Rs. 1120 as interest from B and C, then the sum lent to C is : **(S.S.C. 2003)**

(a) Rs. 700 (b) Rs. 1500 (c) Rs. 4000 (d) Rs. 6500

43. Two equal sums of money were lent at simple interest at 11% p.a. for $3\frac{1}{2}$ years and $4\frac{1}{2}$ years respectively. If the difference in interests for two periods was Rs. 412.50, then each sum is :

(a) Rs. 3250 (b) Rs. 3500 (c) Rs. 3750 (d) Rs. 4250

44. If the simple interest on a certain sum for 15 months at $7\frac{1}{2}\%$ per annum exceeds the simple interest on the same sum for 8 months at $12\frac{1}{2}\%$ per annum by Rs. 32.50, then the sum (in Rs.) is :

(a) Rs. 3000 (b) Rs. 3060 (c) Rs. 3120 (d) Rs. 3250

45. A man invests a certain sum of money at 6% p.a. simple interest and another sum at 7% p.a. simple interest. His income from interest after 2 years was Rs. 354. One-fourth of the first sum is equal to one-fifth of the second sum. The total sum invested was :

(a) Rs. 2600 (b) Rs. 2700 (c) Rs. 2880 (d) Rs. 2900

46. A borrowed some money from B at 12% p.a. S.I. for 3 years. He then added some more money to the borrowed sum and lent it to C for the same period at 14% p.a. rate of interest. If A gains Rs. 93.90 in the whole transaction, how much money did he add from his side ?

(a) Rs. 35 (b) Rs. 55 (c) Rs. 80 (d) Rs. 105

47. A person borrowed Rs. 500 @ 3% per annum S.I. and Rs. 600 @ $4\frac{1}{2}\%$ per annum on the agreement that the whole sum will be returned only when the total interest becomes Rs. 126. The number of years, after which the borrowed sum is to be returned, is :

(a) 2 (b) 3 (c) 4 (d) 5

48. A lent Rs. 5000 to B for 2 years and Rs. 3000 to C for 4 years on simple interest at the same rate of interest and received Rs. 2200 in all from both of them as interest. The rate of interest per annum is : **(C.B.I. 2003)**

(a) 5% (b) 7% (c) $7\frac{1}{8}\%$ (d) 10%

49. A sum of Rs. 725 is lent in the beginning of a year at a certain rate of interest. After 8 months, a sum of Rs. 362.50 more is lent but at the rate twice the former. At the end of the year, Rs. 33.50 is earned as interest from both the loans. What was the original rate of interest ? **(Bank P.O. 2003)**

(*a*) 3.6% (*b*) 4.5% (*c*) 5% (*d*) 6% (*e*) None of these

50. The difference between the simple interest received from two different sources on Rs. 1500 for 3 years is Rs. 13.50. The difference between their rates of interest is :

(*a*) 0.1% (*b*) 0.2% (*c*) 0.3% (*d*) 0.4% (*e*) None of these **(S.S.C. 1999)**

51. Peter invested an amount of Rs. 12,000 at the rate of 10 p.c.p.a. simple interest and another amount at the rate of 20 p.c.p.a. simple interest. The total interest earned at the end of one year on the total amount invested became 14 p.c.p.a. Find the total amount invested. **(S.B.I.P.O. 1999)**

(*a*) Rs. 20,000 (*b*) Rs. 22,000 (*c*) Rs. 24,000 (*d*) Rs. 25,000 (*e*) None of these

52. What should be the least number of years in which the simple interest on Rs. 2600 at $6\frac{2}{3}\%$ will be an exact number of rupees ?

(*a*) 2 (*b*) 3 (*c*) 4 (*d*) 5

53. The rates of simple interest in two banks A and B are in the ratio 5 : 4. A person wants to deposit his total savings in two banks in such a way that he received equal half-yearly interest from both. He should deposit the savings in banks A and B in the ratio :

(*a*) 2 : 5 (*b*) 4 : 5 (*c*) 5 : 2 (*d*) 5 : 4

54. A sum was put at simple interest at a certain rate for 2 years. Had it been put at 3% higher rate, it would have fetched Rs. 72 more. The sum is :

(*a*) Rs. 1200 (*b*) Rs. 1500 (*c*) Rs. 1600 (*d*) Rs. 1800

55. If the annual rate of simple interest increases from 10% to $12\frac{1}{2}\%$, a man's yearly income increases by Rs. 1250. His principal (in Rs.) is : **(S.S.C. 2004)**

(*a*) 45,000 (*b*) 50,000 (*c*) 60,000 (*d*) 65,000

56. A moneylender finds that due to a fall in the annual rate of interest from 8% to $7\frac{3}{4}\%$, his yearly income diminishes by Rs. 61.50. His capital is : **(S.S.C. 2003)**

(*a*) Rs. 22,400 (*b*) Rs. 23,800 (*c*) Rs. 24,600 (*d*) Rs. 26,000

57 What annual payment will discharge a debt of Rs. 6450 due in 4 years at 5% simple interest ?

(*a*) Rs. 1400 (*b*) Rs. 1500 (*c*) Rs. 1550 (*d*) Rs. 1600

58. A sum of Rs. 10 is lent to be returned in 11 monthly instalments of Re. 1 each, interest being simple. The rate of interest is :

(*a*) $9\frac{1}{11}\%$ (*b*) 10% (*c*) 11% (*d*) $21\frac{9}{11}\%$

59. A person takes a loan of Rs. 200 at 5% simple interest. He returns Rs. 100 at the end of 1 year. In order to clear his dues at the end of 2 years, he would pay :

(*a*) Rs. 105 (*b*) Rs. 110 (*c*) Rs. 115 (*d*) Rs. 115.50

60. The price of a T.V. set worth Rs. 20,000 is to be paid in 20 instalments of Rs. 1000 each. If the rate of interest be 6% per annum, and the first instalment be paid at the time of purchase, then the value of the last instalment covering the interest as well will be : **(Hotel Management, 1998)**

(*a*) Rs. 1050 (*b*) Rs. 2050 (*c*) Rs. 3000 (*d*) None of these

61. If the rate increases by 2%, the simple interest received on a sum of money increases by Rs. 108. If the time period is increased by 2 years, the simple interest on the same sum increases by Rs. 180. The sum is :

(*a*) Rs. 1800 (*b*) Rs. 3600 (*c*) Rs. 5400
(*d*) Data inadequate (*e*) None of these

62. Mr. Thomas invested an amount of Rs. 13,900 divided in two different schemes A and B at the simple interest rate of 14% p.a. and 11% p.a. respectively. If the total amount of simple interest earned in 2 years be Rs. 3508, what was the amount invested in Scheme B ? **(R.B.I. 2003)**

(*a*) Rs. 6400 (*b*) Rs. 6500 (*c*) Rs. 7200
(*d*) Rs. 7500 (*e*) None of these

63. A sum of Rs. 2600 is lent out in two parts in such a way that the interest on one part at 10% for 5 years is equal to that on another at 9% for 6 years. The sum lent out at 10% is :

(*a*) Rs. 1150 (*b*) Rs. 1250 (*c*) Rs. 1350 (*d*) Rs. 1450

64. A sum of Rs. 1550 was lent partly at 5% and partly at 8% p.a. simple interest. The total interest received after 3 years was Rs. 300. The ratio of the money lent at 5% to that lent at 8% is :

(*a*) 5 : 8 (*b*) 8 : 5 (*c*) 16 : 15 (*d*) 31 : 6

65. A man lends Rs. 10,000 in four parts. If he gets 8% on Rs. 2000; $7\frac{1}{2}\%$ on Rs. 4000 and $8\frac{1}{2}\%$ on Rs. 1400; what percent must he get for the remainder, if his average annual interest is 8.13% ?

(*a*) 7% (*b*) 9% (*c*) $9\frac{1}{4}\%$ (*d*) $10\frac{1}{2}\%$

66. An amount of Rs. 1,00,000 is invested in two types of shares. The first yields an interest of 9% p.a. and the second, 11% p.a. If the total interest at the end of one year is $9\frac{3}{4}\%$, then the amount invested in each share was : **(M.B.A. 2002)**

(*a*) Rs. 52,500; Rs. 47,500 (*b*) Rs. 62,500; Rs. 37,500
(*c*) Rs. 72,500; Rs. 27,500 (*d*) Rs. 82,500; Rs. 17,500

67. David invested certain amount in three different schemes A, B and C with the rate of interest 10% p.a., 12% p.a. and 15% p.a. respectively. If the total interest accrued in one year was Rs. 3200 and the amount invested in Scheme C was 150% of the amount invested in Scheme A and 240% of the amount invested in Scheme B, what was the amount invested in Scheme B ? **(Bank P.O. 2003)**

(*a*) Rs. 5000 (*b*) Rs. 6500 (*c*) Rs. 8000
(*d*) Cannot be determined (*e*) None of these

68. A person invested in all Rs. 2600 at 4%, 6% and 8% per annum simple interest. At the end of the year, he got the same interest in all the three cases. The money invested at 4% is : **(S.S.C. 2003)**

(*a*) Rs. 200 (*b*) Rs. 600 (*c*) Rs. 800 (*d*) Rs. 1200

69. Divide Rs. 2379 into 3 parts so that their amounts after 2, 3 and 4 years respectively may be equal, the rate of interest being 5% per annum at simple interest. The first part is : **(C.B.I. 1997)**

(*a*) Rs. 759 (*b*) Rs. 792 (*c*) Rs. 818 (*d*) Rs. 828

70. A man invested $\frac{1}{3}$ of his capital at 7%; $\frac{1}{4}$ at 8% and the remainder at 10%. If his annual income is Rs. 561, the capital is :

(*a*) Rs. 5400 (*b*) Rs. 6000 (*c*) Rs. 6600 (*d*) Rs. 7200

ANSWERS

1. (c)	2. (a)	3. (b)	4. (a)	5. (b)	6. (d)	7. (d)	8. (b)	9. (c)
10. (c)	11. (d)	12. (b)	13. (c)	14. (d)	15. (c)	16. (d)	17. (b)	18. (b)
19. (c)	20. (c)	21. (a)	22. (c)	23. (a)	24. (b)	25. (c)	26. (b)	27. (c)
28. (c)	29. (d)	30. (b)	31. (c)	32. (d)	33. (b)	34. (b)	35. (d)	36. (a)
37. (a)	38. (d)	39. (a)	40. (a)	41. (d)	42. (b)	43. (c)	44. (c)	45. (b)
46. (d)	47. (b)	48. (d)	49. (e)	50. (c)	51. (a)	52. (b)	53. (b)	54. (a)
55. (b)	56. (c)	57. (b)	58. (d)	59. (c)	60. (d)	61. (d)	62. (a)	63. (c)
64. (c)	65. (b)	66. (b)	67. (a)	68. (d)	69. (d)	70. (c)		

SOLUTIONS

1. Time = 2 yrs 3 mths = $2\frac{1}{4}$ yrs = $\frac{9}{4}$ yrs.

$\therefore$ S.I. = Rs. $\left(4800 \times \frac{17}{2} \times \frac{9}{4} \times \frac{1}{100}\right)$ = Rs. 918.

2. Time = 9 months = $\frac{3}{4}$ year.

$\therefore$ S.I. = Rs. $\left(16800 \times \frac{25}{4} \times \frac{3}{4} \times \frac{1}{100}\right)$ = Rs. 787.50.

3. Time = (22 + 30 + 21) days = 73 days = $\frac{1}{5}$ year.

$\therefore$ S.I. = Rs. $\left(1820 \times \frac{15}{2} \times \frac{1}{5} \times \frac{1}{100}\right)$ = Rs. 27.30.

4. Gain in 2 yrs. = Rs. $\left[\left(5000 \times \frac{25}{4} \times \frac{2}{100}\right) - \left(\frac{5000 \times 4 \times 2}{100}\right)\right]$ = Rs. (625 – 400) = Rs. 225.

$\therefore$ Gain in 1 year = Rs. $\left(\frac{225}{2}\right)$ = Rs. 112.50.

5. Time = $\left(\frac{100 \times 81}{450 \times 4.5}\right)$ years = 4 years.

6. S.I. = Rs. (15500 – 12500) = Rs. 3000.

Rate = $\left(\frac{100 \times 3000}{12500 \times 4}\right)\%$ = 6%.

7. Time = 2 years 4 months = $2\frac{1}{3}$ years = $\frac{7}{3}$ years.

Rate = $\left(\frac{100 \times 252 \times 3}{1600 \times 7}\right)\%$ = $6\frac{3}{4}\%$.

8. Let rate = R% and time = R years. Then,

$\left(\frac{1200 \times R \times R}{100}\right) = 432 \Leftrightarrow 12R^2 = 432 \Leftrightarrow R^2 = 36 \Leftrightarrow R = 6.$

9. Principal = Rs. $\left(\frac{100 \times 5400}{12 \times 3}\right)$ = Rs. 15000.

10. Let the present worth be Rs. x. Then, S.I. = Rs. $(132 - x)$.

$\therefore \left(\frac{x \times 5 \times 2}{100}\right) = 132 - x \Leftrightarrow 10x = 13200 - 100x \Leftrightarrow 110x = 13200 \Leftrightarrow x = 120.$

11. Principal = Rs. $\left(\frac{100 \times 4016.25}{9 \times 5}\right)$ = Rs. $\left(\frac{401625}{45}\right)$ = Rs. 8925.

12. Sum = $\left(\frac{100 \times \text{S.I.}}{\text{R} \times \text{T}}\right)$ = Rs. $\left(\frac{100 \times x}{x \times x}\right)$ = Rs. $\left(\frac{100}{x}\right)$.

13. S.I. = Rs. (956 − 800) = Rs. 156.

Rate = $\left(\frac{100 \times 156}{800 \times 3}\right)\% = 6\frac{1}{2}\%$.

New rate = $\left(6\frac{1}{2} + 4\right)\% = 10\frac{1}{2}\%$.

New S.I. = Rs. $\left(800 \times \frac{21}{2} \times \frac{3}{100}\right)$ = Rs. 252.

$\therefore$ New amount = Rs. (800 + 252) = Rs. 1052.

14. We need to know the S.I., principal and time to find the rate. Since the principal is not given, so data is inadequate.

15. P = Rs. 800, R = $4\frac{1}{2}\% = \frac{9}{2}\%$, T = 3 years. Then,

S.I. = Rs. $\left(800 \times \frac{9}{2} \times \frac{3}{100}\right)$ = Rs. 108.

Now, P = Rs. 150, S.I. = Rs. 108, R = 8%.

$\therefore$ Time = $\left(\frac{100 \times 108}{150 \times 8}\right)$ years = 9 years.

16. P = Rs. 64, S.I. = Rs. (83.20 − 64) = Rs. 19.20, T = 2 years.

So, rate = $\left(\frac{100 \times 19.20}{64 \times 2}\right)\% = 15\%$.

Now, P = Rs. 86, R = 15%, T = 4 years.

$\therefore$ S.I. = Rs. $\left(\frac{86 \times 15 \times 4}{100}\right)$ = Rs. 51.60

17. S.I. = Rs. 840, R = 5%, T = 8 years.

Principal = Rs. $\left(\frac{100 \times 840}{5 \times 8}\right)$ = Rs. 2100.

Now, P = Rs. 2100, S.I. = Rs. 840, T = 5 years.

$\therefore$ Rate = $\left(\frac{100 \times 840}{2100 \times 5}\right)\% = 8\%$.

18. S.I. = Rs. 202.50, R = 4.5%, T = 1 year.

Principal = Rs. $\left(\frac{100 \times 202.50}{4.5 \times 1}\right)$ = Rs. 4500.

Now, P = Rs. 4500, R = 5%, T = 1 year.

S.I. = Rs. $\left(\frac{4500 \times 5 \times 1}{100}\right)$ = Rs. 225.

$\therefore$ **Difference in interest = Rs. (225 − 202.50) = Rs. 22.50.**

19. Let the sum be Rs. x. Then, S.I. = Rs. $(504 - x)$.

$\therefore \left(\frac{x \times 5 \times 4}{100}\right) = 504 - x \Leftrightarrow 20x = 50400 - 100x \Leftrightarrow 120x = 50400 \Leftrightarrow x = 420.$

Now, P = Rs. 420, R = 10%, T = $\frac{5}{2}$ years.

S.I. = Rs. $\left(\frac{420 \times 10}{100} \times \frac{5}{2}\right)$ = Rs. 105.

$\therefore$ Amount = Rs. (420 + 105) = Rs. 525.

20. Let the principal be P and rate of interest be R%.

$\therefore$ Required ratio = $\left[\frac{\left(\frac{P \times R \times 6}{100}\right)}{\left(\frac{P \times R \times 9}{100}\right)}\right] = \frac{6PR}{9PR} = \frac{6}{9} = 2 : 3.$

21. Let the sum be Rs. x. Then,

$\left(\frac{x \times 6 \times 3}{100}\right) + \left(\frac{x \times 9 \times 5}{100}\right) + \left(\frac{x \times 13 \times 3}{100}\right) = 8160$

$\Leftrightarrow 18x + 45x + 39x = (8160 \times 100) \Leftrightarrow 102x = 816000 \Leftrightarrow x = 8000.$

22. Let the sum be Rs. x. Now, S.I. = Rs. 600, T = 10 years.

Rate = $\left(\frac{100 \times 600}{x \times 10}\right)\% = \left(\frac{6000}{x}\right)\%.$

S.I. for first 5 years = Rs. $\left(\frac{x \times 5 \times 6000}{x \times 100}\right)$ = Rs. 300.

S.I. for last 5 years = Rs. $\left(3x \times 5 \times \frac{6000}{x \times 100}\right)$ = Rs. 900.

$\therefore$ Total interest = Rs. 1200.

23. S.I. = Rs. $\left(10 \times \frac{3}{100} \times 4\right)$ = Rs. 1.20.

24. Let the sum be Rs. 100. Then,

S.I. for first 6 months = Rs. $\left(\frac{100 \times 10 \times 1}{100 \times 2}\right)$ = Rs. 5.

S.I. for last 6 months = Rs. $\left(\frac{105 \times 10 \times 1}{100 \times 2}\right)$ = Rs. 5.25.

So, amount at the end of 1 year = Rs. (100 + 5 + 5.25) = Rs. 110.25.

$\therefore$ Effective rate = (110.25 − 100) = 10.25%.

25. S.I. for 1 year = Rs. (854 − 815) = Rs. 39.

S.I. for 3 years = Rs. (39 × 3) = Rs. 117.

$\therefore$ Principal = Rs. (815 − 117) = Rs. 698.

26. S.I. for 5 years = Rs. (1020 − 720) = Rs. 300.

S.I. for 2 years = Rs. $\left(\frac{300}{5} \times 2\right)$ = Rs. 120.

$\therefore$ Principal = Rs. (720 − 120) = Rs. 600.

27. S.I. for 3 years = Rs. (12005 − 9800) = Rs. 2205.

S.I. for 5 years = Rs. $\left(\frac{2205}{3} \times 5\right)$ = Rs. 3675.

∴ Principal = Rs. (9800 − 3675) = Rs. 6125.

Hence, rate = $\left(\frac{100 \times 3675}{6125 \times 5}\right)\%$ = 12%.

28. S.I. for $1\frac{1}{2}$ years = Rs. (1067.20 − 1012) = Rs. 55.20.

S.I. for $2\frac{1}{2}$ years = Rs. $\left(55.20 \times \frac{2}{3} \times \frac{5}{2}\right)$ = Rs. 92.

∴ Principal = Rs. (1012 − 92) = Rs. 920.

Hence, rate = $\left(\frac{100 \times 92 \times 2}{920 \times 5}\right)\%$ = 4%.

29. Let sum = x. Then, S.I. = x.

∴ Time = $\left(\frac{100 \times \text{S.I.}}{\text{P} \times \text{R}}\right) = \left(\frac{100 \times x}{x \times 12}\right)$ years = $8\frac{1}{3}$ years = 8 years 4 months.

30. Let sum = x. Then, S.I. = x.

∴ Rate = $\left(\frac{100 \times \text{S.I.}}{\text{P} \times \text{T}}\right) = \left(\frac{100 \times x}{x \times 12}\right)\% = \frac{25}{3}\% = 8\frac{1}{3}\%$.

31. Let sum = x. Then, S.I. = $3x$.

∴ Rate = $\left(\frac{100 \times \text{S.I.}}{\text{P} \times \text{T}}\right) = \left(\frac{100 \times 3x}{x \times 15}\right)\%$ = 20%.

32. Let sum = x. Then, S.I. = x.

∴ Rate = $\left(\frac{100 \times x}{x \times 6}\right)\% = \frac{50}{3}\%$.

Now, sum = x, S.I. = $3x$, Rate = $\frac{50}{3}\%$.

∴ Time = $\frac{100 \times 3x}{x \times \frac{50}{3}}$ = 18 years.

33. Let sum = x. Then, S.I. = $2x$, Time = $15\frac{1}{2}$ years = $\frac{31}{2}$ years.

∴ Rate = $\left(\frac{100 \times 2x}{x \times \frac{31}{2}}\right)\% = \frac{400}{31}\%$.

Now, sum = x, S.I. = x, Rate = $\frac{400}{31}\%$.

∴ Time = $\frac{100 \times x}{x \times \frac{400}{31}} = \frac{31}{4}$ years = 7 years 9 months.

34. Let sum be x. Then, S.I. = x.

1. Time = $\frac{100 \times x}{x \times \frac{50}{3}}$ = 6 years (False)

2. Time $= \frac{100 \times x}{x \times 20} = 5$ years (True)

3. Suppose sum = x. Then, S.I. = x and Time = 5 years.

Rate $= \left(\frac{100 \times x}{x \times 5}\right)\% = 20\%$

Now, sum = x, S.I. = $3x$ and Rate = 20%.

$\therefore$ Time $= \left(\frac{100 \times 3x}{x \times 20}\right)$ years = 15 years (False)

So, 2 alone is correct.

35. Let sum = x. Then, S.I. $= \frac{x}{2}$.

$\therefore \frac{x}{2} = \frac{x \times 8 \times 6}{100}$. Clearly, data is inadequate.

36. Let sum = x. Then, S.I. $= \frac{2x}{5}$, Time = 10 years.

$\therefore$ Rate $= \left(\frac{100 \times 2x}{x \times 5 \times 10}\right)\% = 4\%$.

37. Let sum = x. Then, S.I. = $0.125x = \frac{1}{8}x$, R = 10%.

$\therefore$ Time $= \left(\frac{100 \times x}{x \times 8 \times 10}\right)$ years $= \frac{5}{4}$ years $= 1\frac{1}{4}$ years.

38. Let the sum be x. Then, S.I. = 40% of $x = \frac{2x}{5}$; Rate = 5%.

$\therefore$ Time $= \left(100 \times \frac{2x}{5} \times \frac{1}{x \times 5}\right) = 8$ years.

39. Let sum = x. Then, amount $= \frac{7x}{6}$.

S.I. $= \left(\frac{7x}{6} - x\right) = \frac{x}{6}$; Time = 3 years.

$\therefore$ Rate $= \left(\frac{100 \times x}{x \times 6 \times 3}\right)\% = \frac{50}{9}\% = 5\frac{5}{9}\%$.

40. Let sum = x. Then, S.I. $= \frac{x}{9}$.

Let rate = R% and time = R years.

$\therefore \left(\frac{x \times R \times R}{100}\right) = \frac{x}{9} \Leftrightarrow R^2 = \frac{100}{9} \Leftrightarrow R = \frac{10}{3} = 3\frac{1}{3}$.

Hence, rate $= 3\frac{1}{3}\%$.

41. Let sum = x. Then, S.I. $= \frac{9}{16}x$.

Let rate = R% and time = R years.

$\therefore \left(\frac{x \times R \times R}{100}\right) = \frac{9x}{16} \Leftrightarrow R^2 = \frac{900}{16} \Leftrightarrow R = \frac{30}{4} = 7\frac{1}{2}$.

Hence, time $= 7\frac{1}{2}$ years.

42. Let the sum lent to C be Rs. x. Then, $\left(\frac{2500 \times 7 \times 4}{100}\right) + \left(\frac{x \times 7 \times 4}{100}\right) = 1120$

$\Leftrightarrow \quad \frac{7}{25}x = (1120 - 700) \Rightarrow x = \left(\frac{420 \times 25}{7}\right) = 1500.$

43. Let each sum be Rs. x. Then, $\left(\frac{x \times 11 \times 9}{100 \times 2}\right) - \left(\frac{x \times 11 \times 7}{100 \times 2}\right) = 412.50$

$\Leftrightarrow \quad (99x - 77x) = 82500 \quad \Leftrightarrow \quad 22x = 82500 \quad \Leftrightarrow \quad x = 3750.$

44. Let the sum be Rs. x. Then, $\left(x \times \frac{15}{2} \times \frac{5}{4} \times \frac{1}{100}\right) - \left(x \times \frac{25}{2} \times \frac{2}{3} \times \frac{1}{100}\right) = 32.50$

$\Leftrightarrow \quad \frac{75x}{8} - \frac{25x}{3} = 3250 \quad \Leftrightarrow \quad 25x = (3250 \times 24) \quad \Leftrightarrow \quad x = \left(\frac{3250 \times 24}{25}\right) = 3120.$

45. Let the sums be x and y.

$\frac{x \times 6 \times 2}{100} + \frac{y \times 7 \times 2}{100} = 354$ or $6x + 7y = 17700.$ ...(i)

Also, $\frac{x}{4} = \frac{y}{5}$ or $5x - 4y = 0$ ...(ii)

Solving (i) and (ii), we get : $x = 1200$ and $y = 1500$.

$\therefore$ Total sum = Rs. 2700.

46. Let the money added be Rs. x. Then, $\frac{(830 + x) \times 14 \times 3}{100} - \frac{830 \times 12 \times 3}{100} = 93.90$

$\Leftrightarrow \quad 830 \times 42 + 42x - 830 \times 36 = 9390 \quad \Leftrightarrow \quad 42x + 830 \times (42 - 36) = 9390$

$\Leftrightarrow \quad 42x = 9390 - 4980 \quad \Leftrightarrow \quad x = \frac{4410}{42} = 105.$

$\therefore$ Money added = Rs. 105.

47. Let the time be x years. Then, $\left(\frac{500 \times 3 \times x}{100}\right) + \left(\frac{600 \times 9 \times x}{100 \times 2}\right) = 126$

$\Leftrightarrow \quad 15x + 27x = 126 \quad \Leftrightarrow \quad 42x = 126 \quad \Leftrightarrow \quad x = 3.$

$\therefore$ Required time = 3 years.

48. Let the rate be R% p.a. Then, $\left(\frac{5000 \times R \times 2}{100}\right) + \left(\frac{3000 \times R \times 4}{100}\right) = 2200$

$\Leftrightarrow \quad 100R + 120R = 2200 \quad \Leftrightarrow \quad R = \left(\frac{2200}{220}\right) = 10.$

$\therefore$ Rate = 10%.

49. Let the original rate be R%. Then, new rate = (2R)%.

$\therefore \quad \left(\frac{725 \times R \times 1}{100}\right) + \left(\frac{362.50 \times 2R \times 1}{100 \times 3}\right) = 33.50$

$\Leftrightarrow \quad (2175 + 725)\, R = 33.50 \times 100 \times 3 = 10050$

$\Leftrightarrow \quad R = \frac{10050}{2900} = 3.46$

$\therefore$ Original rate = 3.46%.

50. $\left(\frac{1500 \times R_1 \times 3}{100}\right) - \left(\frac{1500 \times R_2 \times 3}{100}\right) = 13.50$

$\Leftrightarrow \quad 4500\,(R_1 - R_2) = 1350 \quad \Leftrightarrow \quad R_1 - R_2 = \frac{1350}{4500} = 0.3\%.$

51. Let the second amount be Rs. x. Then,

$$\left(\frac{12000 \times 10 \times 1}{100}\right) + \left(\frac{x \times 20 \times 1}{100}\right) = \left[\frac{(12000 + x) \times 14 \times 1}{100}\right]$$

$\Leftrightarrow$ $12000 + 20x = 168000 + 14x$ $\Leftrightarrow$ $6x = 48000$ $\Leftrightarrow$ $x = 8000$.

$\therefore$ Total investment = Rs. (12000 + 8000) = Rs. 20000.

52. S.I. = Rs. $\left(2600 \times \frac{20}{3} \times \frac{1}{100} \times T\right)$ = Rs. $\left(\frac{520}{3} \times T\right)$,

which is an exact number of rupees when T = 3.

53. Let the savings be X and Y and the rates of simple interest be $5x$ and $4x$ respectively.

Then, $X \times 5x \times \frac{1}{2} \times \frac{1}{100} = Y \times 4x \times \frac{1}{2} \times \frac{1}{100}$ or $\frac{X}{Y} = \frac{4}{5}$, *i.e.*, X : Y = 4 : 5.

54. Let the sum be Rs. x and original rate be R%. Then, $\frac{x \times (R + 3) \times 2}{100} - \frac{x \times R \times 2}{100} = 72$

$\Leftrightarrow$ $2Rx + 6x - 2Rx = 7200$ $\Leftrightarrow$ $x = 1200$.

55. Let the sum be Rs. x. Then, $\left(x \times \frac{25}{2} \times \frac{1}{100}\right) - \left(\frac{x \times 10 \times 1}{100}\right) = 1250$

$\Leftrightarrow$ $25x - 20x = 250000$ $\Leftrightarrow$ $5x = 250000$ $\Leftrightarrow$ $x = 50000$.

56. Let the capital be Rs. x. Then, $\left(\frac{x \times 8 \times 1}{100}\right) - \left(x \times \frac{31}{4} \times \frac{1}{100}\right) = 61.50$

$\Leftrightarrow$ $32x - 31x = 6150 \times 4$ $\Leftrightarrow$ $x = 24600$.

57. Let the annual instalment be Rs. x. Then,

$$\left[x + \left(\frac{x \times 3 \times 5}{100}\right)\right] + \left[x + \left(\frac{x \times 2 \times 5}{100}\right)\right] + \left[x + \left(\frac{x \times 1 \times 5}{100}\right)\right] + x = 6450$$

$\Leftrightarrow$ $\frac{23x}{20} + \frac{22x}{20} + \frac{21x}{20} + x = 6450$ $\Leftrightarrow$ $86x = 6450 \times 20$ $\Leftrightarrow$ $x = 1500$.

58. Rs. 10 + S.I. on Rs. 10 for 11 months

= Rs. 11 + S.I. on Re. 1 for (1 + 2 + 3 + 4 + ... + 10) months

$\Rightarrow$ Rs. 10 + S.I. on Re. 1 for 110 months = Rs. 11 + S.I on Re. 1 for 55 months

$\Rightarrow$ S.I. on Re. 1 for 55 months = Re. 1.

$\therefore$ Rate = $\left(\frac{100 \times 12}{1 \times 55}\right)\% = 21\frac{9}{11}\%$.

59. Amount to be paid = Rs. $\left(100 + \frac{200 \times 5 \times 1}{100} + \frac{100 \times 5 \times 1}{100}\right)$ = Rs. 115.

60. Money paid in cash = Rs. 1000.

Balance payment = Rs. (20000 − 1000) = Rs. 19000.

61. Let the sum be Rs. x, rate be R% p.a. and time be T years.

Then, $\left[\frac{x \times (R + 2) \times T}{100}\right] - \left(\frac{x \times R \times T}{100}\right) = 108$ $\Leftrightarrow$ $2xT = 10800$ ...(*i*)

And, $\left[\frac{x \times R \times (T + 2)}{100}\right] - \left(\frac{x \times R \times T}{100}\right) = 180$ $\Leftrightarrow$ $2xR = 18000$ ...(*ii*)

Clearly, from (*i*) and (*ii*), we cannot find the value of x.

So, the data is inadequate.

62. Let the sum invested in Scheme A be Rs. x and that in Scheme B be Rs. $(13900 - x)$.

Then, $\left(\frac{x \times 14 \times 2}{100}\right) + \left[\frac{(13900 - x) \times 11 \times 2}{100}\right] = 3508$

$\Leftrightarrow \quad 28x - 22x = 350800 - (13900 \times 22) \quad \Leftrightarrow \quad 6x = 45000 \quad \Leftrightarrow \quad x = 7500.$

So, sum invested in Scheme B = Rs. (13900 − 7500) = Rs. 6400.

63. Let the sum lent at 10% be Rs. x and that lent at 9% be Rs. $(2600 - x)$. Then,

$$\left(\frac{x \times 10 \times 5}{100}\right) = \frac{(2600 - x) \times 9 \times 6}{100}$$

$\Leftrightarrow \quad 50x = (2600 \times 54) - 54x \quad \Rightarrow \quad x = \left(\frac{2600 \times 54}{104}\right) = 1350.$

$\therefore$ Sum lent at 10% = Rs. 1350.

64. Let the sum lent at 5% be Rs. x and that lent at 8% be Rs. $(1550 - x)$. Then,

$$\left(\frac{x \times 5 \times 3}{100}\right) + \left[\frac{(1550 - x) \times 8 \times 3}{100}\right] = 300$$

$\Leftrightarrow \quad 15x - 24x + (1550 \times 24) = 30000 \quad \Leftrightarrow \quad 9x = 7200 \quad \Leftrightarrow \quad x = 800.$

$\therefore$ Required ratio = 800 : 750 = 16 : 15.

65. Let the required rate be R. Then,

$$\left(\frac{20000 \times 8 \times 1}{100}\right) + \left(4000 \times \frac{15}{2} \times \frac{1}{100}\right) + \left(1400 \times \frac{17}{2} \times \frac{1}{100}\right) + \left(2600 \times R \times \frac{1}{100}\right) = \left(\frac{813}{10000} \times 10000\right)$$

$\Leftrightarrow \quad 160 + 300 + 119 + 26R = 813 \quad \Leftrightarrow \quad R = 9.$

66. Let the sum invested at 9% be Rs. x and that invested at 11% be Rs. $(100000 - x)$.

Then, $\left(\frac{x \times 9 \times 1}{100}\right) + \left[\frac{(100000 - x) \times 11 \times 1}{100}\right] = \left(100000 \times \frac{39}{4} \times \frac{1}{100}\right)$

$\Leftrightarrow \quad \frac{9x + 1100000 - 11x}{100} = \frac{39000}{4} = 9750$

$\Leftrightarrow \quad 2x = (1100000 - 975000) = 125000 \quad \Leftrightarrow \quad x = 62500.$

$\therefore$ Sum invested at 9% = Rs. 62500.

Sum invested at 11% = Rs. (100000 − 62500) = Rs. 37500.

67. Let x, y and z be the amounts invested in schemes A, B and C respectively. Then,

$$\left(\frac{x \times 10 \times 1}{100}\right) + \left(\frac{y \times 12 \times 1}{100}\right) + \left(\frac{z \times 15 \times 1}{100}\right) = 3200$$

$\Leftrightarrow \quad 10x + 12y + 15z = 320000$ ...(*i*)

Now, $z = 240\%$ of $y = \frac{12}{5} y$ ...(*ii*)

And, $z = 150\%$ of $x = \frac{3}{2} x \Rightarrow x = \frac{2}{3} z = \left(\frac{2}{3} \times \frac{12}{5}\right) y = \frac{8}{5} y$ ...(*iii*)

From (*i*), (*ii*) and (*iii*), we have

$16y + 12y + 36y = 320000 \quad \Leftrightarrow \quad 64y = 320000 \quad \Leftrightarrow \quad y = 5000.$

$\therefore$ Sum invested in Scheme B = Rs. 5000.

68. Let the parts be x, y and $[2600 - (x + y)]$. Then,

$$\frac{x \times 4 \times 1}{100} = \frac{y \times 6 \times 1}{100} = \frac{[2600 - (x + y)] \times 8 \times 1}{100}$$

$\therefore \quad \frac{y}{x} = \frac{4}{6} = \frac{2}{3}$ or $y = \frac{2}{3}x$.

So, $\frac{x \times 4 \times 1}{100} = \frac{\left(2600 - \frac{5}{3}x\right) \times 8}{100}$

$\Leftrightarrow \quad 4x = \frac{(7800 - 5x) \times 8}{3} \quad \Leftrightarrow \quad 52x = (7800 \times 8) \quad \Leftrightarrow \quad x = \left(\frac{7800 \times 8}{52}\right) = 1200.$

$\therefore$ Money invested at 4% = Rs. 1200

69. Let the parts be x, y and $[2379 - (x + y)]$.

$$x + \left(x \times 2 \times \frac{5}{100}\right) = y + \left(y \times 3 \times \frac{5}{100}\right) = z + \left(z \times 4 \times \frac{5}{100}\right)$$

$\Rightarrow \quad \frac{11x}{10} = \frac{23y}{20} = \frac{6z}{5} = k \quad \Rightarrow \quad x = \frac{10k}{11}, \; y = \frac{20k}{23}, \; z = \frac{5k}{6}$

But $x + y + z = 2379$

$\Rightarrow \quad \frac{10k}{11} + \frac{20k}{23} + \frac{5k}{6} = 2379 \quad \Rightarrow \quad 1380k + 1320k + 1265k = 2379 \times 11 \times 23 \times 6$

$\Rightarrow \quad k = \frac{2379 \times 11 \times 23 \times 6}{3965} = \frac{3 \times 11 \times 23 \times 6}{5}$

$\therefore \quad x = \left(\frac{10}{11} \times \frac{3 \times 11 \times 23 \times 6}{5}\right) = 828.$

Hence, the first part is Rs. 828.

70. Let total capital be Rs. x. Then, $\left(\frac{x}{3} \times \frac{7}{100} \times 1\right) + \left(\frac{x}{4} \times \frac{8}{100} \times 1\right) + \left(\frac{5x}{12} \times \frac{10}{100} \times 1\right) = 561$

$\Leftrightarrow \quad \frac{7x}{300} + \frac{x}{50} + \frac{x}{24} = 561 \quad \Leftrightarrow \quad 51x = (561 \times 600) \quad \Leftrightarrow \quad x = \left(\frac{561 \times 600}{51}\right) = 6600.$

71. Let the sum be Rs. 100 be invested for 1 year. Then,

$$\text{S.I.} = \text{Rs.}\left[\left(\frac{40 \times 15 \times 1}{100}\right) + \left(\frac{30 \times 10 \times 1}{100}\right) + \left(\frac{30 \times 18 \times 1}{100}\right)\right] = \text{Rs. } 14.40.$$

$\therefore$ Effective rate = 14.4%.

EXERCISE 21B

(DATA SUFFICIENCY TYPE QUESTIONS)

Directions (*Questions 1 to 6*) : ***Each of the questions given below consists of a statement and / or a question and two statements numbered I and II given below it. You have to decide whether the data provided in the statement(s) is / are sufficient to answer the question. Read both the statements and***

Give answer (a) if the data in Statement I alone are sufficient to answer the question, while the data in Statement II alone are not sufficient to answer the question;

Give answer (b) if the data in Statement II alone are sufficient to answer the question, while the data in Statement I alone are not sufficient to answer the question;

Give answer (c) if the data either in Statement I or in Statement II alone are sufficient to answer the question;

Give answer (d) if the data in both Statements I and II together are not sufficient to answer the question;

Give answer (e) if the data in both Statements I and II together are necessary to answer the question.

1. What is the rate of simple interest ? **(Bank P.O. 2003)**
   I. The total interest earned was Rs. 4000.
   II. The sum was invested for 4 years.
2. The simple interest on a sum of money is Rs. 50. What is the sum ? **(R.B.I. 2003)**
   I. The interest rate is 10% p.a.
   II. The sum earned simple interest in 10 years.
3. How much money did X invest ?
   I. An increase in the rate of interest from $4\frac{7}{8}\%$ to $5\frac{1}{8}\%$ per annum increases his yearly income by Rs. 25.
   II. The sum invested gets doubled, when invested at 8% p.a. for $12\frac{1}{2}$ years.
4. What percentage of simple interest per annum did Anand pay to Deepak ?
   I. Anand borrowed Rs. 8000 from Deepak for four years.
   II. Anand returned Rs. 8800 to Deepak at the end of two years and settled the loan. **(I.B.P.S. 2002)**
5. A man borrowed a total sum of Rs. 24000 from two moneylenders. For one loan, he paid interest @ $7\frac{1}{2}\%$ p.a. and for the other 9% p.a. How much money did he borrow at each rate ?
   I. The sum of the interests after one year was Rs. 2025.
   II. The interest on one sum was twice that on the other.
6. What is the sum which earned interest ? **(NABARD, 2002)**
   I. The total simple interest was Rs. 7000 after 7 years.
   II. The total of sum and simple interest was double of the sum after 5 years.

Directions (*Questions 7-8*) : *Each of the questions given below consists of a question followed by three statements. You have to study the question and the statements and decide which of the statement(s) is/are necessary to answer the question.*

7. What is the principal sum ?
   I. The sum amounts to Rs. 690 in 3 years at S.I.
   II. The sum amounts to Rs. 750 in 5 years at S.I.
   III. The rate of interest is 5% p.a.
   (*a*) I and III only (*b*) II and III only
   (*c*) I and II only (*d*) I and III only, or II and III only
   (*e*) Any two of the three
8. In how many years will a sum of money put at simple interest treble itself ?
   I. The interest earned in 4 years is half the sum.
   II. The rate of interest is $12\frac{1}{2}\%$.
   III. The sum doubles itself in 8 years at simple interest.
   (*a*) Any one of the three (*b*) Any two of the three
   (*c*) All I, II and III (*d*) II and III only
   (*e*) I and II only

ANSWERS

1. (*d*) 2. (*e*) 3. (*a*) 4. (*e*) 5. (*c*) 6. (*e*) 7. (*e*) 8. (*a*)

SOLUTIONS

1. We know that, $R = \left(\frac{100 \times S.I.}{P \times T}\right)$.

Now, I gives, S.I. = Rs. 4000.

II gives, T = 4 years.

But, P is unknown. So, we cannot find R

So, given data is insufficient to get R.

$\therefore$ Correct answer is (*d*).

2. Given : S.I. = Rs. 50.

I gives, R = 10% p.a.

II gives, T = 10 years.

$$\therefore \quad \text{Sum} = \left(\frac{100 \times S.I.}{T \times R}\right) = \text{Rs.}\left(\frac{100 \times 50}{10 \times 10}\right) = \text{Rs. } 50.$$

Thus, I and II together give the answer.

$\therefore$ Correct answer is (*e*).

3. Suppose X invests Rs. *x*.

I gives : $R_1 = \frac{39}{8}\%$, $R_2 = \frac{41}{8}\%$.

Increase in S.I. = Rs. 25.

$$\Rightarrow \left(\frac{x \times 1 \times \frac{41}{8}}{100}\right) - \left(\frac{x \times 1 \times \frac{39}{8}}{100}\right) = 25$$

$$\Rightarrow (41x - 39x) = (25 \times 800) \Rightarrow x = \left(\frac{25 \times 800}{2}\right) = 10000.$$

Thus, I only gives the answer.

II gives, S.I. = Rs. *x*, R = 8% and T = $\frac{25}{2}$ years.

$$P = \frac{100 \times S.I.}{R \times T} = \left(\frac{100 \times x}{8 \times 25} \times 2\right)$$

Thus, P is not obtained.

$\therefore$ I alone is sufficient to get the answer and II is not sufficient to get the answer.

$\therefore$ Correct answer is (*a*).

4. Let the rate be R% p.a.

I gives, P = Rs. 8000 and T = 4 years.

II gives, S.I. = Rs. (8800 − 8000) = Rs. 800.

$$\therefore \quad R = \frac{100 \times S.I.}{P \times T} = \left(\frac{100 \times 800}{8000 \times 4}\right)\% = 2\frac{1}{2}\% \text{ p.a.}$$

Thus, I and II both are needed to get the answer.

$\therefore$ Correct answer is (*e*).

5. Suppose he borrowed Rs. *x* at $7\frac{1}{2}\%$ p.a. and Rs. (24000 − *x*) at 9% p.a.

I gives, total interest = Rs. 2025.

$\therefore \quad \left(x \times 1 \times \frac{15}{2} \times \frac{1}{100}\right) + \left\{(24000 - x) \times 1 \times \frac{9}{100}\right\} = 2025.$

This gives x.

II gives Interest on Rs. $(24000 - x) = 2 \times$ (interest on Rs x)

$\Rightarrow \quad (24000 - x) \times \frac{9}{100} \times 1 = \left(2 \times x \times \frac{15}{2} \times \frac{1}{100}\right)$

This gives x.

Thus, data in I as well as well as in II are sufficient to answer the question.

$\therefore$ Correct answer is (*c*).

6. Let the sum be Rs. x.

I gives, S.I. = Rs. 7000 and T = 7 years.

II gives, Sum + S.I. for 5 years = 2 × Sum $\Rightarrow$ Sum = S.I. for 5 years

Now, S.I. for 7 years = Rs. 7000

$\therefore$ S.I. for 1 year = Rs. $\frac{7000}{7}$ = Rs. 1000.

S.I. for 5 years = Rs. (1000 × 5) = Rs. 5000.

Thus, I and II both are needed to get the answer.

$\therefore$ Correct answer is (*e*).

7. Clearly, any of the three will give us the answer.

$\therefore$ Correct answer is (*e*).

8. Let sum be Rs. x. Then, S.I. = Rs. $(3x - x)$ = Rs. $2x$, T = ?

I gives : When T = 4, then S.I. = Rs. $\frac{x}{2}$.

$\therefore \quad R = \frac{100 \times S.I.}{P \times T} = \left(100 \times \frac{x}{2} \times \frac{1}{x} \times \frac{1}{4}\right) = 12\frac{1}{2}\%$ p.a.

Now, Sum = Rs. x, S.I. = Rs. $2x$, R = $\frac{25}{2}\%$ p.a., T = ?

$\therefore \quad T = \frac{100 \times S.I.}{P \times R} = \left(\frac{100 \times 2x}{x \times 25} \times 2\right) = 16$ years.

Thus, I only gives the answer.

II gives, R = $\frac{25}{2}\%$ p.a.

$\therefore \quad T = \frac{100 \times S.I.}{P \times R} = \left(\frac{100 \times 2x}{x \times 25} \times 2\right) = 16$ years.

Thus, II only also gives the answer.

III gives, R = 5% p.a.

$\therefore \quad T = \frac{100 \times S.I.}{P \times R} = \left(\frac{100 \times 2x}{x \times 5}\right) = 40$ years.

Thus, III only also gives the answer.

$\therefore$ Correct answer is (*a*).

22. COMPOUND INTEREST

Compound Interest : Sometimes it so happens that the borrower and the lender agree to fix up a certain unit of time, say *yearly* or *half-yearly* or *quarterly* to settle the previous account.

In such cases, the amount after first unit of time becomes the principal for the second unit, the amount after second unit becomes the principal for the third unit and so on.

After a specified period, *the difference between the amount and the money borrowed is called the* ***Compound Interest*** *(abbreviated as C.I.) for that period.*

IMPORTANT FACTS AND FORMULAE

Let Principal = P, Rate = R% per annum, Time = *n* years.

I. When interest is compound Annually :

$$\text{Amount} = P\left(1 + \frac{R}{100}\right)^n$$

II. When interest is compounded Half-yearly :

$$\text{Amount} = P\left[1 + \frac{(R/2)}{100}\right]^{2n}$$

III. When interest is compounded Quarterly :

$$\text{Amount} = P\left[1 + \frac{(R/4)}{100}\right]^{4n}$$

IV. When interest is compounded Annually but time is in fraction, say $3\frac{2}{5}$ years.

$$\text{Amount} = P\left(1 + \frac{R}{100}\right)^3 \times \left(1 + \frac{\frac{2}{5}R}{100}\right)$$

V. When Rates are different for different years, say $R_1\%$, $R_2\%$, $R_3\%$ for 1st, 2nd and 3rd year respectively.

$$\text{Then, Amount} = P\left(1 + \frac{R_1}{100}\right)\left(1 + \frac{R_2}{100}\right)\left(1 + \frac{R_3}{100}\right).$$

VI. Present worth of Rs. *x* due *n* years hence is given by :

$$\text{Present Worth} = \frac{x}{\left(1 + \frac{R}{100}\right)^n}.$$

SOLVED EXAMPLES

Ex. 1. ***Find compound interest on Rs. 7500 at 4% per annum for 2 years, compounded annually.***

Sol. Amount = Rs. $\left[7500 \times \left(1 + \frac{4}{100}\right)^2\right]$ = Rs. $\left(7500 \times \frac{26}{25} \times \frac{26}{25}\right)$ = Rs. 8112.

$\therefore$ C.I. = Rs. (8112 − 7500) = Rs. 612.

Ex. 2. ***Find compound interest on Rs. 8000 at 15% per annum for 2 years 4 months, compounded annually.***

Sol. Time = 2 years 4 months = $2\frac{4}{12}$ years = $2\frac{1}{3}$ years.

Amount = Rs. $\left[8000 \times \left(1 + \frac{15}{100}\right)^2 \times \left(1 + \frac{\frac{1}{3} \times 15}{100}\right)\right]$ = Rs. $\left(8000 \times \frac{23}{20} \times \frac{23}{20} \times \frac{21}{20}\right)$

= Rs. 11109.

$\therefore$ C.I. = Rs. (11109 − 8000) = Rs. 3109.

Ex. 3. ***Find the compound interest on Rs. 10,000 in 2 years at 4% per annum, the interest being compounded half-yearly.*** **(S.S.C. 2000)**

Sol. Principal = Rs. 10000; Rate = 2% per half-year; Time = 2 years = 4 half-years.

$\therefore$ Amount = Rs. $\left[10000 \times \left(1 + \frac{2}{100}\right)^4\right]$ = Rs. $\left(10000 \times \frac{51}{50} \times \frac{51}{50} \times \frac{51}{50} \times \frac{51}{50}\right)$

= Rs. 10824.32.

$\therefore$ C.I. = Rs. (10824.32 − 10000) = Rs. 824.32.

Ex. 4. ***Find the compound interest on Rs. 16,000 at 20% per annum for 9 months, compounded quarterly.***

Sol. Principal = Rs. 16000; Time = 9 months = 3 quarters;

Rate = 20% per annum = 5% per quarter.

$\therefore$ Amount = Rs. $\left[16000 \times \left(1 + \frac{5}{100}\right)^3\right]$ = Rs. $\left(16000 \times \frac{21}{20} \times \frac{21}{20} \times \frac{21}{20}\right)$ = Rs. 18522.

$\therefore$ C.I. = Rs. (18522 − 16000) = Rs. 2522.

Ex. 5. ***If the simple interest on a sum of money at 5% per annum for 3 years is Rs. 1200, find the compound interest on the same sum for the same period at the same rate.***

Sol. Clearly, Rate = 5% p.a., Time = 3 years, S.I. = Rs. 1200.

So, Principal = Rs. $\left(\frac{100 \times 1200}{3 \times 5}\right)$ = Rs. 8000.

Amount = Rs. $\left[8000 \times \left(1 + \frac{5}{100}\right)^3\right]$ = Rs. $\left(8000 \times \frac{21}{20} \times \frac{21}{20} \times \frac{21}{20}\right)$ = Rs. 9261.

$\therefore$ C.I. = Rs. (9261 − 8000) = Rs. 1261.

Ex. 6. ***In what time will Rs. 1000 become Rs. 1331 at 10% per annum compounded annually ?*** **(S.S.C. 2004)**

Sol. Principal = Rs. 1000; Amount = Rs. 1331; Rate = 10% p.a.

Let the time be n years. Then,

$$\left[1000\left(1+\frac{10}{100}\right)^n\right] = 1331 \text{ or } \left(\frac{11}{10}\right)^n = \left(\frac{1331}{1000}\right) = \left(\frac{11}{10}\right)^3$$

$\therefore$ $n = 3$ years.

Ex. 7. ***If Rs. 500 amounts to Rs. 583.20 in two years compounded annually, find the rate of interest per annum.***

Sol. Principal = Rs. 500; Amount = Rs. 583.20; Time = 2 years.

Let the rate be R% per annum. Then,

$$\left[500\left(1+\frac{R}{100}\right)^2\right] = 583.20 \text{ or } \left(1+\frac{R}{100}\right)^2 = \frac{5832}{5000} = \frac{11664}{10000}$$

$$\therefore \left(1+\frac{R}{100}\right)^2 = \left(\frac{108}{100}\right)^2 \text{ or } 1+\frac{R}{100} = \frac{108}{100} \text{ or } R = 8.$$

So, rate = 8% p.a.

Ex. 8. ***If the compound interest on a certain sum at $16\frac{2}{3}\%$ for 3 years is Rs. 1270, find the simple interest on the same sum at the same rate and for the same period.***

Sol. Let the sum be Rs. x. Then,

$$\text{C.I.} = \left[x \times \left(1+\frac{50}{3\times 100}\right)^3 - x\right] = \left(\frac{343x}{216} - x\right) = \frac{127x}{216}.$$

$$\therefore \frac{127x}{216} = 1270 \text{ or } x = \frac{1270 \times 216}{127} = 2160.$$

Thus, the sum is Rs. 2160.

$$\therefore \text{S.I.} = \text{Rs.}\left(2160 \times \frac{50}{3} \times 3 \times \frac{1}{100}\right) = \text{Rs. } 1080.$$

Ex. 9. ***The difference between the compound interest and simple interest on a certain sum at 10% per annum for 2 years is Rs. 631. Find the sum.***

Sol. Let the sum be Rs. x. Then,

$$\text{C.I.} = x\left(1+\frac{10}{100}\right)^2 - x = \frac{21x}{100}, \quad \text{S.I.} = \left(\frac{x \times 10 \times 2}{100}\right) = \frac{x}{5}.$$

$$\therefore (\text{C.I.}) - (\text{S.I.}) = \left(\frac{21x}{100} - \frac{x}{5}\right) = \frac{x}{100}.$$

$$\therefore \frac{x}{100} = 631 \Leftrightarrow x = 63100.$$

Hence, the sum is Rs. 63,100.

Ex. 10. ***The difference between the compound interest and the simple interest accrued on an amount of Rs. 18,000 in 2 years was Rs. 405. What was the rate of interest p.c.p.a.?*** **(Bank P.O. 2003)**

Sol. Let the rate be R% p.a. Then,

$$\left[18000\left(1+\frac{R}{100}\right)^2 - 18000\right] - \left(\frac{18000 \times R \times 2}{100}\right) = 405$$

$$\Leftrightarrow 18000\left[\frac{(100+R)^2}{10000} - 1 - \frac{2R}{100}\right] = 405$$

$$\Leftrightarrow \quad 18000\left[\frac{(100+R)^2-10000-200R}{10000}\right]=405$$

$$\Leftrightarrow \quad \frac{9}{5}R^2=405 \Leftrightarrow R^2=\left(\frac{405\times5}{9}\right)=225 \Leftrightarrow R=15.$$

$\therefore$ Rate = 15%.

Ex. 11. ***Divide Rs. 1301 between A and B, so that the amount of A after 7 years is equal to the amount of B after 9 years, the interest being compounded at 4% per annum.***

Sol. Let the two parts be Rs. x and Rs. $(1301 - x)$.

$$x\left(1+\frac{4}{100}\right)^7=(1301-x)\left(1+\frac{4}{100}\right)^9 \Leftrightarrow \frac{x}{(1301-x)}=\left(1+\frac{4}{100}\right)^2=\left(\frac{26}{25}\times\frac{26}{25}\right).$$

$$\Leftrightarrow \quad 625x=676\ (1301-x) \Leftrightarrow 1301x=676\times1301 \Leftrightarrow x=676.$$

So, the two parts are Rs. 676 and Rs. (1301 – 676) *i.e.* Rs. 676 and Rs. 625.

Ex. 12. ***A certain sum amounts to Rs. 7350 in 2 years and to Rs. 8575 in 3 years. Find the sum and rate percent.***

Sol. S.I. on Rs. 7350 for 1 year = Rs. (8575 – 7350) = Rs. 1225.

$$\therefore \quad \text{Rate}=\left(\frac{100\times1225}{7350\times1}\right)\%=16\frac{2}{3}\%.$$

Let the sum be Rs. x. Then,

$$x\left(1+\frac{50}{3\times100}\right)^2=7350 \Leftrightarrow x\times\frac{7}{6}\times\frac{7}{6}=7350 \Leftrightarrow x=\left(7350\times\frac{36}{49}\right)=5400$$

$\therefore$ Sum = Rs. 5400.

Ex. 13. ***A sum of money amounts to Rs. 6690 after 3 years and to Rs. 10,035 after 6 years on compound interest. Find the sum.***

Sol. Let the sum be Rs. P. Then,

$$P\left(1+\frac{R}{100}\right)^3=6690 \quad \ldots(i) \qquad \text{and } P\left(1+\frac{R}{100}\right)^6=10035 \quad \ldots(ii)$$

On dividing, we get $\left(1+\frac{R}{100}\right)^3=\frac{10035}{6690}=\frac{3}{2}.$

Substituting this value in (*i*), we get :

$$P\times\frac{3}{2}=6690 \text{ or } P=\left(6690\times\frac{2}{3}\right)=4460.$$

Hence, the sum is Rs. 4460.

Ex. 14. ***A sum of money doubles itself at compound interest in 15 years. In how many years will it become eight times ?***

Sol. $P\left(1+\frac{R}{100}\right)^{15}=2P \Rightarrow \left(1+\frac{R}{100}\right)^{15}=\frac{2P}{P}=2 \qquad \ldots(i)$

$$\text{Let } P\left(1+\frac{R}{100}\right)^n=8P \Rightarrow \left(1+\frac{R}{100}\right)^n=8=2^3=\left\{\left(1+\frac{R}{100}\right)^{15}\right\}^3 \quad [\text{using } (i)]$$

$$\Rightarrow \left(1+\frac{R}{100}\right)^n=\left(1+\frac{R}{100}\right)^{45} \Rightarrow n=45.$$

Thus, the required time = 45 years.

Ex. 15. ***What annual payment will discharge a debt of Rs. 7620 due in 3 years at*** $16\frac{2}{3}\%$ ***per annum compound interest ?***

Sol. Let each instalment be Rs. x. Then,

(P.W. of Rs. x due 1 year hence) + (P.W. of Rs. x due 2 years hence) + (P.W. of Rs. x due 3 years hence) = 7620.

$$\therefore \quad \frac{x}{\left(1+\frac{50}{3\times 100}\right)} + \frac{x}{\left(1+\frac{50}{3\times 100}\right)^2} + \frac{x}{\left(1+\frac{50}{3\times 100}\right)^3} = 7620$$

$$\Leftrightarrow \quad \frac{6x}{7} + \frac{36x}{49} + \frac{216x}{343} = 7620 \Leftrightarrow 294x + 252x + 216x = 7620 \times 343$$

$$\Leftrightarrow \quad x = \left(\frac{7620 \times 343}{762}\right) = 3430.$$

$\therefore$ Amount of each instalment = Rs. 3430.

EXERCISE 22A

(OBJECTIVE TYPE QUESTIONS)

Directions : *Mark (✓) against the correct answer* :

1. Albert invested an amount of Rs. 8000 in a fixed deposit scheme for 2 years at compound interest rate 5 p.c.p.a. How much amount will Albert get on maturity of the fixed deposit ? **(Bank P.O. 1999)**
   (*a*) Rs. 8600 (*b*) Rs. 8620 (*c*) Rs. 8800
   (*d*) Rs. 8840 (*e*) None of these
2. What will be the compound interest on a sum of Rs. 25,000 after 3 years at the rate of 12 p.c.p.a. ? **(S.B.I.P.O. 2003)**
   (*a*) Rs. 9000.30 (*b*) Rs. 9720 (*c*) Rs. 10123.20
   (*d*) Rs. 10483.20 (*e*) None of these
3. The compound interest on Rs. 20,480 at $6\frac{1}{4}\%$ per annum for 2 years 73 days, is :
   (*a*) Rs. 2929 (*b*) Rs. 3000 (*c*) Rs. 3131 (*d*) Rs. 3636
4. A man saves Rs. 200 at the end of each year and lends the money at 5% compound interest. How much will it become at the end of 3 years ?
   (*a*) Rs. 565.25 (*b*) Rs. 635 (*c*) Rs. 662.02 (*d*) Rs. 666.50
   (Hotel Management, 2003)
5. Sam invested Rs. 15,000 @ 10% per annum for one year. If the interest is compounded half-yearly, then the amount received by Sam at the end of the year will be :
   (*a*) Rs. 16,500 (*b*) Rs. 16,525.50 (*c*) Rs. 16,537.50
   (*d*) Rs. 18,150 (*e*) None of these **(S.B.I.P.O. 2002)**
6. A bank offers 5% compound interest calculated on half-yearly basis. A customer deposits Rs. 1600 each on 1st January and 1st July of a year. At the end of the year, the amount he would have gained by way of interest is **(N.D.A. 2000)**
   (*a*) Rs. 120 (*b*) Rs. 121 (*c*) Rs. 122 (*d*) Rs. 123
7. What is the difference between the compound interests on Rs. 5000 for $1\frac{1}{2}$ years at 4% per annum compounded yearly and half-yearly ? **(S.S.C. 2000)**
   (*a*) Rs. 2.04 (*b*) Rs. 3.06 (*c*) Rs. 4.80 (*d*) Rs. 8.30

8. Find the compound interest on Rs. 15,625 for 9 months at 16% per annum compounded quarterly. **(R.R.B. 2002)**

(*a*) Rs. 1851 (*b*) Rs. 1941 (*c*) Rs 1951 (*d*) Rs. 1961

9. If the simple interest on a sum of money for 2 years at 5% per annum is Rs. 50, what is the compound interest on the same sum at the same rate and for the same time ?

(*a*) Rs. 51.25 (*b*) Rs. 52 (*c*) Rs. 54.25 (*d*) Rs. 60

(C.B.I. 1997)

10. What will be the difference between simple and compound interest @ 10% per annum on a sum of Rs. 1000 after 4 years ? **(Bank P.O. 2002)**

(*a*) Rs. 31 (*b*) Rs. 32.10 (*c*) Rs. 40.40
(*d*) Rs. 64.10 (*e*) None of these

11. The difference between simple interest and compound interest on Rs. 1200 for one year at 10% per annum reckoned half-yearly is : **(R.R.B. 2002)**

(*a*) Rs. 2.50 (*b*) Rs. 3 (*c*) Rs. 3.75
(*d*) Rs. 4 (*e*) None of these

12. The compound interest on Rs. 30,000 at 7% per annum is Rs. 4347. The period (in years) is : **(L.I.C.A.A.O. 2003)**

(*a*) 2 (*b*) $2\frac{1}{2}$ (*c*) 3 (*d*) 4

13. At what rate of compound interest per annum will a sum of Rs. 1200 become Rs. 1348.32 in 2 years ?

(*a*) 6% (*b*) 6.5% (*c*) 7% (*d*) 7.5%

14. The principal that amounts to Rs. 4913 in 3 years at $6\frac{1}{4}$% per annum compound interest compounded annually, is : **(S.S.C. 2000)**

(*a*) Rs. 3096 (*b*) Rs. 4076 (*c*) Rs. 4085 (*d*) Rs. 4096

15. The present worth of Rs. 169 due in 2 years at 4% per annum compound interest is :

(*a*) Rs. 150.50 (*b*) Rs. 154.75 (*c*) Rs. 156.25 (*d*) Rs. 158

16. In how many years will a sum of Rs. 800 at 10% per annum compounded semi-annually become Rs. 926.10 ? **(Section Officers', 2001)**

(*a*) $1\frac{1}{3}$ (*b*) $1\frac{1}{2}$ (*c*) $2\frac{1}{3}$ (*d*) $2\frac{1}{2}$

17. If the compound interest on a sum for 2 years at $12\frac{1}{2}$% per annum is Rs. 510, the simple interest on the same sum at the same rate for the same period of time is :

(*a*) Rs. 400 (*b*) Rs. 450 (*c*) Rs. 460 (*d*) Rs. 480

(S.S.C. 2004)

18. The compound interest on a certain sum for 2 years at 10% per annum is Rs. 525. The simple interest on the same sum for double the time at half the rate percent per annum is : **(C.B.I. 1997)**

(*a*) Rs. 400 (*b*) Rs. 500 (*c*) Rs. 600 (*d*) Rs. 800

19. The simple interest on a certain sum of money for 3 years at 8% per annum is half the compound interest on Rs. 4000 for 2 years at 10% per annum. The sum placed on simple interest is : **(S.S.C. 2003)**

(*a*) Rs. 1550 (*b*) Rs. 1650 (*c*) Rs. 1750 (*d*) Rs. 2000

20. There is 60% increase in an amount in 6 years at simple interest. What will be the compound interest of Rs. 12,000 after 3 years at the same rate ? **(SIDBI, 2000)**

(*a*) Rs. 2160 (*b*) Rs. 3120 (*c*) Rs. 3972
(*d*) Rs. 6240 (*e*) None of these

21. The difference between compound interest and simple interest on an amount of Rs. 15,000 for 2 years is Rs. 96. What is the rate of interest per annum ?

(*a*) 8 (*b*) 10 (*c*) 12

(*d*) Cannot be determined (*e*) None of these **(R.B.I. 2003)**

22. The difference between simple and compound interests compounded annually on a certain sum of money for 2 years at 4% per annum is Re. 1. The sum (in Rs.) is :

(*a*) 625 (*b*) 630 (*c*) 640 (*d*) 650

(S.S.C. 2003)

23. The compound interest on a sum of money for 2 years is Rs. 832 and the simple interest on the same sum for the same period is Rs. 800. The difference between the compound interest and the simple interest for 3 years will be :

(*a*) Rs. 48 (*b*) Rs. 66.56 (*c*) Rs. 98.56 (*d*) None of these

24. The difference between the simple interest on a certain sum at the rate of 10% per annum for 2 years and compound interest which is compounded every 6 months is Rs. 124.05. What is the principal sum ? **(S.B.I.P.O. 2000)**

(*a*) Rs. 6000 (*b*) Rs. 8000 (*c*) Rs. 10,000

(*d*) Rs. 12,000 (*e*) None of these

25. The difference between compound interest and simple interest on a sum for 2 years at 10% per annum, when the interest is compounded annually is Rs. 16. If the interest were compounded half-yearly, the differ nce in two interests would be :

(*a*) Rs. 24.81 (*b*) Rs. 26.90 (*c*) Rs. 31.61 (*d*) Rs. 32.40

26. A sum of money lent at compound interest for 2 years at 20% per annum would fetch Rs. 482 more, if the interest was payable half-yearly than if it was payable annually. The sum is :

(*a*) Rs. 10,000 (*b*) Rs. 20,000 (*c*) Rs. 40,000 (*d*) Rs. 50,000

27. On a sum of money, the simple interest for 2 years is Rs. 660, while the compound interest is Rs. 696.30, the rate of interest being the same in both the cases. The rate of interest is : **(Hotel Management, 1997)**

(*a*) 10% (*b*) 10.5% (*c*) 12% (*d*) None of these

28. The effective annual rate of interest corresponding to a nominal rate of 6% per annum payable half-yearly is : **(S.S.C. 2000)**

(*a*) 6.06% (*b*) 6.07% (*c*) 6.08% (*d*) 6.09%

29. A person lent out a certain sum on simple interest and the same sum on compound interest at a certain rate of interest per annum. He noticed that the ratio between the difference of compound interest and simple interest of 3 years and that of 2 years is 25 : 8. The rate of interest per annum is :

(*a*) 10% (*b*) 11% (*c*) 12% (*d*) $12\frac{1}{2}\%$

30. Mr. Dua invested money in two schemes A and B offering compound interest @ 8 p.c.p.a. and 9 p.c.p.a. respectively. If the total amount of interest accrued through two schemes together in two years was Rs. 4818.30 and the total amount invested was Rs. 27,000, what was the amount invested in Scheme A ?

(*a*) Rs. 12,000 (*b*) Rs. 13,500 (*c*) Rs. 15,000

(*d*) Cannot be determined (*e*) None of these **(Bank P.O. 2003)**

31. A sum of money invested at compound interest amounts to Rs. 800 in 3 years and to Rs. 840 in 4 years. The rate of interest per annum is : **(S.S.C. 2001)**

(*a*) $2\frac{1}{2}\%$ (*b*) 4% (*c*) 5% (*d*) $6\frac{2}{3}\%$

32 A sum of money invested at compound interest amounts to Rs. 4624 in 2 years and to Rs. 4913 in 3 years. The sum of money is :
(*a*) Rs. 4096 (*b*) Rs. 4260 (*c*) Rs. 4335 (*d*) Rs. 4360

33. A sum of money becomes Rs. 13,380 after 3 years and Rs. 20,070 after 6 years on compound interest. The sum is :
(*a*) Rs 8800 (*b*) Rs. 8890 (*c*) Rs. 8920 (*d*) Rs. 9040

34. A sum of Rs. 12,000 deposited at compound interest becomes double after 5 years. After 20 years, it will become :
(*a*) Rs. 96,000 (*b*) Rs. 1,20,000 (*c*) Rs. 1,24,000 (*d*) Rs. 1,92,000

35. A sum of money placed at compound interest doubles itself in 5 years. It will amount to eight times itself at the same rate of interest in : **(Hotel Management, 2003)**
(*a*) 7 years (*b*) 10 years (*c*) 15 years (*d*) 20 years

36. If a sum on compound interest becomes three times in 4 years, then with the same interest rate, the sum will become 27 times in :
(*a*) 8 years (*b*) 12 years (*c*) 24 years (*d*) 36 years

37. The least number of complete years in which a sum of money put out at 20% compound interest will be more than doubled is : **(N.I.F.T. 2003)**
(*a*) 3 (*b*) 4 (*c*) 5 (*d*) 6

38. A man borrows Rs. 2550 to be paid back with compound interest at the rate of 4% per annum by the end of 2 years in two equal yearly instalments. How much will each instalment be ?
(*a*) Rs. 1275 (*b*) Rs. 1283 (*c*) Rs. 1352 (*d*) Rs. 1377

39. What annual payment will discharge a debt of Rs. 1025 due in 2 years at the rate of 5% compound interest ? **(S.S.C. 2000)**
(*a*) Rs. 550 (*b*) Rs. 551.25 (*c*) Rs. 560 (*d*) Rs. 560.75

40. A man borrows Rs. 12,500 at 20% compound interest. At the end of every year he pays Rs. 2000 as part repayment. How much does he still owe after three such instalments ?
(*a*) Rs. 12,000 (*b*) Rs. 12,864 (*c*) Rs. 15,600 (*d*) None of these

41. A sum of money is borrowed and paid back in two annual instalments of Rs. 882 each allowing 5% compound interest. The sum borrowed was : **(A.I.M.A.T.S. 2002)**
(*a*) Rs. 1620 (*b*) Rs. 1640 (*c*) Rs. 1680 (*d*) Rs. 1700

ANSWERS

1. (*e*)	**2.** (*c*)	**3.** (*a*)	**4.** (*c*)	**5.** (*c*)	**6.** (*b*)	**7.** (*a*)	**8.** (*c*)	**9.** (*a*)
10. (*d*)	**11.** (*b*)	**12.** (*a*)	**13.** (*a*)	**14.** (*d*)	**15.** (*c*)	**16.** (*b*)	**17.** (*d*)	**18.** (*b*)
19. (*c*)	**20.** (*c*)	**21.** (*a*)	**22.** (*a*)	**23.** (*c*)	**24.** (*b*)	**25.** (*a*)	**26.** (*b*)	**27.** (*d*)
28. (*d*)	**29.** (*d*)	**30.** (*a*)	**31.** (*c*)	**32.** (*a*)	**33.** (*c*)	**34.** (*d*)	**35.** (*c*)	**36.** (*b*)
37. (*b*)	**38.** (*c*)	**39.** (*b*)	**40.** (*d*)	**41.** (*b*)				

SOLUTIONS

1. Amount = $\text{Rs.}\left[8000 \times \left(1 + \frac{5}{100}\right)^2\right] = \text{Rs.}\left(8000 \times \frac{21}{20} \times \frac{21}{20}\right) = \text{Rs. } 8820$

2. Amount = $\text{Rs.}\left[25000 \times \left(1 + \frac{12}{100}\right)^3\right] = \text{Rs.}\left(25000 \times \frac{28}{25} \times \frac{28}{25} \times \frac{28}{25}\right) = \text{Rs. } 35123.20.$

$\therefore$ C.I. = Rs. (35123.20 − 25000) = Rs. 10123.20

3. Time $= 2\frac{73}{365}$ years $= 2\frac{1}{5}$ years.

$\therefore$ Amount $= \text{Rs.}\left[20480 \times \left(1 + \frac{25}{4 \times 100}\right)^2 \left(1 + \frac{\frac{1}{5} \times \frac{25}{4}}{100}\right)\right]$

$= \text{Rs.}\left(20480 \times \frac{17}{16} \times \frac{17}{16} \times \frac{81}{80}\right) = \text{Rs. } 23409.$

$\therefore$ C.I. = Rs. (23409 − 20480) = Rs. 2929.

4. Amount $= \text{Rs.}\left[200\left(1 + \frac{5}{100}\right)^3 + 200\left(1 + \frac{5}{100}\right)^2 + 200\left(1 + \frac{5}{100}\right)\right]$

$= \text{Rs.}\left[200 \times \frac{21}{20} \times \frac{21}{20} \times \frac{21}{20} + 200 \times \frac{21}{20} \times \frac{21}{20} + 200 \times \frac{21}{20}\right]$

$= \text{Rs.}\left[200 \times \frac{21}{20}\left(\frac{21}{20} \times \frac{21}{20} + \frac{21}{20} + 1\right)\right] = \text{Rs. } 662.02.$

5. P = Rs. 15000; R = 10% p.a. = 5% per half-year; T = 1 year = 2 half-years.

$\therefore$ Amount $= \text{Rs.}\left[15000 \times \left(1 + \frac{5}{100}\right)^2\right] = \text{Rs.}\left(15000 \times \frac{21}{20} \times \frac{21}{20}\right) = \text{Rs. } 16537.50.$

6. Amount $= \text{Rs.}\left[1600 \times \left(1 + \frac{5}{2 \times 100}\right)^2 + 1600 \times \left(1 + \frac{5}{2 \times 100}\right)\right]$

$= \text{Rs.}\left[1600 \times \frac{41}{40} \times \frac{41}{40} + 1600 \times \frac{41}{40}\right]$

$= \text{Rs.}\left[1600 \times \frac{41}{40}\left(\frac{41}{40} + 1\right)\right] = \text{Rs.}\left(\frac{1600 \times 41 \times 81}{40 \times 40}\right) = \text{Rs. } 3321.$

$\therefore$ C.I. = Rs. (3321 − 3200) = Rs. 121.

7. C.I. when interest is compounded yearly

$= \text{Rs.}\left[5000 \times \left(1 + \frac{4}{100}\right) \times \left(1 + \frac{\frac{1}{2} \times 4}{100}\right)\right] = \text{Rs.}\left(5000 \times \frac{26}{25} \times \frac{51}{50}\right) = \text{Rs. } 5304.$

C.I. when interest is compounded half-yearly

$= \text{Rs.}\left[5000 \times \left(1 + \frac{2}{100}\right)^3\right] = \text{Rs.}\left(5000 \times \frac{51}{50} \times \frac{51}{50} \times \frac{51}{50}\right) = \text{Rs. } 5306.04.$

$\therefore$ Difference = Rs. (5306.04 − 5304) = Rs. 2.04.

8. P = Rs. 15625, n = 9 months = 3 quarters, R = 16% p.a. = 4% per quarter.

Amount $= \text{Rs.}\left[15625 \times \left(1 + \frac{4}{100}\right)^3\right] = \text{Rs.}\left(15625 \times \frac{26}{25} \times \frac{26}{25} \times \frac{26}{25}\right) = \text{Rs. } 17576.$

$\therefore$ C.I. = Rs. (17576 − 15625) = Rs. 1951.

9. Sum = Rs. $\left(\frac{50 \times 100}{2 \times 5}\right)$ = Rs. 500.

Amount = Rs. $\left[500 \times \left(1 + \frac{5}{100}\right)^2\right]$ = Rs. $\left(500 \times \frac{21}{20} \times \frac{21}{20}\right)$ = Rs. 551.25.

$\therefore$ C.I. = Rs. (551.25 − 500) = Rs. 51.25.

10. S.I. = Rs. $\left(\frac{1000 \times 10 \times 4}{100}\right)$ = Rs. 400.

C.I. = Rs. $\left[1000 \times \left(1 + \frac{10}{100}\right)^4 - 1000\right]$ = Rs. 464.10.

$\therefore$ Difference = Rs. (464.10 − 400) = Rs. 64.10.

11. S.I. = Rs. $\left(\frac{1200 \times 10 \times 1}{100}\right)$ = Rs. 120.

C.I. = Rs. $\left[1200 \times \left(1 + \frac{5}{100}\right)^2 - 1200\right]$ = Rs. 123.

$\therefore$ Difference = Rs. (123 − 120) = Rs. 3.

12. Amount = Rs. (30000 + 4347) = Rs. 34347.

Let the time be n years. Then,

$$30000\left(1 + \frac{7}{100}\right)^n = 34347 \Leftrightarrow \left(\frac{107}{100}\right)^n = \frac{34347}{30000} = \frac{11449}{10000} = \left(\frac{107}{100}\right)^2.$$

$\therefore$ $n = 2$ years.

13. Let the rate be R% p.a. Then,

$$1200 \times \left(1 + \frac{R}{100}\right)^2 = 1348.32 \Leftrightarrow \left(1 + \frac{R}{100}\right)^2 = \frac{134832}{120000} = \frac{11236}{10000}$$

$$\therefore \left(1 + \frac{R}{100}\right)^2 = \left(\frac{106}{100}\right)^2 \text{ or } 1 + \frac{R}{100} = \frac{106}{100} \text{ or } R = 6\%.$$

14. Principal = Rs. $\left[\frac{4913}{\left(1 + \frac{25}{4 \times 100}\right)^3}\right]$ = Rs. $\left(4913 \times \frac{16}{17} \times \frac{16}{17} \times \frac{16}{17}\right)$ = Rs. 4096.

15. Present worth = Rs. $\left[\frac{169}{\left(1 + \frac{4}{100}\right)^2}\right]$ = Rs. $\left(169 \times \frac{25}{26} \times \frac{25}{26}\right)$ = Rs. 156.25.

16. Let the time be n years. Then,

$$800 \times \left(1 + \frac{5}{100}\right)^{2n} = 926.10 \text{ or } \left(1 + \frac{5}{100}\right)^{2n} = \frac{9261}{8000}$$

$$\text{or } \left(\frac{21}{20}\right)^{2n} = \left(\frac{21}{20}\right)^3 \text{ or } 2n = 3 \text{ or } n = \frac{3}{2}.$$

$\therefore$ $n = 1\frac{1}{2}$ years.

17. Let the sum be Rs. P. Then,

$$\left[P\left(1+\frac{25}{2\times 100}\right)^2 - P\right] = 510 \text{ or } P\left[\left(\frac{9}{8}\right)^2 - 1\right] = 510 \text{ or } P = \left(\frac{510\times 64}{17}\right) = 1920.$$

$\therefore$ Sum = Rs. 1920.

So, S.I. = Rs. $\left(\frac{1920\times 25\times 2}{2\times 100}\right)$ = Rs. 480.

18. Let the sum be Rs. P. Then,

$$\left[P\left(1+\frac{10}{100}\right)^2 - P\right] = 525 \Leftrightarrow P\left[\left(\frac{11}{10}\right)^2 - 1\right] = 525 \Leftrightarrow P = \left(\frac{525\times 100}{21}\right) = 2500.$$

$\therefore$ Sum = Rs. 2500.

So, S.I. = Rs. $\left(\frac{2500\times 5\times 4}{100}\right)$ = Rs. 500.

19. C.I. = Rs. $\left[4000\times\left(1+\frac{10}{100}\right)^2 - 4000\right]$ = Rs. $\left(4000\times\frac{11}{10}\times\frac{11}{10} - 4000\right)$ = Rs. 840.

$\therefore$ Sum = Rs. $\left(\frac{420\times 100}{3\times 8}\right)$ = Rs. 1750.

20. Let P = Rs. 100. Then, S.I. Rs. 60 and T = 6 years.

$\therefore$ $R = \frac{100\times 60}{100\times 6} = 10\%$ p.a.

Now, P = Rs. 12000, T = 3 years and R = 10% p.a.

$\therefore$ C.I. = Rs. $\left[12000\times\left\{\left(1+\frac{10}{100}\right)^3 - 1\right\}\right]$ = Rs. $\left(12000\times\frac{331}{1000}\right)$ = Rs. 3972.

21. $$\left[15000\times\left(1+\frac{R}{100}\right)^2 - 15000\right] - \left(\frac{15000\times R\times 2}{100}\right) = 96$$

$$\Leftrightarrow 15000\left[\left(1+\frac{R}{100}\right)^2 - 1 - \frac{2R}{100}\right] = 96 \Leftrightarrow 15000\left[\frac{(100+R)^2 - 10000 - 200R}{10000}\right] = 96$$

$$\Leftrightarrow R^2 = \frac{96\times 2}{3} = 64 \Leftrightarrow R = 8.$$

$\therefore$ Rate = 8%.

22. Let the sum be Rs. x. Then,

C.I. = $\left[x\left(1+\frac{4}{100}\right)^2 - x\right] = \left(\frac{676}{625}x - x\right) = \frac{51}{625}x.$

S.I. = $\left(\frac{x\times 4\times 2}{100}\right) = \frac{2x}{25}.$

$\therefore$ $\frac{51x}{625} - \frac{2x}{25} = 1$ or $x = 625.$

23. Difference in C.I. and S.I. for 2 years = Rs. 32.

S.I. for one year = Rs. 400.

$\therefore$ S.I. on Rs. 400 for one year = Rs. 32.

So, Rate $= \left(\frac{100 \times 32}{400 \times 1}\right)\% = 8\%$.

Hence, difference in C.I. and S.I. for 3rd year

$= $ S.I. on Rs. 832 = Rs. $\left(\frac{832 \times 8 \times 1}{100}\right)$ = Rs. 66.56.

Total difference = Rs. (32 + 66.56) = Rs. 98.56.

24. Let the sum be Rs. P. Then

$$P\left[\left(1+\frac{5}{100}\right)^4 - 1\right] - \frac{P \times 10 \times 2}{100} = 124.05$$

$$\Rightarrow P\left[\left(\frac{21}{20}\right)^4 - 1 - \frac{1}{5}\right] = 124.05 \Rightarrow P\left[\frac{194481}{160000} - \frac{6}{5}\right] = \frac{12405}{100}$$

$$\Rightarrow P\left[\frac{194481 - 192000}{160000}\right] = \frac{12405}{100} \Rightarrow P = \left(\frac{12405}{100} \times \frac{160000}{2481}\right) = 8000.$$

25. For first year, S.I. = C.I.

Now, Rs. 16 is the S.I. on S.I. for 1 year.

Rs. 10 is S.I. on Rs. 100.

$\therefore$ Rs. 16 is S.I. on Rs. $\left(\frac{100}{10} \times 16\right)$ = Rs. 160.

So, S.I. on principal for 1 year at 10% is Rs. 160.

$\therefore$ Principal = Rs. $\left(\frac{100 \times 160}{10 \times 1}\right)$ = Rs. 1600.

Amount for 2 years compounded half yearly = Rs. $\left[1600 \times \left(1+\frac{5}{100}\right)^4\right]$ = Rs. 1944.81.

$\therefore$ C.I. = Rs. (1944.81 − 1600) = Rs. 344.81.

S.I. = Rs. $\left(\frac{1600 \times 10 \times 2}{100}\right)$ = Rs. 320.

$\therefore$ (C.I.) − (S.I.) = Rs. (344.81 − 320) = Rs. 24.81.

26. Let the sum be Rs. x. Then,

C.I. when compounded half-yearly $= \left[x \times \left(1+\frac{10}{100}\right)^4 - x\right] = \frac{4641}{10000}x.$

C.I. when compounded annually $= \left[x \times \left(1+\frac{20}{100}\right)^2 - x\right] = \frac{11}{25}x.$

$\therefore \frac{4641}{10000}x - \frac{11}{25}x = 482$ or $x = \frac{482 \times 10000}{241} = 20000.$

27. Difference in C.I. and S.I. for 2 years = Rs. (696.30 − 660) = Rs. 36.30.

S.I. for one year = Rs. 330.

$\therefore$ S.I. on Rs. 330 for 1 year = Rs. 36.30.

$\therefore$ Rate $\left(\frac{100 \times 36.30}{330 \times 1}\right)\% = 11\%.$

28. Amount of Rs. 100 for 1 year when compounded half-yearly

$$= \text{Rs.}\left[100 \times \left(1 + \frac{3}{100}\right)^2\right] = \text{Rs. } 106.09.$$

$\therefore$ Effective rate = $(106.09 - 100)\% = 6.09\%$.

29. Let the principal be Rs. P and rate of interest be R% per annum.

Difference of C.I. and S.I. for 2 years

$$= \left[P \times \left(1 + \frac{R}{100}\right)^2 - P\right] - \left(\frac{P \times R \times 2}{100}\right) = \frac{PR^2}{10^4}.$$

Difference of C.I. and S.I. for 3 years

$$= \left[P \times \left(1 + \frac{R}{100}\right)^3 - P\right] - \left(\frac{P \times R \times 3}{100}\right) = \frac{PR^2}{10^4}\left(\frac{300 + R}{100}\right).$$

$$\therefore \frac{\frac{PR^2}{10^4}\left(\frac{300+R}{100}\right)}{\frac{PR^2}{10^4}} = \frac{25}{8} \Rightarrow \left(\frac{300+R}{100}\right) = \frac{25}{8} \Rightarrow R = \frac{100}{8} = 12\frac{1}{2}\%.$$

30. Let the investment in scheme A be Rs. x.

Then, investment in scheme B = Rs. $(27000 - x)$.

$$\therefore \left[x \times \left\{\left(1 + \frac{8}{100}\right)^2 - 1\right\} + (27000 - x)\left\{\left(1 + \frac{9}{100}\right)^2 - 1\right\}\right] = 4818.30.$$

$$\Leftrightarrow \left(x \times \frac{104}{625}\right) + \frac{1881\,(27000 - x)}{10000} = \frac{481830}{100}$$

$\Leftrightarrow$ $1664x + 1881\,(27000 - x) = 48183000$

$\Leftrightarrow$ $(1881x - 1664x) = (50787000 - 48183000)$

$$\Leftrightarrow 217x = 2604000 \Leftrightarrow x = \frac{2604000}{217} = 12000.$$

31. S.I. on Rs. 800 for 1 year = Rs. $(840 - 800)$ = Rs. 40.

$$\therefore \text{Rate} = \left(\frac{100 \times 40}{800 \times 1}\right)\% = 5\%.$$

32. S.I. on Rs. 4624 for 1 year = Rs. $(4913 - 4624)$ = Rs. 289.

$$\therefore \text{Rate} = \left(\frac{100 \times 289}{4624 \times 1}\right)\% = 6\frac{1}{4}\%.$$

$$\text{Now, } x\left(1 + \frac{25}{4 \times 100}\right)^2 = 4624 \text{ or } x \times \frac{17}{16} \times \frac{17}{16} = 4624$$

$$\therefore x = \left(4624 \times \frac{16}{17} \times \frac{16}{17}\right) = \text{Rs. } 4096.$$

34. $$12000 \times \left(1 + \frac{R}{100}\right)^5 = 24000 \Rightarrow \left(1 + \frac{R}{100}\right)^5 = 2$$

$$\therefore \left[\left(1 + \frac{R}{100}\right)^5\right]^4 = 2^4 = 16 \Rightarrow \left(1 + \frac{R}{100}\right)^{20} = 16 \Rightarrow P\left(1 + \frac{R}{100}\right)^{20} = 16P$$

$$\Rightarrow \quad 12000\left(1+\frac{R}{100}\right)^{20} = 16 \times 12000 = 192000.$$

35. $P\left(1+\frac{R}{100}\right)^5 = 2P \Rightarrow \left(1+\frac{R}{100}\right)^5 = 2$ ...(*i*)

Let $P\left(1+\frac{R}{100}\right)^n = 8P \Rightarrow \left(1+\frac{R}{100}\right)^n = 8 = 2^3 = \left\{\left(1+\frac{R}{100}\right)^5\right\}^3$ [*using* (*i*)]

$$\Rightarrow \left(1+\frac{R}{100}\right)^n = \left(1+\frac{R}{100}\right)^{15} \Rightarrow n = 15.$$

$\therefore$ Required time = 15 years.

36. $P\left(1+\frac{R}{100}\right)^4 = 3P \Rightarrow \left(1+\frac{R}{100}\right)^4 = 3$ ...(*i*)

Let $P\left(1+\frac{R}{100}\right)^n = 27P \Rightarrow \left(1+\frac{R}{100}\right)^n = 27 = (3)^3 = \left\{\left(1+\frac{R}{100}\right)^4\right\}^3$ [*using* (*i*)]

$$\Rightarrow \left(1+\frac{R}{100}\right)^n = \left(1+\frac{R}{100}\right)^{12} \Rightarrow n = 12.$$

$\therefore$ Required time = 12 years.

37. $P\left(1+\frac{20}{100}\right)^n > 2P$ *or* $\left(\frac{6}{5}\right)^n > 2$

Now, $\left(\frac{6}{5}\times\frac{6}{5}\times\frac{6}{5}\times\frac{6}{5}\right) > 2$. So, $n = 4$ years.

38. Let the value of each instalment be Rs. x. Then,
(P.W. of Rs. x due 1 year hence) + (P.W. of Rs. x due 2 years hence) = Rs. 2550

$$\Leftrightarrow \frac{x}{\left(1+\frac{4}{100}\right)} + \frac{x}{\left(1+\frac{4}{100}\right)^2} = 2550 \Leftrightarrow \frac{25x}{26} + \frac{625x}{676} = 2550$$

$$\Leftrightarrow 1275x = 2550 \times 676 \Leftrightarrow x = \left(\frac{2550 \times 676}{1275}\right) = 1352.$$

$\therefore$ Value of each instalment = Rs. 1352.

39. Let each instalment be Rs. x. Then,

$$\frac{x}{\left(1+\frac{5}{100}\right)} + \frac{x}{\left(1+\frac{5}{100}\right)^2} = 1025 \Leftrightarrow \frac{20x}{21} + \frac{400x}{441} = 1025$$

$$\Leftrightarrow 820\,x = 1025 \times 441 \Leftrightarrow x = \left(\frac{1025 \times 441}{820}\right) = 551.25.$$

So, value of each instalment = Rs. 551.25.

40. Balance

$$= \text{Rs.}\left[\left\{12500 \times \left(1+\frac{20}{100}\right)^3\right\} - \left\{2000 \times \left(1+\frac{20}{100}\right)^2 + 2000 \times \left(1+\frac{20}{100}\right) + 2000\right\}\right]$$

$= \text{Rs.}\left[\left(12500 \times \frac{6}{5} \times \frac{6}{5} \times \frac{6}{5}\right) - \left(2000 \times \frac{6}{5} \times \frac{6}{5} + 2000 \times \frac{6}{5} + 2000\right)\right]$

$= \text{Rs.}\ [21600 - (2880 + 2400 + 2000)] = \text{Rs. } 14320.$

41. Principal

= (P.W. of Rs. 882 due 1 year hence) + (P.W. of Rs. 882 due 2 years hence)

$= \left[\frac{882}{\left(1+\frac{5}{100}\right)} + \frac{882}{\left(1+\frac{5}{100}\right)^2}\right] = \left(\frac{882 \times 20}{21} + \frac{882 \times 400}{441}\right) = \text{Rs. } 1640.$

EXERCISE 22B

(DATA SUFFICIENCY TYPE QUESTIONS)

1. The difference between the compound interest and the simple interest earned on a sum of money at the end of 4 years is Rs. 256.40. To find out the sum, which of the following informations given in the statements P and Q is/are necessary ?

P : Amount of simple interest accrued after 4 years.

Q : Rate of interest per annum.

(*a*) Only P is necessary (*b*) Only Q is necessary

(*c*) Either P or Q is necessary (*d*) Neither P nor Q is necessary

(*e*) Both P and Q are necessary

Directions (*Questions 2 to 8*) : *Each of the questions given below consists of a statement and / or a question and two statements numbered I and II given below it. You have to decide whether the data provided in the statement(s) is/are sufficient to answer the given question. Read both the statements and*

Give answer (a) if the data in Statement I alone are sufficient to answer the question, while the data in Statement II alone are not sufficient to answer the question;

Give answer (b) if the data in Statement II alone are sufficient to answer the question, while the data in Statement I alone are not sufficient to answer the question;

Give answer (c) if the data either in Statement I or in Statement II alone are sufficient to answer the question;

Give answer (d) if the data even in both Statements I and II together are not sufficient to answer the question;

Give answer (e) if the data in both Statements I and II together are necessary to answer the question.

2. What is the rate of compound interest ? **(Bank P.O. 2003)**

I. The principal was invested for 4 years.

II. The earned interest was Rs. 1491.

3. What will be the compounded amount ? **(Bank P.O. 1999)**

I. Rs. 200 were borrowed for 192 months at 6% compounded annually.

II. Rs. 200 were borrowed for 16 years at 6%.

4. What is the compound interest earned by Robert at the end of 2 years ?

I. Simple interest at the same rate for one year is Rs. 1020 and the rate of interest is 12 p.c.p.a.

II. The amount invested is Rs. 8500.

5. What is the total compound interest accrued on a sum of money after 5 years ?

I. The sum was Rs. 20,000.

II. The total amount of simple interest on the sum after 5 years was Rs. 4000.

6. What was the total compound interest on a sum after 3 years ? **(Bank P.O. 2003)**

I. The interest after one year was Rs. 100 and the sum was Rs. 1000.

II. The difference between simple and compound interest on a sum of Rs. 1000 at the end of 2 years was Rs. 10.

7. An amount of money was lent for 3 years. What will be the difference between the simple and the compound interest earned on it at the same rate ?

I. The rate of interest was 8 p.c.p.a.

II. The total amount of simple interest was Rs. 1200.

8. What was the rate of interest on a sum of money ? **(S.B.I.P.O. 1998)**

I. The sum fetched a total of Rs. 2522 as compound interest at the end of 3 years.

II. The difference between the simple interest and the compound interest at the end of 2 years at the same rate was Rs. 40.

Directions (*Questions 9 to 12*) : *Each of the questions given below consists of a question followed by three statements. You have to study the question and the statements and decide which of the statement(s) is / are necessary to answer the question* :

9. What is the rate of interest p.c.p.a. ? **(R.B.I. 2002)**

I. An amount doubles itself in 5 years on simple interest.

II. Difference between the compound interest and the simple interest earned on a certain amount in 2 years is Rs. 400.

III. Simple interest earned per annum is Rs. 2000.

(*a*) I only (*b*) II and III only (*c*) All I, II and III

(*d*) Any two of the three (*e*) I only or II and III only

10. A sum of money is put at compound interest. What is the rate of interest ?

I. The sum amounts to Rs. 5290 in 2 years.

II. The sum amounts to Rs. 6083.50 in 3 years.

III. The sum is Rs. 4000.

(*a*) I and II only (*b*) II and III only (*c*) I and III only

(*d*) Any two of the three (*e*) I and III only, or II and III only

11. What will be the compound interest earned on an amount of Rs. 5000 in 2 years ? **(S.B.I.P.O. 2000)**

I. The simple interest on the same amount at the same rate of interest in 5 years in Rs. 2000.

II. The compound interest and the simple interest earned in one year is the same.

III. The amount becomes more than double on compound interest in 10 years.

(*a*) I only (*b*) I and II only (*c*) II and III only

(*d*) I and III only (*e*) None of these

12. A sum of money is placed at compound interest. In how many years will it amount to sixteen times of itself ?

I. The sum doubles itself in 4 years.

II. The sum amounts to eight times of itself in 12 years.

III. The sum amounts to four times of itself in 8 years.

(*a*) I only (*b*) I and II only (*c*) II and III only

(*d*) I and III only (*e*) Any one of the three

Directions (*Questions 13 to 16*) : *In each of the following questions, a question is asked and is followed by three statements. While answering the question, you may or may not require the data provided in all the statements. You have to read, the question and the three statements and then decide whether the question can be answered with any one or two of the statements or all the three statements are required to answer the question. The answer number bearing the statements, which can be dispensed with, if any, while answering the question is your answer.*

13. What would be the difference between the simple interest and the compound interest on a sum of money at the end of four years ?

I. The rate of interest is 5 p.c.p.a.

II. The sum fetches a total of Rs. 2000 as simple interest at the end of 8 years.

III. The difference between the simple interest and the compound interest at the end of 2 years is Rs. 12.50.

(*a*) II only (*b*) III only (*c*) II or III only
(*d*) All I, II and III are required (*e*) None of these

14. Mr. Gupta borrowed a sum of money on compound interest. What will be the amount to be repaid if he is repaying the entire amount at the end of 2 years ?

(Bank P.O. 1999)

I. The rate of interest is 5 p.c.p.a.

II. Simple interest fetched on the same amount in one year is Rs. 600

III. The amount borrowed is 10 times the simple interest in 2 years.

(*a*) I only (*b*) III only (*c*) I or II only
(*d*) I or III only (*e*) All I, II and III are required

15. What is the total compound interest earned at the end of 3 years ? **(S.B.I.P.O. 2001)**

I. Simple interest earned on that amount at the same rate and for the same period is Rs. 4500.

II. The rate of interest is 10 p.c.p.a.

III. Compound interest for 3 years is more than the simple interest for that period by Rs. 465.

(*a*) I and II only (*b*) II and III only (*c*) I and III only
(*d*) Either II or III only (*e*) Any two of the three

16. What is the rate of interest per annum ? **(S.B.I.P.O. 1999)**

I. The amount becomes Rs. 11,025 with compound interest after 2 years.

II. The same amount with simple interest becomes Rs. 11,000 after 2 years.

III. The amount invested is Rs. 10,000.

(*a*) I or II only (*b*) II or III only (*c*) I or III only
(*d*) I or II or III only (*e*) All I, II and III are required

ANSWERS

1. (*b*)	**2.** (*d*)	**3.** (*c*)	**4.** (*a*)	**5.** (*e*)	**6.** (*c*)	**7.** (*e*)	**8.** (*e*)	**9.** (*e*)
10. (*d*)	**11.** (*a*)	**12.** (*e*)	**13.** (*c*)	**14.** (*d*)	**15.** (*d*)	**16.** (*d*)		

SOLUTIONS

1. To find the sum, difference between C.I. and S.I., the time and the rate of interest are needed.

∴ Only Q is necessary.

∴ Correct answer is (*b*).

2. Let Principal = Rs. P and Rate = R% p.a. Then,

Amount = Rs. $\left[P\left(1+\frac{R}{100}\right)^4\right]$.

$\therefore$ C.I. = $P\left[\left(1+\frac{R}{100}\right)^4-1\right] \Rightarrow P\left[\left(1+\frac{R}{100}\right)^4-1\right] = 1491.$

Clearly, it does not give the answer.

$\therefore$ Correct answer is (*d*).

3. I. Amount = Rs. $\left[200\times\left(1+\frac{6}{100}\right)^{16}\right]$.

II. Amount = Rs. $\left[200\times\left(1+\frac{6}{100}\right)^{16}\right]$.

Thus, I as well as II gives the answer.

$\therefore$ Correct answer is (*c*).

4. I. S.I. = Rs. 1020, R = 12% p.a. and T = 1 year.

$\therefore$ $P = \frac{100\times S.I.}{R\times T} \Rightarrow P = \text{Rs.}\left(\frac{100\times 1020}{12\times 1}\right) = \text{Rs. } 8500.$

$\therefore$ C.I. for 2 years = Rs. $\left[8500\times\left\{\left(1+\frac{12}{100}\right)^2-1\right\}\right]$.

II gives : only P and T.

$\therefore$ II alone does not give the answer.

$\therefore$ Correct answer is (*a*).

5. Given : Time = 5 years.

I gives : Sum = Rs. 20000.

II gives : S.I. = Rs. 4000.

Let the rate be R% p.a. Then,

$$R = \frac{100\times S.I.}{P\times T} = \left(\frac{100\times 4000}{5\times 20000}\right) = 4\% \text{ p.a.}$$

$\therefore$ C.I. = Rs. $\left[20000\times\left\{\left(1+\frac{4}{100}\right)^5-1\right\}\right]$

$\therefore$ Both I and II are needed to get the answer.

So, the correct answer is (*e*).

6 I gives : P = Rs. 1000 and S.I. for 1 year = Rs. 100

$\therefore$ Rate = $\frac{100\times S.I.}{P\times T} = \left(\frac{100\times 100}{1000\times 1}\right) = 10\%$ p.a.

Thus, P = Rs. 1000, T = 3 years and R = 10% p.a.

$\therefore$ C.I. may be obtained.

II. Sum = Rs. 1000, [(C.I.) – (S.I.)] for 2 years = Rs. 10.

Let the rate be R% p.a.

$$1000\times\left[\left(1+\frac{R}{100}\right)^2-1\right]-\left(\frac{1000\times R\times 2}{100}\right) = 10.$$

From this, we can find R.

Thus P, T and R are given and therefore, C.I. may be calculated.

Thus, I alone as well as II alone is sufficient to get the answer.

∴ Correct answer is (*c*).

7. Given : T = 3 years.

I gives : R = 8% p.a.

II gives : S.I. = Rs. 1200.

Thus, P = Rs. 5000, R = 8% p.a. and T = 3 years.

∴ Difference between C.I. and S.I. may be obtained.

So, the correct answer is (*e*).

8. I gives : C.I. for 3 years = Rs. 2522.

II gives : (C.I.) − (S.I.) for 2 years at same rate is Rs. 40.

$$P\left[\left(1+\frac{R}{100}\right)^3-1\right] = 2522 \qquad ...(i)$$

$$P\left[\left(1+\frac{R}{100}\right)^2-1\right]-\frac{P\times R\times 2}{100} = 40 \qquad ...(ii)$$

On dividing (*i*) by (*ii*) we get :

$$\frac{\left(1+\frac{R}{100}\right)^3-1}{\left(1+\frac{R}{100}\right)^2-1-\frac{R}{50}} = \frac{2522}{40} \Rightarrow \frac{\frac{R^3}{1000000}+\frac{3R}{100}+\frac{3R^2}{10000}}{\frac{R^2}{10000}} = \frac{1261}{20}$$

$$\Rightarrow \frac{R}{100}+\frac{300}{R} = \frac{1201}{20} \Rightarrow R^2 - 6005R + 30000 = 0$$

$$\Rightarrow R^2 - 6000R - 5R + 30000 = 0$$

$$\Rightarrow R(R - 6000) - 5(R - 6000) = 0$$

$$\Rightarrow (R - 5)(R - 6000) = 0 \Rightarrow R = 5.$$

∴ Both I and II are needed to get R.

∴ Correct answer is (*e*).

9. I. $\frac{P\times R\times 5}{100} = P \Rightarrow R = 20.$

II. $P\left(1+\frac{R}{100}\right)^2 - P - \frac{P\times R\times 2}{100} = 400 \Rightarrow PR^2 = 4000000.$

III. $\frac{P\times R\times 1}{100} = 2000 \Rightarrow PR = 200000$

$$\therefore \frac{PR^2}{PR} = \frac{4000000}{200000} \Rightarrow R = 20.$$

Thus I only or (II & III) give answer.

∴ Correct answer is (*e*).

10. I. $P\left(1+\frac{R}{100}\right)^2 = 5290$ ...(*i*) II. $P\left(1+\frac{R}{100}\right)^3 = 6083.50$ (*ii*)

On dividing (*ii*) by (*i*), we get :

$$\left(1+\frac{R}{100}\right) = \frac{608350}{529000} = \frac{23}{20} \Rightarrow \frac{R}{100} = \left(\frac{23}{20}-1\right) = \frac{3}{20} \Rightarrow R = 15.$$

Thus, I and II give answer.

III. gives P = 4000.

Putting this value of P in (*i*), we get the answer.

Putting this value of P in (*ii*), we get the answer.

∴ (I & II) or (I & III) or (II & III) all give the answer.

Hence, the correct answer is (*d*).

11. P = Rs. 5000 & T = 2 years.

I. S.I. on Rs. 5000 in 5 years is Rs. 2000.

$$\frac{5000 \times R \times 5}{100} = 2000 \Rightarrow R = 8$$

Thus I only gives the answer.

∴ Correct answer is (*a*).

12. I. $P\left(1+\frac{R}{100}\right)^4 = 2P \Rightarrow \left(1+\frac{R}{100}\right)^4 = 2$ ...(*i*)

II. $P\left(1+\frac{R}{100}\right)^{12} = 8P \Rightarrow \left(1+\frac{R}{100}\right)^{12} = 8$ ...(*ii*)

III. $P\left(1+\frac{R}{100}\right)^8 = 4P \Rightarrow \left(1+\frac{R}{100}\right)^8 = 4$ ...(*iii*)

Let the given sum become 16 times in *n* years. Then,

$$P\left(1+\frac{R}{100}\right)^n = 16P \Rightarrow \left(1+\frac{R}{100}\right)^n = 16 \qquad ...(iv)$$

∴ Any one of (*i*), (*ii*) and (*iii*) with (*iv*) will give the value of *n*.

∴ Correct answer is (*e*).

13. I and II will give us, R, S.I. and T.

$$\therefore P = \frac{100 \times S.I.}{R \times T} = \left(\frac{100 \times 2000}{5 \times 8}\right) = 5000.$$

[(C.I.) – (S.I.)] for 4 years may be calculated.

In this case, III is redundant.

I and III give us R and P, using.

$$P\left[\left(1+\frac{5}{100}\right)^2 - 1\right] - \frac{P \times 5 \times 2}{100} = 12.50$$

So, [(C.I.) – (S.I.)] for 4 years may be calculated.

∴ Correct answer is (*c*).

14. I gives, Rate = 5% p.a.

II gives, S.I. for 1 year = Rs. 600.

III gives, sum = 10 × (S.I. for 2 years).

Now, I and II give the sum.

For this sum, C.I. and hence amount can be obtained.

Thus, III is redundant.

Again, II gives S.I. for 2 years = Rs. (600 × 2) = Rs. 1200.

Now, from III, Sum = Rs. (10 × 1200) = Rs. 12000.

$$\text{Thus, Rate} = \frac{100 \times 1200}{2 \times 12000} = 5\% \text{ p.a.}$$

Thus, C.I. for 2 years and therefore, amount can be obtained.

Thus, I is redundant.

Hence, I or III redundant.

15. I gives, S.I. for 3 years = Rs. 4500

II gives, Rate = 10% p.a.

III gives, (C.I.) – (S.I.) = Rs. 465.

Clearly, using I and III we get C.I. = Rs. (465 + 4500).

Thus, II is redundant.

Also, from I and II, we get sum $= \left(\frac{100 \times 4500}{10 \times 3}\right) = 15000.$

Now C.I. on Rs. 15000 at 10% p.a. for 3 years may be obtained.

Thus, III is redundant.

∴ Either II or III is redundant.

16. I gives, Amount after 2 years = Rs. 11025, when compounded.

II gives, Amount after 2 years at S.I. = Rs. 11000.

III gives, Principal = Rs. 10000.

From II and III, we have :

Principal = Rs. 10000, S.I. = Rs. (11000 – 10000) = Rs. 1000 and Time = 2 years.

Hence, Rate can be obtained.

∴ I is redundant.

From I and III, we get $11025 = 10000 \times \left(1 + \frac{R}{100}\right)^2$. This gives R.

∴ II is redundant.

From I and II, we have

$$P\left(1 + \frac{R}{100}\right)^2 = 11025 \quad \ldots(i) \text{ and } P\left[1 + \frac{R \times 2}{100}\right] = 11000 \quad \ldots(ii)$$

On dividing (*i*) by (*ii*), we get $\frac{\left(1 + \frac{R}{100}\right)^2}{(50 + R)} = \frac{11025}{550000}$.

This gives R.

Thus, III is redundant.

Hence I or II or III is redundant.

23. LOGARITHMS

IMPORTANT FACTS AND FORMULAE

I. Logarithm : If a is a positive real number, other than 1 and $a^m = x$, then we write : $m = \log_a x$ and we say that the value of log x to the base a is m.

Example :

(*i*) $10^3 = 1000 \Rightarrow \log_{10} 1000 = 3$ (*ii*) $3^4 = 81 \Rightarrow \log_3 81 = 4$

(*ii*) $2^{-3} = \frac{1}{8} \Rightarrow \log_2 \frac{1}{8} = -3$ (*iv*) $(.1)^2 = .01 \Rightarrow \log_{(.1)} .01 = 2.$

II. Properties of Logarithms :

1. $\log_a (xy) = \log_a x + \log_a y$
2. $\log_a \left(\frac{x}{y}\right) = \log_a x - \log_a y$
3. $\log_x x = 1$
4. $\log_a 1 = 0$
5. $\log_a (x^p) = p (\log_a x)$
6. $\log_a x = \frac{1}{\log_x a}$
7. $\log_a x = \frac{\log_b x}{\log_b a} = \frac{\log x}{\log a}$.

Remember : When base is not mentioned, it is taken as 10.

III. Common Logarithms : Logarithms to the base 10 are known as common logarithms.

IV. The logarithm of a number contains two parts, namely *characteristic* and *mantissa*.

Characteristic : The integral part of the logarithm of a number is called its ***characteristic.***

Case I : When the number is greater than 1.

In this case, the characteristic is one less than the number of digits in the left of the decimal point in the given number.

Case II : When the number is less than 1.

In this case, the characteristic is one more than the number of zeros between the decimal point and the first significant digit of the number and it is negative.

Instead of – 1, – 2, etc. we write, $\bar{1}$ (one bar), $\bar{2}$ (two bar), etc.

Example :

Number	*Characteristic*	*Number*	*Characteristic*
348.25	2	0.6173	$\bar{1}$
46.583	1	0.03125	$\bar{2}$
9.2193	0	0.00125	$\bar{3}$

Mantissa : The decimal part of the logarithm of a number is known is its ***mantissa***. For mantissa, we look through log table.

SOLVED EXAMPLES

Ex. 1. ***Evaluate : (i)*** $\log_3 27$ ***(ii)*** $\log_7 \left(\frac{1}{343}\right)$ ***(iii)*** $\log_{100} (0.01)$

Sol. (*i*) Let $\log_3 27 = n$.

Then, $3^n = 27 = 3^3$ or $n = 3$. $\therefore \log_3 27 = 3$.

(*ii*) Let $\log_7 \left(\frac{1}{343}\right) = n$.

Then, $7^n = \frac{1}{343} = \frac{1}{7^3} = 7^{-3}$ or $n = -3$. $\therefore \log_7 \left(\frac{1}{343}\right) = -3$.

(*iii*) Let $\log_{100} (0.01) = n$.

Then, $(100)^n = 0.01 = \frac{1}{100} = (100)^{-1}$ or $n = -1$ $\therefore \log_{100} (0.01) = -1$.

Ex. 2. ***Evaluate : (i)*** $\log_7 1 = 0$ ***(ii)*** $\log_{34} 34$ ***(iii)*** $36^{\log_6 4}$

Sol. (*i*) We know that $\log_a 1 = 0$, so $\log_7 1 = 0$.

(*ii*) We know that $\log_a a = 1$, so $\log_{34} 34 = 0$.

(*iii*) We know that $a^{\log_a x} = x$.

Now, $36^{\log_6 4} = (6^2)^{\log_6 4} = 6^{2(\log_6 4)} = 6^{\log_6 (4^2)} = 6^{\log_6 16} = 16$.

Ex. 3. ***If*** $\log_{\sqrt{8}} x = 3\frac{1}{3}$, ***find the value of x.***

Sol. $\log_{\sqrt{8}} x = \frac{10}{3} \Leftrightarrow x = (\sqrt{8})^{10/3} = (2^{3/2})^{10/3} = 2^{\left(\frac{3}{2} \times \frac{10}{3}\right)} = 2^5 = 32$.

Ex. 4. ***Evaluate : (i)*** $\log_5 3 \times \log_{27} 25$ ***(ii)*** $\log_9 27 - \log_{27} 9$

Sol. (*i*) $\log_5 3 \times \log_{27} 25 = \frac{\log 3}{\log 5} \times \frac{\log 25}{\log 27} = \frac{\log 3}{\log 5} \times \frac{\log (5^2)}{\log (3^3)} = \frac{\log 3}{\log 5} \times \frac{2 \log 5}{3 \log 3} = \frac{2}{3}$.

(*ii*) Let $\log_9 27 = n$.

Then, $9^n = 27 \Leftrightarrow 3^{2n} = 3^3 \Leftrightarrow 2n = 3 \Leftrightarrow n = \frac{3}{2}$.

Again, let $\log_{27} 9 = m$.

Then, $27^m = 9 \Leftrightarrow 3^{3m} = 3^2 \Leftrightarrow 3m = 2 \Leftrightarrow m = \frac{2}{3}$.

$\therefore \log_9 27 - \log_{27} 9 = (n - m) = \left(\frac{3}{2} - \frac{2}{3}\right) = \frac{5}{6}$.

Ex. 5. ***Simplify :*** $\left(\log \frac{75}{16} - 2 \log \frac{5}{9} + \log \frac{32}{243}\right)$ **(S.S.C. 2000)**

Sol. $\log \frac{75}{16} - 2 \log \frac{5}{9} + \log \frac{32}{243} = \log \frac{75}{16} - \log \left(\frac{5}{9}\right)^2 + \log \frac{32}{243} = \log \frac{75}{16} - \log \frac{25}{81} + \log \frac{32}{243}$

$= \log \left(\frac{75}{16} \times \frac{32}{243} \times \frac{81}{25}\right) = \log 2$.

Ex. 6. ***Find the value of x which satisfies the relation***

$\log_{10} 3 + \log_{10} (4x + 1) = \log_{10} (x + 1) + 1$ **(M.B.A. 2002)**

Sol. $\log_{10} 3 + \log_{10} (4x + 1) = \log_{10} (x + 1) + 1$

$\Leftrightarrow$ $\log_{10} 3 + \log_{10} (4x + 1) = \log_{10} (x + 1) + \log_{10} 10$

$\Leftrightarrow$ $\log_{10} [3 (4x + 1)] = \log_{10} [10 (x + 1)]$

$\Leftrightarrow$ $3 (4x + 1) = 10 (x + 1) \Leftrightarrow 12x + 3 = 10x + 10 \Leftrightarrow 2x = 7 \Leftrightarrow x = \frac{7}{2}$

Ex. 7. ***Simplify*** **:** $\left[\frac{1}{\log_{xy}(xyz)} + \frac{1}{\log_{yz}(xyz)} + \frac{1}{\log_{zx}(xyz)}\right]$

Sol. Given expression $= \log_{xyz}(xy) + \log_{xyz}(yz) + \log_{xyz}(zx)$

$= \log_{xyz}(xy \times yz \times zx) = \log_{xyz}(xyz)^2$

$= 2 \log_{xyz}(xyz) = 2 \times 1 = 2.$ $\left[\because \log_a x = \frac{1}{\log_x a}\right]$

Ex. 8. ***If $\log_{10} 2 = 0.30103$, find the value of $\log_{10} 50$.*** **(C.B.I. 1997)**

Sol. $\log_{10} 50 = \log_{10}\left(\frac{100}{2}\right) = \log_{10} 100 - \log_{10} 2 = 2 - 0.30103 = 1.69897$

Ex. 9. ***If $\log 2 = 0.3010$ and $\log 3 = 0.4771$, find the values of*** **:**

(i) ***log 25*** ***(ii)*** ***log 4.5***

Sol. *(i)* $\log 25 = \log\left(\frac{100}{4}\right) = \log 100 - \log 4 = 2 - 2\log 2 = (2 - 2 \times 0.3010) = 1.398.$

(ii) $\log 4.5 = \log\left(\frac{9}{2}\right) = \log 9 - \log 2 = 2\log 3 - \log 2$

$= (2 \times 0.4771 - 0.3010) = 0.6532.$

Ex. 10. ***If $\log 2 = 0.30103$, find the number of digits in 2^{56}.***

Sol. $\log (2^{56}) = 56 \log 2 = (56 \times 0.30103) = 16.85768.$

Its characteristic is 16. Hence, the number of digits in 2^{56} is 17.

EXERCISE 23

(OBJECTIVE TYPE QUESTIONS)

Directions : ***Mark (✓) against the correct answer*** **:**

1. The value of $\log_2 16$ is : **(M.B.A. 2003)**

(a) $\frac{1}{8}$ (b) 4 (c) 8 (d) 16.

2. The value of $\log_{343} 7$ is :

(a) $\frac{1}{3}$ (b) -3 (c) $-\frac{1}{3}$ (d) 3

3. The value of $\log_5\left(\frac{1}{125}\right)$ is :

(a) 3 (b) -3 (c) $\frac{1}{3}$ (d) $-\frac{1}{3}$

4. The value of $\log_{\sqrt{2}} 32$ is :

(a) $\frac{5}{2}$ (b) 5 (c) 10 (d) $\frac{1}{10}$

5. The value of $\log_{10} (.0001)$ is :

(a) $\frac{1}{4}$ (b) $-\frac{1}{4}$ (c) -4 (d) 4

6. The value of $\log_{(.01)}(1000)$ is :

(a) $\frac{1}{3}$ (b) $-\frac{1}{3}$ (c) $\frac{3}{2}$ (d) $-\frac{3}{2}$

7. The logarithm of 0.0625 to the base 2 is :

(a) − 4 (b) − 2 (c) 0.25 (d) 0.5

8. If $\log_3 x = -2$, then x is equal to :

(a) − 9 (b) − 6 (c) − 8 (d) $\frac{1}{9}$

9. If $\log_8 x = \frac{2}{3}$, then the value of x is :

(a) $\frac{3}{4}$ (b) $\frac{4}{3}$ (c) 3 (d) 4

10. If $\log_x \left(\frac{9}{16}\right) = -\frac{1}{2}$, then x is equal to :

(a) $-\frac{3}{4}$ (b) $\frac{3}{4}$ (c) $\frac{81}{256}$ (d) $\frac{256}{81}$

11. If $\log_x 4 = 0.4$, then the value of x is : **(Asstt. Grade, 1998)**

(a) 1 (b) 4 (c) 16 (d) 32

12. If $\log_{10000} x = -\frac{1}{4}$, then x is equal to :

(a) $\frac{1}{10}$ (b) $\frac{1}{100}$ (c) $\frac{1}{1000}$ (d) $\frac{1}{10000}$

13. If $\log_x 4 = \frac{1}{4}$, then x is equal to :

(a) 16 (b) 64 (c) 128 (d) 256

14. If $\log_x (0.1) = -\frac{1}{3}$, then the value of x is :

(a) 10 (b) 100 (c) 1000 (d) $\frac{1}{1000}$

15. If $\log_{32} x = 0.8$, then x is equal to :

(a) 25.6 (b) 16 (c) 10 (d) 12.8

16. If $\log_x y = 100$ and $\log_2 x = 10$, then the value of y is : **(S.S.C. 1999)**

(a) 2^{10} (b) 2^{100} (c) 2^{1000} (d) 2^{10000}

17. The value of $\log_{(-1/3)} 81$ is equal to :

(a) − 27 (b) − 4 (c) 4 (d) 27

18. The value of $\log_{2\sqrt{3}}(1728)$ is :

(a) 3 (b) 5 (c) 6 (d) 9

19. $\frac{\log \sqrt{8}}{\log 8}$ is equal to : **(I.A.F. 2002)**

(a) $\frac{1}{\sqrt{8}}$ (b) $\frac{1}{4}$ (c) $\frac{1}{2}$ (d) $\frac{1}{8}$

20. Which of the following statements is not correct ? **(M.B.A. 2003)**

(a) $\log_{10} 10 = 1$ (b) $\log(2 + 3) = \log(2 \times 3)$

(c) $\log_{10} 1 = 0$ (d) $\log(1 + 2 + 3) = \log 1 + \log 2 + \log 3$

21. The value of $\log_2 (\log_5 625)$ is :
(*a*) 2 (*b*) 5 (*c*) 10 (*d*) 15

22. If $\log_2 [\log_3 (\log_2 x)] = 1$, then x is equal to :
(*a*) 0 (*b*) 12 (*c*) 128 (*d*) 512

23. The value of $\log_2 \log_2 \log_3 \log_3 27^3$ is :
(*a*) 0 (*b*) 1 (*c*) 2 (*d*) 3

24. If $a^x = b^y$, then : **(Hotel Management, 2001)**
(*a*) $\log \frac{a}{b} = \frac{x}{y}$ (*b*) $\frac{\log a}{\log b} = \frac{x}{y}$ (*c*) $\frac{\log a}{\log b} = \frac{y}{x}$ (*d*) None of these

25. log 360 is equal to :
(*a*) 2 log 2 + 3 log 3 (*b*) 3 log 2 + 2 log 3
(*c*) 3 log 2 + 2 log 3 − log 5 (*d*) 3 log 2 + 2 log 3 + log 5

26. The value of $\left(\frac{1}{3} \log_{10} 125 - 2 \log_{10} 4 + \log_{10} 32\right)$ is :
(*a*) 0 (*b*) $\frac{4}{5}$ (*c*) 1 (*d*) 2

27. $2 \log_{10} 5 + \log_{10} 8 - \frac{1}{2} \log_{10} 4 = ?$ **(M.B.A. 2002)**
(*a*) 2 (*b*) 4 (*c*) $2 + 2 \log_{10} 2$ (*d*) $4 - 4 \log_{10} 2$

28. If $\log_a (ab) = x$, then $\log_b (ab)$ is : **(M.A.T. 2002)**
(*a*) $\frac{1}{x}$ (*b*) $\frac{x}{x+1}$ (*c*) $\frac{x}{1-x}$ (*d*) $\frac{x}{x-1}$

29. If log 2 = x, log 3 = y and log 7 = z, then the value of $\log (4 \cdot \sqrt[3]{63})$ is :
(*a*) $2x + \frac{2}{3} y - \frac{1}{3} z$ (*b*) $2x + \frac{2}{3} y + \frac{1}{3} z$
(*c*) $2x - \frac{2}{3} y + \frac{1}{3} z$ (*d*) $-2x + \frac{2}{3} y + \frac{1}{3} z$ **(S.S.C. 1998)**

30. If $\log_4 x + \log_2 x = 6$, then x is equal to
(*a*) 2 (*b*) 4 (*c*) 8 (*d*) 16

31. If $\log_8 x + \log_8 \frac{1}{6} = \frac{1}{3}$, then the value of x is :
(*a*) 12 (*b*) 16 (*c*) 18 (*d*) 24

32. If $\log_{10} 125 + \log_{10} 8 = x$, then x is equal to :
(*a*) $\frac{1}{3}$ (*b*) .064 (*c*) − 3 (*d*) 3

33. The value of $(\log_9 27 + \log_8 32)$ is :
(*a*) $\frac{7}{2}$ (*b*) $\frac{19}{6}$ (*c*) 4 (*d*) 7

34. $(\log_5 3) \times (\log_3 625)$ equals :
(*a*) 1 (*b*) 2 (*c*) 3 (*d*) 4

35. $(\log_5 5) (\log_4 9) (\log_3 2)$ is equal to :
(*a*) 1 (*b*) $\frac{3}{2}$ (*c*) 2 (*d*) 5

36. If $\log_{12} 27 = a$, then $\log_6 16$ is : **(Assistant Grade, 1998)**
(*a*) $\frac{3-a}{4(3+a)}$ (*b*) $\frac{3+a}{4(3-a)}$ (*c*) $\frac{4(3+a)}{(3-a)}$ (*d*) $\frac{4(3-a)}{(3+a)}$

37. If $\log_{10} 5 + \log_{10} (5x + 1) = \log_{10} (x + 5) + 1$, then x is equal to : **(C.D.S. 2003)**
(a) 1 (b) 3 (c) 5 (d) 10

38. If $\log_5 (x^2 + x) - \log_5 (x + 1) = 2$, then the value of x is :
(a) 5 (b) 10 (c) 25 (d) 32

39. The value of $\left(\frac{1}{\log_3 60} + \frac{1}{\log_4 60} + \frac{1}{\log_5 60}\right)$ is :
(a) 0 (b) 1 (c) 5 (d) 60

40. The value of $(\log_3 4) (\log_4 5) (\log_5 6) (\log_6 7) (\log_7 8) (\log_8 9)$ is :
(a) 2 (b) 7 (c) 8 (d) 33

41. The value of $16^{\log_4 5}$ is :
(a) $\frac{5}{64}$ (b) 5 (c) 16 (d) 25

42. If $\log x + \log y = \log (x + y)$, then :
(a) $x = y$ (b) $xy = 1$ (c) $y = \frac{x-1}{x}$ (d) $y = \frac{x}{x-1}$

43. If $\log \frac{a}{b} + \log \frac{b}{a} = \log (a + b)$, then :
(a) $a + b = 1$ (b) $a - b = 1$ (c) $a = b$ (d) $a^2 - b^2 = 1$

44. $\left[\log\left(\frac{a^2}{bc}\right) + \log\left(\frac{b^2}{ac}\right) + \log\left(\frac{c^2}{ab}\right)\right]$ is equal to :
(a) 0 (b) 1 (c) 2 (d) abc

45. $(\log_b a \times \log_c b \times \log_a c)$ is equal to :
(a) 0 (b) 1 (c) abc (d) $a + b + c$

46. $\left[\frac{1}{(\log_a bc) + 1} + \frac{1}{(\log_b ca) + 1} + \frac{1}{(\log_c ab) + 1}\right]$ is equal to :
(a) 1 (b) $\frac{3}{2}$ (c) 2 (d) 3

47. The value of $\left[\frac{1}{\log_{(p/q)} x} + \frac{1}{\log_{(q/r)} x} + \frac{1}{\log_{(r/p)} x}\right]$ is :
(a) 0 (b) 1 (c) 2 (d) 3

48. If $\log_{10} 7 = a$, then $\log_{10}\left(\frac{1}{70}\right)$ is equal to : **(C.D.S. 2003)**
(a) $-(1 + a)$ (b) $(1 + a)^{-1}$ (c) $\frac{a}{10}$ (d) $\frac{1}{10a}$

49. If $a = b^x$, $b = c^y$ and $c = a^z$, then the value of xyz is equal to :
(a) -1 (b) 0 (c) 1 (d) abc

50. If $\log 27 = 1.431$, then the value of $\log 9$ is : **(Section Officers', 2001)**
(a) 0.934 (b) 0.945 (c) 0.954 (d) 0.958

51. If $\log_{10} 2 = 0.3010$, then $\log_2 10$ is equal to : **(S.S.C. 2000)**
(a) $\frac{699}{301}$ (b) $\frac{1000}{301}$ (c) 0.3010 (d) 0.6990

52. If $\log_{10} 2 = 0.3010$, the value of $\log_{10} 5$ is : **(S.S.C. 2001)**
(a) 0.3241 (b) 0.6911 (c) 0.6990 (d) 0.7525

53. If $\log_{10} 2 = 0.3010$, the value of $\log_{10} 80$ is :
(a) 1.6020 (b) 1.9030 (c) 3.9030 (d) None of these

54. If $\log 3 = 0.477$ and $(1000)^x = 3$, then x equals : **(S.S.C. 2000)**
(a) 0.0159 (b) 0.0477 (c) 0.159 (d) 10

55. If $\log_{10} 2 = 0.3010$, the value of $\log_{10} 25$ is :
(a) 0.6020 (b) 1.2040 (c) 1.3980 (d) 1.5050

56. If $\log 2 = 0.3010$ and $\log 3 = 0.4771$, the value of $\log_5 512$ is : **(M.A.T. 2002)**
(a) 2.870 (b) 2.967 (c) 3.876 (d) 3.912

57. If $\log_{10} 2 = 0.3010$ and $\log_{10} 3 = 0.4771$, then the value of $\log_{10} 1.5$ is :
(a) 0.1761 (b) 0.7116 (c) 0.7161 (d) 0.7611

58. If $\log_{10} 2 = 0.3010$ and $\log_{10} 7 = 0.8451$, then the value of $\log_{10} 2.8$ is :
(a) 0.4471 (b) 1.4471 (c) 2.4471 (d) None of these
(S.S.C. 1999)

59. If $\log (0.57) = \bar{1}.756$, then the value of $\log 57 + \log (0.57)^3 + \log \sqrt{0.57}$ is :
(a) 0.902 (b) $\bar{2}.146$ (c) 1.902 (d) $\bar{1}.146$
(Section Officers', 2003)

60. If $\log 2 = 0.30103$, the number of digits in 2^{64} is : **(C.B.I. 1997)**
(a) 18 (b) 19 (c) 20 (d) 21

61. If $\log 2 = 0.30103$, the number of digits in 4^{50} is :
(a) 30 (b) 31 (c) 100 (d) 200

62. If $\log 2 = 0.30103$, then the number of digits in 5^{20} is :
(a) 14 (b) 16 (c) 18 (d) 25

ANSWERS

1. (b)	**2.** (a)	**3.** (b)	**4.** (c)	**5.** (c)	**6.** (d)	**7.** (a)	**8.** (d)
9. (d)	**10.** (d)	**11.** (d)	**12.** (a)	**13.** (d)	**14.** (c)	**15.** (b)	**16.** (c)
17. (b)	**18.** (c)	**19.** (c)	**20.** (b)	**21.** (a)	**22.** (d)	**23.** (a)	**24.** (c)
25. (d)	**26.** (c)	**27.** (a)	**28.** (d)	**29.** (b)	**30.** (d)	**31.** (a)	**32.** (d)
33. (b)	**34.** (d)	**35.** (a)	**36.** (d)	**37.** (b)	**38.** (c)	**39.** (b)	**40.** (a)
41. (d)	**42.** (d)	**43.** (a)	**44.** (a)	**45.** (b)	**46.** (a)	**47.** (a)	**48.** (a)
49. (c)	**50.** (c)	**51.** (b)	**52.** (c)	**53.** (b)	**54.** (c)	**55.** (c)	**56.** (c)
57. (a)	**58.** (a)	**59.** (a)	**60.** (c)	**61.** (b)	**62.** (a)		

SOLUTIONS

1. Let $\log_2 16 = n$. Then, $2^n = 16 = 2^4 \Rightarrow n = 4$.
$\therefore \log_2 16 = n$.

2. Let $\log_{343} 7 = n$. Then, $(343)^n = 7 \Leftrightarrow (7^3)^n = 7 \Leftrightarrow 3n = 1 \Leftrightarrow n = \frac{1}{3}$.

$\therefore \log_{343} 7 = \frac{1}{3}$.

3. Let $\log_5 \left(\frac{1}{125}\right) = n$. Then, $5^n = \frac{1}{125} \Leftrightarrow 5^n = 5^{-3} \Leftrightarrow n = -3$.

$\therefore \log_5 \left(\frac{1}{125}\right) = -3$.

4. Let $\log_{\sqrt{2}} 32 = n$. Then, $(\sqrt{2})^n = 32 \Leftrightarrow (2)^{n/2} = 2^5 \Leftrightarrow \frac{n}{2} = 5 \Leftrightarrow n = 10$.

$\therefore \log_{\sqrt{2}} 32 = 10$.

5. Let $\log_{10} (.0001) = n$.

Then, $10^n = .0001 \Leftrightarrow 10^n = \frac{1}{10000} = \frac{1}{10^4} \Leftrightarrow 10^n = 10^{-4} \Leftrightarrow n = -4$.

$\therefore \log_{10} (.0001) = -4$.

6. Let $\log_{(.01)} (1000) = n$.

Then, $(.01)^n = 1000 \Leftrightarrow \left(\frac{1}{100}\right)^n = 10^3 \Leftrightarrow \left(10^{-2}\right)^n = 10^3 \Leftrightarrow -2n = 3 \Leftrightarrow n = -\frac{3}{2}$.

7. Let $\log_2 0.0625 = n$.

Then, $2^n = 0.0625 = \frac{625}{10000} \Leftrightarrow 2^n = \frac{1}{16} \Leftrightarrow 2^n = 2^{-4} \Leftrightarrow n = -4$.

$\therefore \log_2 0.0625 = -4$.

8. $\log_3 x = -2 \Leftrightarrow x = 3^{-2} = \frac{1}{3^2} = \frac{1}{9}$.

9. $\log_8 x = \frac{2}{3} \Leftrightarrow x = 8^{2/3} = (2^3)^{2/3} = 2^{\left(3 \times \frac{2}{3}\right)} = 2^2 = 4$.

10. $\log_x \left(\frac{9}{16}\right) = -\frac{1}{2} \Leftrightarrow x^{-1/2} = \frac{9}{16} \Leftrightarrow \frac{1}{\sqrt{x}} = \frac{9}{16} \Leftrightarrow \sqrt{x} = \frac{16}{9}$

$\Leftrightarrow x = \left(\frac{16}{9}\right)^2 = \frac{256}{81}$.

11. $\log_x 4 = 0.4 \Leftrightarrow \log_x 4 = \frac{4}{10} = \frac{2}{5} \Leftrightarrow x^{2/5} = 4 \Leftrightarrow x = 4^{5/2} = (2^2)^{5/2}$

$\Leftrightarrow x = 2^{\left(2 \times \frac{5}{2}\right)} = 2^5 \Leftrightarrow x = 32$.

12. $\log_{10000} x = -\frac{1}{4} \Leftrightarrow x = (10000)^{-1/4} = (10^4)^{-1/4} = 10^{-1} = \frac{1}{10}$.

13. $\log_x 4 = \frac{1}{4} \Leftrightarrow x^{1/4} = 4 \Leftrightarrow x = 4^4 = 256$.

14. $\log_x (0.1) = -\frac{1}{3} \Leftrightarrow x^{-1/3} = 0.1 \Leftrightarrow \frac{1}{x^{1/3}} = 0.1 \Leftrightarrow x^{1/3} = \frac{1}{0.1} = 10$

$\Leftrightarrow x = (10)^3 = 1000$.

15. $\log_{32} x = 0.8 \Leftrightarrow x = (32)^{0.8} = (2^5)^{4/5} = 2^4 = 16$.

16. $\log_2 x = 10 \Rightarrow x = 2^{10}$

$\therefore \log_x y = 100 \Rightarrow y = x^{100} = (2^{10})^{100} \Rightarrow y = 2^{1000}$.

17. Let $\log_{(-1/3)} 81 = x$. Then, $\left(-\frac{1}{3}\right)^x = 81 = 3^4 = (-3)^4 = \left(-\frac{1}{3}\right)^{-4}$

$\therefore x = -4$ *i.e.*, $\log_{(-1/3)} 81 = -4$.

18. Let $\log_{2\sqrt{3}} (1728) = x$.

Then, $(2\sqrt{3})^x = 1728 = (12)^3 = [(2\sqrt{3})^2]^3 = (2\sqrt{3})^6$

$\therefore x = 6$, *i.e.*, $\log_{2\sqrt{3}} (1728) = 6$.

19. $\dfrac{\log \sqrt{8}}{\log 8} = \dfrac{\log (8)^{1/2}}{\log 8} = \dfrac{\frac{1}{2} \log 8}{\log 8} = \dfrac{1}{2}.$

20. (*a*) Since $\log_a a = 1$, so $\log_{10} 10 = 1$.

(*b*) $\log (2 + 3) = 5$ and $\log (2 \times 3) = \log 6 = \log 2 + \log 3$

$\therefore \quad \log (2 + 3) \neq \log (2 \times 3)$.

(*c*) Since $\log_a 1 = 0$, so $\log_{10} 1 = 0$.

(*d*) $\log (1 + 2 + 3) = \log 6 = \log (1 \times 2 \times 3) = \log 1 + \log 2 + \log 3$.

So, (*b*) is incorrect.

21. Let $\log_5 625 = x$. Then, $5^x = 625 = 5^4$ or $x = 4$.

Let $\log_2 (\log_5 625) = y$. Then, $\log_2 4 = y$ or $2^y = 4 = 2^2$ or $y = 2$.

$\therefore \quad \log_2 (\log_5 625) = 2$.

22. $\log_2 [\log_3 (\log_2 x)] = 1 = \log_2 2$

$\Leftrightarrow \log_3 (\log_2 x) = 2 \Leftrightarrow \log_2 x = 3^2 = 9 \Leftrightarrow x = 2^9 = 512$.

23. $\log_2 \log_2 \log_3 (\log_3 27^3) = \log_2 \log_2 \log_3 [\log_3 (3^3)^3] = \log_2 \log_2 \log_3 [\log_3 (3)^9]$

$= \log_2 \log_2 \log_3 (9 \log_3 3) = \log_2 \log_2 \log_3 9 \qquad [\because \log_3 3 = 1]$

$= \log_2 \log_2 [\log_3 (3)^2] = \log_2 \log_2 (2 \log_3 3)$

$= \log_2 \log_2 2 = \log_2 1 = 0$.

24. $a^x = b^y \Rightarrow \log a^x = \log b^y \Rightarrow x \log a = y \log b \Rightarrow \dfrac{\log a}{\log b} = \dfrac{y}{x}$.

25. $360 = (2 \times 2 \times 2) \times (3 \times 3) \times 5$.

So, $\log 360 = \log (2^3 \times 3^2 \times 5) = \log 2^3 + \log 3^2 + \log 5 = 3 \log 2 + 2 \log 3 + \log 5$.

26. $\dfrac{1}{3} \log_{10} 125 - 2 \log_{10} 4 + \log_{10} 32$

$= \log_{10} (125)^{1/3} - \log_{10} (4)^2 + \log_{10} 32 = \log_{10} 5 - \log_{10} 16 + \log_{10} 32$

$= \log_{10} \left(\dfrac{5 \times 32}{16} \right) = \log_{10} 10 = 1$.

27. $2 \log_{10} 5 + \log_{10} 8 - \dfrac{1}{2} \log_{10} 4 = \log_{10} (5^2) + \log_{10} 8 - \log_{10} (4^{1/2})$

$= \log_{10} 25 + \log_{10} 8 - \log_{10} 2 = \log_{10} \left(\dfrac{25 \times 8}{2} \right) = \log_{10} 100 = 2$.

28. $\log_a (ab) = x \quad \Rightarrow \quad \dfrac{\log ab}{\log a} = x \quad \Leftrightarrow \quad \dfrac{\log a + \log b}{\log a} = x$

$\Leftrightarrow \quad 1 + \dfrac{\log b}{\log a} = x \quad \Leftrightarrow \quad \dfrac{\log b}{\log a} = x - 1$

$\Leftrightarrow \quad \dfrac{\log a}{\log b} = \dfrac{1}{x-1} \quad \Leftrightarrow \quad 1 + \dfrac{\log a}{\log b} = 1 + \dfrac{1}{x-1}$

$\Leftrightarrow \quad \dfrac{\log b}{\log b} + \dfrac{\log a}{\log b} = \dfrac{x}{x-1} \quad \Leftrightarrow \quad \dfrac{\log b + \log a}{\log b} = \dfrac{x}{x-1}$

$\Leftrightarrow \quad \dfrac{\log (ab)}{\log b} = \dfrac{x}{x-1} \quad \Leftrightarrow \quad \log_b (ab) = \dfrac{x}{x-1}$.

29. $\log (4 \cdot \sqrt[3]{63}) = \log 4 + \log (\sqrt[3]{63}) = \log 4 + \log (63)^{1/3} = \log (2^2) + \log (7 \times 3^2)^{1/3}$

$= 2 \log 2 + \dfrac{1}{3} \log 7 + \dfrac{2}{3} \log 3 = 2x + \dfrac{1}{3} z + \dfrac{2}{3} y$.

30. $\log_4 x + \log_2 x = 6 \Leftrightarrow \dfrac{\log x}{\log 4} + \dfrac{\log x}{\log 2} = 6$

$\Leftrightarrow \dfrac{\log x}{2 \log 2} + \dfrac{\log x}{\log 2} = 6 \quad \Leftrightarrow 3 \log x = 12 \log 2$

$\Leftrightarrow \log x = 4 \log 2 \Leftrightarrow \log x = \log (2^4) = \log 16 \Leftrightarrow x = 16.$

31. $\log_8 x + \log_8 \left(\dfrac{1}{6}\right) = \dfrac{1}{3} \quad \Leftrightarrow \quad \dfrac{\log x}{\log 8} + \dfrac{\log \frac{1}{6}}{\log 8} = \dfrac{1}{3}$

$\Leftrightarrow \log x + \log \dfrac{1}{6} = \dfrac{1}{3} \log 8 \Leftrightarrow \log x + \log \dfrac{1}{6} = \log (8^{1/3}) = \log 2$

$\Leftrightarrow \log x = \log 2 - \log \dfrac{1}{6} = \log \left(2 \times \dfrac{6}{1}\right) = \log 12$

$\therefore \quad x = 12.$

32. $\log_{10} 125 + \log_{10} 8 = x \Rightarrow \log_{10} (125 \times 8) = x$

$\Rightarrow x = \log_{10} (1000) = \log_{10} (10)^3 = 3 \log_{10} 10 = 3.$

33. Let $\log_9 27 = x$. Then, $9^x = 27 \Leftrightarrow (3^2)^x = 3^3 \Leftrightarrow 2x = 3 \Leftrightarrow x = \dfrac{3}{2}.$

Let $\log_8 32 = y$. Then, $8^y = 32 \Leftrightarrow (2^3)^y = 2^5 \Leftrightarrow 3y = 5 \Leftrightarrow y = \dfrac{5}{3}.$

$\therefore \quad \log_9 27 + \log_8 32 = \left(\dfrac{3}{2} + \dfrac{5}{3}\right) = \dfrac{19}{6}.$

34. Given expression $= \left(\dfrac{\log 3}{\log 5} \times \dfrac{\log 625}{\log 3}\right) = \dfrac{\log 625}{\log 5} = \dfrac{\log (5^4)}{\log 5} = \dfrac{4 \log 5}{\log 5} = 4.$

35. Given expression $= \dfrac{\log 9}{\log 4} \times \dfrac{\log 2}{\log 3}$ $[\because \log_5 5 = 1]$

$= \dfrac{\log 3^2}{\log 2^2} \times \dfrac{\log 2}{\log 3} = \dfrac{2 \log 3}{2 \log 2} \times \dfrac{\log 2}{\log 3} = 1.$

36. $\log_{12} 27 = a \quad \Rightarrow \quad \dfrac{\log 27}{\log 12} = a \quad \Rightarrow \quad \dfrac{\log 3^3}{\log (3 \times 2^2)} = a$

$\Rightarrow \dfrac{3 \log 3}{\log 3 + 2 \log 2} = a \quad \Rightarrow \quad \dfrac{\log 3 + 2 \log 2}{3 \log 3} = \dfrac{1}{a}$

$\Rightarrow \dfrac{\log 3}{3 \log 3} + \dfrac{2 \log 2}{3 \log 3} = \dfrac{1}{a} \quad \Rightarrow \quad \dfrac{2}{3} \dfrac{\log 2}{\log 3} = \dfrac{1}{a} - \dfrac{1}{3} = \left(\dfrac{3 - a}{3a}\right)$

$\Rightarrow \dfrac{\log 2}{\log 3} = \left(\dfrac{3 - a}{2a}\right) \quad \Rightarrow \quad \log 3 = \left(\dfrac{2a}{3 - a}\right) \log 2.$

$$\log_6 16 = \frac{\log 16}{\log 6} = \frac{\log 2^4}{\log (2 \times 3)} = \frac{4 \log 2}{\log 2 + \log 3} = \frac{4 \log 2}{\log 2 \left[1 + \left(\frac{2a}{3 - a}\right)\right]}$$

$$= \frac{4}{\left(\frac{3 + a}{3 - a}\right)} = \frac{4 (3 - a)}{(3 + a)}$$

37. $\log_{10} 5 + \log_{10} (5x + 1) = \log_{10} (x + 5) + 1$

$\Rightarrow \log_{10} 5 + \log_{10} (5x + 1) = \log_{10} (x + 5) + \log_{10} 10$

$\Rightarrow \log_{10} [5 (5x + 1)] = \log_{10} [10 (x + 5)] \Rightarrow 5 (5x + 1) = 10 (x + 5)$

$\Rightarrow 5x + 1 = 2x + 10 \Rightarrow 3x = 9 \Rightarrow x = 3.$

38. $\log_5 (x^2 + x) - \log_5 (x + 1) = 2 \Rightarrow \log_5 \left(\frac{x^2 + x}{x + 1}\right) = 2$

$\Rightarrow \log_5 \left[\frac{x (x + 1)}{x + 1}\right] = 2 \Rightarrow \log_5 x = 2 \Rightarrow x = 5^2 = 25.$

39. Given expression $= \log_{60} 3 + \log_{60} 4 + \log_{60} 5 = \log_{60} (3 \times 4 \times 5) = \log_{60} 60 = 1.$

40. Given expression $= \left(\frac{\log 4}{\log 3} \times \frac{\log 5}{\log 4} \times \frac{\log 6}{\log 5} \times \frac{\log 7}{\log 6} \times \frac{\log 8}{\log 7} \times \frac{\log 9}{\log 8}\right)$

$= \frac{\log 9}{\log 3} = \frac{\log 3^2}{\log 3} = \frac{2 \log 3}{\log 3} = 2.$

41. We know that : $a^{\log_a x} = x.$

$\therefore \quad 16^{\log_4 5} = (4^2)^{\log_4 5} = 4^{2 \log_4 5} = 4^{\log_4 (5^2)} = 4^{\log_4 25} = 25.$

42. $\log x + \log y = \log (x + y) \Rightarrow \log (x + y) = \log (xy)$

$\Rightarrow x + y = xy \Rightarrow y (x - 1) = x \Rightarrow y = \frac{x}{x - 1}.$

43. $\log \frac{a}{b} + \log \frac{b}{a} = \log (a + b) \Rightarrow \log (a + b) = \log \left(\frac{a}{b} \times \frac{b}{a}\right) = \log 1.$

So, $a + b = 1.$

44. Given expression $= \log \left(\frac{a^2}{bc} \times \frac{b^2}{ac} \times \frac{c^2}{ab}\right) = \log 1 = 0.$

45. Given expression $= \left(\frac{\log a}{\log b} \times \frac{\log b}{\log c} \times \frac{\log c}{\log a}\right) = 1.$

46. Given expression $= \frac{1}{\log_a bc + \log_a a} + \frac{1}{\log_b ca + \log_b b} + \frac{1}{\log_c ab + \log_c c}$

$= \frac{1}{\log_a (abc)} + \frac{1}{\log_b (abc)} + \frac{1}{\log_c (abc)} = \log_{abc} a + \log_{abc} b + \log_{abc} c$

$= \log_{abc} (abc) = 1.$

47. Given expression $= \log_x \left(\frac{p}{q}\right) + \log_x \left(\frac{q}{r}\right) + \log_x \left(\frac{r}{p}\right) = \log_x \left(\frac{p}{q} \times \frac{q}{r} \times \frac{r}{p}\right) = \log_x 1 = 0.$

48. $\log_{10} \left(\frac{1}{70}\right) = \log_{10} 1 - \log_{10} 70 = -\log_{10} (7 \times 10) = -(\log_{10} 7 + \log_{10} 10) = -(a + 1).$

49. $a = b^x, b = c^y, c = a^z \Rightarrow x = \log_b a, y = \log_c b, z = \log_a c$

$\Rightarrow xyz = (\log_b a) \times (\log_c b) \times (\log_a c) \Rightarrow xyz = \left(\frac{\log a}{\log b} \times \frac{\log b}{\log c} \times \frac{\log c}{\log a}\right) = 1.$

50. $\log 27 = 1.431 \Rightarrow \log (3^3) = 1.431 \Rightarrow 3 \log 3 = 1.431$

$\Rightarrow \log 3 = 0.477$

$\therefore \log 9 = \log (3^2) = 2 \log 3 = (2 \times 0.477) = 0.954.$

51. $\log_2 10 = \dfrac{1}{\log_{10} 2} = \dfrac{1}{0.3010} = \dfrac{10000}{3010} = \dfrac{1000}{301}$.

52. $\log_{10} 5 = \log_{10}\left(\dfrac{10}{2}\right) = \log_{10} 10 - \log_{10} 2 = 1 - \log_{10} 2 = (1 - 0.3010) = 0.6990.$

53. $\log_{10} 80 = \log_{10} (8 \times 10) = \log_{10} 8 + \log_{10} 10 = \log_{10} (2^3) + 1 = 3 \log_{10} 2 + 1$
$= (3 \times 0.3010) + 1 = 1.9030.$

54. $(1000)^x = 3 \Rightarrow \log [(1000)^x] = \log 3 \Rightarrow x \log 1000 = \log 3$
$\Rightarrow x \log (10^3) = \log 3 \Rightarrow 3x \log 10 = \log 3$
$\Rightarrow 3x = \log 3 \Rightarrow x = \dfrac{0.477}{3} = 0.159.$

55. $\log_{10} 25 = \log_{10}\left(\dfrac{100}{4}\right) = \log_{10} 100 - \log_{10} 4 = 2 - 2 \log_{10} 2 = (2 - 2 \times 0.3010)$
$= (2 - 0.6020) = 1.3980.$

56. $\log_5 512 = \dfrac{\log 512}{\log 5} = \dfrac{\log 2^9}{\log\left(\dfrac{10}{2}\right)} = \dfrac{9 \log 2}{\log 10 - \log 2}$
$= \dfrac{(9 \times 0.3010)}{1 - 0.3010} = \dfrac{2.709}{0.699} = \dfrac{2709}{699} = 3.876.$

57. $\log_{10} (1.5) = \log_{10}\left(\dfrac{3}{2}\right) = \log_{10} 3 - \log_{10} 2 = (0.4771 - 0.3010) = 0.1761.$

58. $\log_{10} (2.8) = \log_{10}\left(\dfrac{28}{10}\right) = \log_{10} 28 - \log_{10} 10$
$= \log_{10} (7 \times 2^2) - 1 = \log_{10} 7 + 2 \log_{10} 2 - 1$
$= 0.8451 + 2 \times 0.3010 - 1 = 0.8451 + 0.602 - 1 = 0.4471.$

59. $\log (0.57) = \bar{1}.756 \Rightarrow \log 57 = 1.756$ [$\because$ mantissa will remain the same]
$\therefore \log 57 + \log (0.57)^3 + \log \sqrt{0.57}$
$= \log 57 + 3 \log\left(\dfrac{57}{100}\right) + \log\left(\dfrac{57}{100}\right)^{1/2}$
$= \log 57 + 3 \log 57 - 3 \log 100 + \dfrac{1}{2} \log 57 - \dfrac{1}{2} \log 100$
$= \dfrac{9}{2} \log 57 - \dfrac{7}{2} \log 100 = \dfrac{9}{2} \times 1.756 - \dfrac{7}{2} \times 2 = 7.902 - 7 = 0.902.$

60. $\log (2^{64}) = 64 \times \log 2 = (64 \times 0.30103) = 19.26592.$
Its characteristic is 19. Hence, the number of digits in 2^{64} is 20.

61. $\log 4^{50} = 50 \log 4 = 50 \log 2^2 = (50 \times 2) \log 2 = 100 \times \log 2 = (100 \times 0.30103) = 30.103.$
$\therefore$ Characteristic = 30. Hence, the number of digits in 4^{50} = 31.

62. $\log 5^{20} = 20 \log 5 = 20 \times \left[\log\left(\dfrac{10}{2}\right)\right] = 20 (\log 10 - \log 2)$
$= 20 (1 - 0.3010) = 20 \times 0.6990 = 13.9800.$
$\therefore$ Characteristic = 13. Hence, the number of digits in 5^{20} is 14.

24. AREA

FUNDAMENTAL CONCEPTS

I. Results on Triangles :

1. Sum of the angles of a triangle is 180°.
2. The sum of any two sides of a triangle is greater than the third side.
3. **Pythagoras Theorem** : In a right-angled triangle,

$$(\text{Hypotenuse})^2 = (\text{Base})^2 + (\text{Height})^2.$$

4. The line joining the mid-point of a side of a triangle to the opposite vertex is called the ***median.***
5. The point where the three medians of a triangle meet, is called ***centroid.*** The centroid divides each of the medians in the ratio 2 : 1.
6. In an isosceles triangle, the altitude from the vertex bisects the base.
7. The median of a triangle divides it into two triangles of the same area.
8. The area of the triangle formed by joining the mid-points of the sides of a given triangle is one-fourth of the area of the given triangle.

II. Results on Quadrilaterals :

1. The diagonals of a parallelogram bisect each other.
2. Each diagonal of a parallelogram divides it into two triangles of the same area.
3. The diagonals of a rectangle are equal and bisect each other.
4. The diagonals of a square are equal and bisect each other at right angles.
5. The diagonals of a rhombus are unequal and bisect each other at right angles.
6. A parallelogram and a rectangle on the same base and between the same parallels are equal in area.
7. Of all the parallelogram of given sides, the parallelogram which is a rectangle has the greatest area.

IMPORTANT FORMULAE

I. 1. Area of a rectangle = (Length × Breadth).

$$\therefore \quad \text{Length} = \left(\frac{\text{Area}}{\text{Breadth}}\right) \text{ and Breadth} = \left(\frac{\text{Area}}{\text{Length}}\right).$$

2. Perimeter of a rectangle = 2 (Length + Breadth).

II. Area of a square $= (\text{side})^2 = \frac{1}{2}(\text{diagonal})^2$.

III. Area of 4 walls of a room = 2 (Length + Breadth) × Height.

IV. 1. Area of a triangle $= \frac{1}{2} \times \text{Base} \times \text{Height}$.

2. Area of a triangle $= \sqrt{s(s-a)(s-b)(s-c)}$, where a, b, c are the sides of the triangle and $s = \frac{1}{2}(a+b+c)$.

3. Area of an equilateral triangle = $\frac{\sqrt{3}}{4} \times (\text{side})^2$

4. Radius of incircle of an equilateral triangle of side $a = \frac{a}{2\sqrt{3}}$.

5. Radius of circumcircle of an equilateral triangle of side $a = \frac{a}{\sqrt{3}}$.

6. Radius of incircle of a triangle of area Δ and semi-perimeter $s = \frac{\Delta}{s}$.

V. 1. Area of a parallelogram = (Base × Height).

2. Area of a rhombus = $\frac{1}{2} \times$ (Product of diagonals).

3. Area of a trapezium = $\frac{1}{2} \times$ (sum of parallel sides) × distance between them.

VI. 1. Area of a circle = πR^2, where R is the radius.

2. Circumference of a circle = $2\pi R$.

3. Length of an arc = $\frac{2\pi R\theta}{360}$, where θ is the central angle.

4. Area of a sector = $\frac{1}{2}(\text{arc} \times R) = \frac{\pi R^2 \theta}{360}$.

VII. 1. Area of a semi-circle = $\frac{\pi R^2}{2}$.

2. Circumference of a semi-circle = πR.

SOLVED EXAMPLES

Ex. 1. ***One side of a rectangular field is 15 m and one of its diagonals is 17 m. Find the area of the field.***

Sol. Other side = $\sqrt{(17)^2 - (15)^2} = \sqrt{289 - 225} = \sqrt{64} = 8$ m.

$\therefore$ Area = $(15 \times 8)\text{ m}^2 = 120\text{ m}^2$.

Ex. 2. ***A lawn is in the form of a rectangle having its sides in the ratio 2 : 3. The area of the lawn is $\frac{1}{6}$ hectares. Find the length and breadth of the lawn.***

Sol. Let length = $2x$ metres and breadth = $3x$ metres.

Now, area = $\left(\frac{1}{6} \times 1000\right)\text{ m}^2 = \left(\frac{5000}{3}\right)\text{ m}^2$.

So, $2x \times 3x = \frac{5000}{3} \Leftrightarrow x^2 = \frac{2500}{9} \Leftrightarrow x = \left(\frac{50}{3}\right)$

$\therefore$ Length = $2x = \frac{100}{3}$ m = $33\frac{1}{3}$ m, and Breadth = $3x = \left(3 \times \frac{50}{3}\right)$ m = 50 m.

Ex. 3. ***Find the cost of carpeting a room 13 m long and 9 m broad with a carpet 75 cm wide at the rate of Rs. 12.40 per square metre.***

Sol. Area of the carpet = Area of the room = $(13 \times 9)\text{ m}^2 = 117\text{ m}^2$.

Length of the carpet = $\left(\frac{\text{Area}}{\text{Width}}\right) = \left(117 \times \frac{4}{3}\right)$ m = 156 m.

$\therefore$ Cost of carpeting = Rs. (156×12.40) = Rs. 1934.40.

Ex. 4. ***If the diagonal of a rectangle is 17 cm long and its perimeter is 46 cm, find the area of the rectangle.***

Sol. Let length = x and breadth = y. Then,

$2(x + y) = 46$ or $x + y = 23$ and $x^2 + y^2 = (17)^2 = 289$.

Now, $(x + y)^2 = (23)^2 \Leftrightarrow (x^2 + y^2) + 2xy = 529 \Leftrightarrow 289 + 2xy = 529 \Leftrightarrow xy = 120$.

$\therefore$ Area = xy = 120 cm^2.

Ex. 5. ***The length of a rectangle is twice its breadth. If its length is decreased by 5 cm and breadth is increased by 5 cm, the area of the rectangle is increased by 75 sq. cm. Find the length of the rectangle.***

Sol. Let breadth = x. Then, length = $2x$. Then,

$(2x - 5)(x + 5) - 2x \times x = 75 \Leftrightarrow 5x - 25 = 75 \Leftrightarrow x = 20$.

$\therefore$ Length of the rectangle = 20 cm.

Ex. 6. ***In measuring the sides of a rectangle, one side is taken 5% in excess, and the other 4% in deficit. Find the error percent in the area calculated from these measurements.*** **(M.B.A. 2003)**

Sol. Let x and y be the sides of the rectangle. Then, Correct area = xy.

Calculated area = $\left(\frac{105}{100}x\right) \times \left(\frac{96}{100}y\right) = \frac{504}{500}xy$.

Error in measurement = $\left(\frac{504}{500}xy\right) - xy = \frac{4}{500}xy$.

$\therefore$ Error % = $\left[\frac{4}{500}xy \times \frac{1}{xy} \times 100\right]\% = \frac{4}{5}\% = 0.8\%$.

Ex. 7. ***A rectangular grassy plot 110 m by 65 m has a gravel path 2.5 m wide all round it on the inside. Find the cost of gravelling the path at 80 paise per sq. metre.***

Sol. Area of the plot = (110×65) m^2 = 7150 m^2.

Area of the plot excluding the path = $[(110 - 5) \times (65 - 5)]$ m^2 = 6300 m^2

$\therefore$ Area of the path = $(7150 - 6300)$ m^2 = 850 m^2

Cost of gravelling the path = Rs. $\left(850 \times \frac{80}{100}\right)$ = Rs. 680.

Ex. 8. ***The perimeters of two squares are 40 cm and 32 cm. Find the perimeter of a third square whose area is equal to the difference of the areas of the two squares.*** **(S.S.C. 2003)**

Sol. Side of first square = $\left(\frac{40}{4}\right)$ cm = 10 cm;

Side of second square = $\left(\frac{32}{4}\right)$ cm = 8 cm.

Area of third square = $[(10)^2 - (8)^2]$ cm^2 = $(100 - 64)$ cm^2 = 36 cm^2.

Side of third square = $\sqrt{36}$ cm = 6 cm.

$\therefore$ Required perimeter = (6×4) cm = 24 cm.

Ex. 9. ***A room 5m 55 cm long and 3m 74 cm broad is to be paved with square tiles. Find the least number of square tiles required to cover the floor.***

Sol. Area of the room = (544×374) cm^2.

Size of largest square tile = H.C.F. of 544 cm and 374 cm = 34 cm.

Area of 1 tile = (34×34) cm^2.

$\therefore$ Number of tiles required = $\left(\frac{544 \times 374}{34 \times 34}\right)$ = 176.

Ex. 10. ***Find the area of a square, one of whose diagonals is 3.8 m long.***

Sol. Area of the square $= \frac{1}{2} \times (\text{diagonal})^2 = \left(\frac{1}{2} \times 3.8 \times 3.8\right) \text{ m}^2 = 7.22 \text{ m}^2$.

Ex. 11. ***The diagonals of two squares are in the ratio of 2 : 5. Find the ratio of their areas.*** **(Section Officers', 2003)**

Sol. Let the diagonals of the squares be $2x$ and $5x$ respectively.

$\therefore$ Ratio of their areas $= \frac{1}{2} \times (2x)^2 : \frac{1}{2} \times (5x)^2 = 4x^2 : 25x^2 = 4 : 25$.

Ex. 12. ***If each side of a square is increased by 25%, find the percentage change in its area.***

Sol. Let each side of the square be a. Then, area $= a^2$.

New side $= \frac{125a}{100} = \frac{5a}{4}$. New area $= \left(\frac{5a}{4}\right)^2 = \frac{25a^2}{16}$.

Increase in area $= \left(\frac{25a^2}{16} - a^2\right) = \frac{9a^2}{16}$.

$\therefore$ Increase % $= \left(\frac{9a^2}{16} \times \frac{1}{a^2} \times 100\right)\% = 56.25\%$.

Ex. 13. ***If the length of a certain rectangle is decreased by 4 cm and the width is increased by 3 cm, a square with the same area as the original rectangle would result. Find the perimeter of the original rectangle.***

Sol. Let x and y be the length and breadth of the rectangle respectively.

Then, $x - 4 = y + 3$ or $x - y = 7$ ...(*i*)

Area of the rectangle $= xy$; Area of the square $= (x - 4)(y + 3)$

$\therefore$ $(x - 4)(y + 3) = xy \Leftrightarrow 3x - 4y = 12$ ...(*ii*)

Solving (*i*) and (*ii*), we get $x = 16$ and $y = 9$.

$\therefore$ Perimeter of the rectangle $= 2(x + y) = [2(16 + 9)]$ cm $= 50$ cm.

Ex. 14. ***A room is half as long again as it is broad. The cost of carpeting the room at Rs. 5 per sq. m is Rs. 270 and the cost of papering the four walls at Rs. 10 per m² is Rs. 1720. If a door and 2 windows occupy 8 sq. m, find the dimensions of the room.***

Sol. Let breadth $= x$ metres, length $= \frac{3x}{2}$ metres, height $=$ H metres.

Area of the floor $= \left(\frac{\text{Total cost of carpeting}}{\text{Rate}/\text{m}^2}\right) \text{m}^2 = \left(\frac{270}{5}\right) \text{m}^2 = 54 \text{ m}^2$.

$\therefore$ $x \times \frac{3x}{2} = 54 \Leftrightarrow x^2 = \left(54 \times \frac{2}{3}\right) = 36 \Leftrightarrow x = 6$.

So, breadth $= 6$ m and length $= \left(\frac{3}{2} \times 6\right)$ m $= 9$ m.

Now, papered area $= \left(\frac{1720}{10}\right) \text{m}^2 = 172 \text{ m}^2$.

Area of 1 door and 2 windows $= 8 \text{ m}^2$.

Total area of 4 walls $= (172 + 8) \text{ m}^2 = 180 \text{ m}^2$.

$\therefore$ $2(9 + 6) \times \text{H} = 180 \Leftrightarrow \text{H} = \left(\frac{180}{30}\right) = 6$ m.

Ex. 15. ***Find the area of a triangle whose sides measure 13 cm, 14 cm and 15 cm.***

Sol. Let $a = 13$, $b = 14$ and $c = 15$. Then, $s = \frac{1}{2}(a + b + c) = 21$.

$\therefore$ $(s - a) = 8$, $(s - b) = 7$ and $(s - c) = 6$.

$\therefore$ Area $= \sqrt{s(s-a)(s-b)(s-c)} = \sqrt{21 \times 8 \times 7 \times 6} = 84 \text{ cm}^2$.

Ex. 16. ***Find the area of a right-angled triangle whose base is 12 cm and hypotenuse 13 cm.***

Sol. Height of the triangle $= \sqrt{(13)^2 - (12)^2}$ cm $= \sqrt{25}$ cm $= 5$ cm.

$\therefore$ Its area $= \frac{1}{2} \times \text{Base} \times \text{Height} = \left(\frac{1}{2} \times 12 \times 5\right) \text{cm}^2 = 30 \text{ cm}^2$.

Ex. 17. ***The base of a triangular field is three times its altitude. If the cost of cultivating the field at Rs. 24.68 per hectare be Rs. 333.18, find its base and height.***

Sol. Area of the field $= \frac{\text{Total cost}}{\text{Rate}} = \left(\frac{333.18}{24.68}\right)$ hectares $= 13.5$ hectares

$= (13.5 \times 10000) \text{ m}^2 = 135000 \text{ m}^2$.

Let altitude $= x$ metres and base $= 3x$ metres.

Then, $\frac{1}{2} \times 3x \times x = 135000 \Leftrightarrow x^2 = 90000 \Leftrightarrow x = 300$.

$\therefore$ Base = 900 m and Altitude = 300 m.

Ex. 18. ***The altitude drawn to the base of an isosceles triangle is 8 cm and the perimeter is 32 cm. Find the area of the triangle.***

Sol. Let ABC be the isosceles triangle and AD be the altitude.

Let $AB = AC = x$. Then, $BC = (32 - 2x)$.

Since, in an isosceles triangle, the altitude bisects the base, so $BD = DC = (16 - x)$.

In ΔADC, $AC^2 = AD^2 + DC^2 \Rightarrow x^2 = (8)^2 + (16 - x)^2$

$\Rightarrow 32x = 320 \Rightarrow x = 10$.

A, x, x, B, D, C

$\therefore$ $BC = (32 - 2x) = (32 - 20)$ cm $= 12$ cm.

Hence, required area $= \left(\frac{1}{2} \times BC \times AD\right) = \left(\frac{1}{2} \times 12 \times 10\right) \text{cm}^2 = 60 \text{ cm}^2$.

Ex. 19. ***Find the length of the altitude of an equilateral triangle of side $3\sqrt{3}$ cm.***

Sol. Area of the triangle $= \frac{\sqrt{3}}{4} \times (3\sqrt{3})^2 = \frac{27\sqrt{3}}{4}$. Let the height be h.

Then, $\frac{1}{2} \times 3\sqrt{3} \times h = \frac{27\sqrt{3}}{4} \Leftrightarrow h = \frac{27\sqrt{3}}{4} \times \frac{2}{3\sqrt{3}} = \frac{9}{2} = 4.5$ cm.

Ex. 20. ***In two triangles, the ratio of the areas is 4 : 3 and the ratio of their heights is 3 : 4. Find the ratio of their bases.***

Sol. Let the bases of the two triangles be x and y and their heights be $3h$ and $4h$ respectively. Then,

$$\frac{\frac{1}{2} \times x \times 3h}{\frac{1}{2} \times y \times 4h} = \frac{4}{3} \Leftrightarrow \frac{x}{y} = \left(\frac{4}{3} \times \frac{4}{3}\right) = \frac{16}{9}.$$

$\therefore$ Required ratio = 16 : 9.

Ex. 21. ***The base of a parallelogram is twice its height. If the area of the parallelogram is 72 sq. cm, find its height.***

Sol. Let the height of the parallelogram be x cm. Then, base = $(2x)$ cm.

$\therefore$ $2x \times x = 72 \Leftrightarrow 2x^2 = 72 \Leftrightarrow x^2 = 36 \Leftrightarrow x = 6.$

Hence, height of the parallelogram = 6 cm.

Ex. 22. ***Find the area of a rhombus one side of which measures 20 cm and one diagonal 24 cm.***

Sol. Let other diagonal = $2x$ cm.

Since diagonals of a rhombus bisect each other at right angles, we have :

$(20)^2 = (12)^2 + x^2 \Leftrightarrow x = \sqrt{(20)^2 - (12)^2} = \sqrt{256} = 16$ cm.

So, other diagonal = 32 cm.

$\therefore$ Area of rhombus = $\frac{1}{2} \times$ (Product of diagonals) = $\left(\frac{1}{2} \times 24 \times 32\right)$ cm^2 = 384 cm^2.

Ex. 23. ***The difference between two parallel sides of a trapezium is 4 cm. The perpendicular distance between them is 19 cm. If the area of the trapezium is 475 cm^2, find the lengths of the parallel sides.*** **(R.R.B. 2002)**

Sol. Let the two parallel sides of the trapezium be a cm and b cm.

Then, $a - b = 4$ ...(*i*)

And, $\frac{1}{2} \times (a + b) \times 19 = 475 \Leftrightarrow (a + b) = \left(\frac{475 \times 2}{19}\right) \Leftrightarrow a + b = 50$ ...(*ii*)

Solving (*i*) and (*ii*), we get : $a = 27$, $b = 23$.

So, the two parallel sides are 27 cm and 23 cm.

Ex. 24. ***Find the length of a rope by which a cow must be tethered in order that it may be able to graze an area of 9856 sq. metres.*** **(M.A.T. 2003)**

Sol. Clearly, the cow will graze a circular field of area 9856 sq. metres and radius equal to the length of the rope.

Let the length of the rope be R metres.

Then, $\pi R^2 = 9856 \Leftrightarrow R^2 = \left(9856 \times \frac{7}{22}\right) = 3136 \Leftrightarrow R = 56.$

$\therefore$ Length of the rope = 56 m.

Ex. 25. ***The area of a circular field is 13.86 hectares. Find the cost of fencing it at the rate of Rs. 4.40 per metre.***

Sol. Area = (13.86×10000) m^2 = 138600 m^2.

$\pi R^2 = 138600 \Leftrightarrow R^2 = \left(138600 \times \frac{7}{22}\right) \Leftrightarrow R = 210$ m.

Circumference = $2\pi R = \left(2 \times \frac{22}{7} \times 210\right)$ m = 1320 m.

$\therefore$ Cost of fencing = Rs. (1320×4.40) = Rs. 5808.

Ex. 26. ***The diameter of the driving wheel of a bus is 140 cm. How many revolutions per minute must the wheel make in order to keep a speed of 66 kmph ?***

Sol. Distance to be covered in 1 min. = $\left(\frac{66 \times 1000}{60}\right)$ m = 1100 m.

Circumference of the wheel = $\left(2 \times \frac{22}{7} \times 0.70\right)$ m = 4.4 m.

$\therefore$ Number of revolutions per min. = $\left(\frac{1100}{4.4}\right)$ = 250.

Ex. 27. ***A wheel makes 1000 revolutions in covering a distance of 88 km. Find the radius of the wheel.***

Sol. Distance covered in one revolution $= \left(\frac{88 \times 1000}{1000}\right)$ m = 88 m.

$\therefore \quad 2\pi R = 88 \Leftrightarrow 2 \times \frac{22}{7} \times R = 88 \Leftrightarrow R = \left(88 \times \frac{7}{44}\right) = 14$ m.

Ex. 28. ***The inner circumference of a circular race track, 14 m wide, is 440 m. Find the radius of the outer circle.***

Sol. Let inner radius be r metres. Then, $2\pi r = 440 \Rightarrow r = \left(440 \times \frac{7}{44}\right) = 70$ m.

$\therefore$ Radius of outer circle = (70 + 14) m = 84 m.

Ex. 29. ***Two concentric circles form a ring. The inner and outer circumferences of the ring are $50\frac{2}{7}$ m and $75\frac{3}{7}$ m respectively. Find the width of the ring.***

Sol. Let the inner and outer radii be r and R metres.

Then, $2\pi r = \frac{352}{7} \Rightarrow r = \left(\frac{352}{7} \times \frac{7}{22} \times \frac{1}{2}\right) = 8$ m.

$2\pi R = \frac{528}{7} \Rightarrow R = \left(\frac{528}{7} \times \frac{7}{22} \times \frac{1}{2}\right) = 12$ m.

$\therefore$ Width of the ring = $(R - r)$ = (12 − 8) m = 4 m.

Ex. 30. ***A sector of 120°, cut out from a circle, has an area of $9\frac{3}{7}$ sq. cm. Find the radius of the circle.*** **(C.B.I. 1997)**

Sol. Let the radius of the circle be r cm. Then,

$\frac{\pi r^2 \theta}{360} = \frac{66}{7} \Leftrightarrow \frac{22}{7} \times r^2 \times \frac{120}{360} = \frac{66}{7} \Leftrightarrow r^2 = \left(\frac{66}{7} \times \frac{7}{22} \times 3\right) = 9 \Leftrightarrow r = 3.$

Hence, radius = 3 cm.

Ex. 31. ***Find the ratio of the areas of the incircle and circumcircle of a square.***

Sol. Let the side of the square be x. Then, its diagonal $= \sqrt{2}\,x$.

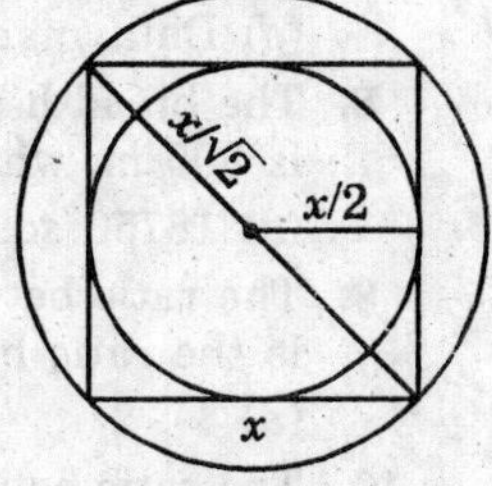

Radius of incircle $= \frac{x}{2}$ and

radius of circumcircle $= \frac{\sqrt{2}\,x}{2} = \frac{x}{\sqrt{2}}$.

$\therefore$ Required ratio $= \left(\frac{\pi x^2}{4} : \frac{\pi x^2}{2}\right) = \frac{1}{4} : \frac{1}{2} = 1 : 2.$

Ex. 32. ***If the radius of a circle is decreased by 50%, find the percentage decrease in its area.***

Sol. Let original radius = R. New radius $= \frac{50}{100} R = \frac{R}{2}$.

Original area $= \pi R^2$ and New area $= \pi \left(\frac{R}{2}\right)^2 = \frac{\pi R^2}{4}$.

$\therefore$ Decrease in area $= \left(\frac{3\pi R^2}{4} \times \frac{1}{\pi R^2} \times 100\right)\% = 75\%.$

EXERCISE 24A

(OBJECTIVE TYPE QUESTIONS)

Directions : *Mark (✓) against the correct answer* :

1. The length of a room is 5.5 m and width is 3.75 m. Find the cost of paving the floor by slabs at the rate of Rs. 800 per sq. metre. **(IGNOU, 2003)**

   (*a*) Rs. 15,000 (*b*) Rs. 15,550 (*c*) Rs. 15,600 (*d*) Rs. 16,500

2. The length of a rectangle is 18 cm and its breadth is 10 cm. When the length is increased to 25 cm, what will be the breadth of the rectangle if the area remains the same ?

   (*a*) 7 cm (*b*) 7.1 cm (*c*) 7.2 cm (*d*) 7.3 cm

3. A rectangular plot measuring 90 metres by 50 metres is to be enclosed by wire fencing. If the poles of the fence are kept 5 metres apart, how many poles will be needed ?

   (*a*) 55 (*b*) 56 (*c*) 57 (*d*) 58

4. The length of a rectangular plot is 60% more than its breadth. If the difference between the length and the breadth of that rectangle is 24 cm, what is the area of that rectangle ? **(Bank P.O. 1998)**

   (*a*) 2400 sq. cm (*b*) 2480 sq. cm (*c*) 2560 sq. cm
   (*d*) Data inadequate (*e*) None of these

5. A rectangular parking space is marked out by painting three of its sides. If the length of the unpainted side is 9 feet, and the sum of the lengths of the painted sides is 37 feet, then what is the area of the parking space in square feet ? **(M.A.T. 2003)**

   (*a*) 46 (*b*) 81 (*c*) 126 (*d*) 252

6. The difference between the length and breadth of a rectangle is 23 m. If its perimeter is 206 m, then its area is : **(Section Officers', 2003)**

   (*a*) 1520 m^2 (*b*) 2420 m^2 (*c*) 2480 m^2 (*d*) 2520 m^2

7. The length of a rectangular plot is 20 metres more than its breadth. If the cost of fencing the plot @ Rs. 26.50 per metre is Rs. 5300, what is the length of the plot in metres ? **(Bank P.O. 1999)**

   (*a*) 40 (*b*) 50 (*c*) 120
   (*d*) Data inadequate (*e*) None of these

8. The breadth of a rectangular field is 60% of its length. If the perimeter of the field is 800 m, what is the area of the field ?

   (*a*) 18750 sq. m (*b*) 37500 sq. m (*c*) 40000 sq. m (*d*) 48000 sq. m

9. The ratio between the length and the perimeter of a rectangular plot is 1 : 3. What is the ratio between the length and breadth of the plot ?

   (*a*) 1 : 2 (*b*) 2 : 1 (*c*) 3 : 2 (*d*) Data inadequate

10. The ratio between the length and the breadth of a rectangular park is 3 : 2. If a man cycling along the boundary of the park at the speed of 12 km / hr completes one round in 8 minutes, then the area of the park (in sq. m) is : **(S.S.C. 2003)**

    (*a*) 15360 (*b*) 153600 (*c*) 30720 (*d*) 307200

11. The length of a rectangular hall is 5 m more than its breadth. The area of the hall is 750 m^2. The length of the hall is : **(S.S.C. 2004)**

    (*a*) 15 m (*b*) 22.5 m (*c*) 25 m (*d*) 30 m

12. The area of a rectangle is 460 square metres. If the length is 15% more than the breadth, what is the breadth of the rectangular field ? **(Bank P.O. 2003)**

    (*a*) 15 metres (*b*) 26 metres (*c*) 34.5 metres
    (*d*) Cannot be determined (*e*) None of these

13. A rectangular field is to be fenced on three sides leaving a side of 20 feet uncovered. If the area of the field is 680 sq. feet, how many feet of fencing will be required ?

(*a*) 34 (*b*) 40 (*c*) 68 (*d*) 88

(R.R.B. 2002)

14. The ratio between the perimeter and the breadth of a rectangle is 5 : 1. If the area of the rectangle is 216 sq. cm, what is the length of the rectangle ?

(*a*) 16 cm (*b*) 18 cm (*c*) 24 cm
(*d*) Data inadequate (*e*) None of these **(B.S.R.B. 1998)**

15. A farmer wishes to start a 100 sq. m rectangular vegetable garden. Since he has only 30 m barbed wire, he fences three sides of the garden letting his house compound wall act as the fourth side fencing. The dimension of the garden is : **(R.R.B. 2003)**

(*a*) 15 m × 6.67 m (*b*) 20 m × 5 m (*c*) 30 m × 3.33 m (*d*) 40 m × 2.5 m

16. The sides of a rectangular field are in the ratio 3 : 4. If the area of the field is 7500 sq. m, the cost of fencing the field @ 25 paise per metre is : **(R.R.B. 2004)**

(*a*) Rs. 55.50 (*b*) Rs. 67.50 (*c*) Rs. 86.50 (*d*) Rs. 87.50

17. A rectangle of certain dimensions is chopped off from one corner of a larger rectangle as shown. AB = 8 cm and BC = 4 cm. The perimeter of the figure ABCPQRA (in cm) is : **(Asstt. Grade, 1998)**

P C R Q 4 cm A B 8 cm

(*a*) 24 (*b*) 28 (*c*) 36 (*d*) 48

18. A large field of 700 hectares is divided into two parts. The difference of the areas of the two parts is one-fifth of the average of the two areas. What is the area of the smaller part in hectares ?

(*a*) 225 (*b*) 280 (*c*) 300 (*d*) 315

19. A rectangular paper, when folded into two congruent parts had a perimeter of 34 cm for each part folded along one set of sides and the same is 38 cm when folded along the other set of sides. What is the area of the paper ? **(S.S.C. 2000)**

(*a*) 140 cm^2 (*b*) 240 cm^2 (*c*) 560 cm^2 (*d*) None of these

20. A rectangular plot is half as long again as it is broad and its area is $\frac{2}{3}$ hectares. Then, its length is :

(*a*) 100 m (*b*) 33.33 m (*c*) 66.66 m (*d*) $\frac{100\sqrt{3}}{3}$ m

21. A courtyard 25 m long and 16 m broad is to be paved with bricks of dimensions 20 cm by 10 cm. The total number of bricks required is :

(*a*) 18000 (*b*) 20000 (*c*) 25000 (*d*) None of these

22. The cost of carpeting a room 18 m long with a carpet 75 cm wide at Rs. 4.50 per metre is Rs. 810. The breadth of the room is :

(*a*) 7 m (*b*) 7.5 m (*c*) 8 m (*d*) 8.5 m

23. The diagonal of the floor of a rectangular closet is $7\frac{1}{2}$ feet. The shorter side of the closet is $4\frac{1}{2}$ feet. What is the area of the closet in square feet ? **(M.B.A. 2003)**

(*a*) $5\frac{1}{4}$ (*b*) $13\frac{1}{2}$ (*c*) 27 (*d*) 37

24. The length of a rectangle is three times of its width. If the length of the diagonal is $8\sqrt{10}$ cm, then the perimeter of the rectangle is : **(S.S.C. 2000)**

(a) $15\sqrt{10}$ cm (b) $16\sqrt{10}$ cm (c) $24\sqrt{10}$ cm (d) 64 cm

25. The diagonal of a rectangle is thrice its smaller side. The ratio of the length to the breadth of the rectangle is :

(a) 3 : 1 (b) $\sqrt{3}$: 1 (c) $\sqrt{2}$: 1 (d) $2\sqrt{2}$: 1

26. A rectangular carpet has an area of 120 sq. metres and a perimeter of 46 metres. The length of its diagonal is :

(a) 15 m (b) 16 m (c) 17 m (d) 20 m

27. The diagonal of a rectangle is $\sqrt{41}$ cm and its area is 20 sq. cm. The perimeter of the rectangle must be : **(Hotel Management, 2002)**

(a) 9 cm (b) 18 cm (c) 20 cm (d) 41 cm

28. A took 15 seconds to cross a rectangular field diagonally walking at the rate of 52 m / min and B took the same time to cross the same field along its sides walking at the rate of 68 m / min. The area of the field is : **(S.S.C. 2003)**

(a) 30 m^2 (b) 40 m^2 (c) 50 m^2 (d) 60 m^2

29. A rectangular carpet has an area of 60 sq. m. If its diagonal and longer side together equal 5 times the shorter side, the length of the carpet is :

(a) 5 m (b) 12 m (c) 13 m (d) 14.5 m

30. The ratio between the length and the breadth of a rectangular field is 3 : 2. If only the length is increased by 5 metres, the new area of the field will be 2600 sq. metres. What is the breadth of the rectangular field ?

(a) 40 metres (b) 60 metres (c) 65 metres
(d) Cannot be determined (e) None of these

31. The length of a blackboard is 8 cm more than its breadth. If the length is increased by 7 cm and breadth is decreased by 4 cm, the area remains the same. The length and breadth of the blackboard (in cm) will be :

(a) 28, 20 (b) 34, 26 (c) 40, 32 (d) 56, 48

32. If the length and breadth of a rectangular room are each increased by 1 m, then the area of floor is increased by 21 sq. m. If the length is increased by 1 m and breadth is decreased by 1 m, then the area is decreased by 5 sq. m. The perimeter of the floor is : **(M.B.A. 2002)**

(a) 30 m (b) 32 m (c) 36 m (d) 40 m

33. The percentage increase in the area of a rectangle, if each of its sides is increased by 20%, is : **(M.A.T. 2004)**

(a) 40% (b) 42% (c) 44% (d) 46%

34. A rectangle has width *a* and length *b*. If the width is decreased by 20% and the length is increased by 10%, then what is the area of the new rectangle in percentage compared to '*ab*'? **(R.R.B. 2002)**

(a) 80% (b) 88% (c) 110% (d) 120%

35. If the length and breadth of a rectangular plot be increased by 50% and 20% respectively, then how many times will its area be increased ? **(Bank P.O. 2003)**

(a) $1\frac{1}{3}$ (b) 2 (c) $3\frac{2}{5}$ (d) $4\frac{1}{5}$ (e) None of these

36. A towel, when bleached, was found to have lost 20% of its length and 10% of its breadth. The percentage of decrease in area is : **(N.I.F.T. 1997)**

(a) 10% (b) 10.08% (c) 20% (d) 28%

37. The length of a rectangle is halved, while its breadth is tripled. What is the percentage change in area ? **(S.S.C. 2000)**

(*a*) 25% increase (*b*) 50% increase (*c*) 50% decrease (*d*) 75% decrease

38. The length of a rectangle is decreased by *r*%, and the breadth is increased by $(r + 5)\%$. Find *r*, if the area of the rectangle is unaltered. **(SCMHRD, 2002)**

(*a*) 5 (*b*) 8 (*c*) 10 (*d*) 15 (*e*) 20

39. The length of a rectangle is increased by 60%. By what percent would the width have to be decreased so as to maintain the same area ? **(M.A.T. 2003)**

(*a*) $37\frac{1}{2}\%$ (*b*) 60% (*c*) 75% (*d*) 120%

40. If the area of a rectangular plot increases by 30% while its breadth remains same, what will be the ratio of the areas of new and old figures ? **(Bank P.O. 2003)**

(*a*) 1 : 3 (*b*) 3 : 1 (*c*) 4 : 7 (*d*) 10 : 13 (*e*) None of these

41. A typist uses a sheet measuring 20 cm by 30 cm lengthwise. If a margin of 2 cm is left on each side and a 3 cm margin on top and bottom, then percent of the page used for typing is : **(M.A.T. 1998)**

(*a*) 40 (*b*) 60 (*c*) 64 (*d*) 72

42. A room is 15 feet long and 12 feet broad. A mat has to be placed on the floor of this room leaving $1\frac{1}{2}$ feet space from the walls. What will be the cost of the mat at the rate of Rs. 3.50 per square feet ? **(R.R.B. 2002)**

(*a*) Rs. 378 (*b*) Rs. 472.50 (*c*) Rs. 496 (*d*) Rs. 630

43. What will be the cost of gardening 1 metre broad boundary around a rectangular plot having perimeter of 340 metres at the rate of Rs. 10 per square metre ?

(*a*) Rs. 1700 (*b*) Rs. 3400 (*c*) Rs. 3440
(*d*) Cannot be determined (*e*) None of these **(Bank P.O. 2003)**

44. 2 metres broad pathway is to be constructed around a rectangular plot on the inside. The area of the plot is 96 sq. m. The rate of construction is Rs. 50 per square metre. Find the total cost of the construction. **(S.B.I.P.O. 2000)**

(*a*) Rs. 2400 (*b*) Rs. 4000 (*c*) Rs. 4800
(*d*) Data inadequate (*e*) None of these

45. Within a rectangular garden 10 m wide and 20 m long, we wish to pave a walk around the borders of uniform width so as to leave an area of 96 m^2 for flowers. How wide should the walk be ?

(*a*) 1 m (*b*) 2 m (*c*) 2.1 m (*d*) 2.5 m

46. A rectangular lawn 55 m by 35 m has two roads each 4 m wide running in the middle of it, one parallel to length and the other parallel to breadth. The cost of gravelling the roads at 75 paise per sq. metre is :

(*a*) Rs. 254.50 (*b*) Rs. 258 (*c*) Rs. 262.50 (*d*) Rs. 270

47. A rectangular park 60 m long and 40 m wide has two concrete crossroads running in the middle of the park and rest of the park has been used as a lawn. If the area of the lawn is 2109 sq. m, then what is the width of the road ? **(M.A.T. 1997)**

(*a*) 2.91 m (*b*) 3 m (*c*) 5.82 m (*d*) None of these

48. A housing society has been allotted a square piece of land measuring 2550.25 sq. m. What is the side of the plot ?

(*a*) 50.25 m (*b*) 50.5 m (*c*) 50.65 m (*d*) None of these

49. The cost of cultivating a square field at the rate of Rs. 135 per hectare is Rs. 1215. The cost of putting a fence around it at the rate of 75 paise per metre would be :

(*a*) Rs. 360 (*b*) Rs. 810 (*c*) Rs. 900 (*d*) Rs. 1800

50. The perimeters of five squares are 24 cm, 32 cm, 40 cm, 76 cm and 80 cm respectively. The perimeter of another square equal in area to the sum of the areas of these squares is : **(S.S.C. 2004)**

(*a*) 31 cm (*b*) 62 cm (*c*) 124 cm (*d*) 961 cm

51. The number of marble slabs of size 20 cm × 30 cm required to pave the floor of a square room of side 3 metres, is :

(*a*) 100 (*b*) 150 (*c*) 225 (*d*) 250

52. 50 square stone slabs of equal size were needed to cover a floor area of 72 sq. m. The length of each stone slab is : **(S.S.C. 2003)**

(*a*) 102 cm (*b*) 120 cm (*c*) 201 cm (*d*) 210 cm

53. The length and breadth of the floor of the room are 20 feet and 10 feet respectively. Square tiles of 2 feet length of different colours are to be laid on the floor. Black tiles are laid in the first row on all sides. If white tiles are laid in the one-third of the remaining and blue tiles in the rest, how many blue tiles will be there ?

(*a*) 16 (*b*) 24 (*c*) 32

(*d*) 48 (*e*) None of these **(S.B.I.P.O. 2000)**

54. What is the least number of square tiles required to pave the floor of a room 15 m 17 cm long and 9 m 2 cm broad ? **(S.S.C. 2003)**

(*a*) 814 (*b*) 820 (*c*) 840 (*d*) 844

55. A rectangular room can be partitioned into two equal square rooms by a partition 7 metres long. What is the area of the rectangular room in square metres ?

(*a*) 49 (*b*) 147 (*c*) 196 (*d*) None of these

56. The perimeter of a square is 48 cm. The area of a rectangle is 4 cm^2 less than the area of the square. If the length of the rectangle is 14 cm, then its perimeter is :

(*a*) 24 cm (*b*) 48 cm (*c*) 50 cm (*d*) 54 cm

(S.S.C. 2002)

57. The area of a rectangle is thrice that of a square. If the length of the rectangle is 40 cm and its breadth is $\frac{3}{2}$ times that of the side of the square, then the side of the square is :

(*a*) 15 cm (*b*) 20 cm (*c*) 30 cm (*d*) 60 cm

58. If the perimeter of a rectangle and a square, each is equal to 80 cm and the difference of their areas is 100 sq. cm, the sides of the rectangle are :

(*a*) 25 cm, 15 cm (*b*) 28 cm, 12 cm (*c*) 30 cm, 10 cm (*d*) 35 cm, 15 cm

59. The cost of fencing a square field @ Rs. 20 per metre is Rs. 10,080. How much will it cost to lay a three metre wide pavement along the fencing inside the field @ Rs. 50 per sq. metre ?

(*a*) Rs. 37,350 (*b*) Rs. 73,800 (*c*) Rs. 77,400 (*d*) None of these

60. A park square in shape has a 3 metre wide road inside it running along its sides. The area occupied by the road is 1764 square metres. What is the perimeter along the outer edge of the road ? **(Bank P.O. 1998)**

(*a*) 576 metres (*b*) 600 metres (*c*) 640 metres

(*d*) Data inadequate (*e*) None of these

61. A man walked diagonally across a square lot. Approximately, what was the percent saved by not walking along the edges ? **(M.B.A. 2003)**

(*a*) 20 (*b*) 24 (*c*) 30 (*d*) 33

62. A man walking at the speed of 4 kmph crosses a square field diagonally in 3 minutes. The area of the field is :

(*a*) 18000 m^2 (*b*) 19000 m^2 (*c*) 20000 m^2 (*d*) 25000 m^2

63. If the length of the diagonal of a square is 20 cm, then its perimeter must be :
(a) $10\sqrt{2}$ cm (b) 40 cm (c) $40\sqrt{2}$ cm (d) 200 cm
(R.R.B. 2003)

64. The area of a square field is 69696 cm^2. Its diagonal will be equal to :
(a) 313.296 m (b) 353.296 m (c) 373.296 m (d) 393.296 m
(S.S.C. 1999)

65. What will be the length of the diagonal of that square plot whose area is equal to the area of a rectangular plot of length 45 metres and breadth 40 metres ?
(a) 42.5 metres (b) 60 metres (c) 75 metres
(d) Data inadequate (e) None of these **(Bank P.O. 1999)**

66. The length of a rectangle is 20% more than its breadth. What will be the ratio of the area of a rectangle to that of a square whose side is equal to the breadth of the rectangle ? **(Bank P.O. 2000)**
(a) 2 : 1 (b) 5 : 6 (c) 6 : 5
(d) Data inadequate (e) None of these

67. A square and a rectangle have equal areas. If their perimeters are p_1 and p_2 respectively, then :
(a) $p_1 < p_2$ (b) $p_1 = p_2$ (c) $p_1 > p_2$ (d) None of these

68. If the perimeters of a square and a rectangle are the same, then the area A and B enclosed by them would satisfy the condition :
(a) A < B (b) A ≤ B (c) A > B (d) A ≥ B

69. The diagonal of a square is $4\sqrt{2}$ cm. The diagonal of another square whose area is double that of the first square, is : **(S.S.C. 2002)**
(a) 8 cm (b) $8\sqrt{2}$ cm (c) $4\sqrt{2}$ cm (d) 16 cm

70. The ratio of the area of a square to that of the square drawn on its diagonal, is :
(a) 1 : 2 (b) 2 : 3 (c) 3 : 4 (d) 4 : 5
(IGNOU, 2003)

71. The ratio of the areas of two squares, one having its diagonal double than the other, is :
(a) 2 : 1 (b) 2 : 3 (c) 3 : 1 (d) 4 : 1

72. If the ratio of areas of two squares is 225 : 256, then the ratio of their perimeters is :
(a) 225 : 256 (b) 256 : 225 (c) 15 : 16 (d) 16 : 15
(S.S.C. 2004)

73. Of the two square fields, the area of one is 1 hectare while the other one is broader by 1%. The difference in their areas is :
(a) 100 m^2 (b) 101 m^2 (c) 200 m^2 (d) 201 m^2

74. If each side of a square is increased by 50%, the ratio of the area of the resulting square to that of the given square is :
(a) 4 : 5 (b) 5 : 4 (c) 4 : 9 (d) 9 : 4

75. What happens to the area of a square when its side is halved ? Its area will :
(a) remain same (b) become half (c) become one-fourth (d) become double
(R.R.B. 2003)

76. An error of 2% in excess is made while measuring the side of a square. The percentage of error in the calculated area of the square is : **(C.D.S. 2003)**
(a) 2% (b) 2.02% (c) 4% (d) 4.04%

77. If the area of a square increases by 69%, then the side of the square increases by :
(a) 13% (b) 30% (c) 39% (d) 69%
(M.A.T. 1998)

78. If the diagonal of a square is made 1.5 times, then the ratio of the areas of two squares is :

(*a*) 4 : 3 (*b*) 4 : 5 (*c*) 4 : 7 (*d*) 4 : 9

79. The length and breadth of a square are increased by 40% and 30% respectively. The area of the resulting rectangle exceeds the area of the square by :

(*a*) 35% (*b*) 42% (*c*) 62% (*d*) 82%

80. The length of one pair of opposite sides of a square is increased by 5 cm on each side; the ratio of the length and the breadth of the newly formed rectangle becomes 3 : 2. What is the area of the original square ? **(Bank P.O. 1999)**

(*a*) 25 sq. cm (*b*) 81 sq. cm (*c*) 100 sq. cm
(*d*) 225 sq. cm (*e*) None of these

81. If the side of a square is increased by 5 cm, the area increases by 165 sq. cm. The side of the square is :

(*a*) 12 cm (*b*) 13 cm (*c*) 14 cm (*d*) 15 cm

82. The difference of the areas of two squares drawn on two line segments of different lengths is 32 sq. cm. Find the length of the greater line segment if one is longer than the other by 2 cm. **(S.S.C. 2003)**

(*a*) 7 cm (*b*) 9 cm (*c*) 11 cm (*d*) 16 cm

83. The areas of a square and a rectangle are equal. The length of the rectangle is greater than the length of any side of the square by 5 cm and the breadth is less by 3 cm. Find the perimeter of the rectangle. **(S.S.C. 2002)**

(*a*) 17 cm (*b*) 26 cm (*c*) 30 cm (*d*) 34 cm

84. A tank is 25 m long, 12 m wide and 6 m deep. The cost of plastering its walls and bottom at 75 paise per sq. m, is : **(C.B.I. 1997)**

(*a*) Rs. 456 (*b*) Rs. 458 (*c*) Rs. 558 (*d*) Rs. 568

85. The dimensions of a room are 10 m × 7 m × 5 m. There are 2 doors and 3 windows in the room. The dimensions of the doors are 1 m × 3 m. One window is of size 2 m × 1.5 m and the other two windows are of size 1 m × 1.5 m. The cost of painting the walls at Rs. 3 per m^2 is :

(*a*) Rs. 474 (*b*) Rs. 578.50 (*c*) Rs. 684 (*d*) Rs. 894

86. The cost of papering the four walls of a room is Rs. 475. Each one of the length, breadth and height of another room is double that of this room. The cost of papering the walls of this new room is :

(*a*) Rs. 712.50 (*b*) Rs. 950 (*c*) Rs. 1425 (*d*) Rs. 1900

87. The ratio of height of a room to its semi-perimeter is 2 : 5. It costs Rs. 260 to paper the walls of the room with paper 50 cm wide at Rs. 2 per metre allowing an area of 15 sq. m for doors and windows. The height of the room is :

(*a*) 2.6 m (*b*) 3.9 m (*c*) 4 m (*d*) 4.2 m

88. The base of a triangle is 15 cm and height is 12 cm. The height of another triangle of double the area having the base 20 cm is : **(S.S.C. 2002)**

(*a*) 8 cm (*b*) 9 cm (*c*) 12.5 cm (*d*) 18 cm

89. ABC is a triangle with base AB. D is a point on AB such that AB = 5 and DB = 3. What is the ratio of the area of Δ ADC to the area of Δ ABC ? **(S.S.C. 2000)**

(*a*) 2 : 3 (*b*) 3 : 2 (*c*) 2 : 5 (*d*) 3 : 5

90. The area of a right-angled triangle is 40 times its base. What is its height ?

(*a*) 45 cm (*b*) 60 cm (*c*) 80 cm
(*d*) Data inadequate (*e*) None of these **(B.S.R.B. 1998)**

91. If the area of a triangle is 1176 cm^2 and base : corresponding altitude is 3 : 4, then the altitude of the triangle is : **(S.S.C. 2000)**

(*a*) 42 cm (*b*) 52 cm (*c*) 54 cm (*d*) 56 cm

92. The three sides of a triangle are 5 cm, 12 cm and 13 cm respectively. Then, its area is :

(*a*) $10\sqrt{3}$ cm^2 (*b*) $10\sqrt{6}$ cm^2 (*c*) 20 cm^2 (*d*) 30 cm^2

93. The sides of a triangle are in the ratio of $\frac{1}{2} : \frac{1}{3} : \frac{1}{4}$. If the perimeter is 52 cm, then the length of the smallest side is : **(M.A.T. 2004)**

(*a*) 9 cm (*b*) 10 cm (*c*) 11 cm (*d*) 12 cm

94. The area of a triangle is 216 cm^2 and its sides are in the ratio 3 : 4 : 5. The perimeter of the triangle is : **(S.S.C. 2004)**

(*a*) 6 cm (*b*) 12 cm (*c*) 36 cm (*d*) 72 cm

95. The sides of a triangle are 3 cm, 4 cm and 5 cm. The area (in cm^2) of the triangle formed by joining the mid-points of the sides of this triangle is : **(S.S.C. 2003)**

(*a*) $\frac{3}{4}$ (*b*) $\frac{3}{2}$ (*c*) 3 (*d*) 6

96. One side of a right-angled triangle is twice the other, and the hypotenuse is 10 cm. The area of the triangle is :

(*a*) 20 cm^2 (*b*) $33\frac{1}{3}$ cm^2 (*c*) 40 cm^2 (*d*) 50 cm^2

97. The perimeter of a right-angled triangle is 60 cm. Its hypotenuse is 26 cm. The area of the triangle is : **(M.B.A. 2002)**

(*a*) 120 cm^2 (*b*) 240 cm^2 (*c*) 390 cm^2 (*d*) 780 cm^2

98. If the perimeter of an isosceles right triangle is $(6 + 3\sqrt{2})$ m, then the area of the triangle is : **(M.A.T. 2003)**

(*a*) 4.5 m^2 (*b*) 5.4 m^2 (*c*) 9 m^2 (*d*) 81 m^2

99. The perimeter of a triangle is 30 cm and its area is 30 cm^2. If the largest side measures 13 cm, then what is the length of the smallest side of the triangle ?

(*a*) 3 cm (*b*) 4 cm (*c*) 5 cm (*d*) 6 cm

(S.S.C. 2003)

100. If the area of an equilateral triangle is $24\sqrt{3}$ sq. cm, then its perimeter is :

(*a*) $2\sqrt{6}$ cm (*b*) $4\sqrt{6}$ cm (*c*) $12\sqrt{6}$ cm (*d*) 96 cm

101. The height of an equilateral triangle is 10 cm. Its area is : **(S.S.C. 2003)**

(*a*) $\frac{100}{3}$ cm^2 (*b*) 30 cm^2 (*c*) 100 cm^2 (*d*) $\frac{100}{\sqrt{3}}$ cm^2

102. From a point in the interior of an equilateral triangle, the perpendicular distance of the sides are $\sqrt{3}$ cm, $2\sqrt{3}$ cm and $5\sqrt{3}$ cm. The perimeter (in cm) of the triangle is :

(*a*) 24 (*b*) 32 (*c*) 48 (*d*) 64

103. If x is the length of a median of an equilateral triangle, then its area is :

(*a*) x^2 (*b*) $\frac{1}{2}x^2$ (*c*) $\frac{\sqrt{3}}{2}x^2$ (*d*) $\frac{\sqrt{3}}{3}x^2$

104. If the area of a square with side a is equal to the area of a triangle with base a, then the altitude of the triangle is : **(B.S.F. 2001)**

(*a*) $\frac{a}{2}$ (*b*) a (*c*) $2a$ (*d*) $4a$

105. An equilateral triangle is described on the diagonal of a square. What is the ratio of the area of the triangle to that of the square ? **(S.S.C. 2002)**

(*a*) $2 : \sqrt{3}$ (*b*) $4 : \sqrt{3}$ (*c*) $\sqrt{3} : 2$ (*d*) $\sqrt{3} : 4$

106. What will be the ratio between the area of a rectangle and the area of a triangle with one of the sides of the rectangle as base and a vertex on the opposite side of the rectangle ? **(S.B.I.P.O. 1999)**

(a) 1 : 2 (b) 2 : 1 (c) 3 : 1
(d) Data inadequate (e) None of these

107. If an equilateral triangle of area X and a square of area Y have the same perimeter, then X is : **(C.D.S. 2003)**

(a) equal to Y (b) greater than Y
(c) less than Y (d) less than or equal to Y

108. A square and an equilateral triangle have equal perimeters. If the diagonal of the square is $12\sqrt{2}$ cm, then the area of the triangle is :

(a) $24\sqrt{2}$ cm^2 (b) $24\sqrt{3}$ cm^2 (c) $48\sqrt{3}$ cm^2 (d) $64\sqrt{3}$ cm^2

109. The ratio of bases of two triangles is $x : y$ and that of their areas is $a : b$. Then the ratio of their corresponding altitudes will be : **(S.S.C. 2004)**

(a) $ax : by$ (b) $\frac{a}{x} : \frac{b}{y}$ (c) $ay : bx$ (d) $\frac{x}{a} : \frac{b}{y}$

110. If the side of an equilateral triangle is decreased by 20%, its area is decreased by :

(a) 36% (b) 40% (c) 60% (d) 64% **(C.B.I. 1997)**

111. If the height of a triangle is decreased by 40% and its base is increased by 40%, what will be the effect on its area ? **(S.B.I.P.O. 2000)**

(a) No change (b) 8% decrease (c) 16% decrease
(d) 16% increase (e) None of these

112. If every side of a triangle is doubled, the area of the new triangle is K times the area of the old one. K is equal to : **(R.R.B. 2003)**

(a) $\sqrt{2}$ (b) 2 (c) 3 (d) 4

113. One side of a parallelogram is 18 cm and its distance from the opposite side is 8 cm. The area of the parallelogram is :

(a) 48 cm^2 (b) 72 cm^2 (c) 100 cm^2 (d) 144 cm^2

114. A parallelogram has sides 30 m and 14 m and one of its diagonals is 40 m long. Then, its area is :

(a) 168 m^2 (b) 336 m^2 (c) 372 m^2 (d) 480 m^2

115. One diagonal of a parallelogram is 70 cm and the perpendicular distance of this diagonal from either of the outlying vertices is 27 cm. The area of the parallelogram (in sq. cm) is :

(a) 1800 (b) 1836 (c) 1890 (d) 1980

116. A triangle and a parallelogram are constructed on the same base such that their areas are equal. If the altitude of the parallelogram is 100 m, then the altitude of the triangle is : **(M.A.T. 2003)**

(a) $10\sqrt{2}$ m (b) 100 m (c) $100\sqrt{2}$ m (d) 200 m

117. If a parallelogram with area P, a rectangle with area R and a triangle with area T are all constructed on the same base and all have the same altitude, then which of the following statements is false ?

(a) P = R (b) P + T = 2R (c) P = 2T (d) T = (1/2) R

118. The area of a rhombus is 150 cm^2. The length of one of its diagonals is 10 cm. The length of the other diagonal is : **(S.S.C. 2004)**

(a) 25 cm (b) 30 cm (c) 35 cm (d) 40 cm

119. One of the diagonals of a rhombus is double the other diagonal. Its area is 25 sq. cm. The sum of the diagonals is : **(S.S.C. 2003)**

(a) 10 cm (b) 12 cm (c) 15 cm (d) 16 cm

120. The perimeter of a rhombus is 56 m and its height is 5 m. Its area is :

(a) 64 sq. m (b) 70 sq. m (c) 78 sq. m (d) 84 sq. m

121. If the diagonals of a rhombus are 24 cm and 10 cm, the area and the perimeter of the rhombus are respectively :

(a) 120 cm^2, 52 cm (b) 120 cm^2, 64 cm (c) 240 cm^2, 52 cm (d) 240 cm^2, 64 cm

122. Each side of a rhombus is 26 cm and one of its diagonals is 48 cm long. The area of the rhombus is : **(R.R.B. 2003)**

(a) 240 cm^2 (b) 300 cm^2 (c) 360 cm^2 (d) 480 cm^2

123. The length of one diagonal of a rhombus is 80% of the other diagonal. The area of the rhombus is how many times the square of the length of the other diagonal ?

(a) $\frac{4}{5}$ (b) $\frac{2}{5}$ (c) $\frac{3}{4}$ (d) $\frac{1}{4}$

124. If a square and a rhombus stand on the same base, then the ratio of the areas of the square and the rhombus is :

(a) greater than 1 (b) equal to 1 (c) equal to $\frac{1}{2}$ (d) equal to $\frac{1}{4}$

125. The two parallel sides of a trapezium are 1.5 m and 2.5 m respectively. If the perpendicular distance between them is 6.5 metres, the area of the trapezium is :

(a) 10 m^2 (b) 13 m^2 (c) 20 m^2 (d) 26 m^2

126. The area of a field in the shape of a trapezium measures 1440 m^2. The perpendicular distance between its parallel sides is 24 m. If the ratio of the parallel sides is 5 : 3, the length of the longer parallel side is : **(S.S.C. 2004)**

(a) 45 m (b) 60 m (c) 75 m (d) 120 m

127. The cross-section of a canal is trapezium in shape. The canal is 12 m wide at the top and 8 m wide at the bottom. If the area of the cross-section is 840 sq. m, the depth of the canal is :

(a) 8.75 m (b) 42 m (c) 63 m (d) 84 m

128. The area of a circle of radius 5 is numerically what percent of its circumference ?

(a) 200 (b) 225 (c) 240 (d) 250 **(S.S.C. 2000)**

129. A man runs round a circular field of radius 50 m at the speed of 12 km / hr. What is the time taken by the man to take twenty rounds of the field ? **(M.A.T. 1997)**

(a) 30 min. (b) 32 min. (c) 34 min. (d) None of these

130. A cow is tethered in the middle of a field with a 14 feet long rope. If the cow grazes 100 sq. ft. per day, then approximately what time will be taken by the cow to graze the whole field ? **(Bank P.O. 2003)**

(a) 2 days (b) 6 days (c) 18 days (d) 24 days (e) None of these

131. A circle and a rectangle have the same perimeter. The sides of the rectangle are 18 cm and 26 cm. What is the area of the circle ? **(Bank P.O. 2004)**

(a) 88 cm^2 (b) 154 cm^2 (c) 1250 cm^2 (d) Cannot be determined (e) None of these

132. The circumference of a circle, whose area is 24.64 m^2, is : **(R.R.B. 2003)**

(a) 14.64 m (b) 16.36 m (c) 17.60 m (d) 18.40 m

133. If the circumference and the area of a circle are numerically equal, then the diameter is equal to : **(S.S.C. 2000)**

(a) $\frac{\pi}{2}$ (b) 2π (c) 2 (d) 4

134. The difference between the circumference and the radius of a circle is 37 cm. The area of the circle is : **(Section Officers', 2001)**

(*a*) 111 cm^2 (*b*) 148 cm^2 (*c*) 154 cm^2 (*d*) 259 cm^2

135. The sum of areas of two circles A and B is equal to the area of a third circle C whose diameter is 30 cm. If the diameter of circle A is 18 cm, then the radius of circle B is :

(*a*) 10 cm (*b*) 12 cm (*c*) 15 cm (*d*) 18 cm

136. Between a square of perimeter 44 cm and a circle of circumference 44 cm, which figure has larger area and by how much ? **(S.S.C. 2000)**

(*a*) Both have equal area (*b*) Square, 33 cm^2

(*c*) Circle, 33 cm^2 (*d*) Square, 495 cm^2

137. A wire can be bent in the form of a circle of radius 56 cm. If it is bent in the form of a square, then its area will be : **(R.R.B. 2002)**

(*a*) 3520 cm^2 (*b*) 6400 cm^2 (*c*) 7744 cm^2 (*d*) 8800 cm^2

138. A wire when bent in the form of a square encloses an area of 484 sq. cm. What will be the enclosed area when the same wire is bent into the form of a circle ?

(*a*) 462 sq. cm (*b*) 539 sq. cm (*c*) 616 sq. cm (*d*) 693 sq. cm

(S.S.C. 2002)

139. A circular wire of radius 42 cm is bent in the form of a rectangle whose sides are in the ratio of 6 : 5. The smaller side of the rectangle is : **(S.S.C. 2004)**

(*a*) 25 cm (*b*) 30 cm (*c*) 36 cm (*d*) 60 cm

140. There is a rectangular tank of length 180 m and breadth 120 m in a circular field. If the area of the land portion of the field is 40000 m^2, what is the radius of the field ?

(*a*) 130 m (*b*) 135 m (*c*) 140 m (*d*) 145 m

141. The areas of two circular fields are in the ratio 16 : 49. If the radius of the latter is 14 m, then what is the radius of the former ? **(IGNOU, 2003)**

(*a*) 4 m (*b*) 8 m (*c*) 18 m (*d*) 32 m

142. If the ratio of areas of two circles is 4 : 9, then the ratio of their circumferences will be : **(R.R.B. 2003)**

(*a*) 2 : 3 (*b*) 3 : 2 (*c*) 4 : 9 (*d*) 9 : 4

143. The perimeter of a circle is equal to the perimeter of a square. Then, their areas are in the ratio :

(*a*) 4 : 1 (*b*) 11 : 7 (*c*) 14 : 11 (*d*) 22 : 7

144. The diameter of a wheel is 1.26 m. How far will it travel in 500 revolutions ?

(*a*) 1492 m (*b*) 1980 m (*c*) 2530 m (*d*) 2880 m

145. The number of revolutions a wheel of diameter 40 cm makes in travelling a distance of 176 m, is : **(S.S.C. 2003)**

(*a*) 140 (*b*) 150 (*c*) 160 (*d*) 166

146. The radius of a wheel is 0.25 m. The number of revolutions it will make to travel a distance of 11 km will be : **(R.R.B. 2003)**

(*a*) 2800 (*b*) 4000 (*c*) 5500 (*d*) 7000

147. The wheel of an engine, $7\frac{1}{2}$ metres in circumference makes 7 revolutions in 9 seconds. The speed of the train in km per hour is :

(*a*) 130 (*b*) 132 (*c*) 135 (*d*) 150

148. The wheel of a motorcycle, 70 cm in diameter, makes 40 revolutions in every 10 seconds. What is the speed of the motorcycle in km / hr ? **(R.R.B. 2002)**

(*a*) 22.32 (*b*) 27.68 (*c*) 31.68 (*d*) 36.24

149. Wheels of diameters 7 cm and 14 cm start rolling simultaneously from X and Y, which are 1980 cm apart, towards each other in opposite directions. Both of them make the same number of revolutions per second. If both of them meet after 10 seconds, the speed of the smaller wheel is : (M.A.T. 2003)

(a) 22 cm / sec (b) 44 cm / sec (c) 66 cm / sec (d) 132 cm / sec

150. A toothed wheel of diameter 50 cm is attached to a smaller wheel of diameter 30 cm. How many revolutions will the smaller wheel make when the larger one makes 15 revolutions ?

(a) 18 (b) 20 (c) 25 (d) 30

151. Find the diameter of a wheel that makes 113 revolutions to go 2 km 26 decametres.

(a) $4\frac{4}{13}$ m (b) $6\frac{4}{11}$ m (c) $12\frac{4}{11}$ m (d) $12\frac{8}{11}$ m

(S.S.C. 2003)

152. The front wheels of a wagon are 2π feet in circumference and the rear wheels are 3π feet in circumference. When the front wheels have made 10 more revolutions than the rear wheels, how many feet has the wagon travelled ? **(M.B.A. 2003)**

(a) 30π (b) 60π (c) 90π (d) 150π

153. A circular ground whose diameter is 35 metres, has a 1.4 m broad garden around it. What is the area of the garden in square metres ? **(S.B.I.P.O. 1999)**

(a) 160.16 (b) 176.16 (c) 196.16

(d) Data inadequate (e) None of these

154. A circular garden has a circumference of 440 m. There is a 7 m wide border inside the garden along its periphery. The area of the border is :

(a) 2918 m^2 (b) 2921 m^2 (c) 2924 m^2 (d) 2926 m^2

155. The areas of two concentric circles forming a ring are 154 sq. cm and 616 sq. cm. The breadth of the ring is :

(a) 7 cm (b) 14 cm (c) 21 cm (d) 28 cm

156. A circular park has a path of uniform width around it. The difference between outer and inner circumferences of the circular path is 132 m. Its width is : **(S.S.C. 2003)**

(a) 20 m (b) 21 m (c) 22 m (d) 24 m

157. A circular swimming pool is surrounded by a concrete wall 4 ft. wide. If the area of the concrete wall surrounding the pool is $\frac{11}{25}$ that of the pool, then the radius of the pool is : **(Assistant Grade, 1998)**

(a) 8 ft (b) 16 ft (c) 20 ft (d) 30 ft

158. The ratio of the outer and the inner perimeters of a circular path is 23 : 22. If the path is 5 metres wide, the diameter of the inner circle is : **(S.S.C. 2004)**

(a) 55 m (b) 110 m (c) 220 m (d) 230 m

159. What will be the area of a semi-circle of 14 m diameter ? **(NABARD, 2002)**

(a) 22 m^2 (b) 77 m^2 (c) 154 m^2 (d) 308 m^2 (e) None of these

160. A semi-circular shaped window has diameter of 63 cm. Its perimeter equals :

(a) 126 cm (b) 162 cm (c) 198 cm (d) 251 cm

(S.S.C. 1999)

161. What will be the area of a semi-circle whose perimeter is 36 cm ?

(a) 154 cm^2 (b) 168 cm^2 (c) 308 cm^2

(d) Data inadequate (e) None of these **(B.S.R.B. 1998)**

162. If a wire is bent into the shape of a square, then the area of the square is 81 sq. cm When the wire is bent into a semi-circular shape, then the area of the semi-circle wil. be : **(S.S.C. 2002)**

(a) 22 cm^2 (b) 44 cm^2 (c) 77 cm^2 (d) 154 cm^2

163. The area of a sector of a circle of radius 5 cm, formed by an arc of length 3.5 cm, is :

(*a*) 7.5 cm^2 (*b*) 7.75 cm^2 (*c*) 8.5 cm^2 (*d*) 8.75 cm^2

(S.S.C. 1999)

164. In a circle of radius 7 cm, an arc subtends an angle of 108° at the centre. The area of the sector is :

(*a*) 43.2 cm^2 (*b*) 44.2 cm^2 (*c*) 45.2 cm^2 (*d*) 46.2 cm^2

165. The area of the greatest circle which can be inscribed in a square whose perimeter is 120 cm, is : **(S.S.C. 2004)**

(*a*) $\frac{22}{7} \times \left(\frac{7}{2}\right)^2$ cm^2 (*b*) $\frac{22}{7} \times \left(\frac{9}{2}\right)^2$ cm^2

(*c*) $\frac{22}{7} \times \left(\frac{15}{2}\right)^2$ cm^2 (*d*) $\frac{22}{7} \times (15)^2$ cm^2

166. The area of the largest circle, that can be drawn inside a rectangle with sides 18 cm by 14 cm, is : **(S.S.C. 2000)**

(*a*) 49 cm^2 (*b*) 154 cm^2 (*c*) 378 cm^2 (*d*) 1078 cm^2

167. The area of a circle is 220 sq. cm. The area of a square inscribed in this circle will be : **(C.B.I. 1997)**

(*a*) 49 cm^2 (*b*) 70 cm^2 (*c*) 140 cm^2 (*d*) 150 cm^2

168. A square is inscribed in a circle whose radius is 4 cm. The area of the portion between the circle and the square is :

(*a*) $(8\pi - 16)$ (*b*) $(8\pi - 32)$ (*c*) $(16\pi - 16)$ (*d*) $(16\pi - 32)$

169. The circumference of a circle is 100 cm. The side of a square inscribed in the circle is : **(C.B.I. 2003)**

(*a*) $50\sqrt{2}$ cm (*b*) $\frac{100}{\pi}$ cm (*c*) $\frac{50\sqrt{2}}{\pi}$ cm (*d*) $\frac{100\sqrt{2}}{\pi}$ cm

170. Four equal sized maximum circular plates are cut off from a square paper sheet of area 784 cm^2. The circumference of each plate is : **(S.S.C. 2003)**

(*a*) 22 cm (*b*) 44 cm (*c*) 66 cm (*d*) 88 cm

171. There are 4 semi-circular gardens on each side of a square-shaped pond with each side 21 m. The cost of fencing the entire plot at the rate of Rs 12.50 per metre is :

(*a*) Rs. 1560 (*b*) Rs. 1650 (*c*) Rs. 3120 (*d*) Rs. 3300

172. The ratio of the areas of the incircle and circumcircle of an equilateral triangle is :

(*a*) 1 : 2 (*b*) 1 : 3 (*c*) 1 : 4 (*d*) 1 : 9

173. The radius of the circumcircle of an equilateral triangle of side 12 cm is :

(*a*) $\frac{4\sqrt{2}}{3}$ cm (*b*) $4\sqrt{2}$ cm (*c*) $\frac{4\sqrt{3}}{3}$ cm (*d*) $4\sqrt{3}$ cm

174. The area of the incircle of an equilateral triangle of side 42 cm is : **(S.S.C. 2004)**

(*a*) $22\sqrt{3}$ cm^2 (*b*) 231 cm^2 (*c*) 462 cm^2 (*d*) 924 cm^2

175. The area of a circle inscribed in an equilateral triangle is 154 cm^2. Find the perimeter of the triangle.

(*a*) 71.5 cm (*b*) 71.7 cm (*c*) 72.3 cm (*d*) 72.7 cm

176. The sides of a triangle are 6 cm, 11 cm and 15 cm. The radius of its incircle is :

(*a*) $3\sqrt{2}$ cm (*b*) $\frac{4\sqrt{2}}{5}$ cm (*c*) $\frac{5\sqrt{2}}{4}$ cm (*d*) $6\sqrt{2}$ cm

(M.A.T. 2001)

177. The perimeter of a triangle is 30 cm and the circumference of its incircle is 88 cm. The area of the triangle is : **(S.S.C. 2003)**
(*a*) 70 cm^2 (*b*) 140 cm^2 (*c*) 210 cm^2 (*d*) 420 cm^2

178. If in a triangle, the area is numerically equal to the perimeter, then the radius of the inscribed circle of the triangle is : **(S.S.C. 2000)**
(*a*) 1 (*b*) 1.5 (*c*) 2 (*d*) 3

179. An equilateral triangle, a square and a circle have equal perimeters. If T denotes the area of the triangle, S, the area of the square and C, the area of the circle, then :
(*a*) S < T < C (*b*) T < C < S (*c*) T < S < C (*d*) C < S < T
(C.D.S. 2003)

180. If an area enclosed by a circle or a square or an equilateral triangle is the same, then the maximum perimeter is possessed by : **(S.C.R.A. 1997)**
(*a*) circle (*b*) square (*c*) equilateral triangle
(*d*) triangle and square have equal perimeters greater than that of circle

181. The area of the largest triangle that can be inscribed in a semi-circle of radius *r*, is :
(*a*) r^2 (*b*) $2r^2$ (*c*) r^3 (*d*) $2r^3$
(Section Officers', 2001)

182. ABC is a right-angled triangle with right angle at B. If the semi-circle on AB with AB as diameter encloses an area of 81 sq. cm and the semi-circle on BC with BC as diameter encloses an area of 36 sq. cm, then the area of the semi-circle on AC with AC as diameter will be :
(*a*) 117 cm^2 (*b*) 121 cm^2 (*c*) 217 cm^2 (*d*) 221 cm^2

183. If the radius of a circle is increased by 75%, then its circumference will increase by :
(*a*) 25% (*b*) 50% (*c*) 75% (*d*) 100%
(C.D.S. 2003)

184. A can go round a circular path 8 times in 40 minutes. If the diameter of the circle is increased to 10 times the original diameter, then the time required by A to go round the new path once, travelling at the same speed as before, is : **(S.S.C. 2000)**
(*a*) 20 min. (*b*) 25 min. (*c*) 50 min. (*d*) 100 min.

185. If the radius of a circle is increased by 6%, then the area is increased by :
(*a*) 6% (*b*) 12% (*c*) 12.36% (*d*) 16.64%
(D.M.R.C. 2003)

186. If the radius of a circle is diminished by 10%, then its area is diminished by :
(*a*) 10% (*b*) 19% (*c*) 20% (*d*) 36%
(Hotel Management, 2003)

187. If the radius of a circle is doubled, its area is increased by : **(C.B.I. 1998)**
(*a*) 100% (*b*) 200% (*c*) 300% (*d*) 400%.

188. If the circumference of a circle increases from 4π to 8π, what change occurs in its area ?
(*a*) It is halved. (*b*) It doubles. (*c*) It triples. (*d*) It quadruples.
(S.S.C. 2000)

189. Three circles of radius 3.5 cm are placed in such a way that each circle touches the other two. The area of the portion enclosed by the circles is : **(S.S.C. 2003)**
(*a*) 1.967 cm^2 (*b*) 1.975 cm^2 (*c*) 19.67 cm^2 (*d*) 21.21 cm^2

190. Four circular cardboard pieces, each of radius 7 cm are placed in such a way that each piece touches two other pieces. The area of the space enclosed by the four pieces is :
(*a*) 21 cm^2 (*b*) 42 cm^2 (*c*) 84 cm^2 (*d*) 168 cm^2

191. Four horses are tethered at four corners of a square plot of side 63 metres so that they just cannot reach one another. The area left ungrazed is :
(*a*) 675.5 m^2 (*b*) 780.6 m^2 (*c*) 785.8 m^2 (*d*) 850.5 m^2

ANSWERS

1. (d) **2.** (c) **3.** (b) **4.** (c) **5.** (c) **6.** (d) **7.** (e) **8.** (b) **9.** (b)
10. (b) **11.** (d) **12.** (e) **13.** (d) **14.** (b) **15.** (b) **16.** (d) **17.** (a) **18.** (d)
19. (a) **20.** (a) **21.** (b) **22.** (b) **23.** (c) **24.** (d) **25.** (d) **26.** (c) **27.** (b)
28. (d) **29.** (b) **30.** (a) **31.** (a) **32.** (d) **33.** (c) **34.** (b) **35.** (e) **36.** (d)
37. (b) **38.** (e) **39.** (a) **40.** (e) **41.** (c) **42.** (a) **43.** (c) **44.** (d) **45.** (b)
46. (b) **47.** (b) **48.** (b) **49.** (c) **50.** (c) **51.** (c) **52.** (b) **53.** (a) **54.** (a)
55. (d) **56.** (b) **57.** (b) **58.** (c) **59.** (b) **60.** (b) **61.** (c) **62.** (c) **63.** (c)
64. (c) **65.** (b) **66.** (c) **67.** (a) **68.** (c) **69.** (a) **70.** (a) **71.** (d) **72.** (c)
73. (d) **74.** (d) **75.** (c) **76.** (d) **77.** (b) **78.** (d) **79.** (d) **80.** (c) **81.** (c)
82. (b) **83.** (d) **84.** (c) **85.** (a) **86.** (d) **87.** (c) **88.** (d) **89.** (b) **90.** (c)
91. (d) **92.** (d) **93.** (d) **94.** (d) **95.** (b) **96.** (a) **97.** (a) **98.** (a) **99.** (c)
100. (c) **101.** (d) **102.** (c) **103.** (d) **104.** (c) **105.** (c) **106.** (b) **107.** (c) **108.** (d)
109. (c) **110.** (a) **111.** (c) **112.** (d) **113.** (d) **114.** (b) **115.** (c) **116.** (d) **117.** (b)
118. (b) **119.** (c) **120.** (b) **121.** (a) **122.** (d) **123.** (b) **124.** (b) **125.** (b) **126.** (c)
127. (d) **128.** (d) **129.** (d) **130.** (b) **131.** (e) **132.** (c) **133.** (d) **134.** (c) **135.** (b)
136. (c) **137.** (c) **138.** (c) **139.** (d) **140.** (c) **141.** (b) **142.** (a) **143.** (c) **144.** (b)
145. (a) **146.** (d) **147.** (b) **148.** (c) **149.** (c) **150.** (c) **151.** (b) **152.** (b) **153.** (a)
154. (d) **155.** (a) **156.** (b) **157.** (c) **158.** (c) **159.** (b) **160.** (b) **161.** (e) **162.** (c)
163. (d) **164.** (d) **165.** (d) **166.** (b) **167.** (c) **168.** (d) **169.** (c) **170.** (b) **171.** (b)
172. (c) **173.** (d) **174.** (c) **175.** (d) **176.** (c) **177.** (c) **178.** (c) **179.** (c) **180.** (c)
181. (a) **182.** (a) **183.** (c) **184.** (c) **185.** (c) **186.** (b) **187.** (c) **188.** (d) **189.** (a)
190. (b) **191.** (d)

SOLUTIONS

1. Area of the floor = $(5.5 \times 3.75)\ m^2 = 20.625\ m^2$.

$\therefore$ Cost of paving = Rs. (800×20.625) = Rs. 16500.

2. Let the breadth be b. Then, $25 \times b = 18 \times 10 \Leftrightarrow b = \left(\frac{18 \times 10}{25}\right)$ cm = 7.2 cm.

3. Perimeter of the plot = $2\,(90 + 50) = 280$ m.

$\therefore$ Number of poles = $\left(\frac{280}{5}\right) = 56$ m.

4. Let breadth = x cm. Then, length = $\left(\frac{160}{100}x\right)$ cm = $\frac{8}{5}x$ cm.

So, $\frac{8}{5}x - x = 24 \Leftrightarrow \frac{3}{5}x = 24 \Leftrightarrow x = \left(\frac{24 \times 5}{3}\right) = 40$.

$\therefore$ Length = 64 cm, Breadth = 40 cm.

Area = $(64 \times 40)\ cm^2 = 2560\ cm^2$.

5. Clearly, we have : $l = 9$ and $l + 2b = 37$ or $b = 14$.

$\therefore$ Area = $(l \times b) = (9 \times 14)$ sq. ft. = 126 sq. ft.

6. We have : $(l - b) = 23$ and $2\,(l + b) = 206$ or $(l + b) = 103$.

Solving the two equations, we get : $l = 63$ and $b = 40$.

$\therefore$ Area = $(l \times b) = (63 \times 40)\ m^2 = 2520\ m^2$.

7. Let breadth = x metres. Then, length = $(x + 20)$ metres.

Perimeter = $\left(\frac{5300}{26.50}\right)$ m = 200 m.

$\therefore$ $2[(x+20)+x] = 200 \Leftrightarrow 2x + 20 = 100 \Leftrightarrow 2x = 80 \Leftrightarrow x = 40$.

Hence, length = $x + 20 = 60$ m.

8. Let length = x metres. Then, breadth = $\left(\frac{60}{100}x\right)$ metres = $\left(\frac{3x}{5}\right)$ metres.

Perimeter = $\left[2\left(x + \frac{3x}{5}\right)\right]$ m = $\left(\frac{16x}{5}\right)$ m.

$\therefore$ $\frac{16x}{5} = 800 \Leftrightarrow x = \left(\frac{800 \times 5}{16}\right) = 250$.

So, length = 250 m; breadth = 150 m.

$\therefore$ Area = (250×150) m^2 = 37500 m^2.

9. $\frac{l}{2(l+b)} = \frac{1}{3} \Rightarrow 3l = 2l + 2b \Rightarrow l = 2b \Rightarrow \frac{l}{b} = \frac{2}{1} = 2 : 1$.

10. Perimeter = Distance covered in 8 min. = $\left(\frac{12000}{60} \times 8\right)$ m = 1600 m.

Let length = $3x$ metres and breadth = $2x$ metres.

Then, $2(3x + 2x) = 1600$ or $x = 160$.

$\therefore$ Length = 480 m and Breadth = 320 m.

$\therefore$ Area = (480×320) m^2 = 153600 m^2.

11. Let breadth = x metres. Then, length = $(x + 5)$ metres.

Then, $x(x+5) = 750 \Leftrightarrow x^2 + 5x - 750 = 0 \Leftrightarrow (x+30)(x-25) = 0 \Leftrightarrow x = 25$.

$\therefore$ Length = $(x + 5)$ = 30 m.

12. Let breadth = x metres. Then, length = $\left(\frac{115x}{100}\right)$ metres.

$\therefore$ $x \times \frac{115x}{100} = 460 \Leftrightarrow x^2 = \left(\frac{460 \times 100}{115}\right) = 400 \Leftrightarrow x = 20$.

13. We have : $l = 20$ ft and $lb = 680$ sq. ft. So, $b = 34$ ft.

$\therefore$ Length of fencing = $(l + 2b) = (20 + 68)$ ft = 88 ft.

14. $\frac{2(l+b)}{b} = \frac{5}{1} \Rightarrow 2l + 2b = 5b \Rightarrow 3b = 2l \Rightarrow b = \frac{2}{3}l$.

Then, Area = 216 cm^2 $\Rightarrow l \times b = 216 \Rightarrow l \times \frac{2}{3}l = 216 \Rightarrow l^2 = 324 \Rightarrow l = 18$ cm.

15. We have : $2b + l = 30 \Rightarrow l = 30 - 2b$.

Area = 100 m^2 $\Rightarrow l \times b = 100 \Rightarrow b(30 - 2b) = 100 \Rightarrow b^2 - 15b + 50 = 0$

$\Rightarrow (b - 10)(b - 5) = 0 \Rightarrow b = 10$ or $b = 5$.

When $b = 10$, $l = 10$ and when $b = 5$, $l = 20$.

Since the garden is rectangular, so its dimension is 20 m × 5 m.

16. Let length = $(3x)$ metres and breadth = $(4x)$ metres.

Then, $3x \times 4x = 7500 \Leftrightarrow 12x^2 = 7500 \Leftrightarrow x^2 = 625 \Leftrightarrow x = 25$.

So, length = 75 m and breadth = 100 m.

Perimeter = $[2(75 + 100)]$ m = 350 m.

$\therefore$ Cost of fencing = Rs. (0.25×350) = Rs. 87.50.

17. Required perimeter = (AB + BC + CP + PQ + QR + RA)

= AB + BC + (CP + QR) + (PQ + RA)

= AB + BC + AB + BC = 2 (AB + BC)

= [2 (8 + 4)] cm = 24 cm.

18. Let the areas of the two parts be x and $(700 - x)$ hectares respectively. Then,

$$[x - (700 - x)] = \frac{1}{5} \times \left[\frac{x + (700 - x)}{2}\right] \Leftrightarrow 2x - 700 = 70 \Leftrightarrow x = 385.$$

So, area of smaller part = (700 − 385) hectares = 315 hectares.

19. When folded along breadth, we have : $2\left(\frac{l}{2} + b\right) = 34$ or $l + 2b = 34$ ...(*i*)

When folded along length, we have : $2\left(l + \frac{b}{2}\right) = 38$ or $2l + b = 38$ ...(*ii*)

Solving (*i*) and (*ii*), we get : $l = 14$ and $b = 10$.

$\therefore$ Area of the paper = $(14 \times 10)\ \text{cm}^2 = 140\ \text{cm}^2$.

20. Let breadth = x metres. Then, length = $\left(\frac{3}{2}x\right)$ metres.

Area = $\left(\frac{2}{3} \times 10000\right)\ \text{m}^2$.

$$\therefore \frac{3}{2} x \times x = \frac{2}{3} \times 10000 \Leftrightarrow x^2 = \frac{4}{9} \times 10000 \Leftrightarrow x = \frac{2}{3} \times 100.$$

$$\therefore \text{Length} = \frac{3}{2} x = \left(\frac{3}{2} \times \frac{2}{3} \times 100\right) \text{m} = 100 \text{ m}.$$

21. Number of bricks = $\left(\frac{\text{Area of courtyard}}{\text{Area of 1 brick}}\right) = \left(\frac{2500 \times 1600}{20 \times 10}\right) = 20000.$

22. Length of the carpet = $\left(\frac{\text{Total cost}}{\text{Rate / m}}\right) = \left(\frac{8100}{45}\right)$ m = 180 m.

Area of the room = Area of the carpet = $\left(180 \times \frac{75}{100}\right) \text{m}^2 = 135\ \text{m}^2$.

$\therefore$ Breadth of the room = $\left(\frac{\text{Area}}{\text{Length}}\right) = \left(\frac{135}{18}\right)$ m = 7.5 m.

23. Other side = $\sqrt{\left(\frac{15}{2}\right)^2 - \left(\frac{9}{2}\right)^2}$ ft = $\sqrt{\frac{225}{4} - \frac{81}{4}}$ ft = $\sqrt{\frac{144}{4}}$ ft = 6 ft.

$\therefore$ Area of the closet = (6 × 4.5) sq. ft = 27 sq. ft.

24. Let breadth = x cm. Then, length = $3x$ cm.

$$x^2 + (3x)^2 = (8\sqrt{10})^2 \Rightarrow 10x^2 = 640 \Rightarrow x^2 = 64 \Rightarrow x = 8.$$

So, length = 24 cm and breadth = 8 cm.

$\therefore$ Perimeter = [2 (24 + 8)] cm = 64 cm.

25. $\sqrt{l^2 + b^2} = 3b \Rightarrow l^2 + b^2 = 9b^2 \Rightarrow l^2 = 8b^2 \Rightarrow \frac{l^2}{b^2} = 8 \Rightarrow \frac{l}{b} = \sqrt{8} = 2\sqrt{2}.$

26. $2(l + b) = 46$ or $l + b = 23$. Also, $lb = 120$.

$\therefore$ Diagonal = $\sqrt{l^2 + b^2} = \sqrt{(l + b)^2 - 2lb} = \sqrt{(23)^2 - 240} = \sqrt{289} = 17$ m.

27. $\sqrt{l^2 + b^2} = \sqrt{41}$ or $l^2 + b^2 = 41$. Also, $lb = 20$.

$(l + b)^2 = (l^2 + b^2) + 2lb = 41 + 40 = 81 \Rightarrow (l + b) = 9.$

$\therefore$ Perimeter = $2(l + b) = 18$ cm.

28. Length of diagonal $= \left(52 \times \frac{15}{60}\right)$ m = 13 m.

Sum of length and breadth $= \left(68 \times \frac{15}{60}\right)$ m = 17 m.

$\therefore \quad \sqrt{l^2 + b^2} = 13$ or $l^2 + b^2 = 169$ and $l + b = 17$.

Area $= lb = \frac{1}{2}(2\,lb) = \frac{1}{2}[(l+b)^2 - (l^2 + b^2)] = \frac{1}{2}[(17)^2 - 169] = \frac{1}{2}(289 - 169) = 60$ m^2.

29. We have : $lb = 60$ and $\sqrt{l^2 + b^2} + l = 5b$.

Now, $l^2 + b^2 = (5b - l)^2 \Rightarrow 24b^2 - 10lb = 0 \Rightarrow 24b^2 - 600 = 0$

$\Rightarrow b^2 = 25 \Rightarrow b = 5$.

$\therefore \quad l = \left(\frac{60}{5}\right)$ m = 12 m. So, length of the carpet = 12 m

30. Let length = $(3x)$ metres and breadth = $(2x)$ metres.
Then, $(3x + 5) \times 2x = 2600 \Leftrightarrow 6x^2 + 10x - 2600 = 0$
$\Leftrightarrow \quad 3x^2 + 5x - 1300 = 0 \Leftrightarrow (3x + 65)(x - 20) = 0 \Leftrightarrow x = 20$.
$\therefore$ Breadth = $2x$ = 40 m.

31. Let breadth = x cm. Then, length = $(x + 8)$ cm.
$\therefore \quad (x + 8)\,x = (x + 15)(x - 4) \Leftrightarrow x^2 + 8x = x^2 + 11x - 60 \Leftrightarrow x = 20$
So, length = 28 cm and breadth = 20 cm.

32. Let length = x metres and breadth = y metres. Then,
$(x + 1)(y + 1) - xy = 21 \Rightarrow x + y = 20$ ...(*i*)
And, $xy - [(x + 1)(y - 1)] = 5 \Leftrightarrow x - y = 6$ ...(*ii*)
Solving (*i*) and (*ii*), we get : $x = 13$ and $y = 7$.
So, length = 13 m and breadth = 7 m.
$\therefore$ Perimeter = [2 (13 + 7)] m = 40 m.

33. Let original length = x metres and original breadth = y metres.
Original area = (xy) m^2.

New length $= \left(\frac{120}{100}x\right)$ m $= \left(\frac{6}{5}x\right)$ m; New breadth $= \left(\frac{120}{100}y\right)$ m $= \left(\frac{6}{5}y\right)$ m.

New Area $= \left(\frac{6}{5}x \times \frac{6}{5}y\right)$ m^2 $= \left(\frac{36}{25}xy\right)$ m^2.

$\therefore$ Increase% $= \left(\frac{11}{25}xy \times \frac{1}{xy} \times 100\right)\% = 44\%$.

34. New area $= \left(\frac{80}{100}a \times \frac{110}{100}b\right) = \left(\frac{4}{5} \times \frac{11}{10}ab\right) = \left(\frac{22}{25}ab\right)$.

$\therefore$ Required percentage $= \left(\frac{22}{25}ab \times \frac{1}{ab} \times 100\right)\% = 88\%$.

35. Let original length = x metres and original breadth = y metres.
Original area = (xy) m^2.

New length $= \left(\frac{150}{100}x\right)$ m $= \left(\frac{3}{2}x\right)$ m; New breadth $= \left(\frac{120}{100}y\right)$ m $= \left(\frac{6}{5}y\right)$ m.

New area $= \left(\frac{3}{2}x \times \frac{6}{5}y\right)$ m^2 $= \left(\frac{9}{5}xy\right)$ m^2.

$\therefore$ Increase $= \left(\frac{\frac{4}{5}xy}{xy}\right) = \frac{4}{5}$ times.

36. Let original length = x and original breadth = y.

Decrease in area $= xy - \left(\frac{80}{100}x \times \frac{90}{100}y\right) = \left(xy - \frac{18}{25}xy\right) = \frac{7}{25}xy.$

$\therefore$ Decrease% $= \left(\frac{7}{25}xy \times \frac{1}{xy} \times 100\right)\% = 28\%.$

37. Let original length = x and original breadth = y.

Original area = xy.

New length $= \frac{x}{2}$; New breadth = $3y$. New Area $= \left(\frac{x}{2} \times 3y\right) = \frac{3}{2}xy.$

$\therefore$ Increase% $= \left(\frac{1}{2}xy \times \frac{1}{xy} \times 100\right)\% = 50\%.$

38. Let original length = x and original breadth = y.

Then, original area = xy.

New area $= \left[\frac{(100-r)}{100} \times x\right]\left[\frac{(105+r)}{100} \times y\right] = \left[\left(\frac{10500 - 5r - r^2}{10000}\right)xy\right]$

$\therefore$ $\left(\frac{10500 - 5r - r^2}{10000}\right)xy = xy \Leftrightarrow r^2 + 5r - 500 = 0 \Leftrightarrow (r+25)(r-20) = 0 \Leftrightarrow r = 20.$

39. Let original length = x and original breadth = y.

Then, original area = xy.

New length $= \frac{160x}{100} = \frac{8x}{5}$. Let new breadth = z.

Then, $\frac{8x}{5} \times z = xy \Rightarrow z = \frac{5y}{8}.$

$\therefore$ Decrease in breadth $= \left(\frac{3y}{8} \times \frac{1}{y} \times 100\right)\% = 37\frac{1}{2}\%.$

40. Let original length = x and original breadth = y.

Then, original area = xy.

New length $= \frac{130}{100}x = \frac{13x}{10}$. New breadth = y. New area $= \left(\frac{13x}{10} \times y\right) = \frac{13xy}{10}.$

$\therefore$ Required ratio $= \left(\frac{\frac{13xy}{10}}{xy}\right) = \frac{13}{10} = 13 : 10.$

41. Area of the sheet = (20 × 30) cm^2 = 600 cm^2.

Area used for typing = [(20 − 4) × (30 − 6)] cm^2 = 384 cm^2.

$\therefore$ Required percentage $= \left(\frac{384}{600} \times 100\right)\% = 64\%.$

42. Area of the mat = [(15 – 3) × (12 – 3)] sq. ft = 108 sq. ft.

∴ Cost of the mat = Rs. (108 × 3.50) = Rs. 378.

43. 2 $(l + b)$ = 340 (Given).

Area of the boundary = $[(l + 2)(b + 2) - lb] = 2(l + b) + 4 = 344$.

∴ Cost of gardening = Rs. (344 × 10) = Rs. 3440.

44. $lb = 96$ (Given).

Area of pathway = $[(l - 4)(b - 4) - lb] = 16 - 4(l + b)$, which cannot be determined. So, data is inadequate.

45. Let the width of walk be x metres. Then,

$(20 - 2x)(10 - 2x) = 96 \Leftrightarrow 4x^2 + 60x - 104 = 0 \Leftrightarrow x^2 + 15x - 26 = 0$

$\Leftrightarrow (x - 13)(x - 2) = 0 \Leftrightarrow x = 2 \quad [\because x \neq 13]$

46. Area of crossroads = $(55 \times 4 + 35 \times 4 - 4 \times 4)$ m² = 344 m².

∴ Cost of gravelling = Rs. $\left(344 \times \frac{75}{100}\right)$ = Rs. 258.

47. Area of the park = (60×40) m² = 2400 m². Area of the lawn = 2109 m².

∴ Area of the crossroads = (2400 – 2109) m² = 291 m².

Let the width of the road be x metres. Then,

$60x + 40x - x^2 = 291 \Leftrightarrow x^2 - 100x + 291 = 0 \Leftrightarrow (x - 97)(x - 3) = 0$

$\Leftrightarrow x = 3 \quad [\because x \neq 97]$.

48. Side = $\sqrt{2550.25} = \sqrt{\frac{255025}{100}} = \frac{505}{10}$ = 50.5 m.

49. Area = $\frac{\text{Total cost}}{\text{Rate}} = \left(\frac{1215}{135}\right)$ hectares = (9×10000) sq. m.

∴ Side of the square = $\sqrt{90000}$ = 300 m.

Perimeter of the field = (300 × 4) = 1200 m.

Cost of fencing = Rs. $\left(1200 \times \frac{3}{4}\right)$ = Rs. 900.

50. The sides of the five squares are $\left(\frac{24}{4}\right), \left(\frac{32}{4}\right), \left(\frac{40}{4}\right), \left(\frac{76}{4}\right), \left(\frac{80}{4}\right)$ *i.e.*, 6 cm, 8 cm, 10 cm, 19 cm, 20 cm.

∴ Area of the new square = $[6^2 + 8^2 + (10)^2 + (19)^2 + (20)^2]$

= (36 + 64 + 100 + 361 + 400) cm² = 961 cm².

Side of the new square = $\sqrt{961}$ cm = 31 cm.

Perimeter of the new square = (4 × 31) cm = 124 cm.

51. Number of marbles = $\left(\frac{300 \times 300}{20 \times 20}\right)$ = 225.

52. Area of each slab = $\left(\frac{72}{50}\right)$ m² = 1.44 m².

∴ Length of each slab = $\sqrt{1.44}$ m = 1.2 m = 120 cm.

53. Area left after laying black tiles = [(20 – 4) × (10 – 4)] sq. ft = 96 sq. ft.

Area under white tiles = $\left(\frac{1}{3} \times 96\right)$ sq. ft = 32 sq. ft.

Area under blue tiles = (96 – 32) sq. ft = 64 sq. ft.

Number of blue tiles = $\frac{64}{(2 \times 2)}$ = 16.

54. Length of largest tile = H.C.F. of 1517 cm and 902 cm = 41 cm.
Area of each tile = (41×41) cm^2.

$\therefore$ Required number of tiles $= \left(\dfrac{1517 \times 902}{41 \times 41}\right) = 814.$

55. Length of the room = (7 + 7) m = 14 m. Breadth of the room = 7 m.

$\therefore$ Area of the room = (14×7) m^2 = 98 m^2.

56. Side of the square = 12 cm. Area of the rectangle = $[(12 \times 12) - 4]$ cm^2 = 140 cm^2.
Now, area = 140 cm^2, length = 14 cm.

$\therefore$ Breadth $= \dfrac{\text{area}}{\text{length}} = \dfrac{140}{14}$ cm = 10 cm.

Hence, Perimeter = $2(l + b) = 2(14 + 10)$ cm = 48 cm.

57. Let the side of the square be x cm. Then, its area = x^2 cm^2.
Area of the rectangle = $(3x^2)$ cm^2.

$\therefore\ 40 \times \dfrac{3}{2} \times x = 3x^2 \Leftrightarrow x = 20.$

58. Side of the square $= \dfrac{80}{4}$ cm = 20 cm.

$2(l + b) = 80 \Rightarrow l + b = 40.$ Now, $(20 \times 20) - lb = 100 \Leftrightarrow lb = 300.$

$(l - b) = \sqrt{(l + b)^2 - 4lb} = \sqrt{(40 \times 40) - (4 \times 300)} = \sqrt{400} = 20.$

Now, $l + b = 40$ and $l - b = 20 \Rightarrow l = 30$ and $b = 10$.

$\therefore$ Sides of the rectangle are 30 cm and 10 cm.

59. Perimeter $= \dfrac{\text{Total cost}}{\text{Cost per m}} = \dfrac{10080}{20}$ m = 504 m.

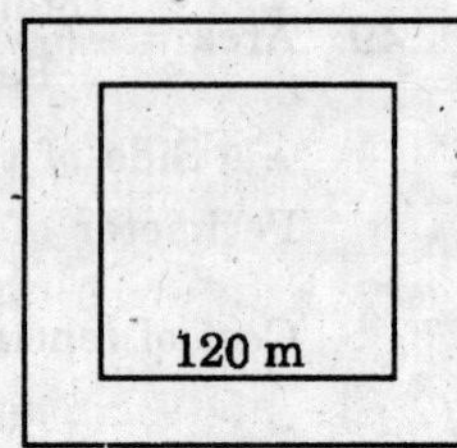

Side of the square $= \dfrac{504}{4}$ m = 126 m.

Breadth of the pavement = 3 m.

Side of inner square = (126 − 6) m = 120 m.

Area of the pavement = $[(126 \times 126) - (120 \times 120)]$ m^2

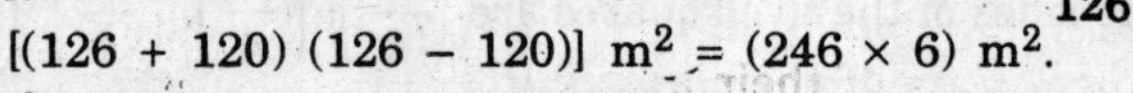

$= [(126 + 120)(126 - 120)]$ m^2 = (246×6) m^2.

$\therefore$ Cost of pavement = Rs. $(246 \times 6 \times 50)$ = Rs. 73800.

60. Let the length of the outer edge be x metres. Then, length of the inner edge = $(x - 6)$ m.

$\therefore\ x^2 - (x - 6)^2 = 1764 \Leftrightarrow x^2 - (x^2 - 12x + 36) = 1764 \Leftrightarrow 12x = 1800 \Leftrightarrow x = 150.$

$\therefore$ Required perimeter = $(4x)$ m = (4×150) m = 600 m.

61. Let the side of the square be x metres.

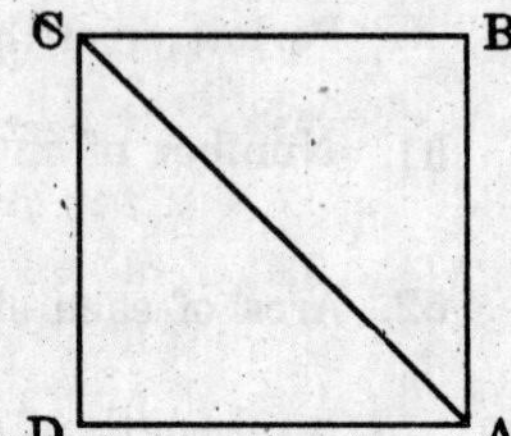

Then, AB + BC = $2x$ metres.

AC = $\sqrt{2}\,x = (1.41x)$ m

Saving on $2x$ metres = $(0.59x)$ m.

Saving% $= \left(\dfrac{0.59x}{2x} \times 100\right)\% = 30\%$ (approx.).

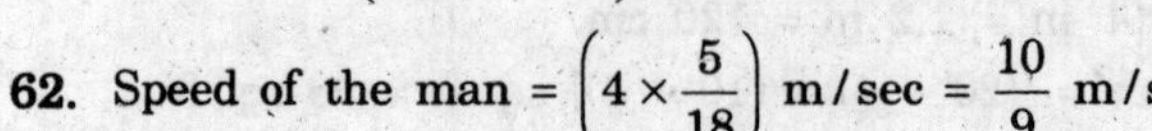

62. Speed of the man $= \left(4 \times \dfrac{5}{18}\right)$ m/sec $= \dfrac{10}{9}$ m/s.

Time taken = (3×60) sec = 180 sec.

Length of diagonal = (speed × time) $= \left(\dfrac{10}{9} \times 180\right)$ m = 200 m.

Area of the field $= \dfrac{1}{2} \times (\text{diagonal})^2 = \left(\dfrac{1}{2} \times 200 \times 200\right)$ m^2 = 20000 m^2.

63. $d = \sqrt{2} \times l \Rightarrow l = \frac{20}{\sqrt{2}}$.

$\therefore$ Perimeter $= (4l)$ cm $= \left(\frac{4 \times 20}{\sqrt{2}} \times \frac{\sqrt{2}}{\sqrt{2}}\right)$ cm $= 40\sqrt{2}$ cm.

64. Side $= \sqrt{69696}$ cm $= 264$ cm.

$\therefore \quad d = \sqrt{2} \times \text{side} = (264 \times \sqrt{2})$ cm $= (264 \times 1.414)$ cm $= 373.296$ cm.

65. Area $= (45 \times 40)$ m^2 $\Leftrightarrow \frac{1}{2} \times (\text{diagonal})^2 = 1800 \Leftrightarrow$ diagonal $= 60$ m.

66. Let breadth be x metres. Then, length $= 120\%$ of $x = \left(\frac{120}{100}x\right) = \frac{6x}{5}$ m.

Required ratio $= \left(\frac{6x}{5} \times x \times \frac{1}{x \times x}\right) = 6 : 5$.

67. A square and a rectangle with equal areas will satisfy the relation p_1

68. Take a square of side 4 cm and a rectangle having $l = 6$ cm, $b = 2$ cm.

Then, perimeter of square = perimeter of rectangle.

Area of square $= 16$ cm^2, area of rectangle $= 12$ cm^2.

$\therefore$ A > B.

69. $d_1 = 4\sqrt{2}$ cm $\Rightarrow$ area $= \frac{1}{2}d_1^2 = \frac{1}{2} \times (4\sqrt{2})^2 = 16$ cm^2.

Area of new square $= (2 \times 16)$ cm^2 $= 32$ cm^2.

$\therefore \frac{1}{2}d_2^2 = 32 \Rightarrow d_2^2 = 64 \Rightarrow d_2 = 8$ cm.

70. Required ratio $= \frac{a^2}{(\sqrt{2}\,a)^2} = \frac{a^2}{2a^2} = \frac{1}{2} = 1 : 2$.

71. Let the diagonals be $2d$ and d.

Then, ratio of their areas $= \frac{\frac{1}{2} \times (2d)^2}{\frac{1}{2} \times d^2} = \frac{4d^2}{d^2} = \frac{4}{1} = 4 : 1$.

72. $\frac{a^2}{b^2} = \frac{225}{256} = \frac{(15)^2}{(16)^2} \Leftrightarrow \frac{a}{b} = \frac{15}{16} \Leftrightarrow \frac{4a}{4b} = \frac{4 \times 15}{4 \times 16} = \frac{15}{16}$.

$\therefore$ Ratio of perimeters $= 15 : 16$.

73. Area $= 1$ hect. $= 10000$ sq. m $\Rightarrow$ side $= \sqrt{10000}$ m $= 100$ m.

Side of the other square $= 101$ m.

Difference in their areas $= [(101)^2 - (100)^2]$ m^2

$= [(101 + 100)(101 - 100)]$ m^2 $= 201$ m^2.

74. Let the sides be x cm and $\frac{150}{100}x = \frac{3x}{2}$ cm.

Required ratio $= \frac{\frac{9}{4}x^2}{x^2} = \frac{9}{4} = 9 : 4$.

75. $A_1 = x^2$ and $A_2 = \left(\frac{1}{2}x\right)^2 = \frac{1}{4}x^2 = \frac{1}{4}A_1$.

76. 100 cm is read as 102 cm.

$\therefore$ $A_1 = (100 \times 100)\ cm^2$ and $A_2 = (102 \times 102)\ cm^2$.

$(A_2 - A_1) = [(102)^2 - (100)^2] = (102 + 100) \times (102 - 100) = 404\ cm^2$.

$\therefore$ Percentage error $= \left(\frac{404}{100 \times 100} \times 100\right)\% = 4.04\%$.

77. Let original area = 100 cm^2. Then, new area = 169 cm^2.

$\Rightarrow$ Original side = 10 cm, New side = 13 cm.

Increase on 10 cm = 3 cm. Increase% $= \left(\frac{3}{10} \times 100\right)\% = 30\%$.

78. Given diagonal = d. New diagonal $= \frac{3}{2}d$.

Original area $= \frac{1}{2}d^2$, New area $= \frac{1}{2} \times \left(\frac{3}{2}d\right)^2 = \frac{9}{8}d^2$.

$\therefore$ Required ratio $= \frac{1}{2}d^2 : \frac{9}{8}d^2 = \frac{1}{2} : \frac{9}{8} = 4 : 9$.

79. Let length = l metres and breadth = b metres. Then, original area = (lb) m^2.

New length = (140% of l) m $= \left(\frac{140}{100} \times l\right)$ m $= \frac{7l}{5}$ m.

New breadth = (130% of b) m $= \left(\frac{130}{100} \times b\right)$ m $= \frac{13b}{10}$ m.

New area $= \left(\frac{7l}{5} \times \frac{13b}{10}\right) = \left(\frac{91}{50}lb\right)$ m^2. Increase $= \left(\frac{91}{50}lb - lb\right) = \frac{41}{50}lb$.

$\therefore$ Increase% $= \left(\frac{41}{50} \times lb \times \frac{1}{lb} \times 100\right)\% = 82\%$.

80. Let original length of each side = x cm. Then, its area = (x^2) cm^2.

Length of rectangle formed = $(x + 5)$ cm and its breadth = x cm.

$\therefore$ $\frac{x+5}{x} = \frac{3}{2} \Leftrightarrow 2x + 10 = 3x \Leftrightarrow x = 10$.

$\therefore$ Original length of each side = 10 cm and its area = 100 cm^2.

81. Let original side = x cm. Then, new side = $(x + 5)$ cm.

$\therefore$ $(x + 5)^2 - x^2 = 165 \Leftrightarrow x^2 + 10x + 25 - x^2 = 165 \Leftrightarrow 10x = 140 \Leftrightarrow x = 14$.

Hence, the side of the square is 14 cm.

82. Let the lengths of the line segments be x cm and $(x + 2)$ cm.

Then, $(x + 2)^2 - x^2 = 32 \Leftrightarrow x^2 + 4x + 4 - x^2 = 32 \Leftrightarrow 4x = 28 \Leftrightarrow x = 7$

$\therefore$ Length of longer line segment = (7 + 2) cm = 9 cm.

83. Let the length of each side of the square be x cm.

Then, length of rectangle = $(x + 5)$ cm and its breadth = $(x - 3)$ cm.

$\therefore$ $(x + 5)(x - 3) = x^2 \Leftrightarrow x^2 + 2x - 15 = x^2 \Leftrightarrow x = \frac{15}{2}$.

$\therefore$ Length $= \left(\frac{15}{2} + 5\right)$ cm $= \frac{25}{2}$ cm, breadth $= \left(\frac{15}{2} - 3\right)$ cm $= \frac{9}{2}$ cm.

Hence, perimeter $= 2(l + b) = 2\left(\frac{25}{2} + \frac{9}{2}\right)$ cm = 34 cm.

84. Area to be plastered = $[2(l + b) \times h] + (l \times b)$
$= \{[2(25 + 12) \times 6] + (25 \times 12)\}\ m^2$
$= (444 + 300)\ m^2 = 744\ m^2$.

$\therefore$ Cost of plastering = Rs. $\left(744 \times \frac{75}{100}\right)$ = Rs. 558.

85. Area of 4 walls = $[2(l + b) \times h] = [2(10 + 7) \times 5]\ m^2 = 170\ m^2$.
Area of 2 doors and 3 windows = $[2(1 \times 3) + (2 \times 1.5) + 2(1 \times 1.5)]\ m^2 = 12\ m^2$.
$\therefore$ Area to be painted = $(170 - 12)\ m^2 = 158\ m^2$.
Cost of painting = Rs. (158×3) = Rs. 474.

86. $A_1 = 2(l + b) \times h;\ A_2 = 2(2l + 2b) \times 2h = 8(l + b) \times h = 4A_1$.
$\therefore$ Required cost = Rs. (4×475) = Rs. 1900.

87. Let $h = 2x$ metres and $(l + b) = 5x$ metres.

Length of the paper = $\frac{\text{Total cost}}{\text{Rate per m}} = \frac{260}{2}$ m = 130 m.

Area of the paper = $\left(130 \times \frac{50}{100}\right) m^2 = 65\ m^2$.

Total area of 4 walls = $(65 + 15)\ m^2 = 80\ m^2$.
$\therefore\ 2(l + b) \times h = 80 \Leftrightarrow 2 \times 5x \times 2x = 80 \Leftrightarrow x^2 = 4 \Leftrightarrow x = 2$.
Height of the room = 4 m.

88. $A_1 = \left(\frac{1}{2} \times 15 \times 12\right) cm^2 = 90\ cm^2$. $A_2 = 2A_1 = 180\ cm^2$.

$\therefore\ \frac{1}{2} \times 20 \times h = 180 \Leftrightarrow h = 18$ cm.

89. $a = 5$, $b = 12$ and $c = 13$. So, $s = \frac{1}{2}(5 + 12 + 13)$ cm = 15 cm.

$\therefore$ Area = $\sqrt{15 \times 10 \times 3 \times 2} = 30\ cm^2$.

$\frac{1}{2} \times 12 \times \text{Height} = 30 \Rightarrow \text{Height} = 5$ cm.

90. $\Delta = \frac{1}{2} \times \text{Base} \times \text{Height} \Rightarrow 40 \times \text{Base} = \frac{1}{2} \times \text{Base} \times \text{Height} \Rightarrow \text{Height} = 80$ cm.

91. Let Base = $3x$ cm and Altitude = $4x$ cm.

Then, $\frac{1}{2} \times 3x \times 4x = 1176 \Leftrightarrow 12x^2 = 2352 \Leftrightarrow x^2 = 196 \Leftrightarrow x = 14$ cm.

$\therefore$ Altitude = (4×14) cm = 56 cm.

92. Since $5^2 + (12)^2 = (13)^2$, so, it is a right-angled triangle with
Base = 12 cm and Height = 5 cm.

$\therefore$ Area = $\left(\frac{1}{2} \times 12 \times 5\right) cm^2 = 30\ cm^2$.

93. Ratio of sides = $\frac{1}{2} : \frac{1}{3} : \frac{1}{4} = 6 : 4 : 3$.

Perimeter = 52 cm. So, sides are $\left(52 \times \frac{6}{13}\right)$ cm, $\left(52 \times \frac{4}{13}\right)$ cm and $\left(52 \times \frac{3}{13}\right)$ cm.

$\therefore\ a = 24$ cm, $b = 16$ cm, $c = 12$ cm.
$\therefore$ Length of smallest side = 12 cm.

94. Let $a = 3x$ cm, $b = 4x$ cm and $c = 5x$ cm. Then, $s = 6x$ cm.

$A = \sqrt{s(s-a)(s-b)(s-c)} = \sqrt{6x \times 3x \times 2x \times x} = (6x^2)\ \text{cm}^2$.

$\therefore\quad 6x^2 = 216 \Leftrightarrow x^2 = 36 \Leftrightarrow x = 6.$

$\therefore\quad a = 18$ cm, $b = 24$ cm and $c = 30$ cm.

Perimeter $= (18 + 24 + 30)$ cm $= 72$ cm.

95. $a = 3$ cm, $b = 4$ cm and $c = 5$ cm.

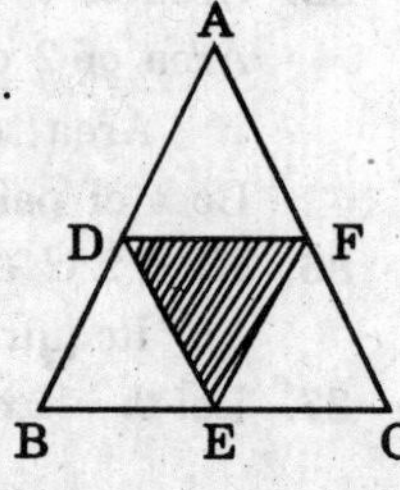

It is a right-angled triangle with base = 3 cm and height = 4 cm.

$\therefore\quad$ Its area $= \left(\frac{1}{2} \times 3 \times 4\right)\ \text{cm}^2 = 6\ \text{cm}^2.$

Area of required triangle $= \left(\frac{1}{4} \times 6\right)\ \text{cm}^2 = \frac{3}{2}\ \text{cm}^2.$

96. Let the sides be a cm and $2a$ cm.

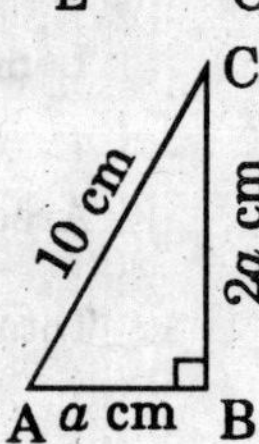

Then, $a^2 + (2a)^2 = (10)^2 \Leftrightarrow 5a^2 = 100 \Leftrightarrow a^2 = 20.$

$\therefore\quad$ Area $= \left(\frac{1}{2} \times a \times 2a\right) = a^2 = 20\ \text{cm}^2.$

97. Let Base = b cm and Height = h cm.

$b + h + 26 = 60 \Leftrightarrow b + h = 34 \Leftrightarrow (b + h)^2 = (34)^2$ ...(i)

Also, $b^2 + h^2 = (26)^2$ ...(ii)

$\therefore\quad (b + h)^2 - (b^2 + h^2) = (34)^2 - (26)^2 \Leftrightarrow 2bh = (34 + 26)(34 - 26) = 480$

$\Leftrightarrow bh = 240 \Leftrightarrow \frac{1}{2} bh = 120.$

$\therefore\quad$ Area $= 120\ \text{cm}^2$.

98. Let the sides be a metres, a metres and b metres.

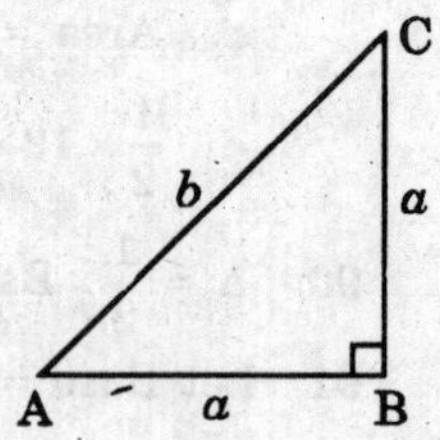

Then, $2a + b = 6 + 3\sqrt{2}$ and $b^2 = a^2 + a^2 = 2a^2 \Leftrightarrow b = \sqrt{2}\,a.$

$\therefore\quad 2a + \sqrt{2}\,a = 6 + 3\sqrt{2} \Leftrightarrow a = 3.$

$\therefore\quad$ Area $= \left(\frac{1}{2} \times 3 \times 3\right)\ \text{m}^2 = 4.5\ \text{m}^2.$

99. Let the smallest side be x cm.

Then, other sides are 13 cm and $(17 - x)$ cm.

Let $a = 13$, $b = x$ and $c = (17 - x)$. So, $s = 15$.

$\therefore\quad$ Area $= \sqrt{s(s-a)(s-b)(s-c)} = \sqrt{15 \times 2 \times (15 - x)(x - 2)}$

$\Leftrightarrow 30 \times (15 - x)(x - 2) = (30)^2 \Leftrightarrow (15 - x)(x - 2) = 30 \Leftrightarrow x^2 - 17x + 60 = 0$

$\Leftrightarrow (x - 12)(x - 5) = 0 \Leftrightarrow x = 12$ or $x = 5$.

$\therefore\quad$ Smallest side = 5 cm.

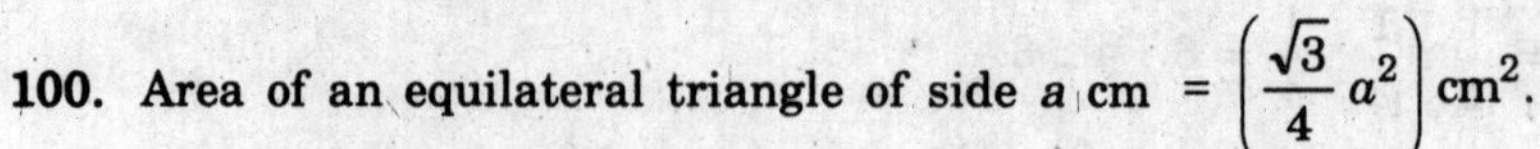

100. Area of an equilateral triangle of side a cm $= \left(\frac{\sqrt{3}}{4} a^2\right)\ \text{cm}^2.$

$\therefore\quad \frac{\sqrt{3}}{4} a^2 = 24\sqrt{3} \Leftrightarrow a^2 = 96 \Leftrightarrow a = 4\sqrt{6}$ cm.

$\therefore\quad$ Perimeter $= 3a = 12\sqrt{6}$ cm.

101. Let each side be a cm.

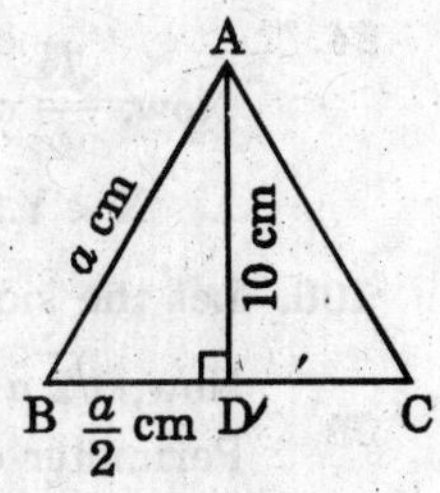

Then, $\left(\frac{a}{2}\right)^2 + (10)^2 = a^2 \Leftrightarrow \left(a^2 - \frac{a^2}{4}\right) = 100$

$\Leftrightarrow \frac{3a^2}{4} = 100 \Leftrightarrow a^2 = \frac{400}{3}.$

$\therefore$ Area $= \frac{\sqrt{3}}{4} \times a^2 = \left(\frac{\sqrt{3}}{4} \times \frac{400}{3}\right) \text{cm}^2 = \frac{100}{\sqrt{3}} \text{cm}^2.$

102. Let each side of the triangle be a cm.

Then, ar (Δ AOB) + ar (Δ BOC) + ar (Δ AOC) = ar (Δ ABC)

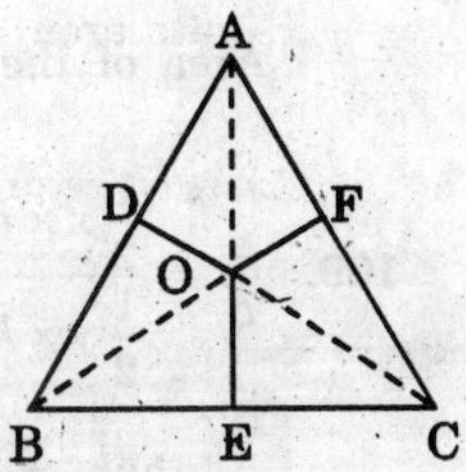

$\Rightarrow \frac{1}{2} \times a \times \sqrt{3} + \frac{1}{2} \times a \times 2\sqrt{3} + \frac{1}{2} \times a \times 5\sqrt{3} = \frac{\sqrt{3}}{4} a^2$

$\Rightarrow \frac{a}{2} \sqrt{3}(1 + 2 + 5) = \frac{\sqrt{3}}{4} a^2 \Rightarrow a = 16.$

$\therefore$ Perimeter = (3 × 16) = 48 cm.

103. Let the side of the triangle be a. Then,

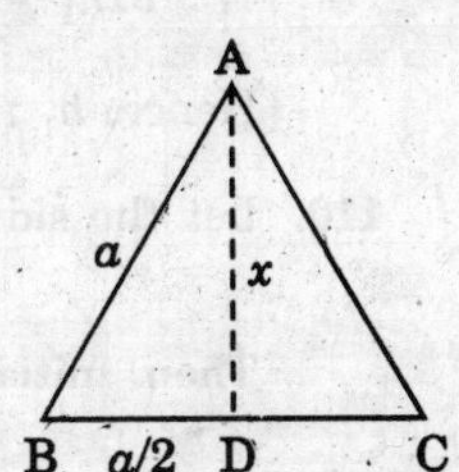

$a^2 = \left(\frac{a}{2}\right)^2 + x^2 \Leftrightarrow \frac{3a^2}{4} = x^2 \Leftrightarrow a^2 = \frac{4x^2}{3}$

$\therefore$ Area $= \frac{\sqrt{3}}{4} a^2 = \frac{\sqrt{3}}{4} \times \frac{4}{3} x^2 = \frac{x^2}{\sqrt{3}} = \frac{x^2 \sqrt{3}}{3}.$

104. Area of a square with side $a = a^2$ sq. units.

Area of a triangle with base $a = \left(\frac{1}{2} \times a \times h\right)$ sq. units.

$\therefore \quad a^2 = \frac{1}{2} \times a \times h \Leftrightarrow h = 2a.$

Hence, the altitude of the triangle is $2a$.

105. Let the side of the square be a cm.

Then, the length of its diagonal $= \sqrt{2}\, a$ cm.

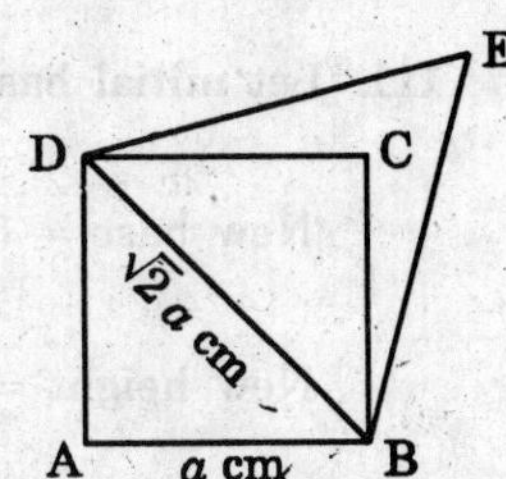

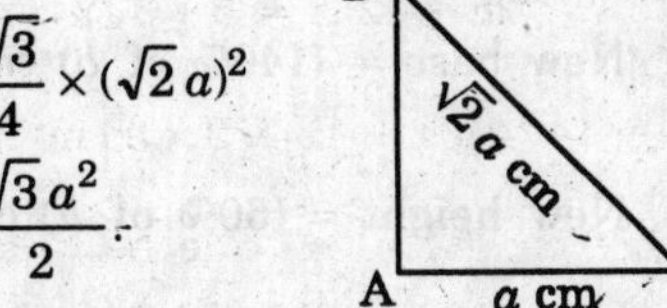

Area of equilateral triangle with side $\sqrt{2}\, a = \frac{\sqrt{3}}{4} \times (\sqrt{2}\, a)^2$

$= \frac{\sqrt{3}\, a^2}{2}.$

$\therefore$ Required ratio $= \frac{\sqrt{3}\, a^2}{2} : a^2 = \sqrt{3} : 2.$

106. Area of rectangle = lb sq. units.

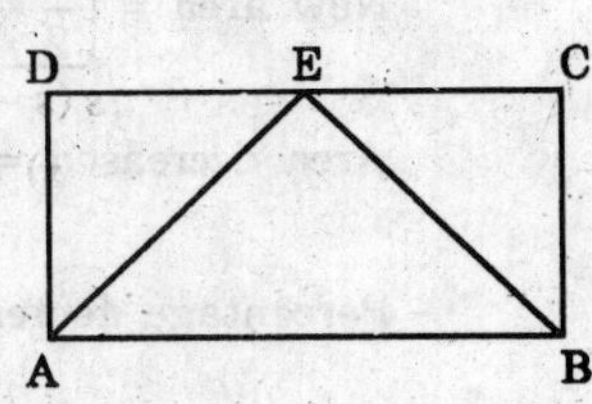

Area of the triangle $= \frac{1}{2} lb$ sq. units.

$\therefore$ Required ratio $= lb : \frac{1}{2} lb = 2 : 1.$

107. Let each side of the triangle be a cm and each side of the square be b cm.

Then, $X = \frac{\sqrt{3}}{4} a^2$ and $Y = b^2$, where $3a = 4b$, *i.e.*, $b = \frac{3a}{4}.$

$\therefore \quad X = \frac{\sqrt{3}}{4} a^2$ and $Y = \frac{9a^2}{16} \quad \left[\because b = \frac{3a}{4}\right]$

Now, $\frac{\sqrt{3}}{4}a^2 = \frac{1.732}{4}a^2 = 0.433\,a^2$ and $\frac{9a^2}{16} = 0.5625\,a^2$.

$\therefore$ X < Y.

108. Let the side of the square be a cm. Then, its diagonal = $\sqrt{2}\,a$ cm.

Now, $\sqrt{2}\,a = 12\sqrt{2} \Rightarrow a = 12$ cm.

Perimeter of the square = $4a$ = 48 cm. Perimeter of the equilateral triangle = 48 cm.

Each side of the triangle = 16 cm.

Area of the triangle = $\left(\frac{\sqrt{3}}{4} \times 16 \times 16\right)$ cm^2 = $(64\sqrt{3})$ cm^2.

109. $\frac{a}{b} = \frac{\frac{1}{2}x \times h_1}{\frac{1}{2}y \times h_2}$ $\left[\text{Ratio of areas} = \frac{a}{b}, \text{ Ratio of base} = x : y\right]$

$\therefore\ bxh_1 = ayh_2 \Leftrightarrow \frac{h_1}{h_2} = \frac{ay}{bx}$.

Hence, $h_1 : h_2 = ay : bx$.

110. Let the sides be x cm and (80% of x) cm = $\frac{4x}{5}$ cm.

Then, initial area = $\frac{\sqrt{3}}{4}x^2$, final area = $\frac{\sqrt{3}}{4}\cdot\left(\frac{4x}{5}\right)^2 = \frac{16\sqrt{3}\,x^2}{100}$.

Decrease in area = $\left(\frac{\sqrt{3}}{4}x^2 - \frac{16\sqrt{3}}{100}x^2\right)$ cm^2 = $\frac{9\sqrt{3}\,x^2}{100}$ cm^2.

$\therefore$ Decrease% = $\left(\frac{9\sqrt{3}\,x^2}{100} \times \frac{4}{\sqrt{3}\,x^2} \times 100\right)\%$ = 36%.

111. Let initial base = b cm and initial height = h cm. Then, initial area = $\left(\frac{1}{2}bh\right)$ cm^2.

New base = (140% of b) cm = $\left(\frac{140b}{100}\right)$ cm = $\left(\frac{7b}{5}\right)$ cm.

New height = (60% of h) cm = $\left(\frac{60h}{100}\right)$ cm = $\left(\frac{3h}{5}\right)$ cm.

New area = $\left(\frac{1}{2} \times \frac{7b}{5} \times \frac{3h}{5}\right)$ cm^2 = $\left(\frac{21}{50}bh\right)$ cm^2.

Area decreased = $\left(\frac{1}{2}bh - \frac{21}{50}bh\right)$ cm^2 = $\left(\frac{4}{50}bh\right)$ cm^2.

Percentage decrease = $\left(\frac{4bh}{50} \times \frac{2}{bh} \times 100\right)\%$ = 16%.

112. $A_1 = \frac{\sqrt{3}}{2}a^2$ and $A_2 = \frac{\sqrt{3}}{2}(2a)^2 = 4 \times \frac{\sqrt{3}}{2}a^2 = 4A_1$.

$\therefore$ K = 4.

113. Area of ||gm = (Base × Height) = (18 × 8) cm^2 = 144 cm^2.

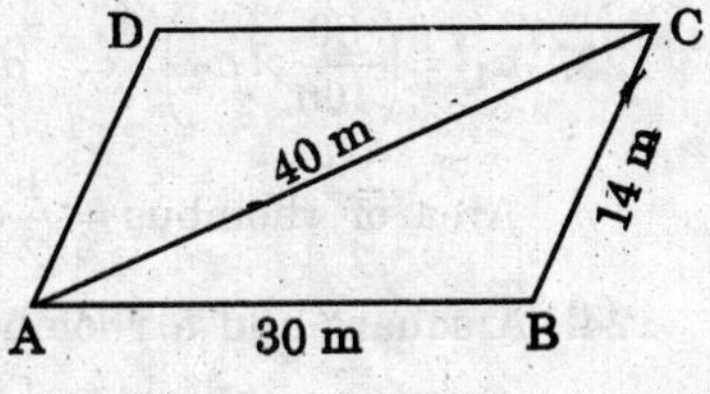

114. Let ABCD be the given ||gm.

Area of ||gm ABCD = 2 × (area of Δ ABC).

Now, a = 30 m, b = 14 m, c = 40 m.

$\therefore \quad s = \frac{1}{2}(30 + 14 + 40)$ m = 42 m.

$\therefore \quad$ Area of ΔABC $= \sqrt{s(s-a)(s-b)(s-c)}$

$= \sqrt{42 \times 12 \times 28 \times 2}$ m² = 168 m².

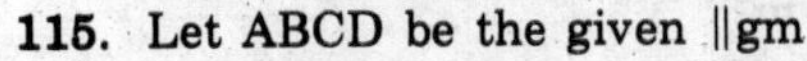

Hence, area of ||gm ABCD = (2 × 168) m² = 336 m².

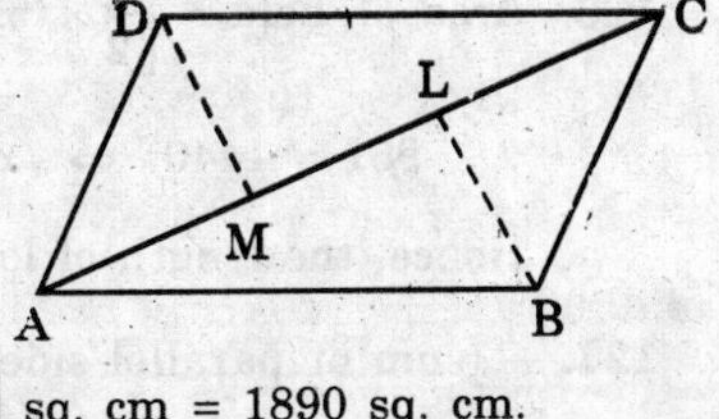

115. Let ABCD be the given ||gm.

Let AC = 70 cm.

Draw BL ⊥ AC and DM ⊥ AC.

Then, DM = BL = 27 cm.

Area of ||gm ABCD = ar (Δ ABC) + ar (Δ ACD)

$= \left[\left(\frac{1}{2} \times 70 \times 27\right) + \left(\frac{1}{2} \times 70 \times 27\right)\right]$ sq. cm = 1890 sq. cm.

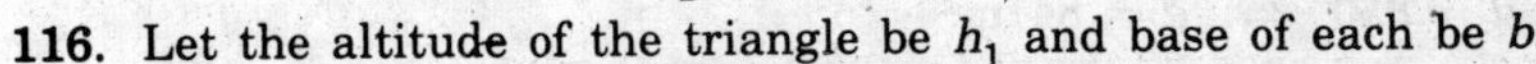

116. Let the altitude of the triangle be h_1 and base of each be b.

Then, $\frac{1}{2} \times b \times h_1 = b \times h_2$, where h_2 = 100 m

$\Leftrightarrow \quad h_1 = 2h_2$ = (2 × 100) m = 200 m.

117. Let each have base = b and height = h. Then, P = $b \times h$, R = $b \times h$, T = $\frac{1}{2} \times b \times h$

So, P = R, P = 2T and T = $\frac{1}{2}$R are all correct statements.

118. $\frac{1}{2} d_1 \times d_2 = 150 \Leftrightarrow \frac{1}{2} \times 10 \times d_2 = 150 \Leftrightarrow d_2 = 30$ cm.

119. $\frac{1}{2} d_1 \times 2d_1 = 25 \Leftrightarrow d_1^2 = 25 \Leftrightarrow d_1 = 5.$

$\therefore$ Sum of lengths of diagonals = (5 + 10) cm = 15 cm.

120. Perimeter of the rhombus = 56 m. Each side of the rhombus = $\frac{56}{4}$ m = 14 m.

Height of the rhombus = 5 m.

$\therefore$ Area = (14 × 5) m² = 70 m².

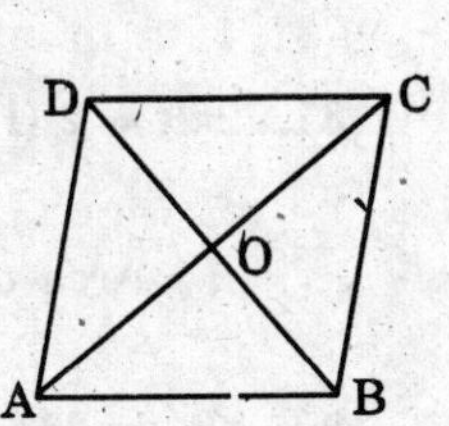

121. Area $= \frac{1}{2} d_1 d_2 = \left(\frac{1}{2} \times 24 \times 10\right)$ cm² = 120 cm².

OA $= \frac{1}{2} d_1 = \left(\frac{1}{2} \times 24\right)$ cm = 12 cm.

OB $= \frac{1}{2} d_2 = \left(\frac{1}{2} \times 10\right)$ cm = 5 cm.

AB² = OA² + OB² = (12)² + 5² = 169 $\Leftrightarrow$ AB = 13 cm.

$\therefore$ Perimeter = (13 × 4) cm = 52 cm.

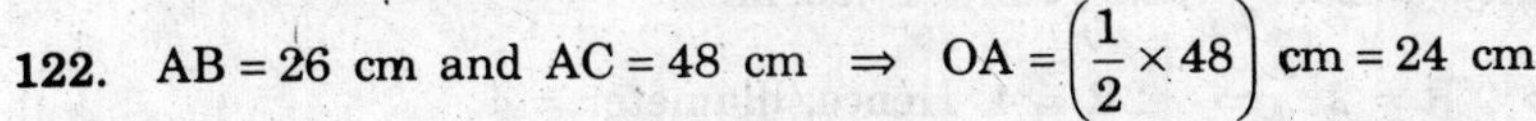

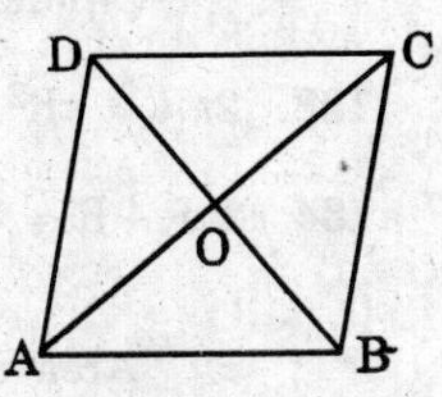

122. AB = 26 cm and AC = 48 cm $\Rightarrow$ OA $= \left(\frac{1}{2} \times 48\right)$ cm = 24 cm.

OB² = AB² − OA² = (26)² − (24)² = (26 + 24) (26 − 24) = 100

$\Rightarrow$ OB = 50 cm $\Rightarrow$ BD = 2 × OB = (2 × 50) cm = 100 cm.

$\therefore$ Area $= \frac{1}{2} \times$ AC × BD $= \left(\frac{1}{2} \times 48 \times 100\right)$ cm² = 2400 cm².

123. $d_1 = \left(\frac{80}{100} \times d_2\right) \Leftrightarrow d_1 = \frac{4d_2}{5}$.

Area of rhombus $= \frac{1}{2} d_1 d_2 = \left(\frac{1}{2} \times \frac{4d_2}{5} \times d_2\right) = \frac{2}{5}(d_2)^2$.

124. A square and a rhombus on the same base are equal in area.

125. Area of trapezium $= \left[\frac{1}{2} \times (1.5 + 2.5) \times 6.5\right]$ m^2 = 13 m^2.

126. Area of field $= \left[\frac{1}{2} \times (5x + 3x) \times 24\right]$ m^2 = $(96x)$ m^2.

$\therefore \quad 96x = 1440 \Leftrightarrow x = \frac{1440}{96} \Leftrightarrow x = 15$.

Hence, the length of longer parallel side = $(5x)$ = 75 m.

127. $\frac{1}{2}$ (sum of parallel sides) × depth = Its area

$\Leftrightarrow \frac{1}{2}(12 + 8) \times d = 840 \Leftrightarrow d = 84$ m.

128. Required% $= \left[\frac{\pi \times (5)^2}{2\pi \times 5} \times 100\right]\% = 250\%$.

129. Speed = 12 km/hr $= \left(12 \times \frac{5}{18}\right)$ m/s $= \frac{10}{3}$ m/s.

Distance covered $= \left(20 \times 2 \times \frac{22}{7} \times 50\right)$ m $= \frac{44000}{7}$ m.

Time taken $= \frac{\text{Distance}}{\text{Speed}} = \left(\frac{44000}{7} \times \frac{3}{10}\right)$ s $= \left(\frac{4400 \times 3}{7} \times \frac{1}{60}\right)$ min

$= \frac{220}{7}$ min $= 31\frac{3}{7}$ min.

130. Area of the field grazed $= \left(\frac{22}{7} \times 14 \times 14\right)$ sq. ft = 616 sq. ft.

Number of days taken to graze the field $= \frac{616}{100}$ days = 6 days (approx.).

131. $2\pi R = 2(l + b) \Leftrightarrow 2\pi R = 2(26 + 18)$ cm $\Leftrightarrow R = \left(\frac{88}{2 \times 22} \times 7\right) = 14$ cm.

$\therefore$ Area of the circle $= \pi R^2 = \left(\frac{22}{7} \times 14 \times 14\right)$ cm^2 = 616 cm^2.

132. $\pi R^2 = 24.64 \Leftrightarrow R^2 = \left(\frac{24.64}{22} \times 7\right) = 7.84 \Leftrightarrow R = \sqrt{7.84} = 2.8$ cm.

$\therefore$ Circumference $= \left(2 \times \frac{22}{7} \times 2.8\right)$ cm = 17.60 m.

133. $2\pi R = \pi R^2 \Leftrightarrow R = 2 \Leftrightarrow 2R = 4$. Hence, diameter = 4.

134. $2\pi R - R = 37 \Leftrightarrow \left(\frac{44}{7} - 1\right) R = 37 \Leftrightarrow R = 7$.

$\therefore$ Area of the circle $= \left(\frac{22}{7} \times 7 \times 7\right)$ cm^2 = 154 cm^2.

135. $\pi R_1^2 + \pi R_2^2 = \pi R_3^2 \Leftrightarrow R_1^2 + R_2^2 = R_3^2 \Leftrightarrow (9)^2 + R_2^2 = (15)^2$

$\Leftrightarrow R_2^2 = (15)^2 - (9)^2 = 144 \Leftrightarrow R_2 = 12$ cm.

136. Side of the square $= \dfrac{44}{4}$ cm = 11 cm.

Area of the square $= (11 \times 11)$ cm^2 = 121 cm^2.

$2\pi R = 44 \Leftrightarrow 2 \times \dfrac{22}{7} \times R = 44 \Leftrightarrow R = 7$ cm.

Area of circle $= \pi R^2 = \left(\dfrac{22}{7} \times 7 \times 7\right)$ cm^2 = 154 cm^2.

$\therefore$ Area of circle is larger by 33 cm^2.

137. Length of wire $= 2\pi \times R = \left(2 \times \dfrac{22}{7} \times 56\right)$ cm = 352 cm.

Side of the square $= \dfrac{352}{4}$ cm = 88 cm.

Area of the square = (88 × 88) cm^2 = 7744 cm^2.

138. Side of the square $= \sqrt{484}$ cm = 22 cm. Perimeter of the square = (22 × 4) cm = 88 cm.

$2\pi R = 88 \Leftrightarrow 2 \times \dfrac{22}{7} \times R = 88 \Leftrightarrow R = \left(88 \times \dfrac{7}{44}\right) = 14$ cm.

$\therefore$ Required area $= \pi R^2 = \left(\dfrac{22}{7} \times 14 \times 14\right)$ cm^2 = 616 cm^2.

139. Length of wire $= 2\pi R = \left(2 \times \dfrac{22}{7} \times 42\right)$ cm = 264 cm.

Perimeter of rectangle = 2 $(6x + 5x)$ cm = $22x$ cm.

$\therefore$ $22x = 264 \Leftrightarrow x = 12$.

Smaller side = (5 × 12) cm = 60 cm.

140. Total area of the field = [(180 × 120)] + 40000] m^2

= (21600 + 40000) m^2 = 61600 m^2.

$\therefore$ $\pi R^2 = 61600 \Leftrightarrow R^2 = \left(61600 \times \dfrac{7}{22}\right) = (400 \times 7 \times 7)$ m

$\Leftrightarrow R = (20 \times 7)$ m = 140 m.

141. $\dfrac{\pi R_1^2}{\pi R_2^2} = \dfrac{16}{49} \Leftrightarrow \dfrac{R_1^2}{(14 \times 14)} = \dfrac{16}{49}$

$\Leftrightarrow R_1^2 = \dfrac{14 \times 14 \times 16}{49} \Leftrightarrow R_1 = \dfrac{14 \times 4}{7} = 8$ m.

142. $\dfrac{\pi R_1^2}{\pi R_2^2} = \dfrac{4}{9} \Leftrightarrow \dfrac{R_1^2}{R_2^2} = \dfrac{4}{9} \Leftrightarrow \dfrac{R_1}{R_2} = \dfrac{2}{3} \Leftrightarrow \dfrac{2\pi R_1}{2\pi R_2} = \dfrac{R_1}{R_2} = \dfrac{2}{3}$.

$\therefore$ Required ratio = 2 : 3.

143. Let the radius of the given circle be R cm and the side of the square be a cm.

Then, $2\pi R = 4a \Leftrightarrow \dfrac{R}{a} = \dfrac{2}{\pi}$.

Ratio of their areas $= \dfrac{\pi R^2}{a^2} = \left(\pi \times \dfrac{4}{\pi^2}\right) = \left(\dfrac{4}{22} \times 7\right) = \dfrac{14}{11} = 14 : 11$.

144. Distance covered in 1 revolution $= 2\pi R = \left(2 \times \frac{22}{7} \times 0.63\right)$ m $= \frac{99}{25}$ m.

Distance covered in 500 revolutions $= \left(\frac{99}{25} \times 500\right)$ m $= 1980$ m.

145. Distance covered in 1 revolution $= 2\pi R = \left(2 \times \frac{22}{7} \times 20\right)$ cm $= \frac{880}{7}$ cm.

Required number of revolutions $= \left(17600 \times \frac{7}{880}\right) = 140.$

146. Distance covered in 1 revolution $= 2\pi R = \left(2 \times \frac{22}{7} \times \frac{25}{100}\right)$ m $= \frac{11}{7}$ m.

$\therefore$ Required number of revolutions $= \left(11000 \times \frac{7}{11}\right) = 7000.$

147. Distance covered in 9 sec $= \left(2 \times \frac{22}{7} \times \frac{15}{2} \times 7\right)$ m $= 330$ m.

Distance covered in 1 sec $= \frac{330}{9}$ m $= \frac{110}{3}$ m.

$\therefore$ Required speed $= \left(\frac{110}{3} \times \frac{18}{5}\right)$ km/hr $= 132$ km/hr.

148. Distance covered in 10 sec $= \left(2 \times \frac{22}{7} \times \frac{35}{100} \times 40\right)$ m $= 88$ m.

Distance covered in 1 sec $= \frac{88}{10}$ m $= 8.8$ m.

$\therefore$ Speed $= 8.8$ m/s $= \left(8.8 \times \frac{18}{5}\right)$ km/hr $= 31.68$ km/hr.

149. Let each wheel make x revolutions per sec. Then

$$\left[\left(2\pi \times \frac{7}{2} \times x\right) + (2\pi \times 7 \times x)\right] \times 10 = 1980$$

$$\Leftrightarrow \left(\frac{22}{7} \times 7 \times x\right) + \left(2 \times \frac{22}{7} \times 7 \times x\right) = 198 \Leftrightarrow 66x = 198 \Leftrightarrow x = 3.$$

Distance moved by smaller wheel in 3 revolutions $= \left(2 \times \frac{22}{7} \times \frac{7}{2} \times 3\right)$ cm $= 66$ cm.

$\therefore$ Speed of smaller wheel $= \frac{66}{3}$ m/s $= 22$ m/s.

150. Distance covered by smaller wheel in 1 revolution $= (2\pi \times 15)$ cm $= (30\pi)$ cm.
Distance covered by larger wheel in 1 revolution $= (2\pi \times 25)$ cm $= (50\pi)$ cm.

Let $k \times 30\pi = 15 \times 50\pi$. Then, $k = \left(\frac{15 \times 50\pi}{30\pi}\right) = 25.$

$\therefore$ Required number of revolutions $= 25$.

151. Let the diameter of the wheel be d metres.
Distance covered in 1 revolution $= (\pi d)$ m.
Distance covered in 113 revolutions $= (113\pi d)$ m.

$\therefore \quad 113 \times \frac{22}{7} \times d = 226 \times 10 \Leftrightarrow d = \left(226 \times 10 \times \frac{7}{22} \times \frac{1}{113}\right)$ m $= 6\frac{4}{11}$ m.

152. Let the rear wheel make x revolutions. Then, the front wheel makes $(x + 10)$ revolutions.

$(x + 10) \times 3\pi = x \times 2\pi \Leftrightarrow 3x + 30 = 2x \Leftrightarrow x = 30.$

Distance travelled by the wagon $= (2\pi \times 30)$ ft $= (60\pi)$ ft.

153. Radius of the ground = 17.5 m. Radius of inner circle = (17.5 – 1.4) m = 16.1 m.

Area of the garden $= \pi \times [(17.5)^2 - (16.1)^2]\ m^2 = \left[\frac{22}{7} \times (17.5 + 16.1)(17.5 - 16.1)\right] m^2$

$= \left(\frac{22}{7} \times 33.6 \times 1.4\right) m^2 = 147.84\ m^2.$

154. $2\pi R = 440 \Leftrightarrow 2 \times \frac{22}{7} \times R = 440 \Leftrightarrow R = \left(440 \times \frac{7}{44}\right) = 70$ m.

Inside radius = (70 – 7) m = 63 m.

Area of the border $= \pi\,[(70)^2 - (63)^2]\ m^2$

$= \left[\frac{22}{7} \times (70 + 63) \times (70 - 63)\right] m^2 = 2926\ m^2.$

155. $\pi R_1^2 = 616 \Leftrightarrow R_1^2 = \left(616 \times \frac{7}{22}\right) = 196 \Leftrightarrow R_1 = 14$ cm.

$\pi R_2^2 = 154 \Leftrightarrow R_2^2 = \left(154 \times \frac{7}{22}\right) = 49 \Leftrightarrow R_2 = 7$ cm.

Breadth of the ring $= (R_1 - R_2)$ cm = (14 – 7) cm = 7 cm.

156. $2\pi R_1 - 2\pi R_2 = 132 \Leftrightarrow 2\pi (R_1 - R_2) = 132 \Leftrightarrow (R_1 - R_2) = \left(\frac{132}{2 \times 22} \times 7\right) = 21$ m.

∴ Required width = 21 m.

157. Let the radius of the pool be R ft. Radius of the pool including the wall = (R + 4) ft.

Area of the concrete wall $= \pi\,[(R + 4)^2 - R^2]$ sq. ft

$= [\pi (R + 4 + R)(R + 4 - R)]$ sq. ft $= 8\pi (R + 2)$ sq. ft.

$8\pi (R + 2) = \frac{11}{25}\pi R^2 \Leftrightarrow 11R^2 = 200 (R + 2) \Leftrightarrow 11R^2 - 200R - 400 = 0$

$\Leftrightarrow 11R^2 - 220R + 20R - 400 = 0$

$\Leftrightarrow 11R (R - 20) + 20 (R - 20) = 0$

$\Leftrightarrow (R - 20)(11R + 20) = 0 \Leftrightarrow R = 20.$

∴ Radius of the pool = 20 ft.

158. $\frac{2\pi R_1}{2\pi R_2} = \frac{23}{22} \Leftrightarrow \frac{R_1}{R_2} = \frac{23}{22} \Leftrightarrow R_1 = \frac{23}{22} R_2.$

Also, $R_1 - R_2 = 5$ m $\Leftrightarrow \frac{23R_2}{22} - R_2 = 5 \Leftrightarrow R_2 = 110.$

∴ Diameter of inner circle = (2 × 110) m = 220 m.

159. Area of the semi-circle $= \frac{1}{2}\pi R^2 = \left(\frac{1}{2} \times \frac{22}{7} \times 7 \times 7\right) m^2 = 77\ m^2.$

160. Perimeter of window $= \pi R + 2R = \left(\frac{22}{7} \times \frac{63}{2} + 63\right)$ cm = (99 + 63) cm = 162 cm.

161. Given : $\pi R + 2R = 36 \Leftrightarrow (\pi + 2) R = 36 \Leftrightarrow R = \frac{36}{\left(\frac{22}{7} + 2\right)}$ cm $= \left(\frac{36 \times 7}{36}\right)$ cm = 7 cm.

$\therefore$ Required area $= \pi R^2 = \left(\frac{22}{7} \times 7 \times 7\right) \text{cm}^2 = 154 \text{ cm}^2$.

162. Length of each side of the square $= \sqrt{81}$ cm = 9 cm.

Length of wire = (9×4) cm = 36 cm.

$\pi R + 2R = 36 \Leftrightarrow (\pi + 2) R = 36 \Leftrightarrow R = \frac{36}{\left(\frac{22}{7} + 2\right)} = 7$ cm.

Area of the semi-circle $= \frac{1}{2} \pi R^2 = \left(\frac{1}{2} \times \frac{22}{7} \times 7 \times 7\right) \text{cm}^2 = 77 \text{ cm}^2$.

163. Area of the sector $= \left(\frac{1}{2} \times \text{arc} \times R\right) = \left(\frac{1}{2} \times 3.5 \times 5\right) \text{cm}^2 = 8.75 \text{ cm}^2$.

164. Area of the sector $= \frac{\pi R^2 \theta}{360} = \left(\frac{22}{7} \times 7 \times 7 \times \frac{108}{360}\right) \text{cm}^2 = 46.2 \text{ cm}^2$.

165. Side of the square $= \frac{120}{4}$ cm = 30 cm.

Radius of the required circle $= \left(\frac{1}{2} \times 30\right)$ cm = 15 cm.

Area of the required circle $= [\pi \times (15)^2] \text{ cm}^2 = \left[\frac{22}{7} \times (15)^2\right] \text{cm}^2$.

166. Radius of the required circle $= \left(\frac{1}{2} \times 14\right)$ cm = 7 cm.

Area of the circle $= \left(\frac{22}{7} \times 7 \times 7\right) \text{cm}^2 = 154 \text{ cm}^2$.

167. $\pi R^2 = 220 \Leftrightarrow R^2 = \left(220 \times \frac{7}{22}\right) = 70$.

Now, $R = \frac{1}{2} \times (\text{diagonal}) \Leftrightarrow \text{diagonal} = 2R$.

$\therefore$ Area of the square $= \frac{1}{2} \times (\text{diagonal})^2$

$= \left(\frac{1}{2} \times 4R^2\right) = 2R^2 = (2 \times 70) \text{ cm}^2 = 140 \text{ cm}^2$.

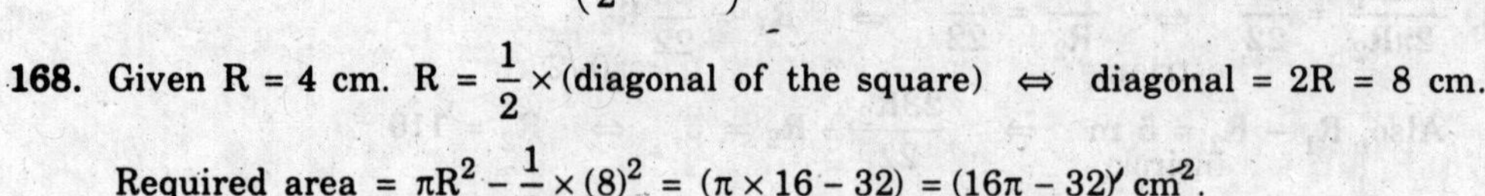

168. Given R = 4 cm. $R = \frac{1}{2} \times (\text{diagonal of the square}) \Leftrightarrow \text{diagonal} = 2R = 8$ cm.

Required area $= \pi R^2 - \frac{1}{2} \times (8)^2 = (\pi \times 16 - 32) = (16\pi - 32) \text{ cm}^2$.

169. $2\pi R = 100 \Leftrightarrow R = \frac{100}{2\pi} = \frac{50}{\pi}$.

$R = \frac{1}{2} \times \text{diagonal} \Leftrightarrow \text{diagonal} = 2R = \frac{2 \times 50}{\pi} = \frac{100}{\pi}$.

$\therefore$ Area of the square $= \frac{1}{2} \times (\text{diagonal})^2 = \frac{1}{2} \times \left(\frac{100}{\pi}\right)^2$

$\Leftrightarrow a^2 = \frac{1}{2} \times \left(\frac{100}{\pi}\right)^2 \Leftrightarrow a = \frac{1}{\sqrt{2}} \times \frac{100}{\pi} = \frac{50\sqrt{2}}{\pi}$ cm.

170. Side of square paper $= \sqrt{784}$ cm $= 28$ cm.

Radius of each circular plate $= \left(\frac{1}{4} \times 28\right)$ cm $= 7$ cm.

Circumference of each circular plate $= \left(2 \times \frac{22}{7} \times 7\right)$ cm $= 44$ cm.

171. Length of the fence $= 4\pi R$, where $R = \frac{21}{2}$ m

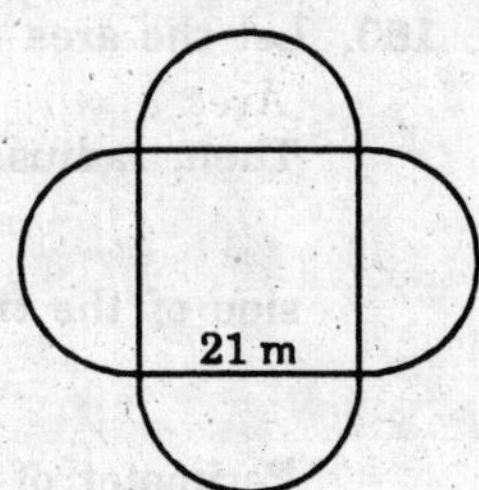

$= \left(4 \times \frac{22}{7} \times \frac{21}{2}\right)$ m $= 132$ m.

Cost of fencing = Rs. $\left(132 \times \frac{25}{2}\right)$ = Rs. 1650.

172. Radius of incircle of an equilateral triangle $= \frac{a}{2\sqrt{3}}$.

Radius of circumcircle of an equilateral triangle $= \frac{a}{\sqrt{3}}$.

$\therefore$ Required ratio $= \frac{\pi a^2}{12} : \frac{\pi a^2}{3} = \frac{1}{12} : \frac{1}{3} = 1 : 4$.

173. Radius of circumcircle $= \frac{a}{\sqrt{3}} = \frac{12}{\sqrt{3}}$ cm $= 4\sqrt{3}$ cm.

174. Radius of incircle $= \frac{a}{2\sqrt{3}} = \frac{42}{2\sqrt{3}}$ cm $= 7\sqrt{3}$ cm.

Area of incircle $= \left(\frac{22}{7} \times 49 \times 3\right)$ cm^2 $= 462$ cm^2.

175. Radius of incircle $= \frac{a}{2\sqrt{3}}$. Area of incircle $= \left(\frac{\pi \times a^2}{12}\right)$ cm^2

$\therefore \frac{\pi a^2}{12} = 154 \Leftrightarrow a^2 = \frac{154 \times 12 \times 7}{22} \Leftrightarrow a = 14\sqrt{3}$.

$\therefore$ Perimeter of the triangle $= (3 \times 14\sqrt{3})$ cm $= (42 \times 1.732)$ cm $= 72.7$ cm (approx.).

176. We have : $a = 6$, $b = 11$, $c = 15$. $s = \frac{1}{2}(6 + 11 + 15) = 16$.

Area of the triangle, $\Delta = \sqrt{16 \times 10 \times 5 \times 1} = 20\sqrt{2}$ cm^2.

Radius of incircle $= \frac{\Delta}{s} = \frac{20\sqrt{2}}{16} = \frac{5\sqrt{2}}{4}$ cm.

177. Let the radius of incircle be r cm. Then, $2\pi r = 88 \Leftrightarrow r = \left(88 \times \frac{7}{22} \times \frac{1}{2}\right) = 14$.

Semi-perimeter, $s = \left(\frac{30}{2}\right)$ cm $= 15$ cm.

$\therefore$ Area of the triangle $= r \times s = (14 \times 15)$ cm^2 $= 210$ cm^2.

178. Radius $= \frac{\text{Area}}{\text{Semi-perimeter}} = \left(\text{Area} \times \frac{2}{\text{Area}}\right) = 2.$

179. Let the perimeter of each be a.

Then, side of the equilateral triangle $= \frac{a}{3}$; side of the square $= \frac{a}{4}$;

radius of the circle $= \frac{a}{2\pi}$.

$\therefore\ T = \frac{\sqrt{3}}{4} \times \left(\frac{a}{3}\right)^2 = \frac{\sqrt{3}\,a^2}{36};\ S = \left(\frac{a}{4}\right)^2 = \frac{a^2}{16};\ C = \pi \times \left(\frac{a}{2\pi}\right)^2 = \frac{a^2}{4\pi} = \frac{7a^2}{88}.$

So, C > S > T.

180. Let the area of each be a.

Then, radius of the circle $= \frac{\sqrt{a}}{\pi}$; side of the square $= \sqrt{a}$;

side of the triangle $= \sqrt{\frac{a \times 4}{\sqrt{3}}}$.

Perimeter of the circle $= 2\pi \sqrt{\frac{a}{\pi}} = 2\sqrt{\pi a} = 2\sqrt{3.14 \times a} = 2 \times 1.77\sqrt{a} = 3.54\sqrt{a}$.

Perimeter of the square $= 4\sqrt{a}$;

Perimeter of the triangle $= 3 \times \sqrt{\frac{4a}{1.732}} = 3 \times \sqrt{2.31a} = 3 \times 1.52\sqrt{a} = 4.56\sqrt{a}$.

Clearly, perimeter of the triangle is the greatest.

181. Required area $= \frac{1}{2} \times \text{base} \times \text{height} = \left(\frac{1}{2} \times 2r \times r\right) = r^2.$

182. Required area $= \frac{\pi}{2} \times \left(\frac{AC}{2}\right)^2 = \frac{\pi}{2} \times \frac{AC^2}{4} = \frac{\pi}{2} \times \frac{AB^2 + BC^2}{4}$

$= \frac{\pi}{2} \times \left(\frac{AB^2}{4} + \frac{BC^2}{4}\right) = \frac{\pi}{2} \times \left(\frac{AB}{2}\right)^2 + \frac{\pi}{2} \times \left(\frac{BC}{2}\right)^2 = 81 + 36 = 117\ \text{cm}^2.$

C
r
A r O r B

183. Let original radius be R cm. Then, original circumference = $(2\pi R)$ cm.

New radius = (175% of R) cm $= \left(\frac{175}{100} \times R\right)$ cm $= \frac{7R}{4}$ cm.

New circumference $= \left(2\pi \times \frac{7R}{4}\right)$ cm $= \frac{7\pi R}{2}$ cm.

Increase in circumference $= \left(\frac{7\pi R}{2} - 2\pi R\right)$ cm $= \frac{3\pi R}{2}$ cm.

Increase% $= \left(\frac{3\pi R}{2} \times \frac{1}{2\pi R} \times 100\right)\% = 75\%.$

184. Let original diameter be d metres. Then, its circumference = (πd) metres.

Time taken to cover $(8\pi d)$ m = 40 min.

New diameter = $(10d)$ m. Then, its circumference = $(\pi \times 10d)$ m.

$\therefore$ Time taken to go round it once $= \left(\frac{40}{8\pi d} \times 10\pi d\right)$ m = 50 min.

185. Let the original radius be R cm. New radius $= \left(\dfrac{106}{100}R\right)$ cm $= \left(\dfrac{53R}{50}\right)$ cm.

Original area $= \pi R^2$.

$$\text{Increase in area} = \pi\left(\frac{53R}{50}\right)^2 - \pi R^2 = \pi R^2\left[\left(\frac{53}{50}\right)^2 - 1\right] = \frac{\pi R^2\,[(53)^2 - (50)^2]}{2500}$$

$$= \frac{\pi R^2\,(103\times 3)}{2500}\ \text{m}^2.$$

$$\text{Increase\%} = \left(\frac{\pi R^2 \times 309}{2500} \times \frac{1}{\pi R^2} \times 100\right)\% = 12.36\%.$$

186. Let the original radius be R cm.

New radius = (90% of R) cm $= \left(\dfrac{90}{100}\times R\right)$ cm $= \dfrac{9R}{10}$ cm.

Original area $= \pi R^2$.

$$\text{Diminished area} = \left[\pi R^2 - \pi\left(\frac{9R}{10}\right)^2\right]\text{cm}^2 = \left[\left(1 - \frac{81}{100}\right)\pi R^2\right]\text{cm}^2 = \left(\frac{19}{100}\pi R^2\right)\text{cm}^2.$$

$$\text{Decrease\%} = \left(\frac{19\pi R^2}{100} \times \frac{1}{\pi R^2} \times 100\right)\% = 19\%.$$

187. Let the original radius be R cm. New radius = 2R.

Original area $= \pi R^2$, New area $= \pi(2R)^2 = 4\pi R^2$.

Increase in area $= (4\pi R^2 - \pi R^2) = 3\pi R^2$.

$$\text{Increase\%} = \left(\frac{3\pi R^2}{\pi R^2} \times 100\right)\% = 300\%.$$

188. $2\pi R_1 = 4\pi$ and $2\pi R_2 = 8\pi \Rightarrow R_1 = 2$ and $R_2 = 4$

$\Rightarrow$ Original area $= (4\pi \times 2^2) = 16\pi$, Increased area $= (4\pi \times 4^2) = 64\pi$.

Thus, the area quadruples.

189. Required area = (Area of an equilateral Δ of side 7 cm)

− (3 × area of sector with $\theta = 60°$ & $r = 3.5$ cm)

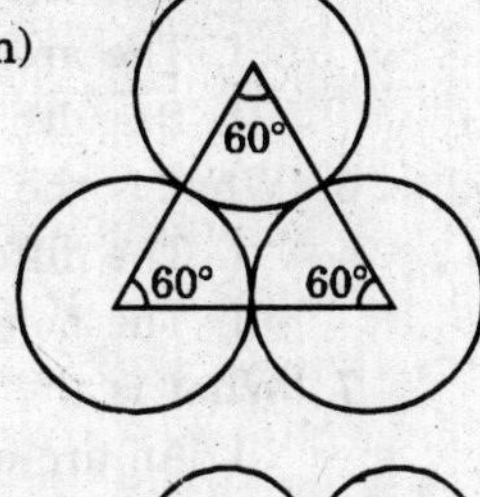

$$= \left[\left(\frac{\sqrt{3}}{4}\times 7\times 7\right) - \left(3\times\frac{22}{7}\times 3.5\times 3.5\times\frac{60}{360}\right)\right]\text{cm}^2$$

$$= \left(\frac{49\sqrt{3}}{4} - 11\times 0.5\times 3.5\right)\text{cm}^2 = (21.217 - 19.25)\ \text{cm}^2 = 1.967\ \text{cm}^2.$$

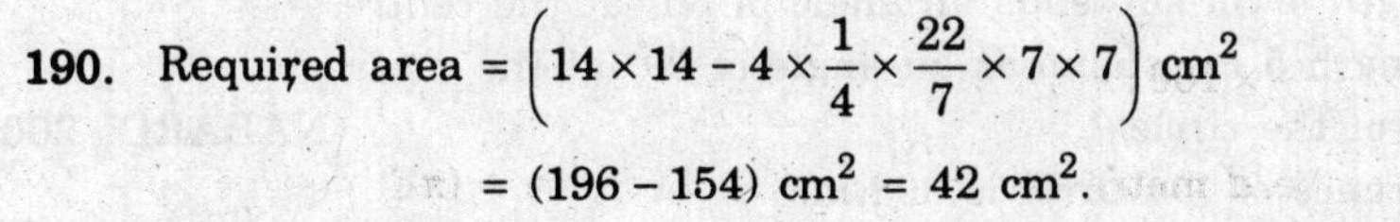

190. Required area $= \left(14\times 14 - 4\times\dfrac{1}{4}\times\dfrac{22}{7}\times 7\times 7\right)\text{cm}^2$

$= (196 - 154)\ \text{cm}^2 = 42\ \text{cm}^2.$

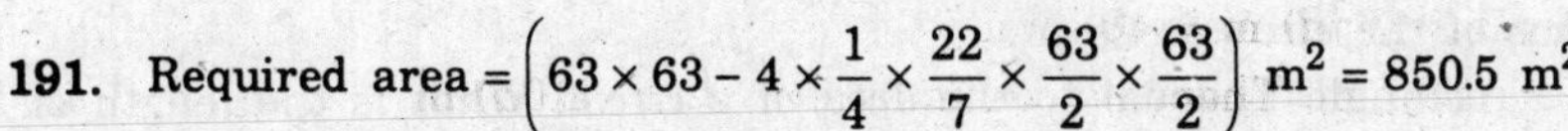

191. Required area $= \left(63\times 63 - 4\times\dfrac{1}{4}\times\dfrac{22}{7}\times\dfrac{63}{2}\times\dfrac{63}{2}\right)\text{m}^2 = 850.5\ \text{m}^2.$

EXERCISE 24B

(DATA SUFFICIENCY TYPE QUESTIONS)

Directions (*Questions 1 to 11*) : ***Each of the questions given below consists of a statement and/or a question and two statements numbered I and II given below it. You have to decide whether the data provided in the statement(s) is/are sufficient to answer the question. Read both the statements and***

Give answer (a) if the data in Statement I alone are sufficient to answer the question, while the data in Statement II alone are not sufficient to answer the question;

Give answer (b) if the data in Statement II alone are sufficient to answer the question, while the data in Statement I alone are not sufficient to answer the question;

Give answer (c) if the data either in Statement I or in Statement II alone are sufficient to answer the question;

Give answer (d) if the data even in both Statements I and II together are not sufficient to answer the question;

Give answer (e) if the data in both Statements I and II together are necessary to answer the question.

1. The area of a playground is 1600 m^2. What is its perimeter ? **(Bank P.O. 2003)**

I. It is a perfect square playground.

II. It costs Rs. 3200 to put a fence around the playground at the rate of Rs. 20 per metre.

2. What is the area of the rectangle ?

I. The ratio of the length and the breadth is 3 : 2.

II. The area of the rectangle is 3.6 times its perimeter.

3. Area of a square is equal to the area of a circle. What is the circumference of the circle ?

I. The diagonal of the square is x inches.

II. The side of the square is y inches. **(S.B.I.P.O. 2003)**

4. The area of a rectangle is equal to the area of a right-angled triangle. What is the length of the rectangle ? **(Bank P.O. 2003)**

I. The base of the triangle is 40 cm.

II. The height of the triangle is 50 cm.

5. What will be the cost of gardening a strip of land inside around a circular field, at the rate of Rs. 85 per sq. metre ?

I. The area of the field is 1386 sq. metres.

II. Breadth and length of the field are in the ratio of 3 : 5 respectively.

6. What is the area of the rectangle ? **(Bank P.O. 2003)**

I. The difference between the sides is 5 cm.

II. The measure of its diagonal is 10 cm.

7. What is the area of the circle ?

I. An arc of length 4 cm subtends an angle of 60° at the centre.

II. A chord of length 5 cm subtends an angle of 90° at the centre.

8. What is the area of the circle ? **(NABARD, 2002)**

I. The circumference of the circle is 308 m.

II. The radius of the circle is 28 m.

9. The area of a rectangle is equal to the area of a circle. What is the length of the rectangle ?

I. The radius of the circle is equal to the breadth of the rectangle.

II. The perimeter of the rectangle is 14 cm more than that of the circle.

10. What is the height of the triangle ? **(Bank P.O. 2002)**

I. The area of the triangle is 20 times its base.

II. The perimeter of the triangle is equal to the perimeter of a square of side 10 cm.

11. What will be the cost of painting the inner walls of a room if the rate of painting is Rs. 20 per square foot ? **(Bank P.O. 2000)**

I. Circumference of the floor is 44 feet.

II. The height of the wall of the room is 12 feet.

Directions (***Questions 12 to 18***) : ***Each of the questions below consists of a question followed by three statements. You have to study the question and the statements and decide which of the statement(s) is/are necessary to answer the question.***

12. What is the area of rectangular field ? **(Bank P.O. 2004)**

I. The perimeter of the field is 110 metres.

II. The length is 5 metres more than the width.

III. The ratio between length and width is 6 : 5 respectively.

(*a*) I and II only (*b*) Any two of the three (*c*) All I, II and III

(*d*) I, and either II or III only (*e*) None of these

13. What is the area of the hall ? **(Bank P.O. 2003)**

I. Material cost of flooring per square metre is Rs. 2.50.

II. Labour cost of flooring the hall is Rs. 3500.

III. Total cost of flooring the hall is Rs. 14,500.

(*a*) I and II only (*b*) II and III only (*c*) All I, II and III

(*d*) Any two of the three (*e*) None of these

14. What is the length of the diagonal of the given rectangle ?

I. The perimeter of the rectangle is 34 cm.

II. The difference between the length and breadth is 7 cm.

III. The length is 140% more than the breadth.

(*a*) Any two of the three (*b*) All I, II and III (*c*) I, and either II or III

(*d*) I and II only (*e*) II and III only

15. What is the cost of flooring the rectangular hall ? **(R.B.I. 2002)**

I. Length and breadth of the hall are in the respective ratio of 3 : 2.

II. Length of the hall is 48 m and cost of flooring is Rs. 85 per sq. m.

III. Perimeter of the hall is 160 m and cost of flooring is Rs. 85 per sq. m.

(*a*) I and II only (*b*) II and III only (*c*) III only

(*d*) I, and either II or III only (*e*) Any two of the three

16. What is the area of a right-angled triangle ? **(S.B.I.P.O. 2000)**

I. The perimeter of the triangle is 30 cm.

II. The ratio between the base and the height of the triangle is 5 : 12.

III. The area of the triangle is equal to the area of a rectangle of length 10 cm

(*a*) I and II only (*b*) II and III only (*c*) I and III only

(*d*) III, and either I or II only (*e*) None of these

17. A path runs around a rectangular lawn. What is the width of the path ?

I. The length and breadth of the lawn are in the ratio of 3 : 1 respectively.

II. The width of the path is ten times the length of the lawn.

III. The cost of gravelling the path @ Rs. 50 per m^2 is Rs. 8832.

(*a*) All I, II and II (*b*) III, and either I or II (*c*) I and III only

(*d*) II and III only (*e*) None of these

18. What is the area of the isosceles triangle ?

I. Perimeter of the isosceles triangle is 18 metres.

II. Base of the triangle is 8 metres.

III. Height of the triangle is 3 metres.

(a) I and II only (b) II and III only (c) I and III only

(d) II, and either I or III only (e) Any two of the three

Directions (*Questions 19 to 22*) : *Each of the questions given below is followed by three statements. You have to study the question and all the three statements given to decide whether any information provided in the statement(s) is/are redundant and can be dispensed with while answering the given question.*

19. What is the cost of painting the two adjacent walls of a hall at Rs. 5 per m^2 which has no windows or doors ? **(S.B.I.P.O. 2001)**

I. The area of the hall is 24 sq. m.

II. The breadth, length and height of the hall are in the ratio of 4 : 6 : 5 respectively.

III. Area of one wall is 30 sq. m.

(a) I only (b) II only (c) III only

(d) Either I or III (e) All I, II and III are required

20. What is the area of the given rectangle ? **(Bank P.O. 1999)**

I. Perimeter of the rectangle is 60 cm.

II. Breadth of the rectangle is 12 cm.

III. Sum of two adjacent sides is 30 cm.

(a) I only (b) II only (c) III only

(d) I and II only (e) I or III only

21. What is the area of the given right-angled triangle ?

I. Length of the hypotenuse is 5 cm.

II. Perimeter of the triangle is four times its base.

III. One of the angles of the triangle is 60°.

(a) II only (b) III only (c) II or III only (d) II and III both

(e) Information given in all the three statements together is not sufficient to answer the question.

22. What will be the cost of painting the four walls of a room with length, width and height 5 m, 3 m and 8 m respectively ? The room has one door, and one window.

I. Cost of painting per sq. m is Rs. 25.

II. Area of window is 2.25 sq. m which is half of the area of the door.

III. Area of the room is 15 sq. m. **(S.B.I.P.O. 1999)**

(a) I only (b) II only (c) III only

(d) II or III only (e) All I, II and III are required

ANSWERS

1. (c)	2. (e)	3. (c)	4. (d)	5. (e)	6. (e)	7. (c)	8. (c)
9. (e)	10. (a)	11. (c)	12. (b)	13. (c)	14. (a)	15. (e)	16. (a)
17. (a)	18. (d)	19. (c)	20. (e)	21. (c)	22. (c)		

SOLUTIONS

1. Area = 1600 m^2.

I. Side = $\sqrt{1600}$ m = 40 m. So, perimeter = (40 × 4) m = 160 m.

∴ I alone gives the answer.

II. Perimeter $= \frac{\text{Total cost}}{\text{Cost per metre}} = \frac{3200}{20}$ m = 160 m.

$\therefore$ II alone gives the answer.

$\therefore$ Correct answer is (*c*).

2. I. Let $l = 3x$ metres and $b = 2x$ metres. Then, area = $(6x^2)$ m^2.

II. Perimeter = $2(3x + 2x)$ m = $(10x)$ m.

$\therefore \quad 6x^2 = 3.6 \times 10x \Leftrightarrow x = \frac{(3.6 \times 10)}{6} = 6.$

$\therefore$ $l = 18$ m and $b = 12$ m and so area can be obtained.

Thus, I and II together give the answer.

$\therefore$ Correct answer is (*e*).

3. I. Area of the circle = Area of the square $= \frac{1}{2}x^2$ sq. inches.

$\Rightarrow \pi r^2 = \frac{1}{2}x^2 \Rightarrow r = \sqrt{\frac{x^2}{2\pi}} = \frac{x}{\sqrt{2\pi}}.$

$\therefore$ Circumference of the circle = $2\pi r$, which can be obtained.

$\therefore$ I alone gives the answer.

II. Area of the circle = Area of the square = y^2 sq. inches.

$\Rightarrow \pi r^2 = y^2 \Rightarrow r = \frac{y}{\sqrt{\pi}}.$

$\therefore$ Circumference of the circle = $2\pi r$, which can be obtained.

Thus, II alone gives the answer.

$\therefore$ Correct answer is (*c*).

4. Given : Area of rectangle = Area of a right-angled triangle

$\Rightarrow l \times b = \frac{1}{2} \times B \times H$

I gives, B = 40 cm.

II gives, H = 50 cm.

Thus, to find l, we need b also, which is not given.

$\therefore$ Given data is not sufficient to give the answer.

$\therefore$ Correct answer is (*d*).

5. I. $\pi R_1^2 = 1386 \Leftrightarrow R_1^2 = \left(1386 \times \frac{7}{22}\right) \Leftrightarrow R_1 = 21$ m.

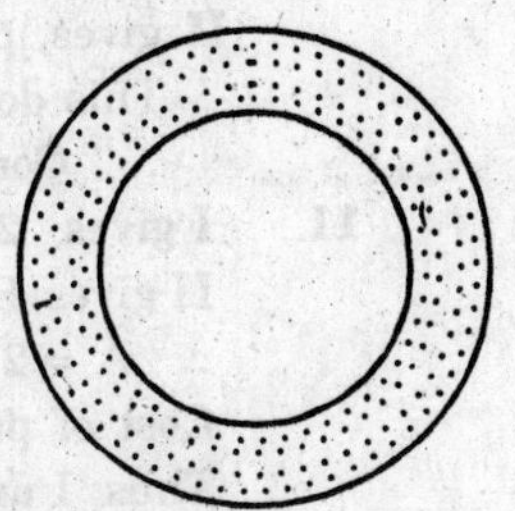

II. $R_2 = (21 - 1.4)$ m = 19.6 m.

$\therefore \quad \text{Area} = \pi(R_1^2 - R_2^2) = \frac{22}{7} \times [(21)^2 - (19.6)^2]$ m^2.

Thus, the required cost may be obtained.

$\therefore$ I and II together will give the answer.

$\therefore$ Correct answer is (*e*).

6. I. Let the sides be x cm and $(x + 5)$ cm.

II. $d = \sqrt{(x+5)^2 + x^2} \Leftrightarrow (x+5)^2 + x^2 = (10)^2 \Leftrightarrow 2x^2 + 10x - 75 = 0$

$\Leftrightarrow x = \frac{-10 \pm \sqrt{100 + 600}}{4} = \frac{-10 + \sqrt{700}}{4} = \frac{-10 + 10\sqrt{7}}{4} = \frac{-10 + 10 \times 2.6}{4}$

Thus, sides and therefore area may be known.

Thus, both I and II are needed to get the answer.

$\therefore$ Correct answer is (*e*).

7. I. Length of arc = $\frac{2\pi R\theta}{360} \Leftrightarrow 4 = \left(\frac{2 \times \frac{22}{7} \times R \times 60}{360}\right)$.

This gives R and therefore, area of the circle = πR^2.

Thus, I only gives the answer.

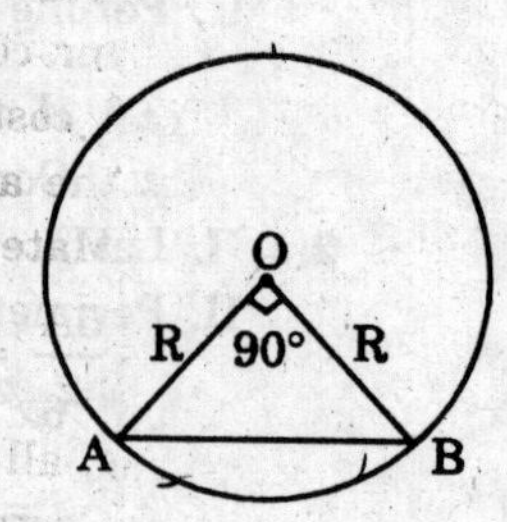

II. $R^2 + R^2 = 5^2 \Leftrightarrow 2R^2 = 25 \Leftrightarrow R^2 = \frac{25}{2}$.

$\therefore$ Area of the circle = $\pi R^2 = \left(\frac{22}{7} \times \frac{25}{2}\right)$ sq. cm.

Thus, II only gives the answer.

$\therefore$ Correct answer is (*c*).

8. I. $2\pi R = 308 \Leftrightarrow 2 \times \frac{22}{7} \times R = 308 \Leftrightarrow R = \left(308 \times \frac{7}{44}\right) = 49.$

Thus, $A = \pi R^2$ can be obtained.

$\therefore$ I alone gives the answer.

II. R = 28 m gives $A = (\pi \times 28 \times 28)$ cm^2.

Thus, II alone gives the answer.

$\therefore$ Correct answer is (*c*).

9. Given : $l \times b = \pi R^2$.

I gives, $R = b$. ...(*i*) ...(*ii*)

From (*i*) and (*ii*), we get $l = \frac{\pi R^2}{b} = \frac{\pi R^2}{R} = \pi R$. ...(*iii*)

II gives, $2(l + b) = 2\pi R + 14 \Rightarrow l + b = \pi R + 7 \Rightarrow l + R = \pi R + 7$

$\Rightarrow l = \pi R - R + 7$

$\Rightarrow l = l - \frac{l}{\pi} + 7$ [Using (*iii*)]

$\Rightarrow l = 7\pi$.

Thus, I and II together give l.

$\therefore$ Correct answer is (*e*).

10. I. $A = 20 \times B \Rightarrow \frac{1}{2} \times B \times H = 20 \times B \Rightarrow H = 40($

$\therefore$ I alone gives the answer.

II gives, perimeter of the triangle = 40 cm.

This does not give the height of the triangle.

$\therefore$ Correct answer is (*a*).

11. I gives, $2\pi R = 44$.

II gives, H = 12.

$\therefore A = 2\pi RH = (44 \times 12)$.

Cost of painting = Rs. $(44 \times 12 \times 20)$.

Thus, I and II together give the answer.

$\therefore$ Correct answer is (*e*).

12. I. $2(l + b) = 110 \Rightarrow l + b = 55$.

II. $l = (b + 5) \Rightarrow l - b = 5$.

III. $\frac{l}{b} = \frac{6}{5} \Rightarrow 5l \quad 6b = 0$.

These are three equations in l and b. We may solve them pairwise.

$\therefore$ Any two of the three will give the answer.

$\therefore$ Correct answer is (*b*).

13. **I.** Material cost = Rs. 2.50 per m^2.
II. Labour cost = Rs. 3500.
III. Total cost = Rs. 14,500.

Let the area be A sq. metres.

$\therefore$ Material cost = Rs. (14500 − 3500) = Rs. 11,000.

$\therefore \frac{5A}{2} = 11000 \Leftrightarrow A = \left(\frac{11000 \times 2}{5}\right) = 4400\ m^2.$

Thus, all I, II and III are needed to get the answer.

$\therefore$ Correct answer is (*c*).

14. **I.** $2(l + b) = 34 \Rightarrow l + b = 17$ ...(*i*)
II. $(l - b) = 7$ ...(*ii*)
III. $l = (100 + 140)\%$ of $b \Rightarrow l - \frac{240}{100}b = 0$

$\Rightarrow 100l - 240b = 0 \Rightarrow 5l - 12b = 0$ ...(*iii*)

These are 3 equations in l and b. We may solve them pairwise.

$\therefore$ Any two of the three will give the answer.

$\therefore$ Correct answer is (*a*).

15. **I.** Let $l = 3x$ metres and $b = 2x$ metres.
II. $l = 48$ m, Rate of flooring = Rs. 85 per m^2.
III. $2(l + b) = 160 \Leftrightarrow l + b = 80$, Rate of flooring = Rs. 85 per m^2.

From I and II, we get $3x = 48 \Leftrightarrow x = 16$

$\therefore l = 48$ m, $b = 32$ m $\Rightarrow$ Area of floor = $(48 \times 32)\ m^2$.

$\therefore$ Cost of flooring = Rs. $(48 \times 32 \times 85)$.

Thus, I and II give the answer.

From II and III, we get $l = 48$ m, $b = (80 - 48)$ m = 32 m.

$\therefore$ Area of floor and cost of flooring is obtained.

Thus, II and III give the answer.

From III and I, we get $3x + 2x = 80 \Leftrightarrow 5x = 80 \Leftrightarrow x = 16$.

$\therefore l = (3 \times 16)$ m = 48 m and $b = (2 \times 16)$ m = 32 m.

$\therefore$ Area of floor and the cost of flooring is obtained.

Thus, III and I give the answer.

Hence, any two of the three will give the answer.

$\therefore$ Correct answer is (*e*).

16. **From II,** base : height = 5 : 12.

Let base = $5x$ and height = $12x$. Then, hypotenuse = $\sqrt{(5x)^2 + (12x)^2} = 13x$.

From I, perimeter of the triangle = 30 cm.

$\therefore 5x + 12x + 13x = 30 \Leftrightarrow x = 1$.

So, base = $5x$ = 5 cm; height = $12x$ = 12 cm.

$\therefore$ Area = $\left(\frac{1}{2} \times 5 \times 12\right)\ cm^2 = 30\ cm^2$.

Thus, I and II together give the answer.

Clearly III is redundant, since the breadth of the rectangle is not given.

$\therefore$ Correct answer is (*a*).

17. III gives area of the path = $\frac{8832}{50}\ m^2 = \frac{4416}{25}\ m^2$.

II gives width of path = 10 × (Length of the lawn).

I gives length = $3x$ metres and breadth = x metres
Clearly, all the three will be required to find the width of the path.
∴ Correct answer is (*a*).

18. II gives base = 8 m.
I gives perimeter = 18 m.
III gives height = 3 m.
From II and I, we get :
$b = 8$ and $a + b + a = 18$ and so $a = 5$.
Thus, the three sides are 5 m, 5 m and 8 m.
From this, the area can be found out.
From II and III, we get : area = $\left(\frac{1}{2} \times 8 \times 3\right) m^2$.
∴ Correct answer is (*d*).

19. **From II**, let $l = 4x$, $b = 6x$ and $h = 5x$.
Then, area of the hall = $(24x^2)$ m^2.
From I. Area of the hall = 24 m^2.
From II and I, we get $24x^2 = 24 \Leftrightarrow x = 1$.
∴ $l = 4$ m, $b = 6$ m and $h = 5$ m.
Thus, area of two adjacent walls = $[(l \times h) + (b \times h)]$ m^2 can be found out and so the cost of painting two adjacent walls may be found out.
Thus, III is redundant.
∴ Correct answer is (*c*).

20. From I and II, we can find the length and breadth of the rectangle and therefore the area can be obtained
So, III is redundant.
Also, from II and III, we can find the length and breadth and therefore the area can be obtained.
So, I is redundant.
∴ Correct answer is (*e*).

21. $\frac{BC}{AC} = \cos 60° = \frac{1}{2} \Rightarrow BC = \frac{5}{2}$ cm [∵ AC = 5 cm]

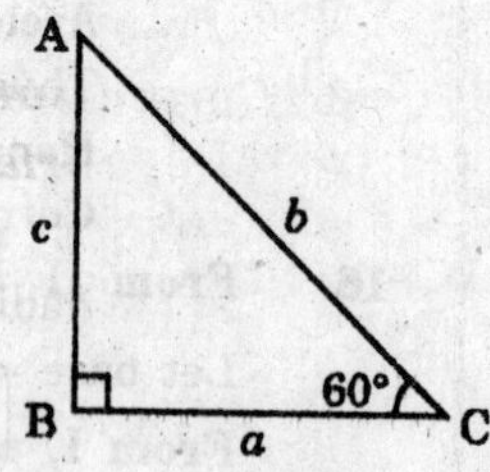

From I and III, we get :
$a = \frac{5}{2}$ cm, $b = 5$ cm and $\theta = 60°$.
∴ $A = \frac{1}{2} ab \sin C$ gives the area.
Thus, I and III give the result.
∴ II is redundant.
Again, II gives $a + b + c = 4a \Rightarrow b + c = 3a \Rightarrow c = 3a - 5$ [∵ $b = 5$ from I]
$a^2 + (3a - 5)^2 = 25$. This gives a and therefore c.
Now, area of Δ ABC = $\frac{1}{2} \times a \times c$, which can be obtained.
Thus I and II give the area.
∴ III is redundant.
∴ Correct answer is (*c*).

22. From given length, breadth and height of the room, its area can be obtained.
So, III is redundant.
∴ Correct answer is (*c*).

25. VOLUME AND SURFACE AREA

IMPORTANT FORMULAE

I. CUBOID

Let length = l, breadth = b and height = h units. Then,

1. ***Volume*** = $(l \times b \times h)$ cubic units.
2. ***Surface area*** = $2(lb + bh + lh)$ sq. units.
3. ***Diagonal*** = $\sqrt{l^2 + b^2 + h^2}$ units.

II. CUBE

Let each edge of a cube be of length a. Then,

1. ***Volume*** = a^3 cubic units.
2. ***Surface area*** = $6a^2$ sq. units.
3. ***Diagonal*** = $\sqrt{3}\,a$ units.

III. CYLINDER

Let radius of base = r and Height (or length) = h. Then,

1. ***Volume*** = $(\pi r^2 h)$ cubic units.
2. ***Curved surface area*** = $(2\pi rh)$ sq. units.
3. ***Total surface area*** = $(2\pi rh + 2\pi r^2)$ sq. units
   = $2\pi r(h + r)$ sq. units.

IV. CONE

Let radius of base = r and Height = h. Then,

1. ***Slant height***, $l = \sqrt{h^2 + r^2}$ units.
2. ***Volume*** = $\left(\frac{1}{3}\pi r^2 h\right)$ cubic units.
3. ***Curved surface area*** = (πrl) sq. units.
4. ***Total surface area*** = $(\pi rl + \pi r^2)$ sq. units.

V. SPHERE

Let the radius of the sphere be r. Then,

1. ***Volume*** = $\left(\frac{4}{3}\pi r^3\right)$ cubic units.
2. ***Surface area*** = $(4\pi r^2)$ sq. units.

VI. HEMISPHERE

Let the radius of a hemisphere be r. Then,

1. ***Volume*** = $\left(\frac{2}{3}\pi r^3\right)$ cubic units.
2. ***Curved surface area*** = $(2\pi r^2)$ sq. units.
3. ***Total surface area*** = $(3\pi r^2)$ sq. units.

Remember : 1 litre = 1000 cm^3.

SOLVED EXAMPLES

Ex. 1. ***Find the volume and surface area of a cuboid 16 m long, 14 m broad and 7 m high.***

Sol. Volume = $(16 \times 14 \times 7)\ m^3 = 1568\ m^3$.

Surface area = $[2 (16 \times 14 + 14 \times 7 + 16 \times 7)]\ cm^2 = (2 \times 434)\ cm^2 = 868\ cm^2$.

Ex. 2. ***Find the length of the longest pole that can be placed in a room 12 m long, 8 m broad and 9 m high.***

Sol. Length of longest pole = Length of the diagonal of the room

$= \sqrt{(12)^2 + 8^2 + 9^2} = \sqrt{289} = 17$ m.

Ex. 3. ***The volume of a wall, 5 times as high as it is broad and 8 times as long as it is high, is 12.8 cu. metres. Find the breadth of the wall.***

Sol. Let the breadth of the wall be x metres.

Then, Height = $5x$ metres and Length = $40x$ metres.

$\therefore \quad x \times 5x \times 40x = 12.8 \Leftrightarrow x^3 = \frac{12.8}{200} = \frac{128}{2000} = \frac{64}{1000}$.

So, $x = \frac{4}{10}$ m $= \left(\frac{4}{10} \times 100\right)$ cm = 40 cm.

Ex. 4. ***Find the number of bricks, each measuring 24 cm × 12 cm × 8 cm, required to construct a wall 24 m long, 8m high and 60 cm thick, if 10% of the wall is filled with mortar ?***

Sol. Volume of the wall = $(2400 \times 800 \times 60)$ cu. cm.

Volume of bricks = 90% of the volume of the wall

$= \left(\frac{90}{100} \times 2400 \times 800 \times 60\right)$ cu. cm.

Volume of 1 brick = $(24 \times 12 \times 8)$ cu. cm.

$\therefore$ Number of bricks $= \left(\frac{90}{100} \times \frac{2400 \times 800 \times 60}{24 \times 12 \times 8}\right) = 45000$.

Ex. 5. ***Water flows into a tank 200 m × 150 m through a rectangular pipe 1.5 m × 1.25 m @ 20 kmph. In what time (in minutes) will the water rise by 2 metres ?***

Sol. Volume required in the tank = $(200 \times 150 \times 2)\ m^3 = 60000\ m^3$.

Length of water column flown in 1 min. $= \left(\frac{20 \times 1000}{60}\right)$ m $= \frac{1000}{3}$ m.

Volume flown per minute $= \left(1.5 \times 1.25 \times \frac{1000}{3}\right) m^3 = 625\ m^3$.

$\therefore$ Required time $= \left(\frac{60000}{625}\right)$ min. = 96 min.

Ex. 6. ***The dimensions of an open box are 50 cm, 40 cm and 23 cm. Its thickness is 3 cm. If 1 cubic cm of metal used in the box weighs 0.5 gms, find the weight of the box.***

Sol. Volume of the metal used in the box = External Volume − Internal Volume

$= [(50 \times 40 \times 23) - (44 \times 34 \times 20)]\ cm^3$

$= 16080\ cm^3$.

$\therefore$ Weight of the metal $= \left(\frac{16080 \times 0.5}{1000}\right)$ kg = 8.04 kg.

Ex. 7. ***The diagonal of a cube is $6\sqrt{3}$ cm. Find its volume and surface area.***

Sol. Let the edge of the cube be a.

$\therefore$ $\sqrt{3}\,a = 6\sqrt{3} \Rightarrow a = 6.$

So, Volume $= a^3 = (6 \times 6 \times 6)\ \text{cm}^3 = 216\ \text{cm}^3.$

Surface area $= 6a^2 = (6 \times 6 \times 6)\ \text{cm}^2 = 216\ \text{cm}^2.$

Ex. 8. ***The surface area of a cube is 1734 sq. cm. Find its volume.***

Sol. Let the edge of the cube be a. Then,

$6a^2 = 1734 \Rightarrow a^2 = 289 \Rightarrow a = 17$ cm.

$\therefore$ Volume $= a^3 = (17)^3\ \text{cm}^3 = 4913\ \text{cm}^3.$

Ex. 9. ***A rectangular block 6 cm by 12 cm by 15 cm is cut up into an exact number of equal cubes. Find the least possible number of cubes.***

Sol. Volume of the block $= (6 \times 12 \times 15)\ \text{cm}^3 = 1080\ \text{cm}^3.$

Side of the largest cube = H.C.F. of 6 cm, 12 cm, 15 cm = 3 cm.

Volume of this cube $= (3 \times 3 \times 3)\ \text{cm}^3 = 27\ \text{cm}^3.$

Number of cubes $= \left(\dfrac{1080}{27}\right) = 40.$

Ex. 10. ***A cube of edge 15 cm is immersed completely in a rectangular vessel containing water. If the dimensions of the base of vessel are 20 cm × 15 cm, find the rise in water level.*** **(R.R.B. 2003)**

Sol. Increase in volume = Volume of the cube $= (15 \times 15 \times 15)\ \text{cm}^3.$

$\therefore$ Rise in water level $= \left(\dfrac{\text{Volume}}{\text{Area}}\right) = \left(\dfrac{15 \times 15 \times 15}{20 \times 15}\right)$ cm $= 11.25$ cm.

Ex. 11. ***Three solid cubes of sides 1 cm, 6 cm and 8 cm are melted to form a new cube. Find the surface area of the cube so formed.***

Sol. Volume of new cube $= (1^3 + 6^3 + 8^3)\ \text{cm}^3 = 729\ \text{cm}^3.$

Edge of new cube $= \sqrt[3]{729}$ cm $= 9$ cm.

$\therefore$ Surface area of the new cube $= (6 \times 9 \times 9)\ \text{cm}^2 = 486\ \text{cm}^2.$

Ex. 12. ***If each edge of a cube is increased by 50%, find the percentage increase in its surface area.***

Sol. Let original length of each edge $= a$.

Then, original surface area $= 6a^2$.

New edge $= (150\%\ \text{of}\ a) = \left(\dfrac{150}{100}a\right) = \dfrac{3a}{2}.$

New surface area $= 6 \times \left(\dfrac{3a}{2}\right)^2 = \dfrac{27}{2}a^2$

Increase percent in surface area $= \left(\dfrac{15}{2}a^2 \times \dfrac{1}{6a^2} \times 100\right)\% = 125\%.$

Ex. 13. ***Two cubes have their volumes in the ratio 1 : 27. Find the ratio of their surface areas.***

Sol. Let their edges be a and b. Then,

$$\frac{a^3}{b^3} = \frac{1}{27} \text{ or } \left(\frac{a}{b}\right)^3 = \left(\frac{1}{3}\right)^3 \text{ or } \frac{a}{b} = \frac{1}{3}.$$

$\therefore$ Ratio of their surface areas $= \dfrac{6a^2}{6b^2} = \dfrac{a^2}{b^2} = \left(\dfrac{a}{b}\right)^2 = \dfrac{1}{9}$, *i.e.*, 1 : 9.

Ex. 14. ***Find the volume, curved surface area and the total surface area of a cylinder with diameter of base 7 cm and height 40 cm.***

Sol. Volume $= \pi r^2 h = \left(\frac{22}{7} \times \frac{7}{2} \times \frac{7}{2} \times 40\right) \text{cm}^3 = 1540 \text{ cm}^3$.

Curved surface area $= 2\pi rh = \left(2 \times \frac{22}{7} \times \frac{7}{2} \times 40\right) \text{cm}^2 = 880 \text{ cm}^2$.

Total surface area $= 2\pi rh + 2\pi r^2 = 2\pi r(h + r)$

$$= \left[2 \times \frac{22}{7} \times \frac{7}{2} \times (40 + 3.5)\right] \text{cm}^2 = 957 \text{ cm}^2.$$

Ex. 15. ***If the capacity of a cylindrical tank is 1848 m³ and the diameter of its base is 14 m, then find the depth of the tank.***

Sol. Let the depth of the tank be h metres. Then,

$$\pi \times (7)^2 \times h = 1848 \Leftrightarrow h = \left(1848 \times \frac{7}{22} \times \frac{1}{7 \times 7}\right) = 12 \text{ m}.$$

Ex. 16. ***2.2 cubic dm of lead is to be drawn into a cylindrical wire 0.50 cm in diameter. Find the length of the wire in metres.***

Sol. Let the length of the wire be h metres. Then,

$$\pi \times \left(\frac{0.50}{2 \times 100}\right)^2 \times h = \frac{2.2}{1000} \Leftrightarrow h = \left(\frac{2.2}{1000} \times \frac{100 \times 100}{0.25 \times 0.25} \times \frac{7}{22}\right) = 112 \text{ m}.$$

Ex. 17. ***How many iron rods, each of length 7 m and diameter 2 cm can be made out of 0.88 cubic metre of iron ?*** **(C.B.I. 1998)**

Sol. Volume of 1 rod $= \left(\frac{22}{7} \times \frac{1}{100} \times \frac{1}{100} \times 7\right)$ cu. m $= \frac{11}{5000}$ cu. m.

Volume of iron = 0.88 cu. m.

Number of rods $= \left(0.88 \times \frac{5000}{11}\right) = 400$.

Ex. 18. ***The radii of two cylinders are in the ratio 3 : 5 and their heights are in the ratio of 2 : 3. Find the ratio of their curved surface areas.***

Sol. Let the radii of the cylinders be $3x$, $5x$ and their heights be $2y$, $3y$ respectively. Then.

Ratio of their curved surface areas $= \frac{2\pi \times 3x \times 2y}{2\pi \times 5x \times 3y} = \frac{2}{5} = 2 : 5$.

Ex. 19. ***If 1 cubic cm of cast iron weighs 21 gms, then find the weight of a cast iron pipe of length 1 metre with a bore of 3 cm and in which thickness of the metal is 1 cm.***

Sol. Inner radius $= \left(\frac{3}{2}\right)$ cm $= 1.5$ cm, Outer radius $= (1.5 + 1) = 2.5$ cm.

$\therefore$ Volume of iron $= [\pi \times (2.5)^2 \times 100 - \pi \times (1.5)^2 \times 100] \text{ cm}^3$

$$= \frac{22}{7} \times 100 \times [(2.5)^2 - (1.5)^2] \text{ cm}^3 = \left(\frac{8800}{7}\right) \text{cm}^3.$$

$\therefore$ Weight of the pipe $= \left(\frac{8800}{7} \times \frac{21}{1000}\right)$ kg $= 26.4$ kg.

Ex. 20. ***Find the slant height, volume, curved surface area and the whole surface area of a cone of radius 21 cm and height 28 cm.***

Sol. Here, $r = 21$ cm and $h = 28$ cm.

$\therefore$ Slant height, $l = \sqrt{r^2 + h^2} = \sqrt{(21)^2 + (28)^2} = \sqrt{1225} = 35$ cm.

$$\text{Volume} = \frac{1}{3}\pi r^2 h = \left(\frac{1}{3}\times\frac{22}{7}\times 21\times 21\times 28\right)\text{ cm}^3 = 12936\text{ cm}^3.$$

$$\text{Curved surface area} = \pi r l = \left(\frac{22}{7}\times 21\times 35\right)\text{ cm}^2 = 2310\text{ cm}^2.$$

$$\text{Total surface area} = (\pi r l + \pi r^2) = \left(2310 + \frac{22}{7}\times 21\times 21\right)\text{ cm}^2 = 3696\text{ cm}^2.$$

Ex. 21. ***Find the length of canvas 1.25 m wide required to build a conical tent of base radius 7 metres and height 24 metres.***

Sol. Here, $r = 7\text{m}$ and $h = 24$ m.

So, $l = \sqrt{r^2 + h^2} = \sqrt{7^2 + (24)^2} = \sqrt{625} = 25$ m.

$$\text{Area of canvas} = \pi r l = \left(\frac{22}{7}\times 7\times 25\right)\text{ m}^2 = 550\text{ m}^2.$$

$$\therefore\quad \text{Length of canvas} = \left(\frac{\text{Area}}{\text{Width}}\right) = \left(\frac{550}{1.25}\right)\text{ m} = 440\text{ m}.$$

Ex. 22. ***The heights of two right circular cones are in the ratio 1 : 2 and the perimeters of their bases are in the ratio 3 : 4. Find the ratio of their volumes.***

Sol. Let the radii of their bases be r and R and their heights be h and $2h$ respectively.

$$\text{Then, } \frac{2\pi r}{2\pi R} = \frac{3}{4} \Rightarrow \frac{r}{R} = \frac{3}{4} \Rightarrow R = \frac{4}{3}r.$$

$$\therefore\quad \text{Ratio of volumes} = \frac{\frac{1}{3}\pi r^2 h}{\frac{1}{3}\pi\left(\frac{4}{3}r\right)^2 (2h)} = \frac{9}{32} = 9:32.$$

Ex. 23. ***The radii of the bases of a cylinder and a cone are in the ratio of 3 : 4 and their heights are in the ratio 2 : 3. Find the ratio of their volumes.***

Sol. Let the radii of the cylinder and the cone be $3r$ and $4r$ and their heights be $2h$ and $3h$ respectively.

$$\therefore\quad \frac{\text{Volume of cylinder}}{\text{Volume of cone}} = \frac{\pi\times(3r)^2\times 2h}{\frac{1}{3}\pi\times(4r^2)\times 3h} = \frac{9}{8} = 9:8.$$

Ex. 24. ***A conical vessel, whose internal radius is 12 cm and height 50 cm, is full of liquid. The contents are emptied into a cylindrical vessel with internal radius 10 cm. Find the height to which the liquid rises in the cylindrical vessel.***

Sol. Volume of the liquid in the cylindrical vessel

$$= \text{Volume of the conical vessel}$$

$$= \left(\frac{1}{3}\times\frac{22}{7}\times 12\times 12\times 50\right)\text{ cm}^3 = \left(\frac{22\times 4\times 12\times 50}{7}\right)\text{ cm}^3.$$

Let the height of the liquid in the vessel be h.

$$\text{Then, } \frac{22}{7}\times 10\times 10\times h = \frac{22\times 4\times 12\times 50}{7} \text{ or } h = \left(\frac{4\times 12\times 50}{10\times 10}\right) = 24\text{ cm}.$$

Ex. 25. ***Find the volume and surface area of a sphere of radius 10.5 cm.***

$$\textbf{Sol.}\quad \text{Volume} = \frac{4}{3}\pi r^3 = \left(\frac{4}{3}\times\frac{22}{7}\times\frac{21}{2}\times\frac{21}{2}\times\frac{21}{2}\right)\text{ cm}^3 = 4851\text{ cm}^3.$$

$$\text{Surface area} = 4\pi r^2 = \left(4\times\frac{22}{7}\times\frac{21}{2}\times\frac{21}{2}\right)\text{ cm}^2 = 1386\text{ cm}^2.$$

Ex. 26. ***If the radius of a sphere is increased by 50%, find the increase percent in volume and the increase percent in the surface area.***

Sol. Let original radius = R. Then, new radius $= \frac{150}{100}R = \frac{3R}{2}$.

Original volume $= \frac{4}{3}\pi R^3$, New volume $= \frac{4}{3}\pi\left(\frac{3R}{2}\right)^3 = \frac{9\pi R^3}{2}$.

Increase % in volume $= \left(\frac{19}{6}\pi R^3 \times \frac{3}{4\pi R^3} \times 100\right)\% = 237.5\%$.

Original surface area $= 4\pi R^2$. New surface area $= 4\pi\left(\frac{3R}{2}\right)^2 = 9\pi R^2$.

Increase % in surface area $= \left(\frac{5\pi R^2}{4\pi R^2} \times 100\right)\% = 125\%$.

Ex. 27. ***Find the number of lead balls, each 1 cm in diameter that can be made from a sphere of diameter 12 cm.***

Sol. Volume of larger sphere $= \left(\frac{4}{3}\pi \times 6 \times 6 \times 6\right)\text{ cm}^3 = 288\pi\text{ cm}^3$.

Volume of 1 small lead ball $= \left(\frac{4}{3}\pi \times \frac{1}{2} \times \frac{1}{2} \times \frac{1}{2}\right)\text{ cm}^3 = \frac{\pi}{6}\text{ cm}^3$.

$\therefore$ Number of lead balls $= \left(288\pi \times \frac{6}{\pi}\right) = 1728$.

Ex. 28. ***How many spherical bullets can be made out of a lead cylinder 28 cm high and with base radius 6 cm, each bullet being 1.5 cm in diameter ?*** **(R.R.B. 2003)**

Sol. Volume of cylinder $= (\pi \times 6 \times 6 \times 28)\text{ cm}^3 = (36 \times 28)\pi\text{ cm}^3$.

Volume of each bullet $= \left(\frac{4}{3}\pi \times \frac{3}{4} \times \frac{3}{4} \times \frac{3}{4}\right)\text{ cm}^3 = \frac{9\pi}{16}\text{ cm}^3$.

Number of bullets $= \frac{\text{Volume of cylinder}}{\text{Volume of each bullet}} = \left[(36 \times 28)\pi \times \frac{16}{9\pi}\right] = 1792$.

Ex. 29. ***A copper sphere of diameter 18 cm is drawn into a wire of diameter 4 mm. Find the length of the wire.***

Sol. Volume of sphere $= \left(\frac{4}{3}\pi \times 9 \times 9 \times 9\right)\text{ cm}^3 = 972\pi\text{ cm}^3$.

Volume of wire $= (\pi \times 0.2 \times 0.2 \times h)\text{ cm}^3$

$\therefore 972\pi = \pi \times \frac{2}{10} \times \frac{2}{10} \times h \Rightarrow h = (972 \times 5 \times 5)\text{ cm} = \left(\frac{972 \times 5 \times 5}{100}\right)\text{ m} = 243\text{ m}.$

Ex. 30. ***Two metallic right circular cones having their heights 4.1 cm and 4.3 cm and the radii of their bases 2.1 cm each, have been melted together and recast into a sphere. Find the diameter of the sphere.***

Sol. Volume of sphere = Volume of 2 cones

$= \left[\frac{1}{3}\pi \times (2.1)^2 \times 4.1 + \frac{1}{3}\pi \times (2.1)^2 \times 4.3\right]\text{ cm}^3 = \frac{1}{3}\pi \times (2.1)^2\,(8.4)\text{ cm}^3.$

Let the radius of the sphere be R.

$\therefore \frac{4}{3}\pi R^3 = \frac{1}{3}\pi(2.1)^3 \times 4$ or $R = 2.1$ cm.

Hence, diameter of the sphere = 4.2 cm.

Ex. 31. ***A cone and a sphere have equal radii and equal volumes. Find the ratio of the diameter of the sphere to the height of the cone.***

Sol. Let radius of each be R and height of the cone be H.

Then, $\frac{4}{3}\pi R^3 = \frac{1}{3}\pi R^2 H$ or $\frac{R}{H} = \frac{1}{4}$ or $\frac{2R}{H} = \frac{2}{4} = \frac{1}{2}$.

$\therefore$ Required ratio = 1 : 2.

Ex. 32. ***Find the volume, curved surface area and the total surface area of a hemisphere of radius 10.5 cm.***

Sol. Volume $= \frac{2}{3}\pi r^3 = \left(\frac{2}{3} \times \frac{22}{7} \times \frac{21}{2} \times \frac{21}{2} \times \frac{21}{2}\right)$ cm^3 = 2425.5 cm^3.

Curved surface area $= 2\pi r^2 = \left(2 \times \frac{22}{7} \times \frac{21}{2} \times \frac{21}{2}\right)$ cm^2 = 693 cm^2.

Total surface area $= 3\pi r^2 = \left(3 \times \frac{22}{7} \times \frac{21}{2} \times \frac{21}{2}\right)$ cm^2 = 1039.5 cm^2.

Ex. 33. ***A hemispherical bowl of internal radius 9 cm contains a liquid. This liquid is to be filled into cylindrical shaped small bottles of diameter 3 cm and height 4 cm. How many bottles will be needed to empty the bowl ?*** **(N.I.F.T. 2003)**

Sol. Volume of bowl $= \left(\frac{2}{3}\pi \times 9 \times 9 \times 9\right)$ cm^3 = 486π cm^3.

Volume of 1 bottle $= \left(\pi \times \frac{3}{2} \times \frac{3}{2} \times 4\right)$ cm^3 = 9π cm^3.

Number of bottles $= \left(\frac{486\pi}{9\pi}\right) = 54$.

Ex. 34. ***A cone, a hemisphere and a cylinder stand on equal bases and have the same height. Find the ratio of their volumes.***

Sol. Let R be the radius of each.

Height of hemisphere = Its radius = R.

$\therefore$ Height of each = R.

Ratio of volumes $= \frac{1}{3}\pi R^2 \times R : \frac{2}{3}\pi R^3 : \pi R^2 \times R = 1 : 2 : 3$.

EXERCISE 25A

(OBJECTIVE TYPE QUESTIONS)

Directions : ***Mark (✓) against the correct answer :***

1. The capacity of a tank of dimensions (8 m × 6 m × 2.5 m) is :
(a) 120 litres (b) 1200 litres (c) 12000 litres (d) 120000 litres

2. Find the surface area of a 10 cm × 4 cm × 3 cm brick. **(R.R.B. 2001)**
(a) 84 sq. cm (b) 124 sq. cm (c) 164 sq. cm (d) 180 sq. cm

3. A cistern 6 m long and 4 m wide contains water up to a depth of 1 m 25 cm. The total area of the wet surface is . **(S.S.C. 2004)**
(a) 49 m^2 (b) 50 m^2 (c) 53.5 m^2 (d) 55 m^2

4. A boat having a length 3 m and breadth 2 m is floating on a lake. The boat sinks by 1 cm when a man gets on it. The mass of man is : **(R.R.B. 2002)**
(a) 12 kg (b) 60 kg (c) 72 kg (d) 96 kg

5. The area of the base of a rectangular tank is 6500 cm^2 and the volume of water contained in it is 2.6 cubic metres. The depth of water in the tank is :
(*a*) 3.5 m (*b*) 4 m (*c*) 5 m (*d*) 6 m

6. Given that 1 cu. cm of marble weighs 25 gms, the weight of a marble block 28 cm in width and 5 cm thick is 112 kg. The length of the block is :
(*a*) 26.5 cm (*b*) 32 cm (*c*) 36 cm (*d*) 37.5 cm

7. Half cubic metre of gold sheet is extended by hammering so as to cover an area of 1 hectare. The thickness of the sheet is :
(*a*) 0.0005 cm (*b*) 0.005 cm (*c*) 0.05 cm (*d*) 0.5 cm

8. In a shower, 5 cm of rain falls. The volume of water that falls on 1.5 hectares of ground is :
(*a*) 75 cu. m (*b*) 750 cu. m (*c*) 7500 cu. m (*d*) 75000 cu. m

9. The height of a wall is six times its width and the length of the wall is seven times its height. If volume of the wall be 16128 cu. m, its width is : **(C.B.I. 1998)**
(*a*) 4 m (*b*) 4.5 m (*c*) 5 m (*d*) 6 m

10. The volume of a rectangular block of stone is 10368 dm^3. Its dimensions are in the ratio of 3 : 2 : 1. If its entire surface is polished at 2 paise per dm^2, then the total cost will be :
(*a*) Rs. 31.50 (*b*) Rs. 31.68 (*c*) Rs. 63 (*d*) Rs. 63.36

11. The edges of a cuboid are in the ratio 1 : 2 : 3 and its surface area is 88 cm^2. The volume of the cuboid is : **(S.S.C. 1999)**
(*a*) 24 cm^3 (*b*) 48 cm^3 (*c*) 64 cm^3 (*d*) 120 cm^3

12. The maximum length of a pencil that can be kept in a rectangular box of dimensions 8 cm × 6 cm × 2 cm, is :
(*a*) $2\sqrt{13}$ cm (*b*) $2\sqrt{14}$ cm (*c*) $2\sqrt{26}$ cm (*d*) $10\sqrt{2}$ cm

13. Find the length of the longest rod that can be placed in a room 16 m long, 12 m broad and $10\frac{2}{3}$ m high. **(S.S.C. 1999)**
(*a*) $22\frac{1}{3}$ m (*b*) $22\frac{2}{3}$ m (*c*) 23 m (*d*) 68 m

14. How many bricks, each measuring 25 cm × 11.25 cm × 6 cm, will be needed to build a wall 8 m × 6 m × 22.5 cm ? **(B.S.F. 2001)**
(*a*) 5600 (*b*) 6000 (*c*) 6400 (*d*) 7200

15. The number of bricks, each measuring 25 cm × 12.5 cm × 7.5 cm, required to construct a wall 6 m long, 5 m high and 0.5 m thick, while the mortar occupies 5% of the volume of the wall, is : **(M.B.A. 2003)**
(*a*) 3040 (*b*) 5740 (*c*) 6080 (*d*) 8120

16. 50 men took a dip in a water tank 40 m long and 20 m broad on a religious day. If the average displacement of water by a man is 4 m^3, then the rise in the water level in the tank will be : **(N.I.F.T. 2000)**
(*a*) 20 cm (*b*) 25 cm (*c*) 35 cm (*d*) 50 cm

17. A tank 4 m long, 2.5 m wide and 1.5 m deep is dug in a field 31 m long and 10 m wide. If the earth dug out is evenly spread out over the field, the rise in level of the field is :
(*a*) 3.1 cm (*b*) 4.8 cm (*c*) 5 cm (*d*) 6.2 cm

18. A river 1.5 m deep and 36 m wide is flowing at the rate of 3.5 km per hour. The amount of water that runs into the sea per minute (in cubic metres) is :
(*a*) 3150 (*b*) 31500 (*c*) 6300 (*d*) 63000

19. A rectangular water tank is 80 m × 40 m. Water flows into it through a pipe 40 sq. cm at the opening at a speed of 10 km / hr. By how much, the water level will rise in the tank in half an hour ? **(M.B.A. 1997)**

(a) $\frac{3}{2}$ cm (b) $\frac{4}{9}$ cm (c) $\frac{5}{8}$ cm (d) None of these

20. A hall is 15 m long and 12 m broad. If the sum of the areas of the floor and the ceiling is equal to the sum of areas of the four walls, the volume of the hall is :

(a) 720 (b) 900 (c) 1200 (d) 1800

(L.I.C. A.A.O. 2003)

21. The sum of the length, breadth and depth of a cuboid is 19 cm and its diagonal is $5\sqrt{5}$ cm. It surface area is :

(a) 125 cm^2 (b) 236 cm^2 (c) 361 cm^2 (d) 486 cm^2

22. A swimming pool 9 m wide and 12 m long is 1 m deep on the shallow side and 4 m deep on the deeper side. Its volume is : **(M.A.T. 1998)**

(a) 208 m^3 (b) 270 m^3 (c) 360 m^3 (d) 408 m^3

23. A metallic sheet is of rectangular shape with dimensions 48 m × 36 m. From each of its corners, a square is cut off so as to make an open box. If the length of the square is 8 m, the volume of the box (in m^3) is : **(M.A.T. 2003)**

(a) 4830 (b) 5120 (c) 6420 (d) 8960

24. An open box is made of wood 3 cm thick. Its external dimensions are 1.46 m, 1.16 m and 8.3 dm. The cost of painting the inner surface of the box at 50 paise per 100 sq. cm is :

(a) Rs. 138.50 (b) Rs. 277 (c) Rs. 415. 50 (d) Rs. 554

25. A cistern of capacity 8000 litres measures externally 3.3 m by 2.6 m by 1.1 m and its walls are 5 cm thick. The thickness of the bottom is : **(S.S.C. 2003)**

(a) 90 cm (b) 1 dm (c) 1 m (d) 1.1 m

26. If a metallic cuboid weighs 16 kg, how much would a miniature cuboid of metal weigh, if all dimensions are reduced to one-fourth of the original ? **(D.M.R.C. 2003)**

(a) 0.25 kg (b) 0.50 kg (c) 0.75 kg (d) 1 kg

27. The areas of the three adjacent faces of a rectangular box which meet in a point are known. The product of these areas is equal to : **(Section Officers', 2003)**

(a) the volume of the box (b) twice the volume of the box

(c) the square of the volume of the box (d) the cube root of the volume of the box

28. If the areas of the three adjacent faces of a cuboidal box are 120 cm^2, 72 cm^2 and 60 cm^2 respectively, then find the volume of the box. **(S.S.C. 2002)**

(a) 720 cm^3 (b) 864 cm^3 (c) 7200 cm^3 (d) $(72)^2$ cm^3

29. If the areas of three adjacent faces of a rectangular block are in the ratio of 2 : 3 : 4 and its volume is 9000 cu. cm; then the length of the shortest side is :

(a) 10 cm (b) 15 cm (c) 20 cm (d) 30 cm

30. The perimeter of one face a of cube is 20 cm. Its volume must be : **(S.S.C. 1999)**

(a) 125 cm^3 (b) 400 cm^3 (c) 1000 cm^3 (d) 8000 cm^3

31. Total surface area of a cube whose side is 0.5 cm is : **(I.M.T. 2002)**

(a) $\frac{1}{4}$ cm^2 (b) $\frac{1}{8}$ cm^2 (c) $\frac{3}{4}$ cm^2 (d) $\frac{3}{2}$ cm^2

32. The cost of the paint is Rs 36.50 per kg. If 1 kg of paint covers 16 square feet, how much will it cost to paint outside of a cube having 8 feet each side ?

(a) Rs. 692 (b) Rs. 768 (c) Rs 876

(d) Rs. 972 (e) None of these **(Bank P.O. 2002)**

33. The dimensions of a piece of iron in the shape of a cuboid are 270 cm × 100 cm × 64 cm. If it is melted and recast into a cube, then the surface area of the cube will be :
(a) 14400 cm^2 (b) 44200 cm^2 (c) 57600 cm^2 (d) 86400 cm^2

34. The cost of painting the whole surface area of a cube at the rate of 13 paise per sq. cm is Rs. 343.98. Then the volume of the cube is : **(S.S.C. 2003)**
(a) 8500 cm^3 (b) 9000 cm^3 (c) 9250 cm^3 (d) 9261 cm^3

35. If the volume of a cube is 729 cm^3, then the surface area of the cube will be :
(a) 456 cm^2 (b) 466 cm^2 (c) 476 cm^2 (d) 486 cm^2

36. The length of an edge of a hollow cube open at one face is $\sqrt{3}$ metres. What is the length of the largest pole that it can accommodate ? **(M.A.T. 1997)**
(a) $\sqrt{3}$ metres (b) 3 metres (c) $3\sqrt{3}$ metres (d) $\frac{3}{\sqrt{3}}$ metres

37. What is the volume of a cube (in cubic cm) whose diagonal measures $4\sqrt{3}$ cm ?
(a) 8 (b) 16 (c) 27 (d) 64
(Hotel Management, 1999)

38. The surface area of a cube is 600 cm^2. The length of its diagonal is :
(a) $\frac{10}{\sqrt{3}}$ cm (b) $\frac{10}{\sqrt{2}}$ cm (c) $10\sqrt{2}$ cm (d) $10\sqrt{3}$ cm

39. If the numbers representing volume and surface area of a cube are equal, then the length of the edge of the cube in terms of the unit of measurement will be :
(a) 3 (b) 4 (c) 5 (d) 6

40. How many cubes of 10 cm edge can be put in a cubical box of 1 m edge ?
(a) 10 (b) 100 (c) 1000 (d) 10000
(R.R.B. 2003)

41. A rectangular box measures internally 1.6 m long, 1 m broad and 60 cm deep. The number of cubical blocks each of edge 20 cm that can be packed inside the box is :
(a) 30 (b) 53 (c) 60 (d) 120

42. How many cubes of 3 cm edge can be cut out of a cube of 18 cm edge ?
(a) 36 (b) 216 (c) 218 (d) 432
(IGNOU, 2003)

43. A cuboidal block of 6 cm × 9 cm × 12 cm is cut up into an exact number of equal cubes. The least possible number of cubes will be : **(Section Officers', 2003)**
(a) 6 (b) 9 (c) 24 (d) 30

44. The size of a wooden block is 5 × 10 × 20 cm. How many such blocks will be required to construct a solid wooden cube of minimum size ?
(a) 6 (b) 8 (c) 12 (d) 16

45. An iron cube of side 10 cm is hammered into a rectangular sheet of thickness 0.5 cm. If the sides of the sheet are in the ratio 1 : 5, the sides are :
(a) 10 cm, 50 cm (b) 20 cm, 100 cm (c) 40 cm, 200 cm (d) None of these
(Hotel Management, 1997)

46. Three cubes of iron whose edges are 6 cm, 8 cm and 10 cm respectively are melted and formed into a single cube. The edge of the new cube formed is :
(a) 12 cm (b) 14 cm (c) 16 cm (d) 18 cm

47. Five equal cubes, each of side 5 cm, are placed adjacent to each other. The volume of the new solid formed will be :
(a) 125 cm^3 (b) 625 cm^3 (c) 15525 cm^3 (d) None of these

48. A cube of edge 5 cm is cut into cubes each of edge 1 cm. The ratio of the total surface area of one of the small cubes to that of the large cube is equal to : **(S.S.C. 2004)**

(*a*) 1 : 5 (*b*) 1 : 25 (*c*) 1 : 125 (*d*) 1 : 625

49. A large cube is formed from the material obtained by melting three smaller cubes of 3, 4 and 5 cm side. What is the ratio of the total surface areas of the smaller cubes and the large cube ? **(M.A.T. 2004)**

(*a*) 2 : 1 (*b*) 3 : 2 (*c*) 25 : 18 (*d*) 27 : 20

50. Three cubes with sides in the ratio 3 : 4 : 5 are melted to form a single cube whose diagonal is $12\sqrt{3}$ cm. The sides of the cubes are : **(M.A.T. 2003)**

(*a*) 3 cm, 4 cm, 5 cm (*b*) 6 cm, 8 cm, 10 cm
(*c*) 9 cm, 12 cm, 15 cm (*d*) None of these

51. If the volumes of two cubes are in the ratio 27 : 1, the ratio of their edges is :

(*a*) 1 : 3 (*b*) 1 : 27 (*c*) 3 : 1 (*d*) 27 : 1

(S.S.C. 1999)

52. The volumes of two cubes are in the ratio 8 : 27. The ratio of their surface areas is :

(*a*) 2 : 3 (*b*) 4 : 9 (*c*) 12 : 9 (*d*) None of these

(Hotel Management, 2003)

53. Two cubes have volumes in the ratio 1 : 27. Then the ratio of the area of the face of one of the cubes to that of the other is :

(*a*) 1 : 3 (*b*) 1 : 6 (*c*) 1 : 9 (*d*) 1 : 12

54. If each edge of a cube is doubled, then its volume :

(*a*) is doubled (*b*) becomes 4 times
(*c*) becomes 6 times (*d*) becomes 8 times

55. If each edge of a cube is increased by 25%, then the percentage increase in its surface area is :

(*a*) 25% (*b*) 48.75% (*c*) 50% (*d*) 56.25%

56. A circular well with a diameter of 2 metres, is dug to a depth of 14 metres. What is the volume of the earth dug out ? **(S.S.C. 1999)**

(*a*) 32 m^3 (*b*) 36 m^3 (*c*) 40 m^3 (*d*) 44 m^3

57. The capacity of a cylindrical tank is 246.4 litres. If the height is 4 metres, what is the diameter of the base ? **(Bank P.O. 2003)**

(*a*) 1.4 m (*b*) 2.8 m (*c*) 14 m (*d*) 28 m (*e*) None of these

58. The volume of a right circular cylinder whose curved surface area is 2640 cm^2 and circumference of its base is 66 cm, is :

(*a*) 3465 cm^3 (*b*) 7720 cm^3 (*c*) 13860 cm^3 (*d*) 55440 cm^3

59. If the volume of a right circular cylinder with its height equal to the radius is $25\frac{1}{7}$ cm^3, then the radius of the cylinder is equal to :

(*a*) π cm (*b*) 2 cm (*c*) 3 cm (*d*) 4 cm

60. The height of a right circular cylinder is 14 cm and its curved surface is 704 sq. cm. Then its volume is :

(*a*) 1408 cm^3 (*b*) 2816 cm^3 (*c*) 5632 cm^3 (*d*) 9856 cm^3

61. A closed metallic cylindrical box is 1.25 m high and its base radius is 35 cm. If the sheet metal costs Rs. 80 per m^2, the cost of the material used in the box is :

(*a*) Rs. 281.60 (*b*) Rs. 290 (*c*) Rs. 340.50 (*d*) Rs. 500

62. The curved surface area of a right circular cylinder of base radius r is obtained by multiplying its volume by :

(*a*) $2r$ (*b*) $\frac{2}{r}$ (*c*) $2r^2$ (*d*) $\frac{2}{r^2}$

63. The ratio of total surface area to lateral surface area of a cylinder whose radius is 20 cm and height 60 cm, is :

(a) 2 : 1 (b) 3 : 2 (c) 4 : 3 (d) 5 : 3

64. A powder tin has a square base with side 8 cm and height 14 cm. Another tin has a circular base with diameter 8 cm and height 14 cm. The difference in their capacities is :

(a) 0 (b) 132 cm^3 (c) 137.1 cm^3 (d) 192 cm^3

65. The ratio between the radius of the base and the height of a cylinder is 2 : 3. If its volume is 12936 cu. cm, the total surface area of the cylinder is :

(a) 2587.2 cm^2 (b) 3080 cm^2 (c) 25872 cm^2 (d) 38808 cm^2

66. The radius of the cylinder is half its height and area of the inner part is 616 sq. cms. Approximately how many litres of milk can it contain ?

(a) 1.4 (b) 1.5 (c) 1.7 (d) 1.9 (e) 2.2

(S.B.I.P.O. 2000)

67. The sum of the radius of the base and the height of a solid cylinder is 37 metres. If the total surface area of the cylinder be 1628 sq. metres, its volume is :

(a) 3180 m^3 (b) 4620 m^3 (c) 5240 m^3 (d) None of these

68. The curved surface area of a cylindrical pillar is 264 m^2 and its volume is 924 m^3. Find the ratio of its diameter to its height. **(S.S.C. 2002)**

(a) 3 : 7 (b) 7 : 3 (c) 6 : 7 (d) 7 : 6

69. The height of a closed cylinder of given volume and the minimum surface area is :

(a) equal to its diameter (b) half of its diameter

(c) double of its diameter (d) None of these **(R.R.B. 2002)**

70. If the radius of the base of a right circular cylinder is halved, keeping the height same, what is the ratio of the volume of the reduced cylinder to that of the original one ?

(a) 1 : 2 (b) 1 : 4 (c) 1 : 8 (d) 8 : 1

71. The radii of two cylinders are in the ratio of 2 : 3 and their heights are in the ratio of 5 : 3. The ratio of their volumes is :

(a) 4 : 9 (b) 9 : 4 (c) 20 : 27 (d) 27 : 20

72. Two right circular cylinders of equal volumes have their heights in the ratio 1 : 2. The ratio of their radii is : **(S.S.C. 1999)**

(a) 1 : 2 (b) 1 : 4 (c) 2 : 1 (d) $\sqrt{2}:1$

73. X and Y are two cylinders of the same height. The base of X has diameter that is half the diameter of the base of Y. If the height of X is doubled, the volume of X becomes :

(a) equal to the volume of Y (b) double the volume of Y

(c) half the volume of Y (d) greater than the volume of Y

(C.B.I. 1997)

74. The radius of a wire is decreased to one-third and its volume remains the same. The new length is how many times the original length ?

(a) 1 time (b) 3 times (c) 6 times (d) 9 times

75. A cylindrical tank of diameter 35 cm is full of water. If 11 litres of water is drawn off, the water level in the tank will drop by : **(S.S.C. 1999)**

(a) $10\frac{1}{2}$ cm (b) $11\frac{3}{7}$ cm (c) $12\frac{6}{7}$ cm (d) 14 cm

76. A well with 14 m inside diameter is dug 10 m deep. Earth taken out of it has been evenly spread all around it to a width of 21 m to form an embankment. The height of the embankment is

(a) $\frac{1}{2}$ m (b) $\frac{2}{3}$ m (c) $\frac{3}{4}$ m (d) $\frac{3}{5}$ m

77. Water flows through a cylindrical pipe of internal diameter 7 cm at 2 m per second. If the pipe is always half full, then what is the volume of water (in litres) discharged in 10 minutes ? **(S.S.C. 2003)**

(*a*) 2310 (*b*) 3850 (*c*) 4620 (*d*) 9240

78. The number of coins of radius 0.75 cm and thickness 0.2 cm to be melted to make a right circular cylinder of height 8 cm and base radius 3 cm is : **(S.S.C. 2003)**

(*a*) 460 (*b*) 500 (*c*) 600 (*d*) 640

79. Two cylindrical vessels with radii 15 cm and 10 cm and heights 35 cm and 15 cm respectively are filled with water. If this water is poured into a cylindrical vessel 15 cm in height, then the radius of the vessel is :

(*a*) 17.5 cm (*b*) 18 cm (*c*) 20 cm (*d*) 25 cm

80. 66 cubic centimetres of silver is drawn into a wire 1 mm in diameter. The length of the wire in metres will be : **(C.B.I. 1998)**

(*a*) 84 (*b*) 90 (*c*) 168 (*d*) 336

81. A hollow garden roller 63 cm wide with a girth of 440 cm is made of iron 4 cm thick. The volume of the iron used is :

(*a*) 54982 cm^3 (*b*) 56372 cm^3 (*c*) 57636 cm^3 (*d*) 58752 cm^3

82. A cylindrical tube open at both ends is made of metal. The internal diameter of the tube is 11.2 cm and its length is 21 cm. The metal everywhere is 0.4 cm thick. The volume of the metal is : **(S.S.C. 2003)**

(*a*) 280.52 cm^3 (*b*) 306.24 cm^3 (*c*) 310 cm^3 (*d*) 316 cm^3

83. What length of solid cylinder 2 cm in diameter mush be taken to cast into a hollow cylinder of external diameter 12 cm, 0.25 cm thick and 15 cm long ?

(*a*) 42.3215 cm (*b*) 44.0123 cm (*c*) 44.0625 cm (*d*) 44.6023 cm

84. A hollow iron pipe is 21 cm long and its external diameter is 8 cm. If the thickness of the pipe is 1 cm and iron weighs 8 g/cm^3, then the weight of the pipe is :

(*a*) 3.6 kg (*b*) 3.696 kg (*c*) 36 kg (*d*) 36.9 kg

(S.S.C. 2004)

85. A circular cylinder can hold 61.6 c.c. of water. If the height of the cylinder is 40 cm and the outer diameter is 16 mm, then the thickness of the material of the cylinder is :

(*a*) 0.2 mm (*b*) 0.3 mm (*c*) 1 mm (*d*) 2 mm

86. The radius of the base and height of a cone are 3 cm and 5 cm respectively whereas the radius of the base and height of a cylinder are 2 cm and 4 cm respectively. The ratio of the volume of cone to that of the cylinder is :

(*a*) 1 : 3 (*b*) 15 : 8 (*c*) 15 : 16 (*d*) 45 : 16

87. The curved surface of a right circular cone of height 15 cm and base diameter 16 cm is : **(S.S.C. 1999)**

(*a*) 60π cm^2 (*b*) 68π cm^2 (*c*) 120π cm^2 (*d*) 136π cm^2

88. What is the total surface area of a right circular cone of height 14 cm and base radius 7 cm ? **(Hotel Management, 2001)**

(*a*) 344.35 cm^2 (*b*) 462 cm^2 (*c*) 498.35 cm^2 (*d*) None of these

89. A right triangle with sides 3 cm, 4 cm and 5 cm is rotated about the side of 3 cm to form a cone. The volume of the cone so formed is : **(S.S.C. 2000)**

(*a*) 12π cm^3 (*b*) 15π cm^3 (*c*) 16π cm^3 (*d*) 20π cm^3

90. The slant height of a right circular cone is 10 m and its height is 8 m. Find the area of its curved surface. **(R.R.B. 2002)**

(*a*) 30π m^2 (*b*) 40π m^2 (*c*) 60π m^2 (*d*) 80π m^2

91. If a right circular cone of height 24 cm has a volume of 1232 cm^3, then the area of its curved surface is : **(S.S.C. 2003)**

(*a*) 154 cm^2 (*b*) 550 cm^2 (*c*) 704 cm^2 (*d*) 1254 cm^2

92. The slant height of a conical mountain is 2.5 km and the area of its base is 1.54 km^2. The height of the mountain is : **(S.S.C. 2002)**
(a) 2.2 km (b) 2.4 km (c) 3 km (d) 3.11 km

93. If the area of the base of a right circular cone is 3850 cm^2 and its height is 84 cm, then the curved surface area of the cone is :
(a) 10001 cm^2 (b) 10010 cm^2 (c) 10100 cm^2 (d) 11000 cm^2

94. Volume of a right circular cone having base radius 70 cm and curved surface area 40040 cm^2 is :
(a) 823400 cm^3 (b) 824000 cm^3 (c) 840000 cm^3 (d) 862400 cm^3

95. The radius and height of a right circular cone are in the ratio 3 : 4. If its volume is 96π cm^3, what is its slant height ? **(C.B.I. 1997)**
(a) 8 cm (b) 9 cm (c) 10 cm (d) 12 cm

96. The length of canvas 1.1 m wide required to build a conical tent of height 14 m and the floor area 346.5 sq. m is :
(a) 490 m (b) 525 m (c) 665 m (d) 860 m

97. If the radius of the base and the height of a right circular cone are doubled, then its volume becomes : **(Asstt. Grade, 2003)**
(a) 2 times (b) 3 times (c) 4 times (d) 8 times

98. If both the radius and height of a right circular cone are increased by 20%, its volume will be increased by : **(S.S.C. 2004)**
(a) 20% (b) 40% (c) 60% (d) 72.8%

99. If the height of a right circular cone is increased by 200% and the radius of the base is reduced by 50%, then the volume of the cone : **(S.S.C. 2000)**
(a) remains unaltered (b) decreases by 25%
(c) increases by 25% (d) increases by 50%

100. If the height of a cone be doubled and radius of base remains the same, then the ratio of the volume of the given cone to that of the second cone will be : **(S.S.C. 2003)**
(a) 1 : 2 (b) 2 : 1 (c) 1 : 8 (d) 8 : 1

101. Two cones have their heights in the ratio of 1 : 3 and radii 3 : 1. The ratio of their volumes is :
(a) 1 : 1 (b) 1 : 3 (c) 3 : 1 (d) 2 : 3

102. The radii of two cones are in the ratio 2 : 1, their volumes are equal. Find the ratio of their heights. **(C.B.I. 1998)**
(a) 1 : 8 (b) 1 : 4 (c) 2 : 1 (d) 4 : 1

103. If the volumes of two cones are in the ratio of 1 : 4 and their diameters are in the ratio of 4 : 5, then the ratio of their heights is :
(a) 1 : 5 (b) 5 : 4 (c) 5 : 16 (d) 25 : 64

104. The volume of the largest right circular cone that can be cut out of a cube of edge 7 cm is : **(M.A.T. 2002)**
(a) 13.6 cm^3 (b) 89.8 cm^3 (c) 121 cm^3 (d) 147.68 cm^3

105. A cone of height 7 cm and base radius 3 cm is carved from a rectangular block of wood 10 cm × 5 cm × 2 cm. The percentage of wood wasted is :
(a) 34% (b) 46% (c) 54% (d) 66%

106. A right circular cone and a right circular cylinder have equal base and equal height. If the radius of the base and the height are in the ratio 5 : 12, then the ratio of the total surface area of the cylinder to that of the cone is :
(a) 3 : 1 (b) 13 : 9 (c) 17 : 9 (d) 34 : 9

107. A cylinder with base radius of 8 cm and height of 2 cm is melted to form a cone of height 6 cm. The radius of the cone will be : **(R.R.B. 2003)**
(*a*) 4 cm (*b*) 5 cm (*c*) 6 cm (*d*) 8 cm

108. A right cylindrical vessel is full of water. How many right cones having the same radius and height as those of the right cylinder will be needed to store that water ?
(*a*) 2 (*b*) 3 (*c*) 4 (*d*) 8

109. A solid metallic cylinder of base radius 3 cm and height 5 cm is melted to form cones, each of height 1 cm and base radius 1 mm. The number of cones is :
(*a*) 450 (*b*) 1350 (*c*) 4500 (*d*) 13500

110. Water flows at the rate of 10 metres per minute from a cylindrical pipe 5 mm in diameter. How long will it take to fill up a conical vessel whose diameter at the base is 40 cm and depth 24 cm ?
(*a*) 48 min. 15 sec. (*b*) 51 min. 12 sec. (*c*) 52 min. 1 sec. (*d*) 55 min.

111. A solid cylindrical block of radius 12 cm and height 18 cm is mounted with a conical block of radius 12 cm and height 5 cm. The total lateral surface of the solid thus formed is : **(Hotel Management, 1998)**
(*a*) 528 cm^2 (*b*) $1357\frac{5}{7}$ cm^2 (*c*) 1848 cm^2 (*d*) None of these

112. Consider the volumes of the following : **(Civil Services, 2002)**
1. A parallelopiped of length 5 cm, breadth 3 cm and height 4 cm
2. A cube of each side 4 cm
3. A cylinder of radius 3 cm and length 3 cm
4. A sphere of radius 3 cm

The volumes of these in the decreasing order is :
(*a*) 1, 2, 3, 4 (*b*) 1, 3, 2, 4 (*c*) 4, 2, 3, 1 (*d*) 4, 3, 2, 1

113. The volume of a sphere is 4851 cu. cm. Its curved surface area is :
(*a*) 1386 cm^2 (*b*) 1625 cm^2 (*c*) 1716 cm^2 (*d*) 3087 cm^2

114. The curved surface area of a sphere is 5544 sq. cm. Its volume is :
(*a*) 22176 cm^3 (*b*) 33951 cm^3 (*c*) 38808 cm^3 (*d*) 42304 cm^3

115. The volume of a sphere of radius r is obtained by multiplying its surface area by :
(*a*) $\frac{4}{3}$ (*b*) $\frac{r}{3}$ (*c*) $\frac{4r}{3}$ (*d*) $3r$

116. If the volume of a sphere is divided by its surface area, the result is 27 cm. The radius of the sphere is : **(R.R.B. 2003)**
(*a*) 9 cm (*b*) 36 cm (*c*) 54 cm (*d*) 81 cm

117. Spheres A and B have their radii 40 cm and 10 cm respectively. The ratio of the surface area of A to the surface area of B is : **(S.S.C. 2003)**
(*a*) 1 : 4 (*b*) 1 : 16 (*c*) 4 : 1 (*d*) 16 : 1

118. Surface area of a sphere is 2464 cm^2. If its radius be doubled, then the surface area of the new sphere will be :
(*a*) 4928 cm^2 (*b*) 9856 cm^2 (*c*) 19712 cm^2 (*d*) Data insufficient

119. If the radius of a sphere is doubled, how many times does its volume become ?
(*a*) 2 times (*b*) 4 times (*c*) 6 times (*d*) 8 times

120. If the radius of a sphere is increased by 2 cm, then its surface area increases by 352 cm^2. The radius of the sphere before the increase was : **(C.B.I. 2003)**
(*a*) 3 cm (*b*) 4 cm (*c*) 5 cm (*d*) 6 cm

121. If the measured value of the radius is 1.5% larger, the percentage error (correct to one decimal place) made in calculating the volume of a sphere is : **(C.B.I. 1997)**
(*a*) 2.1 (*b*) 3.2 (*c*) 4.6 (*d*) 5.4

122. The volumes of two spheres are in the ratio of 64 : 27. The ratio of their surface areas is : **(R.R.B. 2002)**

(*a*) 1 : 2 (*b*) 2 : 3 (*c*) 9 : 16 (*d*) 16 : 9

123. If the surface areas of two spheres are in the ratio of 4 : 25, then the ratio of their volumes is :

(*a*) 4 : 25 (*b*) 25 : 4 (*c*) 125 : 8 (*d*) 8 : 125

124. If three metallic spheres of radii 6 cms, 8 cms and 10 cms are melted to form a single sphere, the diameter of the new sphere will be . **(D.M.R.C. 2003)**

(*a*) 12 cms (*b*) 24 cms (*c*) 30 cms (*d*) 36 cms

125. A solid metallic sphere of radius 8 cm is melted and recast into spherical balls each of radius 2 cm. The number of spherical balls, thus obtained, is :

(*a*) 16 (*b*) 48 (*c*) 64 (*d*) 82

126. A spherical ball of lead, 3 cm in diameter is melted and recast into three spherical balls. The diameter of two of these are 1.5 cm and 2 cm respectively. The diameter of the third ball is :

(*a*) 2.5 cm (*b*) 2.66 cm (*c*) 3 cm (*d*) 3.5 cm

127. If a solid sphere of radius 10 cm is moulded into 8 spherical solid balls of equal radius, then the radius of each such ball is :

(*a*) 1.25 cm (*b*) 2.5 cm (*c*) 3.75 cm (*d*) 5 cm

128. A hollow spherical metallic ball has an external diameter 6 cm and is $\frac{1}{2}$ cm thick. The volume of metal used in the ball is : **(S.S.C. 2004)**

(*a*) $37\frac{2}{3}$ cm^3 (*b*) $40\frac{2}{3}$ cm^3 (*c*) $41\frac{2}{3}$ cm^3 (*d*) $47\frac{2}{3}$ cm^3

129. A solid piece of iron of dimensions 49 × 33 × 24 cm is moulded into a sphere. The radius of the sphere is : **(Hotel Management, 1999)**

(*a*) 21 cm (*b*) 28 cm (*c*) 35 cm (*d*) None of these

130. How many bullets can be made out of a cube of lead whose edge measures 22 cm, each bullet being 2 cm in diameter ?

(*a*) 1347 (*b*) 2541 (*c*) 2662 (*d*) 5324

131. How many lead shots each 3 mm in diameter can be made from a cuboid of dimensions 9 cm × 11 cm × 12 cm ?

(*a*) 7200 (*b*) 8400 (*c*) 72000 (*d*) 84000

132. A sphere and a cube have equal surface areas. The ratio of the volume of the sphere to that of the cube is :

(*a*) $\sqrt{\pi} : \sqrt{6}$ (*b*) $\sqrt{2} : \sqrt{\pi}$ (*c*) $\sqrt{\pi} : \sqrt{3}$ (*d*) $\sqrt{6} : \sqrt{\pi}$

133. The ratio of the volume of a cube to that of a sphere which will fit inside the cube is :

(*a*) 4 : π (*b*) 4 : 3π (*c*) 6 : π (*d*) 2 : π

134. The surface area of a sphere is same as the curved surface area of a right circular cylinder whose height and diameter are 12 cm each. The radius of the sphere is :

(*a*) 3 cm (*b*) 4 cm (*c*) 6 cm (*d*) 12 cm

(S.S.C. 2002)

135. The diameter of the iron ball used for the shot-put game is 14 cm. It is melted and then a solid cylinder of height $2\frac{1}{3}$ cm is made. What will be the diameter of the base of the cylinder ? **(S.S.C. 2004)**

(*a*) 14 cm (*b*) $\frac{14}{3}$ cm (*c*) 28 cm (*d*) $\frac{28}{3}$ cm

136. The volume of the greatest sphere that can be cut off from a cylindrical log of wood of base radius 1 cm and height 5 cm is : **(C.B.I. 1997)**

(a) $\frac{4}{3}\pi$ (b) $\frac{10}{3}\pi$ (c) 5π (d) $\frac{20}{3}\pi$

137. How many spherical bullets can be made out of a lead cylinder 15 cm high and with base radius 3 cm, each bullet being 5 mm in diameter ?

(a) 6000 (b) 6480 (c) 7260 (d) 7800

138. A cylindrical rod of iron whose height is eight times its radius is melted and cast into spherical balls each of half the radius of the cylinder. The number of spherical balls is :

(a) 12 (b) 16 (c) 24 (d) 48

139. The diameter of a sphere is 8 cm. It is melted and drawn into a wire of diameter 3 mm. The length of the wire is :

(a) 36.9 m (b) 37.9 m (c) 38.9 m (d) 39.9 m

140. A cylindrical vessel of radius 4 cm contains water. A solid sphere of radius 3 cm is lowered into the water until it is completely immersed. The water level in the vessel will rise by : **(M.B.A. 2000)**

(a) $\frac{2}{9}$ cm (b) $\frac{4}{9}$ cm (c) $\frac{9}{4}$ cm (d) $\frac{9}{2}$ cm

141. 12 spheres of the same size are made from melting a solid cylinder of 16 cm diameter and 2 cm height. The diameter of each sphere is : **(S.S.C. 2000)**

(a) $\sqrt{3}$ cm (b) 2 cm (c) 3 cm (d) 4 cm

142. A cylindrical tub of radius 12 cm contains water upto a depth of 20 cm. A spherical iron ball is dropped into the tub and thus the level of water is raised by 6.75 cm. The radius of the ball is :

(a) 4.5 cm (b) 6 cm (c) 7.25 cm (d) 9 cm

143. A solid metallic spherical ball of diameter 6 cm is melted and recast into a cone with diameter of the base as 12 cm. The height of the cone is : **(C.B.I. 2003)**

(a) 2 cm (b) 3 cm (c) 4 cm (d) 6 cm

144. A cone of height 9 cm with diameter of its base 18 cm is carved out from a wooden solid sphere of radius 9 cm. The percentage of the wood wasted is : **(S.S.C. 2000)**

(a) 25% (b) 25π% (c) 50% (d) 75%

145. A metallic cone of radius 12 cm and height 24 cm is melted and made into spheres of radius 2 cm each. How many spheres are there ?

(a) 108 (b) 120 (c) 144 (d) 180

146. A hollow sphere of internal and external diameters 4 cm and 8 cm respectively is melted into a cone of base diameter 8 cm. The height of the cone is : **(R.R.B. 2002)**

(a) 12 cm (b) 14 cm (c) 15 cm (d) 18 cm

147. In what ratio are the volumes of a cylinder, a cone and a sphere, if each has the same diameter and the same height ?

(a) 1 : 3 : 2 (b) 2 : 3 : 1 (c) 3 : 1 : 2 (d) 3 : 2 : 1

148. The total surface area of a solid hemisphere of diameter 14 cm, is :

(a) 308 cm^2 (b) 462 cm^2 (c) 1232 cm^2 (d) 1848 cm^2

149. Volume of a hemisphere is 19404 cu. cm. Its radius is :

(a) 10.5 cm (b) 17.5 cm (c) 21 cm (d) 42 cm

150. The capacities of two hemispherical vessels are 6.4 litres and 21.6 litres. The areas of inner curved surfaces of the vessels will be in the ratio of :

(a) $\sqrt{2} : \sqrt{3}$ (b) 2 : 3 (c) 4 : 9 (d) 16 : 81

151. A hemispherical bowl is filled to the brim with a beverage. The contents of the bowl are transferred into a cylindrical vessel whose radius is 50% more than its height. If the diameter is same for both the bowl and the cylinder, the volume of the beverage in the cylindrical vessel is : **(I.A.S. 1999)**

(*a*) $66\frac{2}{3}\%$ (*b*) $78\frac{1}{2}\%$ (*c*) 100%

(*d*) More than 100% (*i.e.*, some liquid will be left in the bowl).

152. A metallic hemisphere is melted and recast in the shape of a cone with the same base radius (R) as that of the hemisphere. If H is the height of the cone, then :

(*a*) H = 2R (*b*) H = 3R (*c*) $H = \sqrt{3}R$ (*d*) $H = \frac{2}{3}R$

(S.S.C. 1999)

153. A hemisphere of lead of radius 6 cm is cast into a right circular cone of height 75 cm. The radius of the base of the cone is :

(*a*) 1.4 cm (*b*) 2 cm (*c*) 2.4 cm (*d*) 4.2 cm

154. A hemisphere and a cone have equal bases. If their heights are also equal, then the ratio of their curved surfaces will be : **(S.S.C. 2002)**

(*a*) 1 : 2 (*b*) 2 : 1 (*c*) $1 : \sqrt{2}$ (*d*) $\sqrt{2} : 1$

155. A sphere of maximum volume is cut out from a solid hemisphere of radius *r*. The ratio of the volume of the hemisphere to that of the cut out sphere is :

(*a*) 3 : 2 (*b*) 4 : 1 (*c*) 4 : 3 (*d*) 7 : 4

ANSWERS

1. (*d*)	2. (*c*)	3. (*a*)	4. (*b*)	5. (*b*)	6. (*b*)	7. (*b*)	8. (*b*)
9. (*a*)	10. (*d*)	11. (*b*)	12. (*c*)	13. (*b*)	14. (*c*)	15. (*c*)	16. (*b*)
17. (*c*)	18. (*a*)	19. (*c*)	20. (*c*)	21. (*b*)	22. (*b*)	23. (*b*)	24. (*b*)
25. (*a*)	26. (*a*)	27. (*c*)	28. (*c*)	29. (*b*)	30. (*a*)	31. (*d*)	32. (*c*)
33. (*d*)	34. (*d*)	35. (*d*)	36. (*b*)	37. (*d*)	38. (*d*)	39. (*d*)	40. (*c*)
41. (*d*)	42. (*b*)	43. (*c*)	44. (*b*)	45. (*b*)	46. (*a*)	47. (*b*)	48. (*b*)
49. (*c*)	50. (*b*)	51. (*c*)	52. (*b*)	53. (*c*)	54. (*d*)	55. (*d*)	56. (*d*)
57. (*e*)	58. (*c*)	59. (*b*)	60. (*b*)	61. (*a*)	62. (*b*)	63. (*c*)	64. (*d*)
65. (*b*)	66. (*b*)	67. (*b*)	68. (*b*)	69. (*a*)	70. (*b*)	71. (*c*)	72. (*d*)
73. (*c*)	74. (*d*)	75. (*b*)	76. (*b*)	77. (*c*)	78. (*d*)	79. (*d*)	80. (*a*)
81. (*d*)	82. (*b*)	83. (*c*)	84. (*b*)	85. (*c*)	86. (*c*)	87. (*d*)	88. (*c*)
89. (*a*)	90. (*c*)	91. (*b*)	92. (*b*)	93. (*b*)	94. (*d*)	95. (*c*)	96. (*b*)
97. (*d*)	98. (*d*)	99. (*b*)	100. (*a*)	101. (*c*)	102. (*b*)	103. (*d*)	104. (*b*)
105. (*a*)	106. (*c*)	107. (*d*)	108. (*b*)	109. (*d*)	110. (*b*)	111. (*d*)	112. (*d*)
113. (*a*)	114. (*c*)	115. (*b*)	116. (*d*)	117. (*d*)	118. (*b*)	119. (*d*)	120. (*d*)
121. (*c*)	122. (*d*)	123. (*d*)	124. (*b*)	125. (*c*)	126. (*a*)	127. (*d*)	128. (*d*)
129. (*a*)	130. (*b*)	131. (*d*)	132. (*d*)	133. (*c*)	134. (*c*)	135. (*c*)	136. (*a*)
137. (*b*)	138. (*d*)	139. (*b*)	140. (*c*)	141. (*d*)	142. (*d*)	143. (*b*)	144. (*d*)
145. (*a*)	146. (*b*)	147. (*c*)	148. (*b*)	149. (*c*)	150. (*c*)	151. (*c*)	152. (*a*)
153. (*c*)	154. (*d*)	155. (*b*)					

SOLUTIONS

1. Capacity of the bank = Volume of the tank

$= \left(\frac{8 \times 100 \times 6 \times 100 \times 2.5 \times 100}{1000}\right)$ litres = 120000 litres.

2. Surface area = $[2\ (10 \times 4 + 4 \times 3 + 10 \times 3)]\ \text{cm}^2 = (2 \times 82)\ \text{cm}^2 = 164\ \text{cm}^2$.

3. Area of the wet surface = $[2\ (lb + bh + lh) - lb] = 2\ (bh + lh) + lb$

$= [2\ (4 \times 1.25 + 6 \times 1.25) + 6 \times 4]\ \text{m}^2 = 49\ \text{m}^2$.

4. Volume of water displaced = $(3 \times 2 \times 0.01)\ \text{m}^3 = 0.06\ \text{m}^3$.

$\therefore$ Mass of man = Volume of water displaced × Density of water

$= (0.06 \times 1000)$ kg = 60 kg.

5. Volume = $(2.6 \times 100 \times 100 \times 100)$ cu. cm.

Depth $= \frac{\text{Volume}}{\text{Area of the base}} = \left(\frac{2.6 \times 100 \times 100 \times 100}{6500}\right)$ cm = 400 cm = 4 m.

6. Let length = x cm. Then, $x \times 28 \times 5 \times \frac{25}{1000} = 112$

$\therefore\quad x = \left(112 \times \frac{1000}{25} \times \frac{1}{28} \times \frac{1}{5}\right)$ cm = 32 cm.

7. Volume of gold $= \left(\frac{1}{2} \times 100 \times 100 \times 100\right)\ \text{cm}^3$.

Area of sheet = $10000\ \text{m}^2 = (10000 \times 100 \times 100)\ \text{cm}^2$

$\therefore$ Thickness of the sheet $= \left(\frac{1 \times 100 \times 100 \times 100}{2 \times 10000 \times 100 \times 100}\right)$ cm = 0.005 cm.

8. Area = $(1.5 \times 10000)\ \text{m}^2 = 15000\ \text{m}^2$.

Depth $= \frac{5}{100}$ m $= \frac{1}{20}$ m.

$\therefore$ Volume = (Area × Depth) $= \left(15000 \times \frac{1}{20}\right)\ \text{m}^3 = 750\ \text{m}^3$.

9. Let the width of the wall be x metres.

Then, Height = $(6x)$ metres and Length = $(42x)$ metres.

$\therefore\quad 42x \times x \times 6x = 16128 \Leftrightarrow x^3 = \left(\frac{16128}{42 \times 6}\right) = 64 \Leftrightarrow x = 4.$

10. Let the dimensions be $3x$, $2x$ and x respectively. Then,

$3x \times 2x \times x = 10368 \Leftrightarrow x^3 = \left(\frac{10368}{6}\right) = 1728 \Leftrightarrow x = 12.$

So, the dimensions of the block are 36 dm, 24 dm, and 12 dm.

Surface area = $[2\ (36 \times 24 + 24 \times 12 + 36 \times 12)]\ \text{dm}^2$

$= [2 \times 144\ (6 + 2 + 3)]\ \text{dm}^2 = 3168\ \text{dm}^2$.

$\therefore$ Cost of polishing = Rs. $\left(\frac{2 \times 3168}{100}\right)$ = Rs. 63.36.

11. Let the dimensions of the cuboid be x, $2x$ and $3x$.

Then, $2\ (x \times 2x + 2x \times 3x + x \times 3x) = 88$

$\Leftrightarrow\quad 2x^2 + 6x^2 + 3x^2 = 44 \Leftrightarrow 11x^2 = 44 \Leftrightarrow x^2 = 4 \Leftrightarrow x = 2.$

$\therefore$ Volume of the cuboid = $(2 \times 4 \times 6)\ \text{cm}^3 = 48\ \text{cm}^3$.

12. Required length $= \sqrt{8^2 + 6^2 + 2^2}$ cm $= \sqrt{104}$ cm $= 2\sqrt{26}$ cm.

13. Required length $= \sqrt{(16)^2 + (12)^2 + \left(\frac{32}{3}\right)^2}$ m $= \sqrt{256 + 144 + \frac{1024}{9}}$ m

$= \sqrt{\frac{4624}{9}}$ m $= \frac{68}{3}$ m $= 22\frac{2}{3}$ m.

14. Number of bricks $= \frac{\text{Volume of the wall}}{\text{Volume of 1 brick}} = \left(\frac{800 \times 600 \times 22.5}{25 \times 11.25 \times 6}\right) = 6400.$

15. Volume of the bricks = 95% of volume of wall $= \left(\frac{95}{100} \times 600 \times 500 \times 50\right)$ cm^3.

Volume of 1 brick $= (25 \times 12.5 \times 7.5)$ cm^3.

$\therefore$ Number of bricks $= \left(\frac{95}{100} \times \frac{600 \times 500 \times 50}{25 \times 12.5 \times 7.5}\right) = 6080.$

16. Total volume of water displaced $= (4 \times 50)$ m^3 = 200 m^3.

$\therefore$ Rise in water level $= \left(\frac{200}{40 \times 20}\right)$ m = 0.25 m = 25 cm.

17. Volume of earth dug out $= \left(4 \times \frac{5}{2} \times \frac{3}{2}\right)$ m^3 = 15 m^3.

Area over which earth is spread $= \left(31 \times 10 - 4 \times \frac{5}{2}\right)$ m^2 = 300 m^2.

$\therefore$ Rise in level $= \left(\frac{\text{Volume}}{\text{Area}}\right) = \left(\frac{15}{300} \times 100\right)$ cm = 5 cm.

18. Length of water column flown in 1 min. $= \left(\frac{3.5 \times 1000}{60}\right)$ m $= \frac{175}{3}$ m.

$\therefore$ Volume flown per minute $= \left(\frac{175}{3} \times 36 \times \frac{3}{2}\right)$ m^3 = 3150 m^3.

19. Length of water column flown in 1 min. $= \left(\frac{10 \times 1000}{60}\right)$ m $= \frac{500}{3}$ m.

Volume flown per minute $= \left(\frac{500}{3} \times \frac{40}{100 \times 100}\right)$ m^3 $= \frac{2}{3}$ m^3.

Volume flown in half an hour $= \left(\frac{2}{3} \times 30\right)$ m^3 = 20 m^3.

$\therefore$ Rise in water level $= \left(\frac{20}{40 \times 80}\right)$ m $= \left(\frac{1}{160} \times 100\right)$ cm $= \frac{5}{8}$ cm.

20. $2(15 + 12) \times h = 2(15 \times 12)$ or $h = \frac{180}{27}$ m $= \frac{20}{3}$ m.

$\therefore$ Volume $= \left(15 \times 12 \times \frac{20}{3}\right)$ m^3 = 1200 m^3.

21. $(l + b + h) = 19$ and $\sqrt{l^2 + b^2 + h^2} = 5\sqrt{5}$ and so $(l^2 + b^2 + h^2) = 125$.

Now, $(l + b + h)^2 = 19^2 \Rightarrow (l^2 + b^2 + h^2) + 2(lb + bh + lh) = 361$

$\Rightarrow 2(lb + bh + lh) = (361 - 125) = 236.$

$\therefore$ Surface area = 236 cm^2.

22. Volume $= \left[12 \times 9 \times \left(\frac{1+4}{2}\right)\right] m^3 = (12 \times 9 \times 2.5)\ m^3 = 270\ m^3$.

23. Clearly, $l = (48 - 16)$ m = 32 m, $b = (36 - 16)$ m = 20 m, h = 8 m.

$\therefore$ Volume of the box $= (32 \times 20 \times 8)\ m^3 = 5120\ m^3$.

24. Internal length = (146 − 6) cm = 140 cm.

Internal breadth = (116 − 6) cm = 110 cm.

Internal depth = (83 − 3) cm = 80 cm.

Area of inner surface $= [2(l + b) \times h] + lb$

$= [2(140 + 110) \times 80 + 140 \times 110]\ cm^2 = 55400\ cm^2$.

$\therefore$ Cost of painting = Rs. $\left(\frac{1}{2} \times \frac{1}{100} \times 55400\right)$ = Rs. 277.

25. Let the thickness of the bottom be x cm.

Then, $[(330 - 10) \times (260 - 10) \times (110 - x)] = 8000 \times 1000$

$\Leftrightarrow$ $320 \times 250 \times (110 - x) = 8000 \times 1000$ $\Leftrightarrow$ $(110 - x) = \frac{8000 \times 1000}{320 \times 250} = 100$

$\Leftrightarrow$ x = 10 cm = 1 dm.

26. Let the dimensions of the bigger cuboid be x, y and z.

Then, Volume of the bigger cuboid = xyz.

Volume of the miniature cuboid $= \left(\frac{1}{4}x\right)\left(\frac{1}{4}y\right)\left(\frac{1}{4}z\right) = \frac{1}{64}xyz$.

$\therefore$ Weight of the miniature cuboid $= \left(\frac{1}{64} \times 16\right)$ kg = 0.25 kg.

27. Let length = l, breadth = b and height = h. Then,

Product of areas of 3 adjacent faces $= (lb \times bh \times lh) = (lbh)^2 = (\text{Volume})^2$.

28. Let the length, breadth and height of the box be l, b and h respectively. Then,

Volume $= lbh = \sqrt{(lbh)^2} = \sqrt{lb \times bh \times lh} = \sqrt{120 \times 72 \times 60} = 720\ cm^3$.

29. Let $lb = 2x$, $bh = 3x$ and $lh = 4x$.

Then, $24x^3 = (lbh)^2 = 9000 \times 9000 \Rightarrow x^3 = 375 \times 9000 \Rightarrow x = 150$.

So, $lb = 300$, $bh = 450$, $lh = 600$ and $lbh = 9000$.

$\therefore$ $h = \frac{9000}{300} = 30$, $l = \frac{9000}{450} = 20$ and $b = \frac{9000}{600} = 15$.

Hence, shortest side = 15 cm.

30. Edge of the cube $= \left(\frac{20}{4}\right)$ cm = 5 cm.

$\therefore$ Volume $= (5 \times 5 \times 5)\ cm^3 = 125\ cm^3$.

31. Surface area $= \left[6 \times \left(\frac{1}{2}\right)^2\right] cm^2 = \frac{3}{2}\ cm^2$.

32. Surface area of the cube $= (6 \times 8^2)$ sq. ft. = 384 sq. ft.

Quantity of paint required $= \left(\frac{384}{16}\right)$ kg = 24 kg.

$\therefore$ Cost of painting = Rs. (36.50 × 24) = Rs. 876.

33. Volume of the cube $= (270 \times 100 \times 64)\ cm^3$.

Edge of the cube $= \sqrt[3]{270 \times 100 \times 64}$ cm $= (3 \times 10 \times 4)$ cm = 120 cm.

$\therefore$ Surface area $= (6 \times 120 \times 120)\ cm^2 = 86400\ cm^2$.

34. Surface area $= \left(\frac{34398}{13}\right) = 2646 \text{ cm}^2$.

$\therefore$ $6a^2 = 2646 \Rightarrow a^2 = 441 \Rightarrow a = 21$.

So, Volume $= (21 \times 21 \times 21) \text{ cm}^3 = 9261 \text{ cm}^3$.

35. $a^3 = 729 \Rightarrow a = 9$.

$\therefore$ Surface area $= (6 \times 9 \times 9) \text{ cm}^2 = 486 \text{ cm}^2$.

36. Required length = Diagonal $= \sqrt{3}\, a = (\sqrt{3} \times \sqrt{3})$ m = 3 m.

37. $\sqrt{3}\, a = 4\sqrt{3} \Rightarrow a = 4$.

$\therefore$ Volume $= (4 \times 4 \times 4) \text{ cm}^3 = 64 \text{ cm}^3$.

38. $6a^2 = 600 \Rightarrow a^2 = 100 \Rightarrow a = 10$.

$\therefore$ Diagonal $= \sqrt{3}\, a = 10\sqrt{3}$ cm.

39. $a^3 = 6a^2 \Rightarrow a = 6$.

40. Number of cubes $= \left(\frac{100 \times 100 \times 100}{10 \times 10 \times 10}\right) = 1000$.

41. Number of blocks $= \left(\frac{160 \times 100 \times 60}{20 \times 20 \times 20}\right) = 120$.

42. Number of cubes $= \left(\frac{18 \times 18 \times 18}{3 \times 3 \times 3}\right) = 216$.

43. Volume of block $= (6 \times 9 \times 12) \text{ cm}^3 = 648 \text{ cm}^3$.

Side of largest cube = H.C.F. of 6 cm, 9 cm, 12 cm = 3 cm.

Volume of this cube $= (3 \times 3 \times 3) = 27 \text{ cm}^3$.

$\therefore$ Number of cubes $= \left(\frac{648}{27}\right) = 24$.

44. Side of smallest cube = L.C.M. of 5 cm, 10 cm, 20 cm = 20 cm.

Volume of the cube $= (20 \times 20 \times 20) \text{ cm}^3 = 8000 \text{ cm}^3$.

Volume of the block $= (5 \times 10 \times 20) \text{ cm}^3 = 1000 \text{ cm}^3$.

$\therefore$ Number of blocks $= \left(\frac{8000}{1000}\right) = 8$.

45. Let the sides of the sheet be x and $5x$. Then,

Volume of the sheet = Volume of the cube

$\Rightarrow x \times 5x \times \frac{1}{2} = 10 \times 10 \times 10 \Rightarrow 5x^2 = 2000 \Rightarrow x^2 = 400 \Rightarrow x = 20$.

$\therefore$ The sides are 20 cm and 100 cm.

46. Volume of the new cube $= (6^3 + 8^3 + 10^3) \text{ cm}^3 = 1728 \text{ cm}^3$.

Let the edge of the new cube be a cm.

$\therefore$ $a^3 = 1728 \Rightarrow a = 12$.

47. The new solid formed is a cuboid of length 25 cm, breadth 5 cm and height 5 cm.

$\therefore$ Volume $= (25 \times 5 \times 5) \text{ cm}^3 = 625 \text{ cm}^3$.

48. Required ratio $= \frac{6 \times 1 \times 1}{6 \times 5 \times 5} = \frac{1}{25} = 1:25$.

49. Volume of the large cube $= (3^3 + 4^3 + 5^3) \text{ cm}^3 = 216 \text{ cm}^3$.

Let the edge of the large cube be a.

So, $a^3 = 216 \Rightarrow a = 6$ cm.

$\therefore$ Required ratio $= \frac{6 \times (3^2 + 4^2 + 5^2)}{6 \times 6^2} = \frac{50}{36} = 25:18$.

50. Let the sides of the three cubes be $3x$, $4x$ and $5x$.

Then, Volume of the new cube $= [(3x)^3 + (4x)^3 + (5x)^3] = 216x^3$.

Edge of the new cube $= (216x^3)^{1/3} = 6x$.

Diagonal of the new cube $= 6\sqrt{3}\,x$.

$\therefore \quad 6\sqrt{3}\,x = 12\sqrt{3} \Rightarrow x = 2$.

So, the sides of the cubes are 6 cm, 8 cm and 10 cm.

51. Let their edges be a and b. Then,

$$\frac{a^3}{b^3} = \frac{27}{1} \Leftrightarrow \left(\frac{a}{b}\right)^3 = \left(\frac{3}{1}\right)^3 \Leftrightarrow \frac{a}{b} = \frac{3}{1} \Leftrightarrow a : b = 3 : 1.$$

52. Let their edges be a and b. Then,

$$\frac{a^3}{b^3} = \frac{8}{27} \Leftrightarrow \left(\frac{a}{b}\right)^3 = \left(\frac{2}{3}\right)^3 \Leftrightarrow \frac{a}{b} = \frac{2}{3} \Leftrightarrow \frac{a^2}{b^2} = \frac{4}{9} \Leftrightarrow \frac{6a^2}{6b^2} = \frac{4}{9}.$$

53. Let their edges be a and b. Then,

$$\frac{a^3}{b^3} = \frac{1}{27} \Leftrightarrow \left(\frac{a}{b}\right)^3 = \left(\frac{1}{3}\right)^3 \Leftrightarrow \frac{a}{b} = \frac{1}{3} \Leftrightarrow \frac{a^2}{b^2} = \frac{1}{9}.$$

54. Let original edge $= a$. Then, volume $= a^3$.

New edge $= 2a$. So, new volume $= (2a)^3 = 8a^3$.

$\therefore$ Volume becomes 8 times.

55. Let original edge $= a$. Then, surface area $= 6a^2$.

New edge $= \frac{125}{100}a = \frac{5a}{4}$.

New surface area $= 6 \times \left(\frac{5a}{4}\right)^2 = \frac{75a^2}{8}$.

Increase in surface area $= \left(\frac{75a^2}{8} - 6a^2\right) = \frac{27a^2}{8}$.

$\therefore$ Increase % $= \left(\frac{27a^2}{8} \times \frac{1}{6a^2} \times 100\right)\% = 56.25\%$.

56. Volume $= \pi r^2 h = \left(\frac{22}{7} \times 1 \times 1 \times 14\right)\ \text{m}^3 = 44\ \text{m}^3$.

57. Volume of the tank $= 246.4$ litres $= 246400\ \text{cm}^3$.

Let the radius of the base be r cm. Then,

$$\left(\frac{22}{7} \times r^2 \times 400\right) = 246400 \Leftrightarrow r^2 = \left(\frac{246400 \times 7}{22 \times 400}\right) = 196 \Leftrightarrow r = 14.$$

$\therefore$ Diameter of the base $= 2r = 28$ cm.

58. $2\pi r = 66 \Rightarrow r = \left(66 \times \frac{1}{2} \times \frac{7}{22}\right) = \frac{21}{2}$ cm.

$\frac{2\pi rh}{2\pi r} = \left(\frac{2640}{66}\right) \Rightarrow h = 40$ cm.

$\therefore$ Volume $= \left(\frac{22}{7} \times \frac{21}{2} \times \frac{21}{2} \times 40\right)\ \text{cm}^3 = 13860\ \text{cm}^3$.

59. Let the radius and height be r cm each.

Then, $\frac{22}{7} \times r^2 \times r = \frac{176}{7} \Rightarrow r^3 = \left(\frac{176}{7} \times \frac{7}{22}\right) = 8 \Rightarrow r = 2.$

60. $\frac{2\pi rh}{h} = \frac{704}{14} \Rightarrow 2\pi r = \frac{704}{14}.$

$\therefore \quad r = \left(\frac{704}{14} \times \frac{1}{2} \times \frac{7}{22}\right) = 8$ cm.

$\therefore \quad$ Volume $= \left(\frac{22}{7} \times 8 \times 8 \times 14\right)$ cm^3 $= 2816$ cm^3.

61. Total surface area $= 2\pi r(h + r) = \left[2 \times \frac{22}{7} \times \frac{35}{100} \times (1.25 + 0.35)\right]$ m^2

$= \left(2 \times \frac{22}{7} \times \frac{35}{100} \times \frac{16}{10}\right)$ m^2 $= 3.52$ m^2.

$\therefore \quad$ Cost of the material = Rs. (3.52 × 80) = Rs. 281.60.

62. Curved surface area $= 2\pi rh = (\pi r^2 h) \cdot \frac{2}{r} = \left(\text{Volume} \times \frac{2}{r}\right).$

63. $\frac{\text{Total surface area}}{\text{Lateral surface area}} = \frac{2\pi rh + 2\pi r^2}{2\pi rh} = \frac{(h + r)}{h} = \frac{80}{60} = \frac{4}{3}.$

64. Difference in capacities $= \left(8 \times 8 \times 14 - \frac{22}{7} \times 4 \times 4 \times 14\right)$ cm^3 $= 192$ cm^3.

65. Let radius $= 2x$ and height $= 3x$. Then,

$\frac{22}{7} \times (2x)^2 \times 3x = 12936 \Leftrightarrow x^3 = \left(12936 \times \frac{7}{22} \times \frac{1}{12}\right) = 343 = 7^3$

$\therefore \quad x = 7$. So, radius = 14 cm and height = 21 cm.

$\therefore \quad$ Total surface area $= 2 \times \frac{22}{7} \times 14 \times (21 + 14) = \left(2 \times \frac{22}{7} \times 14 \times 35\right)$ cm^2 $= 3080$ cm^2.

66. It is given that $r = \frac{1}{2}h$ and $2\pi rh + \pi r^2 = 616$ m^2

$\therefore \quad 2\pi \times \frac{1}{2} h \times h + \pi \times \frac{1}{4} h^2 = 616$

$\Rightarrow \quad \frac{5}{4} \times \frac{22}{7} \times h^2 = 616 \Rightarrow h^2 = \left(616 \times \frac{28}{110}\right) = \frac{28 \times 28}{5}.$

$\therefore \quad$ Volume $= \pi r^2 h = \frac{22}{7} \times \frac{1}{4} h^2 \times h = \frac{22}{7} \times \frac{1}{4} \times \frac{28 \times 28}{5} \times \frac{28}{\sqrt{5}}$ cm^3

$= \left(\frac{22 \times 28 \times 28}{25} \times \sqrt{5}\right)$ cm^3 $= \left(\frac{22 \times 28 \times 28 \times 2.23}{25 \times 1000}\right)$ litres = 1.53 litre.

67. $(h + r) = 37$ and $2\pi r(h + r) = 1628$.

$\therefore \quad 2\pi r \times 37 = 1628$ or $r = \left(\frac{1628}{2 \times 37} \times \frac{7}{22}\right) = 7.$

So, $r = 7$ m and $h = 30$ m.

$\therefore \quad$ Volume $= \left(\frac{22}{7} \times 7 \times 7 \times 30\right)$ m^3 $= 4620$ m^3.

68. $\dfrac{\pi r^2 h}{2\pi rh} = \dfrac{924}{264} \Rightarrow r = \left(\dfrac{924}{264} \times 2\right) = 7$ m.

And, $2\pi rh = 264 \Rightarrow h = \left(264 \times \dfrac{7}{22} \times \dfrac{1}{2} \times \dfrac{1}{7}\right) = 6$ m.

$\therefore$ Required ratio $= \dfrac{2r}{h} = \dfrac{14}{6} = 7:3$.

69. $V = \pi r^2 h$ and $S = 2\pi rh + 2\pi r^2$

$\Rightarrow S = 2\pi r(h + r)$, where $h = \dfrac{V}{\pi r^2}$

$\Rightarrow S = 2\pi r\left(\dfrac{V}{\pi r^2} + r\right) = \dfrac{2V}{r} + 2\pi r^2 \Rightarrow \dfrac{dS}{dr} = \dfrac{-2V}{r^2} + 4\pi r$ and $\dfrac{d^2S}{dr^2} = \left(\dfrac{4V}{r^3} + 4\pi\right) > 0$

$\therefore$ S is minimum when $\dfrac{dS}{dr} = 0$

$\Leftrightarrow \dfrac{-2V}{r^2} + 4\pi r = 0 \Leftrightarrow V = 2\pi r^3 \Leftrightarrow \pi r^2 h = 2\pi r^3 \Leftrightarrow h = 2r$.

70. Let original radius = R. Then, new radius $= \dfrac{R}{2}$.

$$\frac{\text{Volume of reduced cylinder}}{\text{Volume of original cylinder}} = \frac{\pi \times \left(\frac{R}{2}\right)^2 \times h}{\pi \times R^2 \times h} = \frac{1}{4}.$$

71. Let their radii be $2x$, $3x$ and heights be $5y$, $3y$.

Ratio of their volumes $= \dfrac{\pi \times (2x)^2 \times 5y}{\pi \times (3x)^2 \times 3y} = \dfrac{20}{27}$.

72. Let their heights be h and $2h$ and radii be r and R respectively. Then,

$\pi r^2 h = \pi R^2 (2h) \Rightarrow \dfrac{r^2}{R^2} = \dfrac{2h}{h} = \dfrac{2}{1} \Rightarrow \dfrac{r}{R} = \dfrac{\sqrt{2}}{1}$ *i.e.* $\sqrt{2}:1$.

73. Let the height of X and Y be h, and their radii be r and $2r$ respectively. Then,
Volume of X $= \pi r^2 h$ and Volume of Y $= \pi (2r)^2 h = 4\pi r^2 h$.

New height of X $= 2h$.

So, new volume of X $= \pi r^2 (2h) = 2\pi r^2 h = \dfrac{1}{2}(4\pi r^2 h) = \dfrac{1}{2} \times$ (Volume of Y).

74. Let original radius $= r$ and original length $= h$.

New radius $= \dfrac{r}{3}$ and let new length = H.

Then, $\pi r^2 h = \pi\left(\dfrac{r}{3}\right)^2 \times H$ or $H = 9h$.

75. Let the drop in the water level be h cm. Then,

$\dfrac{22}{7} \times \dfrac{35}{2} \times \dfrac{35}{2} \times h = 11000 \Leftrightarrow h = \left(\dfrac{11000 \times 7 \times 4}{22 \times 35 \times 35}\right)$ cm $= \dfrac{80}{7}$ cm $= 11\dfrac{3}{7}$ cm.

76. Volume of earth dug out $= \left(\frac{22}{7} \times 7 \times 7 \times 10\right) m^3 = 1540\ m^3$.

Area of embankment $= \frac{22}{7} \times \left[(28)^2 - (7)^2\right] = \left(\frac{22}{7} \times 35 \times 21\right) m^2 = 2310\ m^2$.

Height of embankment $= \left(\frac{\text{Volume}}{\text{Area}}\right) = \left(\frac{1540}{2310}\right) m = \frac{2}{3}\ m$.

77. Volume of water flown in 1 sec. $= \left(\frac{22}{7} \times \frac{7}{2} \times \frac{7}{2} \times 200\right) cm^3 = 7700\ cm^3$.

Volume of water flown in 10 min. $= (7700 \times 60 \times 10)\ cm^3$

$= \left(\frac{7700 \times 60 \times 10}{1000}\right)$ litres $= 4620$ litres.

78. Volume of one coin $= \left(\frac{22}{7} \times \frac{75}{100} \times \frac{75}{100} \times \frac{2}{10}\right) cm^3 = \frac{99}{280}\ cm^3$.

Volume of larger cylinder $= \left(\frac{22}{7} \times 3 \times 3 \times 8\right) cm^3$.

$\therefore$ Number of coins $= \left(\frac{22 \times 9 \times 8}{7} \times \frac{280}{99}\right) = 640$.

79. Let the radius of the vessel be R. Then,

$\pi R^2 \times 15 = \pi \times (15)^2 \times 35 + \pi \times (10)^2 \times 15$

$\Leftrightarrow \pi R^2 \times 15 = 9375\pi \Leftrightarrow R^2 = 625 \Leftrightarrow R = 25$ cm.

80. Let the length of the wire be h.

Radius $= \frac{1}{2}$ mm $= \frac{1}{20}$ cm. Then,

$\frac{22}{7} \times \frac{1}{20} \times \frac{1}{20} \times h = 66 \Leftrightarrow h = \left(\frac{66 \times 20 \times 20 \times 7}{22}\right) = 8400$ cm $= 84$ m.

81. Circumference of the girth = 440 cm.

$\therefore$ $2\pi R = 440 \Rightarrow R = \left(440 \times \frac{1}{2} \times \frac{7}{22}\right) = 70$ cm.

So, Outer radius = 70 cm. Inner radius = (70 – 4) cm = 66 cm.

Volume of iron $= \pi\ [(70)^2 - (66)^2] \times 63 = \left(\frac{22}{7} \times 136 \times 4 \times 63\right) cm^3 = 58752\ cm^3$.

82. Internal radius $= \left(\frac{11.2}{2}\right)$ cm $= 5.6$ cm, External radius $= (5.6 + 0.4)$ cm $= 6$ cm.

Volume of metal $= \left\{\frac{22}{7} \times [(6)^2 - (5.6)^2] \times 21\right\} cm^3 = (66 \times 11.6 \times 0.4)\ cm^3 = 306.24\ cm^3$.

83. External radius = 6 cm, Internal radius = (6 – 0.25) cm = 5.75 cm.

Volume of material in hollow cylinder

$= \left\{\frac{22}{7} \times [(6)^2 - (5.75)^2] \times 15\right\} cm^3 = \left(\frac{22}{7} \times 11.75 \times 0.25 \times 15\right) cm^3$

$= \left(\frac{22}{7} \times \frac{1175}{100} \times \frac{25}{100} \times 15\right) cm^3 = \left(\frac{11 \times 705}{56}\right) cm^3$.

Let the length of solid cylinder be h. Then,

$\frac{22}{7} \times 1 \times 1 \times h = \left(\frac{11 \times 705}{56}\right) \Leftrightarrow h = \left(\frac{11 \times 705}{56} \times \frac{7}{22}\right)$ cm $= 44.0625$ cm.

84. External radius = 4 cm, Internal radius = 3 cm.

Volume of iron = $\left\{\frac{22}{7} \times [(4)^2 - (3)^2] \times 21\right\}$ cm^3 = $\left(\frac{22}{7} \times 7 \times 1 \times 21\right)$ cm^3 = 462 cm^3.

$\therefore$ Weight of iron = (462 × 8) gm = 3696 gm = 3.696 kg.

85. Let the internal radius of the cylinder be x. Then,

$\frac{22}{7} \times r^2 \times 40 = \frac{616}{10} \Leftrightarrow r^2 = \left(\frac{616 \times 7}{10 \times 22 \times 40}\right) = 0.49 \Leftrightarrow r = 0.7.$

So, internal radius = 0.7 cm = 7 mm.

$\therefore$ Thickness = (8 − 7) mm = 1 mm.

86. $\frac{\text{Volume of cone}}{\text{Volume of cylinder}} = \frac{\frac{1}{3} \times \pi \times (3)^2 \times 5}{\pi \times (2)^2 \times 4} = \frac{45}{48} = \frac{15}{16}.$

87. h = 15 cm, r = 8 cm. So, $l = \sqrt{r^2 + h^2} = \sqrt{8^2 + (15)^2}$ = 17 cm.

$\therefore$ Curved surface area = πrl = (π × 8 × 17) cm^2 = 136π cm^2.

88. h = 14 cm, r = 7 cm. So, $l = \sqrt{(7)^2 + (14)^2} = \sqrt{245} = 7\sqrt{5}$ cm.

$\therefore$ Total surface area = $\pi rl + \pi r^2$ = $\left(\frac{22}{7} \times 7 \times 7\sqrt{5} + \frac{22}{7} \times 7 \times 7\right)$ cm^2

= [154 ($\sqrt{5}$ + 1)] cm^2 = (154 × 3.236) cm^2 = 498.35 cm^2.

89. Clearly, we have r = 3 cm and h = 4 cm.

$\therefore$ Volume = $\frac{1}{3}\pi r^2 h = \left(\frac{1}{3} \times \pi \times 3^2 \times 4\right)$ cm^3 = 12π cm^3.

90. l = 10 m, h = 8 m. So, $r = \sqrt{l^2 - h^2} = \sqrt{(10)^2 - 8^2}$ = 6 m.

$\therefore$ Curved surface area = πrl = (π × 6 × 10) m^2 = 60π m^2.

91. $\frac{1}{3} \times \frac{22}{7} \times r^2 \times 24 = 1232 \Leftrightarrow r^2 = \left(\frac{1232 \times 7 \times 3}{22 \times 24}\right) = 49 \Leftrightarrow r = 7.$

Now, r = 7 cm, h = 24 cm. So, $l = \sqrt{(7)^2 + (24)^2}$ = 25 cm.

$\therefore$ Curved surface area = $\left(\frac{22}{7} \times 7 \times 25\right)$ cm^2 = 550 cm^2.

92. Let the radius of the base be r km. Then,

$\pi r^2 = 1.54 \Rightarrow r^2 = \left(\frac{1.54 \times 7}{22}\right) = 0.49 \Rightarrow r = 0.7$ km.

Now, l = 2.5 km, r = 0.7 km.

$\therefore$ $h = \sqrt{(2.5)^2 - (0.7)^2}$ km = $\sqrt{6.25 - 0.49}$ km = $\sqrt{5.76}$ km = 2.4 km.

So, height of the mountain = 2.4 km.

93. $\pi r^2 = 3850 \Rightarrow r^2 = \left(\frac{3850 \times 7}{22}\right) = 1225 \Rightarrow r = 35.$

Now, r = 35 cm, h = 84 cm.

So, $l = \sqrt{(35)^2 + (84)^2} = \sqrt{1225 + 7056} = \sqrt{8281}$ = 91 cm.

$\therefore$ Curved surface area = $\left(\frac{22}{7} \times 35 \times 91\right)$ cm^2 = 10010 cm^2.

94. $\frac{22}{7} \times 70 \times l = 40040 \Rightarrow l = \left(\frac{40040 \times 7}{22 \times 70}\right) = 182.$

Now, $l = 182$ cm, $r = 70$ cm.

So, $h = \sqrt{(182)^2 - (70)^2} = \sqrt{252 \times 112} = 168$ cm.

$\therefore$ Volume $= \left(\frac{1}{3} \times \frac{22}{7} \times 70 \times 70 \times 168\right) \text{cm}^3 = 862400 \text{ cm}^3.$

95. Let the radius and the height of the cone be $3x$ and $4x$ respectively. Then,

$\frac{1}{3} \times \pi \times (3x)^2 \times 4x = 96\pi \Leftrightarrow 36x^3 = (96 \times 3) \Leftrightarrow x^3 = \left(\frac{96 \times 3}{36}\right) = 8 \Leftrightarrow x = 2.$

$\therefore$ Radius $= 6$ cm, Height $= 8$ cm.

Slant height $= \sqrt{6^2 + 8^2}$ cm $= \sqrt{100}$ cm $= 10$ cm.

96. $\pi r^2 = 346.5 \Rightarrow r^2 = \left(346.5 \times \frac{7}{22}\right) = \frac{441}{4} \Rightarrow r = \frac{21}{2}.$

$\therefore l = \sqrt{r^2 + h^2} = \sqrt{\frac{441}{4} + (14)^2} = \sqrt{\frac{1225}{4}} = \frac{35}{2}.$

So, area of canvas needed $= \pi r l = \left(\frac{22}{7} \times \frac{21}{2} \times \frac{35}{2}\right) \text{m}^2 = \left(\frac{33 \times 35}{2}\right) \text{m}^2.$

$\therefore$ Length of canvas $= \left(\frac{33 \times 35}{2 \times 1.1}\right)$ m $= 525$ m.

97. Let the original radius and height of the cone be r and h respectively.
Then, new radius $= 2r$. New height $= 2h$.

$$\therefore \frac{\text{New Volume}}{\text{Original Volume}} = \frac{\frac{1}{3} \times \pi \times (2r)^2 \times 2h}{\frac{1}{3} \times \pi \times r^2 \times h} = \frac{8}{1}.$$

98. Let the original radius and height of the cone be r and h respectively.

Then, Original volume $= \frac{1}{3}\pi r^2 h.$

New radius $= \frac{120}{100} r = \frac{6}{5} r$, New height $= \frac{6}{5} h.$

New volume $= \frac{1}{3} \pi \times \left(\frac{6}{5} r\right)^2 \times \left(\frac{6}{5} h\right) = \frac{216}{125} \times \frac{1}{3} \pi r^2 h.$

Increase in volume $= \frac{91}{125} \times \frac{1}{3} \pi r^2 h.$

$$\therefore \text{Increase } \% = \left(\frac{\frac{91}{125} \times \frac{1}{3} \pi r^2 h}{\frac{1}{3} \pi r^2 h} \times 100\right) \% = 72.8\%.$$

99. Let the original radius and height of the cone be r and h respectively.

Then, original volume $= \frac{1}{3} \pi r^2 h.$

New radius $= \frac{r}{2}$ and new height $= 3h.$

$$\text{New volume} = \frac{1}{3} \times \pi \times \left(\frac{r}{2}\right)^2 \times 3h = \frac{3}{4} \times \frac{1}{3} \pi r^2 h.$$

$$\therefore \quad \text{Decrease } \% = \left(\frac{\frac{1}{4} \times \frac{1}{3} \pi r^2 h}{\frac{1}{3} \pi r^2 h} \times 100 \right) \% = 25\%.$$

100. $\text{Required ratio} = \dfrac{\frac{1}{3} \pi r^2 h}{\frac{1}{3} \pi r^2 \times (2h)} = \dfrac{1}{2}.$

101. Let their heights be x, $3x$ and their radii be $3y$, y.

$$\text{Then, Ratio of volumes} = \frac{\frac{1}{3} \times \pi \times (3y)^2 \times x}{\frac{1}{3} \times \pi \times y^2 \times (3x)} = \frac{9}{3} = 3 : 1.$$

102. Let their radii be $2x$, x and their heights be h and H respectively. Then,

$$\frac{1}{3} \times \pi \times (2x)^2 \times h = \frac{1}{3} \times \pi \times x^2 \times H \text{ or } \frac{h}{H} = \frac{1}{4}.$$

103. Let their radii be $4x$ and $5x$, and their heights be h and H respectively. Then,

$$\frac{\frac{1}{3} \times \pi \times (4x)^2 \times h}{\frac{1}{3} \times \pi \times (5x)^2 \times H} = \frac{1}{4} \text{ or } \frac{h}{H} = \frac{1}{4} \times \frac{25}{16} = \frac{25}{64}.$$

104. Volume of the largest cone

= Volume of the cone with diameter of base 7 cm and height 7 cm

$$= \left(\frac{1}{3} \times \frac{22}{7} \times 3.5 \times 3.5 \times 7 \right) \text{cm}^3 = \left(\frac{269.5}{3} \right) \text{cm}^3 = 89.8 \text{ cm}^3.$$

105. Volume of the block = $(10 \times 5 \times 2)$ cm^3 = 100 cm^3.

$$\text{Volume of the cone carved out} = \left(\frac{1}{3} \times \frac{22}{7} \times 3 \times 3 \times 7 \right) \text{cm}^3 = 66 \text{ cm}^3.$$

$\therefore$ Wood wasted = $(100 - 66)\% = 34\%$.

106. Let their radius and height be $5x$ and $12x$ respectively.

Slant height of the cone, $l = \sqrt{(5x)^2 + (12x)^2} = 13x$.

$$\frac{\text{Total surface area of cylinder}}{\text{Total surface area of cone}} = \frac{2\pi r (h + r)}{\pi r (l + r)} = \frac{2 (h + r)}{(l + r)} = \frac{2 \times (12x + 5x)}{(13x + 5x)} = \frac{34x}{18x} = \frac{17}{9}.$$

107. Let the radius of the cone be r cm.

$$\text{Then, } \frac{1}{3} \pi \times r^2 \times 6 = \pi \times 8 \times 8 \times 2 \iff r^2 = \left(\frac{8 \times 8 \times 2 \times 3}{6} \right) = 64 \iff r = 8 \text{ cm}.$$

108. Let radius of each be r and height of each be h.

$$\text{Then, number of cones needed} = \frac{\text{Volume of cylinder}}{\text{Volume of 1 cone}} = \frac{\pi r^2 h}{\frac{1}{3} \pi r^2 h} = 3.$$

109. Volume of cylinder = $(\pi \times 3 \times 3 \times 5)$ cm^3 = 45π cm^3.

$$\text{Volume of 1 cone} = \left(\frac{1}{3} \pi \times \frac{1}{10} \times \frac{1}{10} \times 1 \right) \text{cm}^3 = \frac{\pi}{300} \text{ cm}^3$$

$$\therefore \quad \text{Number of cones} = \left(45\pi \times \frac{300}{\pi} \right) = 13500.$$

110. Volume flown in conical vessel $= \frac{1}{3}\pi \times (20)^2 \times 24 = 3200\pi$.

Volume flown in 1 min. $= \left(\pi \times \frac{2.5}{10} \times \frac{2.5}{10} \times 1000\right) = 62.5\pi$.

$\therefore$ Time taken $= \left(\frac{3200\pi}{62.5\pi}\right) = 51$ min. 12 sec.

111. Slant height of the cone, $l = \sqrt{(12)^2 + (5)^2} = 13$ cm.

Lateral surface of the solid = Curved surface of cone + Curved surface of cylinder + Surface area of bottom

$= \pi rl + 2\pi rh + \pi r^2$, where h is the height of the cylinder

$= \pi r\,(l + h + r) = \left[\frac{22}{7} \times 12 \times (13 + 18 + 12)\right] \text{cm}^2$

$= \left(\frac{22}{7} \times 12 \times 43\right) \text{cm}^2 = \left(\frac{11352}{7}\right) \text{cm}^2 = 1621\frac{5}{7} \text{cm}^2$.

112. Volume of parallelopiped $= (5 \times 3 \times 4)$ cm^3 = 60 cm^3.

Volume of cube $= (4)^3$ cm^3 = 64 cm^3.

Volume of cylinder $= \left(\frac{22}{7} \times 3 \times 3 \times 3\right) \text{cm}^3 = 84.86 \text{ cm}^3$.

Volume of sphere $= \left(\frac{4}{3} \times \frac{22}{7} \times 3 \times 3 \times 3\right) = 113.14 \text{ cm}^3$.

113. $\frac{4}{3} \times \frac{22}{7} \times R^3 = 4851 \Rightarrow R^3 = \left(4851 \times \frac{3}{4} \times \frac{7}{22}\right) = \left(\frac{21}{2}\right)^3 \Rightarrow R = \frac{21}{2}$.

$\therefore$ Curved surface area $= \left(4 \times \frac{22}{7} \times \frac{21}{2} \times \frac{21}{2}\right) \text{cm}^2 = 1386 \text{ cm}^2$.

114. $4\pi R^2 = 5544 \Rightarrow R^2 = \left(5544 \times \frac{1}{4} \times \frac{7}{22}\right) = 441 \Rightarrow R = 21$.

$\therefore$ Volume $= \left(\frac{4}{3} \times \frac{22}{7} \times 21 \times 21 \times 21\right) \text{cm}^3 = 38808 \text{ cm}^3$.

115. Volume $= \frac{4}{3}\pi r^3 = \frac{r}{3}(4\pi r^2) = \frac{r}{3} \times$ Surface area.

116. $\dfrac{\frac{4}{3}\pi R^3}{4\pi R^2} = 27 \Rightarrow R = 81$ cm.

117. Let the radii of A and B be r and R respectively.

$\therefore$ Required ratio $= \frac{4\pi r^2}{4\pi R^2} = \frac{r^2}{R^2} = \left(\frac{r}{R}\right)^2 = \left(\frac{40}{10}\right)^2 = 16 : 1$.

118. Let the original radius be r.

Then, original surface area $= 4\pi r^2 = 2464$ cm^2 (given).

New radius $= 2r$.

$\therefore$ New surface area $= 4\pi\,(2r)^2 = 4 \times 4\pi r^2 = (4 \times 2464)$ cm^2 = 9856 cm^2.

119. Let the original radius be r. Then, original volume $= \frac{4}{3}\pi r^3$.

New radius $= 2r$.

$\therefore$ New volume $= \frac{4}{3}\pi\,(2r)^3 = 8 \times \frac{4}{3}\pi r^3 = 8 \times$ original volume.

120. $4\pi (r+2)^2 - 4\pi r^2 = 352 \Leftrightarrow (r+2)^2 - r^2 = \left(352 \times \frac{7}{22} \times \frac{1}{4}\right) = 28.$

$\Leftrightarrow (r+2+r)(r+2-r) = 28 \Leftrightarrow 2r + 2 = 14 \Rightarrow r = \left(\frac{14}{2} - 1\right) = 6 \text{ cm}.$

121. Let the correct radius be 100 cm. Then, measured radius = 101.5 cm.

$\therefore$ Error in volume $= \frac{4}{3}\pi [(101.5)^3 - (100)^3] \text{ cm}^3$

$= \frac{4}{3}\pi (1045678.375 - 1000000) \text{ cm}^3 = \left(\frac{4}{3} \times \pi \times 45678.375\right) \text{ cm}^3.$

$\therefore$ Error % $= \left\{\frac{\frac{4}{3}\pi (45678.375)}{\frac{4}{3}\pi (100 \times 100 \times 100)} \times 100\right\}\% = 4.56\% = 4.6\%$ (app.).

122. Let their radii be R and r. Then,

$\frac{\frac{4}{3}\pi R^3}{\frac{4}{3}\pi r^3} = \frac{64}{27} \Rightarrow \left(\frac{R}{r}\right)^3 = \frac{64}{27} = \left(\frac{4}{3}\right)^3 \Rightarrow \frac{R}{r} = \frac{4}{3}.$

Ratio of surface areas $= \frac{4\pi R^2}{4\pi r^2} = \left(\frac{R}{r}\right)^2 = \left(\frac{4}{3}\right)^2 = \frac{16}{9}.$

123. Let their radii be R and r. Then,

$\frac{4\pi R^2}{4\pi r^2} = \frac{4}{25} \Rightarrow \left(\frac{R}{r}\right)^2 = \left(\frac{2}{5}\right)^2 \Rightarrow \frac{R}{r} = \frac{2}{5}.$

$\therefore$ Ratio of volumes $= \frac{\frac{4}{3}\pi R^3}{\frac{4}{3}\pi r^3} = \left(\frac{R}{r}\right)^3 = \left(\frac{2}{5}\right)^3 = \frac{8}{125}.$

124. Volume of new sphere $= \left[\frac{4}{3}\pi \times (6)^3 + \frac{4}{3}\pi \times (8)^3 + \frac{4}{3}\pi \times (10)^3\right] \text{ cm}^3$

$= \left\{\frac{4}{3}\pi [(6)^3 + (8)^3 + (10)^3]\right\} \text{ cm}^3$

$= \left(\frac{4}{3}\pi \times 1728\right) \text{ cm}^3 = \left[\frac{4}{3}\pi \times (12)^3\right] \text{ cm}^3.$

Let the radius of the new sphere be R. Then,

$\frac{4}{3}\pi R^3 = \frac{4}{3}\pi \times (12)^3 \Rightarrow R = 12 \text{ cm}.$

$\therefore$ Diameter = 2R = 24 cm.

125. Volume of bigger sphere $= \left[\frac{4}{3}\pi \times (8)^3\right] \text{ cm}^3 = \left(\frac{4}{3}\pi \times 512\right) \text{ cm}^3.$

Volume of 1 ball $= \left[\frac{4}{3}\pi \times (2)^3\right] \text{ cm}^3 = \left(\frac{4}{3}\pi \times 8\right) \text{ cm}^3.$

$\therefore$ Number of balls $= \left(\frac{\frac{4}{3}\pi \times 512}{\frac{4}{3}\pi \times 8}\right) = \frac{512}{8} = 64.$

126. Let the radius of the third ball be R cm. Then,

$$\frac{4}{3}\pi \times \left(\frac{3}{4}\right)^3 + \frac{4}{3}\pi \times (1)^3 + \frac{4}{3}\pi \times R^3 = \frac{4}{3}\pi \times \left(\frac{3}{2}\right)^3$$

$$\Rightarrow \frac{27}{64} + 1 + R^3 = \frac{27}{8} \Rightarrow R^3 = \frac{125}{64} = \left(\frac{5}{4}\right)^3 \Rightarrow R = \frac{5}{4}.$$

$\therefore$ Diameter of the third ball = $2R = \frac{5}{2}$ cm = 2.5 cm.

127. Volume of each ball = $\frac{1}{8} \times \left(\frac{4}{3}\pi \times 10 \times 10 \times 10\right)$ cm^3.

$$\therefore \frac{4}{3}\pi R^3 = \frac{1}{8} \times \frac{4}{3}\pi \times 10 \times 10 \times 10 \Rightarrow R^3 = \left(\frac{10}{2}\right)^3 = 5^3 \Rightarrow R = 5.$$

128. External radius = 3 cm, Internal radius = (3 – 0.5) cm = 2.5 cm.

Volume of the metal = $\left[\frac{4}{3} \times \frac{22}{7} \times \{(3)^3 - (2.5)^3\}\right]$ cm^3

$$= \left(\frac{4}{3} \times \frac{22}{7} \times \frac{91}{8}\right) \text{cm}^3 = \left(\frac{143}{3}\right) \text{cm}^3 = 47\frac{2}{3} \text{ cm}^3.$$

129. Volume of the solid = (49 × 33 × 24) cm^3.
Let the radius of the sphere be r.

Then, $\frac{4}{3}\pi r^3 = (49 \times 33 \times 24) \Leftrightarrow r^3 = \left(\frac{49 \times 33 \times 24 \times 3 \times 7}{4 \times 22}\right) = (21)^3 \Leftrightarrow r = 21.$

130. Number of bullets = $\frac{\text{Volume of the cube}}{\text{Volume of 1 bullet}} = \left(\frac{22 \times 22 \times 22}{\frac{4}{3} \times \frac{22}{7} \times 1 \times 1 \times 1}\right) = 2541.$

131. Volume of each lead shot = $\left[\frac{4}{3}\pi \times \left(\frac{0.3}{2}\right)^3\right]$ cm^3 = $\left(\frac{4}{3} \times \frac{22}{7} \times \frac{27}{8000}\right)$ cm^3 = $\frac{99}{7000}$ cm^3.

$\therefore$ Number of lead shots = $\left(9 \times 11 \times 12 \times \frac{7000}{99}\right) = 84000.$

132. $4\pi R^2 = 6a^2 \Rightarrow \frac{R^2}{a^2} = \frac{3}{2\pi} \Rightarrow \frac{R}{a} = \frac{\sqrt{3}}{\sqrt{2\pi}}.$

$$\frac{\text{Volume of sphere}}{\text{Volume of cube}} = \frac{\frac{4}{3}\pi R^3}{a^3} = \frac{4}{3}\pi \cdot \left(\frac{R}{a}\right)^3 = \frac{4}{3}\pi \cdot \frac{3\sqrt{3}}{2\pi\sqrt{2\pi}} = \frac{2\sqrt{3}}{\sqrt{2\pi}} = \frac{\sqrt{12}}{\sqrt{2\pi}} = \frac{\sqrt{6}}{\sqrt{\pi}}.$$

133. Let the edge of the cube be a. Then, volume of the cube = a^3.
Radius of the sphere = $(a/2)$.

Volume of the sphere = $\frac{4}{3}\pi\left(\frac{a}{2}\right)^3 = \frac{\pi a^3}{6}$

$\therefore$ Required ratio = $a^3 : \frac{\pi a^3}{6} = 6 : \pi.$

134. $4\pi R^2 = 2\pi \times 6 \times 12 \Rightarrow R^2 = \left(\frac{6 \times 12}{2}\right) = 36 \Rightarrow R = 6$ cm.

135. Let the radius of the cylinder be R.

Then, $\pi \times R^2 \times \frac{7}{3} = \frac{4}{3}\pi \times 7 \times 7 \times 7$

$\Rightarrow \quad R^2 = \left(\frac{4 \times 7 \times 7 \times 7}{3} \times \frac{3}{7}\right) = 196 = (14)^2 \Rightarrow R = 14$ cm.

$\therefore$ Diameter = 2R = 28 cm.

136. Required volume = Volume of a sphere of radius 1 cm

$= \left(\frac{4}{3}\pi \times 1 \times 1 \times 1\right) \text{cm}^3 = \frac{4}{3}\pi \text{ cm}^3.$

137. Volume of cylinder $= \pi \times (3)^2 \times 15 = 135\pi \text{ cm}^3$.

Radius of 1 bullet $= \frac{5}{2}$ mm $= \frac{5}{20}$ cm $= \frac{1}{4}$ cm.

Volume of 1 bullet $= \left(\frac{4}{3}\pi \times \frac{1}{4} \times \frac{1}{4} \times \frac{1}{4}\right) \text{cm}^3 = \frac{\pi}{48} \text{ cm}^3.$

$\therefore$ Number of bullets $= \left(135\pi \times \frac{48}{\pi}\right) = 6480.$

138. Let the radius of the cylindrical rod be r.

Then, height of the rod = $8r$ and radius of one ball = $\frac{r}{2}$.

$\therefore$ Number of balls $= \frac{\pi \times r^2 \times 8r}{\frac{4}{3}\pi \times \left(\frac{r}{2}\right)^3} = \left(\frac{8 \times 8 \times 3}{4}\right) = 48.$

139. Let the length of the wire be h.

Then, $\pi \times \frac{3}{20} \times \frac{3}{20} \times h = \frac{4}{3}\pi \times 4 \times 4 \times 4$

$\Leftrightarrow \quad h = \left(\frac{4 \times 4 \times 4 \times 4 \times 20 \times 20}{3 \times 3 \times 3}\right) \text{cm} = \left(\frac{102400}{27}\right) \text{cm} = 3792.5 \text{ cm} = 37.9 \text{ m}.$

140. Let the rise in the water level be h cm.

Then, $\pi \times 4 \times 4 \times h = \frac{4}{3}\pi \times 3 \times 3 \times 3 \Rightarrow h = \left(\frac{3 \times 3}{4}\right) = \frac{9}{4}$ cm.

141. Let the radius of each sphere be r cm.

Then, Volume of 12 spheres = Volume of cylinder

$\Rightarrow \quad 12 \times \frac{4}{3}\pi \times r^3 = \pi \times 8 \times 8 \times 2 \Rightarrow r^3 = \left(\frac{8 \times 8 \times 2 \times 3}{12 \times 4}\right) = 8 \Rightarrow r = 2$ cm.

$\therefore$ Diameter of each sphere = $2r$ = 4 cm.

142. Let the radius of the ball be r cm.

Volume of ball = Volume of water displaced by it

$\therefore \quad \frac{4}{3}\pi r^3 = \pi \times 12 \times 12 \times 6.75 \Rightarrow r^3 = 9 \times 9 \times 9 \Rightarrow r = 9$ cm.

143. Let the height of the cone be h cm. Then,

$\frac{1}{3}\pi \times 6 \times 6 \times h = \frac{4}{3}\pi \times 3 \times 3 \times 3 \Rightarrow h = \left(\frac{36 \times 3}{36}\right) = 3$ cm.

144. Volume of sphere = $\left(\frac{4}{3}\pi \times 9 \times 9 \times 9\right)$ cm^3.

Volume of cone = $\left(\frac{1}{3}\pi \times 9 \times 9 \times 9\right)$ cm^3.

Volume of wood wasted = $\left[\left(\frac{4}{3}\pi \times 9 \times 9 \times 9\right) - \left(\frac{1}{3}\pi \times 9 \times 9 \times 9\right)\right]$ cm^3
= $(\pi \times 9 \times 9 \times 9)$ cm^3.

$\therefore$ Required percentage = $\left(\frac{\pi \times 9 \times 9 \times 9}{\frac{4}{3}\pi \times 9 \times 9 \times 9} \times 100\right)\%$ = $\left(\frac{3}{4} \times 100\right)\%$ = 75%.

145. Number of spheres = $\frac{\text{Volume of cone}}{\text{Volume of 1 sphere}} = \frac{\frac{1}{3}\pi \times 12 \times 12 \times 24}{\frac{4}{3}\pi \times 2 \times 2 \times 2} = 108.$

146. Volume of material in the sphere = $\left[\frac{4}{3}\pi \times \{(4)^3 - (2)^3\}\right]$ cm^3 = $\left(\frac{4}{3}\pi \times 56\right)$ cm^3.

Let the height of the cone be h cm.

Then, $\frac{1}{3}\pi \times 4 \times 4 \times h = \left(\frac{4}{3}\pi \times 56\right) \Leftrightarrow h = \left(\frac{4 \times 56}{4 \times 4}\right) = 14$ cm.

147. Let radius = R and height = H. Then,

Ratio of their volumes = $\pi R^2 H : \frac{1}{3}\pi R^2 H : \frac{4}{3}\pi R^3 = H : \frac{1}{3}H : \frac{4}{3}R$

$= H : \frac{1}{3}H : \frac{4}{3} \times \frac{H}{2}$ $\left[\text{In sphere, } H = 2R \text{ or } R = \frac{H}{2}\right]$

= 3 : 1 : 2.

148. Total surface area = $3\pi R^2 = \left(3 \times \frac{22}{7} \times 7 \times 7\right)$ cm^2 = 462 cm^2.

149. Let the radius be R cm. Then,

$\frac{2}{3} \times \frac{22}{7} \times R^3 = 19404 \Leftrightarrow R^3 = \left(19404 \times \frac{21}{44}\right) = (21)^3 \Leftrightarrow R = 21$ cm.

150. Let their radii be R and r. Then,

$\frac{\frac{2}{3}\pi R^3}{\frac{2}{3}\pi r^3} = \frac{6.4}{21.6} \Leftrightarrow \left(\frac{R}{r}\right)^3 = \frac{8}{27} = \left(\frac{2}{3}\right)^3 \Leftrightarrow \frac{R}{r} = \frac{2}{3}.$

$\therefore$ Ratio of curved surface areas = $\frac{2\pi R^2}{2\pi r^2} = \left(\frac{R}{r}\right)^2 = \frac{4}{9}.$

151. Let the height of the vessel be x. Then, radius of the bowl = radius of the vessel = $\frac{x}{2}$.

Volume of the bowl, $V_1 = \frac{2}{3}\pi\left(\frac{x}{2}\right)^3 = \frac{1}{12}\pi x^3.$

Volume of the vessel, $V_2 = \pi\left(\frac{x}{2}\right)^2 x = \frac{1}{4}\pi x^3.$

Since $V_2 > V_1$, so the vessel can contain 100% of the beverage filled in the bowl.

152. $\frac{2}{3}\pi R^3 = \frac{1}{3}\pi R^2 H \Rightarrow H = 2R.$

153. Let the radius of the cone be R cm. Then,

$$\frac{1}{3}\pi \times R^2 \times 75 = \frac{2}{3}\pi \times 6 \times 6 \times 6$$

$$\Leftrightarrow R^2 = \left(\frac{2 \times 6 \times 6 \times 6}{75}\right) = \left(\frac{144}{25}\right) = \left(\frac{12}{5}\right)^2 \Leftrightarrow R = \frac{12}{5} \text{ cm} = 2.4 \text{ cm}.$$

154. Let the radius of each be R. Height of hemisphere, H = R.

So, height of cone = height of hemisphere = R.

Slant height of cone = $\sqrt{R^2 + R^2} = \sqrt{2}\,R.$

$$\frac{\text{Curved surface area of hemisphere}}{\text{Curved surface area of cone}} = \frac{2\pi R^2}{\pi R \times \sqrt{2}\,R} = \sqrt{2} : 1.$$

155. Volume of hemisphere = $\frac{2}{3}\pi r^3.$

Volume of biggest sphere = Volume of sphere with diameter $r = \frac{4}{3}\pi\left(\frac{r}{2}\right)^3 = \frac{1}{6}\pi r^3$

$$\therefore \text{ Required ratio} = \frac{\frac{2}{3}\pi r^3}{\frac{1}{6}\pi r^3} = \frac{4}{1} \text{ i.e. } 4:1.$$

EXERCISE 25B

(DATA SUFFICIENCY TYPE QUESTIONS)

Directions (*Questions 1 to 10*) : *Each of the questions given below consists of a statement and/or a question and two statements numbered I and II given below it. You have to decide whether the data provided in the statement(s) is/are sufficient to answer the given question. Read both the statements and*

Give answer (a) if the data in Statement I alone are sufficient to answer the question, while the data in Statement II alone are not sufficient to answer the question;

Give answer (b) if the data in Statement II alone are sufficient to answer the question, while the data in Statement I alone are not sufficient to answer the question;

Give answer (c) if the data either in Statement I or in Statement II alone are sufficient to answer the question;

Give answer (d) if the data even in both Statements I and II together are not sufficient to answer the question;

Give answer (e) if the data in both Statements I and II together are necessary to answer the question.

1. What is the weight of the iron beam ?
   I. The beam is 9 m long, 40 cm wide and 20 cm high.
   II. Iron weighs 50 kg per cubic metre.
2. What is the volume of 32 metre high cylindrical tank ? **(Bank P.O. 2003)**
   I. The area of its base is 154 m^2.
   II. The diameter of the base is 14 m.
3. What is the volume of a cube ? **(Bank P.O. 2003)**
   I. The area of each face of the cube is 64 square metres.
   II. The length of one side of the cube is 8 metres.

4. What is the total cost of painting the inner surface of an open box at the rate of 50 paise per 100 sq. cm ?

   I. The box is made of wood 3 cm thick.

   II. The external dimensions of the box are 50 cm, 40 cm and 23 cm.

5. What is the capacity of a cylindrical tank ? **(I.B.P.S. 2002)**

   I. Radius of the base is half of its height which is 28 metres.

   II. Area of the base is 616 sq. metres and its height is 28 metres.

6. What is the volume of the cylinder ? **(Bank P.O. 2003)**

   I. Height is equal to the diameter.

   II. Perimeter of the base is 352 cm.

7. What will be the total cost of whitewashing the conical tomb at the rate of 80 paise per square metre ?

   I. The diameter and the slant height of the tomb are 28 m and 50 m.

   II. The height of the tomb is 48 m and the area of its base is 616 sq. m.

8. What is the height of a circular cone ? **(Bank P.O. 1999)**

   I. The area of that cone is equal to the area of a rectangle whose length is 33 cm.

   II. The area of the base of that cone is 154 sq. cm.

9. Is a given rectangular block, a cube ? **(M.A.T. 1999)**

   I. At least 2 faces of the rectangular block are squares.

   II. The volume of the block is 64.

10. A spherical ball of given radius *x* cm is melted and made into a right circular cylinder. What is the height of the cylinder ? **(S.B.I.P.O. 2003)**

    I. The volume of the cylinder is equal to the volume of the ball.

    II. The area of the base of the cylinder is given.

Directions (*Questions 11-13*) : ***Each of the questions given below consists of a question followed by three statements. You have to study the question and the statements and decide which of the statement(s) is/are necessary to answer the question.***

11. What is the capacity of the cylindrical tank ? **(R.B.I. 2003)**

    I. The area of the base is 61,600 sq. cm.

    II. The height of the tank is 1.5 times the radius.

    III. The circumference of base is 880 cm.

    (*a*) Only I and II (*b*) Only II and III (*c*) Only I and III

    (*d*) Any two of the three (*e*) Only II and either I or III

12. A solid metallic cone is melted and recast into a sphere. What is the radius of the sphere ?

    I. The radius of the base of the cone is 2.1 cm.

    II. The height of the cone is four times the radius of its base.

    III. The height of the cone is 8.4 cm.

    (*a*) Only I and II (*b*) Only II and III (*c*) Only I and III

    (*d*) Any two of the three (*e*) All I, II and III

13. What is the total surface area of the cone ?

    I. The area of the base of the cone is 154 cm^2.

    II. The curved surface area of the cone is 550 cm^2.

    III. The volume of the cone is 1232 cm^3.

    (*a*) I, and either II or III (*b*) II, and either I or III

    (*c*) III, and either I or II (*d*) Any two of the three

    (*e*) None of these

ANSWERS

1. (*e*)	2. (*c*)	3. (*c*)	4. (*e*)	5. (*c*)	6. (*e*)	7. (*c*)	8. (*d*)
9. (*d*)	10. (*b*)	11. (*e*)	12. (*d*)	13. (*a*)			

SOLUTIONS

1. I gives, $l = 9$ m, $b = \frac{40}{100}$ m $= \frac{2}{5}$ m and $h = \frac{20}{100}$ m $= \frac{1}{5}$ m.

This gives, volume $= (l \times b \times h) = \left(9 \times \frac{2}{5} \times \frac{1}{5}\right) m^3 = \frac{18}{25} m^3$.

II gives, weight of iron is 50 kg / m^3.

$\therefore$ Weight $= \left(\frac{18}{25} \times 50\right)$ kg $= 36$ kg.

Thus, both I and II are needed to get the answer.

$\therefore$ Correct answer is (*e*).

2. Given, height = 32 m.

I gives, area of the base = 154 m^2.

$\therefore$ Volume = (area of the base × height) = (154 × 32) m^3 = 4928 m^3.

Thus, I alone gives the answer.

II gives, radius of the base = 7 m.

$\therefore$ Volume $= \pi r^2 h = \left(\frac{22}{7} \times 7 \times 7 \times 32\right) m^3 = 4928 \ m^3$.

Thus, II alone gives the answer

$\therefore$ Correct answer is (*c*).

3. Let each edge be a metres. Then,

I. $a^2 = 64 \Rightarrow a = 8$ m $\Rightarrow$ Volume = (8 × 8 × 8) m^3 = 512 m^3.

Thus, I alone gives the answer.

II. $a = 8$ m $\Rightarrow$ Volume = (8 × 8 × 8) m^3 = 512 m^3.

Thus, II alone gives the answer.

$\therefore$ Correct answer is (*c*).

4. I gives, thickness of the wall of the box = 3 cm.

II gives, Internal length = (50 – 6) cm = 44 cm, Internal breadth = (40 – 6) = 34 cm,

Internal height = (23 – 3) cm = 20 cm.

Area to be painted = (area of 4 walls + area of floor) = $[2(l + b) \times h + (l \times b)]$

= [2 (44 + 34) × 20 + (44 × 34)] cm^2 = 4616 cm^2.

Cost of painting = Rs. $\left(\frac{1}{2 \times 100} \times 4616\right)$ = Rs. 23.08.

Thus, both I and II are needed to get the answer.

$\therefore$ Correct answer is (*e*).

5. I gives, $h = 28$ m and $r = 14$ cm.

$\therefore$ Capacity $= \pi r^2 h$, which can be obtained.

Thus, I alone gives the answer.

II gives, $\pi r^2 = 616 \text{ m}^2$ and $h = 28$ m.

$\therefore$ Capacity $= (\pi r^2 \times h) = (616 \times 28) \text{ m}^3$.

Thus, II alone gives the answer.

$\therefore$ Correct answer is (*c*).

6. I gives, $h = 2r$.

II gives, $2\pi r = 352 \Rightarrow r = \left(\frac{352}{2} \times \frac{7}{22}\right)$ cm = 56 cm.

From I and II, we have $r = 56$ cm, $h = (2 \times 56)$ cm = 112 cm.

Thus, we can find the volume.

$\therefore$ Correct answer is (*e*).

7. I gives, $r = 14$ m, $l = 50$ m.

$\therefore$ Curved surface $= \pi rl = \left(\frac{22}{7} \times 14 \times 50\right) \text{m}^2 = 2200 \text{ m}^2$.

Cost of whitewashing = Rs. $\left(2200 \times \frac{80}{100}\right)$ = Rs. 1760

Thus, I alone gives the answer.

II gives, $h = 48$ m, $\pi r^2 = 616 \text{ m}^2$.

These results give r and h and so l can be found out.

$\therefore$ Curved surface $= \pi rl$.

Thus, II alone gives the answer.

$\therefore$ Correct answer is (*c*).

8. II gives the value of r.

But, in I, the breadth of rectangle is not given.

So, we cannot find the surface area of the cone.

Hence, the height of the cone cannot be determined.

$\therefore$ Correct answer is (*d*).

9. I gives, any two of l, b, h are equal.

II gives, $lbh = 64$.

From I and II, the values of l, b, h may be (1, 1, 64), (2, 2, 16), (4, 4, 4).

Thus, the block may be a cube or cuboid.

$\therefore$ Correct answer is (*d*).

10. Clearly, I is not needed, since it is evident from the given question.

From II, we get radius of the base of the cylinder.

Now, $\frac{4}{3}\pi x^3 = \pi r^2 h$ in which x and r are known.

$\therefore$ h can be determined.

$\therefore$ Correct answer is (*b*).

11. Capacity $= \pi r^2 h$.

I gives, $\pi r^2 = 61600$. This gives r.

II gives, $h = 1.5\,r$.

Thus, I and II give the answer.

Again, III gives $2\pi r = 880$. This gives r.

So, II and III also give the answer.

$\therefore$ Correct answer is (*e*).

12. $\frac{4}{3}\pi R^3 = \frac{1}{3}\pi r^2 h.$

Now r and h can be determined from any two of I, II and III.

Thus, R can be calculated.

$\therefore$ Correct answer is (d).

13. **Total surface area of the cone = $(\pi rl + \pi r^2)$ cm^2.**

I gives, $\pi r^2 = 154$. Thus, we can find r.

II gives, $\pi rl = 550$.

From I and II we get the answer.

III gives, $\frac{1}{3}\pi r^2 h = 1232$.

From I and III, we can find h and therefore, l.

Hence the surface area can be determined.

$\therefore$ Correct answer is (a).

---

26. RACES AND GAMES OF SKILL

IMPORTANT FACTS

Races : *A contest of speed in running, riding, driving, sailing or rowing is called a race.*

Race Course : *The ground or path on which contests are made is called a race course.*

Starting Point : *The point from which a race begins is known as a starting point.*

Winning Point or Goal : *The point set to bound a race is called a winning point or a goal.*

Winner : *The person who first reaches the winning point is called a winner.*

Dead Heat Race : *If all the persons contesting a race reach the goal exactly at the same time, then the race is said to be a dead heat race.*

Start : Suppose A and B are two contestants in a race. If before the start of the race, A is at the starting point and B is ahead of A by 12 metres, then we say that '*A gives B, a start of 12 metres*'

To cover a race of 100 metres in this case, A will have to cover 100 metres while B will have to cover only (100 – 12) = 88 metres.

In a 100 m race, '*A can give B 12 m*' or '*A can give B a start of 12 m*' or '*A beats B by 12 m*' means that while A runs 100 m, B runs (100 – 12) = 88 m.

Games : '*A game of 100, means that the person among the contestants who scores 100 points first is the winner*'.

If A scores 100 points while B scores only 80 points, then we say that '*A can give B 20 points*'.

SOLVED EXAMPLES

Ex. 1. ***In a km race, A beats B by 28 metres or 7 seconds. Find A's time over the course.***

Sol. Clearly, B covers 28 m in 7 seconds.

$\therefore$ B's time over the course = $\left(\frac{7}{28} \times 1000\right)$ sec = 250 seconds.

$\therefore$ A's time over the course = (250 – 7) sec = 243 sec = 4 min. 3 sec.

Ex. 2. ***A runs $1\frac{3}{4}$ times as fast as B. If A gives B a start of 84 m, how far must the winning post be so that A and B might reach it at the same time ?***

Sol. Ratio of the rates of A and B = $\frac{7}{4}$: 1 = 7 : 4.

So, in a race of 7 m, A gains 3 m over B.

$\therefore$ 3 m are gained by A in a race of 7 m

$\therefore$ 84 m are gained by A in a race of $\left(\frac{7}{3} \times 84\right)$ m = 196 m.

$\therefore$ Winning post must be 196 m away from the starting point.

Ex. 3. ***A can run 1 km in 3 min. 10 sec. and B can cover the same distance in 3 min. 20 sec. By what distance can A beat B ?***

Sol. Clearly, A beats B by 10 sec.

Distance covered by B in 10 sec. = $\left(\frac{1000}{200} \times 10\right)$ m = 50 m.

$\therefore$ A beats B by 50 metres.

Ex. 4. ***In a 100 m race, A runs at 8 km per hour. If A gives B a start of 4 m and still beats him by 15 seconds, what is the speed of B ?***

Sol. Time taken by A to cover 100 m = $\left(\frac{60 \times 60}{8000} \times 100\right)$ sec = 45 sec.

$\therefore$ B covers (100 − 4) m = 96 m in (45 + 15) sec = 60 sec.

$\therefore$ B's speed = $\left(\frac{96 \times 60 \times 60}{60 \times 1000}\right)$ km/hr = 5.76 km/hr.

Ex. 5. ***A, B and C are three contestants in a km race. If A can give B a start of 40 m and A can give C a start of 64 m, how many metre's start can B give C ?***

Sol. While A covers 1000 m, B covers (1000 − 40) m = 960 m and C covers (1000 − 64) m or 936 m.

When B covers 960 m, C covers 936 m.

When B covers 1000 m, C covers $\left(\frac{936}{960} \times 1000\right)$ m = 975 m.

$\therefore$ B can give C a start of (1000 − 975) or 25 m.

Ex. 6. ***In a game of 80 points, A can give B 5 points and C 15 points. Then how many points B can give C in a game of 60 ?***

Sol. A : B = 80 : 75, A : C = 80 : 65.

$$\frac{B}{C} = \left(\frac{B}{A} \times \frac{A}{C}\right) = \left(\frac{75}{80} \times \frac{80}{65}\right) = \frac{15}{13} = \frac{60}{52} = 60 : 52.$$

$\therefore$ In a game of 60, B can give C 8 points.

EXERCISE 26

(OBJECTIVE TYPE QUESTIONS)

Directions : ***Mark (✓) against the correct answer :***

1. In a 100 m race, A covers the distance in 36 seconds and B in 45 seconds. In this race A beats B by :
   (*a*) 20 m (*b*) 25 m (*c*) 22.5 m (*d*) 9 m
2. In a 200 metres race A beats B by 35 m or 7 seconds. A's time over the course is :
   (*a*) 40 sec (*b*) 47 sec (*c*) 33 sec (*d*) None of these
3. In a 300 m race A beats B by 22.5 m or 6 seconds. B's time over the course is :
   (*a*) 86 sec (*b*) 80 sec (*c*) 76 sec (*d*) None of these
4. A can run 22.5 m while B runs 25 m. In a kilometre race B beats A by :
   (*a*) 100 m (*b*) $111\frac{1}{9}$ m (*c*) 25 m (*d*) 50 m
5. In a 500 m race, the ratio of the speeds of two contestants A and B is 3 : 4. A has a start of 140 m. Then, A wins by :
   (*a*) 60 m (*b*) 40 m (*c*) 20 m (*d*) 10 m

6. A runs $1\frac{2}{3}$ times as fast as B. If A gives B a start of 80 m, how far must the winning post be so that A and B might reach it at the same time ?
(a) 200 m (b) 300 m (c) 270 m (d) 160 m

7. In a 100 m race, A can beat B by 25 m and B can beat C by 4 m. In the same race, A can beat C by :
(a) 21 m (b) 26 m (c) 28 m (d) 29 m

8. In a 100 m race, A can give B 10 m and C 28 m. In the same race B can give C :
(a) 18 m (b) 20 m (c) 27 m (d) 9 m

9. In a 100 m race, A beats B by 10 m and C by 13 m. In a race of 180 m, B will beat C by :
(a) 5.4 m (b) 4.5 m (c) 5 m (d) 6 m

10. In a race of 200 m, A can beat B by 31 m and C by 18 m. In a race of 350 m, C will beat B by :
(a) 22.75 m (b) 25 m (c) 19.5 m (d) $7\frac{4}{7}$ m

11. A and B take part in a 100 m race. A runs at 5 km per hour. A gives B a start of 8 m and still beats him by 8 seconds. The speed of B is :
(a) 5.15 kmph (b) 4.14 kmph (c) 4.25 kmph (d) 4.4 kmph

12. In a game of 100 points, A can give B 20 points and C 28 points. Then, B can give C :
(a) 8 points (b) 10 points (c) 14 points (d) 40 points

13. At a game of billiards, A can give B 15 points in 60 and A can give C 20 points in 60. How many points can B give C in a game of 90 ?
(a) 30 points (b) 20 points (c) 10 points (d) 12 points

ANSWERS

1. (a)	2. (c)	3. (b)	4. (a)	5. (c)	6. (a)	7. (c)	8. (b)
9. (d)	10. (b)	11. (b)	12. (b)	13. (c)			

SOLUTIONS

1. Distance covered by B in 9 sec. = $\left(\frac{100}{45} \times 9\right)$ m = 20 m.

∴ A beats B by 20 metres.

2. B runs 35 m in 7 sec.

∴ B covers 200 m in $\left(\frac{7}{35} \times 200\right)$ = 40 sec.

B's time over the course = 40 sec.

∴ A's time over the course = (40 − 7) sec = 33 sec.

3. B runs $\frac{45}{2}$ m in 6 sec.

∴ B covers 300 m in $\left(6 \times \frac{2}{45} \times 300\right)$ sec = 80 sec.

4. When B runs 25 m, A runs $\frac{45}{2}$ m.

When B runs 1000 m, A runs $\left(\frac{45}{2} \times \frac{1}{25} \times 1000\right)$ m = 900 m.

$\therefore$ B beats A by 100 m.

5. To reach the winning post A will have to cover a distance of (500 – 140) m, *i.e.*, 360 m.
While A covers 3 m, B covers 4 m.

While A covers 360 m, B covers $\left(\frac{4}{3} \times 360\right)$ m = 480 m.

Thus, when A reaches the winning post, B covers 480 m and therefore remains 20 m behind.

$\therefore$ A wins by 20 m.

6. Ratio of the speeds of A and B = $\frac{5}{3} : 1 = 5 : 3$.

Thus, in a race of 5 m, A gains 2 m over B.
2 m are gained by A in a race of 5 m.

80 m will be gained by A in a race of $\left(\frac{5}{2} \times 80\right)$ m = 200 m.

$\therefore$ Winning post is 200 m away from the starting point.

7. A : B = 100 : 75 and B : C = 100 : 96.

$\therefore$ $A : C = \left(\frac{A}{B} \times \frac{B}{C}\right) = \left(\frac{100}{75} \times \frac{100}{96}\right) = \frac{100}{72} = 100 : 72.$

$\therefore$ A beats C by (100 – 72) m = 28 m.

8. A : B = 100 : 90 and A : C = 100 : 72.

$B : C = \frac{B}{A} \times \frac{A}{C} = \frac{90}{100} \times \frac{100}{72} = \frac{90}{72}.$

When B runs 90 m, C runs 72 m.

When B runs 100 m, C runs $\left(\frac{72}{90} \times 100\right)$ m = 80 m.

$\therefore$ B can give C 20 m.

9. A : B = 100 : 90 and A : C = 100 : 87.

$\frac{B}{C} = \frac{B}{A} \times \frac{A}{C} = \frac{90}{100} \times \frac{100}{87} = \frac{30}{29}.$

When B runs 30 m, C runs 29 m.

When B runs 180 m, C runs $\left(\frac{29}{30} \times 180\right)$ m = 174 m.

$\therefore$ B beats C by (180 – 174) m = 6 m.

10. A : B = 200 : 169 and A : C = 200 : 182.

$\frac{C}{B} = \left(\frac{C}{A} \times \frac{A}{B}\right) = \left(\frac{182}{200} \times \frac{200}{169}\right) = 182 : 169.$

When C covers 182 m, B covers 169 m.

When C covers 350 m, B covers $\left(\frac{169}{182} \times 350\right)$ m = 325 m.

11. A's speed = $\left(5 \times \frac{5}{18}\right)$ m/sec = $\frac{25}{18}$ m/sec.

Time taken by A to cover 100 m = $\left(100 \times \frac{18}{25}\right)$ sec = 72 sec.

$\therefore$ Time taken by B to cover 92 m = (72 + 8) sec = 80 sec.

$\therefore$ B's speed = $\left(\frac{92}{80} \times \frac{18}{5}\right)$ kmph = 4.14 kmph.

12. A : B = 100 : 80 and A : C = 100 : 72.

$\therefore \frac{B}{C} = \left(\frac{B}{A} \times \frac{A}{C}\right) = \left(\frac{80}{100} \times \frac{100}{72}\right) = \frac{10}{9} = \frac{100}{90} = 100 : 90.$

$\therefore$ B can give C 10 points.

13. A : B = 60 : 45 and A : C = 60 : 40.

$\therefore \frac{B}{C} = \left(\frac{B}{A} \times \frac{A}{C}\right) = \left(\frac{45}{60} \times \frac{60}{40}\right) = \frac{45}{40} = \frac{90}{80} = 90 : 80.$

$\therefore$ B can give C 10 points in a game of 90.

---

27. CALENDAR

IMPORTANT FACTS AND FORMULAE

We are supposed to find the day of the week on a given date.

For this, we use the concept of *odd days.*

I. Odd Days : In a given period, the number of days more than the complete weeks are called *odd days.*

II. Leap Year :

(*i*) Every year divisible by 4 is a leap year, if it is not a century.

(*ii*) Every 4th century is a leap year and no other century is a leap year.

Note : A leap year has 366 days.

Examples :

(*i*) Each of the years 1948, 2004, 1676 etc. is a leap year.

(*ii*) Each of the years 400, 800, 1200, 1600, 2000 etc. is a leap year.

(*iii*) None of the years 2001, 2002, 2003, 2005, 1800, 2100 is a leap year.

III. Ordinary Year :

The year which is not a leap year is called an ordinary year. An ordinary year has 365 days.

IV. Counting of Odd Days :

(*i*) 1 ordinary year = 365 days = (52 weeks + 1 day).

$\therefore$ *1 ordinary year has 1 odd day.*

(*ii*) 1 leap year = 366 days = (52 weeks + 2 days).

$\therefore$ *1 leap year has 2 odd days.*

(*iii*) 100 years = 76 ordinary years + 24 leap years

= $(76 \times 1 + 24 \times 2)$ odd days = 124 odd days

= (17 weeks + 5 days) $\equiv$ 5 odd days.

$\therefore$ Number of odd days in 100 years = 5

Number of odd days in 200 years = $(5 \times 2) \equiv 3$ odd days

Number of odd days in 300 years = $(5 \times 3) \equiv 1$ odd day.

Number of odd days in 400 years = $(5 \times 4 + 1) \equiv 0$ odd day.

Similarly, each one of 800 years, 1200 years, 1600 years, 2000 years etc. has 0 odd day.

V. Day of the Week Related to Odd Days:

No. of days	0	1	2	3	4	5	6
Day	Sun.	Mon.	Tues.	Wed.	Thurs.	Fri.	Sat.

SOLVED EXAMPLES

Ex. 1 *What was the day of the week on 16th July, 1776 ?*

Sol. 16th July, 1776 = (1775 years + Period from 1.1.1776 to 16.7.1776)

Counting of odd days :

Number of odd days in 1600 years = 0

Number of odd days in 100 years = 5

75 years = 18 leap years + 57 ordinary years

= $(18 \times 2 + 57 \times 1)$ odd days = 93 odd days

= (13 weeks + 2 days) $\equiv$ 2 odd days

$\therefore$ 1775 years have = (0 + 5 + 2) odd days = 7 odd days $\equiv$ 0 odd day.

Jan.		Feb.		March		April		May		June		July	
(31	+	29	+	31	+	30	+	31	+	30	+	16)	= 198 days

198 days = (28 weeks + 2 days) $\equiv$ 2 odd days.

$\therefore$ Total number of odd days = (0 + 2) = 2.

Hence, the required day is Tuesday.

Ex. 2. ***What was the day of the week on 15th August, 1947 ?***

Sol. 15th August, 1947 = (1946 years + Period from 1.1.1947 to 15.8.1947)

Odd days in 1600 years = 0

Odd days in 300 years = $(5 \times 3) = 15 \equiv 1$

46 years = (11 leap years + 35 ordinary years)

= $(11 \times 2 + 35 \times 1)$ odd days = 57 odd days

= (8 weeks + 1 day) $\equiv$ 1 odd day.

$\therefore$ Odd days in 1946 years = $(0 + 1 + 1) = 2$.

Jan.		Feb.		March		April		May		June		July		Aug.	
(31	+	28	+	31	+	30	+	31	+	30	+	31	+	15)	= 227 days

227 days = (32 weeks + 3 days) $\equiv$ 3 odd days.

Total number of odd days = $(2 + 3) = 5$.

Hence, the required day is Friday.

Ex. 3. ***What was the day of the week on 4th June, 2002 ?***

Sol. 4th June, 2002 = (2001 years + Period from 1.1.2002 to 4.6.2002)

Odd days in 1600 years = 0

Odd days in 400 years = 0

Odd days in 1 ordinary year = 1

Odd days in 2001 years = $(0 + 0 + 1) = 1$

Jan.		Feb.		March		April		May		June	
(31	+	28	+	31	+	30	+	31	+	4)	= 155 days
											= 22 weeks + 1 day $\equiv$ 1 odd day

Total number of odd days = $(1 + 1) = 2$

$\therefore$ Required day is Tuesday.

Ex. 4. ***On what dates of March 2005 did Friday fall ?***

Sol. First we find the day on 1.3.2005

1.3.2005 = (2004 years + Period from 1.1.2005 to 1.3.2005)

Odd days in 1600 years = 0

Odd days in 400 years = 0

4 years = (1 leap year + 3 ordinary years)

= $(1 \times 2 + 3 \times 1)$ odd days = 5 odd days

Jan.		Feb.		March	
(31	+	28	+	1)	= 60 days = (8 weeks + 4 days) $\equiv$ 4 odd days.

Total number of odd days = $(0 + 0 + 5 + 4) = 9 \equiv 2$ odd days

$\therefore$ 1.3.2005 was Tuesday. So, Friday lies on 4.3.2005

Hence, Friday lies on 4th, 11th, 18th and 25th of March, 2005.

Ex. 5. ***Prove that the calendar for the year 2003 will serve for the year 2014.***

Sol. We must have same day on 1.1.2003 and 1.1.2014.

So, number of odd days between 31.12.2002 and 31.12.2013 must be 0.

This period has 3 leap years and 8 ordinary years.

Number of odd days = $(3 \times 2 + 8 \times 1) = 14 \equiv 0$ odd day

$\therefore$ Calendar for the year 2003 will serve for the year 2014.

EXERCISE 27

(OBJECTIVE TYPE QUESTIONS)

Mark (✓) against the correct answer in each of the following :

1. January 1, 2007 was Monday. What day of the week lies on Jan. 1, 2008 ?
(*a*) Monday (*b*) Tuesday (*c*) Wednesday (*d*) Sunday

2. January 1, 2008 is Tuesday. What day of the week lies on Jan. 1, 2009 ?
(*a*) Monday (*b*) Wednesday (*c*) Thursday (*d*) Sunday

3. On 8th Dec, 2007 Saturday falls. What day of the week was it on 8th Dec. 2006 ?
(*a*) Sunday (*b*) Thursday (*c*) Tuesday (*d*) Friday

4. On 6th March, 2005 Monday falls. What was the day of the week on 6th March, 2004 ?
(*a*) Sunday (*b*) Saturday (*c*) Tuesday (*d*) Wednesday

5. The calendar for the year 2007 will be the same for the year:
(*a*) 2014 (*b*) 2016 (*c*) 2017 (*d*) 2018

6. On what dates of April, 2001 did Wednesday fall ?
(a) 1st, 8th, 15th, 22nd, 29th (b) 2nd, 9th, 16th, 23rd, 30th
(c) 3rd, 10th, 17th, 24th (d) 4th, 11th, 18th, 25th

7. What was the day of the week on 17th June, 1998 ?
(a) Monday (b) Tuesday (c) Wednesday (d) Thursday

8. What was the day of the week on 28th May, 2006 ?
(a) Thursday (b) Friday (c) Saturday (d) Sunday

9. What will be the day of the week on 15th August, 2010 ?
(a) Sunday (b) Monday (c) Tuesday (d) Friday

10. Today is Monday. After 61 days, it will be
(a) Wednesday (b) Saturday (c) Tuesday (d) Thursday

11. The last day of a century cannot be
(a) Monday (b) Wednesday (c) Tuesday (d) Friday

12. Which of the following is not a leap year ?
(a) 700 (b) 800 (c) 1200 (d) 2000

13. How many days are there in x weeks x days ?
(a) $7x^2$ (b) $8x$ (c) $14x$ (d) 7

14. It was Sunday on Jan 1, 2006. What was the day of the week on Jan 1, 2010 ?
(a) Sunday (b) Saturday (c) Friday (d) Wednesday

15. On 8th Feb, 2005 it was Tuesday. What was the day of the week on 8th Feb, 2004 ?
(a) Tuesday (b) Monday (c) Sunday (d) Wednesday

ANSWERS

1. (b) 2. (c) 3. (d) 4. (b) 5. (d) 6. (d) 7. (c) 8. (d) 9. (a) 10. (b) 11. (c) 12. (a) 13. (b) 14. (c) 15. (c)

SOLUTIONS

1. The year 2007 is an ordinary year. So, it has 1 odd day.
1st day of the year 2007 was Monday.
1st day of the year 2008 will be 1 day beyond Monday.
Hence, it will be Tuesday.

2. The year 2008 is a leap year. So, it has 2 odd days.
1st day of the year 2008 is Tuesday (Given)
So, 1st day of the year 2009 is 2 days beyond Tuesday.
Hence, it will be Thursday.

3. The year 2006 is an ordinary year. So, it has 1 odd day.
So, the day on 8th Dec, 2007 will be 1 day beyond the day on 8th Dec, 2006.
But, 8th Dec, 2007 is Saturday.
$\therefore$ 8th Dec, 2006 is Friday.

4. The year 2004 is a leap year. So, it has 2 odd days.
$\therefore$ The day on 6th March, 2005 will be 2 days beyond the day on 6th March, 2004.
But, 6th March, 2005 is Monday.
$\therefore$ 6th March, 2004 is Saturday.

5. Count the number of odd days from the year 2007 onwards to get the sum equal to 0 odd day.

Year	2007	2008	2009	2010	2011	2012	2013	2014	2015	2016	2017
Odd day	1	2	1	1	1	2	1	1	1	2	1

Sum = 14 odd days $\equiv$ 0 odd day.
$\therefore$ Calendar for the year 2018 will be the same as for the year 2007.

6. We shall find the day on 1st April, 2001.
1st April, 2001 = (2000 years + Period from 1.1.2001 to 1.4.2001)
Odd days in 1600 years = 0
Odd days in 400 years = 0
Jan. Feb. March April
(31 + 28 + 31 + 1) = 91 days $\equiv$ 0 odd days.

Total number of odd days = (0 + 0 + 0) = 0
On 1st April, 2001 it was Sunday.
In April, 2001 Wednesday falls on 4th, 11th, 18th and 25th.

7. 17th June, 1998 = (1997 years + Period from 1.1.1998 to 17.6.1998)
Odd days in 1600 years = 0
Odd days in 300 years = $(5 \times 3) \equiv 1$
97 years has 24 leap years + 73 ordinary years.
Number of odd days in 97 years = $(24 \times 2 + 73)$ = 121 = 2 odd days
Jan. Feb. March April May June
(31 + 28 + 31 + 30 + 31 + 17) = 168 days = 24 weeks = 0 odd day
Total number of odd days = (0 + 1 + 2 + 0) = 3
Given day is Wednesday.

8. 28 May, 2006 = (2005 years + Period from 1.1.2006 to 28.5.2006)
Odd days in 1600 years = 0
Odd days in 400 years = 0
5 years = (4 ordinary years + 1 leap year) = $(4 \times 1 + 1 \times 2)$ odd days
$\equiv$ 6 odd days
Jan. Feb. March April May
(31 + 28 + 31 + 30 + 28) = 148 days = (21 weeks + 1 day)
$\equiv$ 1 odd day
Total number of odd days = (0 + 0 + 6 + 1) = 7 $\equiv$ 0 odd day.
Given day is Sunday.

9. 15th August, 2010 = (2009 years + Period from 1.1.2010 to 15.8.2010)
Odd days in 1600 years = 0
Odd days in 400 years = 0
9 years = (2 leap years + 7 ordinary years)
= $(2 \times 2 + 7 \times 1)$ = 11 odd days $\equiv$ 4 odd days
Jan. Feb. March April May June July Aug.
(31 + 28 + 31 + 30 + 31 + 30 + 31 + 15) = 227 days
= (32 weeks + 3 days) $\equiv$ 3 odd days.
Total number of odd days = (0 + 0 + 4 + 3) = 7 $\equiv$ 0 odd days.
Given day is Sunday.

10. Each day of the week is repeated after 7 days
So, after 63 days, it will be Monday.
∴ After 61 days, it will be Saturday.

11. 100 years contain 5 odd days.
∴ Last day of 1st century is Friday.
200 years contain $(5 \times 2) \equiv 3$ odd days.
∴ Last day of 2nd century is Wednesday.
300 years contain $(5 \times 3) = 15 \equiv 1$ odd day.
∴ Last day of 3rd century is Monday.
400 years contain 0 odd day.
∴ Last day of 4th century is Sunday.
This cycle is repeated.
∴ Last day of a century cannot be Tuesday or Thursday or Saturday.

12. The century divisible by 400 is a leap year.
∴ The year 700 is not a leap year.

13. x weeks x days = $(7x + x)$ days = $8x$ days.

14. On 31st December, 2005 it was Saturday.
Number of odd days from the year 2006 to the year 2009
= (1 + 1 + 2 + 1) = 5 days
∴ On 31st December 2009, it was Thursday.
Thus, on 1st Jan, 2010 it is Friday.

15. The year 2004 is a leap year. It has 2 odd days.
∴ The day on 8th Feb, 2004 is 2 days before the day on 8th Feb, 2005.
Hence, this day is Sunday.

28. CLOCKS

IMPORTANT FACTS

The face or dial of a watch is a circle whose circumference is divided into 60 equal parts, called minute spaces.

A clock has two hands, the smaller one is called the *hour hand* or *short hand* while the larger one is called the *minute hand* or *long hand*.

(*i*) In 60 minutes, the minute hand gains 55 minutes on the hour hand.

(*ii*) In every hour, both the hands coincide once.

(*iii*) The hands are in the same straight line when they are coincident or opposite to each other.

(*iv*) When the two hands are at right angles, they are 15 minute spaces apart.

(*v*) When the hands are in opposite directions, they are 30 minute spaces apart.

(*vi*) Angle traced by hour hand in 12 hrs = 360°.

(*vii*) Angle traced by minute hand in 60 min. = 360°.

Too Fast and Too Slow *: If a watch or a clock indicates 8.15, when the correct time is 8, it is said to be 15 minutes too fast.*

On the other hand, if it indicates 7.45, when the correct time is 8, it is said to be 15 minutes too slow.

SOLVED EXAMPLES

Ex. 1. ***Find the angle between the hour hand and the minute hand of a clock when the time is 3.25.***

Sol. Angle traced by the hour hand in 12 hours = 360°.

Angle traced by it in 3 hrs 25 min. *i.e.* $\frac{41}{12}$ hrs $= \left(\frac{360}{12} \times \frac{41}{12}\right)^\circ = 102\frac{1}{2}^\circ$.

Angle traced by minute hand in 60 min. = 360°.

Angle traced by it in 25 min. $= \left(\frac{360}{60} \times 25\right)^\circ = 150^\circ$.

$\therefore$ Required angle $= \left(150^\circ - 102\frac{1}{2}^\circ\right) = 47\frac{1}{2}^\circ$.

Ex. 2. ***At what time between 2 and 3 o'clock will the hands of a clock be together?***

Sol. At 2 o'clock, the hour hand is at 2 and the minute hand is at 12, *i.e.* they are 10 min. spaces apart.

To be together, the minute hand must gain 10 minutes over the hour hand.

Now, 55 minutes are gained by it in 60 min.

$\therefore$ 10 minutes will be gained in $\left(\frac{60}{55} \times 10\right)$ min. $= 10\frac{10}{11}$ min.

$\therefore$ The hands will coincide at $10\frac{10}{11}$ min. past 2.

Ex. 3. ***At what time between 4 and 5 o'clock will the hands of a clock be at right angle ?***

Sol. At 4 o'clock, the minute hand will be 20 min. spaces behind the hour hand.
Now, when the two hands are at right angles, they are 15 min. spaces apart.
So, they are at right angles in following two cases.

Case I. *When minute hand is 15 min. spaces behind the hour hand* :
In this case min. hand will have to gain (20 – 15) = 5 minute spaces.
55 min. spaces are gained by it in 60 min.

5 min. spaces will be gained by it in $\left(\frac{60}{55} \times 5\right)$ min. $= 5\frac{5}{11}$ min.

$\therefore$ They are at right angles at $5\frac{5}{11}$ min. past 4.

Case II. *When the minute hand is 15 min. spaces ahead of the hour hand* :
To be in this position, the minute hand will have to gain (20 + 15) = 35 minute spaces.
55 min. spaces are gained in 60 min.

35 min. spaces are gained in $\left(\frac{60}{55} \times 35\right)$ min. $= 38\frac{2}{11}$ min.

$\therefore$ They are at right angles at $38\frac{2}{11}$ min. past 4.

Ex. 4. ***Find at what time between 8 and 9 o'clock will the hands of a clock be in the same straight line but not together.***

Sol. At 8 o'clock, the hour hand is at 8 and the minute hand is at 12, *i.e.* the two hands are 20 min. spaces apart.
To be in the same straight line but not together they will be 30 minute spaces apart.
So, the minute hand will have to gain (30 – 20) = 10 minute spaces over the hour hand.
55 minute spaces are gained in 60 min.

10 minute spaces will be gained in $\left(\frac{60}{55} \times 10\right)$ min. $= 10\frac{10}{11}$ min.

$\therefore$ The hands will be in the same straight line but not together at $10\frac{10}{11}$ min. past 8.

Ex. 5. ***At what time between 5 and 6 o'clock are the hands of a clock 3 minutes apart ?***

Sol. At 5 o'clock, the minute hand is 25 min. spaces behind the hour hand.

Case I. *Minute hand is 3 min. spaces behind the hour hand.*
In this case, the minute hand has to gain (25 – 3) = 22 minute spaces.
55 min. are gained in 60 min.

22 min. are gained in $\left(\frac{60}{55} \times 22\right)$ min. = 24 min.

$\therefore$ The hands will be 3 min. apart at 24 min. past 5.

Case II. *Minute hand is 3 min. spaces ahead of the hour hand.*
In this case, the minute hand has to gain (25 + 3) = 28 minute spaces.
55 min. are gained in 60 min.

28 min. are gained in $\left(\frac{60}{55} \times 28\right) = 31\frac{5}{11}$ min.

$\therefore$ The hands will be 3 min. apart at $31\frac{5}{11}$ min. past 5.

Ex. 6. ***The minute hand of a clock overtakes the hour hand at intervals of 65 minutes of the correct time. How much a day does the clock gain or lose ?***

Sol. In a correct clock, the minute hand gains 55 min. spaces over the hour hand in 60 minutes.

To be together again, the minute hand must gain 60 minutes over the hour hand.

55 min. are gained in 60 min.

60 min. are gained in $\left(\frac{60}{55} \times 60\right)$ min. $= 65\frac{5}{11}$ min.

But, they are together after 65 min.

$\therefore$ Gain in 65 min. $= \left(65\frac{5}{11} - 65\right) = \frac{5}{11}$ min.

Gain in 24 hours $= \left(\frac{5}{11} \times \frac{60 \times 24}{65}\right)$ min. $= 10\frac{10}{43}$ min.

$\therefore$ The clock gains $10\frac{10}{43}$ minutes in 24 hours.

Ex. 7. ***A watch which gains uniformly, is 5 min. slow at 8 o'clock in the morning on Sunday and it is 5 min. 48 sec. fast at 8 p.m. on following Sunday. When was it correct ?***

Sol. Time from 8 a.m. on Sunday to 8 p.m. on following Sunday = 7 days 12 hours = 180 hours

$\therefore$ The watch gains $\left(5 + 5\frac{4}{5}\right)$ min. or $\frac{54}{5}$ min. in 180 hrs.

Now $\frac{54}{5}$ min. are gained in 180 hrs.

$\therefore$ 5 min. are gained in $\left(180 \times \frac{5}{54} \times 5\right)$ hrs. = 83 hrs 20 min. = 3 days 11 hrs 20 min.

$\therefore$ Watch is correct 3 days 11 hrs 20 min. after 8 a.m. of Sunday.

$\therefore$ It will be correct at 20 min. past 7 p.m. on Wednesday.

Ex. 8. ***A clock is set right at 5 a.m. The clock loses 16 minutes in 24 hours. What will be the true time when the clock indicates 10 p.m. on 4th day ?***

Sol. Time from 5 a.m. on a day to 10 p.m. on 4th day = 89 hours.

Now 23 hrs 44 min. of this clock = 24 hours of correct clock.

$\therefore$ $\frac{356}{15}$ hrs of this clock = 24 hours of correct clock.

89 hrs of this clock $= \left(24 \times \frac{15}{356} \times 89\right)$ hrs of correct clock.

= 90 hrs of correct clock.

So, the correct time is 11 p.m.

Ex. 9. ***A clock is set right at 8 a.m. The clock gains 10 minutes in 24 hours. What will be the true time when the clock indicates 1 p.m. on the following day ?***

Sol. Time from 8 a.m. on a day to 1 p.m. on the following day = 29 hours.

24 hours 10 min. of this clock = 24 hours of the correct clock.

$\frac{145}{6}$ hrs of this clock = 24 hrs of the correct clock

29 hrs of this clock = $\left(24 \times \frac{6}{145} \times 29\right)$ hrs of the correct clock

= 28 hrs 48 min. of correct clock

∴ The correct time is 28 hrs 48 min. after 8 a.m.

This is 48 min. past 12.

EXERCISE 28

(OBJECTIVE TYPE QUESTIONS)

Directions : ***Mark (✓) against the correct answer*** :

1. A clock is started at noon. By 10 minutes past 5, the hour hand has turned through :
(a) 145° (b) 150° (c) 155° (d) 160°

2. An accurate clock shows 8 o'clock in the morning. Through how many degrees will the hour hand rotate when the clock shows 2 o'clock in the afternoon ? **(I.A.S. 2000)**
(a) 144° (b) 150° (c) 168° (d) 180°

3. At 3.40, the hour hand and the minute hand of a clock form an angle of :
(a) 120° (b) 125° (c) 130° (d) 135°

4. The angle between the minute hand and the hour hand of a clock when the time is 8.30, is :
(a) 80° (b) 75° (c) 60° (d) 105°

5. The angle between the minute hand and the hour hand of a clock when the time is 4.20, is :
(a) 0° (b) 10° (c) 5° (d) 20°

6. At what angle the hands of a clock are inclined at 15 minutes past 5 ?
(a) $58\frac{1}{2}^\circ$ (b) 64° (c) $67\frac{1}{2}^\circ$ (d) $72\frac{1}{2}^\circ$
(L.I.C.A.A.O. 2003)

7. The reflex angle between the hands of a clock at 10.25 is : **(S.C.R.A. 1996)**
(a) 180° (b) $192\frac{1}{2}^\circ$ (c) 195° (d) $197\frac{1}{2}^\circ$

8. How many times do the hands of a clock coincide in a day ?
(a) 20 (b) 21 (c) 22 (d) 24

9. How many times in a day, the hands of a clock are straight ?
(a) 22 (b) 24 (c) 44 (d) 48

10. How many times are the hands of a clock at right angle in a day ? **(I.A.S. 1997)**
(a) 22 (b) 24 (c) 44 (d) 48

11. How many times in a day, are the hands of a clock in straight line but opposite in direction ? **(R.R.B. 2003)**
(a) 20 (b) 22 (c) 24 (d) 48

12. How much does a watch lose per day, if its hands coincide every 64 minutes ?
(a) $32\frac{8}{11}$ min. (b) $36\frac{5}{11}$ min. (c) 90 min. (d) 96 min.

13. At what time, in minutes, between 3 o'clock and 4 o'clock, both the needles will coincide each other ? **(R.R.B. 2002)**
(a) $5\frac{1}{11}''$ (b) $12\frac{4}{11}''$ (c) $13\frac{4}{11}''$ (d) $16\frac{4}{11}''$

14. At what time between 9 and 10 o'clock will the hands of a watch be together ?

(a) 45 min. past 9 (b) 50 min. past 9

(c) $49\frac{1}{11}$ min. past 9 (d) $48\frac{2}{11}$ min. past 9

15. At what time between 7 and 8 o'clock will the hands of a clock be in the same straight line but, not together ? **(A.A.O. Exam. 2003)**

(a) 5 min. past 7 (b) $5\frac{2}{11}$ min. past 7

(c) $5\frac{3}{11}$ min. past 7 (d) $5\frac{5}{11}$ min. past 7

16. At what time between 4 and 5 o'clock will the hands of a watch point in opposite directions ?

(a) 45 min. past 4 (b) 40 min. past 4

(c) $50\frac{4}{11}$ min. past 4 (d) $54\frac{6}{11}$ min. past 4

17. At what time between 5.30 and 6 will the hands of a clock be at right angles ?

(a) $43\frac{5}{11}$ min. past 5 (b) $43\frac{7}{11}$ min. past 5

(c) 40 min. past 5 (d) 45 min. past 5

18. A watch which gains uniformly is 2 minutes low at noon on Monday and is 4 min. 48 sec fast at 2 p.m. on the following Monday. When was it correct ? **(R.R.B. 2001)**

(a) 2 p.m. on Tuesday (b) 2 p.m. on Wednesday

(c) 3 p.m. on Thursday (d) 1 p.m. on Friday

19. A watch which gains 5 seconds in 3 minutes was set right at 7 a.m. In the afternoon of the same day, when the watch indicated quarter past 4 o'clock, the true time is :

(a) $59\frac{7}{12}$ min. past 3 (b) 4 p.m.

(c) $58\frac{7}{11}$ min. past 3 (d) $2\frac{3}{11}$ min. past 4

ANSWERS

1. (c)	**2.** (d)	**3.** (c)	**4.** (b)	**5.** (b)	**6.** (c)	**7.** (d)	**8.** (c)	**9.** (c)	**10.** (c)
11. (b)	**12.** (a)	**13.** (d)	**14.** (c)	**15.** (d)	**16.** (d)	**17.** (b)	**18.** (b)	**19.** (b)	

SOLUTIONS

1. Angle traced by hour hand in 12 hrs = 360°.

Angle traced by hour hand in 5 hrs 10 min. *i.e.* $\frac{31}{6}$ hrs. $= \left(\frac{360}{12} \times \frac{31}{6}\right)^\circ = 155°$

2. Angle traced by the hour hand in 6 hours $= \left(\frac{360}{12} \times 6\right)^\circ = 180°$

3. Angle traced by hour hand in 12 hrs. = 360°.

Angle traced by it in $\frac{11}{3}$ hrs $= \left(\frac{360}{12} \times \frac{11}{3}\right)^\circ = 110°$.

Angle traced by minute hand in 60 min. = 360°.

Angle traced by it in 40 min. = $\left(\frac{360}{60} \times 40\right)^\circ$ = 240°.

∴ Required angle (240 − 110)° = 130°.

4. Angle traced by hour hand in $\frac{17}{2}$ hrs = $\left(\frac{360}{12} \times \frac{17}{2}\right)^\circ$ = 255.

Angle traced by min. hand in 30 min. = $\left(\frac{360}{60} \times 30\right)^\circ$ = 180.

∴ Required angle = (255 − 180)° = 75°.

5. Angle traced by hour hand in $\frac{13}{3}$ hrs = $\left(\frac{360}{12} \times \frac{13}{3}\right)^\circ$ = 130°.

Angle traced by min. hand in 20 min. = $\left(\frac{360}{60} \times 20\right)^\circ$ = 120°.

∴ Required angle = (130 − 120)° = 10°.

6. Angle traced by hour hand in $\frac{21}{4}$ hrs = $\left(\frac{360}{12} \times \frac{21}{4}\right)^\circ = 157\frac{1}{2}^\circ$.

Angle traced by min. hand in 15 min. = $\left(\frac{360}{12} \times 15\right)^\circ$ = 90°.

∴ Required angle = $\left(157\frac{1}{2}\right)^\circ - 90^\circ = 67\frac{1}{2}^\circ$.

7. Angle traced by hour hand in $\frac{125}{12}$ hrs = $\left(\frac{360}{12} \times \frac{125}{12}\right)^\circ = 312\frac{1}{2}^\circ$.

Angle traced by minute hand in 25 min = $\left(\frac{360}{60} \times 25^\circ\right)$ = 150°.

∴ Reflex angle = $360^\circ - \left(312\frac{1}{2} - 150\right)^\circ = 360^\circ - 162\frac{1}{2}^\circ = 197\frac{1}{2}^\circ$.

8. The hands of a clock coincide 11 times in every 12 hours (Since between 11 and 1, they coincide only once, *i.e.* at 12 o'clock).

∴ The hands coincide 22 times in a day.

9. In 12 hours, the hands coincide or are in opposite direction 22 times.

∴ In 24 hours, the hands coincide or are in opposite direction 44 times a day.

10. In 12 hours, they are at right angles 22 times.

∴ In 24 hours, they are at right angles 44 times.

11. The hands of a clock point in opposite directions (in the same straight line) 11 times in every 12 hours (Because between 5 and 7 they point in opposite directions at 6 o'clock only). So, in a day, the hands point in the opposite directions 22 times.

12. 55 min. spaces are covered in 60 min.

60 min. spaces are covered in $\left(\frac{60}{55} \times 60\right)$ min. = $65\frac{5}{11}$ min.

Loss in 64 min. = $\left(65\frac{5}{11} - 64\right) = \frac{16}{11}$ min.

Loss in 24 hrs = $\left(\frac{16}{11} \times \frac{1}{64} \times 24 \times 60\right)$ min. = $32\frac{8}{11}$ min.

13. At 3 o'clock, the minute hand is 15 min. spaces apart from the hour hand.
To be coincident, it must gain 15 min. spaces.
55 min. are gained in 60 min.

15 min. are gained in $\left(\frac{60}{55}\times 15\right)$ min. $= 16\frac{4}{11}$ min.

$\therefore$ The hands are coincident at $16\frac{4}{11}$ min. past 3.

14. To be together between 9 and 10 o'clock, the minute hand has to gain 45 min. spaces.
55 min. spaces gained in 60 min.

45 min. spaces are gained in $\left(\frac{60}{55}\times 45\right)$ min. or $49\frac{1}{11}$ min.

$\therefore$ The hands are together at $49\frac{1}{11}$ min. past 9.

15. When the hands of the clock are in the same straight line but not together, they are 30 minute spaces apart.
At 7 o'clock, they are 25 min. spaces apart.
$\therefore$ Minute hand will have to gain only 5 min. spaces.
55 min. spaces are gained in 60 min.

5 min. spaces are gained in $\left(\frac{60}{55}\times 5\right)$ min $= 5\frac{5}{11}$ min.

$\therefore$ Required time $= 5\frac{5}{11}$ min. past 7.

16. At 4 o'clock, the hands of the watch are 20 min. spaces apart.
To be in opposite directions, they must be 30 min. spaces apart.
$\therefore$ Minute hand will have to gain 50 min. spaces.
55 min. spaces are gained in 60 min.

50 min. spaces are gained in $\left(\frac{60}{55}\times 50\right)$ min. or $54\frac{6}{11}$ min.

$\therefore$ Required time $= 54\frac{6}{11}$ min. past 4.

17. At 5 o'clock, the hands are 25 min. spaces apart.
To be at right angles and that too between 5.30 and 6, the minute hand has to gain $(25 + 15) = 40$ min. spaces.
55 min. spaces are gained in 60 min.

40 min. spaces are gained in $\left(\frac{60}{55}\times 40\right)$ min. $= 43\frac{7}{11}$ min.

$\therefore$ Required time $= 43\frac{7}{11}$ min. past 5.

18. Time from 12 p.m. on Monday to 2 p.m. on the following Monday = 7 days 2 hours
= 170 hours.

$\therefore$ The watch gains $\left(2 + 4\frac{4}{5}\right)$ min. or $\frac{34}{5}$ min. in 170 hrs.

Now. $\frac{34}{5}$ min. are gained in 170 hrs.

$\therefore$ 2 min. are gained in $\left(170 \times \frac{5}{34} \times 2\right)$ hrs = 50 hrs.

$\therefore$ Watch is correct 2 days 2 hrs. after 12 p.m. on Monday *i.e.* it will be correct at 2 p.m. on Wednesday.

19. Time from 7 a.m. to 4.15 p.m. = 9 hrs 15 min. = $\frac{37}{4}$ hrs.

3 min. 5 sec. of this clock = 3 min. of the correct clock.

$\Rightarrow$ $\frac{37}{720}$ hrs of this clock = $\frac{1}{20}$ hrs of the correct clock

$\Rightarrow$ $\frac{37}{4}$ hrs of this clock = $\left(\frac{1}{20} \times \frac{720}{37} \times \frac{37}{4}\right)$ hrs of the correct clock

= 9 hrs of the correct clock

$\therefore$ The correct time is 9 hrs after 7 a.m. *i.e.* 4 p.m.

---

29. STOCK AND SHARES

To start a big business or an industry, a large amount of money is needed. It is beyond the capacity of one or two persons to arrange such a huge amount. However, some persons associate together to form a company. They, then, draft a proposal, issue a prospectus (in the name of the company), explaining the plan of the project and invite the public to invest money in this project. They, thus, pool up the funds from the public, by assigning them ***shares*** of the company.

IMPORTANT FACTS AND FORMULAE

1. **Stock-capital** : *The total amount of money needed to run the company is called the* ***stock-capital.***
2. **Shares or Stock** : *The whole capital is divided into small units, called* **shares** *or* **stock**.

   For each investment, the company issues a *share-certificate*, showing the value of each share and the number of shares held by a person.

   The person who subscribes in shares or stock is called a **share holder** *or* **stock holder**.
3. **Dividend** : *The annual profit distributed among share holders is called* ***dividend.***

   Dividend is paid annually as per share or as a percentage.
4. **Face Value** : *The value of a share or stock printed on the share-certificate is called its* ***Face Value*** *or* ***Nominal Value*** *or* ***Par Value.***
5. **Market Value** : The stocks of different companies are sold and bought in the open market through brokers at stock-exchanges. A share (or stock) is said to be :

   (*i*) ***At premium*** or ***Above par,*** if its market value is more than its face value.

   (*ii*) ***At par,*** if its market value is the same as its face value.

   (*iii*) ***At discount*** or ***Below par,*** if its market value is less than its face value.

   Thus, if a Rs. 100 stock is quoted at a premium of 16, then market value of the stock = Rs. (100 + 16) = Rs. 116.

   Likewise, if a Rs. 100 stock is quoted at a discount of 7, then market value of the stock = Rs. (100 − 7) = Rs. 93.
6. **Brokerage** : *The broker's charge is called* ***brokerage***.

   (*i*) When stock is purchased, brokerage is added to the cost price.

   (*ii*) When stock is sold, brokerage is subtracted from the selling price.

   Remember :

   (*i*) The face value of a share always remains the same.

   (*ii*) The market value of a share changes from time to time.

   (*iii*) Dividend is always paid on the face value of a share.

   (*iv*) Number of shares held by a person

$$= \frac{\text{Total Investment}}{\text{Investment in 1 share}} = \frac{\text{Total Income}}{\text{Income from 1 share}} = \frac{\text{Total Face Value}}{\text{Face value of 1 share}}.$$

Thus, by a Rs. 100, 9% stock at 120, we mean that :

(*i*) Face Value (N.V.) of stock = Rs. 100.

(*ii*) Market Value (M.V.) of stock = Rs. 120.

(*iii*) Annual dividend on 1 share = 9% of face value = 9% of Rs. 100 = Rs. 9.

(*iv*) An investment of Rs. 120 gives an annual income of Rs. 9.

(*v*) Rate of interest p.a. = Annual income from an investment of Rs. 100

$$= \left(\frac{9}{120} \times 100\right)\% = 7\frac{1}{2}\%.$$

SOLVED EXAMPLES

Ex. 1. ***Find the cost of :***

(i) Rs. 7200, 8% stock at 90;

(ii) Rs. 4500, 8.5% stock at 4 premium;

(iii) Rs. 6400, 10% stock at 15 discount.

Sol. (*i*) Cost of Rs. 100 stock = Rs. 90.

Cost of Rs. 7200 stock = Rs. $\left(\frac{90}{100} \times 7200\right)$ = Rs. 6480.

(*ii*) Cost of Rs. 100 stock = Rs. (100 + 4) = Rs. 104.

Cost of Rs. 4500 stock = Rs. $\left(\frac{104}{100} \times 4500\right)$ = Rs. 4680.

(*iii*) Cost of Rs. 100 stock = Rs. (100 − 15) = Rs. 85.

Cost of Rs. 6400 stock = Rs. $\left(\frac{85}{100} \times 6400\right)$ = Rs. 5440.

Ex. 2. ***Find the cash required to purchase Rs. 3200, $7\frac{1}{2}$% stock at 107 $\left(\text{brokerage } \frac{1}{2}\%\right)$.***

Sol. Cash required to purchase Rs. 100 stock = Rs. $\left(107 + \frac{1}{2}\right)$ = Rs. $\frac{215}{2}$.

Cash required to purchase Rs. 3200 stock = Rs. $\left(\frac{215}{2} \times \frac{1}{100} \times 3200\right)$ = Rs. 3440.

Ex. 3. ***Find the cash realised by selling Rs. 2440, 9.5% stock at 4 discount $\left(\text{brokerage } \frac{1}{4}\%\right)$.***

Sol. By selling Rs. 100 stock, cash realised = Rs. $\left[(100 - 4) - \frac{1}{4}\right]$ = Rs. $\frac{383}{4}$.

By selling Rs. 2400 stock, cash realised = Rs. $\left(\frac{383}{4} \times \frac{1}{100} \times 2400\right)$ = Rs. 2298.

Ex. 4. ***Find the annual income derived from Rs. 2500, 8% stock at 106.***

Sol. Income from Rs. 100 stock = Rs. 8.

Income from Rs. 2500 stock = Rs. $\left(\frac{8}{100} \times 2500\right)$ = Rs. 200.

Ex. 5. ***Find the annual income derived by investing Rs. 6800 in 10% stock at 136.***

Sol. By investing Rs. 136, income obtained = Rs. 10.

By investing Rs. 6800, income obtained = Rs. $\left(\frac{10}{136} \times 6800\right)$ = Rs. 500

Ex. 6. ***Which is better investment ? $7\frac{1}{2}$% stock at 105 or $6\frac{1}{2}$% stock at 94.***

Sol. Let the investment in each case be Rs. (105 × 94).

Case I : $7\frac{1}{2}$% stock at 105 :

On investing Rs. 105, income = Rs. $\frac{15}{2}$.

On investing Rs. (105 × 94), income = Rs. $\left(\frac{15}{2} \times \frac{1}{105} \times 105 \times 94\right)$ = Rs. 705.

Case II : $6\frac{1}{2}$% stock at 94 :

On investing Rs. 94, income = Rs. $\frac{13}{2}$.

On investing Rs. (105 × 94), income = Rs. $\left(\frac{13}{2} \times \frac{1}{94} \times 105 \times 94\right)$ = Rs. 682.50.

Clearly, the income from $7\frac{1}{2}$% stock at 105 is more.

Hence, the investment in $7\frac{1}{2}$% stock at 105 is better.

Ex. 7. ***Find the cost of 96 shares of Rs. 10 each at $\frac{3}{4}$ discount, brokerage being $\frac{1}{4}$ per share.*** **(L.I.C. 2003)**

Sol. Cost of 1 share = Rs. $\left[\left(10 - \frac{3}{4}\right) + \frac{1}{4}\right]$ = Rs. $\frac{19}{2}$.

Cost of 96 shares = Rs. $\left(\frac{19}{2} \times 96\right)$ = Rs. 912.

Ex. 8. ***Find the income derived from 88 shares of Rs. 25 each at 5 premium, brokerage being $\frac{1}{4}$ per share and the rate of dividend being $7\frac{1}{2}$% per annum. Also, find the rate of interest on the investment.***

Sol. Cost of 1 share = Rs. $\left(25 + 5 + \frac{1}{4}\right)$ = Rs. $\frac{121}{4}$.

Cost of 88 shares = Rs. $\left(\frac{121}{4} \times 88\right)$ = Rs. 2662.

∴ Investment made = Rs. 2662.

Face value of 88 shares = Rs. (88 × 25) = Rs. 2200.

Dividend on Rs. 100 = $\frac{15}{2}$.

Dividend on Rs. 2200 = Rs. $\left(\frac{15}{2} \times \frac{1}{100} \times 2200\right)$ = Rs. 165.

∴ Income derived = Rs. 165.

Rate of interest on investment = $\left(\frac{165}{2662} \times 100\right)$ = 6.2%.

Ex. 9. ***A man buys Rs. 25 shares in a company which pays 9% dividend. The money invested is such that it gives 10% on investment. At what price did he buy the shares?***

Sol. Suppose he buys each share for Rs. x.

Then, $\left(25 \times \frac{9}{100}\right) = \left(x \times \frac{10}{100}\right)$ or $x = 22.50$.

$\therefore$ Cost of each share = Rs. 22.50.

Ex. 10. ***A man sells Rs. 5000, 12% stock at 156 and invests the proceeds partly in 8% stock at 90 and 9% stock at 108. He thereby increases his income by Rs. 70. How much of the proceeds were invested in each stock ?***

Sol. S.P. of Rs. 5000 stock = Rs. $\left(\frac{156}{100} \times 5000\right)$ = Rs. 7800.

Income from this stock = Rs. $\left(\frac{12}{100} \times 5000\right)$ = Rs. 600.

Let investment in 8% stock be x and that in 9% stock = $(7800 - x)$.

$\therefore \left(x \times \frac{8}{90}\right) + (7800 - x) \times \frac{9}{108} = (600 + 70)$

$\Leftrightarrow \frac{4x}{45} + \frac{7800 - x}{12} = 670 \quad \Leftrightarrow \quad 16x + 117000 - 15x = (670 \times 180) \quad \Leftrightarrow \quad x = 3600.$

$\therefore$ Money invested in 8% stock at 90 = Rs. 3600.

Money invested in 9% at 108 = Rs. (7800 − 3600) = Rs. 4200.

EXERCISE 29

(OBJECTIVE TYPE QUESTIONS)

Directions : *Mark (✓) against the correct answer* :

1. The cost price of a Rs. 100 stock at 4 discount, when brokerage is $\frac{1}{4}$% is :
   (a) Rs. 95.75 (b) Rs. 96 (c) Rs. 96.25 (d) Rs. 104.25
2. The cash realised on selling a 14% stock at Rs. 106.25, brokerage being $\frac{1}{4}$%, is :
   (a) Rs. 105.50 (b) Rs. 106 (c) Rs. 106.50 (d) Rs. 113.75
3. How many shares of market value Rs. 25 each can be purchased for Rs. 12750, brokerage being 2% ? **(M.A.T. 2002)**
   (a) 450 (b) 500 (c) 550 (d) 600
4. A man invests in a 16% stock at 128. The interest obtained by him is :
   (a) 8% (b) 12% (c) 12.5% (d) 16%
5. The income derived from a Rs. 100, 13% stock at Rs. 105, is :
   (a) Rs. 5 (b) Rs. 8 (c) Rs. 13 (d) Rs. 18
6. A man invested Rs. 4455 in Rs. 10 shares quoted at Rs. 8.25. If the rate of dividend be 12%, his annual income is :
   (a) Rs. 207.40 (b) Rs. 534.60 (c) Rs. 648 (d) Rs. 655.60
7. A man invested Rs. 14,400 in Rs. 100 shares of a company at 20% premium. If the company declares 5% dividend at the end of the year, then how much does he get ?
   (a) Rs. 500 (b) Rs. 600 (c) Rs. 650 (d) Rs. 720
   (Hotel Management, 2003)
8. A 6% stock yields 8%. The market value of the stock is :
   (a) Rs. 48 (b) Rs. 75 (c) Rs. 96 (d) Rs. 133.33

9. A 9% stock yields 8%. The market value of the stock is :
(*a*) Rs. 72 (*b*) Rs. 92 (*c*) Rs. 112.50 (*d*) Rs. 116.50

10. A 12% stock yielding 10% is quoted at :
(*a*) Rs. 83.33 (*b*) Rs. 110 (*c*) Rs. 112 (*d*) Rs. 120

11. By investing Rs. 1620 in 8% stock, Michael earns Rs. 135. The stock is then quoted at :
(*a*) Rs. 80 (*b*) Rs. 96 (*c*) Rs. 106 (*d*) Rs 108

12. To produce an annual income of Rs. 1200 from a 12% stock at 90, the amount of stock needed is :
(*a*) Rs. 10,000 (*b*) Rs. 10,800 (*c*) Rs. 14,400 (*d*) Rs. 16,000

13. In order to obtain an income of Rs. 650 from 10% stock at Rs. 96, one must make an investment of :
(*a*) Rs. 3100 (*b*) Rs. 6240 (*c*) Rs. 6500 (*d*) Rs. 9600

14. By investing in $16\frac{2}{3}\%$ stock at 64, one earns Rs. 1500. The investment made is :
(*a*) Rs. 5640 (*b*) Rs. 5760 (*c*) Rs. 7500 (*d*) Rs. 9600

15. A man invested Rs. 1552 in a stock at 97 to obtain an income of Rs. 128. The dividend from the stock is :
(*a*) 7.5% (*b*) 8% (*c*) 9.7% (*d*) None of these.

16. A man bought 20 shares of Rs. 50 at 5 discount, the rate of dividend being $13\frac{1}{2}\%$. The rate of interest obtained is :
(*a*) $12\frac{1}{2}\%$ (*b*) $13\frac{1}{2}\%$ (*c*) 15% (*d*) $16\frac{2}{3}\%$

17. A man buys Rs. 20 shares paying 9% dividend. The man wants to have an interest of 12% on his money. The market value of each share is :
(*a*) Rs. 12 (*b*) Rs. 15 (*c*) Rs. 18 (*d*) Rs. 21

18. A man buys Rs. 50 shares in a company which pays 10% dividend. If the man gets 12.5% on his investment, at what price did he buy the shares ? **(L.I.C.A.A.O. 2003)**
(*a*) Rs. 37.50 (*b*) Rs. 40 (*c*) Rs. 48 (*d*) Rs 52

19. The market value of a 10.5% stock, in which an income of Rs. 756 is derived by investing Rs. 9000, brokerage being $\frac{1}{4}\%$, is :
(*a*) Rs. 108.25 (*b*) Rs. 112.20 (*c*) Rs. 124.75 (*d*) Rs. 125.25

20. Sakshi invests a part of Rs. 12,000 in 12% stock at Rs. 120 and the remainder in 15% stock at Rs. 125. If his total dividend per annum is Rs 1360, how much does he invest in 12% stock at Rs. 120 ?
(*a*) Rs. 4000 (*b*) Rs. 4500 (*c*) Rs. 5500 (*d*) Rs. 6000

21. Rs. 9800 are invested partly in 9% stock at 75 and 10% stock at 80 to have equal amount of incomes. The investment in 9% stock is :
(*a*) Rs. 4800 (*b*) Rs. 5000 (*c*) Rs. 5400 (*d*) Rs. 5600

22. A man invests some money partly in 9% stock at 96 and partly in 12% stock at 120. To obtain equal dividends from both, he must invest the money in the ratio
(*a*) 3 : 4 (*b*) 3 : 5 (*c*) 4 : 5 (*d*) 16 : 15

23. Which is better investment — 11% stock at 143 or $9\frac{3}{4}\%$ stock at 117 ?
(*a*) 11% stock at 143 (*b*) $9\frac{3}{4}\%$ stock at 117 (*c*) Both are equally good
(*d*) Cannot be compared, as the total amount of investment is not given

24. Which is better investment, 12% stock at par with an income tax at the rate of 5 paise per rupee or $14\frac{2}{7}\%$ stock at 120 free from income tax ?

(*a*) 12% stock (*b*) $14\frac{2}{7}\%$ stock (*c*) Both are equally good

(*d*) Cannot be compared

25. A invested some money in 10% stock at 96. If B wants to invest in an equally good 12% stock, he must purchase a stock worth of :

(*a*) Rs. 80 (*b*) Rs. 115.20 (*c*) Rs. 120 (*d*) Rs. 125.40

ANSWERS

1. (*c*)	**2.** (*b*)	**3.** (*b*)	**4.** (*c*)	**5.** (*c*)	**6.** (*c*)	**7.** (*b*)	**8.** (*b*)	**9.** (*c*)	**10.** (*d*)
11. (*b*)	**12.** (*a*)	**13.** (*b*)	**14.** (*b*)	**15.** (*b*)	**16.** (*c*)	**17.** (*b*)	**18.** (*b*)	**19.** (*c*)	**20.** (*a*)
21. (*b*)	**22.** (*d*)	**23.** (*b*)	**24.** (*b*)	**25.** (*b*)					

SOLUTIONS

1. C.P. = Rs. $\left(100 - 4 + \frac{1}{4}\right)$ = Rs. 96.25.

2. Cash realised = Rs. (106.25 − 0.25) = Rs. 106.

3. C.P. of each share = Rs. (25 + 2% of 25) = Rs. 25.50.

$\therefore$ Number of shares = $\left(\frac{12750}{25.50}\right)$ = 500.

4. By investing Rs. 128, income derived = Rs. 16.

By investing Rs. 100, income derived = Rs. $\left(\frac{16}{128} \times 100\right)$ = Rs. 12.5.

$\therefore$ Interest obtained = 12.5%.

5. Income on Rs. 100 stock = Rs. 13.

6. Number of shares = $\left(\frac{4455}{8.25}\right)$ = 540.

Face value = Rs. (540 × 10) = Rs. 5400.

Annual income = Rs. $\left(\frac{12}{100} \times 5400\right)$ = Rs. 648.

Number of shares = $\left(\frac{14400}{120}\right)$ = 120.

Face value = Rs. (100 × 120) = Rs. 12000.

Annual income = Rs. $\left(\frac{5}{100} \times 12000\right)$ = Rs. 600.

8. For an income of Rs. 8, investment = Rs. 100.

For an income of Rs. 6, investment = Rs. $\left(\frac{100}{8} \times 6\right)$ = Rs. 75.

$\therefore$ Market value of Rs. 100 stock = Rs. 75.

9. To obtain Rs. 8, investment = Rs. 100.

To obtain Rs. 9, investment = Rs. $\left(\frac{100}{8} \times 9\right)$ = Rs. 112.50.

$\therefore$ Market value of Rs. 100 stock = Rs. 112.50.

10. To earn Rs. 10, money invested = Rs. 100.

To earn Rs. 12, money invested = Rs. $\left(\frac{100}{10} \times 12\right)$ = Rs. 120.

$\therefore$ Market value of Rs. 100 stock = Rs. 120.

11. To earn Rs. 135, investment = Rs. 1620.

To earn Rs. 8, investment = Rs. $\left(\frac{1620}{135} \times 8\right)$ = Rs. 96.

$\therefore$ Market value of Rs. 100 stock = Rs. 96.

12. For an income of Rs. 12, stock needed = Rs. 100.

For an income of Rs. 1200, stock needed = Rs. $\left(\frac{100}{12} \times 1200\right)$ = Rs. 10,000.

13. To obtain Rs. 10, investment = Rs. 96.

To obtain Rs. 650, investment = Rs. $\left(\frac{96}{10} \times 650\right)$ = Rs. 6240.

14. To earn Rs. $\frac{50}{3}$, investment = Rs. 64.

To earn Rs. 1500, investment = Rs. $\left(64 \times \frac{3}{50} \times 1500\right)$ = Rs. 5760.

15. By investing Rs. 1552, income = Rs. 128.

By investing Rs. 97, income = Rs. $\left(\frac{128}{1552} \times 97\right)$ = Rs. 8.

$\therefore$ Dividend = 8%.

16. Investment = Rs. [20 × (50 − 5)] = Rs. 900.

Face value = Rs. (50 × 20) = Rs. 1000.

Dividend = Rs. $\left(\frac{27}{2} \times \frac{1000}{100}\right)$ = Rs. 135.

Interest obtained = $\left(\frac{135}{900} \times 100\right)\%$ = 15%.

17. Dividend on Rs. 20 = Rs. $\left(\frac{9}{100} \times 20\right)$ = Rs. $\frac{9}{5}$.

Rs. 12 is an income on Rs. 100.

$\therefore$ Rs. $\frac{9}{5}$ is an income on Rs. $\left(\frac{100}{12} \times \frac{9}{5}\right)$ = Rs. 15.

18. Dividend on 1 share = Rs. $\left(\frac{10}{100} \times 50\right)$ = Rs. 5.

Rs. 12.50 is an income on an investment of Rs. 100.

Rs. 5 is an income on an investment of Rs. $\left(100 \times \frac{2}{25} \times 5\right)$ = Rs. 40.

$\therefore$ Cost of 1 share = Rs. 40.

19. For an income of Rs. 756, investment = Rs. 9000.

For an income of Rs. $\frac{21}{2}$, investment = Rs. $\left(\frac{9000}{756} \times \frac{21}{2}\right)$ = Rs. 125.

$\therefore$ For a Rs. 100 stock, investment = Rs. 125.

Market value of Rs. 100 stock = Rs. $\left(125 - \frac{1}{4}\right)$ = Rs. 124.75.

20. Let investment in 12% stock be Rs. x.
Then, investment in 15% stock = Rs. $(12000 - x)$.

$$\frac{12}{120} \times x + \frac{15}{125} \times (12000 - x) = 1360$$

$$\Leftrightarrow \quad \frac{x}{10} + \frac{3}{25}(12000 - x) = 1360$$

$$\Leftrightarrow \quad 5x + 72000 - 6x = 1360 \times 50 \quad \Leftrightarrow \quad x = 4000.$$

21. Let the investment in 9% stock be Rs. x.
Then, investment in 10% stock = Rs. $(9800 - x)$.

$$\frac{9}{75} \times x = \frac{10}{80} \times (9800 - x) \quad \Leftrightarrow \quad \frac{3x}{25} = \frac{9800 - x}{8}$$

$$\Leftrightarrow \quad 24x = 9800 \times 25 - 25x \quad \Leftrightarrow \quad 49x = 9800 \times 25 \quad \Leftrightarrow \quad x = 5000.$$

22. For an income of Re. 1 in 9% stock at 96, investment = Rs. $\left(\frac{96}{9}\right)$ = Rs. $\frac{32}{3}$.

For an income of Re. 1 in 12% stock at 120, investment = Rs. $\left(\frac{120}{12}\right)$ = Rs. 10.

$\therefore$ Ratio of investments = $\frac{32}{3} : 10 = 32 : 30 = 16 : 15$.

23. Let investment in each case be Rs. (143×117).

Income in 1st case = Rs. $\left(\frac{11}{143} \times 143 \times 117\right)$ = Rs. 1287.

Income in 2nd case = Rs. $\left(\frac{39}{4 \times 117} \times 143 \times 117\right)$ = Rs. 1394.25.

Clearly, $9\frac{3}{4}\%$ stock at 117 is better.

24. Let investment in each case = Rs. (100×120).

Income from 12% stock = Rs. $\left(\frac{12}{100} \times 100 \times 120\right)$ = Rs. 1440.

Net income = Rs. $\left(1440 - \frac{5}{100} \times 1440\right)$ = Rs. 1368.

Income from $14\frac{2}{7}\%$ stock = Rs. $\left(\frac{100}{7 \times 20} \times 100 \times 120\right)$ = Rs. 1428.57.

Clearly, $14\frac{2}{7}\%$ stock is better.

25. For an income of Rs. 10, investment = Rs. 96.

For an income of Rs. 12, investment = Rs. $\left(\frac{96}{10} \times 12\right)$ = Rs. 115.20.

30. PERMUTATIONS AND COMBINATIONS

IMPORTANT FACTS AND FORMULAE

Factorial Notation : Let n be a positive integer. Then, factorial n, denoted by $\underline{|n}$ or $n\,!$ is defined as

$$n\,! = n\,(n-1)\,(n-2)\,.....\,3.2.1.$$

Examples : (*i*) $5\,! = (5 \times 4 \times 3 \times 2 \times 1) = 120$; (*ii*) $4\,! = (4 \times 3 \times 2 \times 1) = 24$ etc.

We define, $0\,! = 1$.

Permutations : *The different arrangements of a given number of things by taking some or all at a time, are called permutations.*

Ex. 1. All permutations (or arrangements) made with the letters *a, b, c* by taking two at a time are (***ab, ba, ac, ca, bc, cb***).

Ex. 2. All permutations made with the letters *a, b, c,* taking all at a time are : (***abc, acb, bac, bca, cab, cba***).

Number of Permutations : Number of all permutations of n things, taken r at a time, is given by :

$${}^n\mathrm{P}_r = n\,(n-1)\,(n-2)\,.....\,(n-r+1) = \frac{n\,!}{(n-r)\,!}$$

Examples : (*i*) ${}^6\mathrm{P}_2 = (6 \times 5) = 30$. (*ii*) ${}^7\mathrm{P}_3 = (7 \times 6 \times 5) = 210$.

Cor. ***Number of all permutations of n things, taken all at a time = n !***

An Important Result : *If there are n objects of which p_1 are alike of one kind; p_2 are alike of another kind; p_3 are alike of third kind and so on and p_r are alike of rth kind, such that $(p_1 + p_2 + ... + p_r) = n$.*

Then, ***number of permutations of these n objects is*** :

$$\frac{n\,!}{(p_1\,!)\cdot(p_2\,!)\,.....\,(p_r\,!)}.$$

Combinations : *Each of the different groups or selections which can be formed by taking some or all of a number of objects, is called a combination.*

Ex. 1. Suppose we want to select two out of three boys A, B, C. Then, possible selections are AB, BC and CA.

Note that AB and BA represent the same selection.

Ex. 2. All the combinations formed by *a, b, c,* taking two at a time are ***ab, bc, ca.***

Ex. 3. The only combination that can be formed of three letters *a, b, c* taken all at a time is ***abc.***

Ex. 4. Various groups of 2 out of four persons A, B, C, D are :

AB, AC, AD, BC, BD, CD.

Ex. 5. Note that *ab* and *ba* are two different permutations but they represent the same combination.

Number of Combinations : The number of all combinations of n things, taken r at a time is :

$$^nC_r = \frac{n\,!}{(r\,!)(n-r)\,!} = \frac{n(n-1)(n-2)\,.....\,\text{to } r \text{ factors}}{r\,!}.$$

Note that : $^nC_n = 1$ *and* $^nC_0 = 1.$

An Important Result : $^nC_r = {}^nC_{(n-r)}.$

Example : (*i*) $^{11}C_4 = \frac{(11 \times 10 \times 9 \times 8)}{(4 \times 3 \times 2 \times 1)} = 330.$

(*ii*) $^{16}C_{13} = {}^{16}C_{(16-13)} = {}^{16}C_3 = \frac{16 \times 15 \times 14}{3\,!} = \frac{16 \times 15 \times 14}{3 \times 2 \times 1} = 560.$

SOLVED EXAMPLES

Ex. 1. ***Evaluate*** : $\frac{30\,!}{28\,!}$

Sol. We have, $\frac{30\,!}{28\,!} = \frac{30 \times 29 \times (28\,!)}{28\,!} = (30 \times 29) = 870.$

Ex. 2. ***Find the value of*** (*i*) $^{60}P_3$ (*ii*) $^4P_4$

Sol. (*i*) $^{60}P_3 = \frac{60\,!}{(60-3)\,!} = \frac{60\,!}{57\,!} = \frac{60 \times 59 \times 58 \times (57\,!)}{57\,!} = (60 \times 59 \times 58) = 205320.$

(*ii*) $^4P_4 = 4\,! = (4 \times 3 \times 2 \times 1) = 24.$

Ex. 3. ***Find the value of*** (*i*) $^{10}C_3$ (*ii*) $^{100}C_{98}$ (*iii*) $^{50}C_{50}$

Sol. (*i*) $^{10}C_3 = \frac{10 \times 9 \times 8}{3\,!} = \frac{10 \times 9 \times 8}{3 \times 2 \times 1} = 120.$

(*ii*) $^{100}C_{98} = {}^{100}C_{(100-98)} = {}^{100}C_2 = \left(\frac{100 \times 99}{2 \times 1}\right) = 4950.$

(*iii*) $^{50}C_{50} = 1.$ $[\because {}^nC_n = 1]$

Ex. 4. ***How many words can be formed by using all letters of the word 'BIHAR' ?***

Sol. The word BIHAR contains 5 different letters.

$\therefore$ Required number of words $= {}^5P_5 = 5\,! = (5 \times 4 \times 3 \times 2 \times 1) = 120.$

Ex. 5. ***How many words can be formed by using all the letters of the word 'DAUGHTER' so that the vowels always come together ?***

Sol. Given word contains 8 different letters. When the vowels AUE are always together, we may suppose them to form an entity, treated as one letter.

Then, the letters to be arranged are DGHTR (AUE).

These 6 letters can be arranged in $^6P_6 = 6\,! = 720$ ways.

The vowels in the group (AUE) may be arranged in $3\,! = 6$ ways.

$\therefore$ Required number of words $= (720 \times 6) = 4320.$

Ex. 6. ***How many words can be formed from the letters of the word 'EXTRA', so that the vowels are never together ?***

Sol. The given word contains 5 different letters.

Taking the vowels EA together, we treat them as one letter.

Then, the letters to be arranged are XTR (EA).

These letters can be arranged in 4 ! = 24 ways.

The vowels EA may be arranged amongst themselves in 2 ! = 2 ways.

Number of words, each having vowels together = (24 × 2) = 48.

Total number of words formed by using all the letters of the given words

= 5 ! = (5 × 4 × 3 × 2 × 1) = 120.

Number of words, each having vowels never together = (120 – 48) = 72.

Ex. 7. ***How many words can be formed from the letters of the word 'DIRECTOR' so that the vowels are always together ?***

Sol. In the given word, we treat the vowels IEO as one letter.

Thus, we have DRCTR (IEO).

This group has 6 letters of which R occurs 2 times and others are different.

Number of ways of arranging these letters $= \frac{6\,!}{2\,!} = 360$.

Now 3 vowels can be arranged among themselves in 3 ! = 6 ways.

∴ Required number of ways = (360 × 6) = 2160.

Ex. 8. ***In how many ways can a cricket eleven be chosen out of a batch of 15 players?***

Sol. Required number of ways $= {}^{15}C_{11} = {}^{15}C_{(15-11)} = {}^{15}C_4$

$$= \frac{15 \times 14 \times 13 \times 12}{4 \times 3 \times 2 \times 1} = 1365.$$

Ex. 9. ***In how many ways, a committee of 5 members can be selected from 6 men and 5 ladies, consisting of 3 men and 2 ladies ?***

Sol. (3 men out 6) and (2 ladies out of 5) are to be chosen.

∴ Required number of ways $= ({}^6C_3 \times {}^5C_2) = \left(\frac{6 \times 5 \times 4}{3 \times 2 \times 1} \times \frac{5 \times 4}{2 \times 1}\right) = 200.$

EXERCISE 30

(OBJECTIVE TYPE QUESTIONS)

Directions : ***Mark (✓) against the correct answer :***

1. The value of ${}^{75}P_2$ is :
   (*a*) 2775 (*b*) 150 (*c*) 5550 (*d*) None of these
2. How many 4-letter words with or without meaning, can be formed out of the letters of the word, 'LOGARITHMS', if repetition of letters is not allowed ?
   (*a*) 40 (*b*) 400 (*c*) 5040 (*d*) 2520
3. How many words with or without meaning, can be formed by using all the letters of the word, 'DELHI', using each letter exactly once ?
   (*a*) 10 (*b*) 25 (*c*) 60 (*d*) 120
4. In how many ways can the letters of the word 'APPLE' be arranged
   (*a*) 720 (*b*) 120 (*c*) 60 (*d*) 180 (*e*) None of these
5. In how many ways can the letters of the word 'LEADER' be arranged ?
   (*a*) 72 (*b*) 144 (*c*) 360 (*d*) 720 (*e*) None of these
   (Bank P.O. 2003)

6. In how many different ways can the letters of the word 'RUMOUR' be arranged ?
(a) 180 (b) 90 (c) 30 (d) 720 (e) None of these
(Bank P.O. 2003)

7. How many words can be formed by using all the letters of the word, 'ALLAHABAD' ?
(a) 3780 (b) 1890 (c) 7560 (d) 2520 (e) None of these

8. How many arrangements can be made out of the letters of the word 'ENGINEERING' ?
(a) 277200 (b) 92400 (c) 69300 (d) 23100 (e) None of these

9. How many words can be formed from the letters of the word 'SIGNATURE' so that the vowels always come together ? **(Bank P.O. 2003)**
(a) 720 (b) 1440 (c) 2880 (d) 3600 (e) 17280

10. In how many different ways can the letters of the word 'OPTICAL' be arranged so that the vowels always come together ? **(M.B.A. 2002)**
(a) 120 (b) 720 (c) 4320 (d) 2160 (e) None of these

11. In how many different ways can the letters of the word 'SOFTWARE' be arranged in such a way that the vowels always come together ? **(Bank P.O. 2003)**
(a) 120 (b) 360 (c) 1440 (d) 13440 (e) 720

12. In how many different ways can the letters of the word 'LEADING' be arranged in such a way that the vowels always come together ? **(Bank P.O. 2002)**
(a) 360 (b) 480 (c) 720 (d) 5040 (e) None of these

13. In how many different ways can the letters of the word 'JUDGE' be arranged in such a way that the vowels always come together ? **(S.B.I.P.O. 2001)**
(a) 48 (b) 120 (c) 124 (d) 160 (e) None of these

14. In how many different ways can the letters of the word 'AUCTION' be arranged in such a way that the vowels always come together ? **(S.B.I.P.O. 2000)**
(a) 30 (b) 48 (c) 144 (d) 576 (e) None of these

15. In how many different ways can the letters of the word 'BANKING' be arranged so that the vowels always come together ? **(Bank P.O. 2003)**
(a) 120 (b) 240 (c) 360 (d) 540 (e) 720

16. In how many different ways can the letters of the word 'CORPORATION' be arranged so that the vowels always come together ? **(S.B.I.P.O. 2003)**
(a) 810 (b) 1440 (c) 2880 (d) 50400 (e) 5760

17. In how many different ways can the letters of the word 'MATHEMATICS' be arranged so that the vowels always come together ?
(a) 10080 (b) 4989600 (c) 120960 (d) None of these

18. In how many different ways can the letters of the word 'DETAIL' be arranged in such a way that the vowels occupy only the odd positions ? **(Bank P.O. 2002)**
(a) 32 (b) 48 (c) 36 (d) 60 (e) 120

19. In how many different ways can the letters of the word 'MACHINE' be arranged so that the vowels may occupy only the odd positions ?
(a) 210 (b) 576 (c) 144 (d) 1728 (e) 3456

20. In how many ways can a group of 5 men and 2 women be made out of a total of 7 men and 3 women ? **(Bank P.O. 2003)**
(a) 63 (b) 90 (c) 126 (d) 45 (e) 135

21. In how many ways a committee, consisting of 5 men and 6 women can be formed from 8 men and 10 women ? **(Bank P.O. 2003)**
(a) 266 (b) 5040 (c) 11760 (d) 86400 (e) None of these

22. From a group of 7 men and 6 women, five persons are to be selected to form a committee so that at least 3 men are there on the committee. In how many ways can it be done ? **(M.B.A. 2002)**
(a) 564 (b) 645 (c) 735 (d) 756 (e) None of these

23. In a group of 6 boys and 4 girls, four children are to be selected. In how many different ways can they be selected such that at least one boy should be there ?

(*a*) 159 (*b*) 194 (*c*) 205 (*d*) 209 (*e*) None of these

(S.B.I.P.O. 2000)

24. A box contains 2 white balls, 3 black balls and 4 red balls. In how many ways can 3 balls be drawn from the box, if at least one black ball is to be included in the draw ?

(*a*) 32 (*b*) 48 (*c*) 64 (*d*) 96 (*e*) None of these

(Bank P.O. 1998)

25. How many 3-digit numbers can be formed from the digits 2, 3, 5, 6, 7 and 9, which are divisible by 5 and none of the digits is repeated ? **(S.S.C. 2000)**

(*a*) 5 (*b*) 10 (*c*) 15 (*d*) 20

26. In how many ways can 21 books on English and 19 books on Hindi be placed in a row on a shelf so that two books on Hindi may not be together ?

(*a*) 3990 (*b*) 1540 (*c*) 1995 (*d*) 3672 (*e*) None of these

27. Out of 7 consonants and 4 vowels, how many words of 3 consonants and 2 vowels can be formed ?

(*a*) 210 (*b*) 1050 (*c*) 25200 (*d*) 21400 (*e*) None of these

ANSWERS

1. (*c*)	**2.** (*c*)	**3.** (*d*)	**4.** (*c*)	**5.** (*c*)	**6.** (*a*)
7. (*c*)	**8.** (*a*)	**9.** (*e*)	**10.** (*c*)	**11.** (*e*)	**12.** (*c*)
13. (*a*)	**14.** (*d*)	**15.** (*e*)	**16.** (*d*)	**17.** (*c*)	**18.** (*c*)
19. (*b*)	**20.** (*a*)	**21.** (*c*)	**22.** (*d*)	**23.** (*d*)	**24.** (*c*)
25. (*d*)	**26.** (*b*)	**27.** (*c*)			

SOLUTIONS

1. $^{75}P_2 = \frac{75\,!}{(75-2)\,!} = \frac{75\,!}{73\,!} = \frac{75 \times 74 \times (73\,!)}{73\,!} = (75 \times 74) = 5550.$

2. 'LOGARITHM' contains 10 different letters.

Required number of words = Number of arrangements of 10 letters, taking 4 at a time

$= {}^{10}P_4 = (10 \times 9 \times 8 \times 7) = 5040.$

3. The word 'DELHI' contains 5 different letters.

Required number of words = Number of arrangements of 5 letters, taken all at a time

$= {}^5P_5 = 5\,! = (5 \times 4 \times 3 \times 2 \times 1) = 120.$

4. The word 'APPLE' contains 5 letters, 1A, 2P, 1L and 1E.

$\therefore$ Required number of ways $= \frac{5\,!}{(1\,!)\,(2\,!)\,(1\,!)\,(1\,!)} = 60.$

5. The word 'LEADER' contains 6 letters, namely 1L, 2E, 1A, 1D and 1R.

$\therefore$ Required number of ways $= \frac{6\,!}{(1\,!)\,(2\,!)\,(1\,!)\,(1\,!)\,(2\,!)} = 360.$

6. The word 'RUMOUR' contains 6 letters, namely 2R, 2U, 1M and 1U.

$\because$ Required number of ways $= \frac{6\,!}{(2\,!)\,(2\,!)\,(1\,!)\,(1\,!)} = 180.$

7. The word 'ALLAHABAD' contains 9 letters, namely 4A, 2L, 1H, 1B and 1D.

$\therefore$ Requisite number of words $= \dfrac{9\,!}{(4\,!)\,(2\,!)\,(1\,!)\,(1\,!)\,(1\,!)} = 7560.$

8. The word 'ENGINEERING' contains 11 letters, namely 3E, 3N, 2G, 2I and 1R.

$\therefore$ Required number of arrangements $= \dfrac{11\,!}{(3\,!)\,(3\,!)\,(2\,!)\,(2\,!)\,(1\,!)} = 277200.$

9. The word 'SIGNATURE' contains 9 different letters.

When the vowels IAUE are taken together, they can be supposed to form an entity, treated as one letter.

Then, the letters to be arranged are SGNTR (IAUE).

These 6 letters can be arranged in ${}^6P_6 = 6\,! = 720$ ways.

The vowels in the group (IAUE) can be arranged amongst themselves in

${}^4P_4 = 4\,! = 24$ ways.

$\therefore$ Required number of words $= (720 \times 24) = 17280.$

10. The word 'OPTICAL' contains 7 different letters.

When the vowels OIA are always together, they can be supposed to form one letter.

Then, we have to arrange the letters PTCL (OIA).

Now, 5 letters can be arranged in $5\,! = 120$ ways.

The vowels (OIA) can be arranged among themselves in $3\,! = 6$ ways.

$\therefore$ Required number of ways $= (120 \times 6) = 720.$

11. The word 'SOFTWARE' contains 8 different letters.

When the vowels OAE are always together, they can be supposed to form one letter.

Thus, we have to arrange the letters SFTWR (OAE).

Now, 5 letters can be arranged in $6\,! = 720$ ways.

The vowels (OAE) can be arranged among themselves in $3\,! = 6$ ways.

$\therefore$ Required number of ways $= (720 \times 6) = 4320.$

12. The word 'LEADING' has 7 different letters.

When the vowels EAI are always together, they can be supposed to form one letter.

Then, we have to arrange the letters LDNG (EAI).

Now, 5 letters can be arranged in $5\,! = 120$ ways.

The vowels (EAI) can be arranged among themselves in $3\,! = 6$ ways.

$\therefore$ Required number of ways $= (120 \times 6) = 720.$

13. The word 'JUDGE' has 5 different letters.

When the vowels UE are always together, they can be supposed to form one letter.

Then, we have to arrange the letters JDG (UE).

Now, 4 letters can be arranged in $4\,! = 24$ ways.

The vowels (UE) can be arranged among themselves in $2\,! = 2$ ways.

$\therefore$ Required number of ways $= (24 \times 2) = 48.$

14. The word 'AUCTION' has 7 different letters.

When the vowels AUIO are always together, they can be supposed to form one letter.

Then, we have to arrange the letters CTN (AUIO).

Now, 4 letters can be arranged in $4\,! = 24$ ways.

The vowels (AUIO) can be arranged among themselves in $4\,! = 24$ ways.

$\therefore$ Required number of ways $= (24 \times 24) = 576.$

15. In the word 'BANKING', we treat the two vowels AI as one letter. Thus, we have BNKNG (AI).

This has 6 letters of which N occurs 2 times and the rest are different.

Number of ways of arranging these letters $= \dfrac{6!}{(2!)(1!)(1!)(1!)(1!)} = 360.$

Now, 2 vowels AI can be arranged in $2! = 2$ ways.

$\therefore$ Required number of ways $= (360 \times 2) = 720.$

16. In the word 'CORPORATION', we treat the vowels OOAIO as one letter. Thus, we have CRPRTN (OOAIO).

This has 7 letters of which R occurs 2 times and the rest are different.

Number of ways of arranging these letters $= \dfrac{7!}{2!} = 2520.$

Now, 5 vowels in which O occurs 3 times and the rest are different, can be arranged in $\dfrac{5!}{3!} = 20$ ways.

$\therefore$ Required number of ways $= (2520 \times 20) = 50400.$

17. In the word 'MATHEMATICS' we treat the vowels AEAI as one letter. Thus, we have MTHMTCS (AEAI).

Now, we have to arrange 8 letters, out of which M occurs twice, T occurs twice and the rest are different.

$\therefore$ Number of ways of arranging these letters $= \dfrac{8!}{(2!)(2!)} = 10080.$

Now, AEAI has 4 letters in which A occurs 2 times and the rest are different.

Number of ways of arranging these letters $= \dfrac{4!}{2!} = 12.$

$\therefore$ Required number of words $= (10080 \times 12) = 120960.$

18. There are 6 letters in the given word, out of which there are 3 vowels and 3 consonants. Let us mark these positions as under :

$$(1)\ (2)\ (3)\ (4)\ (5)\ (6)$$

Now, 3 vowels can be placed at any of the three places out of 4, marked 1, 3, 5.

Number of ways of arranging the vowels $= {}^3P_3 = 3! = 6.$

Also, the 3 consonants can be arranged at the remaining 3 positions.

Number of ways of these arrangements $= {}^3P_3 = 3! = 6.$

Total number of ways $= (6 \times 6) = 36.$

19. There are 7 letters in the given word, out of which there are 3 vowels and 4 consonants. Let us mark the positions to be filled up as follows :

$$(1)\ (2)\ (3)\ (4)\ (5)\ (6)\ (7)$$

Now, 3 vowels can be placed at any of the three places, out of the four marked 1, 3, 5, 7.

$\therefore$ Number of ways of arranging the vowels $= {}^4P_3 = (4 \times 3 \times 2) = 24.$

Also, the 4 consonants at the remaining 4 positions may be arranged in $= {}^4P_4 = 4! = 24$ ways.

$\therefore$ Required number of ways $= (24 \times 24) = 576.$

20. Required number of ways $= ({}^7C_5 \times {}^3C_2) = ({}^7C_2 \times {}^3C_1) = \left(\dfrac{7 \times 6}{2 \times 1} \times 3\right) = 63.$

21. Required number of ways $= ({}^8C_5 \times {}^{10}C_6)$

$$= ({}^8C_3 \times {}^{10}C_4) = \left(\frac{8\times7\times6}{3\times2\times1} \times \frac{10\times9\times8\times7}{4\times3\times2\times1}\right) = 11760.$$

22. We may have (3 men and 2 women) or (4 men and 1 woman) or (5 men only)

$\therefore$ Required number of ways $= ({}^7C_3 \times {}^6C_2) + ({}^7C_4 \times {}^6C_1) + ({}^7C_5)$

$$= \left(\frac{7\times6\times5}{3\times2\times1} \times \frac{6\times5}{2\times1}\right) + ({}^7C_3 \times {}^6C_1) + ({}^7C_2)$$

$$= 525 + \left(\frac{7\times6\times5}{3\times2\times1} \times 6\right) + \left(\frac{7\times6}{2\times1}\right)$$

$$= (525 + 210 + 21) = 756.$$

23. We may have (1 boy and 3 girls) or (2 boys and 2 girls) or (3 boys and 1 girl) or (4 boys).

$\therefore$ Required number of ways $= ({}^6C_1 \times {}^4C_3) + ({}^6C_2 \times {}^4C_2) + ({}^6C_3 \times {}^4C_1) + ({}^6C_4)$

$$= ({}^6C_1 \times {}^4C_1) + ({}^6C_2 \times {}^4C_2) + ({}^6C_3 \times {}^4C_1) + ({}^6C_2)$$

$$= (6\times4) + \left(\frac{6\times5}{2\times1} \times \frac{4\times3}{2\times1}\right) + \left(\frac{6\times5\times4}{3\times2\times1} \times 4\right) + \left(\frac{6\times5}{2\times1}\right)$$

$$= (24 + 90 + 80 + 15) = 209.$$

24. We may have (1 black and 2 non-black) or (2 black and 1 non-black) or (3 black).

$\therefore$ Required number of ways $= ({}^3C_1 \times {}^6C_2) + ({}^3C_2 \times {}^6C_1) + ({}^3C_3)$

$$= \left(3 \times \frac{6\times5}{2\times1}\right) + \left(\frac{3\times2}{2\times1} \times 6\right) + 1 = (45 + 18 + 1) = 64.$$

25. Since each desired number is divisible by 5, so we must have 5 at the unit place. So, there is 1 way of doing it.

Tens place can be filled by any of the remaining 5 numbers.

So, there are 5 ways of filling the tens place.

The hundreds place can now be filled by any of the remaining 4 digits. So, there are 4 ways of filling it.

$\therefore$ Required number of numbers $= (1 \times 5 \times 4) = 20.$

26. In order that two books on Hindi are never together, we must place all these books as under :

X E X E X E X ..... X E X

where E denotes the position of an English book and X that of a Hindi book.

Since there are 21 books on English, the number of places marked X are therefore, 22.

Now, 19 places out of 22 can be chosen in ${}^{22}C_{19} = {}^{22}C_3 = \frac{22\times21\times20}{3\times2\times1} = 1540$ ways.

Hence, the required number of ways = 1540.

27. Number of ways of selecting (3 consonants out of 7) and (2 vowels out of 4)

$$= ({}^7C_3 \times {}^4C_2) = \left(\frac{7\times6\times5}{3\times2\times1} \times \frac{4\times3}{2\times1}\right) = 210.$$

Number of groups, each having 3 consonants and 2 vowels = 210.

Each group contains 5 letters.

Number of ways of arranging 5 letters among themselves

$= 5\,! = (5 \times 4 \times 3 \times 2 \times 1) = 120.$

$\therefore$ Required number of words $= (210 \times 120) = 25200.$

31. PROBABILITY

IMPORTANT FACTS AND FORMULAE

1. **Experiment** : An operation which can produce some well-defined outcomes is called an experiment.
2. **Random Experiment** : An experiment in which all possible outcomes are known and the exact output cannot be predicted in advance, is called a random experiment.

   Examples of Performing a Random Experiment :

   (*i*) Rolling an unbiased dice.

   (*ii*) Tossing a fair coin.

   (*iii*) Drawing a card from a pack of well-shuffled cards.

   (*iv*) Picking up a ball of certain colour from a bag containing balls of different colours.

   Details :

   (*i*) When we throw a coin. Then either a Head (H) or a Tail (T) appears

   (*ii*) A dice is a solid cube, having 6 faces, marked 1, 2, 3, 4, 5, 6 respectively. When we throw a die, the outcome is the number that appears on its upper face.

   (*iii*) A pack of cards has 52 cards.
   It has 13 cards of each suit, namely **Spades, Clubs, Hearts** and **Diamonds.**
   Cards of spades and clubs are **black cards.**
   Cards of hearts and diamonds are **red cards.**
   There are 4 honours of each suit.
   These are **Aces, Kings, Queens** and **Jacks.**
   These are called **face cards.**
3. **Sample Space** : When we perform an experiment, then the set S of all possible outcomes is called the **Sample Space.**

   Examples of Sample Spaces :

   (*i*) In tossing a coin, S = {H, T}.

   (*ii*) If two coins are tossed, then S = {HH, HT, TH, TT}.

   (*iii*) In rolling a dice, we have, S = {1, 2, 3, 4, 5, 6}.
4. **Event** : Any subset of a sample space is called an event.
5. **Probability of Occurrence of an Event :**
   Let S be the sample space and let E be an event.
   Then, $E \subseteq S$.

   $$\therefore \quad P(E) = \frac{n(E)}{n(S)}.$$
6. **Results on Probability :**

   (*i*) $P(S) = 1$ (*ii*) $0 \le P(E) \le 1$ (*iii*) $P(\phi) = 0$

   (*iv*) For any events A and B, we have :
   $P(A \cup B) = P(A) + P(B) - P(A \cap B)$

   (*v*) If $\overline{A}$ denotes (not-A), then $P(\overline{A}) = 1 - P(A)$.

SOLVED EXAMPLES

Ex. 1. ***In a throw of a coin, find the probability of getting a head.***

Sol. Here S = {H, T} and E = {H}.

$\therefore \quad P(E) = \dfrac{n(E)}{n(S)} = \dfrac{1}{2}.$

Ex. 2. ***Two unbiased coins are tossed. What is the probability of getting at most one head ?***

Sol. Here S = {HH, HT, TH, T T}.

Let E = event of getting at most one head.

$\therefore$ E = {T T, HT, TH}.

$\therefore \quad P(E) = \dfrac{n(E)}{n(S)} = \dfrac{3}{4}.$

Ex. 3. ***An unbiased die is tossed. Find the probability of getting a multiple of 3.***

Sol. Here S = {1, 2, 3, 4, 5, 6}.

Let E be the event of getting a multiple of 3.

Then, E = {3, 6}

$\therefore \quad P(E) = \dfrac{n(E)}{n(S)} = \dfrac{2}{6} = \dfrac{1}{3}.$

Ex. 4. ***In a simultaneous throw of a pair of dice, find the probability of getting a total more than 7.***

Sol. Here, n (S) = (6 × 6) = 36.

Let E = Event of getting a total more than 7

= {(2, 6), (3, 5), (3, 6), (4, 4), (4, 5), (4, 6), (5, 3), (5, 4), (5, 5), (5, 6), (6, 2) (6, 3), (6, 4), (6, 5), (6, 6)}.

$\therefore \quad P(E) = \dfrac{n(E)}{n(S)} = \dfrac{15}{36} = \dfrac{5}{12}.$

Ex. 5. ***A bag contains 6 white and 4 black balls. Two balls are drawn at random Find the probability that they are of the same colour.***

Sol. Let S be the sample space. Then,

$n(S)$ = Number of ways of drawing 2 balls out of $(6 + 4) = {}^{10}C_2 = \dfrac{(10 \times 9)}{(2 \times 1)} = 45.$

Let E = Event of getting both balls of the same colour. Then,

$n(E)$ = Number of ways of drawing (2 balls out of 6) or (2 balls out of 4)

$= ({}^6C_2 + {}^4C_2) = \dfrac{(6 \times 5)}{(2 \times 1)} + \dfrac{(4 \times 3)}{(2 \times 1)} = (15 + 6) = 21.$

$\therefore \quad P(E) = \dfrac{n(E)}{n(S)} = \dfrac{21}{45} = \dfrac{7}{15}.$

Ex. 6. ***Two dice are thrown together. What is the probability that the sum of the numbers on the two faces is divisible by 4 or 6 ?***

Sol. Clearly, n (S) = 6 × 6 = 36.

Let E be the event that the sum of the numbers on the two faces is divisible by 4 or 6. Then

E = {(1, 3), (1, 5), (2, 2), (2, 4), (2, 6), (3, 1), (3, 3), (3, 5), (4, 2), (4, 4), (5, 1), (5, 3), (6, 2), (6, 6)}

$\therefore$ n (E) = 14.

Hence, $P(E) = \dfrac{n(E)}{n(S)} = \dfrac{14}{36} = \dfrac{7}{18}.$

Ex. 7. ***Two cards are drawn at random from a pack of 52 cards. What is the probability that either both are black or both are queens ?***

Sol. We have $n(S) = {}^{52}C_2 = \frac{(52 \times 51)}{(2 \times 1)} = 1326.$

Let A = event of getting both black cards;

B = event of getting both queens.

$\therefore$ $A \cap B$ = event of getting queens of black cards.

$\therefore$ $n(A) = {}^{26}C_2 = \frac{(26 \times 25)}{(2 \times 1)} = 325,\ n(B) = {}^{4}C_2 = \frac{(4 \times 3)}{(2 \times 1)} = 6$ and $n(A \cap B) = {}^{2}C_2 = 1.$

$\therefore$ $P(A) = \frac{n(A)}{n(S)} = \frac{325}{1326},\ P(B) = \frac{n(B)}{n(S)} = \frac{6}{1326}$ and $P(A \cap B) = \frac{n(A \cap B)}{n(S)} = \frac{1}{1326}.$

$\therefore$ $P(A \cup B) = P(A) + P(B) - P(A \cap B) = \left(\frac{325}{1326} + \frac{6}{1326} - \frac{1}{1326}\right) = \frac{330}{1326} = \frac{55}{221}.$

EXERCISE 31

(OBJECTIVE TYPE QUESTIONS)

Directions : ***Mark (✓) against the correct answer :***

1. In a simultaneous throw of two coins, the probability of getting at least one head is :

   (a) $\frac{1}{2}$ (b) $\frac{1}{3}$ (c) $\frac{2}{3}$ (d) $\frac{3}{4}$

2. Three unbiased coins are tossed. What is the probability of getting at least 2 heads ?

   (a) $\frac{1}{4}$ (b) $\frac{1}{2}$ (c) $\frac{1}{3}$ (d) $\frac{1}{8}$

3. Three unbiased coins are tossed. What is the probability of getting at most two heads ?

   (a) $\frac{3}{4}$ (b) $\frac{1}{4}$ (c) $\frac{3}{8}$ (d) $\frac{7}{8}$

4. In a single throw of a die, what is the probability of getting a number greater than 4 ?

   (a) $\frac{1}{2}$ (b) $\frac{1}{3}$ (c) $\frac{2}{3}$ (d) $\frac{1}{4}$

5. In a simultaneous throw of two dice, what is the probability of getting a total of 7 ?

   (a) $\frac{1}{6}$ (b) $\frac{1}{4}$ (c) $\frac{2}{3}$ (d) $\frac{3}{4}$

6. What is the probability of getting a sum 9 from two throws of a dice ?

   (a) $\frac{1}{6}$ (b) $\frac{1}{8}$ (c) $\frac{1}{9}$ (d) $\frac{1}{12}$

   (M.B.A. 2002)

7. In a simultaneous throw of two dice, what is the probability of getting a doublet ?

   (a) $\frac{1}{6}$ (b) $\frac{1}{4}$ (c) $\frac{2}{3}$ (d) $\frac{3}{7}$

8. In a simultaneous throw of two dice, what is the probability of getting a total of 10 or 11 ?

   (a) $\frac{1}{4}$ (b) $\frac{1}{6}$ (c) $\frac{7}{12}$ (d) $\frac{5}{36}$

9. Two dice are thrown simultaneously. What is the probability of getting two numbers whose product is even ? **(Asstt. PF Commissioner's Exam, 2002)**

(a) $\frac{1}{2}$ (b) $\frac{3}{4}$ (c) $\frac{3}{8}$ (d) $\frac{5}{16}$

10. Tickets numbered 1 to 20 are mixed up and then a ticket is drawn at random. What is the probability that the ticket drawn bears a number which is a multiple of 3 ?

(a) $\frac{3}{10}$ (b) $\frac{3}{20}$ (c) $\frac{2}{5}$ (d) $\frac{1}{2}$

11. Tickets numbered 1 to 20 are mixed up and then a ticket is drawn at random. What is the probability that the ticket drawn has a number which is a multiple of 3 or 5 ?

(a) $\frac{1}{2}$ (b) $\frac{2}{5}$ (c) $\frac{8}{15}$ (d) $\frac{9}{20}$

12. In a lottery, there are 10 prizes and 25 blanks. A lottery is drawn at random. What is the probability of getting a prize ?

(a) $\frac{1}{10}$ (b) $\frac{2}{5}$ (c) $\frac{2}{7}$ (d) $\frac{5}{7}$

13. One card is drawn at random from a pack of 52 cards. What is the probability that the card drawn is a face card ?

(a) $\frac{1}{13}$ (b) $\frac{4}{13}$ (c) $\frac{1}{4}$ (d) $\frac{9}{52}$

14. A card is drawn from a pack of 52 cards. The probability of getting a queen of club or a king of heart is :

(a) $\frac{1}{13}$ (b) $\frac{2}{13}$ (c) $\frac{1}{26}$ (d) $\frac{1}{52}$

15. One card is drawn from a pack of 52 cards. What is the probability that the card drawn is either a red card or a king ?

(a) $\frac{1}{2}$ (b) $\frac{6}{13}$ (c) $\frac{7}{13}$ (d) $\frac{27}{52}$

16. From a pack of 52 cards, one card is drawn at random. What is the probability that the card drawn is a ten or a spade ?

(a) $\frac{4}{13}$ (b) $\frac{1}{4}$ (c) $\frac{1}{13}$ (d) $\frac{1}{26}$

17. The probability that a card drawn from a pack of 52 cards will be a diamond or a king, is :

(a) $\frac{2}{13}$ (b) $\frac{4}{13}$ (c) $\frac{1}{13}$ (d) $\frac{1}{52}$

18. From a pack of 52 cards, two cards are drawn together at random. What is the probability of both the cards being kings ? **(M.B.A. 2002; Railways, 2002)**

(a) $\frac{1}{15}$ (b) $\frac{25}{57}$ (c) $\frac{35}{256}$ (d) $\frac{1}{221}$

19. Two cards are drawn together from a pack of 52 cards. The probability that one is a spade and one is a heart, is : **(M.B.A. 2000)**

(a) $\frac{3}{20}$ (b) $\frac{29}{34}$ (c) $\frac{47}{100}$ (d) $\frac{13}{102}$

20. Two cards are drawn from a pack of 52 cards. The probability that either both are red or both are kings, is :

(a) $\frac{7}{13}$ (b) $\frac{3}{26}$ (c) $\frac{63}{221}$ (d) $\frac{55}{221}$

21. A bag contains 6 black and 8 white balls. One ball is drawn at random. What is the probability that the ball drawn is white ?

(a) $\frac{3}{4}$ (b) $\frac{4}{7}$ (c) $\frac{1}{8}$ (d) $\frac{3}{7}$

22. A box contains 5 green, 4 yellow and 3 white marbles. Three marbles are drawn at random. What is the probability that they are not of the same colour ?

(a) $\frac{3}{44}$ (b) $\frac{3}{55}$ (c) $\frac{52}{55}$ (d) $\frac{41}{44}$

(Bank P.O. 2000)

23. A bag contains 4 white, 5 red and 6 blue balls. Three balls are drawn at random from the bag. The probability that all of them are red, is : **(M.B.A. 2002)**

(a) $\frac{1}{22}$ (b) $\frac{3}{22}$ (c) $\frac{2}{91}$ (d) $\frac{2}{77}$

24. A bag contains 6 white and 4 red balls. Three balls are drawn at random. What is the probability that one ball is red and the other two are white ?

(a) $\frac{1}{2}$ (b) $\frac{1}{12}$ (c) $\frac{3}{10}$ (d) $\frac{7}{12}$

25. A bag contains 2 red, 3 green and 2 blue balls. Two balls are drawn at random. What is the probability that none of the balls drawn is blue ? **(Bank P.O. 2003)**

(a) $\frac{10}{21}$ (b) $\frac{11}{21}$ (c) $\frac{2}{7}$ (d) $\frac{5}{7}$

26. In a box, there are 8 red, 7 blue and 6 green balls. One ball is picked up randomly. What is the probability that it is neither red nor green ? **(Bank P.O. 2002)**

(a) $\frac{2}{3}$ (b) $\frac{3}{4}$ (c) $\frac{7}{19}$ (d) $\frac{8}{21}$ (e) $\frac{9}{21}$

27. A box contains 10 black and 10 white balls. The probability of drawing two balls of the same colour, is :

(a) $\frac{9}{19}$ (b) $\frac{9}{38}$ (c) $\frac{10}{19}$ (d) $\frac{5}{19}$

28. A box contains 4 red balls, 5 green balls and 6 white balls. A ball is drawn at random from the box. What is the probability that the ball drawn is either red or green ?

(a) $\frac{2}{5}$ (b) $\frac{3}{5}$ (c) $\frac{1}{5}$ (d) $\frac{7}{15}$

29. In a class, there are 15 boys and 10 girls. Three students are selected at random. The probability that 1 girl and 2 boys are selected, is :

(a) $\frac{21}{46}$ (b) $\frac{25}{117}$ (c) $\frac{1}{50}$ (d) $\frac{3}{25}$

30. Four persons are chosen at random from a group of 3 men, 2 women and 4 children. The chance that exactly 2 of them are children, is :

(a) $\frac{1}{9}$ (b) $\frac{1}{5}$ (c) $\frac{1}{12}$ (d) $\frac{10}{21}$

31. A box contains 20 electric bulbs, out of which 4 are defective. Two bulbs are chosen at random from this box. The probability that at least one of these is defective, is :

(a) $\frac{4}{19}$ (b) $\frac{7}{19}$ (c) $\frac{12}{19}$ (d) $\frac{21}{95}$

32. In a class, 30% of the students offered English, 20% offered Hindi and 10% offered both. If a student is selected at random, what is the probability that he has offered English or Hindi ?

(a) $\frac{2}{5}$ (b) $\frac{3}{4}$ (c) $\frac{3}{5}$ (d) $\frac{3}{10}$

33. Two dice are tossed. The probability that the total score is a prime number is :

(a) $\frac{1}{6}$ (b) $\frac{5}{12}$ (c) $\frac{1}{2}$ (d) $\frac{7}{9}$

34. A speaks truth in 75% cases and B in 80% of the cases. In what percentage of cases are they likely to contradict each other, narrating the same incident ?

(a) 5% (b) 15% (c) 35% (d) 45%

(Bank P.O. 2000)

35. A man and his wife appear in an interview for two vacancies in the same post. The probability of husband's selection is (1/7) and the probability of wife's selection is (1/5). What is the probability that only one of them is selected ?

(a) $\frac{4}{5}$ (b) $\frac{2}{7}$ (c) $\frac{8}{15}$ (d) $\frac{4}{7}$

ANSWERS

1. (d)	**2.** (b)	**3.** (d)	**4.** (b)	**5.** (a)	**6.** (c)	**7.** (a)	**8.** (d)	**9.** (b)
10. (a)	**11.** (d)	**12.** (c)	**13.** (b)	**14.** (c)	**15.** (c)	**16.** (a)	**17.** (b)	**18.** (d)
19. (d)	**20.** (d)	**21.** (b)	**22.** (d)	**23.** (c)	**24.** (a)	**25.** (a)	**26.** (d)	**27.** (a)
28. (b)	**29.** (a)	**30.** (d)	**31.** (b)	**32.** (a)	**33.** (b)	**34.** (c)	**35.** (b)	

SOLUTIONS

1. Here S = {HH, HT, TH, T T}.

Let E = event of getting at least one head = {HT, TH, HH}.

$\therefore \quad P(E) = \frac{n(E)}{n(S)} = \frac{3}{4}$.

2. Here S = {TTT, TTH, THT, HTT, THH, HTH, HHT, HHH}.

Let E = event of getting at least two heads = {THH, HTH, HHT, HHH}.

$\therefore \quad P(E) = \frac{n(E)}{n(S)} = \frac{4}{8} = \frac{1}{2}$.

3. Here S = {TTT, TTH, THT, HTT, THH, HTH, HHT, HHH}.

Let E = event of getting at most two heads.

Then, E = {TTT, TTH, THT, HTT, THH, HTH, HHT}.

$\therefore \quad P(E) = \frac{n(E)}{n(S)} = \frac{7}{8}$.

4. When a die is thrown, we have S = {1, 2, 3, 4, 5, 6}.

Let E = event of getting a number greater than 4 = {5, 6}.

$\therefore \quad P(E) = \frac{n(E)}{n(S)} = \frac{2}{6} = \frac{1}{3}$.

5. We know that in a simultaneous throw of two dice, $n(S) = 6 \times 6 = 36$.

Let E = event of getting a total of 7 = {(1, 6), (2, 5), (3, 4), (4, 3), (5, 2), (6, 1)}.

$\therefore \quad P(E) = \frac{n(E)}{n(S)} = \frac{6}{36} = \frac{1}{6}$.

6. In two throws of a die, $n(S) = (6 \times 6) = 36$.

Let E = event of getting a sum 9 = {(3, 6), (4, 5), (5, 4), (6, 3)}.

$\therefore \quad P(E) = \frac{n(E)}{n(S)} = \frac{4}{36} = \frac{1}{9}$.

7. In a simultaneous throw of two dice, n (S) = (6 × 6) = 36.

Let E = event of getting a doublet = {(1, 1), (2, 2), (3, 3), (4, 4), (5, 5), (6, 6)}.

$\therefore \quad P(E) = \frac{n(E)}{n(S)} = \frac{6}{36} = \frac{1}{6}.$

8. In a simultaneous throw of two dice, we have n (S) = (6 × 6) = 36.

Let E = event of getting a total of 10 or 11 = {(4, 6), (5, 5), (6, 4), (5, 6), (6, 5)}

$\therefore \quad P(E) = \frac{n(E)}{n(S)} = \frac{5}{36}.$

9. In a simultaneous throw of two dice, we have n (S) = (6 × 6) = 36.

Let E = event of getting two numbers whose product is even.

Then, E = {(1, 2), (1, 4), (1, 6), (2, 1), (2, 2), (2, 3), (2, 4), (2, 5), (2, 6), (3, 2), (3, 4), (3, 6), (4, 1), (4, 2), (4, 3), (4, 4), (4, 5), (4, 6), (5, 2), (5, 4), (5, 6), (6, 1), (6, 2), (6, 3), (6, 4), (6, 5), (6, 6)}.

$\therefore \quad n$ (E) = 27.

$\therefore \quad P(E) = \frac{n(E)}{n(S)} = \frac{27}{36} = \frac{3}{4}.$

10. Here, S = {1, 2, 3, 4, ..., 19, 20}.

Let E = event of getting a multiple of 3 = {3, 6, 9, 12, 15, 18}.

$\therefore \quad P(E) = \frac{n(E)}{n(S)} = \frac{6}{20} = \frac{3}{10}.$

11. Here, S = {1, 2, 3, 4, ..., 19, 20}.

Let E = event of getting a multiple of 3 or 5 = {3, 6, 9, 12, 15, 18, 5, 10, 20}.

$\therefore \quad P(E) = \frac{n(E)}{n(S)} = \frac{9}{20}.$

12. $P\text{ (getting a prize)} = \frac{10}{(10+25)} = \frac{10}{35} = \frac{2}{7}.$

13. Clearly, there are 52 cards, out of which there are 16 face cards.

$\therefore \quad P\text{ (getting a face card)} = \frac{16}{52} = \frac{4}{13}.$

14. Here, n (S) = 52.

Let E = event of getting a queen of club or a king of heart.

Then, n (E) = 2.

$\therefore \quad P(E) = \frac{n(E)}{n(S)} = \frac{2}{52} = \frac{1}{26}.$

15. Here, n (S) = 52.

There are 26 red cards (including 2 kings) and there are 2 more kings.

Let E = event of getting a red card or a king.

Then, n (E) = 28.

$\therefore \quad P(E) = \frac{n(E)}{n(S)} = \frac{28}{52} = \frac{7}{13}.$

16. Here, n (S) = 52.

There are 13 spades (including one ten) and there are 3 more tens.

Let E = event of getting a ten or a spade.

Then, n (E) = (13 + 3) = 16.

$\therefore \quad P(E) = \frac{n(E)}{n(S)} = \frac{16}{52} = \frac{4}{13}.$

17. Here, n (S) = 52.

There are 13 cards of diamond (including one king) and there are 3 more kings.

Let E = event of getting a diamond or a king.

Then, n (E) = (13 + 3) = 16.

$$\therefore \quad P(E) = \frac{n(E)}{n(S)} = \frac{16}{52} = \frac{4}{13}.$$

18. Let S be the sample space. Then,

$$n(S) = {}^{52}C_2 = \frac{(52 \times 51)}{(2 \times 1)} = 1326.$$

Let E = event of getting 2 kings out of 4.

$$\therefore \quad n(E) = {}^4C_2 = \frac{(4 \times 3)}{(2 \times 1)} = 6.$$

$$\therefore \quad P(E) = \frac{n(E)}{n(S)} = \frac{6}{1326} = \frac{1}{221}.$$

19. Let S be the sample space. Then,

$$n(S) = {}^{52}C_2 = \frac{(52 \times 51)}{(2 \times 1)} = 1326.$$

Let E = event of getting 1 spade and 1 heart.

$\therefore$ n (E) = number of ways of choosing 1 spade out of 13 and 1 heart out of 13

$$= ({}^{13}C_1 \times {}^{13}C_1) = (13 \times 13) = 169.$$

$$\therefore \quad P(E) = \frac{n(E)}{n(S)} = \frac{169}{1326} = \frac{13}{102}.$$

20. Clearly, $n(S) = {}^{52}C_2 = \frac{(52 \times 51)}{2} = 1326.$

Let E_1 = event of getting both red cards,

E_2 = event of getting both kings.

Then, $E_1 \cap E_2$ = event of getting 2 kings of red cards.

$$\therefore \quad n(E_1) = {}^{26}C_2 = \frac{(26 \times 25)}{(2 \times 1)} = 325; \; n(E_2) = {}^4C_2 = \frac{(4 \times 3)}{(2 \times 1)} = 6;$$

$$n(E_1 \cap E_2) = {}^2C_2 = 1.$$

$$\therefore \quad P(E_1) = \frac{n(E_1)}{n(S)} = \frac{325}{1326}; \; P(E_2) = \frac{n(E_2)}{n(S)} = \frac{6}{1326}; \; P(E_1 \cap E_2) = \frac{1}{1326}.$$

$$\therefore \quad P(\text{both red or both kings}) = P(E_1 \cup E_2)$$

$$= P(E_1) + P(E_2) - P(E_1 \cap E_2)$$

$$= \left(\frac{325}{1326} + \frac{6}{1326} - \frac{1}{1326}\right) = \frac{330}{1326} = \frac{55}{221}.$$

21. Total number of balls = (6 + 8) = 14.

Number of white balls = 8.

$$P(\text{drawing a white ball}) = \frac{8}{14} = \frac{4}{7}.$$

22. Let S be the sample space. Then,

n (S) = number of ways of drawing 3 marbles out of 12

$$= {}^{12}C_3 = \frac{(12 \times 11 \times 10)}{(3 \times 2 \times 1)} = 220.$$

Let E be the event of drawing 3 balls of the same colour.

Then, E = event of drawing (3 balls out of 5) or (3 balls out of 4) or (3 balls out of 3)

$\Rightarrow \quad n(E) = ({}^5C_3 + {}^4C_3 + {}^3C_3) = ({}^5C_2 + {}^4C_1 + 1) = \frac{(5 \times 4)}{(2 \times 1)} + 4 + 1 = 15.$

$\Rightarrow \quad P(E) = \frac{n(E)}{n(S)} = \frac{15}{220} = \frac{3}{44}.$

$\therefore \quad$ Required probability $= \left(1 - \frac{3}{44}\right) = \frac{41}{44}.$

23. Let S be the sample space. Then,

$n(S)$ = number of ways of drawing 3 balls out of 15 $= {}^{15}C_3 = \frac{(15 \times 14 \times 13)}{(3 \times 2 \times 1)} = 455.$

Let E = event of getting all the 3 red balls.

$\therefore \quad n(E) = {}^5C_3 = {}^5C_2 = \frac{(5 \times 4)}{(2 \times 1)} = 10.$

$\therefore \quad P(E) = \frac{n(E)}{n(S)} = \frac{10}{455} = \frac{2}{91}.$

24. Let S be the sample space. Then,

$n(S)$ = number of ways of drawing 3 balls out of 10

$= {}^{10}C_3 = \frac{(10 \times 9 \times 8)}{(3 \times 2 \times 1)} = 120.$

Let E = event of drawing 1 red and 2 white balls

$\therefore \quad n(E)$ = Number of ways of drawing 1 red ball out of 4 and 2 white balls out of 6

$= ({}^4C_1 \times {}^6C_2) = \left(4 \times \frac{6 \times 5}{2 \times 1}\right) = 60.$

$\therefore \quad P(E) = \frac{n(E)}{n(S)} = \frac{60}{120} = \frac{1}{2}.$

25. Total number of balls = (2 + 3 + 2) = 7.

Let S be the sample space. Then,

$n(S)$ = Number of ways of drawing 2 balls out of 7 $= {}^7C_2 = \frac{(7 \times 6)}{(2 \times 1)} = 21.$

Let E = Event of drawing 2 balls, none of which is blue.

$\therefore \quad n(E)$ = Number of ways of drawing 2 balls out of (2 + 3) balls

$= {}^5C_2 = \frac{(5 \times 4)}{(2 \times 1)} = 10.$

$\therefore \quad P(E) = \frac{n(E)}{n(S)} = \frac{10}{21}.$

26. Total number of balls = (8 + 7 + 6) = 21.

Let E = event that the ball drawn is neither red nor green

= event that the ball drawn is red.

$\therefore \quad n(E) = 8$

$\therefore \quad P(E) = \frac{8}{21}.$

27. Total number of balls = 20.

Let S be the sample space. Then,

$n(S)$ = Number of ways of drawing 2 balls out of 20 $= {}^{20}C_2 = \frac{(20 \times 19)}{(2 \times 1)} = 190.$

Let E = event of drawing 2 balls of the same colour

$n(E)\ (^{10}C_2 + {}^{10}C_2) = 2 \times \left(\frac{10 \times 9}{2 \times 1}\right) = 90.$

$\therefore\quad P(E) = \frac{n(E)}{n(S)} = \frac{90}{190} = \frac{9}{19}.$

28. Total number of balls = (4 + 5 + 6) = 15.

$\therefore\quad n(S) = 15.$

Let E_1 = event of drawing a red ball

and E_2 = event of drawing a green ball.

Then, $E_1 \cap E_2 = \phi$.

$P(E_1 \text{ or } E_2) = P(E_1) + P(E_2) = \left(\frac{4}{15} + \frac{5}{15}\right) = \frac{9}{15} = \frac{3}{5}.$

29. Let S be the sample space and E be the event of selecting 1 girl and 2 boys. Then,

n (S) = Number of ways of selecting 3 students out of 25

$= {}^{25}C_3 = \frac{(25 \times 24 \times 23)}{(3 \times 2 \times 1)} = 2300.$

$n(E) = (^{10}C_1 \times {}^{15}C_2) = \left\{10 \times \frac{(15 \times 14)}{(2 \times 1)}\right\} = 1050.$

$\therefore\quad P(E) = \frac{n(E)}{n(S)} = \frac{1050}{2300} = \frac{21}{46}.$

30. Let S be the sample space and E be the event of choosing four persons such that 2 of them are children. Then,

n (S) = Number of ways of choosing 4 persons out of 9

$= {}^9C_4 = \frac{(9 \times 8 \times 7 \times 6)}{(4 \times 3 \times 2 \times 1)} = 126.$

n (E) = Number of ways of choosing 2 children out of 4 and 2 persons out of (3 + 2) persons

$= (^4C_2 \times {}^5C_2) = \frac{(4 \times 3)}{(2 \times 1)} \times \frac{(5 \times 4)}{(2 \times 1)} = 60.$

$\therefore\quad P(E) = \frac{n(E)}{n(S)} = \frac{60}{126} = \frac{10}{21}.$

31. $P(\text{None is defective}) = \frac{^{16}C_2}{^{20}C_2} = \left(\frac{16 \times 15}{2 \times 1} \times \frac{2 \times 1}{20 \times 19}\right) = \frac{12}{19}.$

$P(\text{at least one is defective}) = \left(1 - \frac{12}{19}\right) = \frac{7}{19}.$

32. $P(E) = \frac{30}{100} = \frac{3}{10}$, $P(H) = \frac{20}{100} = \frac{1}{5}$ and $P(E \cap H) = \frac{10}{100} = \frac{1}{10}.$

$P(E \text{ or } H) = P(E \cup H)$

$= P(E) + P(H) - P(E \cap H)$

$= \left(\frac{3}{10} + \frac{1}{5} - \frac{1}{10}\right) = \frac{4}{10} = \frac{2}{5}.$

33. Clearly, $n(S) = (6 \times 6) = 36$.

Let E = Event that the sum is a prime number.

Then, E = {(1, 1), (1, 2), (1, 4), (1, 6), (2, 1), (2, 3), (2, 5), (3, 2), (3, 4), (4, 1), (4, 3), (5, 2), (5, 6), (6, 1), (6, 5)}

$\therefore \quad n(E) = 15$

$$\therefore \quad P(E) = \frac{n(E)}{n(S)} = \frac{15}{36} = \frac{5}{12}.$$

34. Let A = Event that A speaks the truth

and B = Event that B speaks the truth.

Then, $P(A) = \frac{75}{100} = \frac{3}{4}$, $P(B) = \frac{80}{100} = \frac{4}{5}$.

$$\therefore \quad P(\bar{A}) = \left(1 - \frac{3}{4}\right) = \frac{1}{4} \text{ and } P(\bar{B}) = \left(1 - \frac{4}{5}\right) = \frac{1}{5}.$$

P (A and B contradict each other)

= P [(A speaks the truth and B tells a lie) or (A tells a lie and B speaks the truth)]

$= P[(A \text{ and } \bar{B}) \text{ or } (\bar{A} \text{ and } B)]$

$= P(A \text{ and } \bar{B}) + P(\bar{A} \text{ and } B)$

$= P(A) \cdot P(\bar{B}) + P(\bar{A}) \cdot P(B)$

$$= \left(\frac{3}{4} \times \frac{1}{5}\right) + \left(\frac{1}{4} \times \frac{4}{5}\right) = \left(\frac{3}{20} + \frac{1}{5}\right) = \frac{7}{20} = \left(\frac{7}{20} \times 100\right)\% = 35\%.$$

$\therefore$ A and B contradict each other in 35% of the cases.

35. Let A = Event that the husband is selected

and B = Event that the wife is selected.

Then, $P(A) = \frac{1}{7}$ and $P(B) = \frac{1}{5}$.

$$\therefore \quad P(\bar{A}) = \left(1 - \frac{1}{7}\right) = \frac{6}{7} \text{ and } P(\bar{B}) = \left(1 - \frac{1}{5}\right) = \frac{4}{5}.$$

$\therefore$ Required probability = P [(A and not B) or (B and not A)]

$= P[(A \text{ and } \bar{B}) \text{ or } (B \text{ and } \bar{A})]$

$= P(A \text{ and } \bar{B}) + P(B \text{ and } \bar{A})$

$$= P(A) \cdot P(\bar{B}) + P(B) \cdot P(\bar{A}) = \left(\frac{1}{7} \times \frac{4}{5}\right) + \left(\frac{1}{5} \times \frac{6}{7}\right) = \frac{10}{35} = \frac{2}{7}.$$

32. TRUE DISCOUNT

IMPORTANT CONCEPTS

Suppose a man has to pay Rs. 156 after 4 years and the rate of interest is 14% per annum. Clearly, Rs. 100 at 14% will amount to Rs. 156 in 4 years. So, the payment of Rs. 100 now will clear off the debt of Rs. 156 due 4 years hence. We say that :

Sum due = Rs. 156 due 4 years hence;

Present Worth (P.W.) = Rs. 100;

True Discount (T.D.) = Rs. (156 − 100) = Rs. 56 = (Sum due) − (P.W.).

We define : ***T.D. = Interest on P.W.***

Amount = (P.W.) + (T.D.).

Interest is reckoned on P.W. and true discount is reckoned on the amount.

IMPORTANT FORMULAE

Let rate = R% per annum and Time = T years. Then,

1. $\text{P.W.} = \dfrac{100 \times \text{Amount}}{100 + (\text{R} \times \text{T})} = \dfrac{100 \times \text{T.D.}}{\text{R} \times \text{T}}$.

2. $\text{T.D.} = \dfrac{(\text{P.W.}) \times \text{R} \times \text{T}}{100} = \dfrac{\text{Amount} \times \text{R} \times \text{T}}{100 + (\text{R} \times \text{T})}$.

3. $\text{Sum} = \dfrac{(\text{S.I.}) \times (\text{T.D.})}{(\text{S.I.}) - (\text{T.D.})}$.

4. (S.I.) − (T.D.) = S.I. on T.D.

5. When the sum is put at compound interest, then $\text{P.W.} = \dfrac{\text{Amount}}{\left(1 + \dfrac{\text{R}}{100}\right)^{\text{T}}}$

SOLVED EXAMPLES

Ex. 1. ***Find the present worth of Rs. 930 due 3 years hence at 8% per annum. Also find the discount.***

Sol. $\text{P.W.} = \dfrac{100 \times \text{Amount}}{100 + (\text{R} \times \text{T})} = \text{Rs.} \left[\dfrac{100 \times 930}{100 + (8 \times 3)}\right] = \text{Rs.} \left(\dfrac{100 \times 930}{124}\right) = \text{Rs. } 750.$

T.D. = (Amount) − (P.W.) = Rs. (930 − 750) = Rs. 180.

Ex. 2. ***The true discount on a bill due 9 months hence at 12% per annum is Rs. 540. Find the amount of the bill and its present worth.***

Sol. Let amount be Rs. x. Then,

$$\frac{x \times \text{R} \times \text{T}}{100 + (\text{R} \times \text{T})} = \text{T.D.} \Rightarrow \frac{x \times 12 \times \frac{3}{4}}{100 + \left(12 \times \frac{3}{4}\right)} = 540 \Rightarrow x = \left(\frac{540 \times 109}{9}\right) = \text{Rs. } 6540.$$

∴ Amount = Rs. 6540.

P.W. = Rs. (6540 − 540) = Rs. 6000.

Ex. 3. ***The true discount on a certain sum of money due 3 years hence is Rs. 250 and the simple interest on the same sum for the same time and at the same rate is Rs. 375. Find the sum and the rate percent.***

Sol. T.D. = Rs. 250 and S.I. = Rs. 375.

$\therefore$ Sum due $= \dfrac{\text{S.I.} \times \text{T.D.}}{(\text{S.I.}) - (\text{T.D.})} = \text{Rs.} \left(\dfrac{375 \times 250}{375 - 250}\right) = \text{Rs. } 750.$

Rate $= \left(\dfrac{100 \times 375}{750 \times 3}\right)\% = 16\dfrac{2}{3}\%.$

Ex. 4. ***The difference between the simple interest and true discount on a certain sum of money for 6 months at*** $12\frac{1}{2}\%$ ***per annum is Rs. 25. Find the sum.***

Sol. Let the sum be Rs. x. Then,

$$\text{T.D.} = \frac{x \times \frac{25}{2} \times \frac{1}{2}}{100 + \left(\frac{25}{2} \times \frac{1}{2}\right)} = \left(x \times \frac{25}{4} \times \frac{4}{425}\right) = \frac{x}{17}.$$

$$\text{S.I.} = \left(x \times \frac{25}{2} \times \frac{1}{2} \times \frac{1}{100}\right) = \frac{x}{16}.$$

$$\therefore \quad \frac{x}{16} - \frac{x}{17} = 25 \Rightarrow 17x - 16x = 25 \times 16 \times 17 \Rightarrow x = 6800.$$

Hence, sum due = Rs. 6800.

Ex. 5. ***A bill falls due in 1 year. The creditor agrees to accept immediate payment of the half and to defer the payment of the other half for 2 years. By this arrangement he gains Rs. 40. What is the amount of the bill, if the money be worth*** $12\frac{1}{2}\%$ ***?***

Sol. Let the sum be Rs. x. Then,

$$\left[\frac{x}{2} + \frac{\frac{x}{2} \times 100}{100 + \left(\frac{25}{2} \times 2\right)}\right] - \frac{x \times 100}{100 + \left(\frac{25}{2} \times 1\right)} = 40 \Rightarrow \frac{x}{2} + \frac{2x}{5} - \frac{8x}{9} = 40 \Rightarrow x = 3600.$$

$\therefore$ Amount of the bill = Rs. 3600.

EXERCISE 32

(OBJECTIVE TYPE QUESTIONS)

Directions : ***Mark (✓) against the correct answer :***

1. The present worth of Rs. 2310 due $2\frac{1}{2}$ years hence, the rate of interest being 15% per annum, is :
   (a) Rs. 1750 (b) Rs. 1680 (c) Rs. 1840 (d) Rs. 1443.75
2. If the true discount on a sum due 2 years hence at 14% per annum be Rs. 168, the sum due is :
   (a) Rs. 768 (b) Rs. 968 (c) Rs. 1960 (d) Rs. 2400
3. The true discount on Rs. 2562 due 4 months hence is Rs. 122. The rate percent is :
   (a) 12% (b) $13\frac{1}{3}\%$ (c) 15% (d) 14%

4. The true discount on Rs. 1760 due after a certain time at 12% per annum is Rs. 160. The time after which it is due is :
(a) 6 months (b) 8 months (c) 9 months (d) 10 months

5. The true discount on a bill due 9 months hence at 16% per annum is Rs. 189. The amount of the bill is :
(a) Rs. 1386 (b) Rs. 1764 (c) Rs. 1575 (d) Rs. 2268

6. The interest on Rs. 750 for 2 years is the same as the true discount on Rs. 960 due 2 years hence. If the rate of interest is the same in both cases, it is :
(a) 12% (b) 14% (c) 15% (d) $16\frac{2}{3}\%$

7. The simple interest and the true discount on a certain sum for a given time and at a given rate are Rs. 85 and Rs. 80 respectively. The sum is :
(a) Rs. 1800 (b) Rs. 1450 (c) Rs. 1360 (d) Rs. 6800

8. If Rs. 10 be allowed as true discount on a bill of Rs. 110 due at the end of a certain time, then the discount allowed on the same sum due at the end of double the time is :
(a) Rs. 20 (b) Rs. 21.81 (c) Rs. 22 (d) Rs. 18.33

9. A man wants to sell his scooter. There are two offers, one at Rs. 12,000 cash and the other at a credit of Rs. 12,880 to be paid after 8 months, money being at 18% per annum. Which is the better offer ?
(a) Rs. 12,000 in cash (b) Rs. 12,880 at credit (c) Both are equally good

10. Goods were bought for Rs. 600 and sold the same day for Rs. 688.50 at a credit of 9 months and thus gaining 2%. The rate of interest per annum is :
(a) $16\frac{2}{3}\%$ (b) $14\frac{1}{2}\%$ (c) $13\frac{1}{3}\%$ (d) 15%

11. The present worth of Rs. 1404 due in two equal half-yearly instalments at 8% per annum simple interest is :
(a) Rs. 1325 (b) Rs. 1300 (c) Rs. 1350 (d) Rs. 1500

12. A trader owes a merchant Rs. 10,028 due 1 year hence. The trader wants to settle the account after 3 months. If the rate of interest is 12% per annum, how much cash should he pay ?
(a) Rs. 9025.20 (b) Rs. 9200 (c) Rs. 9600 (d) Rs. 9560

13. A man buys a watch for Rs. 1950 in cash and sells it for Rs. 2200 at a credit of 1 year. If the rate of interest is 10% per annum, the man :
(a) gains Rs. 55 (b) gains Rs. 50 (c) loses Rs. 30 (d) gains Rs. 30

14. A man purchased a cow for Rs. 3000 and sold it the same day for Rs. 3600, allowing the buyer a credit of 2 years. If the rate of interest be 10% per annum, then the man has a gain of :
(a) 0% (b) 5% (c) 7.5% (d) 10%

15. A owes B, Rs. 1573 payable $1\frac{1}{2}$ years hence. Also B owes A, Rs. 1444.50 payable 6 months hence. If they want to settle the account forthwith, keeping 14% as the rate of interest, then who should pay and how much ?
(a) A, Rs. 28.50 (b) B, Rs. 37.50 (c) A, Rs. 50 (d) B, Rs. 50

16. A has to pay Rs. 220 to B after 1 year. B asks A to pay Rs. 110 in cash and defer the payment of Rs. 110 for 2 years. A agrees to it. If the rate of interest be 10% per annum, in this mode of payment :
(a) There is no gain or loss to any one (b) A gains Rs. 7.34
(c) A loses Rs. 7.34 (d) A gains Rs. 11

17. Rs. 20 is the true discount on Rs. 260 due after a certain time. What will be the true discount on the same sum due after half of the former time, the rate of interest being the same ?
(a) Rs. 10 (b) Rs. 10.40 (c) Rs. 15.20 (d) Rs. 13

ANSWERS

1. (*b*) **2.** (*a*) **3.** (*c*) **4.** (*d*) **5.** (*b*) **6.** (*b*) **7.** (*c*) **8.** (*d*) **9.** (*a*)
10. (*a*) **11.** (*a*) **12.** (*b*) **13.** (*b*) **14.** (*a*) **15.** (*d*) **16.** (*b*) **17.** (*b*)

SOLUTIONS

1. P.W. = Rs. $\left[\frac{100 \times 2310}{100 + \left(15 \times \frac{5}{2}\right)}\right]$ = Rs. 1680.

2. P.W. = $\frac{100 \times \text{T.D.}}{\text{R} \times \text{T}} = \frac{100 \times 168}{14 \times 2} = 600.$

∴ Sum = (P.W. + T.D.) = Rs. (600 + 168) = Rs. 768.

3. P.W. = Rs. (2562 – 122) = Rs. 2440.

∴ S.I. on Rs. 2440 for 4 months is Rs. 122.

∴ Rate = $\left(\frac{100 \times 122}{2440 \times \frac{1}{3}}\right)\% = 15\%$.

4. P.W. = Rs. (1760 – 160) = Rs. 1600.

∴ S.I. on Rs. 1600 at 12% is Rs. 160.

∴ Time = $\left(\frac{100 \times 160}{1600 \times 12}\right) = \frac{5}{6}$ years = $\left(\frac{5}{6} \times 12\right)$ months = 10 months.

5. Let P.W. be Rs. x. Then, S.I. on Rs. x at 16% for 9 months = Rs. 189.

∴ $x \times 16 \times \frac{9}{12} \times \frac{1}{100} = 189$ or $x = 1575$.

∴ P.W. = Rs. 1575.

∴ Sum due = P.W. + T.D. = Rs. (1575 + 189) = Rs. 1764.

6. S.I. on Rs. 750 = T.D. on Rs. 960.

This means P.W. of Rs. 960 due 2 years hence is Rs. 750.

∴ T.D. = Rs. (960 – 750) = Rs. 210.

Thus, S.I. on Rs. 750 for 2 years is Rs. 210.

∴ Rate = $\left(\frac{100 \times 210}{750 \times 2}\right)\% = 14\%$.

7. Sum = $\frac{\text{S.I.} \times \text{T.D.}}{(\text{S.I.}) - (\text{T.D.})} = \frac{85 \times 80}{(85 - 80)}$ = Rs. 1360.

8. S.I. on Rs. (110 – 10) for a certain time = Rs. 10.

S.I. on Rs. 100 for double the time = Rs. 20.

T.D. on Rs. 120 = Rs. (120 – 100) = Rs. 20.

T.D. on Rs. 110 = Rs. $\left(\frac{20}{120} \times 110\right)$ = Rs 18.33.

9. P.W. of Rs. 12,880 due 8 months hence

= Rs. $\left[\frac{12880 \times 100}{100 + \left(18 \times \frac{8}{12}\right)}\right]$ = Rs. $\left(\frac{12880 \times 100}{112}\right)$ = Rs. 11500.

Clearly, Rs. 12,000 in cash is a better offer.

10. S.P. = 102% of Rs. 600 = Rs. $\left(\frac{102}{100} \times 600\right)$ = Rs. 612.

Now, P.W. = Rs. 612 and sum = Rs. 688.50.

$\therefore$ T.D. = Rs. (688.50 − 612) = Rs. 76.50.

Thus, S.I. on Rs. 612 for 9 months is Rs. 76.50.

$\therefore$ Rate = $\left(\frac{100 \times 76.50}{612 \times \frac{3}{4}}\right)\% = 16\frac{2}{3}\%$.

11. Required sum = P.W. of Rs. 702 due 6 months hence + P.W. of Rs. 702 due 1 year hence

$= \text{Rs.} \left[\left(\frac{100 \times 702}{100 + 8 \times \frac{1}{2}}\right) + \left(\frac{100 \times 702}{100 + (8 \times 1)}\right)\right]$ = Rs. (675 + 650) = Rs. 1325.

12. Required money = P.W. of Rs. 10028 due 9 months hence

$= \text{Rs.} \left[\frac{10028 \times 100}{100 + \left(12 \times \frac{9}{12}\right)}\right]$ = Rs. 9200.

13. S.P. = P.W. of Rs. 2200 due 1 year hence = Rs. $\left[\frac{2200 \times 100}{100 + (10 \times 1)}\right]$ = Rs. 2000.

$\therefore$ Gain = Rs. (2000 − 1950) = Rs. 50.

14. C.P. = Rs. 3000. S.P. = Rs. $\left[\frac{3600 \times 100}{100 + (10 \times 2)}\right]$ = Rs. 3000.

Gain = 0%.

15. A owes = P.W. of Rs. 1573 due $\frac{3}{2}$ years hence

$= \text{Rs.} \left[\frac{1573 \times 100}{100 + \left(14 \times \frac{3}{2}\right)}\right] = \text{Rs.} \left(\frac{1573 \times 100}{121}\right)$ = Rs. 1300.

B owes = P.W. of Rs. 1444.50 due 6 months hence

$= \text{Rs.} \left[\frac{1444.50 \times 100}{100 + \left(14 \times \frac{1}{2}\right)}\right] = \text{Rs.} \left(\frac{1444.50 \times 100}{107}\right)$ = Rs. 1350.

$\therefore$ B must pay Rs. 50 to A.

16. A has to pay = P.W. of Rs. 220 due 1 year hence = Rs. $\left[\frac{220 \times 100}{100 + (10 \times 1)}\right]$ = Rs. 200.

A actually pays = Rs. 110 + P.W. of Rs. 110 due 2 years hence

$= \left[110 + \frac{110 \times 100}{100 + (10 \times 2)}\right]$ = Rs. 192.66.

$\therefore$ A gains = Rs. (200 − 192.66) = Rs. 7.34.

17. S.I. on Rs. (260 − 20) for a given time = Rs. 20.

S.I. on Rs. 240 for half the time = Rs. 10.

T.D. on Rs. 250 = Rs. 10.

$\therefore$ T.D. on Rs. 260 = Rs. $\left(\frac{10}{250} \times 260\right)$ = Rs. 10.40.

33. BANKER'S DISCOUNT

IMPORTANT CONCEPTS

Banker's Discount : Suppose a merchant A buys goods worth, say Rs. 10,000 from another merchant B at a credit of say 5 months. Then, B prepares a bill, called the bill of exchange. A signs this bill and allows B to withdraw the amount from his bank account after exactly 5 months.

The date exactly after 5 months is called *nominally due date.* Three days (known as *grace days*) are added to it to get a date, known as *legally due date.*

Suppose B wants to have the money before the legally due date. Then he can have the money from the banker or a broker, who deducts S.I. on the face value (*i.e.*, Rs. 10,000 in this case) for the period from the date on which the bill was discounted (*i.e.*, paid by the banker) and the legally due date. This amount is known as ***Banker's Discount (B.D.)***

Thus, **B.D.** *is the S.I. on the face value for the period from the date on which the bill was discounted and the legally due date.*

Banker's Gain (B.G.) = (B.D.) – (T.D.) *for the unexpired time.*

Note : When the date of the bill is not given, grace days are not to be added.

IMPORTANT FORMULAE

1. B.D. = S.I. on bill for unexpired time.

2. $\text{B.G.} = (\text{B.D.}) - (\text{T.D.}) = \text{S.I. on T.D.} = \dfrac{(\text{T.D.})^2}{\text{P.W.}}$.

3. $\text{T.D.} = \sqrt{\text{P.W.} \times \text{B.G.}}$

4. $\text{B.D.} = \left(\dfrac{\text{Amount} \times \text{Rate} \times \text{Time}}{100}\right)$.

5. $\text{T.D.} = \left[\dfrac{\text{Amount} \times \text{Rate} \times \text{Time}}{100 + (\text{Rate} \times \text{Time})}\right]$.

6. $\text{Amount} = \left(\dfrac{\text{B.D.} \times \text{T.D.}}{\text{B.D.} - \text{T.D.}}\right)$.

7. $\text{T.D.} = \left(\dfrac{\text{B.G.} \times 100}{\text{Rate} \times \text{Time}}\right)$

SOLVED EXAMPLES

Ex. 1. ***A bill for Rs. 6000 is drawn on July 14 at 5 months. It is discounted on 5th October at 10%. Find the banker's discount, true discount, banker's gain and the money that the holder of the bill receives.***

Sol. Face value of the bill = Rs. 6000.

Date on which the bill was drawn = July 14 at 5 months.

Nominally due date = December 14. Legally due date = December 17.

Date on which the bill was discounted = October 5.

Unexpired time : Oct. Nov. Dec.

$$26 + 30 + 17 = 73 \text{ days} = \frac{1}{5} \text{ year.}$$

$\therefore$ B.D. = S.I. on Rs. 6000 for $\frac{1}{5}$ year = Rs. $\left(6000 \times 10 \times \frac{1}{5} \times \frac{1}{100}\right)$ = Rs. 120.

T.D. = Rs. $\left[\dfrac{6000 \times 10 \times \frac{1}{5}}{100 + \left(10 \times \frac{1}{5}\right)}\right]$ = Rs. $\left(\frac{12000}{102}\right)$ = Rs. 117.64.

$\therefore$ B.G. = (B.D.) – (T.D.) = Rs. (120 – 117.64) = Rs. 2.36.

Money received by the holder of the bill = Rs. (6000 – 120) = Rs. 5880.

Ex. 2. ***If the true discount on a certain sum due 6 months hence at 15% is Rs. 120, what is the banker's discount on the same sum for the same time and at the same rate?***

Sol. B.G. = S.I. on T.D. = Rs. $\left(120 \times 15 \times \frac{1}{2} \times \frac{1}{100}\right)$ = Rs 9.

$\therefore$ (B.D.) – (T.D.) = Rs. 9.

$\therefore$ B.D. = Rs. (120 + 9) = Rs. 129.

Ex. 3. ***The banker's discount on Rs. 1800 at 12% per annum is equal to the true discount on Rs. 1872 for the same time at the same rate. Find the time.***

Sol. S.I. on Rs. 1800 = T.D. on Rs. 1872.

$\therefore$ P.W. of Rs. 1872 is Rs. 1800.

$\therefore$ Rs. 72 is S.I. on Rs. 1800 at 12%.

$\therefore$ Time = $\left(\frac{100 \times 72}{12 \times 1800}\right)$ year = $\frac{1}{3}$ year = 4 months.

Ex. 4. ***The banker's discount and the true discount on a sum of money due 8 months hence are Rs. 120 and Rs. 110 respectively. Find the sum and the rate percent.***

Sol. Sum = $\left(\frac{\text{B.D.} \times \text{T.D.}}{\text{B.D.} - \text{T.D.}}\right)$ = Rs. $\left(\frac{120 \times 110}{120 - 110}\right)$ = Rs. 1320.

Since B.D. is S.I. on sum due, so S.I. on Rs. 1320 for 8 months is Rs. 120.

$\therefore$ Rate = $\left(\dfrac{100 \times 120}{1320 \times \frac{2}{3}}\right)\%$ = $13\frac{7}{11}\%$.

Ex. 5. ***The present worth of a bill due sometime hence is Rs. 1100 and the true discount on the bill is Rs. 110. Find the banker's discount and the banker's gain.***

Sol. T.D. = $\sqrt{\text{P.W.} \times \text{B.G.}}$

$\therefore$ B.G. = $\frac{(\text{T.D.})^2}{\text{P.W.}}$ = Rs. $\left(\frac{110 \times 110}{1100}\right)$ = Rs. 11.

$\therefore$ B.D. = (T.D. + B.G.) = Rs. (110 + 11) = Rs. 121.

Ex. 6. ***The banker's discount on Rs. 1650 due a certain time hence is Rs. 165. Find the true discount and the banker's gain.***

Sol. Sum = $\frac{\text{B.D.} \times \text{T.D.}}{\text{B.D.} - \text{T.D.}} = \frac{\text{B.D.} \times \text{T.D.}}{\text{B.G.}}$.

$\therefore$ $\frac{\text{T.D.}}{\text{B.G.}} = \frac{\text{Sum}}{\text{B.D.}} = \frac{1650}{165} = \frac{10}{1}$.

Thus, if B.G. is Re 1, T.D. = Rs. 10.

If B.D. is Rs. 11, T.D. = Rs. 10. If B.D. is Rs. 165, T.D. = Rs. $\left(\frac{10}{11} \times 165\right)$ = Rs. 150.

And, B.G. = Rs. (165 – 150) = Rs. 15.

Ex. 7. ***What rate percent does a man get for his money when in discounting a bill due 10 months hence, he deducts 10% of the amount of the bill ?***

Sol. Let, amount of the bill = Rs. 100. Money deducted = Rs. 10.

Money received by the holder of the bill = Rs. (100 – 10) = Rs. 90.

∴ S.I. on Rs. 90 for 10 months = Rs. 10.

∴ $\text{Rate} = \left(\dfrac{100 \times 10}{90 \times \frac{10}{12}}\right)\% = 13\frac{1}{3}\%.$

EXERCISE 33

(OBJECTIVE TYPE QUESTIONS)

Directions : ***Mark (✓) against the correct answer :***

1. The true discount on a bill of Rs. 540 is Rs. 90. The banker's discount is :
(*a*) Rs. 60 (*b*) Rs. 108 (*c*) Rs. 110 (*d*) Rs. 112

2. The present worth of a certain bill due sometime hence is Rs. 800 and the true discount is Rs. 36. The banker's discount is :
(*a*) Rs. 37 (*b*) Rs. 37.62 (*c*) Rs. 34.38 (*d*) Rs. 38.98

3. The present worth of a certain sum due sometime hence is Rs. 1600 and the true discount is Rs. 160. The banker's gain is :
(*a*) Rs. 20 (*b*) Rs. 24 (*c*) Rs. 16 (*d*) Rs. 12

4. The banker's gain of a certain sum due 2 years hence at 10% per annum is Rs. 24. The present worth is :
(*a*) Rs. 480 (*b*) Rs. 520 (*c*) Rs. 600 (*d*) Rs. 960

5. The banker's gain on a bill due 1 year hence at 12% per annum is Rs. 6. The true discount is :
(*a*) Rs. 72 (*b*) Rs. 36 (*c*) Rs. 54 (*d*) Rs. 50

6. The banker's discount on a bill due 4 months hence at 15% is Rs. 420. The true discount is :
(*a*) Rs. 400 (*b*) Rs. 360 (*c*) Rs. 480 (*d*) Rs. 320

7. The banker's gain on a sum due 3 years hence at 12% per annum is Rs. 270. The banker's discount is :
(*a*) Rs. 960 (*b*) Rs. 840 (*c*) Rs. 1020 (*d*) Rs. 760

8. The present worth of a sum due sometime hence is Rs. 576 and the banker's gain is Rs. 16. The true discount is :
(*a*) Rs. 36 (*b*) Rs. 72 (*c*) Rs. 48 (*d*) Rs. 96

9. The banker's discount on Rs. 1600 at 15% per annum is the same as true discount on Rs. 1680 for the same time and at the same rate. The time is :
(*a*) 3 months (*b*) 4 months (*c*) 6 months (*d*) 8 months

10. The banker's discount on a sum of money for $1\frac{1}{2}$ years is Rs. 558 and the true discount on the same sum for 2 years is Rs. 600. The rate percent is :
(*a*) 10% (*b*) 13% (*c*) 12% (*d*) 15%

11. The banker's discount of a certain sum of money is Rs. 72 and the true discount on the same sum for the same time is Rs. 60. The sum due is
(*a*) Rs. 360 (*b*) Rs. 432 (*c*) Rs. 540 (*d*) Rs. 1080

12. The banker's discount on a certain sum due 2 years hence is $\frac{11}{10}$ of the true discount. The rate percent is :

(*a*) 11% (*b*) 10% (*c*) 5% (*d*) 5.5%

13. The banker's gain on a certain sum due $1\frac{1}{2}$ years hence is $\frac{3}{25}$ of the banker's discount. The rate percent is :

(*a*) $5\frac{1}{5}\%$ (*b*) $9\frac{1}{9}\%$ (*c*) $8\frac{1}{8}\%$ (*d*) $6\frac{1}{6}\%$

ANSWERS

1. (*b*)	**2.** (*b*)	**3.** (*c*)	**4.** (*c*)	**5.** (*d*)	**6.** (*a*)	**7.** (*c*)
8. (*d*)	**9.** (*b*)	**10.** (*c*)	**11.** (*a*)	**12.** (*c*)	**13.** (*b*)	

SOLUTIONS

1. P.W. = Rs. (540 − 90) = Rs. 450.

∴ S.I. on Rs. 450 = Rs. 90

S.I. on Rs. 540 = Rs. $\left(\frac{90}{450} \times 540\right)$ = Rs. 108.

∴ B.D. = Rs. 108.

2. $\text{B.G.} = \frac{(\text{T.D.})^2}{\text{P.W.}}$ = Rs. $\left(\frac{36 \times 36}{800}\right)$ = Rs. 1.62.

∴ B.D. = (T.D. + B.G.) = Rs. (36 + 1.62) = Rs. 37.62.

3. $\text{B.G.} = \frac{(\text{T.D.})^2}{\text{P.W.}}$ = Rs. $\left(\frac{160 \times 160}{1600}\right)$ = Rs. 16.

4. $\text{T.D.} = \left(\frac{\text{B.G.} \times 100}{\text{Rate} \times \text{Time}}\right)$ = Rs. $\left(\frac{24 \times 100}{10 \times 2}\right)$ = Rs. 120.

∴ $\text{P.W.} = \frac{100 \times \text{T.D.}}{\text{Rate} \times \text{Time}}$ = Rs. $\left(\frac{100 \times 120}{10 \times 2}\right)$ = Rs. 600.

5. $\text{T.D.} = \frac{\text{B.G.} \times 100}{\text{R} \times \text{T}}$ = Rs. $\left(\frac{6 \times 100}{12 \times 1}\right)$ = Rs. 50.

6. $\text{T.D.} = \frac{\text{B.D.} \times 100}{100 + (\text{R} \times \text{T})}$ = Rs. $\left[\frac{420 \times 100}{100 + \left(15 \times \frac{1}{3}\right)}\right]$ = Rs. $\left(\frac{420 \times 100}{105}\right)$ = Rs. 400.

7. $\text{T.D.} = \left(\frac{\text{B.G.} \times 100}{\text{R} \times \text{T}}\right)$ = Rs. $\left(\frac{270 \times 100}{12 \times 3}\right)$ = Rs. 750.

∴ B.D. = Rs. (750 + 270) = Rs. 1020.

8. $\text{T.D.} = \sqrt{\text{P.W.} \times \text{B.G.}} = \sqrt{576 \times 16} = 96.$

9. S.I. on Rs. 1600 = T.D. on Rs. 1680.

∴ Rs. 1600 is the P.W. of Rs. 1680, *i.e.*, Rs. 80 is S.I. on Rs. 1600 at 15%.

∴ Time = $\left(\frac{100 \times 80}{1600 \times 15}\right)$ year = $\frac{1}{3}$ year = 4 months.

10. B.D. for $\frac{3}{2}$ years = Rs. 558. B.D. for 2 years = Rs. $\left(558 \times \frac{2}{3} \times 2\right)$ = Rs. 744.

T.D. for 2 years = Rs. 600.

$\therefore$ Sum = $\frac{\text{B.D.} \times \text{T.D.}}{\text{B.D.} - \text{T.D.}}$ = Rs. $\left(\frac{744 \times 600}{144}\right)$ = Rs. 3100.

Thus, Rs. 744 is S.I. on Rs. 3100 for 2 years.

$\therefore$ Rate = $\left(\frac{100 \times 744}{3100 \times 2}\right)\%$ = 12%.

11. Sum = $\frac{\text{B.D.} \times \text{T.D.}}{\text{B.D.} - \text{T.D.}}$ = Rs. $\left(\frac{72 \times 60}{72 - 60}\right)$ = Rs. $\left(\frac{72 \times 60}{12}\right)$ = Rs. 360.

12. Let T.D. be Re 1. Then, B.D. = Rs. $\frac{11}{10}$ = Rs. 1.10.

$\therefore$ Sum = Rs. $\left(\frac{1.10 \times 1}{1.10 - 1}\right)$ = Rs. $\left(\frac{110}{10}\right)$ = Rs. 11.

$\therefore$ S.I. on Rs. 11 for 2 years is Rs. 1.10.

$\therefore$ Rate = $\left(\frac{100 \times 1.10}{11 \times 2}\right)\%$ = 5%.

13. Let, B.D. = Re 1. Then, B.G. = Re $\frac{3}{25}$.

$\therefore$ T.D. = (B.D. – B.G.) = Re $\left(1 - \frac{3}{25}\right)$ = Re $\frac{22}{25}$.

Sum = $\left(\frac{1 \times \frac{22}{25}}{1 - \frac{22}{25}}\right)$ = Rs. $\frac{22}{3}$.

S.I. on Rs. $\frac{22}{3}$ for $1\frac{1}{2}$ years is Re 1.

$\therefore$ Rate = $\left(\frac{100 \times 1}{\frac{22}{3} \times \frac{3}{2}}\right)\%$ = $9\frac{1}{9}\%$.

34. HEIGHTS AND DISTANCES

IMPORTANT FACTS AND FORMULAE

1. We already know that :

In a rt. angled Δ OAB, where $\angle$ BOA = θ,

(i) $\sin\theta = \dfrac{\text{Perpendicular}}{\text{Hypotenuse}} = \dfrac{AB}{OB}$;

(ii) $\cos\theta = \dfrac{\text{Base}}{\text{Hypotenuse}} = \dfrac{OA}{OB}$;

(iii) $\tan\theta = \dfrac{\text{Perpendicular}}{\text{Base}} = \dfrac{AB}{OA}$;

(iv) $\text{cosec}\,\theta = \dfrac{1}{\sin\theta} = \dfrac{OB}{AB}$;

(v) $\sec\theta = \dfrac{1}{\cos\theta} = \dfrac{OB}{OA}$;

(vi) $\cot\theta = \dfrac{1}{\tan\theta} = \dfrac{OA}{AB}$.

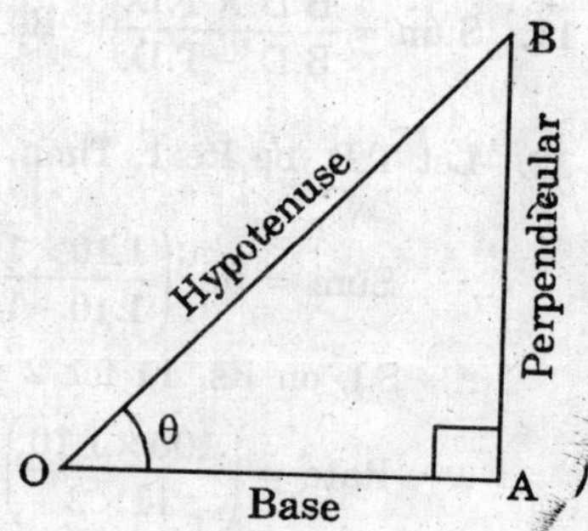

2. Trigonometrical Identities :

(i) $\sin^2\theta + \cos^2\theta = 1$. (ii) $1 + \tan^2\theta = \sec^2\theta$. (iii) $1 + \cot^2\theta = \text{cosec}^2\,\theta$.

3. Values of T-ratios :

θ	0°	($\pi/6$) 30°	($\pi/4$) 45°	($\pi/3$) 60°	($\pi/2$) 90°
$\sin\theta$	0	$\frac{1}{2}$	$\frac{1}{\sqrt{2}}$	$\frac{\sqrt{3}}{2}$	1
$\cos\theta$	1	$\frac{\sqrt{3}}{2}$	$\frac{1}{\sqrt{2}}$	$\frac{1}{2}$	0
$\tan\theta$	0	$\frac{1}{\sqrt{3}}$	1	$\sqrt{3}$	not defined

4. Angle of Elevation : Suppose a man from a point O looks up at an object P, placed above the level of his eye. Then, the angle which the line of sight makes with the horizontal through O, is called the angle of elevation of P as seen from O.

$\therefore$ Angle of elevation of P from O = $\angle$ AOP.

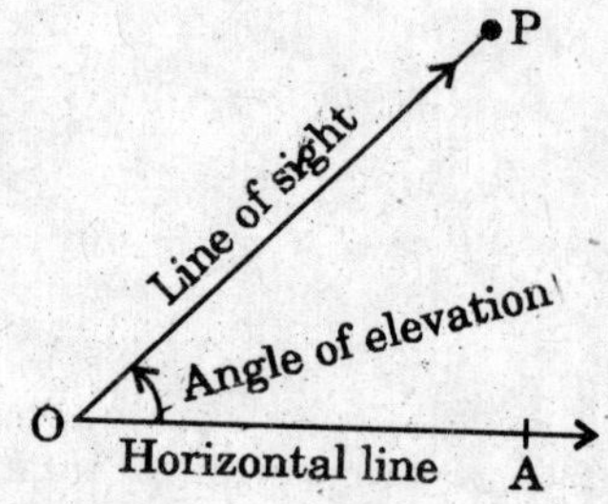

5. **Angle of Depression** : Suppose a man from a point O looks down at an object P, placed below the level of his eye, then the angle which the line of sight makes with the horizontal through O, is called the angle of depression of P as seen from O.

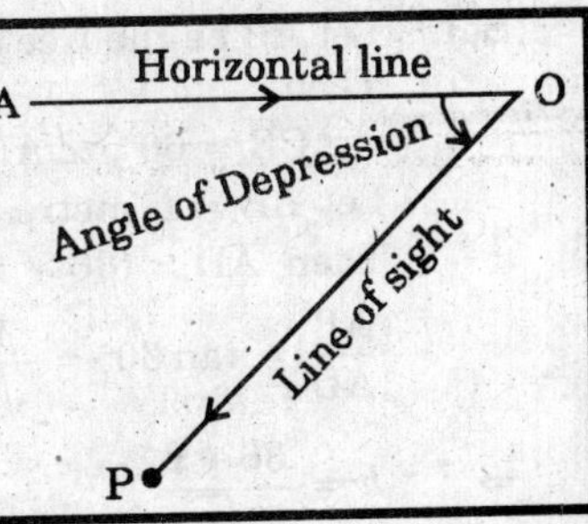

SOLVED EXAMPLES

Ex. 1. ***If the height of a pole is $2\sqrt{3}$ metres and the length of its shadow is 2 metres, find the angle of elevation of the sun.***

Sol. Let AB be the pole and AC be its shadow.

Let angle of elevation, $\angle ACB = \theta$.

Then, $AB = 2\sqrt{3}$ m, $AC = 2$ m.

$$\tan\theta = \frac{AB}{AC} = \frac{2\sqrt{3}}{2} = \sqrt{3} \Rightarrow \theta = 60°$$

So, the angle of elevation is 60°.

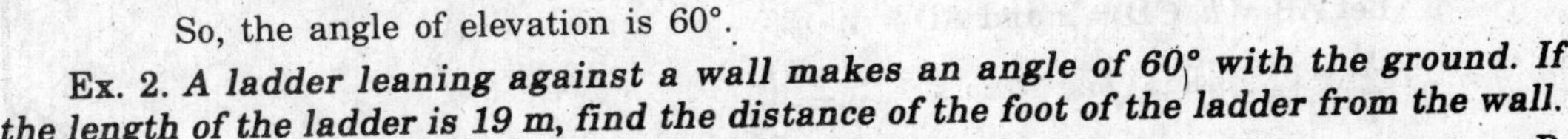

Ex. 2. ***A ladder leaning against a wall makes an angle of 60° with the ground. If the length of the ladder is 19 m, find the distance of the foot of the ladder from the wall.***

Sol. Let AB be the wall and BC be the ladder.

Then, $\angle ACB = 60°$ and $BC = 19$ m.

Let $AC = x$ metres

$$\frac{AC}{BC} = \cos 60° \Rightarrow \frac{x}{19} = \frac{1}{2} \Rightarrow x = \frac{19}{2} = 9.5.$$

$\therefore$ Distance of the foot of the ladder from the wall = 9.5 m.

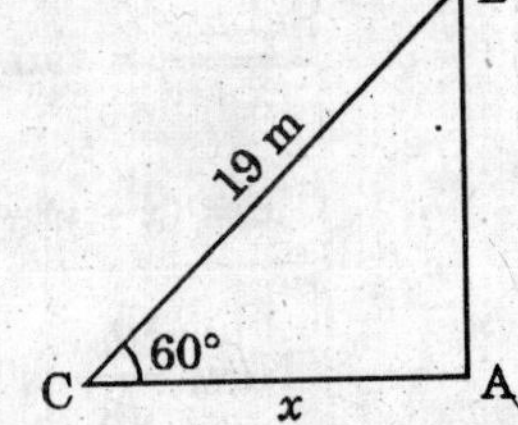

Ex. 3. ***The angle of elevation of the top of a tower at a point on the ground is 30°. On walking 24 m towards the tower, the angle of elevation becomes 60°. Find the height of the tower.***

Sol. Let AB be the tower and C and D be the points of observation. Then,

$$\frac{AB}{AD} = \tan 60° = \sqrt{3} \Rightarrow AD = \frac{AB}{\sqrt{3}} = \frac{h}{\sqrt{3}}.$$

$$\frac{AB}{AC} = \tan 30° = \frac{1}{\sqrt{3}} \Rightarrow AC = AB \times \sqrt{3} = h\sqrt{3}.$$

$$CD = (AC - AD) = \left(h\sqrt{3} - \frac{h}{\sqrt{3}}\right).$$

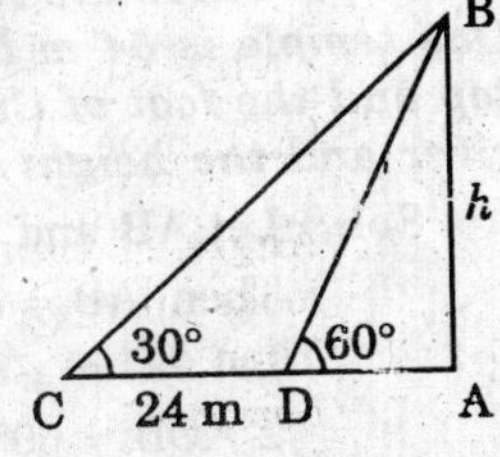

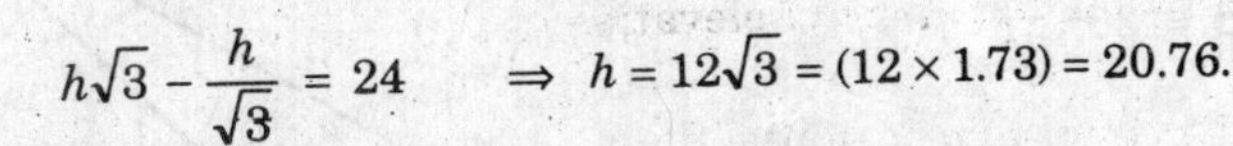

$$\therefore \quad h\sqrt{3} - \frac{h}{\sqrt{3}} = 24 \Rightarrow h = 12\sqrt{3} = (12 \times 1.73) = 20.76.$$

Hence, the height of the tower is 20.76 m.

Ex. 4. ***A man standing on the bank of a river observes that the angle subtended by a tree on the opposite bank is 60°. When he retires 36 m from the bank, he finds the angle to be 30°. Find the breadth of the river.***

Sol. Let AB be the tree and AC be the river. Let C and D be the two positions of the man. Then,

$\angle ACB = 60°$, $\angle ADB = 30°$ and CD = 36 m.

Let AB = h metres and AC = x metres.

Then, AD = $(36 + x)$ metres.

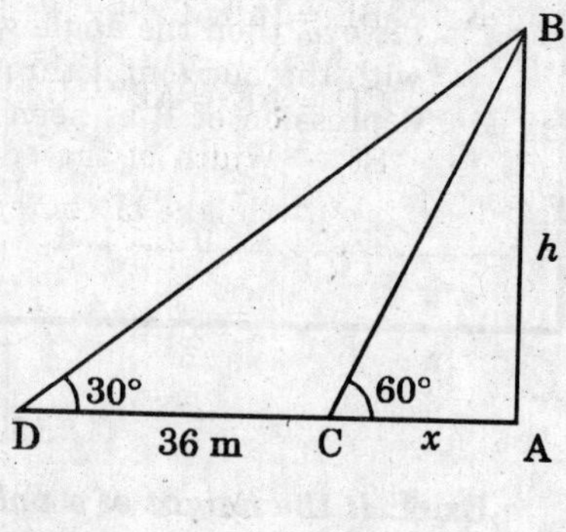

$$\frac{AB}{AD} = \tan 30° = \frac{1}{\sqrt{3}} \Rightarrow \frac{h}{36 + x} = \frac{1}{\sqrt{3}}$$

$$\Rightarrow \quad h = \frac{36 + x}{\sqrt{3}} \qquad ...(i)$$

$$\frac{AB}{AC} = \tan 60° = \sqrt{3} \Rightarrow \frac{h}{x} = \sqrt{3}$$

$$\Rightarrow \quad h = \sqrt{3}\, x \qquad ...(ii)$$

From (*i*) and (*ii*), we get : $\frac{36 + x}{\sqrt{3}} = \sqrt{3}\, x \Rightarrow x = 18$ m.

So, the breadth of the river = 18 m.

Ex. 5. ***A man on the top of a tower, standing on the seashore finds that a boat coming towards him takes 10 minutes for the angle of depression to change from 30° to 60°. Find the time taken by the boat to reach the shore from this position.***

Sol. Let AB be the tower and C and D be the two positions of the boat.

Let AB = h, CD = x and AD = y.

$$\frac{h}{y} = \tan 60° = \sqrt{3} \Rightarrow y = \frac{h}{\sqrt{3}}.$$

$$\frac{h}{x + y} = \tan 30° = \frac{1}{\sqrt{3}} \Rightarrow x + y = \sqrt{3}\, h.$$

$$\therefore \quad x = (x + y) - y = \left(\sqrt{3}\, h - \frac{h}{\sqrt{3}}\right) = \frac{2h}{\sqrt{3}}.$$

Now, $\frac{2h}{\sqrt{3}}$ is covered in 10 min.

$$\therefore \quad \frac{h}{\sqrt{3}} \text{ will be covered in } \left(10 \times \frac{\sqrt{3}}{2h} \times \frac{h}{\sqrt{3}}\right) = 5 \text{ min.}$$

Hence, required time = 5 minutes.

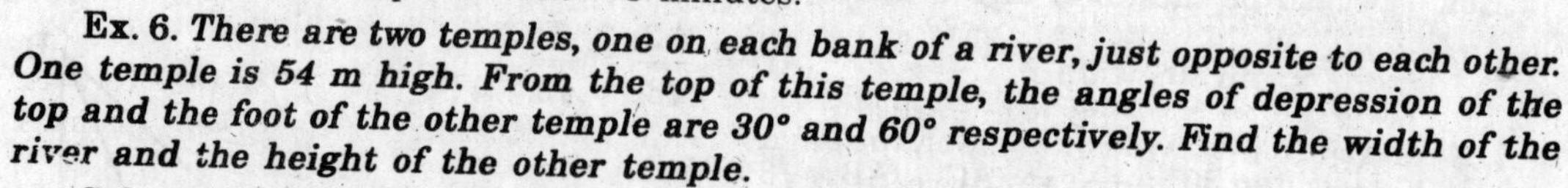

Ex. 6. ***There are two temples, one on each bank of a river, just opposite to each other. One temple is 54 m high. From the top of this temple, the angles of depression of the top and the foot of the other temple are 30° and 60° respectively. Find the width of the river and the height of the other temple.***

Sol. Let AB and CD be the two temples and AC be the river.

Then, AB = 54 m.

Let AC = x metres and CD = h metres.

$\angle ACB = 60°$, $\angle EDB = 30°$.

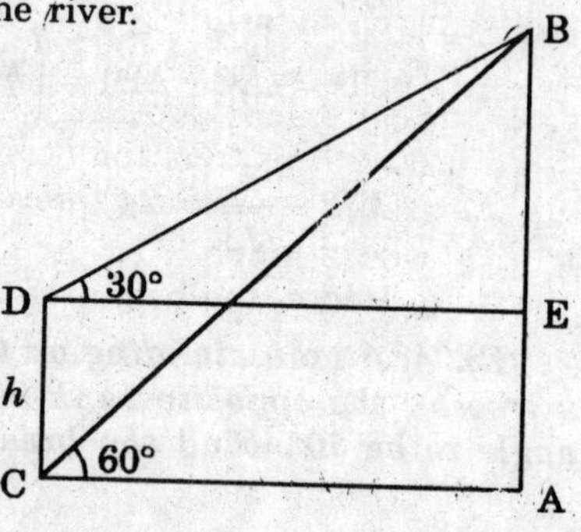

$$\frac{AB}{AC} = \tan 60° = \sqrt{3}$$

$$\Rightarrow \quad AC = \frac{AB}{\sqrt{3}} = \frac{54}{\sqrt{3}} = \left(\frac{54}{\sqrt{3}} \times \frac{\sqrt{3}}{\sqrt{3}}\right) = 18\sqrt{3} \text{ m.}$$

DE = AC = $18\sqrt{3}$ m

$\frac{BE}{DE} = \tan 30° = \frac{1}{\sqrt{3}}$

$\Rightarrow \quad BE = \left(18\sqrt{3} \times \frac{1}{\sqrt{3}}\right) = 18 \text{ m}.$

$\therefore \quad CD = AE = AB - BE = (54 - 18) \text{ m} = 36 \text{ m}.$

So, Width of the river = AC = $18\sqrt{3}$ m = (18×1.73) m = 31.14 m.

Height of the other temple = CD = 18 m.

EXERCISE 34

(OBJECTIVE TYPE QUESTIONS)

Directions : *Mark (✓) against the correct answer* :

1. The angle of elevation of the sun, when the length of the shadow of a tree is $\sqrt{3}$ times the height of the tree, is : **(R.R.B. 2003)**
(*a*) 30° (*b*) 45° (*c*) 60° (*d*) 90°

2. From a point P on a level ground, the angle of elevation of the top of a tower is 30°. If the tower is 100 m high, the distance of point P from the foot of the tower is :
(*a*) 149 m (*b*) 156 m (*c*) 173 m (*d*) 200 m **(R.R.B. 2002)**

3. The angle of elevation of a ladder leaning against a wall is 60° and the foot of the ladder is 4.6 m away from the wall. The length of the ladder is :
(*a*) 2.3 m (*b*) 4.6 m (*c*) 7.8 m (*d*) 9.2 m

4. An observer 1.6 m tall is $20\sqrt{3}$ m away from a tower. The angle of elevation from his eye to the top of the tower is 30°. The height of the tower is :
(*a*) 21.6 m (*b*) 23.2 m (*c*) 24.72 m (*d*) None of these

5. Two ships are sailing in the sea on the two sides of a lighthouse. The angles of elevation of the top of the lighthouse as observed from the two ships are 30° and 45° respectively. If the lighthouse is 100 m high, the distance between the two ships is :
(*a*) 173 m (*b*) 200 m (*c*) 273 m (*d*) 300 m

6. A man standing at a point P is watching the top of a tower, which makes an angle of elevation of 30° with the man's eye. The man walks some distance towards the tower to watch its top and the angle of elevation becomes 60°. What is the distance between the base of the tower and the point P ? **(Bank P.O. 1999)**
(*a*) $4\sqrt{3}$ units (*b*) 8 units (*c*) 12 units
(*d*) Data inadequate (*e*) None of these

7. The angle of elevation of the top of a tower from a certain point is 30°. If the observer moves 20 m towards the tower, the angle of elevation of the top of the tower increases by 15°. The height of the tower is :
(*a*) 17.3 m (*b*) 21.9 m (*c*) 27.3 m (*d*) 30 m

8. A man is watching from the top of a tower a boat speeding away from the tower. The boat makes an angle of depression of 45° with the man's eye when at a distance of 60 metres from the tower. After 5 seconds, the angle of depression becomes 30°. What is the approximate speed of the boat, assuming that it is running in still water ?
(*a*) 32 kmph (*b*) 36 kmph (*c*) 38 kmph
(*d*) 40 kmph (*e*) 42 kmph **(S.B.I.P.O. 1999)**

9. On the same side of a tower, two objects are located. Observed from the top of the tower, their angles of depression are 45° and 60°. If the height of the tower is 150 m, the distance between the objects is :
(*a*) 63.5 m (*b*) 76.9 m (*c*) 86.7 m (*d*) 90 m

10. A man on the top of a vertical observation tower observes a car moving at a uniform speed coming directly towards it. If it takes 12 minutes for the angle of depression to change from 30° to 45°, how soon after this will the car reach the observation tower ?
(*a*) 14 min. 35 sec. (*b*) 15 min. 49 sec. (*c*) 16 min. 23 sec. (*d*) 18 min. 5 sec.
(R.R.B. 2002)

11. The top of a 15 metre high tower makes an angle of elevation of 60° with the bottom of an electric pole and angle of elevation of 30° with the top of the pole. What is the height of the electric pole ?
(*a*) 5 metres (*b*) 8 metres (*c*) 10 metres
(*d*) 12 metres (*e*) None of these

ANSWERS

1. (*a*)	2. (*c*)	3. (*d*)	4. (*a*)	5. (*c*)	6. (*d*)
7. (*c*)	8. (*a*)	9. (*a*)	10. (*c*)	11. (*c*)	

SOLUTIONS

1. Let AB be the tree and AC be its shadow.
Let $\angle ACB = \theta$.
Then, $\frac{AC}{AB} = \sqrt{3} \Rightarrow \cot\theta = \sqrt{3} \Rightarrow \theta = 30°$.

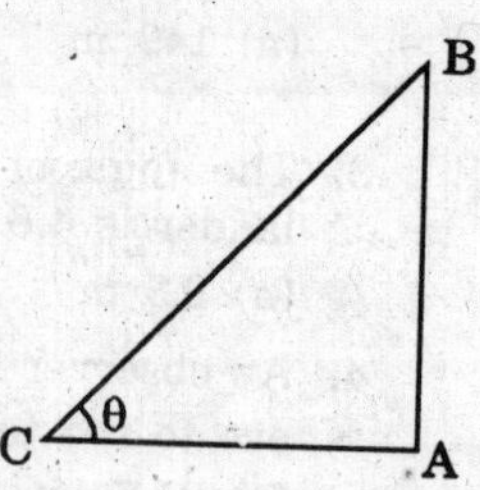

2. Let AB be the tower. Then, $\angle APB = 30°$ and AB = 100 m
$\frac{AB}{AP} = \tan 30° = \frac{1}{\sqrt{3}} \Rightarrow AP = (AB \times \sqrt{3}) = 100\sqrt{3}$ m.

$= (100 \times 1.73)$ m = 173 m.

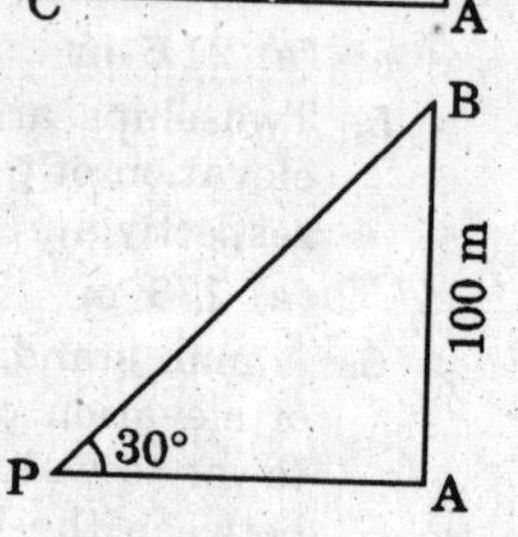

3. Let AB be the wall and BC be the ladder.
Then, $\angle ACB = 60°$ and AC = 4.6 m.
$\frac{AC}{BC} = \cos 60° = \frac{1}{2}$
$\Rightarrow$ BC = 2 × AC = (2 × 4.6) m = 9.2 m.

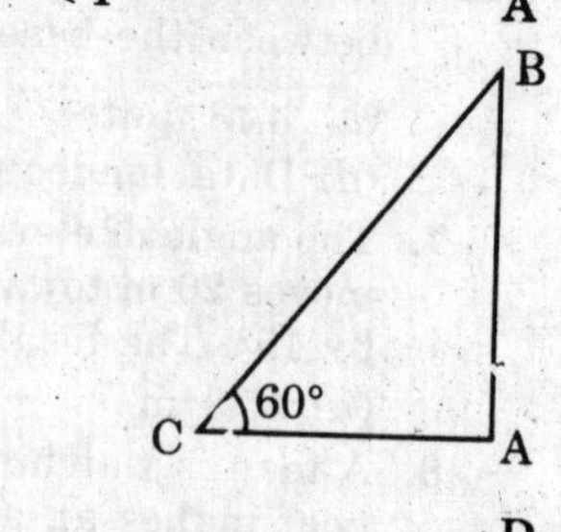

4. Let AB be the observer and CD be the tower.
Draw BE ⊥ CD.
Then, CE = AB = 1.6 m, BE = AC = $20\sqrt{3}$ m.
$\frac{DE}{BE} = \tan 30° = \frac{1}{\sqrt{3}}$
$\Rightarrow DE = \frac{20\sqrt{3}}{\sqrt{3}}$ m = 20 m.
$\therefore$ CD = CE + DE = (1.6 + 20) m = 21.6 m.

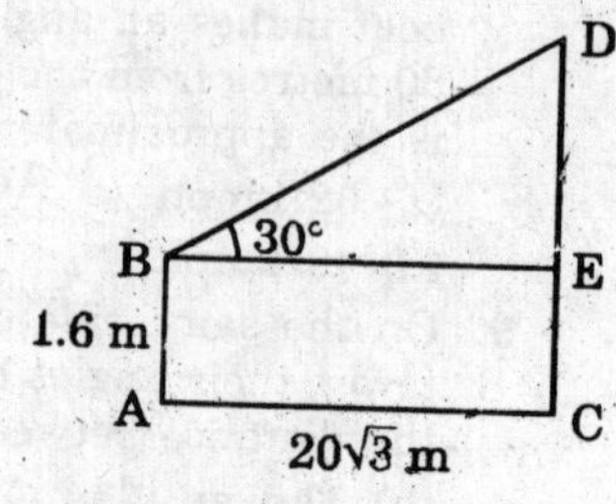

5. Let AB be the lighthouse and C and D be the positions of the ships. Then,
AB = 100 m, $\angle ACB = 30°$ and $\angle ADB = 45°$.

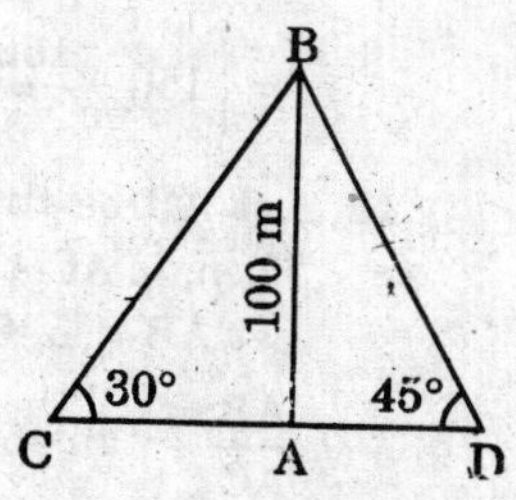

$$\frac{AB}{AC} = \tan 30° = \frac{1}{\sqrt{3}} \Rightarrow AC = AB \times \sqrt{3} = 100\sqrt{3} \text{ m.}$$

$$\frac{AB}{AD} = \tan 45° = 1 \Rightarrow AD = AB = 100 \text{ m.}$$

$$\therefore \quad CD = (AC + AD) = (100\sqrt{3} + 100) \text{ m}$$

$$= 100(\sqrt{3} + 1) \text{ m} = (100 \times 2.73) \text{ m} = 273 \text{ m.}$$

6. One of AB, AD and CD must have been given.
So, the data is inadequate.

7. Let AB be the tower and C and D be the points of observation.
Then, $\angle ACB = 30°$, $\angle ADB = 45°$ and CD = 20 m.
Let AB = h.

Then, $\dfrac{AB}{AC} = \tan 30° = \dfrac{1}{\sqrt{3}} \Rightarrow AC = AB \times \sqrt{3} = h\sqrt{3}$.

And, $\dfrac{AB}{AD} = \tan 45° = 1 \Rightarrow AD = AB = h$.

$CD = 20 \Rightarrow (AC - AD) = 20 \Rightarrow h\sqrt{3} - h = 20$.

$$\therefore \quad h = \frac{20}{(\sqrt{3} - 1)} \times \frac{(\sqrt{3} + 1)}{(\sqrt{3} + 1)} = 10(\sqrt{3} + 1) \text{ m} = (10 \times 2.73) \text{ m} = 27.3 \text{ m.}$$

8. Let AB be the tower and C and D be the two positions of the boats.
Then, $\angle ACB = 45°$, $\angle ADB = 30°$ and AC = 60 m.
Let AB = h.

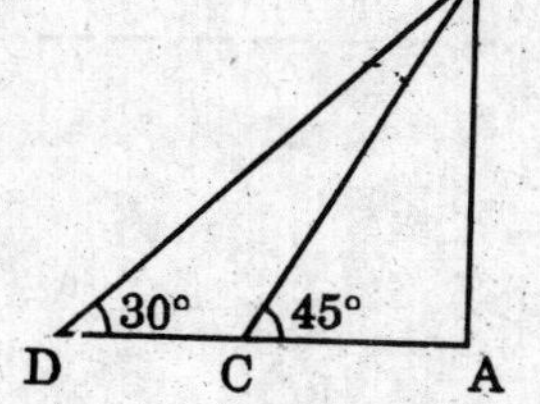

Then, $\dfrac{AB}{AC} = \tan 45° = 1 \Rightarrow AB = AC \Rightarrow h = 60$ m.

And, $\dfrac{AB}{AD} = \tan 30° = \dfrac{1}{\sqrt{3}} \Rightarrow AD = (AB \times \sqrt{3}) = 60\sqrt{3}$ m.

$\therefore \quad CD = (AD - AC) = 60(\sqrt{3} - 1)$ m.

Hence, required speed $= \left[\dfrac{60(\sqrt{3} - 1)}{5}\right]$ m/s $= (12 \times 0.73)$ m/s

$$= \left(12 \times 0.73 \times \frac{18}{5}\right) \text{ km/hr} = 31.5 \text{ km/hr} \approx 32 \text{ km/hr.}$$

9. Let AB be the tower and C and D be the objects
Then, AB = 150 m, $\angle ACB = 45°$ and $\angle ADB = 60°$

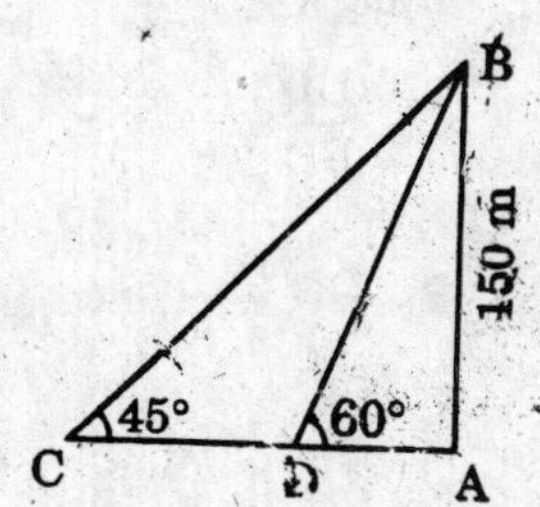

$\dfrac{AB}{AD} = \tan 60° = \sqrt{3} \Rightarrow AD = \dfrac{AB}{\sqrt{3}} = \dfrac{150}{\sqrt{3}}$ m.

$\dfrac{AB}{AC} = \tan 45° = 1 \Rightarrow AC = AB = 150$ m.

$\therefore \quad CD = (AC - AD)$

$$= \left(150 - \frac{150}{\sqrt{3}}\right) \text{ m} = \left[\frac{150(\sqrt{3}-1)}{\sqrt{3}} \times \frac{\sqrt{3}}{\sqrt{3}}\right] \text{ m} = 50(3-\sqrt{3}) \text{ m} = (50 \times 1.27) \text{ m} = 63.5 \text{ m}.$$

10. Let AB be the tower and C and D be the two positions of the car.

Then, $\angle ACB = 45°$, $\angle ADB = 30°$.

Let $AB = h$, $CD = x$ and $AC = y$.

$$\frac{AB}{AC} = \tan 45° = 1 \Rightarrow \frac{h}{y} = 1 \Rightarrow y = h.$$

$$\frac{AB}{AD} = \tan 30° = \frac{1}{\sqrt{3}} \Rightarrow \frac{h}{x+y} = \frac{1}{\sqrt{3}} \Rightarrow x + y = \sqrt{3}\,h.$$

$$\therefore \quad x = (x+y) - y = \sqrt{3}\,h - h = h(\sqrt{3}-1).$$

Now, $h(\sqrt{3}-1)$ is covered in 12 min.

So, h will be covered in $\left[\frac{12}{h(\sqrt{3}-1)} \times h\right] = \frac{12}{(\sqrt{3}-1)}$ min.

$$= \left(\frac{1200}{73}\right) \text{ min.} \approx 16 \text{ min. } 23 \text{ sec.}$$

11. Let AB be the tower and CD be the electric pole.

Then, $\angle ACB = 60°$, $\angle EDB = 30°$ and $AB = 15$ m.

Let $CD = h$. Then, $BE = (AB - AE) = (AB - CD) = (15 - h)$.

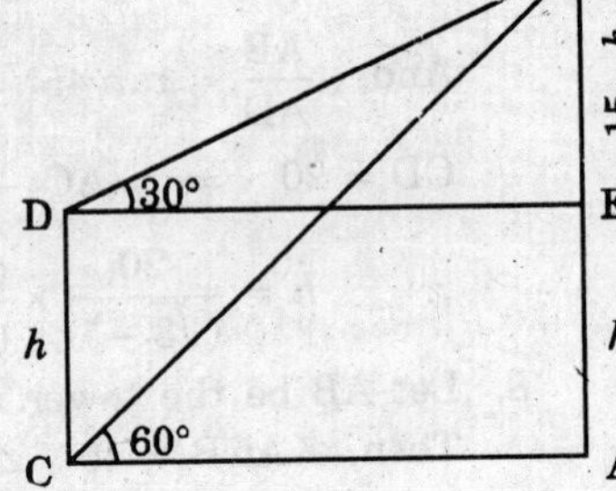

$$\frac{AB}{AC} = \tan 60° = \sqrt{3} \Rightarrow AC = \frac{AB}{\sqrt{3}} = \frac{15}{\sqrt{3}}.$$

And, $\frac{BE}{DE} = \tan 30° = \frac{1}{\sqrt{3}} \Rightarrow DE = (BE \times \sqrt{3})$

$$= \sqrt{3}(15-h).$$

$$AC = DE \Rightarrow \frac{15}{\sqrt{3}} = \sqrt{3}(15-h)$$

$$\Rightarrow 3h = (45 - 15) \Rightarrow h = 10 \text{ m}.$$

35. ODD MAN OUT AND SERIES

EXERCISE 35

Directions : ***Find the odd man out*** :

1. 3, 5, 7, 12, 17, 19
(*a*) 19 (*b*) 17 (*c*) 13 (*d*) 12

2. 10, 14, 16, 18, 21, 24, 26
(*a*) 26 (*b*) 24 (*c*) 21 (*d*) 18

3. 3, 5, 9, 11, 14, 17, 21
(*a*) 21 (*b*) 17 (*c*) 14 (*d*) 9

4. 1, 4, 9, 16, 23, 25, 36
(*a*) 9 (*b*) 23 (*c*) 25 (*d*) 36

5. 6, 9, 15, 21, 24, 28, 30
(*a*) 28 (*b*) 21 (*c*) 24 (*d*) 30

6. 41, 43, 47, 53, 61, 71, 73, 81
(*a*) 61 (*b*) 71 (*c*) 73 (*d*) 81

7. 16, 25, 36, 72, 144, 196, 225
(*a*) 36 (*b*) 72 (*c*) 196 (*d*) 225

8. 10, 25, 45, 54, 60, 75, 80
(*a*) 10 (*b*) 45 (*c*) 54 (*d*) 75

9. 1, 4, 9, 16, 20, 36, 49
(*a*) 1 (*b*) 9 (*c*) 20 (*d*) 49

10. 8, 27, 64, 100, 125, 216, 343
(*a*) 27 (*b*) 100 (*c*) 125 (*d*) 343

11. 1, 5, 14, 30, 50, 55, 91
(*a*) 5 (*b*) 50 (*c*) 55 (*d*) 91

12. 385, 462, 572, 396, 427, 671, 264
(*a*) 385 (*b*) 427 (*c*) 671 (*d*) 264

13. 835, 734, 642, 751, 853, 981, 532
(*a*) 751 (*b*) 853 (*c*) 981 (*d*) 532

14. 331, 482, 551, 263, 383, 242, 111
(*a*) 263 (*b*) 383 (*c*) 242 (*d*) 111

15. 2, 5, 10, 17, 26, 37, 50, 64
(*a*) 50 (*b*) 26 (*c*) 37 (*d*) 64

16. 19, 28, 39, 52, 67, 84, 102
(*a*) 52 (*b*) 102 (*c*) 84 (*d*) 67

17. 253, 136, 352, 460, 324, 631, 244
(*a*) 136 (*b*) 324 (*c*) 352 (*d*) 631

18. 2, 5, 10, 50, 500, 5000
(*a*) 0 (*b*) 5 (*c*) 10 (*d*) 5000

19. 4, 5, 7, 10, 14, 18, 25, 32
(*a*) 7 (*b*) 14 (*c*) 18 (*d*) 33

Directions : ***Find out the wrong number in each sequence :***

20. 22, 33, 66, 99, 121, 279, 594
(*a*) 33 (*b*) 121 (*c*) 279 (*d*) 594

21. 36, 54, 18, 27, 9,18.5, 4.5
(*a*) 4.5 (*b*) 18.5 (*c*) 54 (*d*) 18

22. 582, 605, 588, 611, 634, 617, 600
(*a*) 634 (*b*) 611 (*c*) 605 (*d*) 600

23 46080, 3840, 384, 48, 24, 2, 1
(*a*) 1 (*b*) 2 (*c*) 24 (*d*) 384

24. 1, 8, 27, 64, 124, 216, 343
(*a*) 8 (*b*) 27 (*c*) 64 (*d*) 124

25. 5, 16, 6, 16, 7, 16, 9
(*a*) 9 (*b*) 7 (*c*) 6 (*d*) None of these

26. 6, 13, 18, 25, 30, 37, 40
(*a*) 25 (*b*) 30 (*c*) 37 (*d*) 40

27. 56, 72, 90, 110, 132, 150
(*a*) 72 (*b*) 110 (*c*) 132 (*d*) 150

28. 8, 13, 21, 32, 47, 63, 83
(*a*) 47 (*b*) 63 (*c*) 32 (*d*) 83

29. 25, 36, 49, 81, 121, 169, 225
(*a*) 36 (*b*) 49 (*c*) 121 (*d*) 169

30. 1, 2, 6, 15, 31, 56, 91
(*a*) 31 (*b*) 91 (*c*) 56 (*d*) 15

31. 52, 51, 48, 43, 34, 27, 16
(*a*) 27 (*b*) 34 (*c*) 43 (*d*) 48

32. 105, 85, 60, 30, 0, – 45, – 90
(*a*) 0 (*b*) 85 (*c*) – 45 (*d*) 60

33. 4, 6, 8, 9, 10, 11, 12
(*a*) 10 (*b*) 11 (*c*) 12 (*d*) 9

34. 125, 127, 130, 135, 142, 153, 165
(*a*) 130 (*b*) 142 (*c*) 153 (*d*) 165

35. 16, 36, 64, 81, 100, 144, 190
(*a*) 81 (*b*) 100 (*c*) 190 (*d*) 36

36. 125, 123, 120, 115, 108, 100, 84
(*a*) 123 (*b*) 115 (*c*) 100 (*d*) 84

37. 3, 10, 21, 36, 55, 70, 105
(*a*) 105 (*b*) 70 (*c*) 36 (*d*) 55

38. 4, 9, 19, 39, 79, 160, 319
(*a*) 319 (*b*) 160 (*c*) 79 (*d*) 39

39. 10, 14, 28, 32, 64, 68, 132
(*a*) 32 (*b*) 68 (*c*) 132 (*d*) 28

40. 8, 27, 125, 343, 1331
(*a*) 1331 (*b*) 343 (*c*) 125 (*d*) None of these

Directions : *Insert the missing number :*

41. 4, – 8, 16, – 32, 64, (.....)
(*a*) 128 (*b*) – 128 (*c*) 192 (*d*) – 192

42. 5, 10, 13, 26, 29, 58, 61, (.....)
(*a*) 122 (*b*) 64 (*c*) 125 (*d*) 128

43. 1, 4, 9, 16, 25, 36, 49, (.....)
(*a*) 54 (*b*) 56 (*c*) 64 (*d*) 81

44. 1, 8, 27, 64, 125, 216, (.....)
(*a*) 354 (*b*) 343 (*c*) 392 (*d*) 245

45. 11, 13, 17, 19, 23, 29, 31, 37, 41, (.....)
(*a*) 43 (*b*) 47 (*c*) 53 (*d*) 51

46. 16, 33, 65, 131, 261, (.....)
(*a*) 523 (*b*) 521 (*c*) 613 (*d*) 721

47. 3, 7, 6, 5, 9, 3, 12, 1, 15, (.....)
(*a*) 18 (*b*) 13 (*c*) – 1 (*d*) 3

48. 15, 31, 63, 127, 255, (.....)
(*a*) 513 (*b*) 511 (*c*) 517 (*d*) 523

49. 2, 6, 12, 20, 30, 42, 56, (.....)
(*a*) 60 (*b*) 64 (*c*) 72 (*d*) 70

50. 8, 24, 12, 36, 18, 54, (.....)
(*a*) 27 (*b*) 108 (*c*) 68 (*d*) 72

51. 165, 195, 255,285, 345, (.....)
(*a*) 375 (*b*) 420 (*c*) 435 (*d*) 390

52. 7, 26, 63, 124, 215, 342, (.....)
(*a*) 481 (*b*) 511 (*c*) 391 (*d*) 421

53. 2, 4, 12, 48, 240, (.....)
(*a*) 960 (*b*) 1440 (*c*) 1080 (*d*) 1920

54. 8, 7, 11, 12, 14, 17, 17, 22, (.....)
(*a*) 27 (*b*) 20 (*c*) 22 (*d*) 24

55. 10, 5, 13, 10, 16, 20, 19, (.....)
(*a*) 22 (*b*) 40 (*c*) 38 (*d*) 23

56. 1, 2, 4, 8, 16, 32, 64, (.....), 256
(*a*) 148 (*b*) 128 (*c*) 154 (*d*) 164

57. 71, 76, 69, 74, 67, 72, (.....)
(*a*) 77 (*b*) 65 (*c*) 80 (*d*) 76

58. 9, 12, 11, 14, 13, (.....), 15
(*a*) 12 (*b*) 16 (*c*) 10 (*d*) 17

59. Complete the series : 2, 5, 9, 19, 37, ...
(*a*) 76 (*b*) 74 (*c*) 75 (*d*) None of these

60. Find the wrong number in the series : 3, 8, 15, 24, 34, 48, 63
(*a*) 15 (*b*) 24 (*c*) 34 (*d*) 48 (*e*) 63

61. Find the wrong number in the series : 2, 9, 28, 65, 126, 216, 344
(*a*) 2 (*b*) 28 (*c*) 65 (*d*) 126 (*e*) 216

62. Find out the wrong number in the series : 5, 15, 30, 135, 405, 1215, 3645
(*a*) 3645 (*b*) 1215 (*c*) 405 (*d*) 30 (*e*) 15

63. Find out the wrong number in the series : 125, 106, 88, 76, 65, 58, 53
(*a*) 125 (*b*) 106 (*c*) 88 (*d*) 76 (*e*) 65

Directions : *Find out the wrong number in the series* :

64. 190, 166, 145, 128, 112, 100, 91
(a) 100 (b) 166 (c) 145 (d) 128 (e) 112

65. 1, 1, 2, 6, 24, 96, 720
(a) 720 (b) 96 (c) 24 (d) 6 (e) 2

66. 40960, 10240, 2560, 640, 200, 40, 10
(a) 640 (b) 40 (c) 200 (d) 2560 (e) 10240

67. 64, 71, 80, 91, 104, 119, 135, 155
(a) 71 (b) 80 (c) 104 (d) 119 (e) 135

68. 7, 8, 18, 57, 228, 1165, 6996
(a) 8 (b) 18 (c) 57 (d) 228 (e) 1165

69 3, 7, 15, 27, 63, 127, 255
(a) 7 (b) 15 (c) 27 (d) 63 (e) 127

70. 19, 26, 33, 46, 59, 74, 91
(a) 26 (b) 33 (c) 46 (d) 59 (e) 74

71. 2880, 480, 92, 24, 8, 4, 4
(a) 480 (b) 92 (c) 24 (d) 8 (e) 4

72. 445, 221, 109, 46, 25, 11, 4
(a) 221 (b) 109 (c) 46 (d) 25 (e) 11

73. 3, 7, 15, 39, 63, 127, 255, 511
(a) 7 (b) 15 (c) 39 (d) 63 (e) 127

74. 1, 3, 10, 21, 64, 129, 356, 777
(a) 10 (b) 21 (c) 64 (d) 129 (e) 356

75. 196, 169, 144, 121, 100, 80, 64
(a) 169 (b) 144 (c) 121 (d) 100 (e) 80

76. 6, 12, 48, 100, 384, 768, 3072
(a) 768 (b) 384 (c) 100 (d) 48 (e) 12

77. 10, 26, 74, 218, 654, 1946, 5834
(a) 26 (b) 74 (c) 218 (d) 654 (e) 1946

78. 15, 16, 34, 105, 424, 2124, 12576
(a) 16 (b) 34 (c) 105 (d) 424 (e) 2124

79. 2807, 1400, 697, 347, 171, 84, 41, 20
(a) 697 (b) 347 (c) 171 (d) 84 (e) 41

80. 32, 36, 41, 61, 86, 122, 171, 235
(a) 41 (b) 61 (c) 86 (d) 122 (e) 171

81. 3, 4, 9, 22.5, 67.5, 202.5, 810
(a) 4 (b) 9 (c) 22.5 (d) 67.5 (e) 202.5

82. 1, 2, 8, 33, 148, 760, 4626
(a) 2 (b) 8 (c) 33 (d) 148 (e) 760

83. 3, 8, 18, 46, 100, 210, 432
(a) 8 (b) 18 (c) 46 (d) 100 (e) 210

84. 789, 645, 545, 481, 440, 429, 425
(a) 645 (b) 545 (c) 481 (d) 440 (e) 429

85. 1050, 510, 242, 106, 46, 16, 3
(a) 510 (b) 242 (c) 106 (d) 46 (e) 16

86. 5, 8, 20, 42, 124, 246, 736
(*a*) 8 (*b*) 20 (*c*) 42 (*d*) 124 (*e*) 246

87. 2, 3, 6, 15, 52.5, 157.5, 630
(*a*) 3 (*b*) 6 (*c*) 15 (*d*) 52.5 (*e*) 157.5

88. 888, 440, 216, 104, 48, 22, 6
(*a*) 440 (*b*) 216 (*c*) 104 (*d*) 48 (*e*) 22

89. 4, 5, 15, 49, 201, 1011, 6073
(*a*) 5 (*b*) 15 (*c*) 49 (*d*) 201 (*e*) 1011

ANSWERS

1. (*d*)	**2.** (*c*)	**3.** (*c*)	**4.** (*b*)	**5.** (*a*)	**6.** (*d*)	**7.** (*b*)	**8.** (*c*)	**9.** (*c*)
10. (*b*)	**11.** (*b*)	**12.** (*b*)	**13.** (*a*)	**14.** (*b*)	**15.** (*d*)	**16.** (*b*)	**17.** (*b*)	**18.** (*d*)
19. (*c*)	**20.** (*c*)	**21.** (*b*)	**22.** (*a*)	**23.** (*c*)	**24.** (*d*)	**25.** (*a*)	**26.** (*d*)	**27.** (*d*)
28. (*a*)	**29.** (*a*)	**30.** (*b*)	**31.** (*b*)	**32.** (*a*)	**33.** (*b*)	**34.** (*d*)	**35.** (*c*)	**36.** (*c*)
37. (*b*)	**38.** (*b*)	**39.** (*c*)	**40.** (*d*)	**41.** (*b*)	**42.** (*a*)	**43.** (*c*)	**44.** (*b*)	**45.** (*a*)
46. (*a*)	**47.** (*c*)	**48.** (*b*)	**49.** (*c*)	**50.** (*a*)	**51.** (*c*)	**52.** (*b*)	**53.** (*b*)	**54.** (*b*)
55. (*b*)	**56.** (*b*)	**57.** (*b*)	**58.** (*b*)	**59.** (*c*)	**60.** (*c*)	**61.** (*e*)	**62.** (*d*)	**63.** (*c*)
64. (*d*)	**65.** (*b*)	**66.** (*c*)	**67.** (*e*)	**68.** (*d*)	**69.** (*c*)	**70.** (*b*)	**71.** (*b*)	**72.** (*c*)
73. (*c*)	**74.** (*e*)	**75.** (*e*)	**76.** (*c*)	**77.** (*d*)	**78.** (*e*)	**79.** (*b*)	**80.** (*a*)	**81.** (*a*)
82. (*e*)	**83.** (*b*)	**84.** (*d*)	**85.** (*c*)	**86.** (*b*)	**87.** (*d*)	**88.** (*e*)	**89.** (*a*)	

SOLUTIONS

1. Each of the numbers except 12, is a prime number.

2. Each of the numbers except 21, is an even number.

3. Each of the numbers except 14, is an odd number.

4. Each of the given numbers except 23, is a perfect square.

5. Each of the numbers except 28, is a multiple of 3.

6. Each of the numbers except 81, is a prime number.

7. Each of the numbers except 72, is a perfect square.

8. Each of the numbers except 54, is a multiple of 5.

9. The pattern is $1^2, 2^2, 3^2, 4^2, 5^2, 6^2, 7^2$. But, instead of 5^2, it is 20, which is to be turned out.

10. The pattern is $2^3, 3^3, 4^3, 5^3, 6^3, 7^3$. But, 100 is not a perfect cube.

11. The pattern is 1^2, $1^2 + 2^2$, $1^2 + 2^2 + 3^2$, $1^2 + 2^2 + 3^2 + 4^2$, $1^2 + 2^2 + 3^2 + 4^2 + 5^2$, $1^2 + 2^2 + 3^2 + 4^2 + 5^2 + 6^2$. But, 50 is not of this pattern.

12. In each number except 427, the middle digit is the sum of the other two.

13. In each number except 751, the difference of third and first digit is the middle one.

14. In each number except 383, the product of first and third digits is the middle one.

15. The pattern is $x^2 + 1$, where $x = 1, 2, 3, 4, 5, 6, 7, 8$ etc. But, 64 is out of pattern.

16. The pattern is $x^2 + 3$, where $x = 4, 5, 6, 7, 8, 9$ etc. But, 102 is out of pattern.

17. Sum of the digits in each number, except 324 is 10.

18. Pattern is 1st × 2nd = 3rd; 2nd × 3rd = 4th; 3rd × 4th = 5th.
But, 4th × 5th = 50 × 500 = 25000 ≠ 5000 = 6th.

19. 2nd = (1st + 1); 3rd = (2nd + 2); 4th = (3rd + 3); 5th = (4th + 4).
But, 18 = 6th ≠ 5th + 5 = 14 + 5 = 19.
20. Each number except 279 is a multiple of 11.
21. The terms are alternately multiplied by 1.5 and divided by 3. However, 18.5 does not satisfy it.
22. Alternately 23 is added and 17 is subtracted from the terms. So, 634 is wrong.
23. The terms are successively divided by 12, 10, 8, 6, ... etc. So, 24 is wrong.
24. The numbers are 1^3, 2^3, 3^3, 4^3 etc. So, 124 is wrong; it must have been 5^3 *i.e.,* 125.
25. Terms at odd places are 5, 6, 7, 8 etc. and each term at even place is 16.
So, 9 is wrong.
26. The difference between two successive terms from the beginning are 7, 5, 7, 5, 7, 5.
So, 40 is wrong.
27. The numbers are 7 × 8, 8 × 9, 9 × 10, 10 × 11, 11 × 12, 12 × 13. So, 150 is wrong.
28. Go on adding 5, 8, 11, 14, 17, 20.
So, the number 47 is wrong and must be replaced by 46.
29. The numbers are squares of odd natural numbers, starting from 5 upto 15.
So, 36 is wrong.
30. Add 1^2, 2^2, 3^2, 4^2, 5^2, 6^2. So, 91 is wrong.
31. Subtract 1, 3, 5, 7, 9, 11 from successive numbers. So, 34 is wrong.
32. Subtract 20, 25, 30, 35, 40, 45 from successive numbers. So, 0 is wrong.
33. Each number is a composite number except 11.
34. Prime numbers 2, 3, 5, 7, 11, 13 are to be added successively. So, 165 is wrong.
35. Each number is the square of a composite number except 190.
36. Prime numbers 2, 3, 5, 7, 11, 13 have successively been subtracted.
So, 100 is wrong. It must be (108 – 11) *i.e.,* 97.
37. The pattern is 1 × 3, 2 × 5, 3 × 7, 4 × 9, 5 × 11, 6 × 13, 7 × 15 etc.
38. Double the number and add 1 to it, to get the next number. So, 160 is wrong.
39. Alternately, we add 4 and double the next.
So, 132 is wrong. It must be (68 × 2) *i.e.,* 136.
40. The numbers are cubes of primes *i.e.,* 2^3, 3^3, 5^3, 7^3, 11^3. Clearly, none is wrong.
41. Each number is the preceding number multiplied by – 2.
So, the required number is – 128.
42. Numbers are alternately multiplied by 2 and increased by 3.
So, the missing number = 61 × 2 = 122.
43. Numbers are 1^2, 2^2, 3^2, 4^2, 5^2, 6^2, 7^2. So, the next number is 8^2 = 64.
44. Numbers are 1^3, 2^3, 3^3, 4^3, 5^3, 6^3. So, the missing number is 7^3 = 343.
45. Numbers are all primes. The next prime is 43.
46. Each number is twice the preceding one with 1 added or subtracted alternately.
So, the next number is (2 × 261 + 1) = 523.
47. There are two series, beginning respectively with 3 and 7. In one 3 is added and in another 2 is subtracted. The next number is 1 – 2 = – 1.
48. Each number is double the preceding one plus 1.
So, the next number is (255 × 2) + 1 = 511.
49. The pattern is 1 × 2, 2 × 3, 3 × 4, 4 × 5, 5 × 6, 6 × 7, 7 × 8.
So, the next number is 8 × 9 = 72.
50. Numbers are alternately multiplied by 3 and divided by 2.
So, the next number = 54 ÷ 2 = 27.

51. Each number is 15 multiplied by a prime number i.e., 15×11, 15×13, 15×17, 15×19, 15×23. So, the next number is $15 \times 29 = 435$.

52. Numbers are $(2^3 - 1)$, $(3^3 - 1)$, $(4^3 - 1)$, $(5^3 - 1)$, $(6^3 - 1)$, $(7^3 - 1)$ etc. So, the next number is $(8^3 - 1) = (512 - 1) = 511$.

53. Go on multiplying the given numbers by 2, 3, 4, 5, 6. So, the correct next number is 1440.

54. There are two series (8, 11, 14, 17, 20) and (7, 12, 17, 22) increasing by 3 and 5 respectively.

55. There are two series (10, 13, 16, 19) and (5, 10, 20, 40), one increasing by 3 and the other multiplied by 2.

56. Each previous number is multiplied by 2.

57. Alternately, we add 5 and subtract 7.

58. Alternately, we add 3 and subtract 1.

59. Second number is one more than twice the first; third number is one less than twice the second; fourth number is one more than twice the third; fifth number is one less than the fourth. Therefore, the sixth number is one more than twice the fifth. So, the missing number is 75.

60. The difference between consecutive terms are respectively 5, 7, 9, 11 and 13. So, 34 is a wrong number.

61. $2 = (1^3 + 1)$; $9 = (2^3 + 1)$; $28 = (3^3 + 1)$; $65 = (4^3 + 1)$; $125 = (5^3 + 1)$; $216 \neq (6^3 + 1)$ and $344 = (7^3 + 1)$. So, 216 is a wrong number.

62. Multiply each term by 3 to obtain the next term. Hence, 30 is a wrong number.

63. Go on subtracting prime numbers, 19, 17, 13, 11, 7, 5 from the numbers to get the next number. So, 88 is wrong.

64. Go on subtracting 24, 21, 18, 15, 12, 9 from the numbers to get the next number. Clearly, 128 is wrong.

65. Go on multiplying with 1, 2, 3, 4, 5, 6 to get the next number. So, 96 is wrong.

66. Go on dividing by 4 to get the next number. So, 200 is wrong.

67. Go on adding 7, 9, 11, 13, 15, 17, 19 respectively to obtain the next number. So, 135 is wrong.

68. Let the given numbers be A, B, C, D, E, F, G. Then, A, $A \times 1$, $B \times 2 + 2$, $C \times 3 + 3$, $D \times 4 + 4$, $E \times 5 + 5$, $F \times 6 + 6$ are the required numbers. Clearly, 228 is wrong.

69. Go on multiplying the number by 2 and adding 1 to it to get the next number. So, 27 is wrong.

70. Go on adding 7, 9, 11, 13, 15, 17 respectively to obtain the next number. So, 33 is wrong.

71. Go on dividing by 6, 5, 4, 3, 2, 1 respectively to obtain the next number. Clearly, 92 is wrong.

72. Go on subtracting 3 and dividing the result by 2 to obtain the next number. Clearly, 46 is wrong.

73. Go on multiplying 2 and adding 1 to get the next number. So, 39 is wrong.

74. $A \times 2 + 1$, $B \times 3 + 1$, $C \times 2 + 1$, $D \times 3 + 1$ and so on. So, 356 is wrong.

75. Numbers must be $(14)^2$, $(13)^2$, $(11)^2$, $(10)^2$, $(9)^2$, $(8)^2$. So, 80 is wrong.

76. Each even term of the series is obtained by multiplying the previous term by 2.
2nd term = (1st term) $\times 2 = 6 \times 2 = 12$; 4th term = (3rd term) $\times 2 = 48 \times 2 = 96$;
6th term = (5th term) $\times 2 = 384 \times 2 = 768$.
$\therefore$ 4th term should be 96 instead of 100.

77. 2nd term = (1st term) $\times$ 3 − 4 = 10 $\times$ 3 − 4 = 26;
3rd term = (2nd term) $\times$ 3 − 4 = 26 $\times$ 3 − 4 = 74;
4th term = (3rd term) $\times$ 3 − 4 = 74 $\times$ 3 − 4 = 218;
5th term = (4th term) $\times$ 3 − 4 = 218 $\times$ 3 − 4 = 650.
$\therefore$ 5th term must be 650 instead of 654.

78. 2nd term = (1st term) $\times$ 1 + 1 = 15 $\times$ 1 + 1 = 16;
3rd term = (2nd term) $\times$ 2 + 2 = 16 $\times$ 2 + 2 = 34;
4th term = (3rd term) $\times$ 3 + 3 = 34 $\times$ 3 + 3 = 105;
5th term = (4th term) $\times$ 4 + 4 = 105 $\times$ 4 + 4 = 424;
6th term = (5th term) $\times$ 5 + 5 = 425 $\times$ 5 + 5 = 2125.
$\therefore$ 6th term should be 2125 instead of 2124.

79. 7th term = (8th term) $\times$ 2 + 1 = 20 $\times$ 2 + 1 = 41;
6th term = (7th term) $\times$ 2 + 2 = 41 $\times$ 2 + 2 = 84;
5th term = (6th term) $\times$ 2 + 3 = 84 $\times$ 2 + 3 = 171;
4th term = (5th term) $\times$ 2 + 4 = 171 $\times$ 2 + 4 = 346.
$\therefore$ 4th term should be 346 instead of 347.

80. 2nd term = (1st term) + 2^2 = 32 + 4 = 36; 3rd term = (2nd term) + 3^2 = 36 + 9 = 45;
4th term = (3rd term) + 4^2 = 45 + 16 = 61; 5th term = (4th term) + 5^2 = 61 + 25 = 86.
$\therefore$ 3rd term should be 45 instead of 41.

81. There are two sequences (3, 9, 67.5, 810) and (4, 22.5, 202.5).
Pattern is : (1st term $\times$ 3), (2nd term $\times$ 7.5), (3rd term $\times$ 12) for the first sequence and (1st term $\times$ 5), (2nd term $\times$ 9) and so on for the second sequence.

82. 2nd term = (1st term $\times$ 1 + 1^2) = 1 $\times$ 1 + 1^2 = 2;
3rd term = (2nd term $\times$ 2 + 2^2) = 2 $\times$ 2 + 2^2 = 8;
4th term = (3rd term $\times$ 3 + 3^2) = 8 $\times$ 3 + 3^2 = 33;
5th term = (4th term $\times$ 4 + 4^2) = 33 $\times$ 4 + 4^2 = 148;
6th term = (5th term $\times$ 5 + 5^2) = 148 $\times$ 5 + 5^2 = 765.
$\therefore$ 760 is wrong.

83. 2nd term = (1st term $\times$ 2 + 2) = 3 $\times$ 2 + 2 = 8;
3rd term = (2nd term $\times$ 2 + 4) = 8 $\times$ 2 + 4 = 20;
4th term = (3rd term $\times$ 2 + 6) = 20 $\times$ 2 + 6 = 46;
5th term = (4th term $\times$ 2 + 8) = 46 $\times$ 2 + 8 = 100 and so on.
$\therefore$ 18 is wrong.

84. 2nd term = 1st term − $(12)^2$ = 789 − 144 = 645;
3rd term = (2nd term) − $(10)^2$ = 645 − 100 = 545;
4th term = (3rd term) − $(8)^2$ = 545 − 64 = 481;
5th term = (4th term) − $(6)^2$ = 481 − 36 = 445.
$\therefore$ 440 is wrong.

85. 2nd term = (1st term − 30) ÷ 2 = $\left(\frac{1050-30}{2}\right)$ = 510;

3rd term = (2nd term − 26) ÷ 2 = $\left(\frac{510-26}{2}\right)$ = 242;

4th term = (3rd term − 22) ÷ 2 = $\left(\frac{242-22}{2}\right)$ = 110.

$\therefore$ 106 is wrong.

86. 2nd term = (1st term × 2 – 2) = (5 × 2 – 2) = 8;
3rd term = (2nd term × 3 – 2) = (8 × 3 – 2) = 22;
4th term = (3rd term × 2 – 2) = (22 × 2 – 2) = 42;
5th term = (4th term × 3 – 2) = (42 × 3 – 2) = 124 and so on.
∴ 20 is wrong.

87. 2nd term = (1st term × 1.5) = 2 × 1.5 = 3; 3rd term = (2nd term × 2) = 3 × 2 = 6;
4th term = (3rd term × 2.5) = 6 × 2.5 = 15; 5th term = (4th term × 3) = 15 × 3 = 45.
∴ 52.5 is wrong.

88. 2nd term = $\left(\frac{\text{1st term} - 8}{2}\right) = \left(\frac{888 - 8}{2}\right) = 440;$

3rd term = $\left(\frac{\text{2nd term} - 8}{2}\right) = \left(\frac{440 - 8}{2}\right) = 216;$

4th term = $\left(\frac{\text{3rd term} - 8}{2}\right) = \left(\frac{216 - 8}{2}\right) = 104;$

5th term = $\left(\frac{\text{4th term} - 8}{2}\right) = \left(\frac{104 - 8}{2}\right) = 48;$

6th term = $\left(\frac{\text{5th term} - 8}{2}\right) = \left(\frac{48 - 8}{2}\right) = 20.$

∴ 22 is wrong.

89. 2nd term = (1st term × 1 + 2) = (4 × 1 + 2) = 6;
3rd term = (2nd term × 2 + 3) = (6 × 2 + 3) = 15;
4th term = (3rd term × 3 + 4) = (15 × 3 + 4) = 49;
5th term = (4th term × 4 + 5) = (49 × 4 + 5) = 210 and so on.
∴ 5 is wrong.

SECTION II

DATA INTERPRETATION

36. TABULATION

This section comprises of questions in which certain data regarding common disciplines as production over a period of a few years : imports, exports, incomes of employees in a factory, students applying for and qualifying a certain field of study etc. are given in the form of a table. The candidate is required to understand the given information and thereafter answer the given questions on the basis of comparative analysis of the data.

Thus, here the data collected by the investigator are arranged in a systematic form in a table called the *tabular form*. In order to avoid some heads again and again, tables are made consisting of horizontal lines called *rows* and vertical lines called *columns* with distinctive heads, known as *captions*. Units of measurements are given with the captions.

SOLVED EXAMPLES

Ex. 1. ***The following table gives the sales of batteries manufactured by a company over the years. Study the table and answer the questions that follow :***

(S.B.I.P.O. 1998)

NUMBER OF DIFFERENT TYPES OF BATTERIES SOLD BY A COMPANY OVER THE YEARS (NUMBERS IN THOUSANDS)

Year	TYPES OF BATTERIES					
	4AH	7AH	32AH	35AH	55AH	Total
1992	75	144	114	102	108	543
1993	90	126	102	84	126	528
1994	96	114	75	105	135	525
1995	105	90	150	90	75	510
1996	90	75	135	75	90	465
1997	105	60	165	45	120	495
1998	115	85	160	100	145	605

1. The total sales of all the seven years is the maximum for which battery ?
   (*a*) 4AH (*b*) 7AH (*c*) 32AH (*d*) 35AH (*e*) 55AH
2. What is the difference in the number of 35AH batteries sold in 1993 and 1997 ?
   (*a*) 24000 (*b*) 28000 (*c*) 35000 (*d*) 39000 (*e*) 42000
3. The percentage of 4AH batteries sold to the total number of batteries sold was maximum in the year :
   (*a*) 1994 (*b*) 1995 (*c*) 1996 (*d*) 1997 (*e*) 1998
4. In the case of which battery there was a continuous decrease in sales from 1992 to 1997 ?
   (*a*) 4AH (*b*) 7AH (*c*) 32AH (*d*) 35AH (*e*) 55AH
5. What was the approximate percentage increase in the sales of 55AH batteries in 1998 compared to that in 1992 ?
   (*a*) 28% (*b*) 31% (*c*) 33% (*d*) 34% (*e*) 37%

Sol. 1. (*c*) : The total sales (in thousands) of all the seven years for various batteries are :

For 4AH = 75 + 90 + 96 + 105 + 90 + 105 + 115 = 676

For 7AH = 144 + 126 + 114 + 90 + 75 + 60 + 85 = 694

For 32AH = 114 + 102 + 75 + 150 + 135 + 165 + 160 = 901

For 35 AH = 102 + 84 + 105 + 90 + 75 + 45 + 100 = 601

For 55 AH = 108 + 126 + 135 + 75 + 90 + 120 + 145 = 799.

Clearly, sales are maximum in case of 32AH batteries.

2. (*d*) : Required difference = [(84 – 45) × 1000] = 39000.

3. (*d*) : The percentages of sales of 4AH batteries to the total sales in different years are :

For 1992 $= \left(\frac{75}{543} \times 100\right)\% = 13.81\%$; **For 1993** $= \left(\frac{90}{528} \times 100\right)\% = 17.05\%$;

For 1994 $= \left(\frac{96}{525} \times 100\right)\% = 18.29\%$; **For 1995** $= \left(\frac{105}{510} \times 100\right)\% = 20.59\%$;

For 1996 $= \left(\frac{96}{465} \times 100\right)\% = 19.35\%$; **For 1997** $= \left(\frac{105}{495} \times 100\right)\% = 21.21\%$;

For 1998 $= \left(\frac{115}{605} \times 100\right)\% = 19.01\%$.

Clearly, the percentage is maximum in 1997.

4. (*b*) : From the table it is clear that the sales of 7AH batteries have been decreasing continuously from 1992 to 1997.

5. (*d*) : Required Percentage $= \left[\frac{(145 - 108)}{108} \times 100\right]\% = 34.26\% \approx 34\%.$

Ex. 2. ***Study the following table carefully and answer these questions :*** **(S.B.I.P.O. 2002)**

NUMBER OF CANDIDATES APPEARED AND QUALIFIED IN A COMPETITIVE EXAMINATION FROM DIFFERENT STATES OVER THE YEARS

Year / State	1997		1998		1999		2000		2001	
	App.	**Qual.**	**App.**	**Qual.**	**App.**	**Qual.**	**App.**	**Qual.**	**App.**	**Qual.**
M	5200	720	8500	980	7400	850	6800	775	9500	1125
N	7500	840	9200	1050	8450	920	9200	980	8800	1020
P	6400	780	8800	1020	7800	890	8750	1010	9750	1250
Q	8100	950	9500	1240	8700	980	9700	1200	8950	995
R	7800	870	7600	940	9800	1350	7600	945	7990	885

1. Combining the states P and Q together in 1998, what is the percentage of the candidates qualified to that of the candidates appeared ?

(*a*) 10.87% (*b*) 11.49% (*c*) 12.35% (*d*) 12.54% (*e*) 13.05%

2. The percentage of the total number of qualified candidates to the total number of appeared candidates among all the five states in 1999 is :

(*a*) 11.49% (*b*) 11.84% (*c*) 12.21% (*d*) 12.57% (*e*) 12.73%

3. What is the percentage of candidates qualified from State N for all the years together, over the candidates appeared from State N during all the years together ?

(*a*) 12.36% (*b*) 12.16% (*c*) 11.47% (*d*) 11.15% (*e*) None of these

4. What is the average of candidates who appeared from State Q during the given yeas ?

(*a*) 8700 (*b*) 8760 (*c*) 8810 (*d*) 8920 (*e*) 8990

5. In which of the given years the number of candidates appeared from State P has maximum percentage of qualified candidates ?

(*a*) 1997 (*b*) 1998 (*c*) 1999 (*d*) 2000 (*e*) 2001

6. Total number of candidates qualified from all the states together in 1997 is approximately what percentage of the total number of candidates qualified from all the states together in 1998 ?

(*a*) 72% (*b*) 77% (*c*) 80% (*d*) 83% (*e*) 86%

Sol. 1. (*c*) : Required Percentage $= \left[\frac{(1020 + 1240)}{(8800 + 9500)} \times 100\right]\% = \left(\frac{2260}{18300} \times 100\right)\%$

$= 12.35\%$.

2. (*b*) : Required Percentage $= \left[\frac{(850 + 920 + 890 + 980 + 1350)}{(7400 + 8450 + 7800 + 8700 + 9800)} \times 100\right]\%$

$= \left(\frac{4990}{42150} \times 100\right)\% = 11.84\%$.

3. (*d*) : Required Percentage $= \left[\frac{(840 + 1050 + 920 + 980 + 1020)}{(7500 + 9200 + 8450 + 9200 + 8800)} \times 100\right]\%$

$= \left(\frac{4810}{43150} \times 100\right)\% = 11.15\%$.

4. (*e*) : Required average $= \frac{8100 + 9500 + 8700 + 9700 + 8950}{5} = \frac{44950}{5} = 8990$.

5. (*e*) : The percentages of candidates qualified to candidates appeared from State P during different years are :

For 1997 $= \left(\frac{780}{6400} \times 100\right)\% = 12.19\%$; **For 1998** $= \left(\frac{1020}{8800} \times 100\right)\% = 11.59\%$;

For 1999 $= \left(\frac{890}{7800} \times 100\right)\% = 11.41\%$; **For 2000** $= \left(\frac{1010}{8750} \times 100\right)\% = 11.54\%$;

For 2001 $= \left(\frac{1250}{9750} \times 100\right)\% = 12.82\%$.

$\therefore$ Maximum percentage is for the year 2001.

6. (*c*) : Required Percentage $= \left[\frac{(720 + 840 + 780 + 950 + 870)}{(980 + 1050 + 1020 + 1240 + 940)} \times 100\right]\%$

$= \left(\frac{4160}{5230} \times 100\right)\% = 79.54\% \approx 80\%$.

Ex. 3. ***The following table gives the percentage of marks obtained by seven students in six different subjects in an examination. Study the table and answer the questions based on it. The numbers in the brackets give the maximum marks in each subject.***

(Bank P.O. 2003)

Student \ Subjects (Max. Marks)	Maths (150)	Chemistry (130)	Physics (120)	Geography (100)	History (60)	Computer Science (40)
Ayush	90	50	90	60	70	80
Aman	100	80	80	40	80	70
Sajal	90	60	70	70	90	70
Rohit	80	65	80	80	60	60
Muskan	80	65	85	95	50	90
Tanvi	70	75	65	85	40	60
Tarun	65	35	50	77	80	80

1. What was the aggregate of marks obtained by Sajal in all the six subjects ?
(*a*) 409 (*b*) 419 (*c*) 429 (*d*) 439 (*e*) 449

2. What is the overall percentage of Tarun ?
(*a*) 52.5% (*b*) 55% (*c*) 60% (*d*) 63% (*e*) 64.5%

3. What are the average marks obtained by all the seven students in Physics ? (rounded off to two digits after decimal)
(*a*) 77.26 (*b*) 89.14 (*c*) 91.37 (*d*) 96.11 (*e*) 103.21

4. The number of students who obtained 60% and above marks in all the subjects is :
(*a*) 1 (*b*) 2 (*c*) 3 (*d*) None (*e*) None of these

5. In which subject is the overall percentage the best ?
(*a*) History (*b*) Maths (*c*) Physics (*d*) Chemistry (*e*) Geography

Sol. 1. (*e*) : Aggregate marks obtained by Sajal
$= [(90\% \text{ of } 150) + (60\% \text{ of } 130) + (70\% \text{ of } 120) + (70\% \text{ of } 100) + (90\% \text{ of } 60) + (70\% \text{ of } 40)] = 135 + 78 + 84 + 70 + 54 + 28 = 449.$

2. (*c*) : Aggregate marks obtained by Tarun
$= [(65\% \text{ of } 150) + (35\% \text{ of } 130) + (50\% \text{ of } 120) + (77\% \text{ of } 100) + (80\% \text{ of } 60) + (80\% \text{ of } 40)] = 97.5 + 45.5 + 60 + 77 + 48 + 32 = 360.$

Total maximum marks (of all the six subjects)
$= (150 + 130 + 120 + 100 + 60 + 40) = 600.$

Overall percentage of Tarun $= \left(\frac{360}{600} \times 100\right)\% = 60\%.$

3. (*b*) : Average marks obtained in Physics by all the seven students

$$= \frac{1}{7} \times [(90\% \text{ of } 120) + (80\% \text{ of } 120) + (70\% \text{ of } 120) + (80\% \text{ of } 120) + (85\% \text{ of } 120) + (65\% \text{ of } 120) + (50\% \text{ of } 120)]$$

$$= \frac{1}{7} \times [(90 + 80 + 70 + 80 + 85 + 65 + 50)\% \text{ of } 120]$$

$$= \frac{1}{7} \times [520\% \text{ of } 120] = \frac{624}{7} = 89.14.$$

4. (*b*) : From the table it is clear that Sajal and Rohit have 60% or more marks in each of the six subjects.

5. (*b*) : We shall find the overall percentage (for all the seven students) with respect to each subject.

The overall percentage for any subject is equal to the average of percentages obtained by all the seven students since the maximum marks for any subject is the same for all the students.

Therefore, overall percentage for :

(*i*) Maths $= \left[\frac{1}{7} \times (90 + 100 + 90 + 80 + 80 + 70 + 65)\right]\%$

$= \left[\frac{1}{7} \times (575)\right]\% = 82.14\%.$

(*ii*) Chemistry $= \left[\frac{1}{7} \times (50 + 80 + 60 + 65 + 65 + 75 + 35)\right]\%$

$= \left[\frac{1}{7} \times (430)\right]\% = 61.43\%.$

(*iii*) Physics $= \left[\frac{1}{7} \times (90 + 80 + 70 + 80 + 85 + 65 + 50)\right]\%$

$= \left[\frac{1}{7} \times (520)\right]\% = 74.29\%.$

(*iv*) Geography $= \left[\frac{1}{7} \times (60 + 40 + 70 + 80 + 95 + 85 + 77)\right]\%$

$= \left[\frac{1}{7} \times (507)\right]\% = 72.43\%.$

(*v*) History $= \left[\frac{1}{7} \times (70 + 80 + 90 + 60 + 50 + 40 + 80)\right]\%$

$= \left[\frac{1}{7} \times (470)\right]\% = 67.14\%.$

(*vi*) Computer Science $= \left[\frac{1}{7} \times (80 + 70 + 70 + 60 + 90 + 60 + 80)\right]\%$

$= \left[\frac{1}{7} \times (510)\right]\% = 72.86\%.$

Clearly, this percentage is highest for Maths.

Ex. 4. ***Study the following table carefully and answer the questions given below*** **:**

(Bank P.O. 2001)

CLASSIFICATION OF 100 STUDENTS BASED ON THE MARKS OBTAINED BY THEM IN PHYSICS AND CHEMISTRY IN AN EXAMINATION

Marks out of 50 / Subject	**40 and above**	**30 and above**	**20 and above**	**10 and above**	**0 and above**
Physics	9	32	80	92	100
Chemistry	4	21	66	81	100
(Aggregate) Average	7	27	73	87	100

1. The number of students scoring less than 40% marks in aggregate is :

(*a*) 13 (*b*) 19 (*c*) 20 (*d*) 27 (*e*) 34

2. If at least 60% marks in Physics are required for pursuing higher studies in Physics, how many students will be eligible to pursue higher studies in Physics ?

(*a*) 27 (*b*) 32 (*c*) 34 (*d*) 41 (*e*) 68

3. What is the difference between the number of students passed with 30 as cut-off-marks in Chemistry and those passed with 30 as cut-off marks in aggregate ?

(*a*) 3 (*b*) 4 (*c*) 5 (*d*) 6 (*e*) 7

4. The percentage of the number of students getting at least 60% marks in Chemistry over those getting at least 40% marks in aggregate, is approximately :
(*a*) 21% (*b*) 27% (*c*) 29% (*d*) 31% (*e*) 34%

5. If it is known that at least 23 students were eligible for a Symposium on Chemistry, the minimum qualifying marks in Chemistry for eligibility to Symposium would lie in the range :
(*a*) 40-50 (*b*) 30-40 (*c*) 20-30 (*d*) Below 20 (*e*) Cannot be determined

Sol. 1. (*d*) : We have 40% of 50 = $\left(\frac{40}{100} \times 50\right)$ = 20.

∴ Required number = Number of students scoring less than 20 marks in aggregate
= 100 – number of students scoring 20 and above marks in aggregate = 100 – 73 = 27.

2. (*b*) : We have 60% of 50 = $\left(\frac{60}{100} \times 50\right)$ = 30.

∴ Required number = Number of students scoring 30 and above marks in Physics = 32.

3. (*d*) : Required difference = (Number of students scoring 30 and above marks in Chemistry) – (Number of students scoring 30 and above marks in aggregate) = 27 – 21 = 6.

4. (*c*) : Number of students getting at least 60% marks in Chemistry
= Number of students getting 30 and above marks in Chemistry = 21.
Number of students getting at least 40% marks in aggregate
= Number of students getting 20 and above marks in aggregate = 73.

∴ Required Percentage = $\left(\frac{21}{73} \times 100\right)\%$ = 28.77% ≈ 29%.

5. (*c*) : Since 66 students get 20 and above marks in Chemistry and out of these 21 students get 30 and above marks, therefore to select top 35 students in Chemistry, the qualifying marks should lie in the range 20-30.

EXERCISE 36

Directions (Questions 1 to 6) : ***Study the following table and answer the questions based on it.*** **(Bank P.O. 2003)**

NUMBER OF CANDIDATES APPEARED, QUALIFIED AND SELECTED IN A COMPETITIVE EXAMINATION FROM FIVE STATES DELHI, H.P., U.P., PUNJAB AND HARYANA OVER THE YEARS 1994 TO 1998

	Delhi			H.P.			U.P.			Punjab			Haryana		
Year	**App.**	**Qual.**	**Sel.**	**App.**	**Qual.**	**Sel.**	**App.**	**Qual.**	**Sel.**	**App.**	**Qual.**	**Sel.**	**App.**	**Qual.**	**Sel.**
1997	8000	850	94	7800	810	82	7500	720	78	8200	680	85	6400	700	75
1998	4800	500	48	7500	800	65	5600	620	85	6800	600	70	7100	650	75
1999	7500	640	82	7400	560	70	4800	400	48	6500	525	65	5200	350	55
2000	9500	850	90	8800	920	86	7000	650	70	7800	720	84	6400	540	60
2001	9000	800	70	7200	850	75	8500	950	80	5700	485	60	4500	600	75

1. In the year 1997, which state had the lowest percentage of candidates selected over the candidates appeared ?
(*a*) Delhi (*b*) H.P. (*c*) U.P. (*d*) Punjab (*e*) Haryana

2. The percentage of candidates qualified from Punjab over those appeared from Punjab is highest in the year :
(*a*) 1997 (*b*) 1998 (*c*) 1999 (*d*) 2000 (*e*) 2001

3. The percentage of candidates selected from U.P. over those qualified from U.P. is highest in the year :
(*a*) 1997 (*b*) 1998 (*c*) 1999 (*d*) 2000 (*e*) 2001

4. The number of candidates selected from Haryana during the period under review is approximately what percent of the number selected from Delhi during this period ?
(*a*) 79.5% (*b*) 81% (*c*) 84.5% (*d*) 88.5% (*e*) 92.5%

5. For which state the average number of candidates selected over the years is the maximum ?
(*a*) Delhi (*b*) H.P. (*c*) U.P. (*d*) Punjab (*e*) Haryana

6. What is the approximate percentage of total number of candidates selected to the total number of candidates qualified for all the five states together during the year 1999 ?
(*a*) 10% (*b*) 11% (*c*) 12% (*d*) 13% (*e*) 14%

Directions (Questions 7 to 11) : ***Study the following table to answer the questions that are given below it.*** **(R.B.I. 2003)**

EXPENDITURES OF A COMPANY (IN LAKH RUPEES) PER ANNUM OVER THE GIVEN YEARS

Item of Expenditure / Year	Salary	Fuel and Transport	Bonus	Interest on Loans	Taxes
1998	288	98	3.00	23.4	83
1999	342	112	2.52	32.5	108
2000	324	101	3.84	41.6	74
2001	336	133	3.68	36.4	88
2002	420	142	3.96	49.4	98

7. The ratio between the total expenditure on Taxes for all the years and the total expenditure on Fuel and Transport for all the years respectively is approximately :
(*a*) 4 : 7 (*b*) 10 : 13 (*c*) 15 : 18 (*d*) 5 : 8 (*e*) 2 : 3

8. The total expenditure of the Company over these items during the year 2000 is :
(*a*) Rs. 544.44 lakhs (*b*) Rs. 501.11 lakhs (*c*) Rs. 446.46 lakhs
(*d*) Rs. 478.87 lakhs (*e*) Rs. 612.13 lakhs

9. What is the average amount of interest per year which the Company had to pay during this period ?
(*a*) Rs. 32.43 lakhs (*b*) Rs. 33.72 lakhs (*c*) Rs. 34.18 lakhs
(*d*) Rs. 35.69 lakhs (*e*) Rs. 36.66 lakhs

10. Total expenditure on all these items in 1998 was approximately what percent of the total expenditure in 2002 ?
(*a*) 62% (*b*) 66% (*c*) 69% (*d*) 71% (*e*) 73%

11. The total amount of bonus paid by the Company during the given period is approximately what percent of the total amount of salary paid during this period ?
(*a*) 0.1% (*b*) 0.5% (*c*) 1% (*d*) 1.25% (*e*) 1.11%

Directions (Questions 12 to 16) : ***A school has four sections A, B, C, D of Class IX students. The results of half-yearly and annual examinations are shown in the table given below. Answer the questions based on this table.*** **(Bank P.O. 2000)**

Result	Number of Students			
	Section A	Section B	Section C	Section D
Students failed in both Exams	28	23	17	27
Students failed in half-yearly but passed in Annual Exams	14	12	8	13
Students passed in half-yearly but failed in Annual Exams	6	17	9	15
Students passed in both Exams	64	55	46	76

12. How many students are there in Class IX in the school ?
(*a*) 336 (*b*) 189 (*c*) 335 (*d*) 286 (*e*) 430

13. Which section has the minimum failure rate in half-yearly examination ?
(*a*) A (*b*) B (*c*) C
(*d*) D (*e*) Cannot be determined

14. Which section has the maximum success rate in annual examination ?
(*a*) A (*b*) B (*c*) C
(*d*) D (*e*) Cannot be determined

15. Which section has the maximum pass percentage in at least one of the two examinations ?
(*a*) A (*b*) B (*c*) C
(*d*) D (*e*) Cannot be determined

16. If the number of students passing an examination be considered a criteria for comparison of difficulty level of two examinations, which of the following statements is true in this context ?
(*a*) Half-yearly examinations were more difficult.
(*b*) Annual examinations were more difficult.
(*c*) Both the examinations had almost the same difficulty level.
(*d*) The two examinations cannot be compared for difficulty level.
(*e*) For students of Sections A and B, the annual examinations seem to be more difficult as compared to the half-yearly examinations.

Directions (Questions 17 to 21) : ***The following table shows the number of new employees added to different categories of employees in a Company and also the number of employees from these categories who left the company every year since the foundation of the Company in 1995.*** **(Bank P.O. 2001)**

	Managers		Technicians		Operators		Accountants		Peons	
Year	New	Left	New	Left	New	Left	New	Left	New	Left
1995	760	—	1200	—	880	—	1160	—	820	—
1996	280	120	272	120	256	104	200	100	184	96
1997	179	92	240	128	240	120	224	104	152	88
1998	148	88	236	96	208	100	248	96	196	80
1999	160	72	256	100	192	112	272	88	224	120
2000	193	96	288	112	248	144	260	92	200	104

17. During the period between 1995 and 2000, the total number of Operators who left the Company is what percent of the total number of Operators who joined the Company?
(*a*) 19% (*b*) 21% (*c*) 27% (*d*) 29% (*e*) 32%

18. For which of the following categories the percentage increase in the number of employees working in the Company from 1995 to 2000 was the maximum ?
(*a*) Managers (*b*) Technicians (*c*) Operators (*d*) Accountants (*e*) Peons

19. What is the difference between the total number of Technicians added to the Company and the total number of Accountants added to the Company during the years 1996 to 2000 ?
(*a*) 128 (*b*) 112 (*c*) 96 (*d*) 88 (*e*) 72

20. What was the total number of Peons working in the Company in the year 1999 ?
(*a*) 1312 (*b*) 1192 (*c*) 1088 (*d*) 968 (*e*) 908

21. What is the pooled average of the total number of employees of all categories in the year 1997 ?
(*a*) 1325 (*b*) 1285 (*c*) 1265 (*d*) 1235 (*e*) 1195

Directions (Questions 22 to 25) : ***The following table gives the percentage distribution of population of five states, P, Q, R, S and T on the basis of poverty line and also on the basis of sex. Study the table and answer the questions based on it.***
(Bank P.O. 2000)

State	Percentage of Population below Poverty Line	Proportion of Males and Females	
		Below Poverty Line M : F	Above Poverty Line M : F
P	35	5 : 6	6 : 7
Q	25	3 : 5	4 : 5
R	24	1 : 2	2 : 3
S	19	3 : 2	4 : 3
T	15	5 : 3	3 : 2

22. What will be the number of females above poverty line in the State S if it is known that the population of State S is 7 million ?
(*a*) 3 million (*b*) 2.43 million (*c*) 1.33 million
(*d*) 5.7 million (*e*) 1.61 million

23. If the male population above poverty line for State R is 1.9 million, then the total population of State R is :
(*a*) 4.5 million (*b*) 4.85 million (*c*) 5.35 million
(*d*) 6.25 million (*e*) 7.6 million

24. What will be the male population above poverty line for State P if the female population below poverty line for State P is 2.1 million ?
(*a*) 2.1 million (*b*) 2.3 million (*c*) 2.7 million
(*d*) 3.3 million (*e*) 3.4 million

25. If the population of males below poverty line for State Q is 2.4 million and that for State T is 6 million, then the total populations of states Q and T are in the ratio :
(*a*) 1 : 3 (*b*) 2 : 5 (*c*) 3 : 7 (*d*) 4 : 9 (*e*) 5 : 12

ANSWERS

1. (*d*)	**2.** (*d*)	**3.** (*b*)	**4.** (*d*)	**5.** (*a*)	**6.** (*d*)	**7.** (*b*)	**8.** (*a*)	**9.** (*e*)
10. (*c*)	**11.** (*c*)	**12.** (*e*)	**13.** (*d*)	**14.** (*a*)	**15.** (*d*)	**16.** (*b*)	**17.** (*d*)	**18.** (*a*)
19. (*d*)	**20.** (*b*)	**21.** (*e*)	**22.** (*b*)	**23.** (*d*)	**24.** (*d*)	**25.** (*b*)		

SOLUTIONS

1. The percentages of candidates selected over the candidates appeared in 1997, for various states are :

(*i*) For Delhi = $\left(\frac{94}{8000}\times 100\right)\% = 1.175\%$; (*ii*) For H.P. = $\left(\frac{82}{7800}\times 100\right)\% = 1.051\%$;

(*iii*) For U.P. = $\left(\frac{78}{7500}\times 100\right)\% = 1.040\%$; (*iv*) For Punjab = $\left(\frac{85}{8200}\times 100\right)\% = 1.037\%$;

(*v*) For Haryana = $\left(\frac{75}{6400}\times 100\right)\% = 1.172\%$.

Clearly, this percentage is lowest for Punjab.

2. The percentages of candidates qualified from Punjab over those appeared from Punjab during different years are :

For 1997 = $\left(\frac{680}{8200}\times 100\right)\% = 8.29\%$; **For 1998** = $\left(\frac{600}{6800}\times 100\right)\% = 8.82\%$;

For 1999 = $\left(\frac{525}{6500}\times 100\right)\% = 8.08\%$; **For 2000** = $\left(\frac{720}{7800}\times 100\right)\% = 9.23\%$;

For 2001 = $\left(\frac{485}{5700}\times 100\right)\% = 8.51\%$.

Clearly, this percentage is highest for the year 2000.

3. The percentages of candidates selected from U.P. over those qualified from U.P. during different years are :

For 1997 = $\left(\frac{78}{720}\times 100\right)\% = 10.83\%$; **For 1998** = $\left(\frac{85}{620}\times 100\right)\% = 13.71\%$;

For 1999 = $\left(\frac{48}{400}\times 100\right)\% = 12\%$; **For 2000** = $\left(\frac{70}{650}\times 100\right)\% = 10.77\%$;

For 2001 = $\left(\frac{80}{950}\times 100\right)\% = 8.42\%$.

Clearly, this percentage is highest for the year 1998.

4. Required Percentage = $\left[\frac{(75+75+55+60+75)}{(94+48+82+90+70)}\times 100\right]\%$

$= \left(\frac{340}{384}\times 100\right)\% = 88.54\% \approx 88.5\%.$

5. The average number of candidates selected over the given period for various states are :

For Delhi = $\frac{94+48+82+90+70}{5} = \frac{384}{5} = 76.8$

For H.P. = $\frac{82+65+70+86+75}{5} = \frac{378}{5} = 75.6$

For U.P. $= \dfrac{78+85+48+70+80}{5} = \dfrac{361}{5} = 72.2$

For Punjab $= \dfrac{85+70+65+84+60}{5} = \dfrac{364}{4} = 72.8$

For Haryana $= \dfrac{75+75+55+60+75}{5} = \dfrac{340}{5} = 68.$

Clearly, this average is maximum for Delhi.

6. Required Percentage $= \left[\dfrac{(82+70+48+65+55)}{(640+560+400+525+350)} \times 100\right]\%$

$= \left(\dfrac{320}{2475} \times 100\right)\% = 12.93\% \approx 13\%.$

7. Required Ratio $= \dfrac{(83+108+74+88+98)}{(98+112+101+133+142)} = \dfrac{451}{586} \approx \dfrac{1}{1.3} = \dfrac{10}{13}.$

8. Total expenditure of the Company during 2000
$=$ Rs. $(324 + 101 + 3.84 + 41.6 + 74)$ lakhs $=$ Rs. 544.44 lakhs.

9. Average amount of interest paid by the Company during the given period
$=$ Rs. $\left(\dfrac{23.4+32.5+41.6+36.4+49.4}{5}\right)$ lakhs $=$ Rs. $\left(\dfrac{183.3}{5}\right)$ lakh
$=$ Rs. 36.66 lakhs.

10. Required Percentage $= \left[\dfrac{(288+98+3.00+23.4+83)}{(420+142+3.96+49.4+98)} \times 100\right]\%$

$= \left(\dfrac{495.4}{713.36} \times 100\right)\% \approx 69.45\%.$

11. Required Percentage $= \left[\dfrac{(3.00+2.52+3.84+3.68+3.96)}{(288+342+324+336+420)} \times 100\right]\%$

$= \left(\dfrac{17}{1710} \times 100\right)\% \approx 1\%.$

12. Since the classification of the students on the basis of their results and sections form independent groups, so the total number of students in the class :
$= (28 + 23 + 17 + 27 + 14 + 12 + 8 + 13 + 6 + 17 + 9 + 15 + 64 + 55 + 46 + 76) = 430.$

13. Total number of failures in half-yearly exams in a section
$=$ [(Number of students failed in both exams) + (Number of students failed in half-yearly but passed in Annual exams)] in that section

$\therefore$ Failure rate in half-yearly exams in **Section A**

$= \left[\dfrac{\text{Number of students of Section A failed in half-yearly}}{\text{Total number of students in Section A}} \times 100\right]\%$

$= \left[\dfrac{(28+14)}{(28+14+6+64)} \times 100\right]\% = \left(\dfrac{42}{112} \times 100\right)\% = 37.5\%$

Similarly, failure rate in half-yearly exams in .

Section B $= \left[\dfrac{(23+12)}{(23+12+17+55)} \times 100\right]\% = \left(\dfrac{35}{107} \times 100\right)\% = 32.71\%$

Section C $= \left[\dfrac{(17+8)}{(17+8+9+46)} \times 100\right]\% = \left(\dfrac{25}{80} \times 100\right)\% = 31.25\%$

Section D $= \left[\frac{(27+13)}{(27+13+15+76)} \times 100\right]\% = \left(\frac{40}{131} \times 100\right)\% = 30.53\%$

Clearly, the failure rate is minimum for Section D.

14. Total number of students passed in annual exams in a section

= [(Number of students failed in half-yearly but passed in annual exams) + (Number of students passed in both exams)] in that section

∴ Success rate in annual examination in **Section A**

$= \left[\frac{\text{Number of students of Section A passed in annual exams}}{\text{Total number of students in Section A}} \times 100\right]\%$

$= \left[\frac{(14+64)}{(28+14+6+64)} \times 100\right]\% = \left(\frac{78}{112} \times 100\right)\% = 69.64\%$

Similarly, success rate in annual examinations in :

Section B $= \left[\frac{(12+55)}{(23+12+17+55)} \times 100\right]\% = \left(\frac{67}{107} \times 100\right)\% = 62.62\%$

Section C $= \left[\frac{(8+46)}{(17+8+9+46)} \times 100\right]\% = \left(\frac{54}{80} \times 100\right)\% = 67.5\%$

Section D $= \left[\frac{(13+76)}{(27+13+15+76)} \times 100\right]\% = \left(\frac{89}{131} \times 100\right)\% = 67.94\%$

Clearly, the success rate in annual examination is maximum for Section A.

15. Pass percentages in at least one of the two examinations for different sections are :

For **Section A** $= \left[\frac{(14+6+64)}{(28+14+6+64)} \times 100\right]\% = \left(\frac{84}{112} \times 100\right)\% = 75\%$

For **Section B** $= \left[\frac{(12+17+55)}{(23+12+17+55)} \times 100\right]\% = \left(\frac{84}{107} \times 100\right)\% = 78.5\%$

For **Section C** $= \left[\frac{(8+9+46)}{(17+8+9+46)} \times 100\right]\% = \left(\frac{63}{80} \times 100\right)\% = 78.75\%$

For **Section D** $= \left[\frac{(13+15+76)}{(27+13+15+76)} \times 100\right]\% = \left(\frac{104}{131} \times 100\right)\% = 79.39\%$

Clearly, the pass percentage is maximum for Section D.

16. Number of students who passed half-yearly exams in the school

= (Number of students passed in half-yearly but failed in annual exams) + (Number of students passed in both exams) = (6 + 17 + 9 + 15) + (64 + 55 + 46 + 76) = 288

Also, Number of students who passed annual exams in the school

= (Number of students failed in half-yearly but passed in annual exams) + (Number of students passed in both exams) = (14 + 12 + 8 + 13) + (64 + 55 + 46 + 76) = 288

Since, the number of students passed in half-yearly = the number of students passed in annual exams, therefore, it can be inferred that both the examinations had almost the same difficulty level.

Thus, Statements (*a*), (*b*) and (*d*) are false and Statement (*c*) is true.

Also, number of students from Sections A and B who passed the annual exams

= (14 + 12) + (64 + 55) = 145

And, number of students from Sections A and B who passed the half-yearly exams

= (6 + 17) + (64 + 55) = 142.

Since the number of students of Sections A and B who passed the annual exams is greater than those who passed the half-yearly exams it implies that for students of Sections A and B, the half-yearly exams were more difficult as compared to annual exams.

Hence, Statement (*e*) is false.

17. Total number of Operators who left the Company during 1995-2000

$= (104 + 120 + 100 + 112 + 144) = 580.$

Total number of Operators who joined the Company during 1995-2000

$= (880 + 256 + 240 + 208 + 192 + 248) = 2024.$

$\therefore$ Required Percentage $= \left(\frac{580}{2024} \times 100\right)\% = 28.66\% \approx 29\%.$

18. Number of Managers working in the Company :

In **1995** = 760.

In **2000** = (760 + 280 + 179 + 148 + 160 + 193) – (120 + 92 + 88 + 72 + 96) = 1252.

$\therefore$ Percentage increase in the number of Managers

$= \left[\frac{(1252 - 760)}{760} \times 100\right]\% = 64.74\%.$

Number of Technicians working in the Company :

In **1995** = 1200.

In **2000** = (1200 + 272 + 240 + 236 + 256 + 288) – (120 + 128 + 96 + 100 + 112) = 1936.

$\therefore$ Percentage increase in the number of Technicians

$= \left[\frac{(1936 - 1200)}{1200} \times 100\right]\% = 61.33\%.$

Number of Operators working in the Company :

In **1995** = 880.

In **2000** = (880 + 256 + 240 + 208 + 192 + 248) – (104 + 120 + 100 + 112 + 144) = 1444.

$\therefore$ Percentage increase in the number of Operators

$= \left[\frac{(1444 - 880)}{880} \times 100\right]\% = 64.09\%$

Number of Accountants working in the Company :

In **1995** = 1160.

In **2000** = (1160 + 200 + 224 + 248 + 272 + 260) – (100 + 104 + 96 + 88 + 92) = 1884.

$\therefore$ Percentage increase in the number of Accountants

$= \left[\frac{(1884 - 1160)}{1160} \times 100\right]\% = 62.41\%$

Number of Peons working in the Company :

In **1995** = 820.

In **2000** = (820 + 184 + 152 + 196 + 224 + 200) – (96 + 88 + 80 + 120 + 104) = 1288.

$\therefore$ Percentage increase in the number of Peons

$= \left[\frac{(1288 - 820)}{820} \times 100\right]\% = 57.07\%$

Clearly, the percentage increase is maximum in case of Managers.

19. Required difference = (272 + 240 + 236 + 256 + 288) − (200 + 224 + 248 + 272 + 260) = 88.

20. Total number of Peons working in the Company in 1999
= (820 + 184 + 152 + 196 + 224) − (96 + 88 + 80 + 120) = 1192.

21. Total number of employees of various categories working in the Company in 1997 are:

Managers = (760 + 280 + 179) − (120 + 92) = 1007

Technicians = (1200 + 272 + 240) − (120 + 128) = 1464

Operators = (880 + 256 + 240) − (104 + 120) = 1152

Accountants = (1160 + 200 + 224) − (100 + 104) = 1380

Peons = (820 + 184 + 152) − (96 + 88) = 972

∴ Pooled average of all the five categories of employees working in the Company in 1997 = $\frac{1}{5} \times (1007 + 1464 + 1152 + 1380 + 972) = \frac{1}{5} \times 5975 = 1195.$

22. Total population of State S = 7 million.

∴ Population above poverty line = [(100 − 19)% of 7] million
= (81% of 7) million = 5.67 million.

And so, the number of females above poverty line in State S = $\left(\frac{3}{7} \times 5.67\right)$ million
= 2.43 million.

23. Let the total population of State R be x million.

Then, population of State R above poverty line = [(100 − 24)% of x] million
= $\left(\frac{76}{100} \times x\right)$ million.

And so, male population of State R above poverty line = $\left[\frac{2}{5} \times \left(\frac{76}{100} \times x\right)\right]$ million

But, it is given that male population of State R above poverty line = 1.9 million

∴ $\frac{2}{5} \times \left(\frac{76}{100} \times x\right) = 1.9 \Rightarrow x = \frac{5 \times 100 \times 1.9}{76 \times 2} = 6.25.$

∴ Total population of State R = 6.25 million.

24. Female population below poverty line for State P = 2.1 million.

Let the male population below poverty line for State P be x million.

Then, $5 : 6 = x : 2.1 \Rightarrow x = \frac{2.1 \times 5}{6} = 1.75$

∴ Population below poverty line for State P = (2.1 + 1.75) million = 3.85 million.

Let the population above poverty line for State P be y million.

Since, 35% of the total population of State P is below poverty line, therefore, 65% of the total population of State P is above poverty line *i.e.*, the ratio of population below poverty line to that above poverty line for State P is 35 : 65.

∴ $35 : 65 = 3.85 : y \Rightarrow y = \frac{65 \times 3.85}{35} = 7.15$

i.e., population above poverty line for State P = 7.15 million and so, male population above poverty line for State P = $\left(\frac{6}{13} \times 7.15\right)$ million = 3.3 million.

25. For State Q :

Male population below poverty line = 2.4 million.

Let the female population below poverty line be x million.

Then, $3 : 5 = 2.4 : x \Rightarrow x = \frac{5 \times 2.4}{3} = 4$

$\therefore$ Total population below poverty line = (2.4 + 4) = 6.4 million.

If N_q be the total population of State Q, then,

25% of N_q = 6.4 million $\Rightarrow N_q = \left(\frac{6.4 \times 100}{25}\right)$ million = 25.6 million.

For State T :

Male population below poverty line = 6 million.

Let the female population below poverty line be y million.

Then, $5 : 3 = 6 : y \Rightarrow y = \frac{3 \times 6}{5} = 3.6$

$\therefore$ Total population below poverty line = (6 + 3.6) = 9.6 million.

If N_t be the total population of State T, then

15% of N_t = 9.6 million $\Rightarrow N_t = \left(\frac{9.6 \times 100}{15}\right)$ million = 64 million.

Thus, required ratio $= \frac{N_q}{N_t} = \frac{25.6}{64} = 0.4 = \frac{2}{5}$.

37. BAR GRAPHS

This section comprises of questions in which the data collected in a particular discipline are represented in the form of vertical or horizontal bars drawn by selecting a particular scale. One of the parameters is plotted on the horizontal axis and the other on the vertical axis. The candidate is required to understand the given information and thereafter answer the given questions on the basis of data analysis.

Ex. 1. ***The bar graph given below shows the foreign exchange reserves of a country (in million US $) from 1991-92 to 1998-99. Answer the questions based on this graph.***

(Bank P.O. 2001)

FOREIGN EXCHANGE RESERVES OF A COUNTRY

(in million US $)

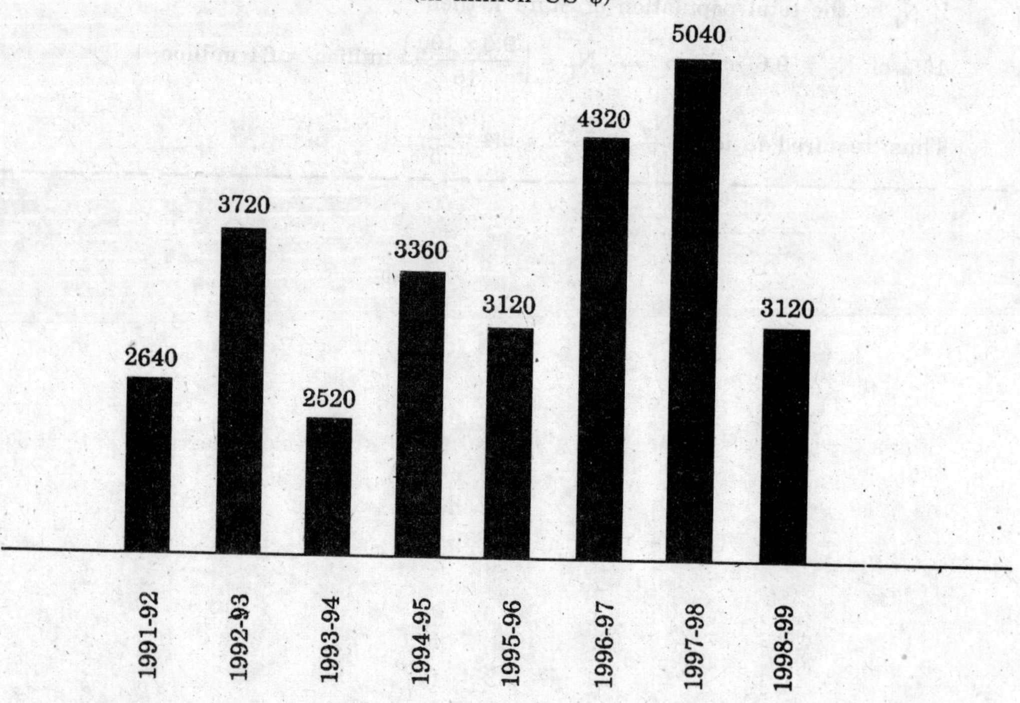

1. The foreign exchange reserves in 1997-98 was how many times that in 1994-95 ?

(*a*) 0.7 (*b*) 1.2 (*c*) 1.4 (*d*) 1.5 (*e*) 1.8

2. What was the percentage increase in the foreign exchange reserves in 1997-98 over 1993-94 ?

(*a*) 100 (*b*) 150 (*c*) 200 (*d*) 620 (*e*) 2520

3. For which year, the percent increase of foreign exchange reserves over the previous year, is the highest ?

(*a*) 1992-93 (*b*) 1993-94 (*c*) 1994-95 (*d*) 1996-97 (*e*) 1997-98

4. The foreign exchange reserves in 1996-97 were approximately what percent of the average foreign exchange reserves over the period under review ?

(*a*) 95% (*b*) 110% (*c*) 115% (*d*) 125% (*e*) 140%

5. The ratio of the number of years, in which the foreign exchange reserves are above the average reserves, to those in which the reserves are below the average reserves, is :

(*a*) 2 : 6 (*b*) 3 : 4 (*c*) 3 : 5 (*d*) 4 : 4 (*e*) 5 : 3

Sol. 1. (*d*) : Required ratio $= \frac{5040}{3360} = 1.5.$

2. (*a*) : Foreign exchange reserves in 1997-98 = 5040 million US $

Foreign exchange reserves in 1993-94 = 2520 million US $.

$\therefore$ Increase = (5040 – 2520) = 2520 million US $.

$\therefore$ Percentage increase $= \left(\frac{2520}{2520} \times 100\right)\% = 100\%.$

3. (*a*) : There is an increase in foreign exchange reserves during the years 1992-93, 1994-95, 1996-97 and 1997-98 as compared to previous year (as shown by bar-graph).

The percentage increase in reserves during these years compared to previous year are :

(*i*) For **1992-93** $= \left[\frac{(3720 - 2640)}{2640} \times 100\right]\% = 40.91\%$

(*ii*) For **1994-95** $= \left[\frac{(3360 - 2520)}{2520} \times 100\right]\% = 33.33\%$

(*iii*) For **1996-97** $= \left[\frac{(4320 - 3120)}{3120} \times 100\right]\% = 38.46\%$

(*iv*) For **1997-98** $= \left[\frac{(5040 - 4320)}{4320} \times 100\right]\% = 16.67\%$

Clearly, the percentage increase over previous year is highest for 1992-93.

4. (*d*) : Average foreign exchange reserves over the given period

$= \left[\frac{1}{8} \times (2640 + 3720 + 2520 + 3360 + 3120 + 4320 + 5040 + 3120)\right]$ million US $

= 3480 million US $.

Foreign exchange reserves in 1996-97 = 4320 million US $.

$\therefore$ Required Percentage $= \left(\frac{4320}{3480} \times 100\right)\% = 124.14\% \approx 125\%.$

5. (*c*) : Average foreign exchange reserves over the given period = 3480 million US $.

The country had reserves above 3480 million US $ during the years 1992-93, 1996-97 and 1997-98 *i.e.*, for 3 years and below 3480 million US $ during the years 1991-92, 1993-94, 1994-95, 1995-96 and 1998-99 *i.e.*, for 5 years.

Hence, required ratio = 3 : 5.

Ex. 2. ***The bar-graph provided on next page gives the sales of books (in thousand numbers) from six branches of a publishing company during two consecutive years 2000 and 2001. Answer the questions based on this bar-graph.*** **(Bank P.O. 2003)**

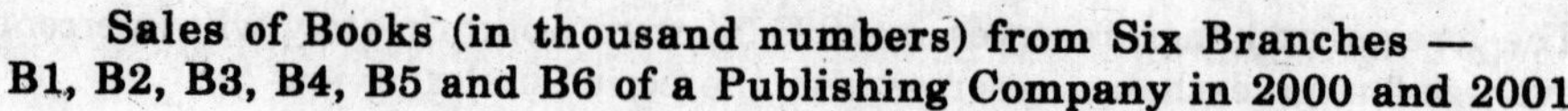

Sales of Books (in thousand numbers) from Six Branches — B1, B2, B3, B4, B5 and B6 of a Publishing Company in 2000 and 2001

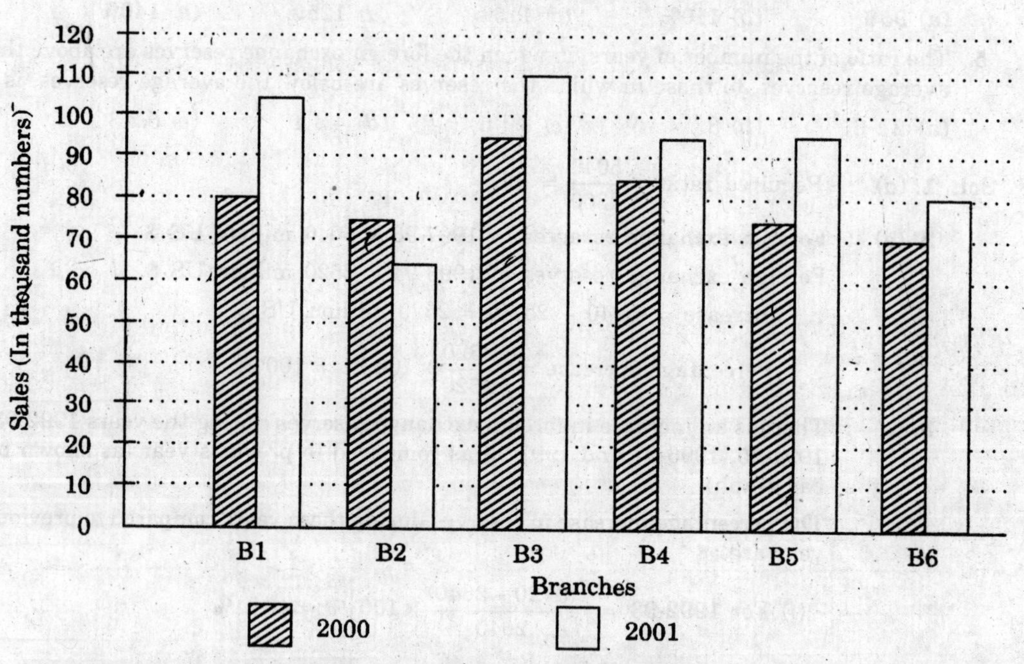

1. Total sales of branches B1, B3 and B5 together for both the years (in thousand numbers) is :

   (*a*) 250 (*b*) 310 (*c*) 435 (*d*) 560 (*e*) 585

2. Total sales of branch B6 for both the years is what percent of the total sales of branch B3 for both the years ?

   (*a*) 68.54% (*b*) 71.11% (*c*) 73.17% (*d*) 75.55% (*e*) 77.26%

3. What is the average sale of all the branches (in thousand numbers) for the year 2000 ?

   (*a*) 73 (*b*) 80 (*c*) 83 (*d*) 88 (*e*) 96

4. What is the ratio of the total sales of branch B2 for both years to the total sales of branch B4 for both years ?

   (*a*) 2 : 3 (*b*) 3 : 5 (*c*) 4 : 5 (*d*) 5 : 7 (*e*) 7 : 9

5. What percent of the average sales of branches B1, B2 and B3 in 2001 is the average sales of branches B1, B3 and B6 in 2000 ?

   (*a*) 75% (*b*) 77.5% (*c*) 82.5% (*d*) 85% (*e*) 87.5%

Sol. 1. (*d*) : Total sales of branches B1, B3 and B5 for both the years (in thousand numbers) = (80 + 105) + (95 + 110) + (75 + 95) = 560.

2. (*c*) : Required Percentage $= \left[\dfrac{(70+80)}{(95+110)} \times 100\right]\% = \left(\dfrac{150}{205} \times 100\right)\% = 73.17\%.$

3. (*b*) : Average sales of all the six branches (in thousand numbers) for the year 2000 $= \dfrac{1}{6} \times [80 + 75 + 95 + 85 + 75 + 70] = 80.$

4. (*e*) : Required ratio $= \dfrac{(75+65)}{(85+95)} = \dfrac{140}{180} = \dfrac{7}{9}$

5. (*e*) : Average sales (in thousand numbers) of branches B1 B3 and B6 in 2000

$$= \frac{1}{3} \times (80 + 95 + 70) = \left(\frac{245}{3}\right).$$

Average sales (in thousand numbers) of branches B1, B2 and B3 in 2001

$$= \frac{1}{3} \times (105 + 65 + 110) = \left(\frac{280}{3}\right).$$

$$\therefore \text{ Required Percentage} = \left[\frac{\left(\frac{245}{3}\right)}{\left(\frac{280}{3}\right)} \times 100\right]\% = \left(\frac{245}{280} \times 100\right)\% = 87.5\%.$$

Ex. 3. ***The bar graph provided below gives the data of the production of paper (in lakh tonnes) by three different companies X, Y and Z over the years. Study the graph and answer the questions that follow.*** **(Bank P.O. 2001)**

Production of Paper (in lakh tonnes) by Three Companies X, Y and Z over the Years

Year	X	Y	Z
1996	30	25	35
1997	45	35	40
1998	25	35	45
1999	50	40	35
2000	40	50	35

(Quantity in Lakh Tons; Years)

1. What is the difference between the production of Company Z in 1998 and Company Y in 1996 ?
   (*a*) 2,00,000 tons (*b*) 20,00,000 tons (*c*) 20,000 tons
   (*d*) 2,00,00,000 tons (*e*) None of these
2. What is the ratio of the average production of Company X in the period 1998-2000 to the average production of Company Y in the same period ?
   (*a*) 1 : 1 (*b*) 15 : 17 (*c*) 23 : 25 (*d*) 27 : 29 (*e*) None of these
3. What is the percentage increase in the production of Company Y from 1996 to 1999 ?
   (*a*) 30% (*b*) 45% (*c*) 50% (*d*) 60% (*e*) 75%
4. The average production for five years was maximum for which Company ?
   (*a*) X (*b*) Y (*c*) Z (*d*) X and Y both (*e*) X and Z both

5. For which of the following years, the percentage rise / fall in production from the previous year is the maximum for Company Y ?

(*a*) 1997 (*b*) 1998 (*c*) 1999 (*d*) 2000 (*e*) 1997 and 2000

6. In which year was the percentage of production of Company Z to the production of Company Y the maximum ?

(*a*) 1996 (*b*) 1997 (*c*) 1998 (*d*) 1999 (*e*) 2000

Sol. 1. (*b*) : Required difference = [(45 − 25) × 1,00,000] tons = 20,00,000 tons.

2. (*c*) : Average production of Company X in the period 1998-2000

$$= \left[\frac{1}{3} \times (25 + 50 + 40)\right] = \left(\frac{115}{3}\right) \text{ lakh tons.}$$

Average production of Company Y in the period 1998-2000

$$= \left[\frac{1}{3} \times (35 + 40 + 50)\right] = \left(\frac{125}{3}\right) \text{ lakh tons.}$$

$$\therefore \quad \text{Required ratio} = \frac{\left(\frac{115}{3}\right)}{\left(\frac{125}{3}\right)} = \frac{115}{125} = \frac{23}{25}.$$

3. (*d*) : Percentage increase in the production of Company Y from 1996 to 1999

$$= \left[\frac{(40 - 25)}{25} \times 100\right]\% = \left(\frac{15}{25} \times 100\right)\% = 60\%.$$

4. (*e*) : Average production (in lakh tons) in five years for the three companies are :

$$\text{For Company } X = \left[\frac{1}{5} \times (30 + 45 + 25 + 50 + 40)\right] = \frac{190}{5} = 38$$

$$\text{For Company } Y = \left[\frac{1}{5} \times (25 + 35 + 35 + 40 + 50)\right] = \frac{185}{5} = 37$$

$$\text{For Company } Z = \left[\frac{1}{5} \times (35 + 40 + 45 + 35 + 35)\right] = \frac{190}{5} = 38.$$

∴ Average production of five years is maximum for both the Companies X and Z.

5. (*a*) : Percentage change (rise / fall) in the production of Company Y in comparison to the previous year, for different years are :

$$\text{For 1997} = \left[\frac{(32 - 25)}{25} \times 100\right]\% = 40\%$$

$$\text{For 1998} = \left[\frac{(35 - 35)}{25} \times 100\right]\% = 0\%$$

$$\text{For 1999} = \left[\frac{(40 - 35)}{35} \times 100\right]\% = 14.29\%$$

$$\text{For 2000} = \left[\frac{(50 - 40)}{40} \times 100\right]\% = 25\%$$

Hence, the maximum percentage rise / fall in the production of Company Y is for 1997.

6. (a) : The percentages of production of Company Z to the production of Company Z for various years are :

$$\text{For 1996} = \left(\frac{35}{25} \times 100\right)\% = 140\%; \text{ For 1997} = \left(\frac{40}{35} \times 100\right)\% = 114.29\%;$$

$$\text{For 1998} = \left(\frac{45}{35} \times 100\right)\% = 128.57\%; \text{ For 1999} = \left(\frac{35}{40} \times 100\right)\% = 87.5\%;$$

$$\text{For 2000} = \left(\frac{35}{50} \times 100\right)\% = 70\%.$$

Clearly, this percentage is highest for 1996.

Ex. 4. ***Out of the two bar graphs provided below, one shows the amounts (in Lakh Rs.) invested by a Company in purchasing raw materials over the years and the other shows the values (in Lakh Rs.) of finished goods sold by the Company over the years. Study the two bar graphs and answer the questions based on them.***

Amount Invested in Raw Materials and the Value of Sales of Finished Goods for a Company over the Years

Amount Invested in Raw Materials (Rs. in Lakhs)

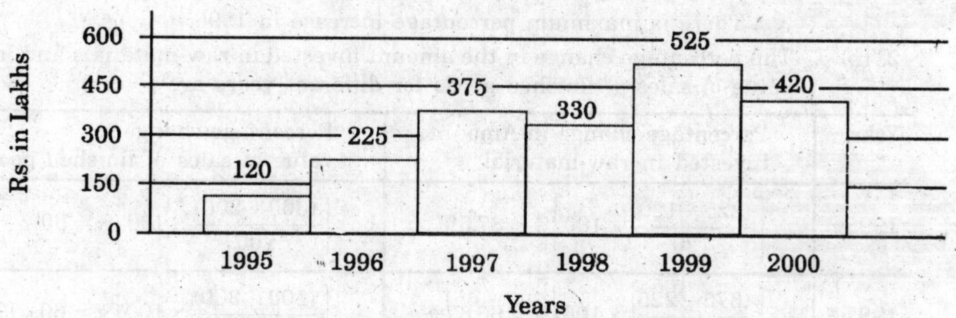

Value of Sales of Finished Goods (Rs. in Lakhs)

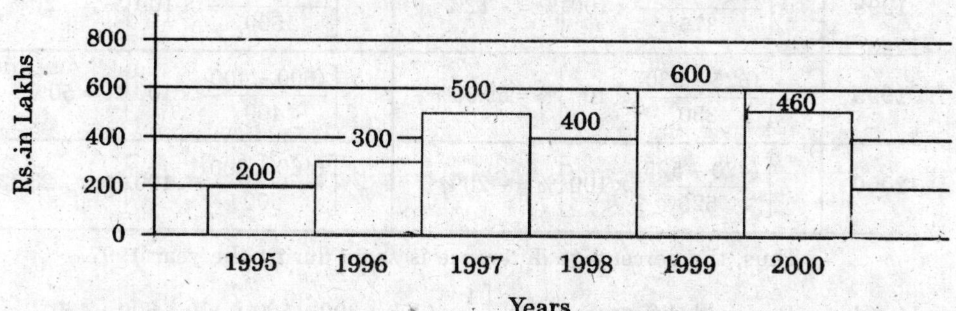

1. In which year, there has been a maximum percentage increase in the amount invested in Raw Materials as compared to the previous year ?
   (a) 1996 (b) 1997 (c) 1998 (d) 1999 (e) 2000
2. In which year, the percentage change (compared to the previous year) in the investment on Raw Materials is the same as that in the value of sales of finished goods ?
   (a) 1996 (b) 1997 (c) 1998 (d) 1999 (e) 2000
3. What was the difference between the average amount invested in Raw Materials during the given period and the average value of sales of finished goods during this period ?
   (a) Rs. 62.5 lakhs (b) Rs. 68.5 lakhs (c) Rs. 71.5 lakhs
   (d) Rs. 77.5 lakhs (e) Rs. 83.5 lakhs

4. The value of sales of finished goods in 1999 was approximately what percent of the average amount invested in Raw Materials in the years 1997, 1998 and 1999 ?
(a) 33% (b) 37% (c) 45% (d) 49% (e) 53%

5. The maximum difference between the amount invested in Raw Materials and the value of sales of finished goods was during the year :
(a) 1995 (b) 1996 (c) 1997 (d) 1998 (e) 1999

Sol. 1. (a) : The percentage increase in the amount invested in raw-materials as compared to the previous year, for different years are :

$$\text{For 1996} = \left[\frac{(225-120)}{120}\times 100\right]\% = 87.5\%$$

$$\text{For 1997} = \left[\frac{(375-225)}{225}\times 100\right]\% = 66.67\%$$

For 1998 there is a decrease.

$$\text{For 1999} = \left[\frac{(525-330)}{330}\times 100\right]\% = 59.09\%$$

For 2000 there is a decrease.

∴ There is maximum percentage increase in 1996.

2. (b) : The percentage change in the amount invested in raw-materials and in the value of sales of finished goods for different years are :

Year	Percentage change in Amount invested in raw-material	Percentage change in value of sales of finished goods
1996	$\left[\frac{(225-120)}{120}\times 100\right]\% = 87.5\%$	$\left[\frac{(300-200)}{200}\times 100\right]\% = 50\%$
1997	$\left[\frac{(375-225)}{225}\times 100\right]\% = 66.67\%$	$\left[\frac{(500-300)}{300}\times 100\right]\% = 66.67\%$
1998	$\left[\frac{(330-375)}{375}\times 100\right]\% = -12\%$	$\left[\frac{(400-500)}{500}\times 100\right]\% = -20\%$
1999	$\left[\frac{(525-330)}{330}\times 100\right]\% = 59.09\%$	$\left[\frac{(600-400)}{400}\times 100\right]\% = 50\%$
2000	$\left[\frac{(420-525)}{525}\times 100\right]\% = -20\%$	$\left[\frac{(460-600)}{600}\times 100\right]\% = -23.33\%$.

Thus, the percentage difference is same during the year 1997.

3. (d) : Required difference $= \text{Rs.}\left[\frac{1}{6}\times(200+300+500+400+600+460) - \frac{1}{6}\times(120+225+375+330+525+420)\right]$ lakhs

$= \text{Rs.}\left[\left(\frac{2460}{6}\right)-\left(\frac{1995}{6}\right)\right]$ lakhs $=$ Rs. (410 − 332.5) lakhs = Rs. 77.5 lakhs.

4. (d) : Required percentage $= \left[\frac{600}{(375+330+525)}\times 100\right]\% = 48.78\% \approx 49\%.$

5. (*c*) : The differences between the amount invested in raw material and the value of sales of finished goods for various years are :

For 1995 = Rs. (200 − 120) lakhs = Rs. 80 lakhs.
For 1996 = Rs. (300 − 225) lakhs = Rs. 75 lakhs.
For 1997 = Rs. (500 − 375) lakhs = Rs. 125 lakhs.
For 1998 = Rs. (400 − 330) lakhs = Rs. 70 lakhs.
For 1999 = Rs. (600 − 525) lakhs = Rs. 75 lakhs.
For 2000 = Rs. (460 − 420) lakhs = Rs. 40 lakhs.

Clearly, maximum difference was during 1997.

EXERCISE 37

Directions (Questions 1 to 5) : ***Study the following bar-graph and answer the questions given below.*** **(Bank P.O. 2002)**

Production of Fertilizers by a Company (in 10000 tonnes) over the Years

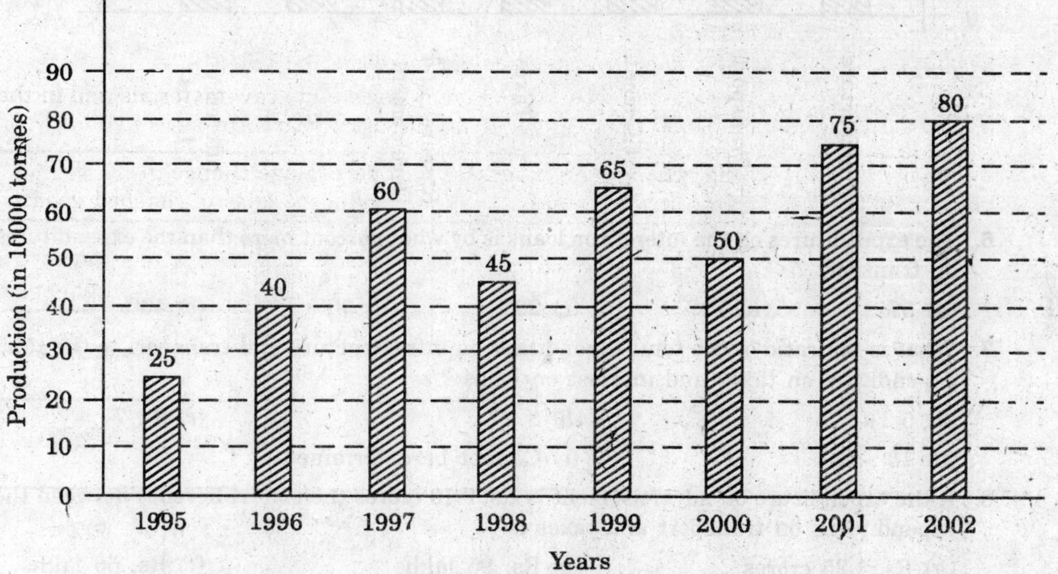

1. In how many of the given years was the production of fertilizers more than the average production of the given years ?
(*a*) 1 (*b*) 2 (*c*) 3 (*d*) 4 (*e*) 5

2. The average production of 1996 and 1997 was exactly equal to the average production of which of the following pairs of years ?
(*a*) 2000 and 2001 (*b*) 1999 and 2000 (*c*) 1998 and 2000
(*d*) 1995 and 1999 (*e*) 1995 and 2001

3. What was the percentage decline in the production of fertilizers from 1997 to 1998 ?
(*a*) $33\frac{1}{3}\%$ (*b*) 30% (*c*) 25% (*d*) 21% (*e*) 20%

4. In which year was the percentage increase in production as compared to the previous year the maximum ?
(*a*) 2002 (*b*) 2001 (*c*) 1999 (*d*) 1997 (*e*) 1996

5. What was the percentage increase in production of fertilizers in 2002 compared to that in 1995 ?

(*a*) 320% (*b*) 300% (*c*) 220% (*d*) 200% (*e*) 150%

Directions (Questions 6 to 10) : ***The bar-graph given below shows the percentage distribution of total expenditures of a Company under various expense heads during 2003. Study the graph and answer the questions that follow :***

Percentage Distribution of Total Expenditures of a Company

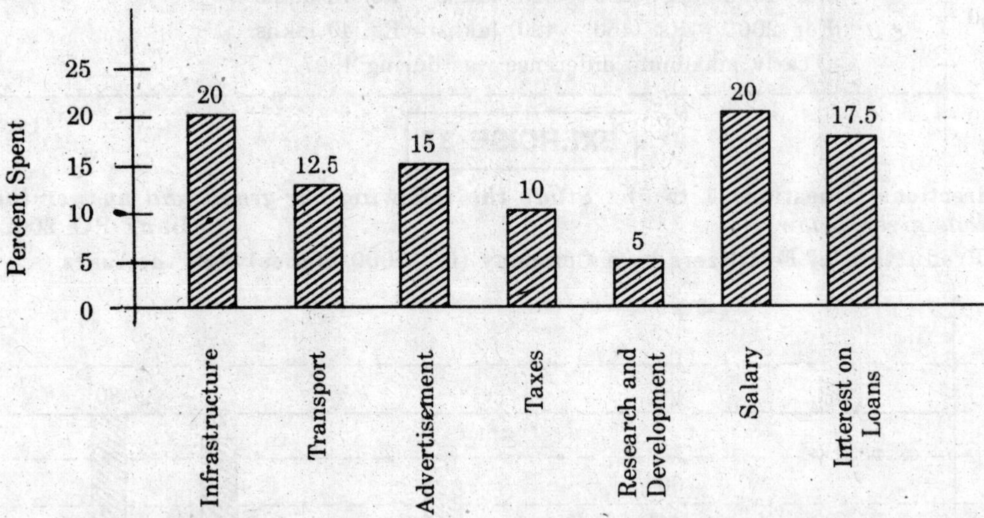

6. The expenditures on the interest on loans is by what percent more than the expenditures on transport ?

(*a*) 5% (*b*) 10% (*c*) 20% (*d*) 30% (*e*) 40%

7. What is the ratio of the total expenditure on infrastructure and transport to the total expenditure on taxes and interest on loans ?

(*a*) 5 : 4 (*b*) 8 : 7 (*c*) 9 : 7
(*d*) 13 : 11 (*e*) Cannot be determined

8. If the expenditure on advertisement is Rs. 2.10 crores then the difference between the expenditures on transport and taxes is :

(*a*) Rs. 1.25 crores (*b*) Rs. 95 lakhs (*c*) Rs. 65 lakhs
(*d*) Rs. 35 lakhs (*e*) Rs. 25 lakhs

9. The total amount of expenditures of the Company is how many times the expenditure on research and development ?

(*a*) 27 (*b*) 20 (*c*) 18 (*d*) 8 (*e*) 5

10. If the interest on loans amounted to Rs. 2.45 crores then the total amount of expenditure on advertisement, taxes and research and development is

(*a*) Rs. 7 crores (*b*) Rs. 5.4 crores (*c*) Rs. 4.2 crores
(*d*) Rs. 3 crores (*e*) Rs. 2.4 crores

Directions (Questions 11 to 15) : ***A cosmetic company produces five different products. The sales of these five products (in lakh number of packs) during 1995 and 2000 are shown in the following bar-graph. The questions given below are based on this graph.***

(Bank P.O. 2001)

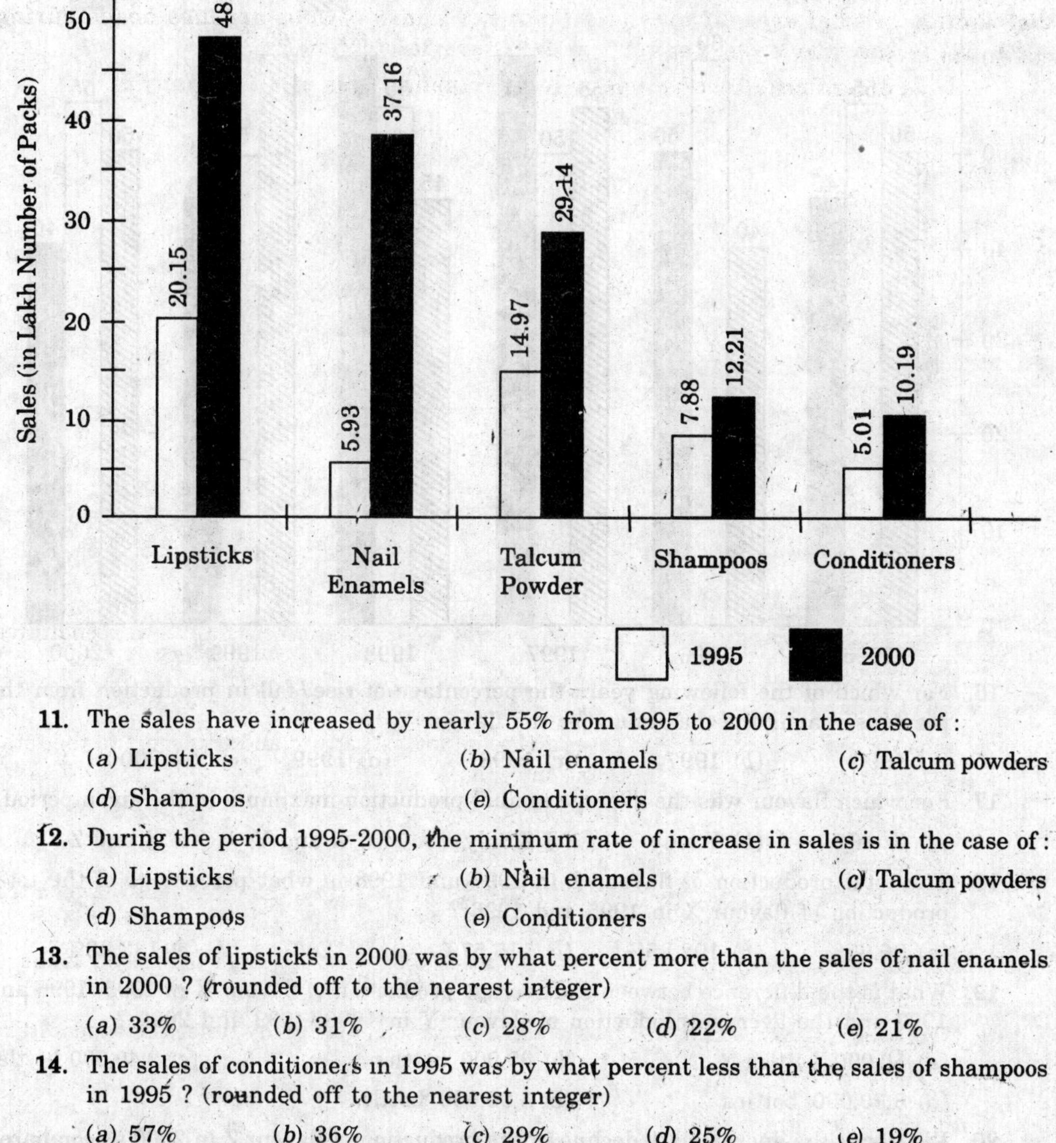

11. The sales have increased by nearly 55% from 1995 to 2000 in the case of :

(*a*) Lipsticks (*b*) Nail enamels (*c*) Talcum powders

(*d*) Shampoos (*e*) Conditioners

12. During the period 1995-2000, the minimum rate of increase in sales is in the case of :

(*a*) Lipsticks (*b*) Nail enamels (*c*) Talcum powders

(*d*) Shampoos (*e*) Conditioners

13. The sales of lipsticks in 2000 was by what percent more than the sales of nail enamels in 2000 ? (rounded off to the nearest integer)

(*a*) 33% (*b*) 31% (*c*) 28% (*d*) 22% (*e*) 21%

14. The sales of conditioners in 1995 was by what percent less than the sales of shampoos in 1995 ? (rounded off to the nearest integer)

(*a*) 57% (*b*) 36% (*c*) 29% (*d*) 25% (*e*) 19%

15. What is the approximate ratio of the sales of nail enamels in 2000 to the sales of Talcum powders in 1995 ?

(*a*) 7 : 2 (*b*) 5 : 2 (*c*) 4 : 3 (*d*) 2 : 1 (*e*) 5 : 3

Directions (Questions 16 to 20) : ***A soft-drink company prepares drinks of three different flavours — X, Y and Z. The production of the three flavours over a period of six years has been expressed in the bar-graph provided below. Study the graph and answer the questions based on it.*** **(I.B.P.S. 2002)**

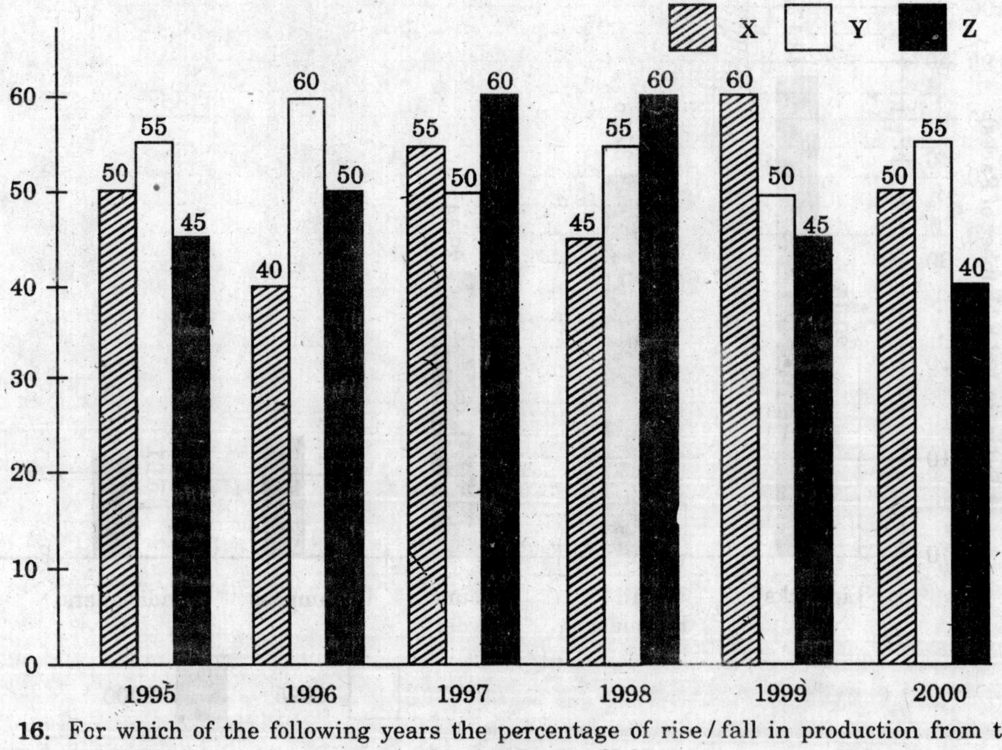

16. For which of the following years the percentage of rise / fall in production from the previous year is the maximum for the flavour Y ?

(*a*) 1996 (*b*) 1997 (*c*) 1998 (*d*) 1999 (*e*) 2000

17. For which flavour was the average annual production maximum in the given period ?

(*a*) X only (*b*) Y only (*c*) Z only (*d*) X and Y (*e*) X and Z

18 The total production of flavour Z in 1997 and 1998 is what percentage of the total production of flavour X in 1995 and 1996 ?

(*a*) 96.67% (*b*) 102.25% (*c*) 115.57% (*d*) 120% (*e*) 133.33%

19. What is the difference between the average production of flavour X in 1995, 1996 and 1997 and the average production of flavour Y in 1998, 1999 and 2000 ?

(*a*) 50,000 bottles (*b*) 80,000 bottles (*c*) 2,40,000 bottles

(*d*) 3,30,000 bottles (*e*) 5,00,000 bottles

20. What was the approximate decline in the production of flavour Z in 2000 as compared to the production in 1998 ?

(*a*) 50% (*b*) 42% (*c*) 33% (*d*) 25% (*e*) 22.5%

Directions (Questions 21 to 25) : ***The bar-graph given below shows the percentage distribution of the total production of a car manufacturing company into various models over two years. Study the graph carefully and answer the questions that follow.***

(Bank P.O. 2001)

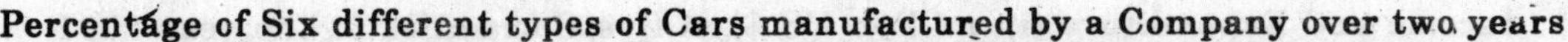

Percentage of Six different types of Cars manufactured by a Company over two years

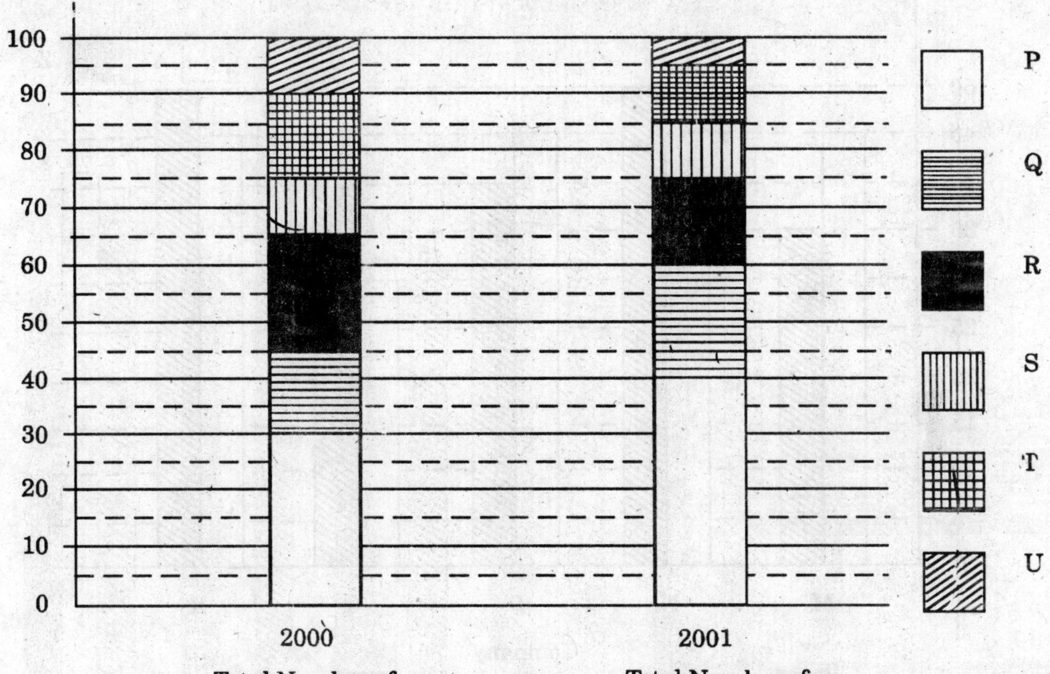

Total Number of Cars produced = 3,50,000 | Total Number of Cars produced = 4,40,000

21. Total number of cars of models P, Q and T manufactured in 2000 is :

(*a*) 2,45,000 (*b*) 2,27,500 (*c*) 2,10,000 (*d*) 1,92,500 (*e*) 1,57,500

22. For which model the percentage rise / fall in production from 2000 to 2001 was minimum ?

(*a*) Q (*b*) R (*c*) S (*d*) T (*e*) U

23. What was the difference in the number of Q type cars produced in 2000 and that produced in 2001 ?

(*a*) 35,500 (*b*) 27,000 (*c*) 22,500 (*d*) 17,500 (*e*) 16,000

24. If the percentage production of P type cars in 2001 was the same as that in 2000, then the number of P type cars produced in 2001 would have been :

(*a*) 1,40,000 (*b*) 1,32,000 (*c*) 1,17,000 (*d*) 1,05,000 (*e*) 97,000

25. If 85% of the S type cars produced in each year were sold by the Company, how many S type cars remained unsold ?

(*a*) 7650 (*b*) 9350 (*c*) 11,850 (*d*) 12,250 (*e*) 13,350

Directions (Questions 26 to 30) : ***The following bar-graph shows the Income and Expenditures (in million US $) of five Companies in the year 2001. The percent profit or loss of a Company is given by***

$$(\text{Profit / Loss})\% = \frac{\text{Income} - \text{Expenditure}}{\text{Expenditure}} \times 100.$$

Study the graph and answer the questions that are based on it. (S.B.I.P.O. 2002)

Income and Expenditure (in million US $) of five Companies in the year 2001

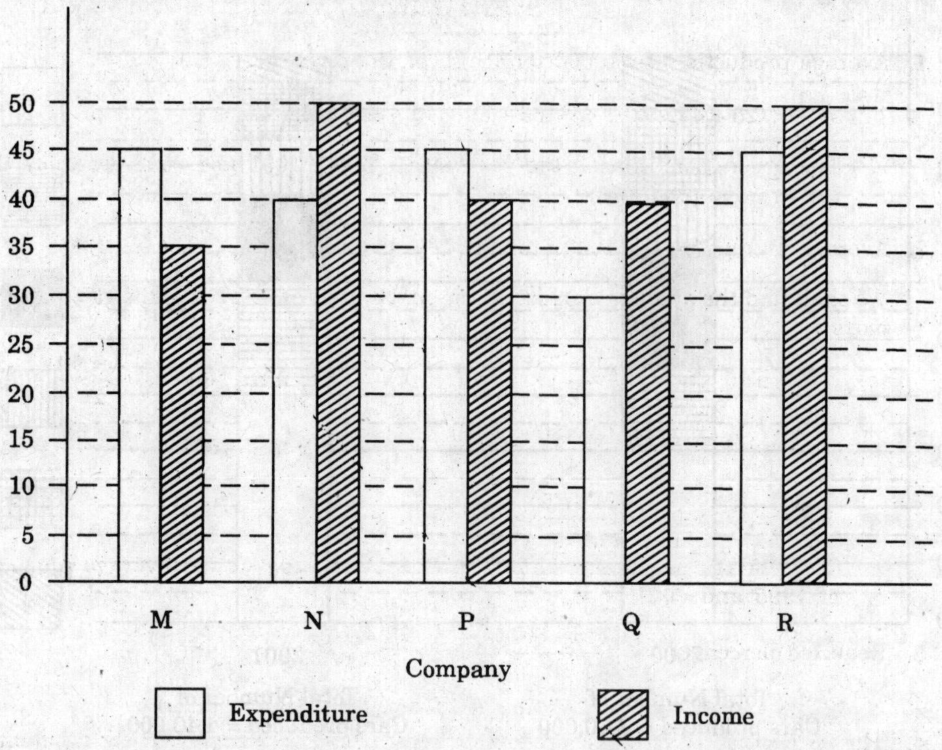

50
45
40
35
30
25
20
15
10
5
0

M N P Q R

Company

Expenditure Income

26. Which Company earned the maximum percentage profit in the year 2001 ?

(*a*) M (*b*) N (*c*) P (*d*) Q (*e*) R

27. The Companies M and N together had a percentage profit / loss of :

(*a*) 12% loss (*b*) 10% loss (*c*) 10% profit
(*d*) 12% profit (*e*) There was no loss or profit

28. In 2001 what was the approximate percentage of profit / loss of all the five Companies taken together ?

(*a*) 5% profit (*b*) 6.5% profit (*c*) 4% loss (*d*) 7% loss (*e*) 10% profit

29. If the income of Company Q in 2001 was 10% more than its income in 2000 and the Company had earned a profit of 20% in 2000, then its expenditure in 2000 (in million US $) was :

(*a*) 28.28 (*b*) 30.30 (*c*) 32.32 (*d*) 34.34 (*e*) 36.36

30. For Company R, if the expenditure had increased by 20% in year 2001 from year 2000 and the Company had earned a profit of 10% in 2000, what was the Company's income in 2000 (in million US $) ?

(*a*) 35.75 (*b*) 37.25 (*c*) 38.5 (*d*) 41.25 (*e*) 42.75

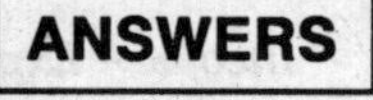

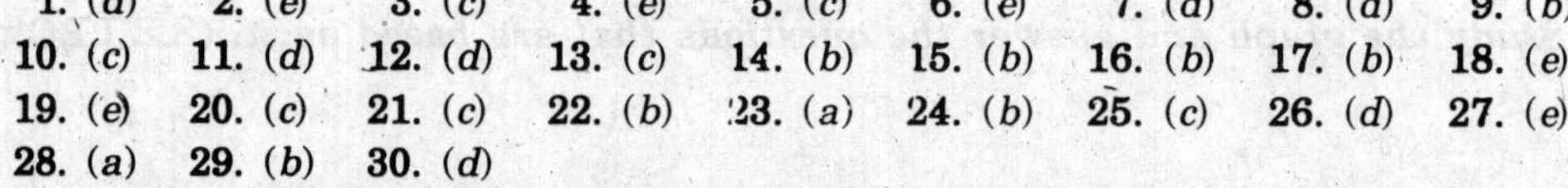

1. (*d*) **2.** (*e*) **3.** (*c*) **4.** (*e*) **5.** (*c*) **6.** (*e*) **7.** (*d*) **8.** (*d*) **9.** (*b*)
10. (*c*) **11.** (*d*) **12.** (*d*) **13.** (*c*) **14.** (*b*) **15.** (*b*) **16.** (*b*) **17.** (*b*) **18.** (*e*)
19. (*e*) **20.** (*c*) **21.** (*c*) **22.** (*b*) **23.** (*a*) **24.** (*b*) **25.** (*c*) **26.** (*d*) **27.** (*e*)
28. (*a*) **29.** (*b*) **30.** (*d*)

SOLUTIONS

1. Average production (in 10000 tonnes) over the given years

$$= \frac{1}{8} \times (25 + 40 + 60 + 45 + 65 + 50 + 75 + 80) = 55$$

∴ The productions during the years 1997, 1999, 2001 and 2002 are more than the average production.

2. Average production (in 10000 tonnes) of 1996 and 1997 $= \frac{40 + 60}{2} = 50.$

We shall find the average production (in 10000 tonnes) for each of the given alternative pairs :

(*a*) **2000 and 2001** $= \frac{50 + 75}{2} = 62.5$ (*b*) **1999 and 2000** $= \frac{65 + 50}{2} = 57.5$

(*c*) **1998 and 2000** $= \frac{45 + 50}{2} = 47.5$ (*d*) **1995 and 1999** $= \frac{25 + 65}{2} = 45$

(*e*) **1995 and 2001** $= \frac{25 + 75}{2} = 50.$

∴ The average production of 1996 and 1997 is equal to the average production of 1995 and 2001.

3. Required percentage $= \left[\frac{(45 - 60)}{60} \times 100\right]\% = -25\%.$

∴ There is a decline of 25% in production from 1997 to 1998.

4. The percentage increase in production compared to previous year for different years are :

In **1996** $= \left[\frac{(40 - 25)}{25} \times 100\right]\% = 60\%;$ In **1997** $= \left[\frac{(60 - 40)}{40} \times 100\right]\% = 50\%$

In **1998** there is a decrease in production.

In **1999** $= \left[\frac{(65 - 45)}{45} \times 100\right]\% = 44.44\%$

In **2000** there is a decrease in production.

In **2001** $= \left[\frac{(75 - 50)}{50} \times 100\right]\% = 50\%;$ In **2002** $= \left[\frac{(80 - 75)}{75} \times 100\right]\% = 6.67\%$

Clearly, there is maximum percentage increase in production in 1996.

5. Required percentage $= \left[\frac{(80 - 25)}{25} \times 100\right]\% = 220\%.$

6. Let the total amount of expenditures be Rs. x.

Then, the expenditure on interest on loans = Rs. (17.5% of x) = Rs. $\left(\frac{17.5}{100} x\right)$

and the expenditure on transport = Rs. (12.5% of x) = Rs. $\left(\frac{12.5}{100} x\right)$

∴ Difference between the two expenditures = Rs. $\left(\frac{17.5}{100} x - \frac{12.5}{100} x\right)$ = Rs. $\left(\frac{5x}{100}\right)$

and so, the required percentage $= \left[\frac{\left(\frac{5x}{100}\right)}{\left(\frac{12.5x}{100}\right)} \times 100\right]\% = 40\%.$

7. Let the total amount of expenditures be Rs. x.

Then, the total expenditure on infrastructure and transport

$$= \text{Rs. } [(20 + 12.5)\% \text{ of } x] = \text{Rs. } (32.5\% \text{ of } x) = \text{Rs. } \left(\frac{32.5x}{100}\right)$$

and total expenditure on taxes and interest on loans

$$= \text{Rs. } [(10 + 17.5)\% \text{ of } x] = \text{Rs. } (27.5\% \text{ of } x) = \text{Rs. } \left(\frac{27.5x}{100}\right)$$

$$\therefore \text{ Required ratio } = \frac{\left(\frac{32.5x}{100}\right)}{\left(\frac{27.5x}{100}\right)} = 13 : 11.$$

8. Let the total expenditure be Rs. x crores.

Then, 15% of $x = 2.10 \Rightarrow x = \left(\frac{2.10 \times 100}{15}\right) = 14.$

$\therefore$ Total expenditure = Rs. 14 crores

and so, the difference between the expenditures on transport and taxes

= Rs. [(12.5 – 10)% of 14] crores = Rs. (2.5% of 14) crores

= Rs. 0.35 crores = Rs. 35 lakhs.

9. Let the total expenditures be Rs. x.

Then, the expenditure on Research and Development = Rs. (5% of x) = Rs. $\left(\frac{x}{20}\right)$.

$\therefore$ Ratio of the total expenditure to the expenditure on Research and Development

$$= \frac{x}{\left(\frac{x}{20}\right)} = \frac{20}{1}.$$

Thus, the total expenditure is 20 times the expenditure on Research and Development.

10. Let the total expenditure be Rs. x crores. Then, 17.5% of $x = 2.45 \Rightarrow x = 14$.

$\therefore$ Total expenditure = Rs. 14 crores

and so, the total expenditure on advertisement, taxes and research and development = Rs. [(15 + 10 + 5)% of 14] crores

= Rs. (30% of 14) crores = Rs. 4.2 crores.

11. The percentage increase from 1995 to 2000 for various products are :

Lipsticks $= \left[\frac{(48.17 - 20.15)}{20.15} \times 100\right]\% = 139.06$

Nail enamels $= \left[\frac{(37.76 - 5.93)}{5.93} \times 100\right]\% = 536.76\%$

Talcum powders $= \left[\frac{(29.14 - 14.97)}{14.97} \times 100\right]\% = 94.66\%$

Shampoos $= \left[\frac{(12.21 - 7.88)}{7.88} \times 100\right]\% = 54.95\% \approx 55\%$

Conditioners $= \left[\frac{(10.19 - 5.01)}{5.01} \times 100\right]\% = 103.39\%.$

12. As calculated in the Solution of Q. 11, the minimum rate of increase in sales from 1995 to 2000 is in the case of Shampoos.

13. Required percentage $= \left[\dfrac{(48.17 - 37.76)}{37.76} \times 100\right]\% = 27.57\% \approx 28\%.$

14. Required percentage $= \left[\dfrac{(7.88 - 5.01)}{7.88} \times 100\right]\% = 36.42\% \approx 36\%.$

15. Required ratio $= \dfrac{37.76}{14.97} \approx 2.5 = \dfrac{5}{2}.$

16. The percentage rise / fall in production from the previous year for flavour Y during various years are :

In **1996** $= \left[\dfrac{(60 - 55)}{55} \times 100\right]\% = 9.09\%$ (increase)

In **1997** $= \left[\dfrac{(60 - 50)}{60} \times 100\right]\% = 16.67\%$ (decrease)

In **1998** $= \left[\dfrac{(55 - 50)}{55} \times 100\right]\% = 10\%$ (increase)

In **1999** $= \left[\dfrac{(55 - 50)}{55} \times 100\right] = 9.09\%$ (decrease)

In **2000** $= \left[\dfrac{(55 - 50)}{50} \times 100\right]\% = 10\%$ (increase)

$\therefore$ Maximum change is decrease of 16.67% during 1997.

17. Average annual productions over the given period for various flavours are :

For *flavour X* $= \left[\dfrac{1}{6} \times (50 + 40 + 55 + 45 + 60 + 50)\right]$ lakh bottles = 50 lakh bottles.

For *flavour Y* $= \left[\dfrac{1}{6} \times (55 + 60 + 50 + 55 + 50 + 55)\right]$ lakh bottles

= 54.17 lakh bottles.

For *flavour Z* $= \left[\dfrac{1}{6} \times (45 + 50 + 60 + 60 + 45 + 40)\right]$ lakh bottles = 50 lakh bottles.

$\therefore$ Maximum average production is for flavour Y.

18. Required percentage $= \left[\dfrac{(60 + 60)}{(50 + 40)} \times 100\right]\% = \left(\dfrac{120}{90} \times 100\right)\% = 133.33\%.$

19. Average production of flavour X in 1995, 1996 and 1997 $= \left[\dfrac{1}{3} \times (50 + 40 + 55)\right]$

$= \left(\dfrac{145}{3}\right)$ lakh bottles.

Average production of flavour Y in 1998, 1999 and 2000 $= \left[\dfrac{1}{3} \times (55 + 50 + 55)\right]$

$= \left(\dfrac{160}{3}\right)$ lakh bottles.

$\therefore$ Difference $= \left(\dfrac{160}{3} - \dfrac{145}{3}\right) = \dfrac{15}{3} = 5$ lakh bottles = 5,00,000 bottles.

20. Percentage decline in the production of flavour Z in 2000 as compared to the production in 1998 $= \left[\frac{(60-40)}{60} \times 100\right]\% = \left(\frac{20}{60} \times 100\right)\% = 33.33\% \approx 33\%.$

21. We shall first determine the number of cars of each model produced by the Company during the two years :

In 2000 : Total number of cars produced = 3,50,000.

P = (30 – 0)% of 3,50,000 = 30% of 3,50,000 = 1,05,000

Q = (45 – 30)% of 3,50,000 = 15% of 3,50,000 = 52,500

R = (65 – 45)% of 3,50,000 = 20% of 3,50,000 = 70,000

S = (75 – 65)% of 3,50,000 = 10% of 3,50,000 = 35,000

T = (90 – 75)% of 3,50,000 = 15% of 3,50,000 = 52,500

U = (100 – 90)% of 3,50,000 = 10% of 3,50,000 = 35,000.

In 2001 : Total number of cars produced = 4,40,000.

P = (40 – 0)% of 4,40,000 = 40% of 4,40,000 = 1,76,000

Q = (60 – 40)% of 4,40,000 = 20% of 4,40,000 = 88,000

R = (75 – 60)% of 4,40,000 = 15% of 4,40,000 = 66,000

S = (85 – 75)% of 4,40,000 = 10% of 4,40,000 = 44,000

T = (95 – 85)% of 4,40,000 = 10% of 4,40,000 = 44,000

U = (100 – 95)% of 4,40,000 = 5% of 4,40,000 = 22,000.

Now, we shall solve the questions.

Total number of cars of models P, Q and T manufactured in 2000

= (105000 + 52500 + 52500) = 2,10,000.

22. Using the above calculation, the percentage change (rise / fall) in production from 2000 to 2001 for various models is :

For P $= \left[\frac{(176000-105000)}{105000} \times 100\right]\%$ = 67.62%, rise.

For Q $= \left[\frac{(88000-52500)}{52500} \times 100\right]\%$ = 67.62%, rise.

For R $= \left[\frac{(70000-66000)}{70000} \times 100\right]\%$ = 5.71%, fall

For S $= \left[\frac{(44000-35000)}{35000} \times 100\right]\%$ = 25.71%, rise.

For T $= \left[\frac{(52500-44000)}{52500} \times 100\right]\%$ = 16.19%, fall.

For U $= \left[\frac{(35000-22000)}{35000} \times 100\right]\%$ = 37.14%, fall.

∴ Minimum percentage rise / fall in production is in the case of model R.

23. Required difference = 88000 – 52500 = 35500

(Using calculations in the Solution of Q. 21)

24. If the percentage production of P type cars in 2001 = percentage production of P type cars in 2000 = 30%

then, number of P type cars produced in 2001 = 30% of 440000 = 132000.

25. Number of S type cars which remained unsold in 2000 = 15% of 35000

and number of S type cars which remained unsold in 2001 = 15% of 44000

$\therefore$ Total number of S type cars which remained unsold

$= 15\%$ of $(35000 + 44000) = 15\%$ of $79000 = 11850$.

26. The percentage profit / loss in the year 2001 for various companies are :

$$\textit{For } M = \left[\frac{(30-45)}{45} \times 100\right]\% = -33.33\% \text{ i.e. } \%\text{Loss} = 33.33\%$$

$$\textit{For } N = \left[\frac{(50-40)}{40} \times 100\right]\% = 25\% \text{ i.e. } \%\text{Profit} = 25\%$$

$$\textit{For } P = \left[\frac{(40-45)}{45} \times 100\right]\% = -11.11\% \text{ i.e. } \%\text{Loss} = 11.11\%$$

$$\textit{For } Q = \left[\frac{(40-30)}{30} \times 100\right]\% = 33.33\% \text{ i.e. } \%\text{Profit} = 33.33\%$$

$$\textit{For } R = \left[\frac{(50-45)}{45} \times 100\right]\% = 11.11\% \text{ i.e. } \%\text{Profit} = 11.11\%$$

Clearly, the Company Q earned the maximum profit in 2001.

27. Total income of companies M and N together $= (35 + 50)$ million US \$

$= 85$ million US \$

Total expenditure of companies M and N together $= (45 + 40)$ million US \$

$= 85$ million US \$

$\therefore$ Percent Profit / Loss of companies M and N together

$$\%\text{Profit / Loss} = \left(\frac{85-85}{85} \times 100\right) = 0\%.$$

Thus, there was neither loss nor profit for companies M and N together.

28. Total income of all five companies $= (35 + 50 + 40 + 40 + 50) = 215$ million US \$

Total expenditure of all five companies $= (45 + 40 + 45 + 30 + 45)$

$= 205$ million US \$

$$\therefore \quad \%\text{Profit} = \left[\frac{(215-205)}{205} \times 100\right]\% = 4.88\% \approx 5\%.$$

29. Let the income of Company Q in 2000 $= x$ million US \$

Then, income of Company Q in 2001 $= \left(\frac{110}{100}x\right)$ million US \$

$$\therefore \quad \frac{110}{100}x = 40 \Rightarrow x = \left(\frac{400}{11}\right).$$

i.e. income of Company Q in 2000 $= \left(\frac{400}{11}\right)$ million US \$.

Let the expenditure of Company Q in 2000 be E million US \$.

$$\text{Then, } 20 = \frac{\left[\left(\frac{400}{11}\right) - E\right]}{E} \times 100 \quad [\because \%\text{Profit} = 20\%]$$

$$\Rightarrow 20 = \left[\left(\frac{400}{11E}\right) - 1\right] \times 100 \Rightarrow E = \frac{400}{11} \times \frac{100}{120} = 30.30.$$

$\therefore$ Expenditure of Company Q in 2000 $= 30.30$ million US \$.

30. Let the expenditure of Company R in 2000 be x million US \$.

Then, expenditure of Company R in 2001 = $\left(\frac{120}{100}x\right)$ million US \$.

$\therefore \quad \frac{120}{100}x = 45 \Rightarrow x = 37.5$

i.e. expenditure of Company R in 2000 = 37.5 million US \$.

Let the income of Company R in 2000 be I million US \$.

Then, $10 = \frac{(I - 37.5)}{37.5} \times 100 \quad [\because \text{ \% profit in 2000} = 10\%]$

$\Rightarrow \quad I - 37.5 = 3.75 \Rightarrow I = 41.25$

i.e. Income of Company R in 2000 = 41.25 million US \$.

---

38. PIE-CHARTS

IMPORTANT FACTS AND FORMULAE

The **pie-chart** or a **pie-graph** is a method of representing a given numerical data in the form of sectors of a circle.

The sectors of the circle are constructed in such a way that the area of each sector is proportional to the corresponding value of the component of the data.

From geometry, we know that the area of the sector of a circle is proportional to the central angle.

So, the central angle of each sector must be proportional to the corresponding value of the component.

Since the sum of all the central angles is 360°, we have

$$\text{Central angle of the component} = \left(\frac{\text{Value of the component}}{\text{Total value}} \times 360\right)^\circ$$

SOLVED EXAMPLES

The procedure of solving problems based on pie-charts will be clear from the following solved examples.

Example 1. ***The following pie-chart shows the sources of funds to be collected by the National Highways Authority of India (NHAI) for its Phase II projects. Study the pie-chart and answer the questions that follow.***

SOURCES OF FUNDS TO BE ARRANGED BY NHAI FOR PHASE II PROJECTS (IN CRORES RS.)

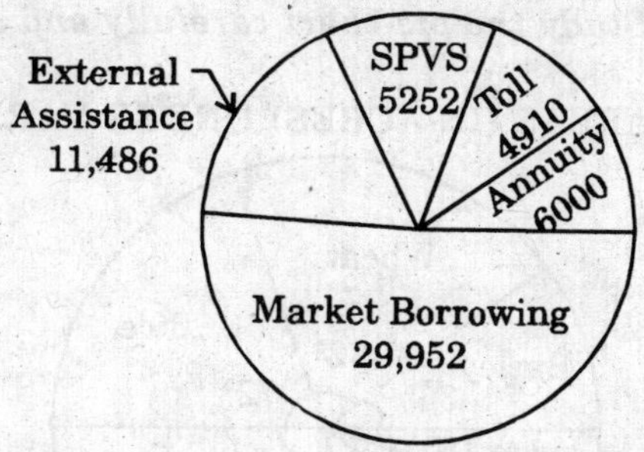

Total funds to be arranged for Projects (Phase II) = Rs. 57,600 crores.

1. Near about 20% of the funds are to be arranged through :
   (*a*) SPVS (*b*) External Assistance
   (*c*) Annuity (*d*) Market Borrowing
2. The central angle corresponding to Market Borrowing is :
   (*a*) 52° (*b*) 137.8% (*c*) 187.2° (*d*) 192.4°
3. The approximate ratio of the funds to be arranged through Toll and that through Market Borrowing is :
   (*a*) 2 : 9 (*b*) 1 : 6 (*c*) 3 : 11 (*d*) 2 : 5

4. If NHAI could receive a total of Rs. 9695 crores as External Assistance, by what percent (approximately) should it increase the Market Borrowings to arrange for the shortage of funds ?

(a) 4.5% (b) 7.5% (c) 6% (d) 8%

5. If the toll is to be collected through an outsourced agency by allowing a maximum 10% commission, how much amount should be permitted to be collected by the outsourced agency, so that the project is supported with Rs. 4910 crores ?

(a) Rs. 6213 crores (b) Rs. 5827 crores (c) Rs. 5401 crores (d) Rs. 5216 crores

SOLUTION

1. (b) : 20% of the total funds to be arranged = Rs. (20% of 57600) crores = Rs. 11520 crores ≈ Rs. 11486 crores.

Rs. 11486 crores is the amount of funds to be arranged through External Assistance.

2. (c) : Central angle corresponding to Market Borrowing $= \left(\frac{29952}{57600} \times 360°\right) = 187.2°$

3. (b) : Required ratio $= \frac{4910}{29952} = \frac{1}{6.1} \approx \frac{1}{6}$.

4. (c) : Shortage of funds arranged through External Assistance = Rs. (11486 − 9695) crores = Rs. 1791 crores.

∴ Increase required in Market Borrowings = Rs. 1791 crores.

Percentage increase required $= \left(\frac{1791}{29952} \times 100\right)\% = 5.98\% \approx 6\%$.

5. (c) : Amount permitted = (Funds required from Toll for projects of Phase II) + (10% of these funds)

= Rs. 4910 crores + Rs. (10% of 4910) crores

= Rs. (4910 + 491) crores = Rs. 5401 crores

Example 2. ***The pie-chart provided below gives the distribution of land (in a village) under various food crops. Study the pie-chart carefully and answer the questions that follow.***

DISTRIBUTION OF AREAS (IN ACRES) UNDER VARIOUS FOOD CROPS

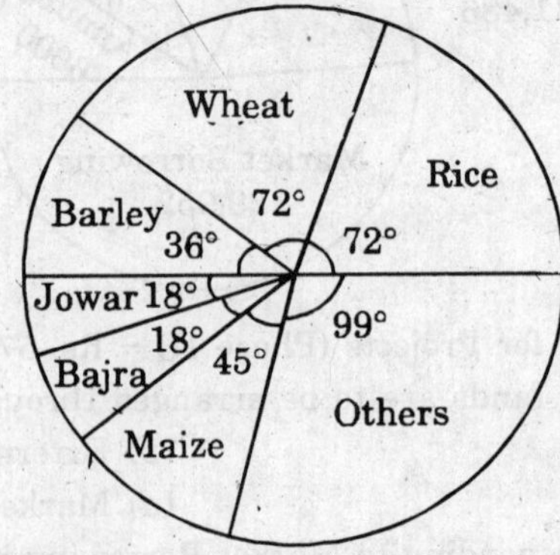

1. Which combination of three crops contribute to 50% of the total area under the food crops ?

(a) Wheat, Barley and Jowar (b) Rice, Wheat and Jowar

(c) Rice Wheat and Barley (d) Bajra, Maize and Rice

2. If the total area under jowar was 1.5 million acres, then what was the area (in million acres) under rice ?

(a) 6 (b) 7.5 (c) 9 (d) 4.5

3. If the production of wheat is 6 times that of barley, then what is the ratio between the yield per acre of wheat and barley ?

(*a*) 3 : 2 (*b*) 3 : 1 (*c*) 12 : 1 (*d*) 2 : 3

4. If the yield per acre of rice was 50% more than that of barley, then the production of barley is what percent of that of rice ?

(*a*) 30% (*b*) $33\frac{1}{3}\%$ (*c*) 35% (*d*) 36%

5. If the total area goes up by 5%, and the area under wheat production goes up by 12%, then what will be the angle for wheat in the new pie-chart ?

(*a*) 62.4° (*b*) 76.8° (*c*) 80.6° (*d*) 84.2°

SOLUTION

1. (*c*) : The total of the central angles corresponding to the three crops which cover 50% of the total area, should be 180°. Now, the total of the central angles for the given combinations are :

(*i*) Wheat, Barley and Jowar = (72° + 36° + 18°) = 126°

(*ii*) Rice, Wheat and Jowar = (72° + 72° + 18°) = 162°

(*iii*) Rice, Wheat and Barley = (72° + 72° + 36°) = 180°

(*iv*) Bajra. Maize and Rice = (18° + 45° + 72°) = 135°

Clearly, (*iii*) is the required combination.

2. (*a*) : The area under any of the food crops is proportional to the central angle corresponding to that crop.

Let, the area under rice production be *x* million acres.

Then, $18 : 72 = 1.5 : x \Rightarrow x = \left(\frac{72 \times 1.5}{18}\right) = 6.$

Thus, the area under rice production = 6 million acres.

3. (*b*) : Let the total production of barley be T tonnes and let Z acres of land be put under barley production.

Then, the total production of wheat = (6T) tonnes.

Also, area under wheat production = (2Z) acres.

$$\left[\because \frac{\text{Area under Wheat production}}{\text{Area under Barley production}} = \frac{72^\circ}{36^\circ} = 2\right.$$

$$\left.\text{and therefore, Area under wheat} = 2 \times \text{Area under barley} = (2Z) \text{ acres}\right]$$

Now, yield per acre for wheat = $\left(\frac{6T}{2Z}\right)$ tonnes/ acre = $\left(\frac{3T}{Z}\right)$ tonnes/ acre

and yield per acre for barley = $\left(\frac{T}{Z}\right)$ tonnes/ acre.

$\therefore$ Required Ratio = $\left(\frac{3T/Z}{T/Z}\right) = 3 : 1.$

4. (*b*) : Let Z acres of land be put under barley production.

Then, $\frac{\text{Area under rice production}}{\text{Area under barley production}} = \frac{72^\circ}{36^\circ} = 2.$

$\therefore$ Area under Rice production = 2 × area under barley production = (2Z) acres.

Now, if *p* tonnes be the yield per acre of barley then, yield per acre of rice

$$= (p + 50\% \text{ of } p) \text{ tonnes} = \left(\frac{3}{2}p\right) \text{ tonnes.}$$

$\therefore$ Total production of rice = (yield per acre) × (area under production)

$$= \left(\frac{3}{2}p\right) \times 2Z = (3pZ) \text{ tonnes.}$$

And, Total production of barley = (pZ) tonnes.

$\therefore$ Percentage production of barley to that of rice = $\left(\frac{pZ}{3pZ} \times 100\right)\% = 33\frac{1}{3}\%$.

5. (*b*) : Initially, let t acres be the total area under consideration.

Then, area under wheat production initially was = $\left(\frac{72}{360} \times t\right)$ acres = $\left(\frac{t}{5}\right)$ acres.

Now, if the total area under consideration be increased by 5%, then the new value of the total area = $\left(\frac{105}{100}t\right)$ acres.

Also, if the area under wheat production be increased by 12%, then the new value of the area under wheat = $\left[\frac{t}{5} + \left(12\% \text{ of } \frac{t}{5}\right)\right]$ acres = $\left(\frac{112t}{500}\right)$ acres.

$\therefore$ Central angle corresponding to wheat in the new pie-chart

$$= \left[\frac{\text{Area under wheat (new)}}{\text{Total area (new)}} \times 360\right]^\circ = \left[\frac{\left(\frac{112t}{500}\right)}{\left(\frac{105t}{100}\right)} \times 360\right]^\circ = 76.8^\circ.$$

Example 3. ***The following pie-charts show the distribution of students of graduate and post-graduate levels in seven different institutes — M, N, P, Q, R, S and T in a town.*** **(Bank P.O. 2003)**

DISTRIBUTION OF STUDENTS AT GRADUATE AND POST-GRADUATE LEVELS IN SEVEN INSTITUTES — M, N, P, Q, R, S AND T

Total Number of Students of Graduate Level = 27300

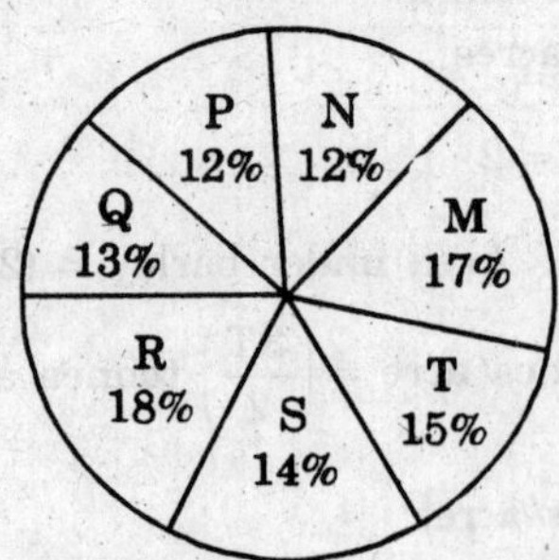

Total Number of Students of Post-Graduate Level = 24700

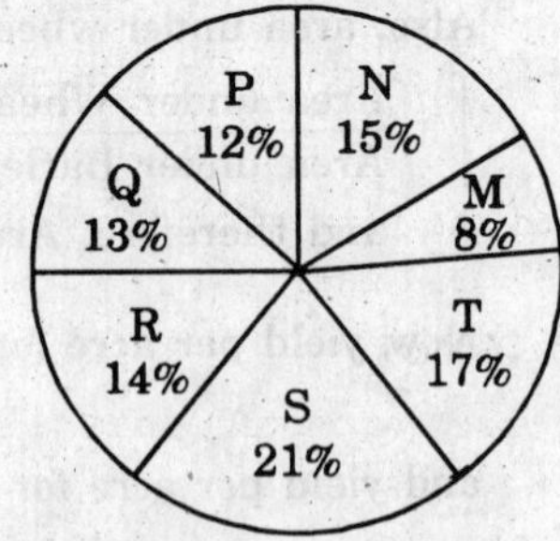

1. How many students of institutes M and S are studying at graduate level ?
(*a*) 7516 (*b*) 8463 (*c*) 9127 (*d*) 9404

2. Total number of students studying at post-graduate level from institutes N and P is :
(*a*) 5601 (*b*) 5944 (*c*) 6669 (*d*) 7004

3. What is the total number of graduate and post-graduate level students in institute R ?
(*a*) 8320 (*b*) 7916 (*c*) 9116 (*d*) 8372

4. What is the ratio between the number of students studying at post-graduate and graduate levels respectively from institute S ?
(*a*) 14 : 19 (*b*) 19 : 21 (*c*) 17 : 21 (*d*) 19 : 14

5. What is the ratio between the number of students studying at post-graduate level from institute S and the number of students studying at graduate level from institute Q ?

(*a*) 13 : 19 (*b*) 21 : 13 (*c*) 13 : 8 (*d*) 19 : 13

SOLUTION

1. (*b*) : Students of institute M at graduate level = 17% of 27300 = 4641.
Students of institute S at graduate level = 14% of 27300 = 3822.
∴ Total number of students at graduate level in institutes M and S
= 4641 + 3822 = 8463.

2. (*c*) : Required number = (15% of 24700) + (12% of 24700) = 3705 + 2964 = 6669.

3. (*d*) : Required number = (18% of 27300) + (14% of 24700) = 4914 + 3458 = 8372.

4. (*d*) : Required ratio $= \frac{(21\% \text{ of } 24700)}{(14\% \text{ of } 27300)} = \frac{21 \times 24700}{14 \times 27300} = \frac{19}{14}$.

5. (*d*) : Required ratio $= \frac{(21\% \text{ of } 24700)}{(13\% \text{ of } 27300)} = \frac{21 \times 24700}{13 \times 27300} = \frac{19}{13}$.

Example 4. ***Study the following pie-chart and the table and answer the questions based on them.*** **(S.B.I.P.O. 1999)**

PROPORTION OF POPULATION OF SEVEN VILLAGES IN 1997

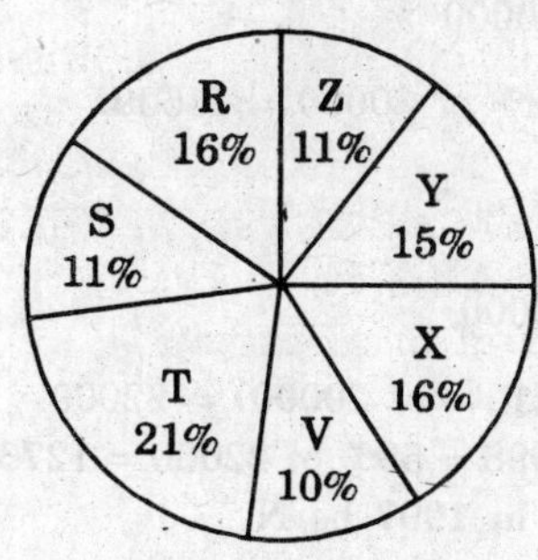

Village	% Population Below Poverty Line
X	38
Y	52
Z	42
R	51
S	49
T	46
V	58

1. Find the population of village S if the population of village X below poverty line in 1997 is 12160.

(*a*) 18500 (*b*) 20500 (*c*) 22000 (*d*) 26000

2. The ratio of population of village T below poverty line to that of village Z below poverty line in 1997 is :

(*a*) 11 : 23 (*b*) 13 : 11 (*c*) 23 : 11 (*d*) 11 : 13

3. If the population of village R in 1997 is 32000, then what will be the population of village Y below poverty line in that year ?

(*a*) 14100 (*b*) 15600 (*c*) 16500 (*d*) 17000

4. If in 1998, the population of villages Y and V increase by 10% each and the percentage of population below poverty line remains unchanged for all the villages, then find the population of village V below poverty line in 1998, given that the population of village Y in 1997 was 30000.

(*a*) 11250 (*b*) 12760 (*c*) 13140 (*d*) 13780

5. If in 1999, the population of village R increases by 10% while that of village Z reduces by 5% compared to that in 1997 and the percentage of population below poverty line remains unchanged for all the villages, then find the approximate ratio of population of village R below poverty line to the ratio of population of village Z below poverty line for the year 1999.

(*a*) 2 : 1 (*b*) 3 : 2 (*c*) 4 : 3 (*d*) 5 : 4

SOLUTION

1. (*c*) : Let the population of village X be *x*.

Then, 38% of $x = 12160 \Rightarrow x = \frac{12160 \times 100}{38} = 32000.$

Now, if *s* be the population of village S, then

$16 : 11 = 32000 : s \Rightarrow s = \frac{11 \times 32000}{16} = 22000.$

2. (*c*) : Let N be the total population of all the seven villages.

Then, population of village T below poverty line = 46% of (21% of N)

and population of village Z below poverty line = 42% of (11% of N)

$\therefore$ Required ratio $= \frac{46\% \text{ of } (21\% \text{ of N})}{42\% \text{ of } (11\% \text{ of N})} = \frac{46 \times 21}{42 \times 11} = \frac{23}{11}.$

3. (*b*) : Population of village R = 32000 (given).

Let the population of village Y be *y*.

Then, $16 : 15 = 32000 : y \Rightarrow y = \frac{15 \times 32000}{16} = 30000$

$\therefore$ Population of village Y below poverty line = 52% of 30000 = 15600.

4. (*b*) : Population of village Y in 1997 = 30000 (given).

Let the population of village V in 1997 be *v*.

Then, $15 : 10 = 30000 : v \Rightarrow v = \frac{30000 \times 10}{15} = 20000.$

Now, population of village V in 1998 = 20000 + (10% of 20000) = 22000.

$\therefore$ Population of village V below poverty line in 1998 = 58% of 22000 = 12760.

5. (*a*) : Let the total population of all the seven villages in 1997 be N.

Then, population of village R in 1997 = 16% of N $= \frac{16}{100}$N

and population of village Z in 1997 = 11% of N $= \frac{11}{100}$N.

$\therefore$ Population of village R in 1999 $= \left\{\frac{16}{100}\text{N} + \left(10\% \text{ of } \frac{16}{100}\text{N}\right)\right\} = \frac{1760}{10000}\text{N}$

and population of village Z in 1999 $= \left\{\frac{11}{100}\text{N} - \left(5\% \text{ of } \frac{11}{100}\text{N}\right)\right\} = \frac{1045}{10000}\text{N}$

Now, population of village R below poverty line for 1999 = 51% of $\left(\frac{1760}{10000}\text{N}\right)$

and population of village Z below poverty line for 1999 = 42% of $\left(\frac{1045}{10000}\text{N}\right)$.

$$\therefore \text{Required ratio} = \frac{51\% \text{ of } \left(\frac{1760}{10000}\text{N}\right)}{42\% \text{ of } \left(\frac{1045}{10000}\text{N}\right)} = \frac{51 \times 1760}{42 \times 1045} \approx \frac{2}{1}.$$

EXERCISE 38

1. The following pie-chart shows the percentage of Literate and Illiterate — Males and Females in a city. **(Bank P.O. 2003)**

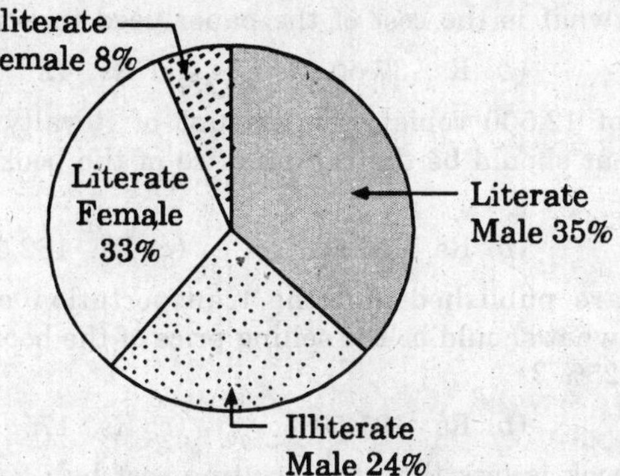

Total number = 2,50,000.

What is the difference between the number of Literate Males and Literate Females ?

(*a*) 75,000 (*b*) 1,500 (*c*) 5,000 (*d*) 500

Directions (Questions 2 to 10) : ***The following pie-chart shows the percentage distribution of the expenditure incurred in publishing a book. Study the pie-chart and answer the questions based on it.*** **(Bank P.O. 2002)**

VARIOUS EXPENDITURES (IN PERCENTAGE) INCURRED IN PUBLISHING A BOOK

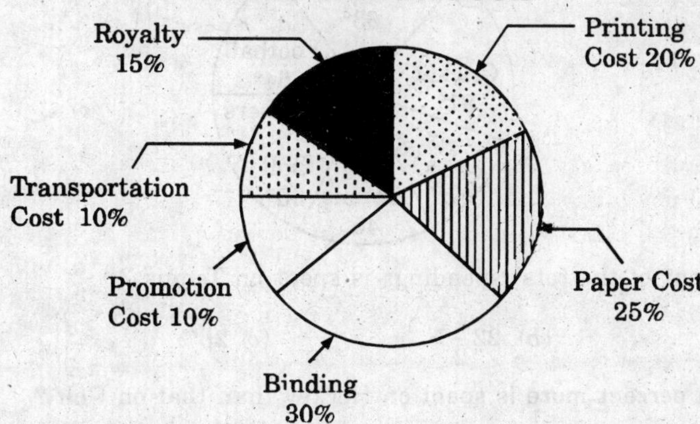

2. What is the central angle of the sector corresponding to the expenditure incurred on Royalty ?

(*a*) 15° (*b*) 24° (*c*) 54° (*d*) 48°

3. Which two expenditures together have a central angle of 108° ?

(*a*) Binding Cost and Transportation Cost (*b*) Printing Cost and Paper Cost

(*c*) Royalty and Promotion Cost (*d*) Binding Cost and Paper Cost

4. If the difference between the two expenditures are represented by 18° in the pie-chart, then these expenditures possibly are :

(*a*) Binding Cost and Promotion Cost (*b*) Paper Cost and Royalty

(*c*) Binding Cost and Printing Post (*d*) Paper Cost and Printing Cost

5. If for an edition of the book, the cost of paper is Rs. 56250, then find the promotion cost for this edition

(*a*) Rs. 20,000 (*b*) Rs. 22.500 (*c*) Rs. 25,500 (*d*) Rs. 28,125

6. If for a certain quantity of books, the publisher has to pay Rs. 30,600 as printing cost, then what will be the amount of royalty to be paid for these books ?

(a) Rs. 19,450 (b) Rs. 21,200 (c) Rs. 22,950 (d) Rs. 26,150

7. The price of the book is marked 20% above the C.P. If the marked price of the book is Rs. 180, then what is the cost of the paper used in a single copy of the book ?

(a) Rs. 36 (b) Rs. 37.50 (c) Rs. 42 (d) Rs. 44.25

8. For an edition of 12,500 copies, the amount of Royalty paid by the publisher is Rs. 2,81,250. What should be the selling price of the book if the publisher desires a profit of 5% ?

(a) Rs. 152.50 (b) Rs. 157.50 (c) Rs. 162.50 (d) Rs. 167.50

9. If 5500 copies are published and the transportation cost on them amounts to Rs. 82,500, then what should be the selling price of the book so that the publisher can earn a profit of 25% ?

(a) Rs. 187.50 (b) Rs. 191.50 (c) Rs. 175 (d) Rs. 180

10. Royalty on the book is less than the printing cost by :

(a) 5% (b) $33\frac{1}{3}\%$ (c) 20% (d) 25%

Directions (Questions 11 to 15) : ***The circle-graph given here shows the spendings of a country on various sports during a particular year. Study the graph carefully and answer the questions given below it.***

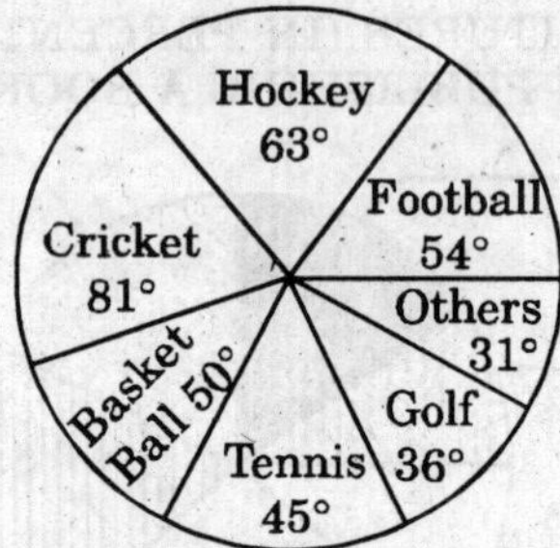

11. What percent of the total spendings is spent on Tennis ?

(a) $12\frac{1}{2}\%$ (b) $22\frac{1}{2}\%$ (c) 25% (d) 45%

12. How much percent more is spent on Hockey than that on Golf ?

(a) 27% (b) 35% (c) 37.5% (d) 75%

13. How much percent less is spent on Football than that on Cricket ?

(a) $22\frac{2}{9}\%$ (b) 27% (c) $33\frac{1}{3}\%$ (d) $37\frac{1}{2}\%$

14. If the total amount spent on sports during the year was Rs. 2 crores, the amount spent on Cricket and Hockey together was :

(a) Rs. 8,00,000 (b) Rs. 80,00,000 (c) Rs. 1,20,00,000 (d) Rs. 1,60,00,000

15. If the total amount spent on sports during the year be Rs. 1,80,00,000, the amount spent on Basketball exceeds that on Tennis by :

(a) Rs. 2,50,000 (b) Rs. 3,60,000 (c) Rs. 3,75,000 (d) Rs. 4,10,000

Directions (Questions 16 to 20) : ***Study the following graph carefully and answer the questions given below :*** **(Bank P.O. 2002)**

DISTRIBUTION OF CANDIDATES WHO WERE ENROLLED FOR MBA ENTRANCE EXAM AND THE CANDIDATES (OUT OF THOSE ENROLLED) WHO PASSED THE EXAM IN DIFFERENT INSTITUTES

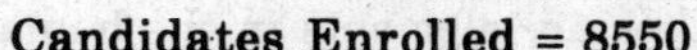

Candidates Enrolled = 8550 **Candidates who Passed the Exam = 5700**

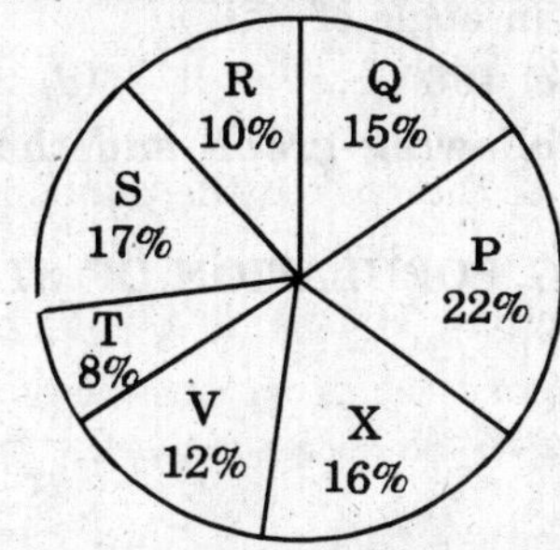

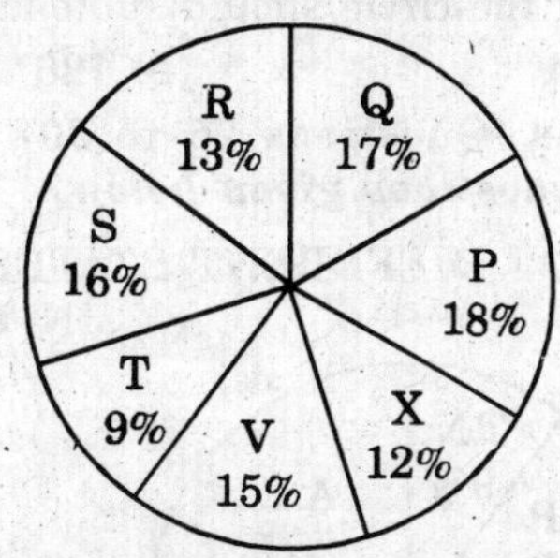

16. What percentage of candidates passed the Exam from institute T out of the total number of candidates enrolled from the same institute ?

(*a*) 50% (*b*) 62.5% (*c*) 75% (*d*) 80%

17. What is the ratio of candidates passed to the candidates enrolled from institute P ?

(*a*) 9 : 11 (*b*) 14 : 17 (*c*) 6 : 11 (*d*) 9 : 17

18. What is the percentage of candidates passed to the candidates enrolled for institutes Q and R together ?

(*a*) 68% (*b*) 80% (*c*) 74% (*d*) 65%

19. Which institute has the highest percentage of candidates passed to the candidates enrolled ?

(*a*) Q (*b*) R (*c*) V (*d*) T

20. The number of candidates passed from institutes S and P together exceeds the number of candidates enrolled from institutes T and R together by :

(*a*) 228 (*b*) 279 (*c*) 399 (*d*) 407

Directions (Questions 21 to 25) : ***Study the following pie-diagrams carefully and answer the questions given below it.***

PERCENTAGE COMPOSITION OF HUMAN BODY

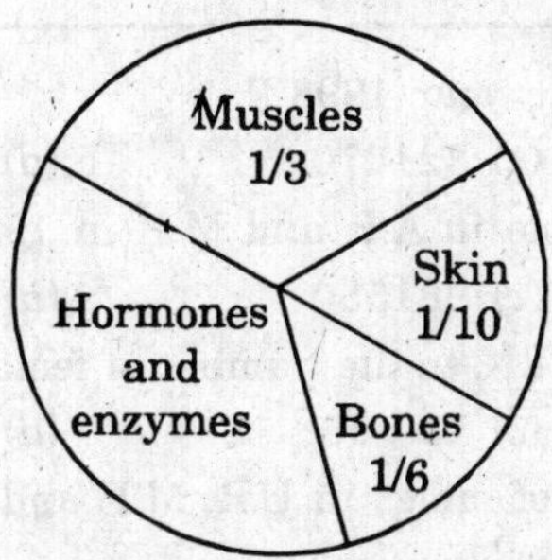

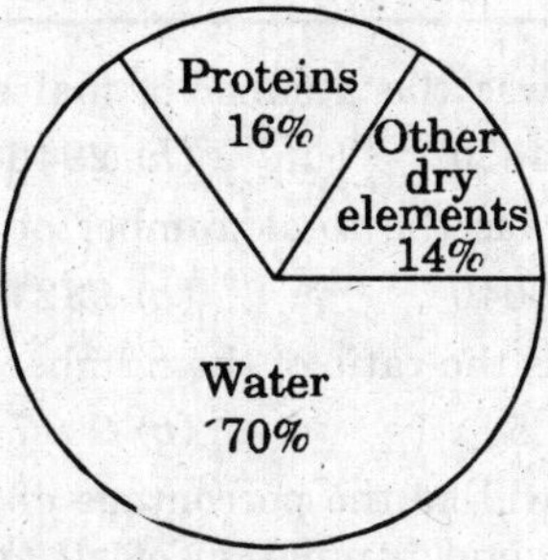

21. In the human body, what part is made of neither bones nor skin ?

(*a*) $\frac{1}{40}$ (*b*) $\frac{3}{80}$ (*c*) $\frac{2}{5}$ (*d*) None of these

22. What is the ratio of the distribution of proteins in the muscles to that of the distribution of proteins in the bones ?

(*a*) 1 : 18 (*b*) 1 : 2 (*c*) 2 : 1 (*d*) 18 : 1

23. What will be the quantity of water in the body of a person weighing 50 kg ?

(*a*) 20 kg (*b*) 35 kg (*c*) 41 kg (*d*) 42.5 kg

24. What percent of the total weight of human body is equivalent to the weight of the proteins in skin in human body ?

(*a*) 0.016 (*b*) 1.6 (*c*) 0.16 (*d*) Data inadequate

25. To show the distribution of proteins and other dry elements in the human body, the arc of the circle should subtend at the centre an angle of :

(*a*) 54° (*b*) 126° (*c*) 108° (*d*) 252°

Directions (Questions 26 to 30) : ***Study the following graph and the table and answer the questions given below.***

DATA OF DIFFERENT STATES REGARDING POPULATION OF STATES IN THE YEAR 1998

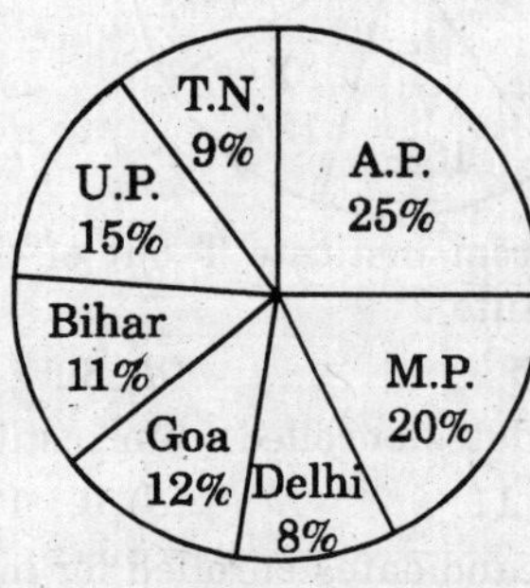

Total Population of the given States = 3276000

States	Sex and Literacy wise Population Ratio					
	Sex			Literacy		
	M	—	F	Literate	—	Illiterate
A.P.	5	:	3	2	:	7
M.P.	3	:	1	1	:	4
Delhi	2	:	3	2	:	1
Goa	3	:	5	3	:	2
Bihar	3	:	4	5	:	1
U.P.	3	:	2	7	:	2
T.N.	3	:	4	9	:	4

26. What was the number of males in U.P. in the year 1998 ?

(*a*) 254650 (*b*) 294840 (*c*) 321470 (*d*) 341200

27. What was the total number of illiterate people in A.P. and M.P. in 1998 ?

(*a*) 876040 (*b*) 932170 (*c*) 981550 (*d*) 1161160

28. What is the ratio of the number of females in T.N. to the number of females in Delhi ?

(*a*) 7 : 5 (*b*) 9 : 7 (*c*) 13 : 11 (*d*) 15 : 14

29. What will be the percentage of total number of males in U.P., M.P. and Goa together to the total population of all the given states ?

(*a*) 25% (*b*) 27.5% (*c*) 28.5% (*d*) 31.5%

30. If in the year 1998, there was an increase of 10% in the population of U.P. and 12% in the population of M.P. compared to the previous year, then what was the ratio of populations of U.P. and M.P. in 1997 ?

(*a*) 42 : 55 (*b*) 48 : 55 (*c*) 7 : 11 (*d*) 4 : 5

ANSWERS

1. (c)	2. (c)	3. (a)	4. (d)	5. (b)	6. (c)	7. (b)	8. (b)	9. (a)
10. (d)	11. (a)	12. (d)	13. (c)	14. (b)	15. (a)	16. (c)	17. (c)	18. (b)
19. (b)	20. (c)	21. (d)	22. (c)	23. (b)	24. (b)	25. (c)	26. (b)	27. (d)
28. (d)	29. (c)	30. (a)						

SOLUTIONS

1. Difference = (35% of 2,50,000) – (33% of 2,50,000)
= (35% – 33%) of 2,50,000 = 2% of 2,50,000 = 5000.

2. Central angle corresponding to Royalty = $(15\% \text{ of } 360)° = 54°$.

3. Central angle of 108° = $\left(\frac{108}{360} \times 100\right)\%$ of the total expenditure
= 30% of the total expenditure.

From the pie-chart it is clear that :
Binding Cost + Transportation Cost = (20% + 10%) of the total expenditure
= 30% of the total expenditure.

∴ Binding Cost and Transportation Cost together have a central angle of 108°.

4. Central angle of 18° = $\left(\frac{18}{360} \times 100\right)\%$ of the total expenditure
= 5% of the total expenditure.

From the pie-chart it is clear that :
Out of the given combinations, only in combination (*d*) the difference is 5% *i.e.*
Paper Cost – Printing Cost = (25% – 20%) of total expenditure
= 5% of total expenditure.

5. Let the Promotion Cost for this edition be Rs. *p*.

Then, 25 : 10 = 56250 : $p \Rightarrow p$ = Rs. $\left(\frac{56250 \times 10}{25}\right)$ = Rs. 22500.

6. Let the amount of Royalty to be paid for these books be Rs. *r*.

Then, 20 : 15 = 30600 : $r \Rightarrow r$ = Rs. $\left(\frac{30600 \times 15}{20}\right)$ = Rs. 22950.

7. Clearly, marked price of the book = 120% of C.P.
Also, cost of paper = 25% of C.P.
Let the cost of paper for a single book be Rs. *n*.

Then, 120 : 25 = 180 : $n \Rightarrow n$ = Rs. $\left(\frac{25 \times 180}{120}\right)$ = Rs. 37.50.

8. Clearly, S.P. of the book = 105% of C.P.
Let the selling price of this edition (of 12500 books) be Rs. *x*.

Then, 15 : 105 = 281250 : $x \Rightarrow x$ = Rs. $\left(\frac{105 \times 281250}{15}\right)$ = Rs. 1968750.

∴ S.P. of one book = Rs. $\left(\frac{1968750}{12500}\right)$ = Rs. 157.50.

9. For the publisher to earn a profit of 25%, S.P. = 125% of C.P.
Also Transportation Cost = 10% of C.P.
Let the S.P. of 5500 books be Rs. x.
Then, $10 : 125 = 82500 : x \Rightarrow x = \text{Rs.}\left(\frac{125 \times 82500}{10}\right) = \text{Rs. } 1031250.$

$\therefore$ S.P. of one book = Rs. $\left(\frac{1031250}{5500}\right)$ = Rs. 187.50.

10. Printing Cost of book = 20% of C.P.
Royalty on book = 15% of C.P.
Difference = (20% of C.P.) – (15% of C.P.) = 5% of C.P.

$\therefore$ Percentage difference $= \left(\frac{\text{Difference}}{\text{Printing Cost}} \times 100\right)\%$

$= \left(\frac{5\% \text{ of C.P.}}{20\% \text{ of C.P.}} \times 100\right)\% = 25\%.$

Thus, Royalty on the book is 25% less than the Printing Cost.

11. Percentage of money spent on Tennis $= \left(\frac{45}{360} \times 100\right)\% = 12\frac{1}{2}\%.$

12. Let the total spendings on sports be Rs. x. Then,

Amount spent on Golf = Rs. $\left(\frac{36}{360} \times x\right)$ = Rs. $\frac{x}{10}$.

Amount spent on Hockey = Rs. $\left(\frac{63}{360} \times x\right)$ = Rs. $\frac{7}{40}x$.

Difference = Rs. $\left(\frac{7}{40}x - \frac{x}{10}\right)$ = Rs. $\frac{3x}{40}$.

$\therefore$ Required Percentage $= \left[\left(\frac{3x/40}{x/10}\right) \times 100\right]\% = 75\%$

13. Let the total spendings on sports be Rs. x. Then,

Amount spent on Cricket = Rs. $\left(\frac{81}{360} \times x\right)$ = Rs. $\left(\frac{9}{40}x\right)$.

Amount spent on Football = Rs. $\left(\frac{54}{360} \times x\right)$ = Rs. $\left(\frac{3}{20}x\right)$.

Difference = Rs. $\left(\frac{9}{40}x - \frac{3}{20}x\right)$ = Rs. $\frac{3}{40}x$.

$\therefore$ Required Percentage $= \left[\left(\frac{3x/40}{9x/40}\right) \times 100\right]\% = 33\frac{1}{3}\%.$

14. Amount spent on Cricket and Hockey together

$= \text{Rs.}\left[\frac{(81+63)}{360} \times 2\right]$ crores = Rs. 0.8 crores = Rs. 8000000.

15. Amount spent on Basketball exceeds that on Tennis by :

Rs. $\left[\frac{(50-45)}{360} \times 18000000\right]$ = Rs. 250000.

16. Required percentage $= \left(\frac{9\% \text{ of } 5700}{8\% \text{ of } 8550} \times 100\right)\% = \left(\frac{9 \times 5700}{8 \times 8550} \times 100\right)\% = 75\%.$

17. Required ratio $= \left(\frac{18\% \text{ of } 5700}{22\% \text{ of } 8550}\right) = \left(\frac{18 \times 5700}{22 \times 8550}\right) = \frac{6}{11}.$

18. Candidates passed from institutes Q and R together

$= [(13\% + 17\%) \text{ of } 5700] = 30\% \text{ of } 5700.$

Candidates enrolled from institutes Q and R together

$= [(15\% + 10\%) \text{ of } 8550] = 25\% \text{ of } 8550.$

$\therefore$ Required Percentage $= \left(\frac{30\% \text{ of } 5700}{25\% \text{ of } 8550} \times 100\right)\% = \left(\frac{30 \times 5700}{25 \times 8550} \times 100\right)\% = 80\%.$

19. The percentage of candidates passed to candidates enrolled can be determined for each institute as under :

(*i*) $P = \left[\left(\frac{18\% \text{ of } 5700}{22\% \text{ of } 8550}\right) \times 100\right]\% = \left[\frac{18 \times 5700}{22 \times 8550} \times 100\right]\% = \left[\frac{18 \times 2}{22 \times 3} \times 100\right]\% = 54.55\%.$

(*ii*) $Q = \left[\left(\frac{17\% \text{ of } 5700}{15\% \text{ of } 8550}\right) \times 100\right]\% = 75.56\%.$

(*iii*) $R = \left[\left(\frac{13\% \text{ of } 5700}{10\% \text{ of } 8550}\right) \times 100\right]\% = 86.67\%.$

(*iv*) $S = \left[\left(\frac{16\% \text{ of } 5700}{17\% \text{ of } 8550}\right) \times 100\right]\% = 62.75\%.$

(*v*) $T = \left[\left(\frac{9\% \text{ of } 5700}{8\% \text{ of } 8550}\right) \times 100\right]\% = 75\%.$

(*vi*) $V = \left[\left(\frac{15\% \text{ of } 5700}{12\% \text{ of } 8550}\right) \times 100\right]\% = 83.33\%.$

(*vii*) $X = \left[\left(\frac{12\% \text{ of } 5700}{16\% \text{ of } 8550}\right) \times 100\right]\% = 50\%.$

Highest of these is 86.67% corresponding to institute R.

20. Required difference $= [(16\% + 18\%) \text{ of } 5700] - [(8\% + 10\%) \text{ of } 8550]$

$= [(34\% \text{ of } 5700) - (18\% \text{ of } 8550)] = (1938 - 1539) = 399.$

21. Part of the body made of neither bones nor skin $= 1 - \left(\frac{1}{6} + \frac{1}{10}\right) = \frac{11}{15}.$

22. Required ratio $= \dfrac{16\% \text{ of } \frac{1}{3}}{16\% \text{ of } \frac{1}{6}} = \frac{6}{3} = \frac{2}{1}.$

23. Quantity of water in the body of a person weighing 50 kg = (70% of 50) kg = 35 kg.

24. Let the body weight be x kg.

Then, weight of skin protein in the body $= \left[16\% \text{ of } \left(\frac{1}{10} \text{ of } x\right)\right] \text{ kg} = \left(\frac{16}{1000}x\right) \text{ kg}$

$\therefore$ Required percentage $= \left[\frac{\left(\frac{16}{1000}x\right)}{x} \times 100\right]\% = 1.6\%.$

25. Percentage of proteins and other dry elements in the body = (16% + 14%) = 30%

$\therefore$ Central angle corresponding to proteins and other dry elements together

$= 30\% \text{ of } 360° = 108°.$

26. Number of males in U.P. $= \left[\frac{3}{5} \text{ of } (15\% \text{ of } 3276000)\right] = \frac{3}{5} \times \frac{15}{100} \times 3276000 = 294840.$

27. No. of illiterate people in A.P. $= \left[\frac{7}{9} \text{ of } (25\% \text{ of } 3276000)\right] = 637000.$

No. of illiterate people in M.P. $= \left[\frac{4}{5} \text{ of } (20\% \text{ of } 3276000)\right] = 524160.$

Total number = (637000 + 524160) = 1161160.

28. Required ratio $= \dfrac{\frac{4}{7} \text{ of } (9\% \text{ of } 3276000)}{\frac{3}{5} \text{ of } (8\% \text{ of } 3276000)} = \dfrac{\left(\frac{4}{7} \times 9\right)}{\left(\frac{3}{5} \times 8\right)} = \left(\frac{4}{7} \times 9 \times \frac{5}{3} \times \frac{1}{8}\right) = \frac{15}{14}.$

29. Number of males in U.P. $= \left[\frac{3}{5} \text{ of } (15\% \text{ of N})\right] = \frac{3}{5} \times \frac{15}{100} \times N = 9 \times \frac{N}{100}$

where N = 3276000.

Number of males in M.P. $= \left[\frac{3}{4} \text{ of } (20\% \text{ of N})\right] = \frac{3}{4} \times \frac{20}{100} \times N = 15 \times \frac{N}{100};$

Number of males in Goa $= \left[\frac{3}{8} \text{ of } (12\% \text{ of N})\right] = \frac{3}{8} \times \frac{12}{100} \times N = 4.5 \times \frac{N}{100}.$

$\therefore$ Total number of males in these three states $= (9 + 15 + 4.5) \times \frac{N}{100} = \left(28.5 \times \frac{N}{100}\right).$

$\therefore$ Required Percentage $= \left[\dfrac{\left(28.5 \times \frac{N}{100}\right)}{N} \times 100\right]\% = 28.5\%.$

30. Let x be the population of U.P. in 1997. Then,

Population of U.P. in 1998 = 110% of $x = \frac{110}{100} \times x.$

Also, let y be the population of M.P. in 1997. Then,

Population of M.P. in 1998 = 112% of $y = \frac{112}{100} \times y.$

Ratio of populations of U.P. and M.P. in 1998 $= \dfrac{\left(\frac{110}{100} \times x\right)}{\left(\frac{112}{100} \times y\right)} = \frac{110x}{112y}.$

From the pie-chart, this ratio is $\frac{15}{20}$.

$\therefore \frac{110x}{112y} = \frac{15}{20} \Rightarrow \frac{x}{y} = \frac{15}{20} \times \frac{112}{110} = \frac{42}{55}.$

Thus, ratio of populations of U.P. and M.P. in 1997 = $x : y = 42 : 55$.

39. LINE-GRAPHS

This section comprises of questions in which the data collected in a particular discipline are represented by specific points joined together by straight lines. The points are plotted on a two-dimensional plane taking one parameter on the horizontal axis and the other on the vertical axis. The candidate is required to analyse the given information and thereafter answer the given questions on the basis of the analysis of data.

SOLVED EXAMPLES

Ex. 1. ***In a school the periodical examinations are held every second month. In a session during Apr. 2001 – Mar. 2002, a student of Class IX appeared for each of the periodical exams. The aggregate marks obtained by him in each periodical exam are represented in the line-graph given below. Study the graph and answer the questions based on it.*** **(S.B.I.P.O. 2003)**

MARKS OBTAINED BY A STUDENT IN SIX PERIODICAL EXAMS HELD IN EVERY TWO MONTHS DURING THE YEAR IN THE SESSION 2001-02

Maximum Total Marks in each Periodical Exam = 500

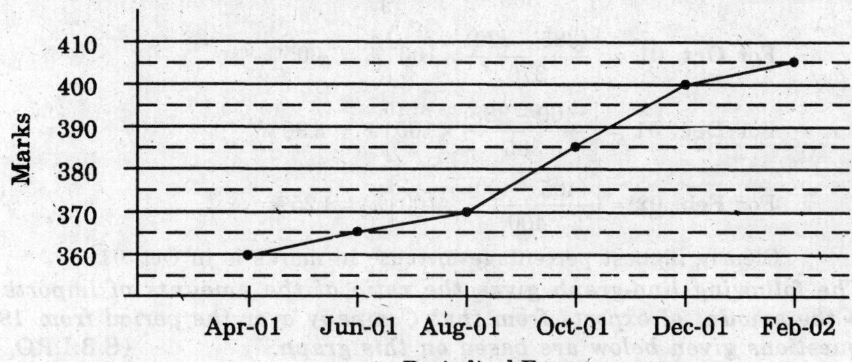

1. The total number of marks obtained in Feb. 02 is what percent of the total marks obtained in Apr. 01 ?
(*a*) 110% (*b*) 112.5% (*c*) 115% (*d*) 116.5% (*e*) 117.5%

2. What are the average marks obtained by the student in all the periodical exams during the session ?
(*a*) 373 (*b*) 379 (*c*) 381 (*d*) 385 (*e*) 389

3. What is the percentage of marks obtained by the student in the periodical exams of Aug. 01 and Oct. 01 taken together ?
(*a*) 73.25% (*b*) 75.5% (*c*) 77% (*d*) 78.75% (*e*) 79.5%

4. In which periodical exams there is a fall in percentage of marks as compared to the previous periodical exams ?
(*a*) None (*b*) Jun. 01 (*c*) Oct. 01 (*e*) Feb. 02 (*e*) None of these

5 In which periodical exams did the student obtain the highest percentage increase in marks over the previous periodical exams ?
(*a*) Jun. 01 (*b*) Aug. 01 (*c*) Oct. 01 (*d*) Dec. 01 (*e*) Feb. 02

Sol. Here it is clear from the graph that the student obtained 360, 365, 370, 385, 400 and 405 marks in periodical exams held in Apr. 01. Jun. 01, Aug. 01, Oct. 01, Dec. 01 and Feb. 02 respectively.

1. (*b*) : Required percentage $= \left(\frac{405}{360} \times 100\right)\% = 112.5\%$.

2. (*c*) : Average marks obtained in all the periodical exams

$= \frac{1}{6} \times [360 + 365 + 370 + 385 + 400 + 405] = 380.83 \approx 381.$

3. (*b*) : Required percentage $= \left[\frac{(370 + 385)}{(500 + 500)} \times 100\right]\% = \left(\frac{755}{1000} \times 100\right)\% = 75.5\%$.

4. (*a*) : As is clear from the graph, the total marks obtained in periodical exams, go on increasing. Since, the maximum marks for all the periodical exams are same, it implies that the percentage of marks also goes on increasing. Thus, in none of the periodical exams, there is a fall in percentage of marks compared to the previous exam.

5. (*c*) : Percentage increase in marks in various periodical exams compared to the previous exams are :

For **Jun. 01** $= \left[\frac{(365 - 360)}{360} \times 100\right]\% = 1.39\%$

For **Aug. 01** $= \left[\frac{(370 - 365)}{365} \times 100\right]\% = 1.37\%$

For **Oct. 01** $= \left[\frac{(385 - 370)}{370} \times 100\right]\% = 4.05\%$

For **Dec. 01** $= \left[\frac{(400 - 385)}{385} \times 100\right]\% = 3.90\%$

For **Feb. 02** $= \left[\frac{(405 - 400)}{400} \times 100\right]\% = 1.25\%$.

Clearly, highest percentage increase in marks is in Oct. 01.

Ex. 2. ***The following line-graph gives the ratio of the amounts of imports by a Company to the amount of exports from that Company over the period from 1995 to 2001. The questions given below are based on this graph.*** **(S.B.I.P.O. 2001)**

Ratio of Value of Imports to Exports by a Company over the Years

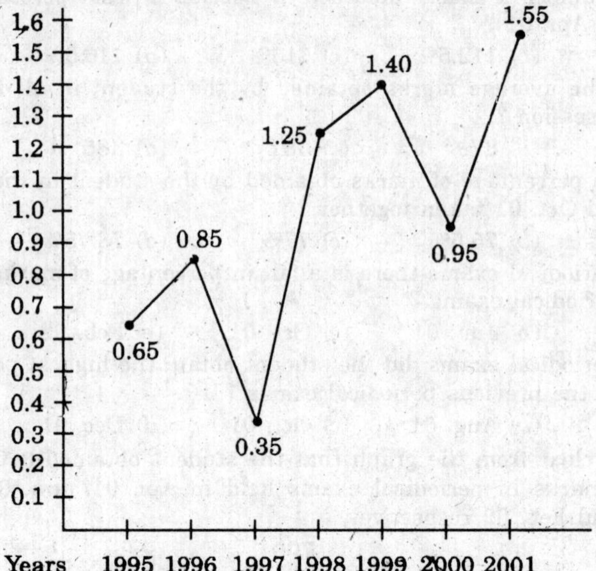

1. In how many of the given years were the exports more than the imports ?

(a) 1 (b) 2 (c) 3 (d) 4 (e) None of these

2. The imports were minimum proportionate to the exports of the Company in the year :

(a) 1995 (b) 1996 (c) 1997 (d) 2000 (e) 2001

3. If the imports of the Company in 1996 was Rs. 272 crores, the exports from the Company in 1996 was :

(a) Rs. 370 crores (b) Rs. 320 crores (c) Rs. 280 crores
(d) Rs. 275 crores (e) Rs. 264 crores

4. What was the percentage increase in imports from 1997 to 1998 ?

(a) 72 (b) 56 (c) 28 (d) None of these (e) Data inadequate

5. If the imports in 1998 was Rs. 250 crores and the total exports in the years 1998 and 1999 together was Rs. 500 crores, then the imports in 1999 was :

(a) Rs. 250 crores (b) Rs. 300 crores (c) Rs. 357 crores
(d) Rs. 420 crores (e) None of these

Sol. 1. (*d*) : The exports are more than the imports implies that the ratio of value of imports to exports is less than 1.

Now, this ratio is less than 1 in the years 1995, 1996, 1997 and 2000.

Thus, there are four such years.

2. (*c*) : The imports are minimum proportionate to the exports implies that the ratio of the value of imports to exports has the minimum value.

Now, this ratio has a minimum value of 0.35 in 1997, *i.e.*, the imports are minimum proportionate to the exports in 1997.

3. (*b*) : Ratio of imports to exports in the year 1996 = 0.85.

Let the exports in 1996 = Rs. x crores.

Then, $\dfrac{272}{x} = 0.85 \Rightarrow x = \dfrac{272}{0.85} = 320.$

$\therefore$ Exports in 1996 = Rs. 320 crores.

4. (*e*) : The graph gives only the ratio of imports to exports for different years. To find the percentage increase in imports from 1997 to 1998, we require more details such as the value of imports or exports during these years. Hence, the data is inadequate to answer this question.

5. (*d*) The ratio of imports to exports for the years 1998 and 1999 are 1.25 and 1.40 respectively.

Let the exports in the year 1998 = Rs. x crores.

Then, the exports in the year 1999 = Rs. $(500 - x)$ crores.

$\therefore \quad 1.25 = \dfrac{250}{x} \Rightarrow x = \dfrac{250}{1.25} = 200$ [Using ratio for 1998]

Thus, the exports in the year 1999 = Rs. (500 – 200) crores = Rs. 300 crores.

Let the imports in the year 1999 = Rs. y crores.

Then, $1.40 = \dfrac{y}{300} \Rightarrow y = (300 \times 1.40) = 420.$

$\therefore$ Imports in the year 1999 = Rs. 420 crores.

Ex. 3. ***Study the following line-graph and answer the questions based on it.***

(R.B.I. 2003)

Number of Vehicles Manufactured by Two Companies over the Years
(Number in Thousands)

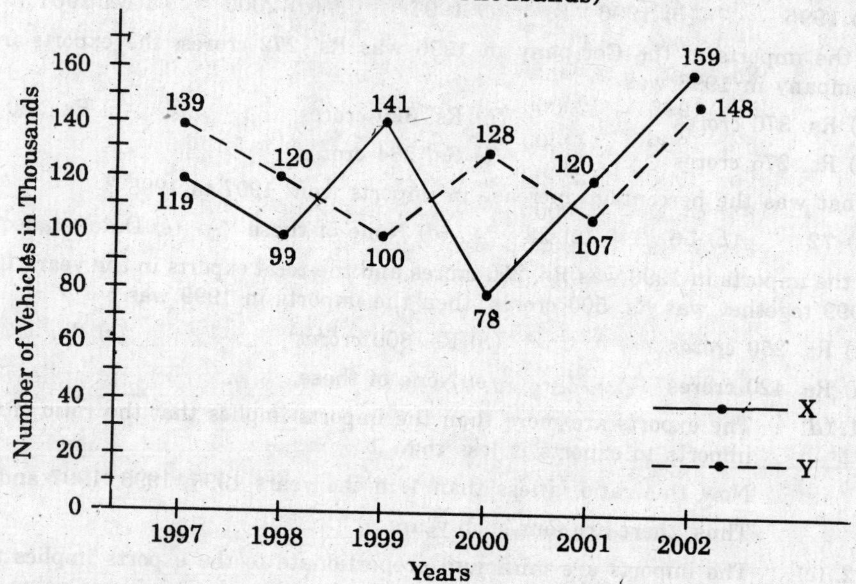

1. What is the difference between the total productions of the two Companies in the given years ?
   (*a*) 19000 (*b*) 22000 (*c*) 26000 (*d*) 28000 (*e*) 29000
2. What is the difference between the numbers of vehicles manufactured by Company Y in 2000 and 2001 ?
   (*a*) 50000 (*b*) 42000 (*c*) 33000 (*d*) 21000 (*e*) 13000
3. What is the average number of vehicles manufactured by Company X over the given period ? (rounded off to the nearest integer)
   (*a*) 119333 (*b*) 113666 (*c*) 112778 (*d*) 111223 (*e*) None of these
4. In which of the following years, the difference between the productions of Companies X and Y was the maximum among the given years ?
   (*a*) 1997 (*b*) 1998 (*c*) 1999 (*d*) 2000 (*e*) 2001
5. The production of Company Y in 2000 was approximately what percent of the production of Company X in the same year ?
   (*a*) 173 (*b*) 164 (*c*) 132 (*d*) 97 (*e*) 61

Sol. From the line-graph it is clear that the productions of Company X in the years 1997, 1998, 1999, 2000, 2001 and 2002 are 119000, 99000, 141000, 78000, 120000 and 159000 respectively and those of Company Y are 139000, 120000, 100000, 128000, 107000 and 148000 respectively.

1. (*c*) : Total production of Company X from 1997 to 2002

= 119000 + 99000 + 141000 + 78000 + 120000 + 159000 = 716000,

and total production of Company Y from 1997 to 2002

= 139000 + 120000 + 100000 + 128000 + 107000 + 148000 = 742000.

Difference = 742000 − 716000 = 26000.

2. (*d*) : Required difference = 128000 − 107000 = 21000.

3. (*a*) : Average number of vehicles manufactured by Company X

$$= \frac{1}{6} \times (119000 + 99000 + 141000 + 78000 + 120000 + 159000) = 119333.$$

4. (*d*) : The difference between the productions of Companies X and Y in various years are :

For 1997 = (139000 − 119000) = 20000;

For 1998 = (120000 − 99000) = 21000;

For 1999 = (141000 − 100000) = 41000;

For 2000 = (128000 − 78000) = 50000;

For 2001 = (120000 − 107000) = 13000;

For 2002 = (159000 − 148000) = 11000.

Clearly, maximum difference was in 2000.

5. (*b*) : Required percentage $= \left(\frac{128000}{78000} \times 100\right)\% \approx 164\%.$

Ex. 4. ***The following line-graph gives the percent profit earned by two Companies X and Y during the period 1996 – 2001. Study the line-graph and answer the questions that are based on it.*** **(NABARD, 2002)**

Percentage Profit Earned by Two Companies X and Y over the Given Years

$$\% \text{Profit / Loss} = \frac{\text{Income} - \text{Expenditure}}{\text{Expenditure}} \times 100$$

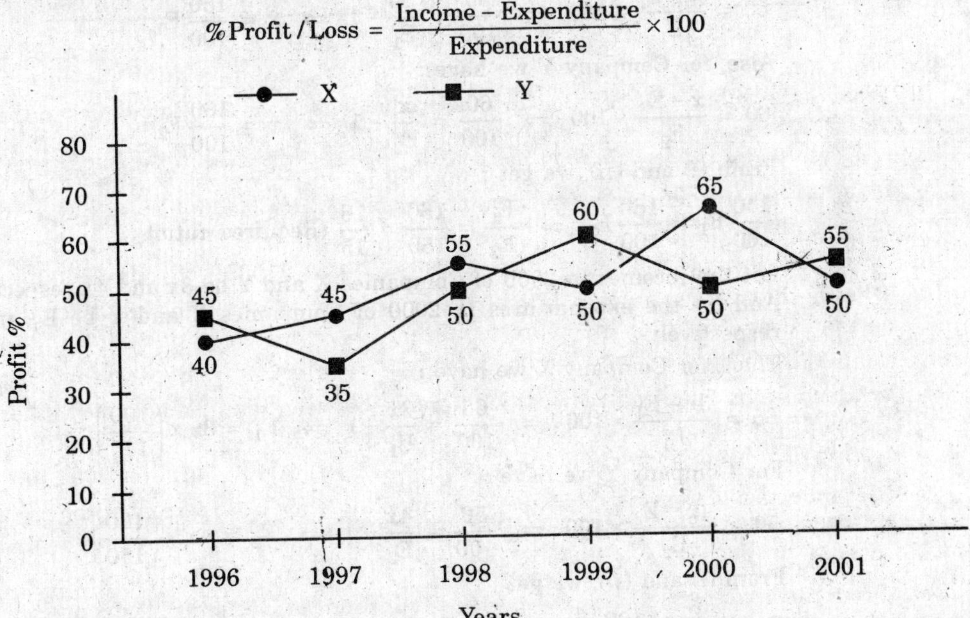

1. If the expenditure of Company Y in 1997 was Rs. 220 crores, what was its income in 1997 ?
   (*a*) Rs. 312 crores (*b*) Rs. 297 crores (*c*) Rs. 283 crores
   (*d*) Rs 275 crores (*e*) Rs. 261 crores
2. If the incomes of the two Companies were equal in 1999, then what was the ratio of expenditure of Company X to that of Company Y in 1999 ?
   (*a*) 6 : 5 (*b*) 5 : 6 (*c*) 11 : 6 (*d*) 16 : 15 (*e*) 15 : 16
3. The incomes of the Companies X and Y in 2000 were in the ratio of 3 : 4 respectively. What was the respective ratio of their expenditures in 2000 ?
   (*a*) 7 : 22 (*b*) 14 : 19 (*c*) 15 : 22 (*d*) 27 : 35 (*e*) 33 : 40

4. If the expenditures of Companies X and Y in 1996 were equal and the total income of the two Companies in 1996 was Rs. 342 crores, what was the total profit of the two Companies together in 1996 ? (Profit = Income − Expenditure)

(a) Rs. 240 crores (b) Rs. 171 crores (c) Rs. 120 crores
(d) Rs. 102 crores (e) None of these

5. The expenditure of Company X in the year 1998 was Rs. 200 crores and the income of Company X in 1998 was the same as its expenditure in 2001. The income of Company X in 2001 was :

(a) Rs. 465 crores (b) Rs. 385 crores (c) Rs. 335 crores
(d) Rs. 295 crores (e) Rs. 255 crores

Sol. 1. (b) : Profit percent of Company Y in 1997 = 35.

Let the income of Company Y in 1997 be Rs. x crores.

Then, $35 = \dfrac{x - 220}{220} \times 100 \Rightarrow x = 297.$

$\therefore$ Income of Company Y in 1997 = Rs. 297 crores.

2. (d) : Let the incomes of each of the two Companies X and Y in 1999 be Rs. x. And let the expenditures of Companies X and Y in 1999 be E_1 and E_2 respectively.

Then, for Company X we have :

$$50 = \frac{x - E_1}{E_1} \times 100 \Rightarrow \frac{50}{100} = \frac{x}{E_1} - 1 \Rightarrow x = \frac{150}{100} E_1 \qquad ...(i)$$

Also, for Company Y we have :

$$60 = \frac{x - E_2}{E_2} \times 100 \Rightarrow \frac{60}{100} = \frac{x}{E_2} - 1 \Rightarrow x = \frac{160}{100} E_2 \qquad ...(ii)$$

From (i) and (ii), we get :

$$\frac{150}{100} E_1 = \frac{160}{100} E_2 \Rightarrow \frac{E_1}{E_2} = \frac{160}{150} = \frac{16}{15} \text{ (Required ratio).}$$

3. (c) : Let the incomes in 2000 of Companies X and Y be $3x$ and $4x$ respectively. And let the expenditures in 2000 of Companies X and Y be E_1 and E_2 respectively.

Then, for Company X we have :

$$65 = \frac{3x - E_1}{E_1} \times 100 \Rightarrow \frac{65}{100} = \frac{3x}{E_1} - 1 \Rightarrow E_1 = 3x \times \left(\frac{100}{165}\right) \qquad ...(i)$$

For Company Y we have :

$$50 = \frac{4x - E_2}{E_2} \times 100 \Rightarrow \frac{50}{100} = \frac{4x}{E_2} - 1 \Rightarrow E_2 = 4x \times \left(\frac{100}{150}\right) \qquad ...(ii)$$

From (i) and (ii), we get :

$$\frac{E_1}{E_2} = \frac{3x \times \left(\frac{100}{165}\right)}{4x \times \left(\frac{100}{150}\right)} = \frac{3 \times 150}{4 \times 165} = \frac{15}{22} \text{ (Required ratio).}$$

4. (d) : Let the expenditures of each of the Companies X and Y in 1996 be Rs. x crores. And let the income of Company X in 1996 be Rs. z crores so that the income of Company Y in 1996 = Rs. $(342 - z)$ crores.

Then, for Company X we have :

$$40 = \frac{z - x}{x} \times 100 \Rightarrow \frac{40}{100} = \frac{z}{x} - 1 \Rightarrow x = \frac{100z}{140} \qquad ...(i)$$

Also, for Company Y we have :

$$45 = \frac{(342 - z) - x}{x} \times 100 \Rightarrow \frac{45}{100} = \frac{(342 - z)}{x} - 1 \Rightarrow x = \frac{(342 - z) \times 100}{145} \quad ...(ii)$$

From (*i*) and (*ii*), we get :

$$\frac{100z}{140} = \frac{(342 - z) \times 100}{145} \Rightarrow z = 168.$$

Substituting $z = 168$ in (*i*), we get : $x = 120$.

∴ Total expenditure of Companies X and Y in 1996 = $2x$ = Rs. 240 crores.

Total income of Companies X and Y in 1996 = Rs. 342 crores.

∴ Total profit = Rs. (342 − 240) crores = Rs. 102 crores.

5. (*a*) : Let the income of Company X in 1998 be Rs. x crores.

Then, $55 = \frac{x - 200}{200} \times 100 \Rightarrow x = 310.$

∴ Expenditure of Company X in 2001

= Income of Company X in 1998 = Rs. 310 crores

Let the income of Company X in 2001 be Rs. z crores.

Then, $50 = \frac{z - 310}{310} \times 100 \Rightarrow z = 465.$

∴ Income of Company X in 2001 = Rs. 465 crores.

EXERCISE 39

Directions (Questions 1 to 5) : ***The following line-graph gives the percentage of the number of candidates who qualified an examination out of the total number of candidates who appeared for the examination over a period of seven years from 1994 to 2000. Study the graph and answer the questions based on it.*** **(Bank P.O. 2000)**

Percentage of Candidates Qualified to Appeared in an Examination Over the Years

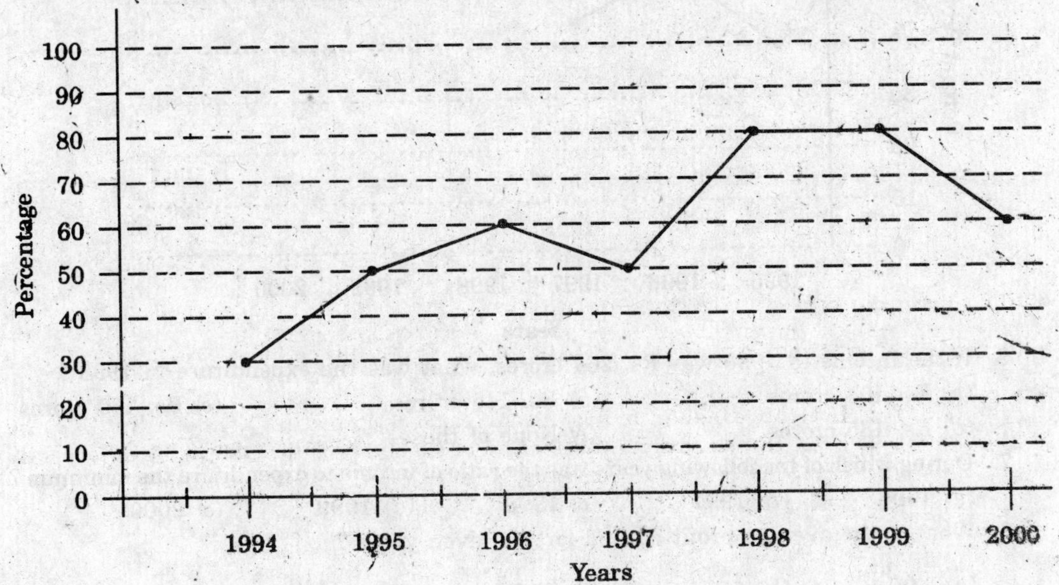

1. The difference between the percentages of candidates qualified to appeared was maximum in which of the following pairs of years ?

(a) 1994 and 1995 (b) 1997 and 1998 (c) 1998 and 1999
(d) 1999 and 2000 (e) 1994 and 1997

2. In which pair of years was the number of candidates qualified, the same ?

(a) 1995 and 1997 (b) 1995 and 2000 (c) 1998 and 1999
(d) 1996 and 2000 (e) Data inadequate

3. If the number of candidates qualified in 1998 was 21200, what was the number of candidates appeared in 1998 ?

(a) 32000 (b) 28500 (c) 26500 (d) 25000 (e) 24500

4. If the total number of candidates appeared in 1996 and 1997 together was 47400, then the total number of candidates qualified in these two years together was :

(a) 34700 (b) 32100 (c) 31500
(d) None of these (e) Data inadequate

5. The total number of candidates qualified in 1999 and 2000 together was 33500 and the number of candidates appeared in 1999 was 26500. What was the number of candidates appeared in 2000 ?

(a) 24500 (b) 22000 (c) 20500 (d) 19000 (e) 18500

Directions (Questions 6 to 13) : ***The following line-graph gives the annual percent profit earned by a Company during the period 1995-2000. Study the line-graph and answer the questions that are based on it.*** **(R.B.I. 2003)**

Percent Profit Earned by a Company Over the Years

$$\% \text{Profit} = \frac{\text{Income} - \text{Expenditure}}{\text{Expenditure}} \times 100$$

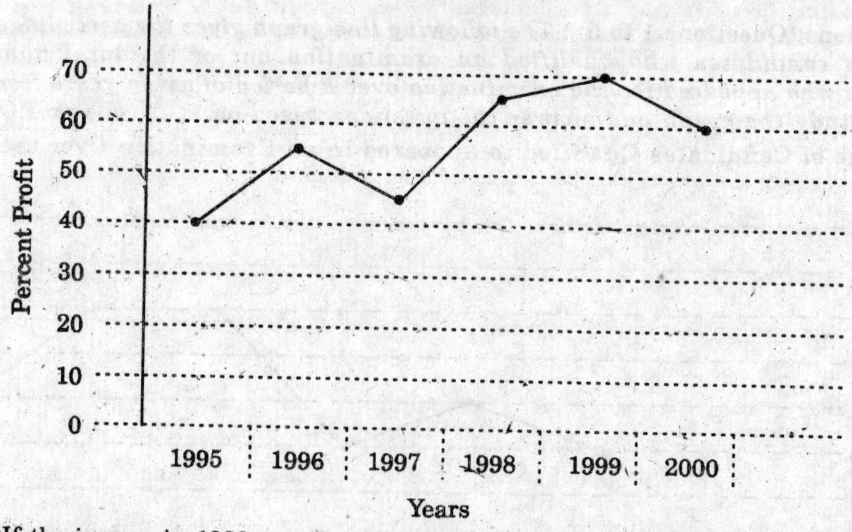

6. If the income in 1998 was Rs. 264 crores, what was the expenditure in 1998 ?

(a) Rs. 104 crores (b) Rs. 145 crores (c) Rs. 160 crores
(d) Rs. 185 crores (e) None of these

7. During which of the following years was the ratio of income to expenditure the minimum ?

(a) 1996 (b) 1997 (c) 1998 (d) 1999 (e) 2000

8. What is the average profit earned for the given years ?

(a) $50\frac{2}{3}$ (b) $55\frac{5}{6}$ (c) $60\frac{1}{6}$ (d) 336 (e) None of these

9. During which year the ratio of percentage profit earned to that in the previous year is the minimum ?
(*a*) 1996 (*b*) 1997 (*c*) 1998 (*d*) 1999 (*e*) 2000

10. If the expenditures in 1996 and 1999 are equal, then the approximate ratio of the incomes in 1996 and 1999 respectively, is :
(*a*) 1 : 1 (*b*) 2 : 3 (*c*) 9 : 10
(*d*) 13 : 14 (*e*) Cannot be determined

11. If the expenditure in 2000 is 25% more than the expenditure in 1997, then the income in 1997 is what percent less than the income in 2000 ?
(*a*) 22.5% (*b*) 25% (*c*) 27.5% (*d*) 31.25% (*e*) 32.5%

12. If the profit in 1999 was Rs. 4 crores, what was the profit in 2000 ?
(*a*) Rs. 4.2 crores (*b*) Rs. 6.6 crores (*c*) Rs. 6.8 crores
(*d*) Cannot be determined (*e*) None of these

13. In which year is the expenditure minimum ?
(*a*) 2000 (*b*) 1997 (*c*) 1996
(*d*) Cannot be determined (*e*) None of these

Directions (Questions 14 to 18) : ***Answer the questions based on the line-graph given below.*** **(Bank P.O. 2003)**

Ratio of Exports to Imports (in terms of money in Rs. crores) of Two Companies Over the Years

Years	1995	1996	1997	1998	1999	2000
Company A	1.75	1.5	1.75	0.75	0.75	1.0
Company B	0.75	0.75	1.0	1.25	1.0	1.25

14. In how many of the given years were the exports more than the imports for Company A ?
(*a*) 2 (*b*) 3 (*c*) 4 (*d*) 5 (*e*) 6

15. In which year(s) was the difference between imports and exports of Company B the maximum ?
(*a*) 2000 (*b*) 1996 (*c*) 1998 and 2000
(*d*) Cannot be determined (*e*) None of these

16. If the exports of Company A in 1998 were Rs. 237 crores, what was the amount of imports in that year ?
(*a*) Rs. 189.6 crores (*b*) Rs. 243 crores (*c*) Rs. 281 crores
(*d*) Rs. 316 crores (*e*) None of these

17. If the imports of Company A in 1997 were increased by 40 percent, what would be the ratio of exports to the increased imports ?

(a) 1.20 (b) 1.25 (c) 1.30
(d) None of these (e) Cannot be determined

18. In 1995, the export of Company A was double that of Company B. If the imports of Company A during the year was Rs. 180 crores, what was the approximate amount of imports of Company B during that year ?

(a) Rs. 190 crores (b) Rs. 210 crores (c) Rs. 225 crores
(d) Cannot be determined (e) None of these

Directions (Questions 19 to 23) : ***Two different finance companies declare fixed annual rate of interest on the amounts invested with them by investors. The rate of interest offered by these companies may differ from year to year depending on the variation in the economy of the country and the banks' rate of interest. The annual rate of interest offered by the two Companies P and Q over the years are shown by the line-graph provided below. Answer the questions based on this graph.*** **(Bank P.O. 2003)**

ANNUAL RATE OF INTEREST OFFERED BY TWO FINANCE COMPANIES OVER THE YEARS

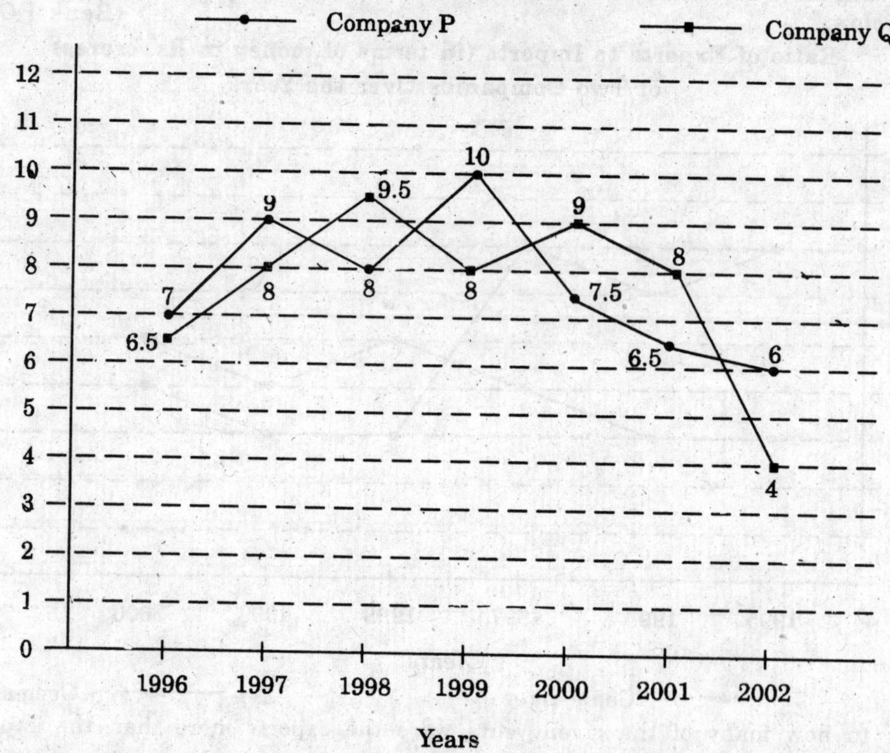

19. If two different amounts in the ratio 8 : 9 are invested in Companies P and Q respectively in 2002, then the amounts received after one year as interests from Companies P and Q are respectively in the ratio :

(a) 2 : 3 (b) 3 : 4 (c) 6 : 7 (d) 4 : 3 (e) 9 : 8

20. In 2000, a part of Rs. 30 lakhs was invested in Company P and the rest was invested in Company Q for one year. The total interest received was Rs. 2.43 lakhs. What was the amount invested in Company P ?

(a) Rs. 9 lakhs (b) Rs. 11 lakhs (c) Rs. 12 lakhs
(d) Rs. 14 lakhs (e) Rs. 18 lakhs

21. A sum of Rs. 4.75 lakhs was invested in Company Q in 1999 for one year. How much more interest would have been earned if the sum was invested in Company P ?
(*a*) Rs. 19,000 (*b*) Rs. 14,250 (*c*) Rs. 11,750 (*d*) Rs. 9500 (*e*) Rs. 7500

22. An investor invested a sum of Rs. 12 lakhs in Company P in 1998. The total amount received after one year was reinvested in the same Company for one more year. The total appreciation received by the investor on his investment was :
(*a*) Rs. 2,96,200 (*b*) Rs. 2,42,000 (*c*) Rs. 2,25,600
(*d*) Rs. 2,16,000 (*e*) Rs. 2,03,500

23. An investor invested Rs. 5 lakhs in Company Q in 1996. After one year, the entire amount along with the interest was transferred as investment to Company P in 1997 for one year. What amount will be received from Company P, by the investor ?
(*a*) Rs. 5,94,550 (*b*) Rs. 5,80,425 (*c*) Rs. 5,77,800
(*d*) Rs. 5,77,500 (*e*) Rs. 5,75,075

Directions (Questions 24 to 30) : ***Study the following line-graph which gives the number of students who joined and left the school in the beginning of year for six years, from 1996 to 2001.***

Initial strength of the school in 1995 = 3000.

The questions given below the graph are based on this line-graph. **(S.B.I.P.O 2001)**

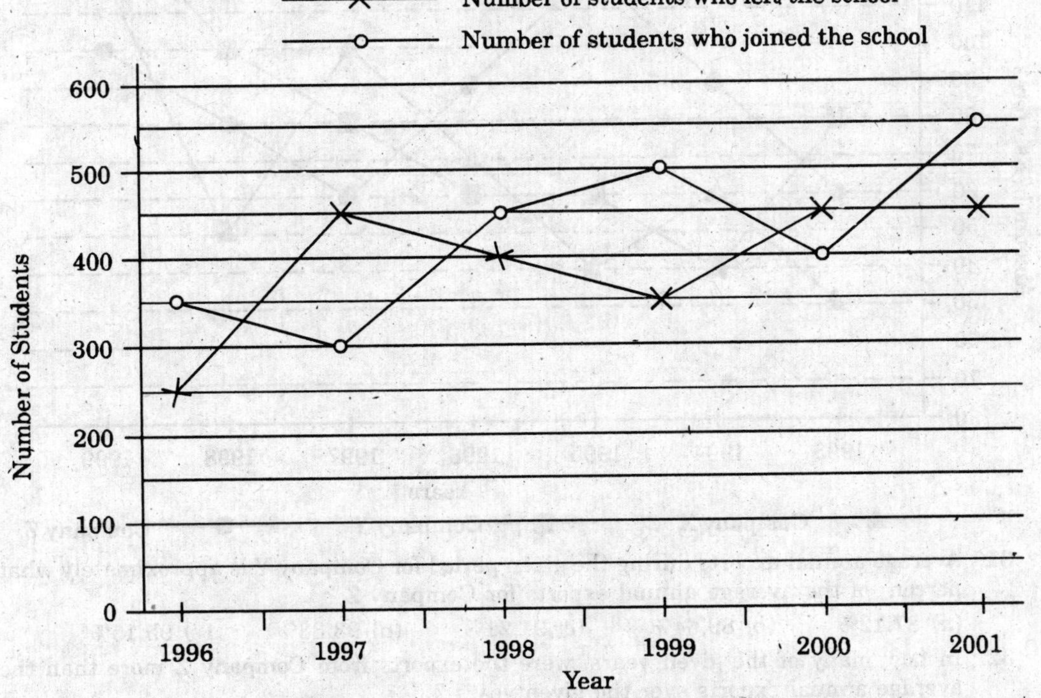

24. The strength of the school increased / decreased from 1997 to 1998 by approximately what percent ?
(*a*) 1.2% (*b*) 1.7% (*c*) 2.1% (*d*) 2.4% (*e*) 2.6%

25. The number of students studying in the school during 1999 was :
(*a*) 2950 (*b*) 3000 (*c*) 3100 (*d*) 3150 (*e*) 3200

26. During which of the following pairs of years, the strength of the school was same ?
(*a*) 1999 and 2001 (*b*) 1998 and 2000 (*c*) 1997 and 1998
(*d*) 1996 and 2000 (*e*) 1999 and 2000

27. The number of students studying in the school in 1998 was what percent of the number of students studying in the school in 2001 ?
(*a*) 92.13% (*b*) 93.75% (*c*) 96.88% (*d*) 97.25% (*e*) 99%

28. Among the given years, the largest number of students joined the school in the year :
(*a*) 1996 (*b*) 1998 (*c*) 1999 (*d*) 2000 (*e*) 2001

29. For which year, the percentage rise / fall in the number of students who left the school compared to the previous year is maximum ?
(*a*) 1997 (*b*) 1998 (*c*) 1999 (*d*) 2000 (*e*) 2001

30. The ratio of the least number of students who joined the school to the maximum number of students who left the school in any of the years during the given period is :
(*a*) 7 : 9 (*b*) 4 : 5 (*c*) 3 : 4 (*d*) 9 : 11 (*e*) 2 : 3

Directions (Questions 31 to 35) : ***Study the following graph and answer the questions based on it.*** **(S.B.I.P.O. 2000)**

Exports from Three Companies Over the Years (in Crore Rs.)

Amount in Rs. crores
140 130 120 110 100 90 80 70 60 50 40 30 20 10 0
1993 1994 1995 1996 1997 1998 1999
Years
Company X Company Y Company Z

31. Average annual exports during the given period for Company Y is approximately what percen of the average annual exports for Company Z ?
(*a*) 87.12% (*b*) 89.64% (*c*) 91.21% (*d*) 93.33% (*e*) 95.15%

32. In how many of the given years, were the exports from Company Z more than the average annual exports over the given years ?
(*a*) 2 (*b*) 3 (*c*) 4 (*d*) 5 (*e*) 6

33. What was the difference between the average exports of the three Companies in 1993 and the average exports in 1998 ?
(*a*) Rs. 15.33 crores (*b*) Rs. 18.67 crores (*c*) Rs. 20 crores
(*d*) Rs. 22.17 crores (*e*) Rs. 25 crores

34. In which year was the difference between the exports from Companies X and Y the minimum ?
(*a*) 1994 (*b*) 1995 (*c*) 1996 (*d*) 1997 (*e*) None of these

35. For which of the following pairs of years the total exports from the three Companies together are equal ?

(*a*) 1995 and 1998 (*b*) 1996 and 1998 (*c*) 1997 and 1998
(*d*) 1995 and 1996 (*e*) 1993 and 1994

ANSWERS

1. (*b*)	**2.** (*e*)	**3.** (*c*)	**4.** (*e*)	**5.** (*c*)	**6.** (*c*)	**7.** (*b*)	**8.** (*b*)	**9.** (*b*)
10. (*a*)	**11.** (*c*)	**12.** (*d*)	**13.** (*d*)	**14.** (*b*)	**15.** (*d*)	**16.** (*d*)	**17.** (*b*)	**18.** (*b*)
19. (*d*)	**20.** (*e*)	**21.** (*d*)	**22.** (*c*)	**23.** (*b*)	**24.** (*b*)	**25.** (*d*)	**26.** (*d*)	**27.** (*b*)
28. (*e*)	**29.** (*a*)	**30.** (*e*)	**31.** (*d*)	**32.** (*c*)	**33.** (*c*)	**34.** (*c*)	**35.** (*d*)	

SOLUTIONS

1. The differences between the percentages of candidates qualified to appeared for the given pairs of years are :

For *1994 and 1995* = 50 − 30 = 20; For *1997 and 1998* = 80 − 50 = 30;
For *1998 and 1999* = 80 − 80 = 0; For *1999 and 2000* = 80 − 60 = 20;
For *1994 and 1997* = 50 − 30 = 20.

Thus, the maximum difference is between the years 1997 and 1998.

2. The graph gives the data for the percentage of candidates qualified to appeared and unless the absolute values of number of candidates qualified or candidates appeared is known we cannot compare the absolute values for any two years. Hence, the data is inadequate to solve this question.

3. Let the number of candidates appeared in 1998 be *x*.

Then, 80% of $x = 21200 \Rightarrow x = \frac{21200 \times 100}{80} = 26500$ (required number).

4. The total number of candidates qualified in 1996 and 1997 together, cannot be determined until we know at least, the number of candidates appeared in any one of the two years 1996 or 1997 or the percentage of candidates qualified to appeared in 1996 and 1997 together. Hence, the data is inadequate.

5. The number of candidates qualified in 1999 = 80% of 26500 = 21200.

∴ Number of candidates qualified in 2000 = 33500 − 21200 = 12300.

Let the number of candidates appeared in 2000 be *x*.

Then, 60% of $x = 12300 \Rightarrow x = \frac{12300 \times 100}{60} = 20500$.

6. Let the expenditure in 1998 be Rs. *x* crores.

Then, $65 = \frac{264 - x}{x} \times 100 \Rightarrow \frac{65}{100} = \frac{264}{x} - 1 \Rightarrow x = \frac{264 \times 100}{165} = 160.$

∴ Expenditure in 1998 = Rs. 160 crores.

7. It is given that : $\%\text{Profit} = \frac{\text{Income} - \text{Expenditure}}{\text{Expenditure}} \times 100$

$$\Rightarrow \frac{\%\text{Profit}}{100} = \frac{\text{Income}}{\text{Expenditure}} - 1 \Rightarrow \frac{\text{Income}}{\text{Expenditure}} = \frac{\%\text{Profit}}{100} + 1.$$

From this it is clear that the ratio of income to expenditure is minimum for the year in which the % profit has the minimum value. Since, out of the given years (*i.e.*, out of 1996, 1997, 1998, 1999 and 2000), the Company has the minimum % profit in the year 1997, so the minimum ratio of income to expenditure is in the year 1997.

8. Average percent profit earned for the given years

$$= \frac{1}{6} \times [40 + 55 + 45 + 65 + 70 + 60] = \frac{335}{6} = 55\frac{5}{6}.$$

9. The ratio of percentage profit earned to that in the previous year, for different years are :

For 1996 $= \frac{55}{40} = 1.38$; **For 1997** $= \frac{45}{55} = 0.82$; **For 1998** $= \frac{65}{45} = 1.44$;

For 1999 $= \frac{70}{65} = 1.08$; **For 2000** $= \frac{60}{70} = 0.86$.

Clearly, this ratio is minimum for 1997.

10. Let the expenditure in 1996 = expenditure in 1999 = x.

Also, let the incomes in 1996 and 1999 be I_1 and I_2 respectively.

Then, for the year 1996, we have :

$$55 = \frac{I_1 - x}{x} \times 100 \Rightarrow \frac{55}{100} = \frac{I_1}{x} - 1 \Rightarrow I_1 = \frac{155x}{100} \quad ...(i)$$

And, for the year 1999, we have :

$$70 = \frac{I_2 - x}{x} \times 100 \Rightarrow \frac{70}{100} = \frac{I_2}{x} - 1 \Rightarrow I_2 = \frac{170x}{100} \quad ...(ii)$$

From (i) and (ii), we get :

$$\frac{I_1}{I_2} = \frac{\left(\frac{155x}{100}\right)}{\left(\frac{170x}{100}\right)} = \frac{155}{170} \approx \frac{0.91}{1} \approx 9 : 10.$$

11. Let the expenditure in 1997 be x.

Then, expenditure in 2000 $= x + (25\% \text{ of } x) = \frac{5}{4}x.$

Also, let the incomes in 1997 and 2000 be I_1 and I_2 respectively.

Then, for the year 1997, we have :

$$45 = \frac{I_1 - x}{x} \times 100 \Rightarrow \frac{45}{100} = \frac{I_1}{x} - 1 \Rightarrow I_1 = \frac{145x}{100} = 1.45x.$$

Also, for the year 2000, we have :

$$60 = \frac{\left(I_2 - \frac{5}{4}x\right)}{\left(\frac{5}{4}x\right)} \times 100 \Rightarrow \frac{60}{100} = \frac{4I_2}{5x} - 1 \Rightarrow I_2 = \frac{160}{100} \times \frac{5x}{4} = 2x.$$

Difference between the two incomes $= (2x - 1.45x) = 0.55x.$

$\therefore$ Percentage by which I_1 is less than $I_2 = \left(\frac{0.55x}{2x} \times 100\right)\% = 27.5\%.$

12. From the line-graph we obtain information about the percentage profit only. To find the profit in 2000 we must have the data for the income or expenditure in 2000. Therefore, the profit for 2000 cannot be determined.

13. The line-graph gives the comparison of percent profit for different years but the comparison of the expenditures is not possible without more data. Therefore, the year with minimum expenditure cannot be determined.

14. The exports are more than the imports in those years for which the exports to imports ratio is more than 1. For Company A, such years are 1995, 1996 and 1997. Thus, during these 3 years, the exports are more than the imports for Company A.

15. We shall try to find the difference between the imports and exports of Company B for various years one by one :

For 1995 : We have

$\frac{E}{I} = 0.75$ (where E = amount of exports and I = amount of imports in 1995)

$\Rightarrow E = 0.75I \quad \therefore \quad I - E = I - 0.75I = 0.25I.$

Thus, the difference between the imports and exports of Company B in 1995 is dependent on the amount of imports of Company B in 1995.

Similarly, the difference for other years can be determined only if the amount of imports for these years are known. Since the imports or exports for various years are not known, the differences between imports and exports for various years cannot be determined.

16. Let the amount of imports of Company A in 1998 be Rs. x crores.

Then, $\frac{237}{x} = 0.75 \Rightarrow x = \frac{237}{0.75} = 316.$

$\therefore$ Amount of imports of Company A in 1998 = Rs. 316 crores.

17. In 1997 for Company A we have :

$\frac{E}{I} = 1.75$ *i.e.*, $E = 1.75I$ ...(*i*)

[where E = amount of exports and I = amount of imports of Company A in 1997]

Now, the required imports $I_1 = I + 40\%$ of $I = 1.4I$.

$\therefore$ Required ratio $= \frac{E}{I_1} = \frac{1.75I}{1.4I} = 1.25.$

18. In 1995 for Company A we have :

$\frac{E_A}{I_A} = 1.75$ ...(*i*) [where E_A = amount of exports and I_A = amount of imports of Company A in 1995]

In 1995 for Company B we have :

$\frac{E_B}{I_B} = 0.75$ ...(*ii*) [where E_B = amount of exports and I_B = amount of imports of Company B in 1995]

Also, we have $E_A = 2E_B$ ...(*iii*)

Substituting I_A = Rs. 180 crores (given) in (*i*), we get

E_A = Rs. (180 × 1.75) crores = Rs. 315 crores.

Using E_A = Rs. 315 crores in (*iii*), we get : $E_B = \frac{E_A}{2} = \text{Rs.} \left(\frac{315}{2}\right)$ crores.

Substituting $E_B = \text{Rs.} \left(\frac{315}{2}\right)$ crores in (*ii*), we get :

$I_B = \frac{E_B}{0.75} = \text{Rs.} \left(\frac{315}{2 \times 0.75}\right)$ crores = Rs. 210 crores.

i.e., amount of imports of Company B in 1995 = Rs. 210 crores.

19. Let the amounts invested in 2002 in Companies P and Q be Rs. $8x$ and Rs. $9x$ respectively.

Then, interest received after one year from Company P

$= \text{Rs. } (6\% \text{ of } 8x) = \text{Rs. } \frac{48}{100}x$

and interest received after one year from Company Q

$$= \text{Rs. } (4\% \text{ of } 9x) = \text{Rs. } \frac{36}{100}x.$$

$$\therefore \quad \text{Required ratio} = \frac{\left(\frac{48}{100}x\right)}{\left(\frac{36}{100}x\right)} = \frac{4}{3}.$$

20. Let Rs. x lakhs be invested in Company P in 2000, then amount invested in Company Q in 2000 = Rs. $(30 - x)$ lakhs.

Total interest received from the two Companies after 1 year

$$= \text{Rs. } [(7.5\% \text{ of } x) + \{9\% \text{ of } (30 - x)\}] \text{ lakhs} = \text{Rs. } \left[2.7 - \left(\frac{1.5x}{100}\right)\right] \text{ lakhs.}$$

$$\therefore \quad \left[2.7 - \left(\frac{1.5x}{100}\right)\right] = 2.43 \Rightarrow x = 18.$$

i.e., amount invested in Company P = Rs. 18 lakhs.

21. Difference = Rs. [(10% of 4.75) – (8% of 4.75)] lakhs

= Rs. (2% of 4.75) lakhs = Rs. 0.095 lakhs = Rs. 9500.

22. Amount received from Company P after one year (*i.e.*, in 1999) on investing Rs. 12 lakhs in it = Rs. [12 + (8% of 12)] lakhs = Rs. 12.96 lakhs.

Amount received from Company P after one year on investing Rs. 12.96 lakhs in the year 1999 = Rs. [12.96 + (10% of 12.96)] lakhs = Rs. 14.256 lakhs.

Appreciation received on investment during the period of two years

= Rs. (14.256 – 12) lakhs = Rs. 2.256 lakhs = Rs. 2,25,600.

23. Amount received from Company Q after one year on investment of Rs. 5 lakhs in the year 1996 = Rs. [5 + (6.5% of 5)] lakhs = Rs. 5.325 lakhs.

Amount received from Company P after one year on investment of Rs. 5.325 lakhs in the year 1997 = Rs. [5.325 + (9% of 5.325)] lakhs = Rs. 5.80425 lakhs = Rs. 5,80,425.

Questions 24 to 30 :

Before solving the questions, we shall analyse the graph :

From the graph it is clear that :

In 1996 : Number of students left = 250 and number of students joined = 350.

In 1997 : Number of students left = 450 and number of students joined = 300.

In 1998 : Number of students left = 400 and number of students joined = 450.

In 1999 : Number of students left = 350 and number of students joined = 500.

In 2000 : Number of students left = 450 and number of students joined = 400.

In 2001 : Number of students left = 450 and number of students joined = 550.

Therefore, the numbers of students studying in the school (*i.e.*, strength of the school) in various years :

In 1995 = 3000 (given); **In 1996** = 3000 – 250 + 350 = 3100;

In 1997 = 3100 – 450 + 300 = 2950; **In 1998** = 2950 – 400 + 450 = 3000;

In 1999 = 3000 – 350 + 500 = 3150; **In 2000** = 3150 – 450 + 400 = 3100;

In 2001 = 3100 – 450 + 550 = 3200.

Now we shall solve the questions.

24. Percentage increase in the strength of the school from 1997 to 1998

$$= \left[\frac{(3000 - 2950)}{2950} \times 100\right]\% = 1.69\% \approx 1.7\%.$$

25. As calculated above, the number of students studying in the school during 1999 = 3150.

26. As calculated above, in the years 1996 and 2000 the strength of the school was same *i.e.*, 3100.

27. Using the calculations above we have :

Required percentage = $\left(\frac{3000}{3200} \times 100\right)\% = 93.75\%$.

28. As calculated above, the largest number of students (*i.e.*, 550) joined the school in the year 2001.

29. The percentage rise / fall in the number of students who left the school (compared to the previous year) during various years are :

For 1997 = $\left[\frac{(450-250)}{250} \times 100\right]\% = 80\%$ (rise);

For 1998 = $\left[\frac{(450-400)}{450} \times 100\right]\% = 11.11\%$ (fall);

For 1999 = $\left[\frac{(400-350)}{400} \times 100\right]\% = 12.5\%$ (fall);

For 2000 = $\left[\frac{(450-350)}{350} \times 100\right]\% = 28.57\%$ (rise);

For 2001 = $\left[\frac{(450-450)}{450} \times 100\right]\% = 0\%$.

Clearly, the maximum percentage rise / fall is for 1997.

30. Using the calculations above we get :

Required ratio = $\frac{300}{450} = \frac{2}{3}$.

Questions 31 to 35 :

Analysis of the graph : From the graph it is clear that

(*i*) The amount of exports of Company X (in crore Rs.) in the years 1993, 1994, 1995, 1996, 1997, 1998 and 1999 are 30, 60, 40, 70, 100, 50 and 120 respectively.

(*ii*) The amount of exports of Company Y (in crore Rs.) in the years 1993, 1994, 1995, 1996, 1997, 1998 and 1999 are 80, 40, 60, 60, 80, 100 and 140 respectively.

(*iii*) The amount of exports of Company Z (in crore Rs.) in the years 1993, 1994, 1995, 1996, 1997, 1998 and 1999 are 60, 90, 120, 90, 60, 80 and 100 respectively.

31. Average annual exports (in Rs. crore) of Company Y during the given period

$= \frac{1}{7} \times (80 + 40 + 60 + 60 + 80 + 100 + 140) = \frac{560}{7} = 80.$

Average annual exports (in Rs. crore) of Company Z during the given period

$= \frac{1}{7} \times (60 + 90 + 120 + 90 + 60 + 80 + 100) = \left(\frac{600}{7}\right).$

$\therefore$ Required percentage = $\left[\frac{80}{\left(\frac{600}{7}\right)} \times 100\right]\% \approx 93.33\%.$

32. Average annual exports of Company Z during the given period

$= \text{Rs.}\left[\frac{1}{7} \times (60 + 90 + 120 + 90 + 60 + 80 + 100)\right] \text{ crores} = \text{Rs.}\left(\frac{600}{7}\right) \text{ crores}$

= Rs. 85.71 crores.

From the analysis of graph the exports of Company Z are more than the average annual exports of Company Z (*i.e.*, Rs. 85.71 crores) during the years 1994, 1995, 1996 and 1999, *i.e.*, during 4 of the given years.

33. Average exports of the three Companies X, Y and Z in 1993

$$= \text{Rs.} \left[\frac{1}{3} \times (30 + 80 + 60)\right] \text{ crores} = \text{Rs.} \left(\frac{170}{3}\right) \text{ crores.}$$

Average exports of the three Companies X, Y and Z in 1998

$$= \text{Rs.} \left[\frac{1}{3} \times (50 + 100 + 80)\right] \text{ crores} = \text{Rs.} \left(\frac{230}{3}\right) \text{ crores.}$$

$$\text{Difference} = \text{Rs.} \left[\left(\frac{230}{3}\right) - \left(\frac{170}{3}\right)\right] \text{ crores} = \text{Rs.} \left(\frac{60}{3}\right) \text{ crores} = \text{Rs. 20 crores.}$$

34. The differences between the exports from the Companies X and Y during various years are :

In 1993 = Rs. (80 – 30) crores = Rs. 50 crores;
In 1994 = Rs. (60 – 40) crores = Rs. 20 crores;
In 1995 = Rs. (60 – 40) crores = Rs. 20 crores;
In 1996 = Rs. (70 – 60) crores = Rs. 10 crores;
In 1997 = Rs. (100 – 80) crores = Rs. 20 crores;
In 1998 = Rs. (100 – 50) crores = Rs. 50 crores;
In 1999 = Rs (140 – 120) crores = Rs. 20 crores.

Clearly, tne difference is minimum in the year 1996.

35. Total exports of the three Companies X, Y and Z together, during various years are :

In 1993 = Rs. (30 + 80 + 60) crores = Rs. 170 crores.
In 1994 = Rs. (60 + 40 + 90) crores = Rs. 190 crores.
In 1995 = Rs. (40 + 60 + 120) crores = Rs. 220 crores.
In 1996 = Rs. (70 + 60 + 90) crores = Rs. 220 crores.
In 1997 = Rs. (100 + 80 + 60) crores = Rs. 240 crores.
In 1998 = Rs. (50 + 100 + 80) crores = Rs. 230 crores.
In 1999 = Rs. (120 + 140 + 100) crores = Rs. 360 crores.

Clearly, the total exports of the three Companies X, Y and Z together are same during the years 1995 and 1996.